Prente Hall Physical Science

Prentice H Physial Sciene

Physical Science (spine)

BACHER · HURD · McLAUGHLIN · SILVER

Prentice Hall

The difference between memorizing facts and __understanding__ science.

from Prente Hall Allyn & Bacon

Comprehensive coverage organized in a motivating and easy-to-learn format

8 UNITS, INCLUDING 28 CHAPTERS, provide for a full-year course in physical science.

UP-TO-DATE CONTENT, including a special unit on science and technology, relates physical science to today's world and everyday life.

EXCITING UNIT OPENERS with dynamic visuals, vivid introductory paragraphs, and lists of chapter titles get students interested in each unit.

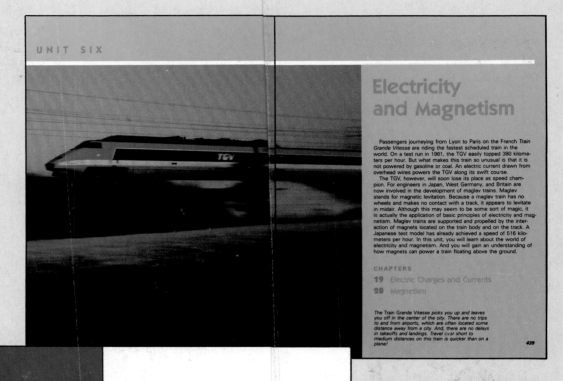

UNIT SIX

Electricity and Magnetism

Passengers journeying from Lyon to Paris on the French *Train Grande Vitesse* are riding the fastest scheduled train in the world. On a test run in 1981, the TGV easily topped 380 kilometers per hour. But what makes this train so unusual is that it is not powered by gasoline or coal. An electric current drawn from overhead wires powers the TGV along its swift course.

The TGV, however, will soon lose its place as speed champion. For engineers in Japan, West Germany, and Britain are now involved in the development of maglev trains. Maglev stands for magnetic levitation. Because a maglev train has no wheels and makes no contact with a track, it appears to levitate in midair. Although this may seem to be some sort of magic, it is actually the application of basic principles of electricity and magnetism. Maglev trains are supported and propelled by the interaction of magnets located on the train body and on the track. A Japanese test model has already achieved a speed of 516 kilometers per hour. In this unit, you will learn about the world of electricity and magnetism. And you will gain an understanding of how magnets can power a train floating above the ground.

CHAPTERS

19 Electric Charges and Currents

20 Magnetism

The Train Grande Vitesse picks you up and leaves you off in the center of the city. There are no trips to and from airports, which are often located some distance away from a city. And, there are no delays in takeoffs and landings. Travel over short to medium distances on this train is quicker than on a plane!

439

Motion · 12

CHAPTER SECTIONS

12–1 Frames of Reference
12–2 Speed and Velocity
12–3 Acceleration
12–4 Momentum

CHAPTER OBJECTIVES

After completing this chapter, you will be able to

12–1 Describe a frame of reference.

12–2 Calculate speed.

12–2 Distinguish between speed and velocity.

12–3 Define and calculate acceleration and deceleration.

12–4 Describe momentum.

The eyes of the crowd on the sleek, dazzling skier as he sweeps ski jump track at 100 kilometers per hour. The bottom of the track, he leaps into the air. Wind lashes at his face. Even with goggles on, led by the glare of the snow on the mountain—far below.

Then, in an attempt gravity, he leans forward. His body and ski form of an airplane wing as he rides the wind. Finally, his skis make contact with the snow-ending area. The snow flies up in his face in tens. The sound of the cheering crowd mingle sound of the wind. His ride is over.

The scene is the Vympics. And the ski jumper has just flown 1 through the air to set a new record for distances his gold medal not only to courage and training but also to an understanding of moti

In this sense, ski jump merely a sport. It is also a science. Learn the science of motion may not earn you an Gedal, but it can be a leap into adventure any.

Although this ski jumper seems to be floating in midair, his body is really in motion. You would quickly observe this fact if you were watching the ski jump from the ground below.

287

ATTENTION-GRABBING CHAPTER OPENERS relate physical science topics to everyday life through full-color pictures and interesting stories to discuss in class.

Chapter openers include **A LIST OF CHAPTER SECTIONS** for previewing the chapter and **CHAPTER OBJECTIVES** for identifying learning goals.

Especially written so your students can read and understand science

SECTION OBJECTIVES are skills-oriented and show students what is important in each section.

A FLOWING NARRATIVE STYLE clearly explains concepts through interesting examples and anecdotes at the reading level of your students.

HUNDREDS OF PHOTOGRAPHS AND ILLUSTRATIONS motivate students and reinforce the text material.

8–1 Nature of Chemical Reactions

Section Objective

To describe the characteristics of chemical reactions

Here's a chemical puzzle for you. What do the rusting of iron, the burning of gasoline, and the cooking of sugar have in common? They are all examples of **chemical reactions.** A chemical reaction is a process in which the physical and chemical properties of the original substances change as new substances with different physical and chemical properties are formed. Can you name some other examples of chemical reactions?

Characteristics of Chemical Reactions

In any chemical reaction, a new substance is formed. **When a chemical reaction takes place, there is always a change in the properties and in the energy of the substances involved in the chemical reaction.** Both the physical and chemical properties of the substances are changed.

Figure 8–1 *Rusting is a chemical reaction in which iron combines with oxygen to form the compound iron oxide (left). Rusting takes place very slowly, and only a very small amount of heat energy is given off. Fighting brush fires involves a chemical reaction in which noncombustible products are formed (right). This chemical reaction occurs rapidly. What two things always change in a chemical reaction?*

For example, inside a flashbulb is a small coil of shiny gray metal. This metal is magnesium. The bulb is also filled with the invisible gas oxygen. When the flashbulb is set off, the magnesium combines with the oxygen in a chemical reaction. Energy is released in the form of light, and a fine white powder is produced. You can see this powder on the inside of the bulb. The powder is magnesium oxide, a compound with physical and chemical properties very different from the elements magnesium and oxygen. So a chemical reaction has occurred.

In any chemical reaction, there are always two kinds of substances: the substances that are present before the change and the substances that are formed by the change. A substance that enters into a chemical reaction is called a **reactant** (ree-AK-tehnt). A substance that is produced by a chemical reaction is called a **product.** So a general description of a chemical reaction could be stated as reactants changing into products. In the example of the flashbulb, what are the reactants? The product?

In addition to changes in properties, chemical reactions always involve a change in energy. Energy is either absorbed or released during a chemical reaction. For example, heat energy is absorbed when sugar changes into caramel. When gasoline burns, heat energy is released. Later in this chapter you

Figure 8–2 *Inside this flashbulb is a thin coil of magnesium metal and the invisible gas oxygen (top). When the flashbulb is set off, a chemical reaction takes place in which the magnesium combines with oxygen to form magnesium oxide (bottom). How can you tell a chemical reaction has occurred?*

Figure 8–3 *The ability of substances to burn fueled the Voyager 1 spacecraft on its mission to the outer planets (right). The ability of substances not to burn helped this firefighter extinguish a bog fire (left). What type of property is the ability to burn?*

A LARGE, READABLE TYPE SIZE makes learning easier and more enjoyable.

SHORT, MANAGEABLE PARAGRAPHS help students grasp ideas easily.

VOCABULARY WORDS and **KEY IDEAS** are highlighted in boldface type. Phonetic respellings help, too!

Skills-oriented for "doing" and "thinking" science

SHARPEN YOUR SKILLS provides quick and easy activities that develop science skills . . . hands-on activities, field investigations, computational activities, library assignments, and science writing activities for every ability level.

Sharpen Your Skills

Viewing Vibrations

Sound is caused by vibration. You can observe this by experimenting with a tuning fork.

1. Strike the prongs of a tuning fork with a pencil and then hold the fork close to your ear. What happens? What happens when you touch the prongs of the fork?
2. Next, strike the prongs of the tuning fork and place the ends of the prongs in a glass of water. What happens?
3. Tie a small piece of cork to a string and hold the string in one hand so the cork can swing freely. Strike the prongs of the tuning fork and hold one prong against the cork. Observe what happens.

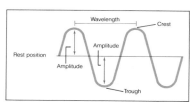

Figure 22–6 *Some of the basic characteristics of a sound wave can be seen in this diagram. What three characteristics can you identify?*

Intensity determines the loudness of a sound. The greater the intensity of a sound, the louder the sound is to the ear. Thunder sounds louder than a handclap because the intensity of thunder is much greater than the intensity of a handclap.

Intensity is measured in units called **decibels.** A sound with an intensity of 0 decibels is so soft that it can barely be heard. Thunder, on the other hand, has an intensity of 120 decibels. Thunder is a very

---

15 LABORATORY INVESTIGATION
Mechanical Advantage of an Inclined Plane

Problem

How are the ideal and the actual mechanical advantage of an inclined plane determined?

Materials *(per group)*
wooden ramp at least 0.80 m long
wooden block or brick
spring scale calibrated in newtons (0–5 N)
meterstick
2 books
string

Procedure

1. Place one end of the wooden ramp on top of the two books.
2. Measure the length and height of the ramp. Take both measurements from the bottom of the ramp, as indicated in the accompanying figure. Record each measurement to the nearest 0.1 centimeter.
3. Tie one end of a string around the block or brick. Attach the other end of the string to the spring scale. Record the weight of the block to the nearest 0.1 newton.
4. Pull the block up the ramp with the spring scale. Read the scale while pulling the block. Record this value as the effort force to the nearest 0.1 newton.

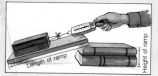

Observations

1. Calculate the work done in lifting the block without the ramp.
2. Calculate the work done in lifting the block with the ramp.
3. Calculate the ideal mechanical advantage using the formula

   IMA = length of ramp/height of ramp

4. Calculate the actual mechanical advantage using the formula

   AMA = weight of block/effort force

Length of inclined plane	cm
Height of inclined plane	cm
Weight of block	N
Effort force	N

Conclusions

1. What simple machine is the ramp? How does it make a job easier?
2. Does it require more or less force to lift the block using the ramp?
3. Is more or less work done in lifting the block when the ramp is used?
4. How does the ideal mechanical advantage compare with the actual mechanical advantage?
5. What force causes a difference in the ideal and actual mechanical advantage? How could this force be reduced?

LABORATORY INVESTIGATIONS in every chapter reinforce the scientific method and develop manipulative laboratory and critical thinking skills. These easy-to-follow experiments use inexpensive materials, and include clear directions, useful visuals, and questions for drawing conclusions.

---

4. A <u>transverse</u> wave is a series of compressions and rarefactions.
5. The distance between two consecutive crests is one <u>amplitude</u>.
6. Frequency is measured in <u>hertz</u>.

9. When ... ... from each other, <u>destructive</u> interference occurs.
10. Constructive interference and destructive interference producing stationary nodes and antinodes is called a <u>diffraction</u> wave.

CONCEPT REVIEW: SKILL BUILDING

Use the skills you have developed in the chapter to complete each activity.

1. **Applying concepts** Waves travel slower through a denser medium. Although water is denser than air, sound waves travel faster in water. Explain why.
2. **Making calculations** Complete the following table.

Speed (m/sec)	Frequency (Hz)	Wavelength (m)
150	2.0	
	250	1.5
200		0.5
	200	1.0

3. **Identifying relationships** State the effect on the frequency and speed of a wave if the amplitude is increased; wavelength is increased; wavelength is decreased.

4. **Interpreting diagrams** Answer the following questions using these diagrams.

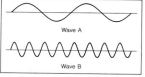

Wave A

Wave B

a. Which wave has the largest amplitude?
b. Which wave has the shorter wavelength?
c. Which wave has a higher frequency?

CONCEPT REVIEW: ESSAY

Discuss each of the following in a brief paragraph.

1. How do density and elasticity of a medium affect the speed ... ...

4. Describe what ... ... to an incident ... ... hitti... ... angle.

SKILL-BUILDING EXERCISES at the end of each chapter provide more interesting and challenging questions to develop thinking skills.

Relates physical science to everyday life

SCIENCE GAZETTES include exciting and provoking articles that focus on current adventures and issues in science. And there are science reading skills activities in the Teachers Resource Book for each article.

SCIENCE GAZETTE

Adventures in Science

DICK RUTAN AND JEANA YEAGER: MAKING AVIATION HISTORY

"Look! Up in the sky . . . It's a bird . . . It's a plane . . . It's a very unusual plane!" This airplane, named the *Voyager*, does not look like any conventional aircraft. Its long, narrow wings are tipped with tiny upright "winglets." An extra wing streams out on either side of its nose. Two narrow fuel-filled booms suspended along either side of its body complete its design.

The *Voyager* is one of the wo[rld's] and most extraordinary aircraft. I[ts] wingspan is greater than that of a[...] But its mass is only 8427 kilo[grams] about half the mass of a sma[ll...] although this remarkable aircraft [...] to carry up to five times its weight[...] for only two people. But that's no[...] that is exactly how the *Voyager* w[...]

388

SCIENCE GAZETTE

Issues in Science

NUCLEAR POWER: PROMISE OR PERIL?

A fiery explosion on April 26, 1986, rocked a city in the Soviet Union and terrified the rest of the world. The accident occurred at the Chernobyl Nuclear Power Plant, near Kiev. An explosion in a nuclear reactor blew off the roof of the plant and triggered a fire that burned for days. A cloud of radioactive particles rose into the air and was carried by winds throughout Europe. Chernobyl was the most serious nuclear accident in history.

Several people were killed instantly by the explosion at the Chernobyl plant. Others died

soon after from burns or radiation po[isoning.] How many more will die in future y[ears as a] result of radiation remains unknown. [...] ple may not be the only casualties o[f the ex-]plosion. The future of nuclear powe[r in the] United States has been gravely threa[tened by] the accident at Chernobyl.

BENEFITS VERSUS RISKS

The popularity of nuclear power [in the] United States had begun to decline lon[g...]

CAREERS in every chapter feature realistic opportunities for students to explore . . . whether they have a high school diploma or a Ph.D.!

CAREER

Food Chemist

HELP WANTED: FOOD CHEMIST to develop new food products and processing techniques. Candidates for this position should have a college degree in food science or chemistry.

If you were alive one hundred years ago, you probably would have spent much of your time growing and preparing your own food. What you did not grow or process yourself, you would have purchased fresh nearly every day. Packaged and canned foods were not common then. And there were no mechanical refrigerators.

Today, most people can reach into the refrigerator or cabinet for a snack or easy-to-prepare meal. Much of the food you eat has been processed for you by a food processing company. Almost every method of food processing involves chemical reactions. **Food chemists** use their knowledge of chemistry to develop these food processing methods.

Some food chemists develop new foods or new flavors. Others develop improved packag-

ing and storage methods for foods. Food chemists might work in the plants where food is processed. Food chemists may test samples of a product to be sure that the nutrients in the food match the nutritional information printed on the package.

If you are interested in a career as a food chemist, write to the Institute of Food Technologists, Career Guidance, Suite 300, 221 North LaSalle Street, Chicago, IL 60601.

And on the right side? You should count 1. Now try the same thing for oxygen. There are 2 oxygen atoms on the left but only 1 on the right. This cannot be correct, since atoms can be neither created nor destroyed during a chemical reaction.

To balance this equation, you must represent more than 1 atom of oxygen and more than one molecule of magnesium oxide:

$$2Mg + O_2 \longrightarrow 2MgO + energy$$

If you count atoms again, you will find 2 magnesium atoms on each side of the equation, as well as 2 oxygen atoms. The equation is balanced. It can be read: 2 atoms of magnesium combine with 1 molecule of oxygen to yield 2 molecules of magnesium oxide. Notice that when no coefficient is written, such as in front of the molecule of oxygen, the number is understood to be 1. Remember that to balance a chemical equation, you can change coefficients but never symbols or formulas.

Chemical equations are easy to write and balance. Follow the rules in Figure 8–7 and on page 188.

Figure 8–7 *These are the steps to follow in balancing a chemical equation. What law must a chemical equation obey?*

BALANCING EQUATIONS

$$H_2 + O_2 \longrightarrow H_2O$$

1. Write a chemical equation with correct symbols and formulas.
2. Count the number of atoms of each element on each side of the arrow.

$$2H_2 + O_2 \longrightarrow 2H_2O$$

3. Balance atoms by using coefficients.
4. Check your work by counting atoms of each element.

187

18–2 Insulation

Once heat is brought into a room or building, it will quickly begin to escape if the area lacks proper **insulation.** Insulation materials reduce heat transfer because they are poor conductors of heat. **Insulation prevents heat loss by reducing the transfer of heat that occurs by conduction and convection.**

A common insulating material is **fiberglass.** Fiberglass consists of long, thin strands of glass packed together. In between the strands are air spaces. Glass is a poor conductor of heat. So is the air that is trapped between the fibers.

Insulating materials are packed beneath roofs and in the outside walls of buildings. Insulation can also be used around doors and windows. This type of insulation is called weather stripping. Weather stripping prevents heat loss by closing up spaces through which heat is transferred by convection. Double-pane window glass is another effective insulator. The air trapped between the panes of glass does not conduct heat well. And the air space is so small that convection cannot take place either.

Section Objective

To explain how insulation prevents heat loss

Figure 18–8 *The long, shaggy hair of a musk ox provides insulation from the cold Arctic winter. During the fall, the ox grows an inner matting of hair, which combined with the outer coat gives a double blanket of protection.*

Figure 18–9 *Invisible heat energy, or infrared energy, can be "seen" by using a device called a thermograph. This thermogram, or heat picture, reveals heat loss from a house. Generally, the lighter and brighter the color, the greater the heat loss. How can a thermogram be useful to homeowners?*

Sharpen Your Skills

Effectiveness of Insulating Materials

The effectiveness of insulating materials is measured according to *R-value.* Using books and other reference materials in the library, find out what the R-value of insulating materials is based on. Find out how the R-values of common insulating materials such as brick, concrete, stucco, fiberglass, wood, and foam. Rank the materials according to their effectiveness.

423

REAL-LIFE APPLICATIONS AND UP-TO-DATE CONTENT help students relate physical science concepts to their everyday lives.

Student involvement on every page

Figure 2–23 *As the leaves change color each autumn in Vermont, this old piece of farm equipment rusts a little more (left). Fireworks dot the Houston skyline during a Fourth of July celebration (right). What three chemical changes can you identify in the photographs?*

digestion are chemical changes you could not live without. Photosynthesis, or the food-making process in green plants, is a chemical change. Rusting and the changing colors of leaves in the fall are chemical changes. Can you name some other examples?

Chemical changes are often called **chemical reactions.** Chemical reactions involve chemically combining different substances. The chemical reaction produces new substances with new and different physical and chemical properties. However, matter is never destroyed in a chemical reaction. The particles of one substance are rearranged to form a new substance, but the same number of particles exists before and after the reaction.

SECTION REVIEW

1. How is a chemical property different from a chemical change?
2. Give an example of a chemical property and a chemical change.
3. What is the difference between a physical property and a chemical property? Between a physical change and a chemical change?
4. What is a chemical reaction?
5. Identify the following processes as either physical changes or chemical changes: boiling water, digesting food, burning coal, melting butter, tarnishing silver, baking brownies, dissolving sugar, exploding TNT.

INTERACTIVE QUESTIONS in the text and in the figure captions are great for class discussions—to get all students interested and to sharpen critical thinking skills!

SAMPLE PROBLEMS with step-by-step instruction takes the mystery out of science word problems.

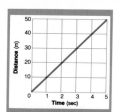

CONSTANT SPEED Figure 12–6 is a distance–time graph of a runner's motion. Distance is plotted on the vertical, or Y, axis. Time is plotted on the horizontal, or X, axis. According to the graph, how many meters did the runner travel after 1 second? You are right if you said 10 meters. The runner's speed was 10 m/sec. After 3 seconds, the runner had run 30 meters. So his speed was 30 m/3 sec = 10 m/sec. The runner's speed did not change. Speed that does not change is called **constant speed.** The speed at any particular instant can be found by dividing distance by time. Notice that a distance–time graph for constant speed is a straight line.

In Figure 12–7, the motions of two swimmers are plotted on a graph. Are the speeds of both swimmers constant? How can you tell? Now use the graph to determine if both swimmers are moving at the same speed. Swimmer 1 swims 100 meters in 50 seconds. So her speed is 100 m/50 sec = 2 m/sec. Swimmer 2 swims 50 meters in 50 seconds. Her speed is 50 m/50 sec = 1 m/sec. Swimmer 1 is the faster swimmer. If you compare the graphs of the two swimmers, you will see that the graph for swimmer 1 has a steeper, or greater, **slope.** The slope of a distance–time graph is directly related to the speed. The steeper the slope, the faster the speed.

Figure 12–6 *In a distance–time graph, the distance an object travels is plotted as a function of the time it takes the object to go that distance. How do you know that the object whose motion is shown here traveled at a constant speed?*

Figure 12–7 *Study the distance–time graphs for the two lead swimmers in this race. Which graph has the steepest slope? What does that tell you about the speed of the two swimmers?*

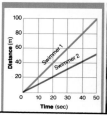 

AVERAGE SPEED The speed of a moving object is not always constant. Look at Figure 12–8. The distance–time graph describing this motion is not a straight line. According to the graph, after the first

GRAPHS, CHARTS, AND MAPS help students organize, interpret, and use scientific information accurately.

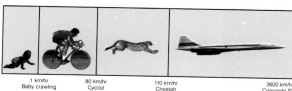

| 1 km/hr | 80 km/hr | 110 km/hr | 3600 km/hr |
| Baby crawling | Cyclist | Cheetah | Concorde SST |

Figure 12–5 *You can compare the speeds of some common objects on this scale. Where do you think your walking speed would fit?*

Speed

Speed is the distance traveled by a moving object per unit of time. You can calculate the **speed** of a moving object by dividing the distance the object travels by the time it takes to travel that distance.

$$speed = \frac{distance}{time}$$

Since distance is measured in meters or kilometers and time is measured in seconds or hours, the units of speed are meters per second (m/sec) or kilometers per hour (km/hr). What was the speed of the winning runner?

Sample Problem		A car travels 300 kilometers in 6 hours. What is the speed of the car?
Solution		
Step 1	Write the formula	$speed = \dfrac{distance}{time}$
Step 2	Substitute given numbers and units	$speed = \dfrac{300 \text{ kilometers}}{6 \text{ hours}}$
Step 3	Solve for unknown variable	$speed = \dfrac{50 \text{ kilometers}}{hour}$ or 50 kilometers/hour
Practice Problems		
		1. What is the speed of a jet plane that flies 7200 km in 9 hours?
		2. The speed of a cruise ship is 50 km/hr. How far will the ship travel in 14 hours?

PRACTICE PROBLEMS emphasize real-life applications and provide plenty of opportunities for students to sharpen problem-solving skills.

Thorough review and reinforcement exercises to master concepts and skills

from a diving board, you encounter air resistance. It is a relatively small amount of air resistance, so your motion is slowed down only a little. But the fluid resistance of the water is great enough to stop your motion before you reach the bottom of the pool.

Fluid friction usually opposes motion less than sliding friction does. Substances called **lubricants** change sliding friction to fluid friction. This reduces the friction and makes motion easier. Oil, grease, and wax are examples of lubricants.

Friction is not always an "unfriendly" force. Friction can be helpful. You often want to increase friction rather than decrease it. Tires have treads to increase the friction of the wheels on the road. Car brakes use friction to stop motion. Why do you suppose increasing friction is desirable?

Without friction you could not walk. The friction between the soles of your shoes and the ground keeps you from slipping and sliding. Why do you think sand is placed on icy streets?

Figure 13-4 *Friction can be a helpful force. Without friction between the tires and the track, these bikes would continue to move in a straight line instead of curving around the track. What purpose does the banking of the track serve?*

SECTION REVIEW

1. What is force?
2. What is friction? What are the three types of friction?
3. What type of friction is involved in the following situations: a train moving along a track, a bird in flight, skiing, walking?

309

SECTION REVIEWS provide a quick check for understanding.

COMPREHENSIVE CHAPTER REVIEWS check recall, build critical thinking skills, and provide a variety of questions . . . multiple-choice, completions, true or false, essay, and skill-building exercises . . . for review and enrichment at every ability level.

CHAPTER REVIEW

SUMMARY

8–1 Nature of Chemical Reactions

❏ When a chemical reaction takes place, there is always a change in the properties and in the energy of the substances.

❏ A reactant is a substance that enters into a chemical reaction. A product is a substance that is produced by a chemical reaction.

❏ An atom forms chemical bonds with other atoms in order to complete its outermost energy level. The arrangement of electrons in an atom determines the atom's bonding capacity, or its ability to undergo chemical reactions.

8–2 Chemical Equations

❏ A chemical equation is an expression in which symbols and formulas are used to represent a chemical reaction. Reactants are written to the left of the arrow in such an equation and products are written to the right.

❏ The law of conservation of mass states that matter can be neither created nor destroyed in a chemical reaction.

❏ Four basic rules should be followed in balancing equations: Write a word equation and a chemical equation, count the number of atoms of each element on each side of the arrow, use coefficients to balance the equation, check your work.

8–3 Types of Chemical Reactions

❏ In a synthesis reaction, two or more simple substances combine to form a new, more complex substance.

❏ In a decomposition reaction, a complex substance breaks down into two or more simpler substances.

❏ In a single-replacement reaction, an uncombined element replaces an element that is part of a compound.

❏ In a double-replacement reaction, different atoms in two different compounds replace each other.

8–4 Energy of Chemical Reactions

❏ When chemical reactions occur, energy can either be released or absorbed.

❏ A chemical reaction in which energy is released is called an exothermic reaction. A chemical reaction in which energy is absorbed is called an endothermic reaction.

❏ In order for reactants to form products, activation energy is needed.

8–5 Rates of Chemical Reactions

❏ The rate of a reaction is a measure of how quickly reactants turn into products.

❏ An increase in the concentration of reactants increases the rate of a reaction.

❏ An increase in the surface area of reactants increases the rate of a reaction.

❏ An increase in temperature generally increases the rate of a reaction.

❏ A catalyst is a substance that increases the rate of a reaction without itself being changed by the reaction.

VOCABULARY

Define each term in a complete sentence.

activation energy	concentration	endothermic reaction	reactant
catalyst	decomposition reaction	exothermic reaction	reaction rate
chemical equation		kinetics	single-replacement

CHAPTER SUMMARIES list all key concepts by section.

VOCABULARY exercises reinforce important scientific terms introduced in the chapter.

CONTENT REVIEW: MULTIPLE CHOICE

On a separate sheet of paper, write the letter of the answer that best completes each statement.

1. The substances to the left of the arrow in a chemical equation are called
   a. coefficients. b. products. c. subscripts. d. reactants.
2. An atom's ability to undergo chemical reactions is determined by
   a. protons. b. neutrons. c. innermost electrons. d. outermost electrons.
3. In a balanced chemical equation,
   a. atoms are conserved. b. molecules are equal.
   c. coefficients are equal. d. energy is not conserved.
4. Two or more simple substances combine to form a new substance in a
   a. decomposition reaction. b. double-replacement reaction.
   c. single-replacement reaction. d. synthesis reaction.
5. A reaction in which energy is absorbed is called
   a. exothermic. b. endothermic. c. analytic. d. catalytic.
6. In an exothermic reaction, heat is
   a. absorbed. b. released. c. destroyed. d. conserved.
7. The energy required for reactants to form products is called
   a. energy of motion. b. potential energy.
   c. activation energy. d. synthetic energy.
8. The rate of a chemical reaction can be increased by
   a. decreasing concentration. b. decreasing temperature.
   c. increasing surface area. d. all of the above.
9. Concentration is a measure of molecular
   a. energy. b. speed. c. number per unit of volume. d. temperature.
10. Adding a catalyst to a reaction increases rate by
    a. increasing molecular motion. b. decreasing molecular motion.
    c. lowering activation energy. d. increasing concentration.

CONTENT REVIEW: COMPLETION

On a separate sheet of paper, write the word or words that best complete each statement.

1. In a _____ change, one kind of matter is turned into another.
2. A chemical reaction is accompanied by a change in the _____ and _____ of the substances.
3. A (An) _____ means "yields."
4. According to the law of _____ matter can be neither created nor destroyed during a chemical reaction.
5. Two or more simple substances combine to form a new, more complex substance in a (an) _____ reaction.
6. An uncombined element replaces an element that is part of a compound in a (an) _____ reaction.
7. A reaction in which energy is released is called a (an) _____ reaction.
8. In an endothermic reaction, the _____ have more energy.
9. The study of reaction rates is called _____
10. A substance that increases the rate of a chemical reaction without itself being changed is called a (an) _____

202

CONTENT REVIEW: TRUE OR FALSE

Determine whether each statement is true or false. Then on a separate sheet of paper, write "true" if it is true. If it is false, change the underlined word or words to make the statement true.

1. The substances formed as a result of a chemical reaction are called reactants.
2. A chemical equation uses symbols and formulas to represent a reaction.
3. A number written in front of a chemical symbol or formula is a (an) coefficient.
4. To balance the following equation, the number 2 should be placed in front of O_2: $KClO_3 \longrightarrow KCl + O_2$.
5. In a synthesis reaction, complex substances form simpler substances.
6. The formation of carbon dioxide during combustion of a fuel is an example of a decomposition reaction.
7. In an exothermic reaction, products have more energy than reactants.
8. The collision theory can be used to account for the factors that affect reaction rates.
9. Concentration is a measure of the energy of motion of molecules.
10. Increasing surface area increases reaction rate.

CONCEPT REVIEW: SKILL BUILDING

Use the skills you have developed in the chapter to complete each activity.

1. **Making calculations** Balance the following equations:
   a. $PbO_2 \longrightarrow PbO + O_2$
   b. $Ca + H_2O \longrightarrow Ca(OH)_2 + H_2$
   c. $Zn + S \longrightarrow ZnS$
   d. $BaCl_2 + Na_2SO_4 \longrightarrow BaSO_4 + NaCl$
   e. $Al + Fe_2O_3 \longrightarrow Al_2O_3 + Fe$
   f. $C_{12}H_{22}O_{11} \longrightarrow C + H_2O$
   c. $4C + 6H_2 + O_2 \longrightarrow 2C_2H_6O$
   d. $2LiI + Pb(NO_3)_2 \longrightarrow 2LiNO_3 + PbI_2$
   e. $2H_2O + O_2 \longrightarrow 2H_2O_2$

2. **Classifying reactions** Identify the general type of reaction represented by each equation. Explain your answers.
   a. $NiCl_2 \longrightarrow Ni + Cl_2$
   b. $MgBr_2 + 2K \longrightarrow Mg + 2KBr$

3. **Relating cause and effect** Iron is often galvanized, or covered with the more active metal zinc, in order to protect the iron from corroding. Explain why this method is effective.

4. **Developing a model** Draw an energy diagram of an exothermic reaction that has a high activation energy. On your diagram, indicate how an increase in temperature would affect the rate of this reaction. Do the same for the addition of a catalyst.

CONCEPT REVIEW: ESSAY

Discuss each of the following in a brief paragraph.

1. Why do substances react chemically?
2. State the law of conservation of mass and explain its role in chemical reactions.
3. Use the collision theory to explain the effects on reaction rate of (a) increased concentration, (b) catalysts, and (c) increased surface area.
4. Give two reasons why collisions between molecules of reactants may not be effective in forming products.
5. Explain how the heat content of the products of a reaction compares with that of the reactants when the reaction is (a) exothermic or (b) endothermic.

203

Total Teaching Support for building understanding and testing knowledge

ANNOTATED TEACHER'S EDITION contains background information, teaching strategies, demonstrations, enrichment activities, and answers to all questions in the text in an easy-to-use wrap-around format.

The comprehensive, easy-to-use **LABORATORY MANUAL** includes 67 experiments that emphasize physical science concepts, skills development, and everyday life applications.

LABORATORY MANUAL ANNOTATED TEACHER'S EDITION gives you all the information you need for successful labs including safety guidelines, materials and supplier lists, answers to questions, and more!

COMPUTER TEST BANK contains test questions and answer keys on easy-to-use software and in book format in a handy 3-ring binder.

DIAL-A-TEST™ offers you customized tests by phone or mail to save time and work!

TEACHER'S RESOURCE BOOK gives you everything you need for successful teaching . . . daily Lesson Plans, Master Forms, Vocabulary Skills, Using Science Skills, Sharpen Your Skills, Laboratory Investigations, and Problem-Solving Worksheets, plus Chapter and Unit Tests with Answer Keys. It also includes a special Science Reading Skills section, a Science Graphing Skills section, and a Problem-Solving Skills section, Plus Full-Color Transparencies, Posters, a Science Fair Manual, a Spanish Physical Science Glossary, and the Prentice Hall Physical Science Activity Exchange.

PHYSICAL SCIENCE CRITICAL THINKING SKILLS TRANSPARENCIES provide exciting visual aids to use in class.

PRENTICE HALL SCIENCE COURSEWARE includes 10 easy-to-use interactive software programs that reinforce and extend physical science concepts and skills through dynamic graphics and a sound educational design.

Prentice Hall
Physical Science

DEAN HURD

Physical Science Instructor
Carlsbad High School
Carlsbad, California

MYRNA SILVER

Physical Science Instructor
Richardson Independent School District
Richardson, Texas

ANGELA BORNN BACHER

Chemistry Instructor
Methacton School District
Fairview Village, Pennsylvania

CHARLES WILLIAM McLAUGHLIN

Chemistry Instructor
Central High School
St. Joseph, Missouri

Prentice-Hall, Inc., Englewood Cliffs, New Jersey 07632

FIRST EDITION

© 1988 by Prentice-Hall, Inc., Englewood Cliffs, New Jersey 07632. All rights reserved. No part of this book may be reproduced in any form or by any means without permission in writing from the publisher.
Printed in the United States of America.

0-13-700576-8

10 9 8 7 6 5 4

Prentice-Hall of Australia, Pty. Ltd., Sydney
Prentice-Hall of Canada Inc., Toronto
Prentice-Hall Hispanoamericana, S.A., Mexico
Prentice-Hall of India Private Ltd., New Delhi
Prentice-Hall International, Inc., London
Prentice-Hall of Japan, Inc., Tokyo
Prentice-Hall of Southeast Asia Pte. Ltd., Singapore
Editora Prentice-Hall do Brasil Ltda., Rio de Janeiro

Contents of Annotated Teacher's Edition

Other Components of *Prentice Hall Physical Science*

Prentice Hall Physical Science has been designed as a complete program for use with junior high or middle school physical science students. The student text contains the topics most widely covered by physical science courses. The auxiliary materials described below are available to augment the program.

ANNOTATED TEACHER'S EDITION

This comprehensive teacher's edition includes all the information needed to teach *Prentice Hall Physical Science.* It features pedagogical aids for science instruction; teaching strategies for units, chapters, and chapter sections; background information; historical notes; interesting facts and figures; suggested teacher demonstrations; answers to all text and end-of-chapter questions; additional end of chapter questions; section previews; section performance objectives; and shading in of key topic sentences. A comprehensive list of laboratory materials, science suppliers, teacher's bibliography, and audiovisual and software suggestions are also included.

LABORATORY MANUAL—STUDENT EDITION

Each textbook has an accompanying laboratory manual. The manuals are 8½ inches by 11 inches, are five-hole punched, and are consumable. Each laboratory activity is keyed to a particular chapter in the student text. There is at least one lab per chapter. These laboratory investigations provide a traditional laboratory approach to the topics presented in the text and employ standard laboratory equipment.

Each investigation begins with background information for the student, a comprehensive list of materials, a step-by-step procedure, safety caution of symbols keyed to specific steps in the procedure, an observations section, a conclusions section, a section that poses additional critical thinking and application questions, and a going further section that allows industrious students to do further experiments.

LABORATORY MANUAL— ANNOTATED TEACHER'S EDITION

Each annotated teacher's edition provides answers to questions posed in the investigations, includes setup instructions, and suggests places to purchase special equipment, if any is required.

TEACHER'S RESOURCE BOOK

Each Teacher's Resource Book, or TRB, contains a wide variety of skills-related material for the teacher, most of which is clearly keyed to various academic levels. Materials in the TRB are presented on a chapter-by-chapter basis, that is, correlated to the chapters in the student text and presented in the same sequence. Materials for each chapter include

1. Daily lesson plans integrating all components of *Prentice Hall Physical Science*
2. Chapter outline sheets
3. Vocabulary Skill Worksheets
4. Using Science Skills Worksheets
5. Sharpen Your Skills Worksheets
6. Laboratory Investigation Worksheets
7. Problem-Solving Worksheets
8. Transparency Master Forms
9. Chapter and Unit Tests

In addition to the chapter-by-chapter materials, the TRB contains a section on science reading skills, a booklet on science graphing skills, a section on problem-solving strategies with additional problem-solving worksheets, a section on laboratory safety and assessment that includes a safety contract and laboratory practicals, a section on study skills with accompanying worksheets, a section on running a science fair, four-color physical science transparencies, physical science wall posters, a physical science Spanish glossary, and Prentice-Hall's exclusive activity exchange.

SCIENCE COURSEWARE

Prentice Hall Computer Software Programs provide a vast multiprogram project under the general title: Science Courseware. Such courseware employs "state of the art" graphics in order to present on the computer screen events, concepts, and data that cannot be presented in the traditional classroom setting. The goal of Prentice Hall Courseware is to allow the student—through a maximum of student participation and interaction—to master science material that cannot be easily grasped through the printed word, through laboratory experiences, or by using other traditional classroom materials and techniques.

All Prentice Hall science courseware is correlated to chapters in the textbook and offers review, reteaching, glossaries, basic skills instruction, simulations, tests, and a complete management system.

COMPUTER TEST BANK WITH DIAL-A-TEST™ SERVICE AND SOFTWARE

The Computer Test Bank is packaged in a convenient three-ring binder and provides you with unparalleled flexibility in creating tests. Printed chapter tests are presented as blackline masters ready for photocopying. Software allows you to create your own customized tests, accompanied by illustrations photocopied from the Illustration Masters. Dial-A-Test™ gives you the option of phoning in question numbers and receiving customized tests in the mail.

Each question in the Computer Test Bank is keyed to chapter objectives for criterion-referenced evaluation. Multiple Choice questions test students' knowledge of basic facts.

True or False questions test students' ability to determine which statements are correct. Completion questions require students to provide the correct term or terms to make a statement accurate. Using Science Skills questions include questions based on visuals that test students' ability to read and understand illustrations. Critical Thinking and Application questions require students to comprehend, analyze, and synthesize information.

PHYSICAL SCIENCE CRITICAL THINKING SKILLS TRANSPARENCIES

Packaged in a convenient three-ring binder, the four-color phycial science transparencies allow the teacher to use visual aids to demonstrate difficult physical science concepts and processes. Each transparency is accompanied by five questions which test critical thinking skills. The questions are ordered by difficulty, with the first few questions testing basic observing and comparing skills, while the last questions test more complex critical thinking skills such as inferring, relating, applying, and predicting. These transparencies are in addition to the four-color transparencies in the Teacher's Resource Book.

To the Teacher

RATIONALE OF THE PROGRAM

Science education is a vital force in helping your students recognize the critical importance of scientific developments in today's world—and tomorrow's. The authors and editors of *Prentice Hall Physical Science* have designed this textbook and its auxiliary materials to meet this educational goal. This program provides your students with the basic knowledge of physical science as it relates to them and to their own range of experiences. However, this program goes even farther. It makes it possible for young people to use their abilities to develop an appreciation of the basic concepts in physics and chemistry. Historical achievements in the field of physical science, career paths, and some thoughts on the future will all contribute to the growth and development of your students.

BALANCED PHYSICAL SCIENCE PROGRAM

The *Prentice Hall Physical Science* program has been developed in accordance with basic principles of science education. The program offers a balance between textual and investigative material, with enough flexibility to suit individual teaching styles and classroom needs.

The textual material presents relevant and recent facts that are used to build science concepts. Illustrations, teaching captions, and in-text questions encourage students to participate, to draw on previously learned information, to make judgements, and to inquire, thereby forming a basis for conceptual learning.

SKILLS IN PHYSICAL SCIENCE PROGRAM

The *Prentice Hall Physical Science* program provides for the full development of science skills that are inherent in physical science, as well as in other branches of science. The skills package within the textbook includes Laboratory Investigations, Sharpen Your Skills marginal activities, and Skill Building activities at the end of each chapter. Through these investigations and activities, students gain firsthand experience with such learning skills and processes as *observing, classifying, identifying, measuring, inferring, hypothesizing, interpreting,* and *predicting.*

By utilizing the skills package provided in the textbok, teachers can be assured that their students will receive a comprehensive program that reinforces and extends all the skills that are applicable to physical science. Furthermore, since most skills investigations and activities require report writing and the recording of data, teachers can easily assess whether their students have developed proficiency in skills development.

READABILITY AND STUDENT COMPREHENSION AND INTEREST

The authors and editors of *Prentice Hall Physical Science* have taken many steps to improve the readability of this text as a means of facilitating student comprehension and interest.

Prentice Hall Physical Science is designed with an open, clean format that uses exciting and relevant visuals to enhance student interest. The text is written in a style that appeals to and accommodates the wide range of comprehension levels found in the junior high or middle school. The readability of the text has been carefully controlled so that most students will be able to understand the physical science content and concepts presented.

Studies have shown that students often feel hindered and frustrated by scientific terms because the words are alien to them, are usually difficult to pronounce, and are hard to remember. To remedy this situation, *Prentice Hall Physical Science* introduces scientific terms in boldfaced type. Definitions accompany the new terms, and phonetic pronunciation guides are given where necessary.

In addition, photographs and illustrations, most of which are in full color, visually reinforce the text material, thereby aiding readability and comprehension. Most photographs and illustrations include an explanatory caption and frequently an inductive question. The answers to these caption questions can be discerned by the student in three ways:

1. Referring back to text material
2. Basing the response directly on the photograph or illustration
3. Using previously acquired knowledge

Other aids to readability and comprehension include single-concept paragraphs, frequent in-text questions, section checkup questions, chapter summaries, and end-of-chapter questions. These features help to make the text more readable by providing immediate learning evaluations and by continually eliciting student participation and response.

Since a clear guide to what students will be expected to learn in each chapter is a proven readability aid, *Prentice Hall Physical Science* includes an outline of chapter sections with objectives keyed to each section on the chapter opening pages. Moreover, each numbered section within the text provides a skill-oriented section objective to further guide students. In each section, a key idea statement tying together the most important concepts in the section is included in boldfaced type. These boldfaced key ideas are extremely helpful for students who need some guidance as to what is the most important information in each section.

Overview of Science Education

READING AND LANGUAGE DEVELOPMENT IN THE SCIENCE CLASSROOM

The type of reading required of secondary students is different from that required of elementary students. The vocabulary is more difficult, the sentence structure is more complex, the writing is denser, and the concepts presented are more challenging. In addition, reading in the science area presents difficulties of its own. Students must be able to isolate important facts and organize them, form hypotheses based on these facts, test alternatives, and draw conclusions.

In order for students to utilize any text, appropriate readability is essential. The Dale-Chall formula indicates that this text is written on the reading level of most junior high school students. The introduction of new terms in boldfaced type, the pronunciation guides and definitions, and the review questions at the end of each section and chapter improve the readability of this test. However, you will still need to help your students develop the specialized skills they need to read in the science area.

Vocabulary in the Science Area

Reading in the science area presents students with a largely unfamiliar technical vocabulary. Terms such as exothermic and orbital motion do not come up in everyday conversation. In addition, terms with which students may be familiar in an everyday context, such as electricity, have a specialized meaning in a scientific context. Students may require some assistance in dealing with these difficult terms. Try doing the following before giving a reading assignment from this text:
1. Identify the key concepts and vocabulary words in each chapter.
2. Pronounce all new words. Each new scientific term in each unit is introduced in boldfaced type and followed by a phonetic pronunciation guide where necessary. It is important for you to pronounce these terms and any others with which your students may have trouble. The pronunciation key is located at the beginning of the Glossary.
3. Define all new and potentially difficult terms. New terms are defined in-text and, for most terms, again in the Glossary.
4. Draw students' attention to the charts, drawings, and photographs that will help them understand new words and concepts. All photographs and artwork have been carefully selected to help students visualize concepts presented throughout the text.

Reading in the Science Area

Besides helping students develop a science vocabulary, a science course should also help them develop skills in the following:
1. Reading for exact meaning
2. Identifying the main ideas expressed in chapter sections
3. Classifying information and organizing ideas obtained from reading the text
4. Noting cause-and-effect relationships
5. Gaining accurate information from the visual representations throughout the text
6. Understanding the scientific formulas and symbols in the text
7. Reading directions accurately, especially for carrying out Laboratory Investigations and activities suggested in the text

8. Locating and using different sources of information

Science teachers sometimes overlook the development of these specialized reading skills. These skills are necessary for students to develop into mature and independent readers both inside and outside of the science classroom.

Writing in the Science Area

Developing good writing skills goes hand-in-hand with developing good reading skills. Both are important for effective communication.

Because our society relies heavily on written expression and printed material, it is important for students to possess effective writing skills. Your students will have frequent opportunities to display and develop their writing skills while using the *Prentice Hall Physical Science* text. When using this textbook, you should expect your students to
1. Keep records of all investigations and activities. Many investigations and activities require students to write a short report detailing observations and conclusions made during an investigation or activity.
2. Record notes from text material and your lectures and discussions. For students to fully comprehend the material presented by such sources, they need to learn to organize and summarize information. Writing the information will help students retain and understand the material better.
3. Write the answers to Section Review questions, as well as the questions at the end of each chapter. Essay questions at the end of each chapter require students to write brief essays on topics related to the chapter. All such exercises should be used not only for reinforcement and as an evaluative and diagnostic aid, but also as an opportunity to develop writing skills.

Speaking in the Science Area

The *Prentice Hall Physical Science* text offers many opportunities to develop communication skills. When students have a chance to express their own thoughts or to interpret the thoughts of others, oral and written communication improve and become a means for learning. Thus, speaking is another important language skill that can and should be further developed in the science classroom. Oral communication is the most effective and common means of communicating and is the basis for a sound program in reading and writing.
1. **Presentations.** Students of this age are curious about their surroundings and the natural events that occur in their environment. Have students make oral presentations to

their classmates about any physics or chemistry collections, physical science topics that interest them, or results obtained from investigations and activities. Encourage students in the audience to participate by asking relevant questions.

2. **Discussion.** Encourage students to participate in class discussions. Techniques for encouraging student involvement in discussions are presented in a later section, Questioning in the Science Area.

3. **Dramatizations.** Have students act out concepts presented in this text, such as important discoveries of scientists or the impact pollution may have on a town or an individual.

Listening in the Science Area

Even though speaking is the most common form of communication, it is ineffective without a listener. Listening skills should be developed concurrently with speaking skills. Students need to learn to respect each other's viewpoints.

Encourage good listening habits in your students by being a good listener yourself. Pause after asking a question. If no student offers an answer, rephrase the question. Teaching effective listening is important in helping all your students become better science students.

Listening constitutes a major portion of the communication process. Listening skills can be developed by encouraging students to

1. Listen to questions posed by the teacher and other students. For example, before proceeding with a laboratory investigation, you may ask a question such as "What conditions do you think bring about a chemical change?" A question of this nature would involve the entire class in a discussion and would require students to listen to responses from their classmates.

2. Listen to directions for carrying out investigations. It is important for students to be able to follow directions, especially safety precautions, in a science class.

   Have your students practice this listening skills by giving them oral instructions on how to make something—a paper airplane, for instance. Repeat the directions frequently and ask your students to repeat the instructions as they follow them. This activity will prepare students for laboratory investigations by helping them follow a thought sequence and by emphasizing the need for accuracy in communication and interpretation.

3. Listen to explanations or descriptions of natural phenomena provided by you, other students, or guest speakers. You can help your students listen properly by telling them what to listen for, how to listen to the material presented, and how to mentally organize or write down what they hear.

Questioning in the Science Area

Developing communication in your science classroom involves your participation. Much of a teacher's class time is spent asking questions. In fact, research has shown that teachers use questioning more frequently than any other single teaching technique. You ask questions to develop creative learning situations, evaluate your students' progress, give directions, correct behavior, and initiate instructions.

It is important to understand and use good questioning techniques and strategies during the instructional process. Thought-provoking questions and improved questioning techniques can help you develop and sustain student interest, provide new ways to deal with subject matter, and give purpose to your student evaluations.

You should design your objectives at a variety of cognitive levels. Your questions should also reflect the various levels of your performance objectives. Research indicates that many teachers unconsciously concentrate most of their questions at the lowest level in the cognitive domain—knowledge. Answering questions at this level requires a simple recall of facts. For instance,

1. What does the word element mean?
2. In what year was the first periodic table developed?

   Notice that each question requires only a short response or the recall of a definition or fact. These questions could be rephrased to require your students to operate at a higher thinking level. For instance,

1. Explain the difference between an element and a compound.
2. How did the development of the periodic table affect basic chemistry concepts?

   These questions would result in longer student responses, would require answers that go beyond the simple recall of facts, and would probably encourage greater discussion in your classroom. Questions should, therefore, be asked at a variety of cognitive levels.

   Besides the type of question you ask, the number of questions you ask affects student response. It is easy to ask too many questions during an instruction period. Studies have found that some teachers ask questions at a rate of 180 questions per science lesson! This rapid-fire method of questioning and calling on a student to respond immediately after the question is asked leads to brief student responses.

Thus, wait-time serves a twofold purpose in the classroom: (1) It provides an atmosphere more conducive to discussion and learning, and (2) students learn to use wait-time to organize a more complete answer.

Along with waiting 3 to 5 seconds after asking a question, pausing after a student response is also helpful. This second pause, or silent-time, increases the chances that the student will add to his or her response or that other students will add to the initial response. If you follow these simple techniques of waiting before and after a student's response, more students may become involved, you may not need to ask as many questions, and the questions you do ask will probably be of a higher cognitive level.

TEACHING HETEROGENEOUS CLASSES

Prentice Hall Physical Science has been designed to meet the needs of students of all ability levels. Through careful analysis of readability, the text has been monitored to ensure that students in the junior high or middle school can read and comprehend the material presented in the text. Moreover, large photographs and illustrations, which reinforce and extend the material in the text, are important tools in helping students comprehend facts and concepts in physical science.

In order to help teachers meet the needs of students of varying ability levels in a heterogeneous classroom, all of the marginal Sharpen Your Skills activities have been keyed to an ability level in the Annotated Teacher's Edition. These ability levels are remedial, average, and enriched. In this way, the teacher can assign activities on an individual basis, depending on the ability level of different students in the classroom.

TEACHING "SPECIAL" STUDENTS

Certain state and federal laws have mandated that all students are to have access to the least restrictive learning environment possible. Thus, many "special" students, those with physical and mental disabilities, are being "mainstreamed" into nonspecialized classes. This action challenges the teacher to accommodate a much wider range of student abilities, needs, and interests.

Students With Learning Problems

Learning processes that include inferences and abstract reasoning are often more difficult for students who have learning problems. Such students include those who have some degree of mental retardation. In order to better help such students grasp facts and concepts in physical science, it is important to provide daily learning goals at a pace that will allow the goals to be achieved. These students will benefit greatly from the use of concrete examples in the classroom that relate back to daily life. The need to reinforce lessons is also important to such students. Furthermore, since many of these students will have experienced failure in their studies, it is vital to provide as much positive reinforcement as possible. Emphasize success and minimize failure whenever you can.

Students With Visual Problems

Students who are blind, as well as those with limited sight, are more dependent on senses such as hearing than other students. As a result, such students should always be seated where they will be able to hear the teacher and their classmates most easily. Tape recording lessons will help these students study and go over material at their own pace. Also, classmates can be a great aid by providing descriptions of photographs and illustrations in the text.

Students With Hearing Problems

Students with hearing problems are far more dependent on the written word than other students. Usually, these students should be seated near the front of the room so that they can read the teacher's lips. The teacher should enunciate every word and avoid talking too quickly. All instructions and assignments should be written down for these students. Allow students who cannot hear well to copy the notes taken in class by classmates.

Students With Other Physical Problems

Students who have physical problems that require crutches or wheelchairs will need extra room to get around in the classroom. Take care to make sure such students do not try to stretch their limits beyond their physical capabilities, but do not treat them any more differently than necessary so that they will feel an integral part of the class.

Students who have physical problems due to disorders such as muscular dystrophy, or other disorders that deter motor coordination, will often have trouble in the laboratory setting.

Holding flasks, pouring liquids, and using other equipment may be beyond their capabilities. If these students can write, it is often best to assign them the task of recording during investigations while their lab partners carry out the more physical aspects of the investigation.

Some students may have illnesses such as diabetes or epilepsy. In general, such students will not need any special care. However, the teacher should be aware of any special problems or symptoms these illnesses might present in order to obtain prompt medical attention when necessary.

Features of the Student Text

Prentice Hall Physical Science has been set up to provide a flexible and varied approach to teaching science. The text is divided into eight units, sufficiently self-contained to be taught separately and in any order. Since science cannot be compartmentalized into discrete packets of information, there are areas in which topics in one unit overlap with topics in other units. However, in order to retain the flexibility of the program and allow the teacher to begin with any unit he or she desires, any concept or definition introduced for the first time in any unit is considered unfamiliar and taught as if the topic is a new one.

One exception to this flexibility is Chapter I: Exploring Physical Science. This chapter introduces students to the scientific method, the various branches of physical science, the metric system, tools of measurement, and the need for safety in the laboratory. It is recommended that all students complete Chapter I first. At that point, the teacher can jump to the unit in the text that best fits her or his curriculum needs.

UNIT OPENERS

Each unit begins with a two-page spread that includes a large, dramatic photograph or illustration. Accompanying the visual is a short overview that both introduces the topics to be discussed in the unit and provides motivational text to capture student interest. A listing of the chapters in the unit is also included in the unit opening spread.

CHAPTER OPENERS

Each chapter begins with a two-page spread. Like the unit openers, large photographs and illustrations are employed to "grab" student attention immediately. A short, concise caption informs the reader as to the nature of the visual. The visual can also be readily identified through the chapter opening text. This text, often written in an anecdotal style, serves to entice the student to read further. Intriguing questions and unusual data are employed to hold the student's attention and to thrust the student into the text with the desire to find out more about the topic.

Also included in the chapter opening spread is a list of the main sections in each chapter. This listing serves as an instructional outline for both student and teacher. Moreover, chapter objectives are provided in the chapter opening spread. Thus, the chapter opener serves the dual purpose of initiating the student's desire to learn more about the material and of alerting the student to the specific objectives, or goals, that he or she is expected to grasp when the chapter is completed.

CHAPTER SECTIONS

As noted, each main chapter section is listed in the chapter opening. These sections are numbered consecutively on both the chapter opening page and in the text itself. Numbering the main sections helps distinguish the main topics in the chapter from the subtopics. Subtopics in each main section are set apart and boldfaced.

Beside each numbered chapter section is a Section Objective for that section. The Section Objective alerts the student to the particular science skill that is developed in that section. For example, in a section dealing with the various types of mixtures, the objective would tell the student that the science skill needed or developed in that section is classifying types of mixtures.

In most sections, the students will find in-text questions based on the material the student has just read. Some in-text questions require simple factual recall. Other in-text questions employ more advanced critical thinking skills such as predicting and relating.

Within each main section are numerous photographs and illustrations that help teach and reinforce the topics found in the section. Most visuals are large and in color to further hold student interest. Data charts and graphs are interspersed in the text as well, to provide further information. Each numbered section also contains one sentence that is set apart in boldfaced type. This sentence alerts the student to the key idea of that section.

SAMPLE PROBLEMS

In selected sections where formulas requiring mathematical skills are presented, a clearly delineated box containing sample problems is included. The first problem is presented and worked out in a step-by-step method that shows students exactly how to tackle such problems. Following the sample problem, two additional practice problems are provided in order to reinforce concepts that have been illustrated by the sample problem.

Whenever possible within a section, interesting motivational information is presented to help generate student interest. This motivational material may relate to students' everyday life, or present interesting anecdotes that help students grasp the processes involved in scientific experimentation. Motivational material is usually written in a storylike, flowing narrative. Basic information presented in the chapter is found in the paragraphs following motivational material. Most paragraphs are written to begin with a topic sentence that provides the student with a clear idea of the information that is to follow.

At the end of every numbered section is a Section Review. These review questions, usually short answer questions, allow the teacher to quickly verify whether the important topics in that section have been grasped by the student. In general, at least one review question relates back to the Section Objective listed at the beginning of that section.

MARGINAL ACTIVITIES

In most cases, each main numbered section of the text contains at least one Sharpen Your Skills marginal activity. These activities are placed in the margin to avoid disrupting the student's reading of the text. These activities can be used in a variety of ways, including homework, extra credit, and class projects. Each activity is keyed to an academic level—remedial, average, or enriched—in the annotated teacher's edition. In this way, teachers can assign those marginal activities they think are most appropriate for a particular student's academic needs.

The marginal activities appear with the generic term Sharpen Your Skills. However, on page T-12 of the Annotated Teacher's Edition is a detailed skills scope and sequence for all marginal activities, as well as Laboratory Investigations and skill building questions found at the end of each chapter. There are five types of marginal activities. These are hands-on, computational, reading comprehension/vocabulary, library, and field activities. All such activities require the student to utilize science skills applicable to all scientific endeavors. Such skills range from simple skills such as observing and comparing to more high-level skills such as relating, predicting, and applying. In many activities, the student is required to write a report, prepare a visual presentation in the form of charts and diagrams, or graph any observations and data.

CAREERS

Each chapter contains a career feature that introduces students to a possible career choice in science related to that particular chapter. Careers, it should be noted, range from those requiring a high school diploma to those requiring a doctorate. Each career feature consists of a full-color photograph depicting a person in this career at work, a description of the work done by people in this career, and an address to which interested students may write for further information. In order to increase career awareness and encourage students to contemplate and begin planning their own futures, a Help Wanted ad is included in each career to help relate such careers to real life career possibilities.

LABORATORY INVESTIGATIONS

Each chapter contains one full-page laboratory investigation just prior to the chapter summary page. Such investigations provide students with the opportunity to work in the laboratory and actively participate in investigating science problems. Most of the investigations are designed to reinforce concepts presented in the text, but a few are designed to supplement the material in the text. Easy-to-obtain materials are used in such investigations.

Each laboratory investigation clearly outlines the Problem to be investigated, the Materials needed, and the Procedure to follow. A section called Observations alerts students to any observations or data they are to collect, and tells students how to organize their data. In general, data is organized in the form of charts or graphs. A Conclusions section ties up the laboratory investigation, calling upon students to analyze their data and draw various conclusions. Often the Conclusions section asks students to use their data to reinforce or further establish a scientific concept or theory. In addition, special safety symbols alert students when important safety precautions must be observed.

CHAPTER REVIEW

Chapter Summary and Vocabulary

At the end of every chapter is a chapter summary section. The summary is divided into groupings based on the main, numbered sections in the chapter. Under each grouping is a list of key sentences that describe the most important concepts presented in the chapter. The chapter summary might be considered a detailed outline of the chapter content.

Following the summary is a listing of the vocabulary words included in the chapter. The vocabulary words include all the boldfaced terms from the chapter.

End-of-Chapter Questions

A wide variety of questions end each chapter. The first three question sections are Content Review questions. These questions are listed in the order in which the material is introduced in the chapter. Content Review questions are broken down into ten multiple choice questions, ten completions questions, and ten true or false questions. The true or false questions are of the type that the student must not only identify an incorrect statement, but then must make it correct by substituting the correct word or phrase into the statement.

Also included in the end-of-chapter questions are two Concept Review sections. The first is titled Skill Building. Skill building questions require the student to draw upon science skills and are based on material presented in the chapter. Skill building questions range from simple computational questions to more difficult questions utilizing higher order skills such as inferring and relating. Often the student is asked to examine illustrations in the chapter and then analyze the illustrations in the form of charts and graphs.

The second type of Concept Review questions are essay questions. Essay questions reinforce and extend concepts, both scientific and societal. Since they require the student to write his or her answer in paragraph form, essay questions enhance the student's ability to write and report on science topics.

END-OF-UNIT MATERIAL

Science Gazettes

At the end of every unit are two Science Gazette articles, each of which is two pages in length. Each Science Gazette is a science reader written and designed in a motivational magazine format. The first article, called an Adventure In Science, profiles a particular scientist and the path the scientist took, or is taking, to make a significant discovery. The second article, called an Issue In Science, presents a nonbiased discussion of a contemporary scientific issue.

The articles of the Science Gazette have been carefully chosen and designed to maximize the motivation of students of all levels in their study of science. Each article is related to topics presented in the unit. The articles can be used to stimulate class discussions, as the basis for individual short essay homework assignments; to introduce or wrap-up lessons on related topics, and to develop science reading skills.

In the Annotated Teacher's Edition, additional background material is included on each Science Gazette article. In addition, a teaching strategy for each article is presented, as well as Additional Questions and Topic Suggestions. Moreover, in the Teacher's Resource Book, specific activities and handouts related to each gazette article are included in the Science

Reading Skills section. These activities test basic science reading skills and provide the teacher with an excellent framework for assessing whether students have grasped the concepts in the Science Gazette articles.

END-OF-TEXT FEATURES

Following the text are several features designed to aid students in their understanding of physical science.

For Further Reading

A bibliography for each chapter in the textbook is provided in a section called For Further Reading. The books listed in the bibliography will help students who wish to do further research on a topic they find interesting, as well as helping students reinforce the material they have learned.

Appendices

A variety of appendices are located in the back of the textbook. Appendix A details the metric system and provides methods of converting metric figures into their English equivalents and vice-versa. Appendix B lists a wide variety of safety rules that the students must use in any laboratory setting. Appendix C provides a mathematics refresher to help students with basic mathematical concepts and processes that they will employ while studying *Prentice Hall Physical Science*. Appendix D lists all of the important formulas and equations students will encounter during their study of physical science. Appendix E lists some of the more common elements and provides basic information about these elements. In addition a reproduction of the periodic table has been included in the end paper of the text for easy reference.

Glossary

Scientific terms introduced in the text are listed in the Glossary in alphabetical order. Each term is clearly defined.

Index

The Index provides students with an easy-to-use reference listing of subjects covered in the text.

Prentice Hall Physical Science
Skills Scope and Sequence

The following charts provide the basic skills framework presented in *Prentice Hall Physical Science*. Basic skills through more complex critical thinking skills are included in these charts. The skills scope and sequence keys in all Sharpen Your Skills marginal activities, all Laboratory Investigations, and all end-of-chapter Skill Building questions.

CHAPTER 1 EXPLORING PHYSICAL SCIENCE pp. 4–31

TEXT REFERENCE	HANDS-ON	COMPUTATIONAL	VOCABULARY/WRITING	LIBRARY	FIELD	OBSERVING	COMPARING	MANIPULATIVE	RELATING	MEASURING	INFERRING	RECORDING	SAFETY	APPLYING	DIAGRAMING	DESIGNING	CLASSIFYING	HYPOTHESIZING	PREDICTING
Sharpen Your Skills: Changing Theories, p. 7			X	X										X					
Sharpen Your Skills: Expanding Water, p. 8	X					X		X	X	X				X					
Sharpen Your Skills: Prefixes and Suffixes, p. 14			X						X					X					
Sharpen Your Skills: Metric Research, p. 18		X		X															
Sharpen Your Skills: Metric Conversions, p. 20		X					X												
Sharpen Your Skills: Metric Measurements, p. 22	X	X								X		X							
Laboratory Investigation 1: Uncertainty of Measurements, p. 28						X	X	X		X	X	X	X						
Skill Building 1, p. 31														X					
Skill Building 2, p. 31		X																	
Skill Building 3, p. 31										X									
Skill Building 4, p. 31																X			

CHAPTER 2 PROPERTIES OF MATTER pp. 32–59

TEXT REFERENCE	HANDS-ON	COMPUTATIONAL	VOCABULARY/WRITING	LIBRARY	FIELD	OBSERVING	COMPARING	MANIPULATIVE	RELATING	MEASURING	INFERRING	RECORDING	SAFETY	APPLYING	DIAGRAMING	DESIGNING	CLASSIFYING	HYPOTHESIZING	PREDICTING
Sharpen Your Skills: Demonstrating Inertia, p. 36	X					X		X	X										
Sharpen Your Skills: A Quick Weight Change, p. 37		X																	
Sharpen Your Skills: Determining the Volume of a Solid, p. 38	X							X		X									
Sharpen Your Skills: Determining Particle Space, p. 41	X					X		X											
Sharpen Your Skills: Observing Viscosity, p. 43	X					X	X	X											
Sharpen Your Skills: Charles's Law, p. 44	X							X	X										
Sharpen Your Skills: Melting and Freezing Water, p. 51	X					X	X	X											
Sharpen Your Skills: Physical and Chemical Changes, p. 54	X					X		X			X								
Laboratory Investigation: Observing a Candle, p. 56	X					X		X			X	X	X						

CHAPTER 2 PROPERTIES OF MATTER pp. 32–59 (continued)

TEXT REFERENCE	HANDS-ON	COMPUTATIONAL	VOCABULARY/WRITING	LIBRARY	FIELD	OBSERVING	COMPARING	MANIPULATIVE	RELATING	MEASURING	INFERRING	RECORDING	SAFETY	APPLYING	DIAGRAMING	DESIGNING	CLASSIFYING	HYPOTHESIZING	PREDICTING
Skill Building 1, p. 59							X												
Skill Building 2, p. 59														X					
Skill Building 3, p. 59														X					
Skill Building 4, p. 59															X	X			

CHAPTER 3 CLASSIFICATION OF MATTER pp. 60-81

TEXT REFERENCE	HANDS-ON	COMPUTATIONAL	VOCABULARY/WRITING	LIBRARY	FIELD	OBSERVING	COMPARING	MANIPULATIVE	RELATING	MEASURING	INFERRING	RECORDING	SAFETY	APPLYING	DIAGRAMING	DESIGNING	CLASSIFYING	HYPOTHESIZING	PREDICTING
Sharpen Your Skills: Is It a Solution, p. 68	X					X		X			X								
Sharpen Your Skills: Collecting Elements, p. 71	X					X	X		X										
Sharpen Your Skills: Classifying Common Objects, p. 74	X					X		X			X						X		
Sharpen Your Skills: Counting Atoms, p. 76		X																	
Laboratory Investigation: Making Models of Chemical Reactions, p. 78	X						X	X	X		X			X					
Skill Building 1, p. 81																	X		
Skill Building 2, p. 81														X					
Skill Building 3, p. 81									X										
Skill Building 4, p. 81																X			
Skill Building 5, p. 81		X																	

CHAPTER 4 STRUCTURE OF MATTER pp. 86–109

TEXT REFERENCE	HANDS-ON	COMPUTATIONAL	VOCABULARY/WRITING	LIBRARY	FIELD	OBSERVING	COMPARING	MANIPULATIVE	RELATING	MEASURING	INFERRING	RECORDING	SAFETY	APPLYING	DIAGRAMING	DESIGNING	CLASSIFYING	HYPOTHESIZING	PREDICTING
Sharpen Your Skills: Making Indirect Observations, p. 91	X					X	X	X			X								
Sharpen Your Skills: Constructing Atomic Models, p. 94	X							X											
Sharpen Your Skills: Maria Goeppart Mayer, p. 96			X	X															
Sharpen Your Skills: Atomic Math, p. 101		X									X								
Sharpen Your Skills: Probability: Finding Your Friend, p. 102	X								X										
Laboratory Investigation: Shoe-Box Atoms, p. 106	X					X		X			X	X							
Skill Building 1, p. 109											X			X					
Skill Building 2, p. 109									X					X					
Skill Building 3, p. 109											X			X					

CHAPTER 5 THE PERIODIC LAW pp. 110–129

TEXT REFERENCE	HANDS-ON	COMPUTATIONAL	VOCABULARY/WRITING	LIBRARY	FIELD	OBSERVING	COMPARING	MANIPULATIVE	RELATING	MEASURING	INFERRING	RECORDING	SAFETY	APPLYING	DIAGRAMING	DESIGNING	CLASSIFYING	HYPOTHESIZING	PREDICTING
Sharpen Your Skills: Mendeleev—Chemical Superstar, p. 114	X			X					X					X					
Sharpen Your Skills: Classifying Objects, p. 117	X						X		X					X			X		
Sharpen Your Skills: Metals and Nonmetals, p. 121	X					X	X				X			X					
Sharpen Your Skills: The Frasch Process, p. 122			X	X							X								
Sharpen Your Skills: Predicting Formulas, p. 125	X	X							X		X			X					X
Laboratory Investigation 5: Graphing Trends in the Periodic Table, p. 126		X									X			X					X
Skill Building 1, p. 129																	X		
Skill Building 2, p. 129							X												
Skill Building 3, p. 129															X				
Skill Building 4, p. 129														X					
Skill Building 5, p. 129														X					
Skill Building 6, p. 129							X												
Skill Building 7, p. 129														X					

CHAPTER 6 FAMILIES OF ELEMENTS pp. 130–151

TEXT REFERENCE	HANDS-ON	COMPUTATIONAL	VOCABULARY/WRITING	LIBRARY	FIELD	OBSERVING	COMPARING	MANIPULATIVE	RELATING	MEASURING	INFERRING	RECORDING	SAFETY	APPLYING	DIAGRAMING	DESIGNING	CLASSIFYING	HYPOTHESIZING	PREDICTING
Sharpen Your Skills: Heat Conductivity in Metals, p. 134	X					X	X	X			X							X	
Sharpen Your Skills: Metal or Nonmetal?, P. 140	X					X	X	X			X								
Sharpen Your Skills: Getting to Know the Elements, p. 142	X		X			X	X										X		
Sharpen Your Skills: Deep-Sea Danger, p. 146			X	X															
Sharpen Your Skills: Ellen Richards, p. 147			X	X															
Laboratory Investigation 6: Flame Tests, p. 148						X	X	X	X		X		X	X				X	
Skill Building 1, p. 151														X					
Skill Building 2, p. 151															X				
Skill Building 3, p. 151														X					
Skill Building 4, p. 151														X					
Skill Building 5, p. 151																			X
Skill Building 6, p. 151																	X		
Skill Building 7, p. 151											X								
Skill Building 8, p. 151		X																	

CHAPTER 7 ATOMS AND BONDING pp. 158–179

TEXT REFERENCE	HANDS-ON	COMPUTATIONAL	VOCABULARY/WRITING	LIBRARY	FIELD	OBSERVING	COMPARING	MANIPULATIVE	RELATING	MEASURING	INFERRING	RECORDING	SAFETY	APPLYING	DIAGRAMING	DESIGNING	CLASSIFYING	HYPOTHESIZING	PREDICTING
Sharpen Your Skills: A Model of Energy Levels, p. 162	X							X						X	X				
Sharpen Your Skills: Growing Crystals, p. 166	X					X		X	X										
Sharpen Your Skills: Determining Oxidation Numbers, p. 175		X												X					
Laboratory Investigation 7: Properties of Ionic and Covalent Compounds, p. 176						X	X	X	X	X		X	X	X					
Skill Building 1, p. 179																			X
Skill Building 2, p. 179														X					X
Skill Building 3, p. 179															X				
Skill Building 4, p. 179															X				
Skill Building 5, p. 179																			X
Skill Building 6, p. 179														X					

CHAPTER 8 CHEMICAL REACTIONS pp. 180–203

TEXT REFERENCE	HANDS-ON	COMPUTATIONAL	VOCABULARY/WRITING	LIBRARY	FIELD	OBSERVING	COMPARING	MANIPULATIVE	RELATING	MEASURING	INFERRING	RECORDING	SAFETY	APPLYING	DIAGRAMING	DESIGNING	CLASSIFYING	HYPOTHESIZING	PREDICTING
Sharpen Your Skills: Mass and a Chemical Reaction, p. 186	X					X	X	X	X	X	X							X	
Sharpen Your Skills: A Balancing Act, p. 188		X							X										X
Sharpen Your Skills: Preventing a Chemical Reaction, p. 189	X					X	X		X					X				X	
Sharpen Your Skills: Double Replacement Reaction, p. 191	X					X		X	X		X								X
Sharpen Your Skills: Helpful Prefixes, p. 193			X	X															
Sharpen Your Skills: Kitchen Chemistry, p. 194	X			X		X			X		X			X					
Sharpen Your Skills: Rate of Reaction, p. 196	X					X	X				X							X	
Sharpen Your Skills: Temperature and Reaction Rate, p. 198	X					X	X	X			X							X	
Laboratory Investigation 8: Determining Reaction Rates, p. 200						X	X	X		X	X	X	X					X	
Skill Building 1, p. 203		X																	
Skill Building 2, p. 203																	X		
Skill Building 3, p. 203									X										
Skill Building 4, p. 203															X				

CHAPTER 9 SOLUTION CHEMISTRY pp. 204–231

TEXT REFERENCE	HANDS-ON	COMPUTATIONAL	VOCABULARY/WRITING	LIBRARY	FIELD	OBSERVING	COMPARING	MANIPULATIVE	RELATING	MEASURING	INFERRING	RECORDING	SAFETY	APPLYING	DIAGRAMING	DESIGNING	CLASSIFYING	HYPOTHESIZING	PREDICTING
Sharpen Your Skills: Solubility of a Gas in a Liquid, p. 211	X					X	X	X	X									X	
Sharpen Your Skills: Helpful Prefixes, p. 216			X											X					
Sharpen Your Skills: Emulsifying Action, p. 219	X					X		X	X					X					
Sharpen Your Skills: Naming Acids, p. 222			X	X			X							X					
Sharpen Your Skills: Acid–Base Testing, p. 225	X					X	X	X									X		
Sharpen Your Skills: A Homemade Indicator, p. 226	X					X	X	X											
Sharpen Your Skills: Predicting Salt Formation, p. 227		X												X					X
Laboratory Investigation 9: Acids, Bases, and Salts, p. 228						X	X		X	X		X	X	X				X	
Skill Building 1, p. 231																	X		
Skill Building 2, p. 231														X					
Skill Building 3, p. 231																X			

CHAPTER 9 SOLUTION CHEMISTRY pp. 204–231 (continued)

TEXT REFERENCE	HANDS-ON	COMPUTATIONAL	VOCABULARY/WRITING	LIBRARY	FIELD	OBSERVING	COMPARING	MANIPULATIVE	RELATING	MEASURING	INFERRING	RECORDING	SAFETY	APPLYING	DIAGRAMING	DESIGNING	CLASSIFYING	HYPOTHESIZING	PREDICTING
Skill Building 4, p. 231		X																	
Skill Building 5, p. 231														X					
Skill Building 6, p. 231									X										
Skill Building 7, p. 231											X								

CHAPTER 10 CARBON CHEMISTRY pp. 232–255

TEXT REFERENCE	HANDS-ON	COMPUTATIONAL	VOCABULARY/WRITING	LIBRARY	FIELD	OBSERVING	COMPARING	MANIPULATIVE	RELATING	MEASURING	INFERRING	RECORDING	SAFETY	APPLYING	DIAGRAMING	DESIGNING	CLASSIFYING	HYPOTHESIZING	PREDICTING
Sharpen Your Skills: Isomers, p. 237	X							X	X					X					
Sharpen Your Skills: Octane Rating, p. 240					X		X		X					X					
Sharpen Your Skills: The Structure of Benzene, p. 244				X					X										
Sharpen Your Skills: Food Additives, p. 249	X			X			X		X					X					
Sharpen Your Skills: Saturated and Unsaturated Fats, p. 251	X			X			X		X					X					
Laboratory Investigation 10: Preparing and Identifying Esters, p. 252						X	X	X	X	X		X	X	X					
Skill Building 1, p. 255																	X		
Skill Building 2, p. 255							X												
Skill Building 3, p. 255															X				
Skill Building 4, p. 255																	X		
Skill Building 5, p. 255														X					
Skill Building 6, p. 255							X												
Skill Building 7, p. 255															X				

CHAPTER 11 NUCLEAR CHEMISTRY pp. 256–279

TEXT REFERENCE	HANDS-ON	COMPUTATIONAL	VOCABULARY/WRITING	LIBRARY	FIELD	OBSERVING	COMPARING	MANIPULATIVE	RELATING	MEASURING	INFERRING	RECORDING	SAFETY	APPLYING	DIAGRAMING	DESIGNING	CLASSIFYING	HYPOTHESIZING	PREDICTING
Sharpen Your Skills: What Is a Quark, p. 262		X	X						X					X					
Sharpen Your Skills: Writing Nuclear Equations, p. 265		X							X		X			X					
Sharpen Your Skills: A Model of Half-Life, p. 267	X	X							X					X	X				X
Sharpen Your Skills: The Case of the Missing Mass, p. 269				X					X					X					
Sharpen Your Skills: Radioactivity in Medicine, p. 275						X	X		X					X					
Laboratory Investigation 11: The Half-Life of a Sugar Cube, p. 276		X						X	X		X	X		X	X				
Skill Building 1, p. 279		X																	
Skill Building 2, p. 279		X																	
Skill Building 3, p. 279														X					
Skill Building 4, p. 279											X								
Skill Building 5, p. 279		X																	
Skill Building 6, p. 279														X					
Skill Building 7, p. 279																X			

CHAPTER 12 MOTION pp. 286–303

TEXT REFERENCE	HANDS-ON	COMPUTATIONAL	VOCABULARY/WRITING	LIBRARY	FIELD	OBSERVING	COMPARING	MANIPULATIVE	RELATING	MEASURING	INFERRING	RECORDING	SAFETY	APPLYING	DIAGRAMING	DESIGNING	CLASSIFYING	HYPOTHESIZING	PREDICTING
Sharpen Your Skills: Frames of Reference, p. 288	X					X		X			X								
Sharpen Your Skills: Marble Motion, p. 293	X					X	X	X		X		X						X	
Sharpen Your Skills: Sensing Motion, p. 296	X					X					X								
Sharpen Your Skills: Momentum, p. 298		X					X				X			X					
Laboratory Investigation 12: Measuring Constant Speed, p. 300						X	X											X	
Skill Building 1, p. 303														X					
Skill Building 2, p. 303		X																	
Skill Building 3, p. 303														X					
Skill Building 4, p. 303		X																	
Skill Building 5, p. 303														X					
Skill Building 6, p. 303									X										
Skill Building 7, p. 303														X					

CHAPTER 13 FORCES pp. 304–327

TEXT REFERENCE	HANDS-ON	COMPUTATIONAL	VOCABULARY/WRITING	LIBRARY	FIELD	OBSERVING	COMPARING	MANIPULATIVE	RELATING	MEASURING	INFERRING	RECORDING	SAFETY	APPLYING	DIAGRAMING	DESIGNING	CLASSIFYING	HYPOTHESIZING	PREDICTING
Sharpen Your Skills: Move That Barge, p. 311		X													X				
Sharpen Your Skills: Newton's First Law of Motion, p. 313	X					X		X	X		X								
Sharpen Your Skills: Newton's Third Law of Motion, p. 316	X					X			X		X								
Sharpen Your Skills: Reaction Engines, p. 318				X	X														
Sharpen Your Skills: Projectile Motion, p. 320	X					X		X	X										
Sharpen Your Skills: A Speeding Snowball, p. 321		X												X					
Laboratory Investigation 13: Would a Gorilla Fall Faster Than a Banana?, p. 324	X					X	X	X	X			X						X	X
Skill Building 1, p. 327														X					
Skill Building 2. p. 327														X					
Skill Building 3, p. 327														X					
Skill Building 4, p. 327									X										
Skill Building 5, p. 327									X										
Skill Building 6, p. 327		X																	

CHAPTER 14 FORCES IN FLUIDS pp. 328–345

TEXT REFERENCE	HANDS-ON	COMPUTATIONAL	VOCABULARY/WRITING	LIBRARY	FIELD	OBSERVING	COMPARING	MANIPULATIVE	RELATING	MEASURING	INFERRING	RECORDING	SAFETY	APPLYING	DIAGRAMING	DESIGNING	CLASSIFYING	HYPOTHESIZING	PREDICTING
Sharpen Your Skills: Air Pressure, p. 332	X					X		X						X				X	
Sharpen Your Skills: Buoyancy, p. 334	X					X		X										X	
Sharpen Your Skills: A Bathtub Submarine, p. 336	X					X		X	X										
Sharpen Your Skills: Bernoulli's Principle, p. 340	X							X	X		X							X	
Laboratory Investigation 14: A Cartesian Diver, p. 342						X		X	X									X	
Skill Building 1, p. 345																X			
Skill Building 2, p. 345											X								
Skill Building 3, p. 345								X											
Skill Building 4, p. 345														X					
Skill Building 5, p. 345														X					
Skill Building 6, p. 345																X			
Skill Building 7, p. 345								X											
Skill Building 8, p. 345														X					

CHAPTER 15 WORK, POWER, AND SIMPLE MACHINES pp. 346–369

TEXT REFERENCE	HANDS-ON	COMPUTATIONAL	VOCABULARY/WRITING	LIBRARY	FIELD	OBSERVING	COMPARING	MANIPULATIVE	RELATING	MEASURING	INFERRING	RECORDING	SAFETY	APPLYING	DIAGRAMING	DESIGNING	CLASSIFYING	HYPOTHESIZING	PREDICTING
Sharpen Your Skills: Work and Power, p. 351	X	X					X		X	X				X					
Sharpen Your Skills: James Watt and the Steam Engine, p. 352			X	X															
Sharpen Your Skills: An Imaginary Machine, p. 356			X											X					
Sharpen Your Skills: Simple Machines in Your Environment, p. 359	X					X	X		X			X		X					
Sharpen Your Skills: Levers, p. 362	X	X				X	X	X	X					X					
Sharpen Your Skills: Compound Machines, p. 365			X											X		X			
Laboratory Investigation 15: Mechanical Advantage of an Inclined Plane, p. 366		X				X	X	X	X	X	X	X		X					
Skill Building 1, p. 369														X					
Skill Building 2, p. 369														X					
Skill Building 3, p. 369														X					
Skill Building 4, p. 369		X																	
Skill Building 5, p. 369															X				
Skill Building 6, p. 369									X										

TEXT REFERENCE	HANDS-ON	COMPUTATIONAL	VOCABULARY/WRITING	LIBRARY	FIELD	OBSERVING	COMPARING	MANIPULATIVE	RELATING	MEASURING	INFERRING	RECORDING	SAFETY	APPLYING	DIAGRAMING	DESIGNING	CLASSIFYING	HYPOTHESIZING	PREDICTING
Sharpen Your Skills: Forms of Energy, p. 474	X													X			X		
Sharpen Your Skills: Observing Gravitational Potential Energy, p. 377	X					X	X				X								
Sharpen Your Skills: Computing Kinetic Energy, p. 379		X							X										
Sharpen Your Skills: The Pendulum, p. 381	X					X	X		X		X								
Sharpen Your Skills: Measuring Energy, p. 382			X	X															
Laboratory Investigation 16: Relating Mass, Velocity, and Kinetic Energy, p. 384	X					X	X	X	X	X	X	X	X						
Skill Building 1, p. 387														X					
Skill Building 2, p. 387									X										
Skill Building 3, p. 387		X												X					
Skill Building 4, p. 387						X													
Skill Building 5, p. 387														X					
Skill Building 6, p. 387									X										
Skill Building 7, p. 387														X					
Skill Building 8, p. 387						X													

CHAPTER 17 HEAT pp. 394–415

TEXT REFERENCE	HANDS-ON	COMPUTATIONAL	VOCABULARY/WRITING	LIBRARY	FIELD	OBSERVING	COMPARING	MANIPULATIVE	RELATING	MEASURING	INFERRING	RECORDING	SAFETY	APPLYING	DIAGRAMING	DESIGNING	CLASSIFYING	HYPOTHESIZING	PREDICTING
Sharpen Your Skills: The Discoveries of Rumford and Joule, p. 396			X																
Sharpen Your Skills: Heat Loss, p. 398					X	X	X		X		X			X					
Sharpen Your Skills: Investigating Molecular Motion, p. 400	X					X	X	X	X		X								
Sharpen Your Skills: Solve the Mystery, p. 406		X							X		X			X					
Sharpen Your Skills: Food Calories, p. 407		X		X										X					
Sharpen Your Skills: Thermal Expansion, p. 409	X					X			X	X	X								
Sharpen Your Skills: Associated Meanings, p. 411			X																
Skill Building 1, p. 415														X					
Skill Building 2, p. 415										X				X					
Skill Building 3, p. 415							X												
Skill Building 4, p. 415														X					
Skill Building 5, p. 415														X	X				

CHAPTER 18 USES OF HEAT pp. 416–433

TEXT REFERENCE	HANDS-ON	COMPUTATIONAL	VOCABULARY/WRITING	LIBRARY	FIELD	OBSERVING	COMPARING	MANIPULATIVE	RELATING	MEASURING	INFERRING	RECORDING	SAFETY	APPLYING	DIAGRAMING	DESIGNING	CLASSIFYING	HYPOTHESIZING	PREDICTING
Sharpen Your Skills: History of Heating Systems, p. 419			X				X				X								
Sharpen Your Skills: Effectiveness of Insulating Materials, p. 423				X															
Sharpen Your Skills: Evaporation as a Cooling Process, p. 424	X					X	X	X			X			X					
Sharpen Your Skills: Technology and Social Change, P. 426			X				X		X		X			X					
Laboratory Investigation 18: Constructing a Solar Collector, p. 430	X					X	X	X		X	X	X	X	X					
Skill Building 1, p. 433															X				
Skill Building 2, p. 433														X					
Skill Building 3, p. 433																	X		
Skill Building 4, p. 433														X					

CHAPTER 19 ELECTRIC CHARGES AND CURRENTS pp. 440–465

TEXT REFERENCE	HANDS-ON	COMPUTATIONAL	VOCABULARY/WRITING	LIBRARY	FIELD	OBSERVING	COMPARING	MANIPULATIVE	RELATING	MEASURING	INFERRING	RECORDING	SAFETY	APPLYING	DIAGRAMING	DESIGNING	CLASSIFYING	HYPOTHESIZING	PREDICTING
Sharpen Your Skills: Balloon Electricity, p. 444	X					X												X	
Sharpen Your Skills: Spark, Crackle, Move, p. 445	X					X													
Sharpen Your Skills: Observing Static Electricity, p. 449	X					X		X										X	
Sharpen Your Skills: Electric Forces, p. 452	X					X	X	X				X							
Sharpen Your Skills: Ohm's Law, p. 453		X												X					
Sharpen Your Skills: How Much Electricity Do You Use?, p. 460		X												X					
Sharpen Your Skills: Electricity in Your Home, p. 461	X					X								X	X				
Laboratory Investigation 19: Electricity From a Lemon, p. 462						X	X	X		X	X	X	X	X				X	
Skill Building 1, p. 465														X					
Skill Building 2, p. 465		X																	
Skill Building 3, p. 465									X										
Skill Building 4, p. 465																X			

CHAPTER 20 MAGNETISM pp. 466–487

TEXT REFERENCE	HANDS-ON	COMPUTATIONAL	VOCABULARY/WRITING	LIBRARY	FIELD	OBSERVING	COMPARING	MANIPULATIVE	RELATING	MEASURING	INFERRING	RECORDING	SAFETY	APPLYING	DIAGRAMING	DESIGNING	CLASSIFYING	HYPOTHESIZING	PREDICTING
Sharpen Your Skills: Experiencing Magnetic Forces, p. 471	X					X	X	X										X	
Sharpen Your Skills: Mapping Lines of Magnetic Force, p. 472	X					X		X	X						X				
Sharpen Your Skills: Cork-and-Needle Compass, p. 473	X					X		X			X								
Sharpen Your Skills: A Model of Magnetic Domains, p. 475	X						X							X				X	
Sharpen Your Skills: Constructing an Electromagnet, p. 479	X					X		X											
Sharpen Your Skills: History of Electricity, p. 480		X	X																
Sharpen Your Skills: Electromagnets and the Telephone, p. 482				X										X					
Laboratory Investigation 20: Electromagnetism, p. 484	X					X	X						X	X				X	
Skill Building 1, p. 487									X										

CHAPTER 20 MAGNETISM pp. 466–487 (continued)

TEXT REFERENCE	HANDS-ON	COMPUTATIONAL	VOCABULARY/WRITING	LIBRARY	FIELD	OBSERVING	COMPARING	MANIPULATIVE	RELATING	MEASURING	INFERRING	RECORDING	SAFETY	APPLYING	DIAGRAMING	DESIGNING	CLASSIFYING	HYPOTHESIZING	PREDICTING
Skill Building 2, p. 487														X					
Skill Building 3, p. 487															X				
Skill Building 4, p. 487							X												
Skill Building 5, p. 487														X					

CHAPTER 21 WAVES pp. 494–511

TEXT REFERENCE	HANDS-ON	COMPUTATIONAL	VOCABULARY/WRITING	LIBRARY	FIELD	OBSERVING	COMPARING	MANIPULATIVE	RELATING	MEASURING	INFERRING	RECORDING	SAFETY	APPLYING	DIAGRAMING	DESIGNING	CLASSIFYING	HYPOTHESIZING	PREDICTING
Sharpen Your Skills: Earthquake Waves, p. 498	X			X											X		X		
Sharpen Your Skills: Waves on a Rope, p. 502	X					X	X	X	X					X					
Sharpen Your Skills: Law of Reflection, p. 505	X					X	X	X	X										
Sharpen Your Skills: Law of Refraction, p. 506	X						X	X	X	X								X	
Sharpen Your Skills: Waves in Your Bathtub, p. 507	X					X		X											
Laboratory Investigation 21: Observing Wave Properties of a Slinky, p. 508						X	X	X	X		X								
Skill Building 1, p. 511														X					
Skill Building 2, p. 511		X																	
Skill Building 3, p. 511									X										
Skill Building 4, p. 511						X													

CHAPTER 22 SOUND pp. 512-533

TEXT REFERENCE	HANDS-ON	COMPUTATIONAL	VOCABULARY/WRITING	LIBRARY	FIELD	OBSERVING	COMPARING	MANIPULATIVE	RELATING	MEASURING	INFERRING	RECORDING	SAFETY	APPLYING	DIAGRAMING	DESIGNING	CLASSIFYING	HYPOTHESIZING	PREDICTING
Sharpen Your Skills: Viewing Vibrations, p. 518	X					X	X	X	X					X					
Sharpen Your Skills: Changing Pitch on Stringed Instruments, p. 519	X					X	X	X			X								
Sharpen Your Skills: The Doppler Effect, p. 520	X					X	X		X					X					
Sharpen Your Skills: Sound Through Bones, p. 528	X					X	X	X	X										
Sharpen Your Skills: Model of a Wave, p. 529	X					X	X	X	X					X					
Laboratory Investigation 22: Speed of Sound in Air, p. 530		X				X		X		X	X	X	X	X				X	
Skill Building 1, p. 533							X												
Skill Building 2, p. 533		X																	
Skill Building 3, p. 533																	X		
Skill Building 4, p. 533														X					
Skill Building 5, p. 533		X																	

CHAPTER 22 SOUND pp. 512–533 (Continued)

TEXT REFERENCE	HANDS-ON	COMPUTATIONAL	VOCABULARY/WRITING	LIBRARY	FIELD	OBSERVING	COMPARING	MANIPULATIVE	RELATING	MEASURING	INFERRING	RECORDING	SAFETY	APPLYING	DIAGRAMING	DESIGNING	CLASSIFYING	HYPOTHESIZING	PREDICTING
Skill Building 6, p. 533										X	X								
Skill Building 7, p. 533									X										
Skill Building 8, p. 533									X										
Skill Building 9, p. 533																			X
Skill Building 10, p. 533														X					

CHAPTER 23 LIGHT pp. 534–557

TEXT REFERENCE	HANDS-ON	COMPUTATIONAL	VOCABULARY/WRITING	LIBRARY	FIELD	OBSERVING	COMPARING	MANIPULATIVE	RELATING	MEASURING	INFERRING	RECORDING	SAFETY	APPLYING	DIAGRAMING	DESIGNING	CLASSIFYING	HYPOTHESIZING	PREDICTING
Sharpen Your Skills: Shadows, p. 537	X					X		X	X					X				X	
Sharpen Your Skills: Hole in Your Hand, p. 538	X					X		X	X										
Sharpen Your Skills: X-Rays, p. 543			X	X			X		X										
Sharpen Your Skills: Light—Particle or Wave?, p. 545	X					X	X	X	X		X			X					
Sharpen Your Skills: Firewater!, p. 547	X					X		X					X						
Sharpen Your Skills: Penny in a Cup, p. 549	X					X		X			X			X					
Sharpen Your Skills: Color "Magic", p. 553	X					X			X		X							X	
Laboratory Investigation 23: Regular Reflection, p. 554						X	X	X	X	X	X	X	X	X				X	
Skill Building 1, p. 557									X										
Skill Building 2, p. 557														X					
Skill Building 3, p. 557									X										
Skill Building 4, p. 557																			X
Skill Building 5, p. 557														X					
Skill Building 6, p. 557															X				

CHAPTER 24 LIGHT AND ITS USES pp. 558–579

TEXT REFERENCE	HANDS-ON	COMPUTATIONAL	VOCABULARY/WRITING	LIBRARY	FIELD	OBSERVING	COMPARING	MANIPULATIVE	RELATING	MEASURING	INFERRING	RECORDING	SAFETY	APPLYING	DIAGRAMING	DESIGNING	CLASSIFYING	HYPOTHESIZING	PREDICTING
Sharpen Your Skills: Heat and Light, p. 561	X					X	X	X	X	X				X					
Sharpen Your Skills: Using a Plane Mirror, p. 565	X					X	X		X										
Sharpen Your Skills: Reflection in a Spoon, p. 566	X					X		X									X		
Sharpen Your Skills: Using Lenses, p. 567	X					X	X	X	X									X	
Sharpen Your Skills: Forming an Image, p. 571	X					X		X	X		X								
Sharpen Your Skills: Color Photography, p. 572			X						X										
Laboratory Investigation 24: Convex Lenses, p. 576						X	X	X	X	X		X	X	X					
Skill Building 1, p. 579														X					
Skill Building 2, p. 579									X										
Skill Building 3, p. 579														X					
Skill Building 4, p. 579		X																	
Skill Building 5, p. 579							X												
Skill Building 6, p. 579									X					X					

CHAPTER 25 ENERGY RESOURCES pp. 586–607

TEXT REFERENCE	HANDS-ON	COMPUTATIONAL	VOCABULARY/WRITING	LIBRARY	FIELD	OBSERVING	COMPARING	MANIPULATIVE	RELATING	MEASURING	INFERRING	RECORDING	SAFETY	APPLYING	DIAGRAMING	DESIGNING	CLASSIFYING	HYPOTHESIZING	PREDICTING
Sharpen Your Skills: Where Is the Oil?, p. 590	X			X					X						X				
Sharpen Your Skills: Dinosaur Power, p. 593				X										X					X
Sharpen Your Skills: Timing Tides, p. 595		X					X		X										
Sharpen Your Skills: A Model Chain Reaction, p. 597	X						X			X									
Laboratory Investigation 25: Solar Heating, p. 604						X		X	X	X	X	X	X	X	X			X	
Skill Building 1, p. 607																			X
Skill Building 2, p. 607																	X		
Skill Building 3, p. 607											X								
Skill Building 4, p. 607														X					
Skill Building 5, p. 607						X													
Skill Building 6, p. 607									X										
Skill Building 7, p. 607																	X		
Skill Building 8, p. 607											X								

CHAPTER 26 ENERGY AND THE ENVIRONMENT pp. 608–625

TEXT REFERENCE	HANDS-ON	COMPUTATIONAL	VOCABULARY/WRITING	LIBRARY	FIELD	OBSERVING	COMPARING	MANIPULATIVE	RELATING	MEASURING	INFERRING	RECORDING	SAFETY	APPLYING	DIAGRAMING	DESIGNING	CLASSIFYING	HYPOTHESIZING	PREDICTING
Sharpen Your Skills: Greenhouse Effect, p. 614			X	X					X										X
Sharpen Your Skills: Local Pollution, p. 617	X					X	X		X					X	X				
Sharpen Your Skills: The Year 2050, p. 619			X								X								X
Sharpen Your Skills: Car Pooling, p. 620	X					X	X		X			X		X					
Laboratory Investigation 26: Observing Air Pollution, p. 622						X	X	X	X	X		X	X	X				X	
Skill Building 1, p. 625															X				
Skill Building 2, p. 625															X				
Skill Building 3, p. 625									X										
Skill Building 4, p. 625			X																
Skill Building 5, p. 625									X										
Skill Building 6, p. 625														X					

CHAPTER 27 CHEMICAL TECHNOLOGY pp. 626–639

TEXT REFERENCE	HANDS-ON	COMPUTATIONAL	VOCABULARY/WRITING	LIBRARY	FIELD	OBSERVING	COMPARING	MANIPULATIVE	RELATING	MEASURING	INFERRING	RECORDING	SAFETY	APPLYING	DIAGRAMING	DESIGNING	CLASSIFYING	HYPOTHESIZING	PREDICTING
Sharpen Your Skills: Homemade Adhesives, p. 632	X						X	X	X					X		X			
Sharpen Your Skills: Kapton Calculations, p. 635		X																	
Laboratory Investigation 27: Comparing Natural and Synthetic Polymers, p. 636						X	X	X	X		X		X	X					
Skill Building 1, p. 639		X							X										
Skill Building 2, p. 639																			X
Skill Building 3, p. 639														X					
Skill Building 4, p. 639											X			X					

CHAPTER 28 ELECTRONICS AND COMPUTERS pp. 640–661

TEXT REFERENCE	HANDS-ON	COMPUTATIONAL	VOCABULARY/WRITING	LIBRARY	FIELD	OBSERVING	COMPARING	MANIPULATIVE	RELATING	MEASURING	INFERRING	RECORDING	SAFETY	APPLYING	DIAGRAMING	DESIGNING	CLASSIFYING	HYPOTHESIZING	PREDICTING
Sharpen Your Skills: Electronics in Your Home, p. 643	X				X	X			X		X			X					
Sharpen Your Skills: Telephone and Radio History, p. 652				X					X										
Sharpen Your Skills: Computing Speed, p. 653		X					X												
Sharpen Your Skills: Building ENIAC, p. 655		X												X					
Sharpen Your Skills: Computer Language, p. 656				X													X		
Sharpen Your Skills: Helpful Prefixes, p. 657			X						X					X					
Laboratory Investigation 28: The First Calculator: The Abacus, p. 658		X						X	X					X					
Skill Building 1, p. 661															X				
Skill Building 2, p. 661									X										
Skill Building 3, p. 661		X																	
Skill Building 4, p. 661																	X		
Skill Building 5, p. 661														X					
Skill Building 6, p. 661														X					

Features of the Annotated Teacher's Edition

The *Prentice Hall Physical Science* Annotated Teacher's Edition is the most complete, comprehensive, and pedagogically sound teacher's edition available for the junior high/middle school physical science teacher. The basic structure of this teacher's edition provides reduced student pages. This reduction allows a wide variety of teaching materials to be wrapped around the student page, but the reduction is not so great that the teacher cannot easily read all student material.

You will immediately note that on most pages the right and left margin columns have a blue-tinted background color. All material found in these margin columns pertains to background information for the teacher, interesting facts and figures the teacher may want to present to the class, answers and additional information relating to all marginal Sharpen Your Skills activities, teacher demonstration ideas, and other extremely useful information. The exact nature of the components of these margin columns will be explained in the pages that follow.

You will also immediately notice that an area boxed in red is found at the bottom of most teacher pages. This boxed-in area has been designed to provide teaching strategies specifically geared to the information presented in the text. Thus, by separating teaching strategies in one box and including other relevant information in the side columns only, the teacher can use this annotated teacher's edition with a minimum of training or experience. The kinds of teaching strategies included for each lesson will be discussed in detail in the pages that follow.

One important aspect of this wrap-around annotated teacher's edition is that all relevant material is right there along with the student pages for easy reference. Ease of use was an important criterion in the development of this teacher's edition. Of equal importance is the fact that the teaching material and marginal column material have been carefully controlled so that all material relates directly to the two-page spread in the student edition. That is, all material on the teacher's edition page refers directly to those same student pages. Teachers need not try to decipher which teaching instructions or background information is applicable to which student pages. All applicable material is included directly along with the student pages so no flipping of pages to look for answers or teaching strategies is required. Again, this makes the *Prentice Hall Physical Science* Annotated Teacher's Edition the most comprehensive and functional teacher's edition available.

UNIT OPENERS

Wrapped around the two-page unit openers in *Prentice Hall Physical Science* are a wide variety of instructional materials and teaching information. In the blue-tinted side columns you will find a Unit Overview, which provides a short overview of the facts and important concepts covered in a particular unit. Following the overview are Unit Objectives, which tie together the facts and concepts in objective form that are employed in the entire unit. Thus, through unit objectives, the teacher is presented with a basic understanding of the broad objectives students should meet during their study of a particular unit. Also included in the side columns is a list of each chapter in the unit and a brief description of the topics covered in each chapter.

At the bottom of each unit opener, located in the red-bordered strategy box, is a teaching strategy for introducing the unit. In general, the strategy calls upon the teacher to first have students observe the unit-opening photograph. Questions based on the photograph are often provided. Many are open-ended and require some degree of critical thinking. A basic design feature of all questions posed in this teacher's edition is that a small bullet is placed before each question. The question is set in boldfaced type so that all suggested questions are immediately obvious at a glance. The answers to such questions are placed in parentheses immediately after the question.

After students observe the photograph, they are called upon to read the text material that accompanies the unit-opening visual. Again, questions and teaching strategies are included in order to motivate and provide general interest to the student.

CHAPTER OPENERS

The blue-tinted columns that wrap-around the chapter-opening pages begin with a Chapter Overview. Like the Unit Overview, the Chapter Overview provides the teacher with the basic facts and concepts that will be presented in the chapter. Following the overview is a Teacher Demonstration, which has been written to motivate students and provide a conceptual framework for the information that is to come in the chapter. Also included in the marginal columns of the chapter opener are a listing of appropriate audiovisual materials, a bibliography for teachers and students, and appropriate software materials for the chapter.

The bottom of the chapter-opening spread is reserved for a chapter-opening teaching strategy and is called Introducing the Chapter. The format for the chapter introductory teacher materials is similar in scope and design to the unit-opening introductory teacher materials.

CHAPTER SECTION MATERIALS

Each major section in *Prentice Hall Physical Science* is numbered for easy reference. The column in the margin directly next to the numbered section begins with a Section Preview. The Section Preview alerts the teacher to the basic facts and concepts that will be presented in that specific section of the chapter. Following the Section Preview is a numbered listing of Performance Objectives for that particular section. Following the Performance Objectives are all the boldfaced vocabulary words found in that section, which are listed under the title Science Terms. In addition, the page on which each term is introduced is included along with the term.

The blue-tinted columns on the right and left that follow each numbered section contain a wide variety of instructional materials. These instructional materials appear, whenever applicable, only in the marginal columns. Background Information provides the teacher with extra information about the topics being covered. Historical Notes provide a historical framework for the concepts being covered. Aside from the Teacher Demonstration that is used to introduce each chapter, at least one more Teacher Demonstration, and often more than one, is included within the margin columns of each chapter. Again, these demonstrations are meant to be motivational and often include questions to be asked before and after the demonstration. A feature called Facts and Figures may also be found in the marginal columns of each chapter. This feature provides interesting information that the teacher may want to present to the class.

Since physical science cannot be taught in a vacuum, *Prentice Hall Physical Science* provides numerous Tie-Ins to other areas of science and to other curriculum areas such as history,

government, and art. These Tie-Ins help relate physical science to other areas of science, as well as to the students' everyday life.

Also included in the marginal columns of the annotated teacher's edition are the instructional materials related to the Sharpen Your Skills activities in the text. These teaching notes are always found directly on the same two-page spread on which they are located in the student text. Usually, they are found right beside the accompanying student activity. The teacher is provided with the skills to be employed with each activity, the type of activity that is being assigned, the level of each activity (remedial, average, or enriched), any materials that are required, and the answers or suggested answers to the activity.

Finally, the column materials that pertain to the student text pages include an Annotation Key. The Annotation Key is a key to all in-text questions as well as a key to all thinking skills employed on a particular text page. You will note that the student pages in the annotated teacher's edition contain small numbers in red beside each in-text or caption question. The same number, in red, is found in the Annotation Key with the correct answer. In parentheses after the answer is the science skill that the student must employ to answer the question. You will also note small numbers in blue next to paragraphs on the student pages of the annotated teacher's edition. These blue numbers are repeated in the Annotation Key and alert the teacher as to the types of thinking skills that the student must use to read, grasp, and understand the facts and concepts presented in the chapter. Each two-page spread in the text material for each chapter contains an Annotation Key. In this way, all answers and thinking skills employed on the spread in the student book are immediately visible and answered on the accompanying teacher page. No flipping between pages is necessary to find all the answers and thinking skills.

Below the student pages in the annotated teacher's edition is an area boxed in red. This area is reserved for teaching strategies. Each numbered section in the text begins with a teaching strategy called Motivation. The strategy employed in Motivation is to present students with an activity, a thought question, a demonstration, or some type of teaching tool to help interest and motivate students. Motivation strategies are also employed throughout the section. Following the motivational ideas that begin each section is a teaching strategy called Content Development. Content Development information is designed to help the teacher teach the basic facts and concepts presented in the chapter. Like Motivation strategies, Content Development ideas are interspersed throughout each section. Another feature that is located in the teaching strategy box is called Skills Development. Under this title is a listing of the skills that will be developed, followed by an activity or a set of questions to help test basic science skills. Yet another strategy employed in the teaching strategy box is called Reinforcement. These features help the teacher reinforce basic concepts and facts for students who may not always grasp the facts and concepts without some extra help. For students who are highly academic, a feature called Enrichment is also interspersed throughout each chapter. These Enrichment ideas provide the teacher with a way to help academic students go beyond the text material. Finally, at the end of each numbered section in the text are the answers to Section Review questions presented in the textbook. Section Review answers are set in red type for easy reference.

On occasion and when applicable, a special teaching strategy title called Common Errors is included. This strategy usually accompanies student pages in which sample and practice problems are introduced. The section called Common Errors points out some of the ways students might make a mistake while performing the practice problems.

In selected chapters, yet another feature has been included. This feature is called a Cross-Unit Reference. This Cross-Unit Reference tells the teacher when he or she may want to jump from a particular chapter to a chapter in the last unit on technology that relates to a particular chapter. For example, after students read about electricity and magnetism in Unit Six, the teacher is given the option of skipping to Chapter 28 on Electronics and Computers. This skipping is not necessary, but allows the teacher the flexibility of teaching the technology unit at one time, or incorporating the technology chapters into other units when they are appropriate.

As you look over the student pages in your annotated teacher's edition, you will notice that certain sentences have been shaded in pink. This shading provides teachers with the most important topic sentences and concepts that are being taught in a particular chapter. The shading basically provides an outline of key facts and figures in each chapter.

LABORATORY INVESTIGATION ANNOTATIONS

The laboratory investigations in the *Prentice Hall Physical Science* textbook are always located at the back of the chapter, just prior to the Chapter Summary materials. In the an-

notated teacher's edition, a great deal of extra information is provided for the teacher on each investigation. All such information is provided on blue-tinted pages. The first feature for all lab investigations is called Before The Lab. This tells the teacher when to prepare any materials for the investigation and any special instructions that may be necessary prior to the investigation. The next feature is called Pre-Lab Discussion. This section tells the teacher which concepts presented in the chapter should be reviewed prior to the investigation, as well as other general information to be discussed with students prior to their doing the investigation. Variables and hypotheses are brought out in the Pre-Lab Discussion, whenever applicable.

Following the Pre-Lab Discussion is a section called Skill Development. This section alerts the teacher to which skills students will employ while completing the investigation. After the Skill Development feature is a section called Safety Tips. While the student text includes safety symbols alerts, this Safety Tips section alerts the teacher to any potential safety problems that may occur if students do not follow accepted safety practices in the laboratory.

A section called Teaching Strategy for Lab Procedure is next. It provides the teacher, when necessary, with a strategy to be employed while students complete the investigation. Next comes a section called Observations in which answers to questions in the Observation section of the investigation are provided. The same is true for the section called Conclusions, in which all answers are provided.

Finally, for each investigation there is a section called Going Further: Enrichment. This section may include additional activities that can be undertaken in the lab, it may include critical-thinking questions based on the lab, it may include application questions related to the lab, as well as other enrichment ideas.

END-OF-CHAPTER QUESTIONS

The last two pages in each chapter contain end of chapter questions. Answers to all multiple choice, completion, true or false, skill building, and essay questions are provided in the annotated teacher's edition. Also included in the annotated teacher's edition are Additional Questions and Topic Suggestions. These may be additional activities or questions teachers may want to assign their students. Finally, a section called Issues in Science is included in the annotated teacher's edition. This section provides one or more issues that can be discussed, debated, or assigned for homework.

...ES

...very unit are two Science Gazette articles. ...re in Science profile of a scientist or group ...scientists. The other is an Issues in Science article, presenting a current scientific issue in a nonbiased manner. In the annotated teacher's edition, extra background information is presented on each gazette article. Also included are questions, many of which are critical thinking in nature, which are based on the gazette article. A teaching strategy for each science gazette, as well as suggested debate topics are also included in the annotated teacher's edition.

Science Safety Guidelines

SCIENCE SAFETY CLASSROOM DO'S AND DON'T'S

It is essential that students follow safety guidelines whenever performing an investigation or activity. Make sure your students read the safety section in Chapter 1, as well as the list of safety rules in Appendix B. You may also want to read the following do's and don't's to your class.

Do

1. Wear protective goggles when working with chemicals, burners, or any substance that might get into your eyes. Many materials in a lab can cause injury to the eyes and even blindness.
2. Learn what to do in case of specific accidents such as getting acid in your eyes or on your skin. (Rinse acids on your body with lots of water.)
3. Before starting any Laboratory Investigation or other experiment, make a list of the things that could go wrong that might hurt you. Then make a list of what you should do if the accident happens.
4. Make sure you have a fire extinguisher nearby to put out a fire.
5. Work with a friend, when you can, under the supervision of a science teacher or adult who understands lab safety rules.
6. Work in a well-ventilated area.
7. Learn how to use first aid to quickly treat burns, cuts, and bruises. Seek help if you are injured.
8. Read directions for an experiment carefully two or more times. Follow the directions exactly as they are written.

Don't

1. Mix chemicals "for the fun of it." You might produce an explosive reaction that could seriously injure you.
2. Taste, touch, or smell any chemical that you don't know for a fact is harmless. Many chemicals are poisonous.
3. Heat any chemical that you are not instructed to heat. A chemical that is harmless when cool can be dangerous when heated.
4. Heat a liquid in a closed container. The expanding gases produced may blow the container apart, injuring you.
5. Perform an experiment in which you must connect wires to house current. You could electrocute yourself. (Use dry cells instead.)
6. Tilt a test tube toward yourself or anyone else (or hold it upright) when you are heating its contents. (Always tilt the tube away from yourself and others.)
7. Perform any experiment for which you do not have written instructions (in a text or from your teacher).

FIELD TRIP SAFETY

This text offers a variety of field investigations, or field trips, that can be used to extend your students' studies and interests in science. Although the program outlined in this book can be successfully carried out within the confines of a classroom, the suggested field investigations have been included to provide an opportunity for your students to have firsthand evidence and experiences outside of the classroom.

1. **Site Selection:** The text suggests possible field trip sites, but it is up to you to select an appropriate field trip site for your students, depending upon your locale. To aid you

in making the necessary arrangements, we suggest that you make a school file of available sites in your area. The file should contain specific instructions concerning who to contact at the site, directions or a map to the site, fees (if any), the hours the site is open to the public, and availability of meal facilities and restrooms.

It is suggested that you make a visit to the site prior to the field trip to inspect the facilities. While you are there, locate and inventory work-study areas. Make a list of specific equipment your students will need and note the site restrictions and danger spots. Also note facilities for the handicapped if any of your students have physical limitations.

2. **Planning the Trip:** Be sure that the field trip is justified in view of the school's educational program and your individual lesson objectives. Request written permission for the trip from school personnel and keep this written permission on file. After being granted permission, send a written statement of your destination, departure and arrival times, mode of transportation, and necessary expenditures to each student's parent or guardian.

Meanwhile, provide time in class for advance research on the site. Correlate the projected field trip with your lessons and text material. Tell your students the why, where, and when of the field trip. Be sure to inform them of any special equipment or clothing they will need—special shoes, shorts, hand lenses, notebooks, and so on.

3. **The Actual Field Trip:** Make a head count of your students at each boarding and departure and periodically during the trip. Each adult should be provided with a list of the students he or she is to supervise and should remain with that group throughout the entire trip. While you are on the way to the site, discuss the investigation with your students. When you arrive at the site, keep the group together unless you have planned otherwise.

Make certain the students understand the purpose of the field trip. Have them make sketches, drawings, plans, or maps or take notes. Do not allow students to remove anything from its natural setting unless carefully selected items are taken for observation and returned to their natural habitats.

Most importantly, be enthusiastic but don't rush. Don't try to crowd too much into one field trip. Keep in contact with the individuals in the group and be alert for the "teachable moment."

4. **Follow-up Activities:** A good field trip provides a base experience for other class activities. While you are returning to the school, have students exchange ideas and discuss their experiences and observations at the site. Encourage students to ask questions and propose future activities related to the field trip. Schedule individual or group reports and have the students evaluate the trip.

Later, you may want to have your students prepare exhibits or displays using their sketches, maps, photographs, or other materials from the trip. Have them use the library to investigate questions arising from the trip. A number of library investigations can usually be proposed after a successful field trip. Remember, the learning value of a field trip depends largely on you and the type of follow-up activities you provide or encourage.

List of Suppliers

LABORATORY MATERIALS AND ADDRESSES

Carolina Biological Supply Company
Burlington, NC 27215

DAMON/Educational Division
115 Fourth Avenue
Needham, MA 02194

Edmund Scientific Company
103 Gloucester Pike
Barrington, NJ 08007

Fisher Scientific Company
Stansi Educational Materials Division
1259 Wood Street
Chicago, IL 60622

Hubbard Scientific Company
2855 Shermer Road
Northbrook, IL 60062

La Pine Scientific Company
6001 Knox Avenue
Chicago, IL 60018

Prentice-Hall Equipment Division
10 Oriskany Drive
Tonawanda, NY 14150

Sargeant-Welch Scientific Company
7300 North Linder Avenue
Skokie, IL 60076

Science Kit, Inc.
777 East Park Drive
Tonawanda, NY 14150

Scientific Glass Apparatus Company
737 Broad Street
Bloomfield, NJ 07003

Turtox/Cambosco
Macmillan Science Company, Inc.
8200 South Hoyne Avenue
Chicago, IL 60620

A-V SUPPLIERS AND ADDRESSES

BFA
Phoenix/BFA Films
468 Park Avenue South
New York, NY 10016

Cor
Coronet/MTI Film and Video
108 Wilmot Road
Deerfield, IL 60015

EBE
Encyclopedia Britannica
Educational Corporation
425 N. Michigan Avenue
Chicago, IL 60611

Eye Gate
Eye Gate Media
146-01 Archer Avenue
Jamaica, NY 11435

NGS
National Geographic Society
Educational Services
Dept. 79
Washington, DC 20036

Guidance Associates/Center for the Humanities
90 South Bedford Street
Mt. Kisco, NY 10546
Note: Materials from **PH Media** *can now be ordered from this supplier.*

Walt Disney
Walt Disney Educational Media Company
500 South Buena Vista Street
Burbank, CA 91521

COMPUTER SOFTWARE SUPPLIERS

Carolina Biological Supply Company
2700 York Road
Burlington, NC 27215

Datatech Software Systems
19312 East Eldorado Drive
Aurora, CA 80013

Educational Dimensions Group
P.O. Box 126
Stamford, CT 06904

Focus Media, Inc.
839 Stewart Avenue
Garden City, NY 11530

Prentice Hall, Inc.
Educational Book Division
Englewood Cliffs, NJ 07632

Comprehensive List of Laboratory Materials

Item	Quantities per group	Chapter
Acid, mild (lime or lemon juice or vinegar)	150 mL	27
Acid solutions (H_2SO_4, HCL, HNO_3)	5 mL	9
Aluminum foil holder	1	2
Aluminum foil	1 small piece	20
Abacus	1	28
Balance, triple-beam	1	1, 4, 13
Basic solutions (KOH, NaOH, $Ca(OH)_2$)	5 mL	9
Battery, dry-cell	1	7
Beaker		
medium	3	1, 10
100-mL	2	7
250-mL	3	8
medium	1	9
250-mL	2	17, 18
Bleach, liquid	200 mL	27
Book	2	15
Bottle, large clear-plastic with airtight lid	1	14
Bowl, large	1	11
Box, cardboard, to fit compass	1	19
Bunsen burner	1	6, 7
Butyric acid	5 mL	10
Candle, small	1	2
Cardboard, corrugated 30 cm x 20 cm	1 piece	23
Chloride test solutions (LiCl, $CaCl_2$, KCl, $CuCl_2$, $SrCl_2$, $NaCl_2$, $BaCl_2$, unknown)	5 mL	6
Clock	1	25
Cloth samples, 15 cm x 15 cm		
Polyester, nylon, acetate	1 of each	27
Wool, cotton, linen	1 of each	27

Item	Quantities per group	Chapter
Coins		
dime, nickel, penny	1 of each	20
dime	1	19
penny	2	19
Compass	1	19
Connecting wire	3	7
Container, 1-L	1	18
metal or plastic with plastic lids	2	25
Copper sheet	small piece	20
Cork	1	6
Cups, Styrofoam	3	17
	12	27
Dry cell	1	20
Ethanol	10 mL	10
Evaporating dish	1	9
Food coloring, red, yellow, green, blue	1 small bottle of each	3
any color	1 small bottle	11
Funnel	1	18
Glacial acetic acid	5 mL	10
Glass	1	14
Glass plate	1	2
	3	10
Gloves, rubber	1 pair	27
Graduated cylinder		
medium	1	1, 18
	2	8
100-mL	2	17
1000-mL	1	22
Hot plate	1	10, 17
Hydrocholoric acid, dilute	1 small bottle	6
Lemon	1	19
Lens, convex	1	24
Lens holder	1	24
Light bulb	1	7, 24
Light bulb socket	1	7, 24

Item	Quantities per group	Chapter
Litmus paper, red and blue	small box	9
Magnifying lens	1	26
Magnet	1	4
Marshmallows, large	25	3
Matches	1 book	2
Medicine dropper	1	9, 10, 11, 14, 27
Meterstick	1	1, 4, 15, 16, 22, 24
Methanol	5 mL	10
Metric ruler	1	1, 12, 23, 27
Mirror, plane	1	23
Nails, 10 cm long	5	20
Newspaper, painted black	several sheets	18
Objects, irregular	1	1
regular	1	1
Oil, vegetable	50 mL	7
	6 drops	27
Paper		
construction, black	few sheets	25
construction, white	few sheets	25
graph	2 sheets	5
graph	1 sheet	12, 26
graph, 30 cm x 20 cm	1 sheet	23
Paper clips	6	20
Paper towel	1	1, 27
Pebble, small	1	1
Pen, marking	1	27
Pencils		
2 different colors	1 of each	5
glass-marking	1	7, 26
Petri dishes	6	26
Petri dish cover	1	26
Petroleum jelly	1 small jar	26
Phenolphthalein	few drops	9
Pins, straight	4	23
Plastic wrap	50 cm x 50 cm sheet	18

Item	Quantities per group	Chapter
Protractor	1	23
Ramp, wooden, at least 0.80 m long	1	15
Ring stand and ring	1	18
Rubber band	1	16, 23
Safety goggles	1	6, 7, 8, 9, 10
Salicylic acid	1 g	10
Salt	small sample	7
Sandpaper	small piece	19
Scissors	1	19, 25, 27
Shoe box	1	4
painted black	1	18
Slinky, or other coiled spring	1	21
Spring scale, calibrated in Newtons (0–5N)	1	15
Stirring rod	1	7, 8, 9, 17
Stopwatch (or one with sweep second hand)	1	8
Straight edge	1	5
String	50 cm	15
Styrofoam,		
10 cm x 15 cm x 2.5 cm	1 pad	13
Sugar	small sample	7
Sugar cubes	250	11
Sulfuric acid, concentrated	5 mL	10
Tape	1 roll	25
Test tubes, medium	8	6
	4	7
	6	9
	3	10
Test tube holder	1	10
Test tube rack	1	6, 9, 10
Test tube tongs	1	7
Thumbtacks	3	16
Timer	1	7
Toothpicks	1 box	3
Thermometer, Celsius	1	1, 17, 18
	2	25

Tubing, rubber or plastic, 1 mm diameter, 1 mm length	1	18
Tubing, glass 2.5 cm x 45 cm, hollow	1	22
Tuning fork, of known frequency	1	22
Watch	1	25
Washers	12	16
Wire, nichrome or platinum, 30 cm	1	6
copper, 25 cm	1	14
bell, 150 cm	1	19
bell, 20 m	1	20
Wood, 10 cm x 15 cm x 2.5	1	13
block or brick	1	15, 23
Wooden board, 15 cm x 100 cm	1	16

Laboratory Skills Assessment Record Chart

The Laboratory Skills Assessment Record Chart that follows is designed to help you assess students' progress in the laboratory setting. By filling out one chart per student for each laboratory investigation, you can monitor individual student performance in a particular laboratory investigation as well as each student's continuing progress as the year evolves.

Use a proficiency rating scale from 1 to 5, with 1 showing absence of laboratory skills proficiency and 5 showing complete proficiency. Carefully monitor students who achieve low proficiency ratings in certain categories at the beginning of the year for improvement. Further instruction may be required for students who do not improve as the year progresses.

Student's Name _____ Class _____ Date _____

Laboratory Investigation Title _____

SKILL	PROFICIENCY RATING
Instructional Skills	
• Reads lab before class	
• Understands purpose of investigation	
• Follows all directions as written or spoken	
• Does not improvise without permission	
• Contributes to the lab group	
• Records all observations and data accurately	
• Achieves expected results	
• Answers questions accurately, based on data	
• Relates investigation to textbook material	
Manipulative Skills	
• Sets up all equipment as instructed	
• Uses measurement instruments accurately	
Safety Skills	
• Understands and follows all safety regulations	
• Uses safety goggles and heat-resistant gloves when necessary	
• Treats glassware carefully	
• Handles and disposes of chemicals properly	
• Does not fool around in class	
• Cleans up work area	

PRENTICE HALL
Physical
Science

Prentice Hall
Physical Science

Dean Hurd

Physical Science Instructor
Carlsbad High School
Carlsbad, California

Myrna Silver

Physical Science Instructor
Richardson Independent School District
Richardson, Texas

Angela Bornn Bacher

Chemistry Instructor
Methacton School District
Fairview Village, Pennsylvania

Charles William McLaughlin

Chemistry Instructor
Central High School
St. Joseph, Missouri

Prentice-Hall, Inc., Englewood Cliffs, New Jersey 07632

Prentice Hall Physical Science Program

Student Text and Annotated Teacher's Edition

Laboratory Manual with Annotated Teacher's Edition

Teacher's Resource Book

Test Bank with Software and DIAL-A-TEST™ Service

Physical Science Critical Thinking Skills Transparencies

Physical Science Courseware

Other programs in this series

Prentice Hall Life Science © 1988

Prentice Hall Earth Science © 1988

Prentice Hall Physical Science presents science as a process that involves research, experimentation, and the development of theories that can hold great explanatory and predictive power. This approach reflects the challenges and intellectual rewards available to students in the ever-changing discipline of science.

Photograph credits begin on p. 695

The photograph on the cover shows the pattern of concentric circles formed when an object is dropped into a pool of water and the energy spreads out from the source in a series of waves. The small drop suspended above the pool is actually a drop of water that was forced upward by the energy of the object making contact with the water. Also illustrated is the reflection of light off the surface of the water.
(Richard Megna/Fundamental Photographs)

FIRST EDITION

ISBN 0-13-700568-7

10 9 8 7 6 5 4 3 2

Prentice-Hall of Australia Pty. Ltd., Sydney
Prentice-Hall of Canada Inc., Toronto
Prentice-Hall Hispanoamericana, S.A., Mexico
Prentice-Hall of India Private Ltd., New Delhi
Prentice-Hall International (UK) Limited, London
Prentice-Hall of Japan, Inc., Tokyo
Prentice-Hall of Southeast Asia Pte. Ltd., Singapore
Editora Prentice-Hall do Brasil Ltda., Rio de Janeiro

Physical Science Reviewers:

Edward A. Dalton
President
National Energy Foundation
Salt Lake City, Utah

Jack Grube
Science Coordinator
Eastside Union High School
San Jose, California

John D. Hunt
Physics/Chemistry Instructor
Judson High School
Converse, Texas

Kenneth L. Krause
Physical Science Instructor
Harriet Tubman Middle School
Portland, Oregon

Ernest Kuehl
Physics Instructor
Lawrence High School
Cedarhurst, New York

David LaHart
Senior Instructor
Florida Solar Energy Center
Cape Canaveral, Florida

Joyce K. Walsh
Physical Science Instructor
Chesterfield School District
Chesterfield, Virginia

Reading Consultant

Patricia N. Schwab
Department of Education
University of South Carolina
Sumter, South Carolina

Contents

UNIT THREE Interactions of Matter 156–283

UNIT FOUR Motion, Forces, and Energy 284–391

UNIT FIVE Heat Energy 392–437

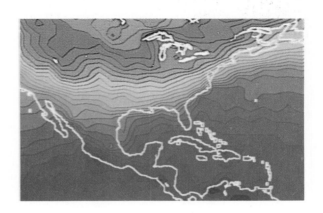

UNIT SIX Electricity and Magnetism 438–491

UNIT SEVEN Waves: Sound and Light 492–583

UNIT EIGHT Physical Science and Technology 584–665

Reference Section

Unit One

DIVERSITY OF MATTER

UNIT OVERVIEW

In Unit One, students first explore the general nature of physical science. They learn about the steps involved in scientific method and about experimentation, measurement, and safety in the laboratory.

Next, they apply what they have learned to investigate the properties of matter. They learn about matter's general properties and then about the phases and phase changes of matter. The differences between chemical and physical properties are also explored, as are chemical changes.

Finally, students learn how to classify materials on the basis of whether the materials are heterogeneous mixtures, homogeneous mixtures, or true solutions. The students also read about the differences between elements and compounds and about the use of chemical symbols, formulas, and equations.

UNIT OBJECTIVES

1. **Describe the steps generally involved in scientific method.**
2. **State the basic metric units of measurement.**
3. **Describe the general properties of matter.**
4. **Classify matter on the basis of phase.**
5. **Distinguish between physical and chemical properties and between physical and chemical changes, and make use of chemical symbols, formulas, and equations.**
6. **Classify materials as elements, compounds, or mixtures.**

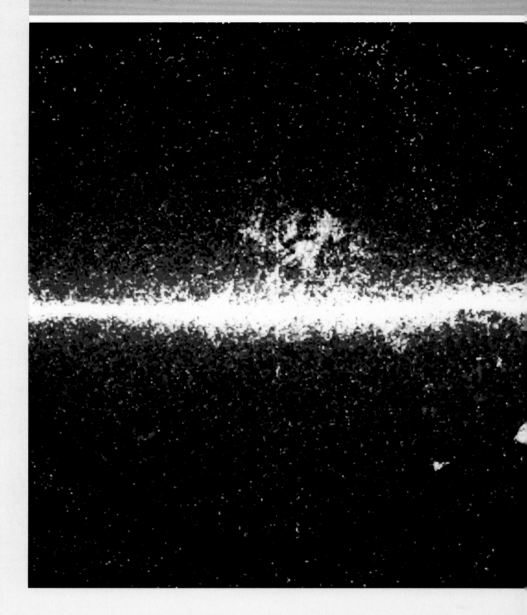

INTRODUCING UNIT ONE

Begin your teaching of the unit by directing students' attention to the unit-opening photograph. Have them read the caption, as well. The photograph is a projection of the entire sky by IRAS, a joint project of the U.S., the Netherlands, and the United Kingdom. It shows more than 250,000 point sources of infrared radiation. The plane of the Milky Way, our galaxy, runs horizontally across the middle of the picture. The yellowish-purple region above the center is in the constellation Ophiuchus, and the similar region at the right, just below the center, is in Orion. The two white blobs below the center and toward the right are the Large and Small Magellenic clouds, small galaxies that orbit the Milky Way. The chain of dots above the galactic center is a concentration of galaxies near the Milky Way that is called the Local Supercluster.

You may wish to have students speculate on certain aspects of the illustration. Ask them the following questions. If they are unable to infer or guess the correct answers, provide them to them.

• **What do the black areas represent?** (They are areas not scanned by IRAS.)
• **Are the colors shown actually those visible if the different features are seen through a telescope?** (No.

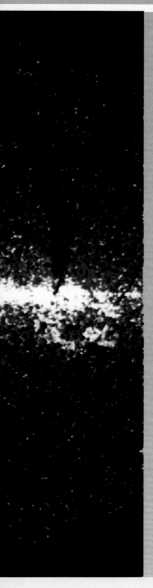

Diversity of Matter

In January 1983, the Infrared Astronomy Satellite (IRAS) was launched into space. Its job was to observe the universe through infrared sensors. Infrared is a form of light that is invisible to the human eye. Surveying the entire sky, IRAS discovered five new comets and a new asteroid. It examined galaxies hundreds of times brighter than the Milky Way. It even probed the gas and dust clouds between the stars. While scanning the star Vega, IRAS made an important discovery. A dusty ring surrounds this star. As yet, matter in the ring has not clumped together to form planets. But the existence of the ring is the first clear evidence that stars other than our sun may have planetary systems.

Spectacular photographs of a universe never before seen have been radioed back to the earth by IRAS. Scientists examining the data have confirmed an amazing scientific fact. All visible objects—be they huge galaxies of stars or tiny particles of matter floating in space—are made of the same matter that is found on the earth. Nowhere in the universe is there matter unlike that which exists "at home." For even the fiery stars are composed of the same basic materials as the air, the rocks, the seas, and you!

CHAPTERS

This image of the entire sky was assembled from data from the Infrared Astronomical Satellite (IRAS).

3

CHAPTER DESCRIPTIONS

1 Exploring Physical Science Chapter 1 deals first with the steps that scientists generally use in investigating a question or problem. Experimental and control setups are contrasted, and metric units of measurement and laboratory tools and safety rules are introduced.

2 Properties of Matter Mass, weight, volume, and density are explained. Matter is then classified according to phases, and the Gas Laws are introduced. Phase changes are presented, and, finally, physical properties and physical changes are contrasted, as are chemical properties and chemical changes.

3 Classification of Matter Materials are classified on the basis of whether they are heterogeneous mixtures, homogeneous mixtures, true solutions, elements, or compounds. The use of chemical symbols, formulas, and equations is also introduced.

following questions to the class in order to initiate class discussions.

• **Why should the ring around Vega suggest that other stars may have planetary systems, if Vega itself does not have planets?** (The presence of the ring suggests that planets will eventually form around Vega. Since Vega does not seem to be a unique star in any way, it is reasonable to assume that other stars once had such a surrounding ring that, by the same mechanism, resulted in the formation of planets.)

• **Why is it assumed that matter everywhere in the universe is basically the same as that on earth?** (The assumption is made because no new kinds of matter have as yet been found, despite a great deal of investigation. It is, however, theoretically possible, if unlikely, that somewhere in the universe a different kind of matter may exist.)

The light photographed was infrared, which is invisible to the eye. The colors were created for coding purposes.)

• **What do the different colors represent?** (The colors represent different temperatures. The warmest material is color-coded blue, material of intermediate temperature is green, and relatively cool material is red.)

• **What do you think the yellow-green dots that appear uniformly across the picture represent?** (They are other galaxies.)

• **What do you think may be occurring in the yellowish-purple regions near the center?** (They are intense regions of star formation in our galaxy, near the sun.)

Now have students read the unit introduction. The material in it should serve as the basis for various discussions that will better motivate students to go on to read the chapters that follow. You may wish to pose the

Chapter 1
EXPLORING PHYSICAL SCIENCE

CHAPTER OVERVIEW

Physical Science is curiosity. It is the world filled with wonder and excitement. It is built on exploration, energy, and persistence. It is the why, what, and how of our everyday living.

Through Physical Science we learn the scientific method to research, form opinions, and explain problems. Every scientific method has six basic steps: stating a problem, gathering information about the problem, forming an opinion or hypothesis, performing experiments to test our hypothesis, recording and analyzing data, and stating a conclusion.

Learning to solve problems is one of the most important objectives in Physical Science. Learning to collect accurate information through measurement, research, and safe experimentation develops a scientific attitude.

TEACHER DEMONSTRATION

Collect three skillets. A plain metal skillet, one with a "Teflon coating," and the third with a "Silverstone" or other nonscratchable nonstick surface. Point out to students that the plain metal skillet has been used for many years.
- **Is there some way we could improve on this type of cooking skillet?** (Accept all logical answers.)

Explain that through research, scientists found that food did not stick to a Teflon-coated surface. Point out that with the Teflon surface we have to use

INTRODUCING CHAPTER 1

Have students observe the photograph on page 4. Point out that the photo is of a computer chip. Tell the class that a computer chip is a small piece of semiconducting material, usually silicon, on which an integrated circuit is fabricated.
- **How could we improve this chip?** (Accept all answers.)

Explain that a problem has developed: computer users are finding these expensive chips wear out over a period of time. This has caused scientists to experiment with new materials to give longer life to the computer chips. Tell the students that scientists are developing a new method to coat these chips with a synthetic diamond material. Explain that diamonds are extremely hard and resistant to wear.
- **Do you know of any other products**

that use diamonds? (Accept all logical answers, but lead students to suggest that many stereo needles have a diamond point.)

Explain to students that many of the things we use today have a coating on them to make them better. Tell students we laminate books to give them a nice appearance and to keep them clean.
- **What else do we coat to make it look better and help keep it clean?**

Exploring Physical Science 1

CHAPTER OBJECTIVES

After completing this chapter, you will be able to

1–1 Describe the steps scientists use to investigate a question or problem.

1–1 Explain the difference between an experimental setup and a control setup.

1–2 Compare the different units of measurement in the metric system.

1–3 Identify the common laboratory tools used to measure length, volume, mass, and temperature.

1–4 List the important safety rules you must follow in the science laboratory.

What do a razor blade, a rocket engine, and swamp gas have in common? Today, researchers at Penn State University are hard at work to provide an answer. These scientists are trying to find a way to coat various objects with a thin film of synthetic diamond. Synthetic diamonds are made in the laboratory.

How do scientists go about making a synthetic diamond coating? They start with swamp gas, which is called methane. Methane is a chemical substance made of one carbon atom linked to four hydrogen atoms. The first step in the process is to "strip away" the hydrogen atoms from the carbon atom. When this happens, the carbon atoms from thousands of methane particles are left behind.

Diamonds are made of carbon atoms. By carefully controlling conditions in the laboratory, scientists can make the carbon atoms link together to form synthetic diamonds. As they link together they are deposited on the object to be coated. The synthetic diamonds are virtually 100 percent pure.

Diamonds are extremely hard and resistant to wear. By placing a diamond coating on a razor blade, the blade will last longer and stay sharper. Diamond coatings on rocket engines and cutting tools will increase their resistance to wear. In addition, diamond coatings can make lenses and windows almost scratchproof. The list of uses goes on and on.

As you read this book, you will be introduced to the realm of physical science. And you will learn about many other exciting discoveries that may change your world. Perhaps one day in a laboratory of the future, you will be working on a new scientific project!

Silicon chips coated with synthetic diamond will be sturdier, more efficient, and not overheat as quickly.

5

plastic or nonmetal spoons and spatulas.

• **Could we improve on this skillet?** (Accept all answers.)

Hold up the Silverstone skillet. Explain that with more research and experimentation, scientists discovered that a coating could be made that did not scratch with metal utensils and still kept food from sticking.

TEACHER RESOURCES

Audiovisuals

Chemistry/What Is Science?, 4 filmstrips with 4 cassettes, PH Media
Doing Better in Science, 2 filmstrips with 2 cassettes, LA
Physics/What Is Science? 4 filmstrips with 4 cassettes, PH Media
What Is Science?, 16 mm film, Cor

Books

Arons, Arnold, *The Various Languages: An Inquiry Approach to the Physical Sciences,* Oxford University Press
Highsmith, Philip E., and Andrew S. Howard, *Adventures in Physics*, Saunders
Penny, R. K., *The Experimental Method,* Longman
Whitman, Nancy C., and Frederick G. Brown, *The Metric System: A Laboratory Approach for Teachers,* Wiley

(Accept all logical answers, but lead students to suggest we coat floors and furniture with a vinyl or wax.)

Explain that the heads of tape decks are coated with Sendust for clear sound reproduction. The tapes themselves are plastic that has been coated with magnetic particles.

• **How do you think these things came into being?** (Accept all answers, but lead students to suggest that someone had to develop the products.)

Point out that almost everything we use has been developed by a person. Explain that the person decided there was a problem and a need for a product. Through research with trial and error, retesting, rethinking, and reexperimenting, a temporary solution was found. Explain that like the computer "chip," people like them will find new and better methods to deal with tomorrow's problems.

1-1 WHAT IS SCIENCE?

SECTION PREVIEW 1-1

We are all scientists. We observe and question the things around us. We learn by investigating new methods of doing old things. We change our opinions after learning new information. We develop methods that suit the individual job.

We as scientists attempt to find answers to questions. Scientists seek facts, and from these facts they propose explanations or theories to events they observe in the world. They use a systematic approach to problem solving, which is called the scientific method.

PERFORMANCE OBJECTIVES 1-1

1. Describe the steps scientists use to investigate a question or problem.
2. Explain each step in the scientific method.
3. Explain the difference between an experimental setup and a control setup.

SCIENCE TERMS 1-1

theory p. 7
law p. 7
scientific method p. 7
hypothesis p. 9
variable p. 10
experimental setup p. 10
control setup p. 11
data p. 11
chemistry p. 14
physics p. 14

TEACHING STRATEGY 1-1

Motivation

Begin this section by asking all of the scientists in the class to raise their hand.
• **What did you observe on the way to school today?** (Accept all answers.)

Select one or two of the students to describe in detail what they observed.
• **Could you have taken another route to school?** (Accept all answers.)
• **Would you still have ended up at school?** (Accept all answers.)
• **Would you have observed the same things if you had traveled another way?** (Accept all answers.)

Point out that even though they would have arrived at school, they probably would not have observed the very same things.

Content Development

Point out to students that they are all scientists. Scientists observe the world around them. Explain that "science" comes from the Latin word *scire,* which means "to know."

Skills Development

Skill: Relating facts

Have the students make a list of the things they know about themselves, such as gender, address, phone number, name, age, school, friends' names, etc.
• **Are you absolutely sure these are things you know?** (Accept all answers, but lead students to suggest they are absolutely sure of their knowledge in this area.)

1–1 What Is Science?

You may not realize it, but you are a scientist. Does that statement surprise you? If it does, it is probably because you do not understand exactly what a scientist is. But if you have ever observed a rainbow or seen a fire burn, you were acting like a scientist. You also are a scientist when you watch waves breaking in the ocean and lightning bolts brightening the night sky. Or perhaps you have noticed drops of dew on the morning grass or a roller coaster dipping up and down the track. Whenever you observe the world around you, you are acting like a scientist. Does that give you a clue to the nature of science and scientists? ❶

Scientists observe the world around them. But they do more than that. The word *science* comes from the Latin word *scire,* which means "to know." Science is more than just observing. And real scientists do more than just observe. They question what they see. They wonder what makes things the way they are. They attempt to find answers to their questions.

Figure 1–1 *It has long been a theory that a liquid does not retain its shape when removed from its container. However, scientists were forced to modify this theory after observing the photograph you see here. The photograph, taken with an exposure of a millionth of a second, shows that the water in the balloon retained its balloon shape for 12 to 13 milliseconds after the balloon had been burst by a dart.*

Theories and Laws

Scientists seek basic truths about nature. Such truths are often called facts. An example of a fact is that the sun is the source of heat and light on the earth. But scientists do more than seek facts. They use the facts to solve deeper mysteries of the universe. To do so, they must often tie together several facts in an orderly way. Using the facts they have learned, scientists propose explanations for the events they observe in their world. Then they perform experiments to test their explanations.

After a study of facts, observations, and experiments, scientists may develop a **theory**. A theory is the most logical explanation of events that occur in nature. Once a scientific theory has been proposed, it must be tested over and over again. If test results do not agree, the theory may be changed or even rejected. When a scientific theory has been tested many times and is generally accepted as true, scientists may call it a **law**. But even laws can be changed as a result of future observations and experiments. This points out the heart of science: Always allow questions to be asked and new scientific explanations to be considered.

Scientific Methods

Scientists investigate problems every day. Sometimes it takes many years to solve a problem and develop a theory. Sometimes a problem is quickly solved, especially when the tools needed to investigate the problem are available. And sometimes a problem goes unsolved.

When scientists try to solve a problem, they usually search for an answer in an orderly and systematic manner. To do so, scientists use the **scientific method.** The scientific method is a systematic approach to problem solving. **The basic steps in any scientific method are**

Stating the problem
Gathering information on the problem
Forming a hypothesis
Performing experiments to test the hypothesis ❸
Recording and analyzing data
Stating a conclusion

7

ANNOTATION KEY

❶ Science involves observing the world and its events (Relating concepts)
❶ Thinking Skill: Observing
❷ Thinking Skill: Applying concepts
❸ Thinking Skill: Sequencing

that theories are tested over and over. If a theory proves to be correct every time it is tested, it may be called a law. But, even in a science, a law can be changed if further observation and experimentation do not support the law.

• **Why do you think science allows us to come up with new answers for old ideas?** (Accept all logical answers.)

Point out that allowing for questions and new scientific explanations is the heart of science. Scientists are always looking for new and better ways of explaining and understanding the things around us.

Skills Development
Skill: Applying concepts
Tell the students that their problem is that one of their favorite VCR programs or musical tapes is missing. Using the scientific method, they are to write an explanation on how they would go about finding it. Students might share and discuss their solutions.

• **Would you say these are "facts"?** (Accept all answers.)
Explain that in order "to know," we must question the things we observe and the "facts."
• **Could any of the facts about you change?** (Accept all answers, but lead the students to agree that they could move and change addresses, girls marry and change last names, their age changes every year, they could live in a different house, etc.)

• **Which "facts" about you are not likely to change?** (Accept all answers, but lead students to suggest that during their lifetime many "facts" about them will change.)

Content Development
Explain that after observations, collecting facts, and experimenting, scientists may develop a theory. A theory is the most logical explanation of events that occur in nature. Point out

Sharpen Your Skills

Expanding Water
Skills: Observing, manipulative, relating, applying, inferring
Level: Remedial
Type: Hands-on
Materials: small pan, water, freezer unit

Through this activity, students will discover that unlike most substances, water expands when it freezes. Students will easily be able to see this since the frozen water will have risen above the top of the container.

1-1 (continued)

Motivation

Hold up a pencil for the students to observe. Write the word *observations* on the chalkboard. Without saying the word "pencil," ask:
• **What do you observe about this object?** (Accept all logical answers.)

Write all of their observations except the word "pencil" on the chalkboard. When the students say it's a pencil, ask:
• **How do you know?** (Accept all answers.)

Explain to the students that the only reason they "know" the object is a pencil is because it looks like a pencil, writes like a pencil, and they were told it was a pencil.

Content Development

Explain to the students that any time scientists have a problem, they develop

Figure 1–2 *The cracks in these rocks were produced by a process called frost action. How can freezing water form such cracks?* ❶

Sharpen Your Skills

Expanding Water

Most substances on the earth contract, or become smaller in volume, when they freeze. Water, however, is most unusual in that it expands when it freezes. You can investigate the expansion of water for yourself.

1. Fill a small pan to the brim with water.

2. Carefully place the pan in a freezer, making sure not to spill any of the water.

3. Wait one or two hours until all of the water has frozen.

4. Did the water expand when it froze? How can you tell?

8

To see how the scientific method is used, consider the following problem. It is one you might have observed yourself. Let's see how a scientist would try to solve it.

Stating the Problem

Suppose you stay at a friend's house one cold winter night. In the morning, your friend's father decides to drive you to school. However, when he turns the key in the ignition, the car does not start. Your friend discovers that there is a pool of ice under the car's engine.

A quick check with a mechanic provides an explanation. The water in the engine's cooling system froze overnight. As the water froze, it expanded and caused the engine to crack in places. Some water leaked onto the ground where it, too, froze. "I forgot to put antifreeze in my car," states the father. You nod your head in agreement, without any real idea about what antifreeze does.

How is it that an engine with antifreeze and water in its cooling system will not freeze on a cold night, while an engine without antifreeze will? If
❶ you have ever wondered about this, you have taken the first step toward recognizing a scientific problem. This kind of problem is one a scientist might try to solve.

Before investigating any problem, a scientist must develop a clear statement defining the problem. In this example, a physical scientist might state the problem this way: In what way does antifreeze keep the water in a car's engine from freezing on cold nights?

Gathering Information on the Problem

Once the problem has been clearly stated, all available information related to the problem must be gathered. In this example, a scientist would discover that antifreeze is needed to prevent freezing only in areas where the temperature goes below the freezing point of water. The freezing point of water is the temperature at which liquid water becomes ice. A scientist would also discover that people who

a clear statement, defining the problem.
• **Why is it necessary to develop a clear statement?** (Accept all logical answers.)
• **Why would it be easier to reach a conclusion if you had a definite and clear stated problem?** (Accept all logical answers. Lead students to suggest that only when a problem is recognized can a solution be found.)

Motivation

Have the students observe Figure 1-3. Read the caption.
• **Why do we put antifreeze in our cars?** (Accept all logical answers. Lead students to suggest either for cold, heat, or both.)
• **What do you predict happens when antifreeze is added to the radiator?** (Accept all logical answers.)

Figure 1–3 *Motorists know that it is as important to put antifreeze in a car's engine during the winter (left) as it is during the summer (right). How does antifreeze protect a car's engine during both seasons?* ❷

live in extremely cold areas must put more antifreeze in their cars than people who live in moderately cold areas. Finally, a scientist would note that water normally freezes at zero degrees Celsius, 0°C.

Forming a Hypothesis

After gathering all available information on the problem, a scientist would suggest a possible solution. A proposed solution to a scientific problem is called a **hypothesis** (high-PAHTH-uh-sihs). One hypothesis that might be considered is that antifreeze ❷ prevents water from freezing by lowering the temperature at which water freezes. A scientist might state the hypothesis as a question: Does antifreeze lower the freezing point of water?

Performing Experiments

A scientist does not stop once a hypothesis has been formed. Evidence that either supports or does not support the hypothesis must be found. So a scientist must test a hypothesis to see if it is correct. Such testing is usually done by performing one or more experiments.

A scientist performs experiments according to specific rules, so that the evidence uncovered will

9

clearly support or not support the hypothesis. How might a scientist go about testing the hypothesis that antifreeze lowers the freezing point of water?

First a scientist would obtain two containers. Each container would be the same size and made of the same material. A measured amount of water would be placed in the first container. The same amount of water would be placed in the second container. A measured amount of antifreeze would then be added to the second container.

Next a thermometer would be placed in one container, just below the water line. The same kind of thermometer would be placed in the second container, just below the water–antifreeze mixture line. Then each container would be placed in a freezer or cooling device.

It may appear to you as if two experiments are being performed—one with water and one with a water–antifreeze mixture. Actually, both containers are part of the same experiment. But there is a difference between the two containers. One container holds antifreeze and the other does not. In this experiment, the antifreeze is the **variable.** A variable in any experiment is the one factor that is being tested. The part of the experiment that contains the variable is called the **experimental setup.**

In any experiment, a scientist attempts to test one variable and only one variable at a time. This is done to ensure that the results of the experiment are due to the variable and not some hidden factor. To make sure that the results of an experiment

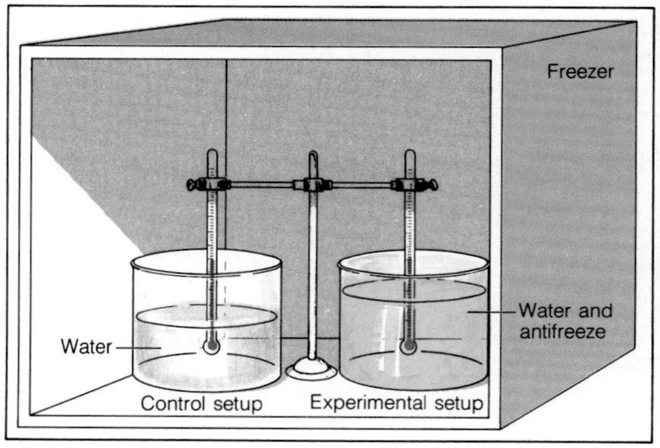

Figure 1–4 *What is the variable in this experiment?* ❶

Freezer

Water

Water and antifreeze

Control setup   Experimental setup

10

1-1 (continued)

Motivation

Show the class a tennis ball. Drop the ball and let it bounce. Discuss the bounce of the ball.

• **How many things could we change or vary to cause the ball to bounce higher?** (Accept all logical answers.)

Content Development

Explain to the students that after a hypothesis is made, a scientist must test the hypothesis by performing experiments. Point out that there should be only one *variable* in an experimental setup. A variable is a single thing that might change the results of the experiment.

Skills Development

Skill: Applying concepts

• **What is a variable?** (A variable is something that might change the results of the experiment.)

• **Why is it important to have only one variable?** (If there were more than one variable, you wouldn't know which variable caused the result.)

Explain that in an experiment a known fact or constant must be present.

• **Why would it be necessary to have**

something we already know to be present when we experiment? (Accept all answers.)

Explain that this constant is called a control setup. It assures us that the results will be based on a known value.

• **What would happen if we experimented without a control setup?** (Accept all answers, but lead students to suggest that "too many things could go wrong" and we wouldn't know what caused what to happen.)

Skills Development

Skill: Applying definitions

Have the students observe Figure 1-4. Read the caption. Discuss the experiment and the concepts of a "variable" and "control" by using the following questions.

• **What is the control setup in this experiment?** (Students should reply "the water.")

• **Why was water used as the control setup?** (Students should reply that the

HELP WANTED: SCIENCE TEACHER to teach junior high school science classes. Responsibilities include classroom, laboratory, and field activities. Teaching certification required. College degree in science preferred.

The bell rings and the last student enters the classroom to find a seat at a shiny, black lab table. The **science teacher** closes the door and eagerly looks out at the smiling faces of this year's science students.

A science teacher guides students in gathering information and learning new facts about the wonderful world of science. A science teacher helps students explore the weather, the stars, the nature of life, and the principles of physics. Frequently, these things cannot be seen, even with special equipment.

So the challenge to a science teacher is to present complex and abstract information in interesting, exciting, and clear ways. Satisfaction comes when students understand concepts they previously knew nothing about.

In addition to developing lesson plans for different topics, a science teacher must prepare lectures, demonstrations, laboratory projects, and field trips. A teacher must have a solid understanding of the material and be aware of the changes taking place in the world of scientific knowledge.

If you are interested in a career as a science teacher, contact the National Science Teachers Association, 1742 Connecticut Avenue NW, Washington, DC 20009.

are not caused by a hidden factor, a **control setup** is also run. A control setup is exactly like the experimental setup except the control setup does not contain the variable. By running a control setup, a scientist can be sure that the results of the experimental setup were due only to the variable. Which part of the antifreeze experiment is the control setup? ❷

Recording and Analyzing Data

In any experiment, a scientist must observe the experiment and write down important information. Recorded observations and measurements are called **data.** In the antifreeze experiment, a scientist would ❸ observe the containers in both the experimental and the control setups at specific time intervals—perhaps every 10 minutes. The temperature in each container would be recorded every 10 minutes. And the temperature at which liquid froze in each container

11

that a back lower corner of the freezer could be colder than the upper front part, which is closer to the door.
• **How could we make sure of the results of our experiment?** (Accept all logical answers, but lead students to suggest the experiment should be done in several places in the freezer at the same time.)

Content Development
Explain that scientists must test and retest to be sure their results are consistent and accurate. Tell the students that scientists must keep very accurate records of each experiment to check their results.

Skills Development
Skill: Designing an experiment
Have students design an experiment to test the hypothesis "Does salt lower the boiling point of water?" After the experiment has been designed, students might do the experiment.

Reinforcement
Have students think about other common substances that might lower or raise the boiling or freezing points of water. Then have teams state their hypothesis as a question, design an experiment, and conduct the experiment.

major hypothesis was "Does antifreeze lower the freezing point of water?" Therefore, water must be used as the controlling substance in the setup.)
• **Why was the same amount of water used in both setups?** (Without the same amount of water, another variable would have entered into the experiment.)
• **How might the amount of antifreeze used in the experiment change the results?** (Accept all answers but

lead students to suggest that several experiments using different amounts of antifreeze could give different results.)
• **What other "hidden" variable has not been discussed?** (Accept all logical answers.)

Concept Development
Point out to the students that the temperatures in different parts of the freezer could be different. Explain

would be noted. To record the data, a scientist would set up data tables similar to the following:

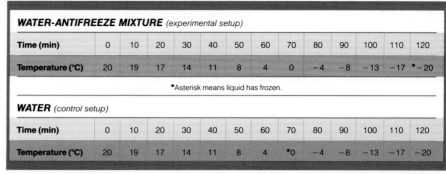

WATER-ANTIFREEZE MIXTURE (experimental setup)													
Time (min)	0	10	20	30	40	50	60	70	80	90	100	110	120
Temperature (°C)	20	19	17	14	11	8	4	0	−4	−8	−13	−17	*−20

*Asterisk means liquid has frozen.

WATER (control setup)													
Time (min)	0	10	20	30	40	50	60	70	80	90	100	110	120
Temperature (°C)	20	19	17	14	11	8	4	*0	−4	−8	−13	−17	−20

Figure 1–5 *Scientists often record their observations in data tables. According to these data tables, what is the time interval for measurements?* ❶

To visually compare the data, a scientist would next construct a graph from the data in each table. Since each data table contains two sets of measurements—time and temperature—the graph would have two axes. See Figure 1–6. The horizontal axis of the graph represents time. As you can see from this graph, the horizontal axis must be clearly labeled with the measurement and its units. Since ❶ time measurements were made at 10-minute intervals, the horizontal axis is marked in intervals of 10 minutes. The space between equal intervals must be equal. That is, the space between 10 minutes and 20 minutes must be the same as the space between 20 minutes and 30 minutes.

The vertical axis of the graph represents temperature. This axis too is clearly labeled with the measurement and its units. Since the experiment began at 20°C and ended at −20°C, the vertical axis would go from 20°C to −20°C.

After the axes for each graph were chosen and labeled, a scientist would graph the data from the experimental setup. Each pair of data points from ❷ the data table would be plotted. At 0 minutes, the temperature was 20°C. So a dot would be placed where 0 minutes and 20°C intersected on the graph—in the upper left corner. When each set of data points had been plotted on the graph, a scientist would draw a line connecting all the dots.

12

The same procedure would be followed for the data from the control setup. Soon a scientist would have a graph of the experimental setup side by side with a graph of the control setup. For these particular graphs, the final thing would be to indicate at what temperature the liquid in each container froze.

Stating a Conclusion

The results from a single experiment are not enough to reach a conclusion. A scientist must run an experiment over and over again before the data can be considered accurate.

Once the antifreeze experiment had been run many times, a scientist would examine the data and state a conclusion. Since the plain water froze at a temperature of 0°C and the water with antifreeze froze at a temperature of −20°C, a scientist would conclude that antifreeze lowers the temperature at which water freezes. The original hypothesis in this case would be correct.

Is the scientist finished? Actually, a good scientist would then ask *why* antifreeze lowers the freezing point of water. And that, of course, sounds very much like the beginning of a new problem. It often

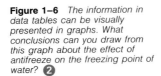

Figure 1–6 *The information in data tables can be visually presented in graphs. What conclusions can you draw from this graph about the effect of antifreeze on the freezing point of water?* ❷

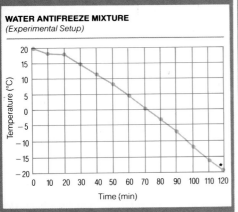
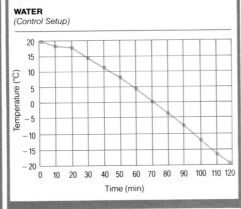
data are not always easy to interpret in table form. A scientist will frequently use a graph to help understand the data.

Have the students observe Figure 1-6. Explain that the data from Figure 1-5 was plotted on a grid to make the graphs. Point out the horizontal axis showing time in minutes and the vertical axis showing temperature in degrees Celsius.

Skills Development
Skill: Interpreting graphs
- **Which axis shows the time elapsed?** (The horizontal axis shows the time elapsed.)
- **Which axis shows the temperature?** (The horizontal axis shows the temperature.)
- **Which graph shows the control setup?** (The graph at the right shows the control setup.)
- **Which graph shows the experi-**

mental setup? (The graph at the left shows the experimental setup.)
- **How are the graphs similar?** (Both graphs have the same scales on the axes, and the lines connecting the dots are the same.)
- **How are the graphs different?** (One graph shows the control data, and the other graph shows the experimental data. The freezing point is different on the graphs.)

Content Development
Explain that after the results from many experiments have been gathered and recorded, a scientist can *sometimes* state a conclusion to the problem. In this experiment a scientist might conclude that "Antifreeze lowers the temperature at which water freezes." The original hypothesis, "Does antifreeze lower the freezing point of water?" would be answered yes.

Point out that a scientist might decide to go further into the investigation and ask another question, such as, "How does antifreeze lower the freezing point of water?"

Reinforcement
Have students research magazines to find graphs. Teams might share and discuss how each graph helps the reader to interpret the data.

ANNOTATION KEY
❶ Ten-minute intervals (Interpreting charts)
❷ Antifreeze lowers the freezing point of water. (Interpreting graphs)
❶ Thinking Skill: Making graphs
❷ Thinking Skill: Relating facts
❸ Thinking Skill: Drawing conclusions

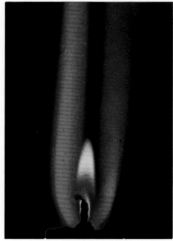

Figure 1–7 *Chemistry is the study of matter and the changes it undergoes (left). The laws of motion (right) are part of the science of physics.*

ANNOTATION KEY

❶ Turn together or meet (Applying definitions)

❶ Thinking Skill: Classifying

❷ Thinking Skill: Using root words

Sharpen Your Skills

Prefixes and Suffixes
Skills: Applying concepts, applying definitions, relating
Level: Average
Type: Vocabulary/writing comprehension

This activity will help reinforce the concept that learning prefixes and suffixes will be of great help to students in determining the meanings of unfamiliar science terms.

1-1 (continued)

Section Review 1-1

1. Stating a problem, gathering information on the problem, forming a hypothesis, performing experiments, recording and analyzing data, stating a conclusion

2. If an experiment has more than one variable, a scientist cannot be sure which variable affected the results of the experiment.

3. Antifreeze raises the boiling point of water and helps prevent cars from overheating.

TEACHING STRATEGY 1-2

Motivation

Have 4–6 pencils of *different* lengths available. Divide the class into teams of six students. Give each team one of the pencils. Tell the teams to measure the length of a student desk and record the distance on the chalkboard using "pencil" as the unit name. Discuss the motivation activity.

Sharpen Your Skills

Prefixes and Suffixes

Study the list of common science prefixes and suffixes in Figure 1–8.

1. Select three science words that have a prefix listed on the chart.

2. Select two science words that have a suffix listed on the chart.

3. Write a paragraph using the five words you have chosen.

4. Do you know any additional science prefixes and suffixes that you think should be added to the chart? Share your findings with your class.

14

---

happens in science that the solution to one problem leads to yet another problem. The cycle of discovery in science goes on and on.

Branches of Physical Science

Science is divided into many branches, depending on the subject matter being studied. Physical science is the study of matter and energy. There are two main branches of physical science—**chemistry** and **physics.** Chemistry involves the study of what substances are made of and how they change and combine. Physics is the study of forms of energy and the laws of motion.

Just as with any branch of science, physical science has many special terms that may be unfamiliar to you. The chart in Figure 1–8 gives the meanings of some prefixes and suffixes commonly used in science vocabulary. If you learn the meanings of these prefixes and suffixes, you will find it easier to learn new science terms. And knowing the meaning of science terms will increase your understanding of physical science. For example, suppose you come upon the term *exothermic reaction.* You know from the chart that *exo-* means out and *-therm* means heat. So you probably can guess that in an exothermic reaction heat goes out, or heat is given off.

• **We all measured similar desks. Why are the measures so different?** (The measures are different because the pencils must have been different. If we had a short pencil, our measure is the biggest number. If we had a long pencil, our measure is the smallest number.)

• **What is wrong with having different measures for the same thing?** (Accept all answers. Lead students to state that we all need to use the same unit for measuring in order to communicate.)

• **What would happen if all shoes were sized using different units of measure?** (Accept all answers, and reinforce the need for using the same unit of measure for "fit" and to communicate with others.)

• **What could we do to be sure that our measures of the same desk were the same?** (We should all use the same unit of measure.)

SOME COMMON SCIENCE PREFIXES AND SUFFIXES

Prefix	Meaning	Prefix	Meaning	Suffix	Meaning
anti-	against	in-	inside	-ation	the act of
atmo-	vapor	inter-	between	-escent	becoming
chromo-	color	iso-	equal	-graphy	description of
con-	together	macro-	large	-logy	study of
di-	double	micro-	small	-meter	device for measuring
endo-	within	photo-	light	-scope	instrument for seeing
exo-	outside	sub-	under	-sphere	round
hetero-	different	syn-	together	-stasis	stationary condition
homo-	same	tele-	distant	-therm	heat
hydro-	water	trans-	across	-verge	turn

Figure 1–8 *A working knowledge of prefixes and suffixes used in science vocabulary will be of great help to you. According to this chart, what is the meaning of the term converge?* ❶

SECTION REVIEW

1. Identify the steps in a scientific method.
2. Explain why any experiment must have only one variable.
3. People usually put antifreeze in a car engine during the summer when temperatures get very high. What effect do you think antifreeze has on water that makes it useful on very hot days?

1–2 Scientific Measurements

Section Objective

To identify the metric units used in scientific measurements

As you learned, experimenting is an important part of any scientific method. And most experiments involve measurements. Measurements made during experiments must be reliable and accurate as well as easily communicated to others. So a system of measurements based on standard units is used by scientists. With this system, scientists around the world can compare and analyze data.

15

1-2 SCIENTIFIC MEASUREMENTS

SECTION PREVIEW 1-2

The standard system used by scientists throughout the world is the metric system. The metric system is a decimal system. Scientists use metric units to measure length, volume, mass, and temperature. The metric unit of distance is the meter. An object's volume is measured in liters and cubic centimeters in the metric system. Metric mass is measured using units called grams and kilograms. The Celsius degree (°C) is the metric unit for measuring temperature. Scientists use other units of metric measure that are derived from the base units.

PERFORMANCE OBJECTIVES 1-2

1. **Compare the different units of measurement in the metric system.**
2. **Explain how to measure distance, volume, mass, and temperature in standard metric units.**
3. **Demonstrate how to measure using standard metric units of distance, volume, mass, and temperature.**

SCIENCE TERMS 1-2

metric system p. 16	kilogram p. 18
meter p. 16	milligram p. 18
centimeter p. 16	gram p. 18
millimeter p. 17	density p. 18
kilometer p. 17	Celsius p. 19
liter p. 17	dimensional analysis p. 19
milliliter p. 17	conversion factor p. 19
cubic centimeter p. 18	

Content Development

Explain that in ancient times each country, kingdom, or state used its own unit of measure. In those days, travel was limited and the need for a worldwide standard was not so important. Today, we travel and communicate with people all over the world. Point out that a standard unit of measure must be used to be able to communicate with others.

Skills Development

Skill: Using a model

Prepare 4–6 one-meter long unmarked sticks, from broomsticks or other available materials. Divide the class into groups of four to six. Show the class the sticks and tell them that it is a "model" of a standard unit. Give each group a model of the standard stick. Have the teams measure the length and width of the classroom. Tell the teams to record their measures on the chalkboard. Compare and discuss the team measures.

• **What did you find out?** (Most of the measures were the same.)
• **Why did we all get almost the same measures?** (We all used the standard model unit.)
• **All of the measures were *not exactly* the same. What caused this to happen when we all used the same standard?** (Accept all logical answers.)

TIE-IN/HISTORY

Have students do library research to find out about some of the ancient units of measure. Students should find out about a cubit, digit, span, pace, and other ancient units of measure.

TEACHER DEMONSTRATION

Have a new unsharpened pencil available in your desk. Tell the class that you have a "secret" unit of distance. Ask the class to use their hands to demonstrate how long they *guess* the secret unit distance might be. Then, show the secret pencil length to the class. Discuss how the pencil might be used to measure various distances.

• **How would you use the secret pencil length to measure the height of a desk?** (Compare and count how many pencil lengths it takes to reach the height of the desk.)

Have several students follow the suggested procedure to measure the height of the desk.

• **How would you use the secret pencil length to measure the height of the door?** (Compare and count how many pencil lengths it takes to reach the height of the door.)

Have several students follow the suggested procedure to measure the height of the door.

• **What unit did we use to measure the height of the door?** (We used the secret pencil unit.)

• **What is measuring?** (Accept all logical answers. Lead students to state that measuring is comparing and counting how many units fit into a distance.)

The standard system used by all scientists is the **metric system.** The metric system is also referred to as the International System of Units, or SI. The metric system is a decimal system. That is, it is based on the number 10 and multiples of 10.

❶ Scientists use metric units to measure length, volume, mass, density, and temperature. Some frequently used metric units and their abbreviations are listed in Figure 1–9.

Length

The basic unit of length in the metric system is the **meter (m).** A meter is equal to about 39.4 inches. Your height would be measured in meters. Most students your age are between 1½ and 2 meters tall.

To measure the length of an object smaller than a meter, the metric unit called the **centimeter (cm)** is used. The prefix *centi-* means one-hundredth. So there are 100 centimeters in a meter. The height of this book is about 26 centimeters.

Figure 1–9 *The metric system is easy to use because it is based on units of ten. How many centimeters are there in 10 meters?* ❶

COMMONLY USED METRIC UNITS	
Length	**Mass**
Length is the distance from one point to another.	Mass is the amount of matter in an object.
A meter is slightly longer than a yard.	A gram has a mass equal to about one paper clip.
1 meter (m) = 100 centimeters (cm)	
1 meter = 1000 millimeters (mm)	1 kilogram (kg) = 1000 grams (g)
1 meter = 1,000,000 micrometers (μm)	1 gram = 1000 milligrams (mg)
1 meter = 1,000,000,000 nanometers (nm)	1000 kilograms = 1 metric ton (t)
1 meter = 10,000,000,000 angstroms (Å)	
1000 meters = 1 kilometer (km)	
Volume	**Temperature**
Volume is the amount of space an object takes up.	Temperature is the measure of hotness or coldness in degrees Celsius (°C).
A liter is slightly larger than a quart.	
1 liter (L) = 1000 milliliters (mL) or 1000 cubic centimeters (cm³)	0°C = freezing point of water
	100°C = boiling point of water

16

1-2 (continued)

Motivation

Show the class a "standard" unit model stick. Discuss the different lengths that might be measured using the standard unit model stick.

• **Would a standard unit model stick be a good unit for measuring the length or width of the classroom? Why?** (Yes, because the room is larger than the standard unit model stick.)

• **Would a standard unit model stick be a good unit for measuring the length or width of a football field?**

Why? (Yes, because the standard unit model stick is smaller than a football field.)

• **Would a standard unit model stick be a good unit for measuring the length or width of your finger? Why?** (No, because the stick is longer than a finger, we would have to guess.)

Content Development

Point out to the students that using a standard unit of measure is very

important in science. Explain that scientists around the world must be able to communicate with each other.

Skills Development

Skill: Developing a model

• **What are some ways we might improve the standard unit model stick?** (Accept all logical answers, but lead students to suggest the need for a smaller standard unit or dividing the standard unit into smaller sections.)

Figure 1–10 *This spectacular photograph of the rings of Saturn was taken by the Voyager satellite as it passed by the distant planet. Which metric unit is best for measuring the distance to Saturn?* ❷

To measure even smaller objects, the metric unit called the **millimeter (mm)** is used. The prefix *milli-* means one-thousandth. As you might expect, there ❷ are 1000 millimeters in a meter. How many millimeters are there in a centimeter? ❸

Sometimes scientists want to measure long distances, such as the length of the Nile River in Africa. Such lengths can be measured in meters, centimeters, or even millimeters. But when measuring long distances with small units, the numbers become very large and difficult to work with. For example, the length of the Nile River is about 6,649,000,000 millimeters. To avoid such large numbers, the metric unit called the **kilometer (km)** is used. The prefix *kilo-* means one thousand. So there are 1000 meters in a kilometer. The length of the Nile River is about 6649 kilometers. How many meters is this? How many centimeters are there in one kilometer? How many millimeters? ❹

Volume

Volume is the amount of space an object takes up. The basic unit of volume in the metric system is the **liter (L).** A liter is slightly more than a quart. To measure volumes smaller than a liter, scientists ❸ use the **milliliter (mL).** There are 1000 milliliters in a liter. An ordinary drinking glass holds about 200 milliliters of liquid.

17

in one meter. However, when we try to measure to get *exactly* 100 centimeters that are *exactly* the same size, we have problems. These problems lead us to understand that measurements can only be reasonably precise, depending on the unit being used.

Point out that the prefix *milli* means 1/1000th (0.001). A millimeter is 1/1000th of a meter and 1/100th of a centimeter.

• **How could we measure something much longer than a meter?** (Accept all logical answers.)

Motivation

Hold up a glass of water. Explain that volume is the amount of space an object takes up. When we measure the volume of containers, we also call it capacity.

• **How could we measure the volume of the water in this glass?** (Accept all logical answers.)

Hold up a small stick (such as a toothpick) that has been cut the length of a centimeter.

• **Would a standard unit the size of this stick be good for measuring small distances?** (Most students will reply that it would.)

Content Development

Explain that 100 of the small stick lengths would equal the length of the standard unit model stick. If 100 small sticks fit the standard length, then the small stick is 1/100th (0.01) as long as the large standard unit model stick.

Explain that the base unit of measure in the metric system is the meter, and that the standard unit model stick was really a meter. Point out that a centimeter (cm) is 1/100th (0.01) of a meter, or there are 100 centimeters in one meter.

Using the standard metric definition, there are *exactly* 100 centimeters

The Founding Fathers of our American republic used a type of metric system in currency that we still use today. They established our decimal system of coinage, with 100 cents equal to one dollar. All United States monies are decimal multiples or decimal fractions of the base dollar.

Sharpen Your Skills

Metric Research
Skill: Making calculations
Level: Enriched
Type: Library/computational

In their library research, students will probably find the measurements in nonmetric units. As such, they will have to convert to the proper metric unit. Students should find that a football field is 91.44 meters; Golden Gate Bridge is 1280 meters; distance to sun is 150,000,000 kilometers (average distance); light year is 9.65 trillion kilometers; mass of mouse is 22.39 grams; Wright brothers' plane is 340 kilograms; hottest temperature is 58°C; coldest temperature is −90°C.

1-2 (continued)

Motivation

Show the students a block of wood.
• **How could we find the volume of this piece of wood?** (Accept all logical answers.)

Content Development

Point out that in the metric system the volume of a liquid or gas is measured in liters (L) and milliliters (mL). The volume of a container is referred to as capacity.

The volume of a solid is measured in cubic centimeters (cm³). To find the volume of a solid measure the length, width, and height of the object in centimeter units. Then multiply the measures (V = 1 × w × h) to find the volume in cubic centimeters. Explain that a cubic centimeter (cm³) is equal to a milliliter (mL).

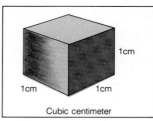

Figure 1–11 *A cubic centimeter (cm³, or cc) is the volume of a cube that measures 1 cm by 1 cm by 1 cm. How many milliliters are in a cubic centimeter?* ❷

Sharpen Your Skills

Metric Research

Using reference books from the library, find out the values for the following objects:

- length of a football field in meters
- length of the Golden Gate Bridge in meters
- distance to the sun in kilometers
- distance light travels in one year, which is called a light-year, in kilometers
- average mass of a mouse in grams
- mass of Wright brothers' plane in kilograms
- hottest temperature ever recorded on the earth in degrees Celsius
- coldest temperature ever recorded on the earth in degrees Celsius

❶

18

Motivation

Have the students observe Figure 1-12. Explain that many times scientists want to measure the amount of matter in an object.
• **How could we measure the amount of matter in the real animals shown in Figure 1-12?** (Accept all logical answers.)
• **What would we need to measure mass?** (Accept all answers. Lead students to suggest that a standard unit

---

Liters and milliliters are used to measure the volume of liquids. The metric unit used to measure the volume of solids is called the **cubic centimeter (cm³ or cc).** A cubic centimeter is equal to a milliliter. Cubic centimeters often are used in measuring the volume of liquids as well as solids. How many cubic centimeters are there in a liter? ❶

Mass

The basic unit of mass in the metric system is the **kilogram (kg).** Mass is a measure of the amount of matter in an object. For example, there is more matter in a dumptruck than in a compact car. So a dumptruck has more mass than a compact car. A kilogram is about 2.2 pounds. What is your mass in kilograms?

The kilogram is used to measure the mass of large objects. To measure the mass of small objects, such as a nickel, the **gram (g)** is used. If you remember what the term *kilo-* means, then you know that a kilogram contains 1000 grams. A nickel has a mass of about 5 grams.

The mass of even smaller objects is measured in **milligrams (mg).** A milligram is one-thousandth of a gram. So there are 1000 milligrams in a gram. How many milligrams are there in a kilogram? ❸

Density

Sometimes it is useful to know the amount of mass in a given volume of an object. This quantity is known as **density.** Density is defined as the mass per unit volume of a substance. The following formula shows the relationship between density, mass, and volume:

$$\text{density} = \frac{\text{mass}}{\text{volume}}$$

Suppose a substance has a mass of 10 grams and a volume of 10 milliliters. If you divide the mass of 10 grams by the volume of 10 milliliters, you obtain the density of the substance:

$$\frac{10\text{ g}}{10\text{ mL}} = \frac{1\text{ g}}{\text{mL}}$$

---

of mass is needed.)

Content Development

Explain that the amount of matter in an object is called its mass. The base metric unit of mass is a kilogram (kg). Kilogram is pronounced KIL-oh-gram. One liter of water has a mass of one kilogram. Kilogram units are used to measure the mass of large things.

Point out that to measure the mass of small things, such as the mouse, the

Figure 1–12 *The hippopotamus is one of the largest land animals on the earth. Harvest field mice are the smallest mice on the earth. Which metric unit would be best for measuring the mass of a hippopotamus? Of field mice?* ❹

As it turns out, this substance is water. The density of water is 1 g/mL. Objects with a density less than that of water will float on water. Objects with a density greater than that of water will sink in water. Does wood have a density less than or greater than 1 g/mL? ❺

Temperature

In the metric system, temperature is measured on the **Celsius** (SEHL-see-uhs) scale. On the Celsius temperature scale, water freezes at 0°C and boils at 100°C. There are exactly 100 degrees between the freezing point and boiling point of water. Each Celsius degree represents 1/100 of this temperature range. Normal body temperature in humans is 37°C. Comfortable room temperature is about 21°C.

Dimensional Analysis

Now that you know the basic units of the metric system, it is important that you understand how to go from one unit to another. The skill of converting one unit to another is called **dimensional analysis.** Dimensional analysis involves determining in what units a problem is given, in what units the answer should be, and the factor to be used to make the conversion from one unit to another.

To perform dimensional analysis, you must use a **conversion factor.** A conversion factor is a fraction

Figure 1–13 *Notice the steam rising out of the sulfur springs on the island of Saint Lucia. What instrument would be used to measure the temperature of the sulfur springs?* ❻

19

Motivation
Show the students a block of Styrofoam. Explain that the Styrofoam block has both mass and volume. Cut or break the block into two pieces. Point out that each piece also has both mass and volume.

Content Development
Tell the students that sometimes it is useful to know the relationship between the mass and the volume of a substance. Explain that the density of a substance is the ratio of the mass to the volume (mass per unit volume). The density of an object is equal to the mass divided by the volume (density = mass/volume).

Explain that if an object is cut into smaller pieces, each piece would have a mass of its own and a volume of its own. And the mass and volume of one small piece would be less than the mass and volume of the large object it was cut from. However, the density of the same pure substance is always the same.

scientist would need a smaller unit. Explain that things with small masses are measured in grams (g). A paper clip has a mass of about one gram. One gram is equal to one one-thousandth (1/1000 kg or 0.001 kg) of a kilogram. One thousand grams equals one kilogram (1000 g × 1 kg).

Skills Development
Skill: Classifying mass
Have the class make a list of large and small objects or things. Remind the students that the mass of an object or thing could be measured in either kilograms or grams.

• **Which unit, gram or kilogram, would you use to measure the mass of each object?** (The mass of large objects such as cars, people, and airplanes should be measured in kilogram units. The mass of small objects such as pencils, pens, and erasers should be measured in gram units.)

ANNOTATION KEY

❶ **Thinking Skill: Applying formulas**
❷ **Thinking Skill: Making generalizations**

1-2 (continued)

Skills Development
Skill: Applying formulas
Have students make additional conversions between grams and kilograms. If necessary, write the conversion factor on the chalkboard and show both the cancellation and multiplication for each problem. Encourage students to use the symbols g and kg.
• **How many kilograms are equal to 1357 grams?** (1357 g × 1 kg/1000 g = 1.357 kg)
• **How many kilograms are equal to 791 grams?** (791 g × 1 kg/1000 g = 0.791 kg)
• **How many grams are equal to 3.184 kilograms?** (3.184 kg × 1000 g/1 kg = 3184 g)

20

that always equals 1. For example, 1 kilometer equals 1000 meters. So the fraction 1 kilometer/1000 meters equals 1. So does the fraction 1000 meters/1 kilometer. The top number in a fraction is called the numerator. The bottom number in a fraction is called the denominator. In a conversion fraction the numerator always equals the denominator so that the fraction always equals 1.

Let's see how dimensional analysis works. Suppose you are told to convert 2500 grams to kilograms. This means that grams are your given unit and you must express your answer in kilograms. The conversion factor you choose must contain a relationship between grams and kilograms that has a value of 1. You have two possible choices:

$$\frac{1000 \text{ grams}}{1 \text{ kilogram}} = 1 \quad \text{or} \quad \frac{1 \text{ kilogram}}{1000 \text{ grams}} = 1$$

To convert one metric unit to another, you must multiply the given value times the conversion factor. Remember that multiplying a number by 1 does not change the value of the number. So multiplying by a conversion factor does not change the value, just the units.

Now, which conversion factor should you use to change 2500 grams into kilograms? Since you are going to multiply by the conversion factor, you want the unit to be converted to cancel out during the multiplication. This is just what will happen if the denominator of the conversion factor has the same units as the value you wish to convert. Since you are converting grams into kilograms, the denominator of the conversion factor must be in grams and the numerator in kilograms. The first step in dimensional analysis, then, is to write out the value given, the correct conversion factor, and a multiplication symbol between them:

❶
$$2500 \text{ grams} \times \frac{1 \text{ kilogram}}{1000 \text{ grams}}$$

The next step is to cancel out the same units:

$$2500 \text{ grams} \times \frac{1 \text{ kilogram}}{1000 \text{ grams}}$$

• **How many grams are equal to 0.31 kilograms?** (0.31 kg × 1000 g/1 kg = 310 g)

Section Review 1-2

1. Meter; liter; kilogram; degree Celsius
2. Kilometers. The distance is so large that using smaller units would involve very large numbers.
3. There are 10 billion Angstroms in a meter.

4. If the object has a density less than 1 g/mL, it will float on water.

TEACHING STRATEGY 1-3

Motivation
Hold up a metric ruler. Ask:
• **What type of measurement do you think we will use this for?** (Most students will predict that the metric ruler will be used for measuring distances

The last step is to multiply:

$$2500 \times \frac{1 \text{ kilogram}}{1000} = \frac{2500 \text{ kilograms}}{1000}$$

$$\frac{2500 \text{ kilograms}}{1000} = 2.5 \text{ kilograms}$$

SECTION REVIEW

1. What are the basic units of length, volume, mass, and temperature in the metric system?
2. What metric unit of length would be appropriate for expressing the distance from the earth to the sun? Why?
3. To measure the size of atoms, scientists use the unit called the Angstrom. An Angstrom is one ten-billionth of a meter. How many Angstroms are in a meter?
4. Without placing an object in water, how can you determine if it will float?

1–3 Tools of Measurement

Section Objective

To describe how common laboratory tools are used to make scientific measurements

Physical scientists use a wide variety of tools in order to study the world around them. Some of these tools are rather complex; others are relatively simple. As you read this book, you will be introduced to many of these tools. You will have an opportunity to use some of these laboratory tools when you perform physical science experiments. **The basic laboratory tools that you will learn to use are the metric ruler, triple-beam balance, graduated cylinder, and Celsius thermometer.** ②

Measuring Length

A metric ruler is used to measure the length of objects. A metric ruler is divided into centimeters. Common metric rulers are 15 or 25 centimeters in length. Each centimeter is further divided into 10 millimeters. Figure 1–14 on page 22 shows a metric ruler and the centimeter and millimeter divisions. Keep in mind that this ruler is not drawn to scale. You cannot use it to make calculations.

21

1-3 TOOLS OF MEASUREMENT

SECTION PREVIEW 1-3

The Physical Scientist uses a wide variety of tools to study the world. The basic scientific tools of measurement are the metric ruler, meterstick, triple-beam balance, graduated cylinder, and Celsius thermometer.

Learning to measure with the proper tools is very important. The metric ruler will be used to measure the length of an object. With the triple-beam balance we can measure the mass of an object. To find the volume of a liquid we use a graduated cylinder. Scientists use a Celsius thermometer to measure temperature.

PERFORMANCE OBJECTIVES 1-3

1. Identify the common laboratory tools used to measure length, volume, mass, and temperature.
2. Explain the base units of metric measurement.
3. Describe the relationship between metric base units and the prefixes *centi*, *milli*, and *kilo*.

SCIENCE TERMS 1-3
meniscus p. 24

such as the length, width, height, or thickness of things.)

Explain that a metric ruler is divided into smaller units called centimeters. The symbol for centimeters is cm. Each centimeter is then divided into ten equal parts called a millimeter. The symbol for millimeter is mm. One millimeter is 1/10th of a centimeter (1 mm = 0.1 cm). Ten millimeters equals one centimeter (10 mm = 1 cm).

Content Development
Point out that each scientific measuring tool performs a different job or function. Explain that when tools are used for measuring, we are measuring directly. In direct measurement, the thing being measured is compared directly to the standard unit. The accuracy of a measurement depends on three things: (1) the smallest unit on the measuring scale, (2) the ability of the observer to read the scale prop-

erly, and (3) the degree of precision of the measuring instrument and scale.

Skills Development
Skill: Taking measurements
Divide the class into teams of 4–6 students. Have each team measure ten different classroom distances. Each measured distance should be recorded in millimeters, centimeters, and meters.

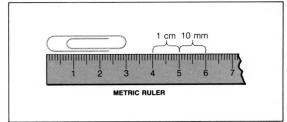

To measure an object whose length is longer than a metric ruler, you would use a meterstick. A meterstick is one meter long and contains 100 centimeters. How many millimeters are in a meterstick? ❷

Measuring Mass

Recall that the kilogram is the basic unit of mass in the metric system. A kilogram contains 1000 grams. Most of the measurements you will make in physical science will be in grams. One of the most common tools used to measure mass in grams is the triple-beam balance shown in Figure 1–15.

As you might expect, a triple-beam balance has three beams. Each beam is marked, or calibrated, in grams. The front beam is the 10-gram beam. Markings divide the beam into 10 segments of 1 gram each. On some triple-beam balances, each 1-gram segment on the front beam is further divided into units of one-tenth gram. The middle beam, often called the 500-gram beam, is divided into 5 segments of 100 grams each. The back beam, or 100-gram beam, is divided into 10 segments of 10 grams each. What is the largest mass you can measure with a triple-beam balance? ❸

To measure the mass of a solid, such as a small rock, follow these steps. First, place the rock on the flat pan of the balance. Then slide the rider on the middle beam notch by notch until the pointer drops below zero. Move the rider back one notch. Next, ❶ slide the rider on the back beam notch by notch until the pointer drops below zero. Move this rider back one notch. Finally, move the rider on the front beam notch by notch until the pointer points exactly to the zero mark. The mass of the object is equal to the *sum* of the readings on the three beams.

Sharpen Your Skills

Metric Measurements
Skills: Measuring, calculating, recording
Level: Average
Type: Hands-on/computational
This activity will help students relate metric units to their everyday lives. Students answers will vary, depending on the objects they measure.

Sharpen Your Skills

Metric Measurements

Here are some measurements you can make about yourself and your surroundings. Use the metric units of length, mass, volume, and temperature. Record your measurements on a chart.

Make the following measurements about yourself:

 height
 arm length
 body temperature
 volume of water you drink in a day

Make the following measurements about your environment:

 outdoor temperature
 automobile speed limit on your street
 distance to school
 total mass of ingredients in your favorite cake recipe
 mass of your favorite sports equipment

22

1-3 (continued)

Motivation
Ask students to observe their pencils carefully.
• **What are the properties of your pencil?** (Students are likely to suggest color, size, shape, length, width, diameter, volume, and mass.)
Tell the students to hold the pencil out at arm's length in front of their body.

• **What would happen to the pencil if you released your grip?** (The pencil would fall down.)
• **What would gravity pull on to make the pencil fall down?** (Gravity would pull on the mass of the pencil.)

Content Development
Explain that everything in the universe that is made of matter has mass. Mass is the quantity of matter in any object or substance.

Have students observe Figure 1-15. Remind students that the metric units of mass are the kilogram (kg) and gram (g). Explain that the balance in the photograph is the same kind they will be using in the laboratory. Point out the positions of the pan, large rider on the middle beam, middle rider on the back beam, small rider on the front beam, pointer, pointer scale, and zero adjustment knob.

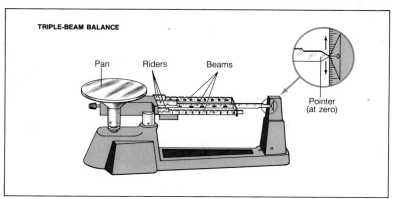

TRIPLE-BEAM BALANCE

Pan   Riders   Beams

Pointer
(at zero)

If you want to find the mass of a powder or of crystals, you will have to place the sample on a sheet of filter paper on top of the pan. You must never place such a sample directly on the balance pan. The mass of the filter paper must first be determined. Once this is done, you can pour the sample onto the filter paper and find the mass of the filter paper and sample combined. Subtract the mass of the filter paper from the mass of filter paper and sample to determine the mass of the sample.

A similar method can be used to find the mass of a liquid. In this case, place an empty beaker or flask on the pan and find its mass. Then pour the liquid into the beaker. Find the combined mass of ❷ the beaker and liquid. Subtract the mass of the beaker from the mass of the beaker and liquid to determine the mass of the liquid.

Figure 1–15 *A triple-beam balance is one of the instruments used to measure mass in grams. Can mass in kilograms be measured by using a triple-beam balance? Explain your answer.* ❹

Figure 1–16 *A triple-beam balance is used to determine the mass of an object. What is the mass of the solid?* ❺

Measuring Volume

You learned that the basic unit of volume in the metric system is the liter. Most of the measurements you will make in physical science, however, will be in milliliters or cubic centimeters. Remember there are 1000 milliliters or cubic centimeters in a liter.

To find the volume of a liquid, you will use a graduated cylinder. See Figure 1–17. A graduated cylinder is usually calibrated in milliliters. Each line ❸ on the graduated cylinder is one milliliter. To measure the volume of a liquid, pour the liquid into the graduated cylinder. You will notice that the surface of the liquid is curved. To determine the volume of

23

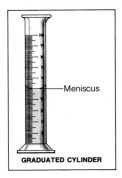
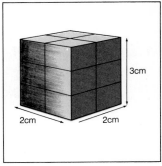

Figure 1–17 *A graduated cylinder is used to measure volume (left). To get an accurate measurement, where should you read the markings on the graduated cylinder? What is the volume of this rectangular block in cubic centimeters (cm³) (right)?* ❶

the liquid, read the milliliter marking at the *bottom* of the curve. This curve is called the **meniscus** (mih-NIHS-kuhs). Keep in mind that although a graduated cylinder is marked off in milliliters, each milliliter is equal to one cubic centimeter.

To find the volume of a solid that is rectangular in shape, you will use a metric ruler. A rectangular solid is often called a regular solid. The volume of a regular solid is determined by multiplying the length of the solid times the width of the solid times the height of the solid. The formula you can use to find the volume of a regular solid is

volume = height times length times width

or

❶ **v = h × l × w**

Figure 1–17 shows a rectangular solid with a length of 2 centimeters, a width of 2 centimeters, and a height of 3 centimeters. If you multiply 2 cm times 2 cm times 3 cm, you obtain the volume, which is 12 cm³, or 12 cc. What is the volume of a regular solid 3 cm by 4 cm by 5 cm? ❷

Suppose you wish to determine the volume of a solid that is not rectangular in shape, or an irregular solid. You cannot measure its height, width, or length with a metric ruler. So to determine the volume of an irregular solid, you will use a graduated cylinder again. First fill the cylinder about half full with water. Record the volume of the water. Then ❷ carefully place the solid into the liquid. Record the volume of the liquid and solid combined. Then subtract the volume of the liquid from the combined volume of the liquid and solid. The answer will be

24

1-3 (continued)

Content Development

Have the students observe Figure 1-18. Explain that to find the volume of a rectangular solid, you start by measuring the solid with a metric ruler. Point out how to find the volume of a rectangular solid by using the formula: volume = height × length × width. Write the formula on the chalkboard.

Skills Development

Skill: Using formulas

Have students calculate the volume of the following rectangular solids:

2 cm × 4 cm × 6 cm = 48 cm³
1 cm × 3 cm × 2 cm = 6 cm³
2 cm × 5 cm × 12 cm = 120 cm³

Point out to students that when you multiply cm × cm × cm, you will get cubic centimeters. The metric symbol for cubic centimeters is cm³.

Content Development

Explain that if a solid is not rectangular in shape, you must measure the volume indirectly. Have the students observe Figure 1-17. Read the caption. Point out that the scale is read at the bottom curve of the meniscus.

Content Development

Explain that the volume of the rock was not obtained by a direct measurement of the rock. Instead, the volume of the rock was obtained by measuring the amount of water that the rock displaced. This is called indirect measurement.

Skills Development

Skill: Taking indirect measurements

Divide the class into groups 2–3 students. Give each group a graduated cylinder and several rocks, bolts, or other heavy objects that will fit into the graduated cylinders. Water and several empty containers should be available for each group. Have each group use the demonstrated procedure to determine the volume of the objects by indirect measurement.

Content Development

Point out that metric temperature is

the volume of the irregular solid. Will the volume be in milliliters or in cubic centimeters? ❸

Measuring Temperature

To measure temperature, you will use a Celsius thermometer. The two fixed points on a Celsius thermometer are the freezing point of water, 0°C, and the boiling point of water, 100°C. Some Celsius thermometers go as low as −25°C so that temperatures below the freezing point of water can be measured. Each calibration on a Celsius thermometer is equal to one degree Celsius.

Within the glass tube of a Celsius thermometer is a colored liquid. Alcohol or mercury are the two liquids most commonly used. In order to measure the temperature of a substance, place the thermometer in the substance. The liquid in the thermometer will begin to change. Wait until the liquid stops changing. Then read the number next to the mark on the thermometer that lines up with the top of the liquid. This number is the temperature of the substance.

SECTION REVIEW

1. Each side of a regular solid is 5 centimeters long. What is the volume of the solid?
2. What instrument would you use to measure length? Mass? Volume? Temperature?
3. If you want to find the density of an irregular object, what tools will you need? How will you go about making this measurement?

1–4   Science Safety in the Laboratory

Section Objective

To apply safety rules in the laboratory

The science laboratory is a place of adventure and discovery. Some of the most exciting events in the history of science have taken place in laboratories. The discovery of X-rays is one example. Another example is the discovery of oxygen. The relationship between electricity and magnetism was also discovered by scientists working in a laboratory. The list goes on and on.

Figure 1–18 *A Celsius thermometer is used to measure temperature. What is the temperature of the ice-water mixture in the beaker?* ❹

25

1-4 SCIENCE SAFETY IN THE LABORATORY

SECTION PREVIEW 1-4

A science laboratory is an exciting place of discovery. It can provide the answers to our changing times. It is the birthplace of ideas, understandings, and skills. It is a place to satisfy our curiosity.

Added to this is the skill of sensing problems and solving them in a scientific way, so that the results are dependable. To do this, we must work with scientific tools. And like all tools, they must be treated with care and purpose.

Most scientific experiments can be safe. But first, students must learn to always follow the teacher's directions or the directions in the textbook exactly as stated. Students should *never* try anything in the laboratory on their own without the teacher's consent.

Procedures and equipment should always be handled with the utmost care. Rules are made to keep the laboratory safe for everyone. Make sure to have students follow safety rules at all times.

PERFORMANCE OBJECTIVES 1-4

1. **List the important safety rules you must follow in the classroom.**
2. **Explain the reasons for each laboratory safety rule.**
3. **Describe how to respond to possible laboratory emergencies.**

TEACHING STRATEGY 1-4

Motivation

Point out that a laboratory can be a very exciting place—a place of discovery and challenge, a place where history is made in the fields of science and technology. Explain that many discoveries such as (1) the X-ray, which is used in medicine, computer screens, and television, (2) insulin for people with diabetes, (3) the heart pump, and many others were first developed in a science laboratory. Point out that every person, including themselves, who enters a laboratory is a scientist working on a new or different discovery.

measured with a Celsius thermometer. Explain that a Celsius thermometer has two fixed points, the freezing point at 0°C and the boiling point at 100°C. There are 100 spaces between 0°C and 100°C. Each space on a Celsius thermometer is equal to one degree Celsius.

Section Review 1-3
1. 125 cm³ or 125 cc
2. Length: metric ruler or meterstick; Mass: triple-beam balance; Volume: metric ruler or graduated cylinder; Temperature: Celsius thermometer
3. You will need a triple-beam balance and a graduated cylinder. First find the mass of the object with the balance. Then use water and the graduated cylinder to find the volume of the object. Since density is mass divided by volume, you can determine the density by dividing the object's mass by its volume.

TEACHER DEMONSTRATION

Pour 125 mL of water into a 500-mL beaker. Point out that water is a common substance. Add 50 mL of white vinegar. Remark that vinegar and water are both common everyday substances. Place the beaker on a ring stand and heat over a Bunsen burner until boiling. Show the students a box of baking soda.

- **What is baking soda used for?** (Accept all logical answers.)

Point out that almost every kitchen has a box of baking soda. Measure 15 mL of baking soda. Pour the baking soda into the heated mixture and stir— the mixture will bubble up rapidly.

Explain to the students that in a laboratory, we must always *expect* the *unexpected.*

1-4 (continued)

Motivation
Collect several magazine or newspaper pictures showing explosions, burning buildings, bandaged people, or other disaster events or results. Show the pictures to the class.
Why wouldn't you want to be involved in this? (Accept all logical answers.)
Could these accidents have been prevented? How? (Accept all logical answers.)
What are some possible accidents that could happen with improper use of glassware? (Accept all logical answers.)
How could such accidents be prevented? (Accept all logical answers.)
What would you do to help a victim of such an accident? (Accept all logical answers.)

Content Development
Make a transparency and/or enlarged photocopy of each of the seven safety precaution symbols. Use the copy as a

To better understand the facts and concepts you will read about in physical science, you may work in the laboratory this year. If you follow instructions and are as careful as a scientist would be, the laboratory will turn out to be an exciting experience.

When working in the laboratory, scientists know that it is very important to follow safety procedures. All of the work you will do in the laboratory this year will include experiments that have been done over and over again. When done properly, the experiments are interesting and safe. However, if they are done improperly, accidents can occur. How can you avoid such problems?

First and foremost, always follow your teacher's directions or the directions in your textbook exactly as stated. Never try anything on your own without asking your teacher first. And when you are not sure what you should do, always ask first. As you read the laboratory investigations in the textbook, you will see safety alert symbols next to certain procedures that require special safety care. Look at Figure 1–20 to learn the meanings of the safety symbols and the important safety precautions you should take.

In addition to the safety procedures listed in Figure 1–20, there is a more detailed list of safety procedures in Appendix B on page 669 of this textbook. Before you enter the laboratory for the first time, make sure that you have read each rule carefully. Then read them over again. Make sure that you understand each rule. If you do not

Figure 1–19 *It is important to always point a test tube that is being heated away from yourself and your classmates (left). What two safety precautions is this student taking before picking up a hot beaker (right)?* ❶

focal point during a discussion of laboratory safety rules, precautions, and emergency procedures. Point out and quiz students on each listed safety precaution. In addition to the items listed, you might ask (or explain) the following:
Glassware Safety
- **What should you do if you accidentally get cut with broken glass?** (Accept all logical answers and explain the procedures for your school.)

Fire Safety
- **Where is the closest fire extinguisher? How is it used in an emergency?** (Accept all logical answers and explain the procedures for your school.)
- **Where is the closest fire blanket? How is it used in an emergency?** (Accept all logical answers and explain the procedures for your school.)
- **How should we report a fire?** (Accept all logical answers and explain

SAFETY PRECAUTION SYMBOLS

Glassware Safety

1. Whenever you see this symbol, you will know that you are working with glassware that can easily be broken. Take particular care to handle such glassware safely. And never use broken glassware.
2. Never heat glassware that is not thoroughly dry. Never pick up any glassware unless you are sure it is not hot. If it is hot, use heat-resistant gloves.
3. Always clean glassware thoroughly before putting it away.

Fire Safety

1. Whenever you see this symbol, you will know that you are working with fire. Never use any source of fire without wearing safety goggles.
2. Never heat anything—particularly chemicals—unless instructed to do so.
3. Never heat anything in a closed container.
4. Never reach across a flame.
5. Always use a clamp, tongs, or heat-resistant gloves to handle hot objects.
6. Always maintain a clean work area, particularly when using a flame.

Heat Safety

Whenever you see this symbol, you will know that you should put on heat-resistant gloves to avoid burning your hands.

Chemical Safety

1. Whenever you see this symbol, you will know that you are working with chemicals that could be hazardous.
2. Never smell any chemical directly from its container. Always use your hand to waft some of the odors from the top of the container toward your nose—and only when instructed to do so.
3. Never mix chemicals unless instructed to do so.

4. Never touch or taste any chemical unless instructed to do so.
5. Keep all lids closed when chemicals are not in use. Dispose of all chemicals as instructed by your teacher.
6. Immediately rinse with water any chemicals, particularly acids, off your skin and clothes. Then notify your teacher.

Eye and Face Safety

1. Whenever you see this symbol, you will know that you are performing an experiment in which you must take precautions to protect your eyes and face by wearing safety goggles.
2. Always point away from you and others a test tube or bottle that is being heated. Chemicals can splash or boil out of the heated test tube.
3. Always wear safety goggles when you see this symbol.

Sharp Instrument Safety

1. Whenever you see this symbol, you will know that you are working with a sharp instrument.
2. Always use single-edged razors; double-edged razors are too dangerous.
3. Handle any sharp instrument with extreme care. Never cut any material toward you; always cut away from you.
4. Notify your teacher immediately if you are cut in the lab.

Electrical Safety

1. Whenever you see this symbol, you will know that you are using electricity in the laboratory.
2. Never use long extension cords to plug in an electrical device. Do not plug too many different appliances into one socket or you may overload the socket and cause a fire.
3. Never touch an electrical appliance or outlet with wet hands.

understand a rule, ask your teacher to explain it. You may even want to suggest further rules that apply to your particular classroom.

Figure 1–20 *This chart shows the safety precaution symbols you will often find next to the procedure in the laboratory investigations in this book. Which symbol would you expect to see when the investigation calls for using a Bunsen burner?* ❷

SECTION REVIEW

1. What is the most important general rule to follow when working in the laboratory?
2. Why is it important to point a test tube away from yourself and others when it is being heated?
3. Where is the nearest fire extinguisher located in your laboratory or classroom?

27

the procedures for your school.)
Heat Safety
• **Where would you find the heat resistant gloves?** (Accept all logical answers and explain the procedures for your school.)
• **What should you do if you accidentally burn your fingers or hands?** (Accept all logical answers and explain the procedures for your school.)
Chemical Safety
• **What should you do if a chemical is accidentally spilled on your face, skin, or clothing?** (Accept all logical answers and explain the procedures for your school. Point out the location of the nearest shower and eye wash station.)
Eye and Face Safety
• **What should you do if your face or eyes are accidentally injured?** (Accept all logical answers and explain the procedures for your school. Point out the location of the nurse's station.)

Sharp Instrument Safety
• **What should you do if you accidentally cut yourself?** (Accept all logical answers and explain the procedures for your school.)
Electrical Safety
• **What should you do if you see an electrical cord close to spilled water?** (Accept all logical answers and explain the procedures for your school.)

Place copies of the safety precaution page in a conspicuous place around the laboratory. Reinforce and/or explain the safety precautions as appropriate for each laboratory investigation.

Section Review 1-4

1. Always follow directions, whether printed or from your teacher.
2. Chemicals heated in a test tube can splash or boil out and injure someone unless the test tube is pointed away from people.
3. Answers will vary, depending on location.

LABORATORY INVESTIGATION
UNCERTAINTY OF MEASUREMENTS

BEFORE THE LAB
1. **Divide the class into groups of 3–6 students.**
2. **Gather all materials at least one day prior to the investigation. You should have enough supplies to meet your class needs, assuming 3–6 students per group.**
3. **Prepare a class data table so that students can record all class data for each work station.**

PRE-LAB DISCUSSION
Have students read the complete laboratory procedure. Discuss the procedure by asking questions similar to the following:
- **What is the purpose of the laboratory investigation?** (To find out about the uncertainty of measurement or how accurately matter can be measured using common laboratory instruments)
- **STATION 1: What is the smallest unit shown on the meterstick?** (The smallest unit shown on the meterstick is 1 mm, or 0.1 cm.)
- **STATION 2: How do you find the volume of an object when you know the length, width, and height?** (Multiply the length times the width times the height.)
- **STATION 3: Which part of the meniscus should be read?** (The bottom curve of the meniscus should be read.)
- **STATION 3: What is the smallest unit shown on the graduated cylinder?** (The smallest unit shown on the graduated cylinder is 1 mL.) (*Note*: Some graduated cylinders may have different graduations.)
- **STATION 4: Why is it important for the riders to start at zero?** (The riders should start at zero so you can see that the balance starts even at zero grams.)
- **STATION 5: How can we change milliliters to cubic centimeters?** (One cubic centimeter is equal to 1 mL. Keep the same number and change the unit symbol.)
- **STATION 6: What is the smallest unit on this Celsius scale?** (One degree Celsius is the smallest unit on the thermometer scale.) (*Note*: Some thermometers may have different graduations.)

SKILL DEVELOPMENT
Students will use the following skills while completing this investigation.
1. Manipulative
2. Safety
3. Observing
4. Comparing
5. Applying
6. Inferring
7. Measuring
8. Recording

SAFETY TIPS
Alert students to be cautious with the measuring instruments.

TEACHING STRATEGY FOR LAB PROCEDURE
1. Assign a starting station to each

Purpose
How accurately can matter be measured?

Materials *(per station)*
Station 1: meterstick
Station 2: metric ruler
　　　　　regular object
Station 3: graduated cylinder
　　　　　beaker with colored liquid
Station 4: triple-beam balance
　　　　　small pebble
Station 5: graduated cylinder
　　　　　beaker of water
　　　　　irregular object
Station 6: Celsius thermometer
　　　　　beaker with ice and water
　　　　　paper towel

Procedure
1. Station 1: Use the meterstick to measure the length and width of the desk or lab table. If the table is irregular, measure the shortest width and the longest length. Express your measurements in centimeters.
2. Station 2: Use the metric ruler to find the volume of the regular object. Express the volume in cubic centimeters.
3. Station 3: Use the graduated cylinder to find the volume of the colored liquid in the beaker. Then pour the liquid back into the beaker. Express your measurement in milliliters.
4. Station 4: Place the pebble on the pan of the triple-beam balance. Move the riders until the pointer is at zero. Record the mass of the pebble in grams. Remove the pebble and return all riders back to zero.
5. Station 5: Fill the graduated cylinder half full with water. Find the volume of the irregular object. Express the volume of the object in cubic centimeters. Carefully

28

remove the object from the graduated cylinder. Pour the water back into the beaker.
6. Station 6: Use the Celsius thermometer to find the temperature of the ice water. Record the temperature in degrees Celsius. Remove the thermometer and carefully dry it with a paper towel.

Observation
Your teacher will construct a large class data table for each of the work stations. Record the data from each group on the class data table.

Conclusions
1. Do all the class measurements have the exact same value for each station?
2. Which station had measurements that were most nearly alike? Explain why these measurements were so similar.
3. Which station had measurements that were most varied? Explain why these measurements were so varied.

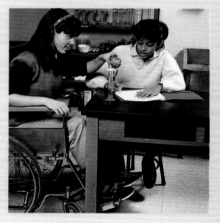

CHAPTER REVIEW

SUMMARY

1-1 What Is Science?

❏ A theory is the most logical explanation of events that occur in nature.

❏ When a scientific theory has been tested many times and is accepted as true, scientists may call it a law.

❏ The scientific method is a systematic approach to problem solving.

❏ A variable is the one factor that is being tested in an experiment.

❏ The two main branches of physical science are chemistry and physics.

1-2 Scientific Measurements

❏ The standard system of measurement used by all scientists is the metric system.

❏ The basic unit of length in the metric system is the meter. One meter is equal to 100 centimeters or 1000 millimeters.

❏ A kilometer is equal to 1000 meters.

❏ The basic unit of volume in the metric system is the liter. A liter contains 1000 milliliters or 1000 cubic centimeters.

❏ The kilogram is the basic unit of mass in the metric system.

❏ A kilogram is equal to 1000 grams.

❏ Density is defined as the mass per unit volume of an object.

❏ The basic unit of temperature in the metric system is the degree Celsius.

❏ Dimensional analysis is a method of converting from one unit to another in the metric system by multiplying the given unit by a conversion factor.

1-3 Tools of Measurement

❏ The metric ruler is used to measure length. A metric ruler is divided into centimeters and millimeters.

❏ The triple-beam balance is used to measure mass.

❏ A graduated cylinder is used to find the volume of a liquid or the volume of an irregular solid.

❏ The volume of a regular solid can be determined by multiplying its height by its width by its length.

❏ A Celsius thermometer is used to measure temperature.

1-4 Science Safety in the Laboratory

❏ When working in the laboratory, it is important to take all necessary safety precautions. These include using safety equipment and following all instructions carefully.

❏ If all safety rules are followed, the laboratory can be a safe and exciting place.

VOCABULARY

Define each term in a complete sentence.

Celsius	density	law	physics
centimeter	dimensional	liter	scientific
chemistry	analysis	meniscus	method
control setup	experimental	meter	theory
conversion	setup	metric system	variable
factor	gram	milligram	
cubic	hypothesis	milliliter	
centimeter	kilogram	millimeter	
data	kilometer		

29

---

team. After the teams have completed one station, they should proceed to the next station. Allow about 5 minutes per station.

2. Have the teams follow the directions carefully as they work in the laboratory.

3. You might ask the teams to write down what they *guess* each measure will be *before* the actual measurement.

OBSERVATIONS

Check that students have accu-rately copied the class data on their class data table.

CONCLUSIONS

1. It is unlikely that class data for each station will be exactly the same. In fact, you can probably assume that groups that have the exact same data for each station worked together or compared their data prior to recording it.

2. Answers will vary. In most cases, Stations 2, 3, and 4 will have the closest data. The reason being that the object being measured was very exact and the class teams are likely to arrive at very similar figures.

3. Answers will vary. In most cases, Stations 1, 5, and 6 will be the most dissimilar. In particular, Station 6, in which students measure the temperature of ice water, will likely have quite different measurements. The reason for this is that the ice may melt. Also, as the cold water sits on the table during the entire lab, it will absorb heat from its surroundings and become warmer than at the beginning of the lab.

GOING FURTHER: ENRICHMENT

Part 1

Have students *count* the number of centimeters in a meter. The answer should be 100, because we counted. There are *exactly* 100 centimeters in one meter. However, when we measure, we always have to estimate to the nearest half or whole unit on the scale. Therefore, measurements can be "accurate" or even "precise" but seldom exact.

Part 2

Have students calculate the average (mean) of the measurements at each station. To do this, add each measurement to find a total and then divide by the number of measurements. Point out that an average (mean) tends to balance large number with small numbers. Tell them that an average of several measurements is usually more precise than a single measurement.

Part 3

Have students do the investigation again. Tell them to *really* aim for the *best precision* and *accuracy possible* in their measurements by following the suggestions just given. Chart the measurements as before and calculate an average for each station.

Have students compare the measurements and averages for the two trials. Discuss factors that led to more precise measurements.

CHAPTER REVIEW

MULTIPLE CHOICE

1. c	3. d	5. b	7. c	9. a
2. d	4. c	6. a	8. b	10. b

COMPLETION

1. law
2. proposed solution
3. experimental setup
4. physics
5. metric system
6. kilometer
7. milliliters; cubic centimeters
8. boils; freezes
9. fraction
10. meniscus

TRUE OR FALSE

1. F   one variable
2. T
3. T
4. F   one thousand
5. F   1000 milliliters
6. F   grams or kilograms or milligrams
7. F   mass; volume
8. T
9. F   middle beam
10. T

SKILL BUILDING

1. Graduated cylinder/milliliters; metric ruler/centimeters; graduated cylinder and triple-beam balance/grams; meterstick/meters; graduated cylinder/cubic centimeters; triple-beam balance/grams; Celsius thermometer/degrees Celsius.
2. a. 3300 cm; b. 45,000 mm; c. 8800 m; 2500 mg; 6,300,000 g
3. Answers will vary in terms of when the temperature of the water begins to rise, due to the amount of heat generated by the stove burner. Answers will also vary in terms of how long it took the water to boil. However, all students should note that the amount the water rises in temperature each minute is not the same. For the first few minutes, there will be little rise in temperature. Then the temperature will rise rapidly. If students continue to observe the water as it boils, they will note that the water does not rise in temperature during a change of phase. That is, the water does not rise in temperature as the water evaporates from a liquid to a gas.
4. Students' experiments should be similar to that described in the text. However, this time the containers will be heated instead of cooled. Make sure students describe the control and variable in their design. Also, see if students can devise a way to ensure that the heat being added to each container is the same for each container. You may want to point out to students that antifreeze raises the boiling point of water, much the way it lowers the freezing point.

CONTENT REVIEW: MULTIPLE CHOICE

On a separate sheet of paper, write the letter of the answer that best completes each statement.

1. An orderly, systematic approach to problem solving is called a (an)
   a. experiment.   b. conclusion.
   c. scientific method.   d. dimensional analysis.
2. A proposed solution to a scientific problem is called a
   a. conclusion.   b. theory.   c. data.   d. hypothesis.
3. In any experiment, the one factor being tested is the
   a. data.   b. control.   c. hypothesis.   d. variable.
4. The basic unit of length in the metric system is the
   a. kilometer.   b. centimeter.   c. meter.   d. liter.
5. A cubic centimeter is equal in volume to a
   a. liter.   b. milliliter.   c. gram.   d. milligram.
6. The basic unit of mass in the metric system is the
   a. kilogram.   b. liter.   c. milligram.   d. gram.
7. The amount of matter in an object is called its
   a. volume.   b. density.   c. mass.   d. dimension.
8. To measure the mass of a solid, you should use a
   a. graduated cylinder.   b. triple-beam balance.
   c. meterstick.   d. Celsius thermometer.
9. A graduated cylinder is calibrated in
   a. milliliters.   b. liters.   c. grams.   d. degrees Celsius.
10. When working with a flame, always wear
    a. heat-resistant gloves.   b. safety goggles.
    c. a short-sleeved shirt.   d. a laboratory apron.

CONTENT REVIEW: COMPLETION

On a separate sheet of paper, write the word or words that best complete each statement.

1. When a theory is accepted as true, scientists may call it a _____.
2. A hypothesis is a _____ to a problem.
3. In any experiment, the part of the experiment that contains the variable is called the _____.
4. The branch of physical science that deals with the laws of motion is called _____.
5. The _____ is the standard system of measurement used by scientists.
6. To measure the distance across the United States, you would likely use the unit of measurement called the _____.
7. A liter contains 1000 _____, or 1000 _____.
8. On the Celsius temperature scale, water _____ at 100°C and _____ at 0°C.
9. A conversion factor is a _____ that always equals one.
10. The bottom of the curve formed by a liquid in a graduated cylinder is called the _____.

30

ESSAY

1. The steps are stating the problem; gathering information on the problem; forming a hypothesis; performing experiments to test the hypothesis; recording and analyzing data; stating a conclusion. Students' descriptions of these steps should be similar to the text discussion of each step.
2. If there are two variables, the person performing the experiment cannot be sure which variable caused the results.

CONTENT REVIEW: TRUE OR FALSE

Determine whether each statement is true or false. Then on a separate sheet of paper, write "true" if it is true. If it is false, change the underlined word or words to make the statement true.

1. An experiment should have <u>two variables</u>.
2. The <u>experimental setup</u> contains the variable.
3. Recorded observations are called <u>data</u>.
4. The prefix *kilo-* means <u>one hundred</u>.
5. A liter contains <u>100 milliliters</u>.
6. Mass is measured in <u>liters</u>.
7. Density is <u>volume</u> per unit <u>mass</u>.
8. A conversion fraction must equal <u>one</u>.
9. The <u>front beam</u> of a triple-beam balance is often called the 500-gram beam.
10. To find the volume of a regular solid, you <u>multiply</u> height times width times length.

CONCEPT REVIEW: SKILL BUILDING

Use the skills you have developed in this chapter to complete each activity.

1. **Applying concepts** What tool or tools would you use to make the following measurements? What units would you use to express your answers?

   volume of a glass of water
   length of a sheet of paper
   mass of a liter of milk
   length of a football field
   volume of an irregular object
   mass of a hockey puck
   ocean temperature

2. **Making calculations** Use dimensional analysis to convert each of the following:
   a. A blue whale is about 33 meters in length. How many centimeters is this?
   b. The Statue of Liberty is about 45 meters tall. How tall is the statue in millimeters?
   c. Mount Everest is about 8.8 kilometers high. How high is it in meters?
   d. A Ping-Pong ball has a mass of about 2.5 grams. What is its mass in milligrams?
   e. An elephant is about 6300 kilograms in mass. What is its mass in grams?

3. **Making measurements** Fill a cooking pan half full with water. Place the pan on the burner of your stove at home. Turn the dial to the lowest setting. **CAUTION:** *Be very careful when working with an open flame or electric burner.* Hold a Celsius thermometer in the water, making sure you do not let the thermometer touch the sides or bottom of the pan. Have a classmate or parent record the temperature of the water at one-minute intervals until the water begins to boil. Make a graph of your data with temperature versus time axes. At what point did the temperature of the water begin to rise? How long did it take before the water began to boil? Did the heated water rise in temperature by the same amount each minute?

4. **Designing an experiment** Antifreeze is put into a car's cooling system during hot summer months. Design an experiment to test whether antifreeze has any effect on the boiling point of water. Make sure you include an experimental and control setup. If you were to graph your data, how would you label the two axes of the graph?

CONCEPT REVIEW: ESSAY

Discuss each of the following in a brief paragraph.

1. Describe the steps in a scientific method.
2. Explain why the results of an experiment are not valid if there are two variables.
3. Describe the need for a standard system of measurement.
4. Explain how you are a scientist.

31

ADDITIONAL QUESTIONS AND TOPIC SUGGESTIONS

1. Seven students had the following heights:

   Johnny is 1 m 45 cm tall, Mary 1 m 20 cm,
   George is 129 cm, Frank is 1 m 43 cm,
   Jerry is 124 cm, Carol is 1 m 25 cm, and
   Charles is 164 cm. What is the average height of the students?

   Johnny: 1 m 45 cm = 1.45 m
   Mary: 1 m 20 cm   = 1.20 m
   George: 129 cm   = 1.29 m
   Frank: 1 m 43 cm = 1.43 m
   Jerry: 124 cm   = 1.24 m
   Carol: 1 m 25 cm = 1.25 m
   Charles: 164 cm   = 1.64 m
   Sum of heights   = 9.45 m
   9.45 m/7 = 1.35 m, or 1 m 35 cm

2. Mary wants to find the density of her new locket. She finds it as a mass of 35 g. She places it in 50 mL of water and the water rises to 55 mL. What is the density of the locket?

   density = mass/volume
   density = 35 g/2 cm^3
   density = 17.5 g/cm^3

3. The density of lead is 11.3 g/cm^3. What is the volume of a 248.6-g piece of lead?

   density = mass/volume, or
   volume = mass/density
   volume = 248.6 g/11.3 g/cm^3
   volume = 22 cm^3

ISSUES IN SCIENCE

The following issues can be used as a springboard for class debate, or they can be assigned as a writing homework.
1. Some scientists believe that taking many "accurate" measurements and averaging them still gives an "accurate not precise" measure. Other scientists believe that taking many "accurate" measurements and averaging them gives a "precise" measure. What is your opinion and why?

Or they cannot be sure if the results were caused by a combination of both variables. Since an experiment is set up to test a particular hypothesis and the variable relates directly to the hypothesis, the experiment is completely invalid with more than one variable.
3. Without a standard system of measurement, scientists all over the world cannot be sure they are comparing their data accurately, nor can they transmit data and be sure their

data is being interpreted correctly.
4. The first, and most basic, step scientists usually take is to make an observation and then try to explain what they have seen. Since all people make observations and wonder about what they have observed, all people are scientists. However, a real scientist goes beyond wondering about an observation and follows the scientific method to investigate an unusual observation.

Chapter 2
PROPERTIES OF MATTER

CHAPTER OVERVIEW

Everything in the world is made up of matter. In this chapter, students will learn the basic properties of matter. These properties include mass, weight, volume, and density.

Students will also learn that matter can exist in four phases—solid, liquid, gas, and plasma. The first three of these phases are familiar, and students will have no trouble identifying many examples of each. The fourth phase, plasma, may be less familiar, because it rarely exists on earth. In some ways, plasma resembles a gas, but unlike a gas, it consists of electrically charged particles. The surface of the sun and other stars consists of plasma.

Within the three phases found on earth, matter can change from one phase to another. Students will learn that energy must be added to or subtracted from a substance in order for a phase change to occur.

In the last part of this chapter, students will learn about chemical properties of matter. They will come to understand that while the identity of a substance remains intact during a physical change, a new substance is formed during a chemical change.

INTRODUCING CHAPTER 2

Direct students' attention to the photograph of frozen oranges. Ask them to describe what they see. Most students will point out that the oranges are frozen and probably ruined. Now have them read the chapter introduction. Ask,
- **How do you keep your hands warm on a cold day?** (by wearing gloves or mittens)
- **What would you think if someone suggested that you keep your hands warm by coating them with ice?** (Answers will vary; most will probably say that the idea sounds crazy!)
- **Why do you think the oranges in the picture are frozen?** (to protect them from the cold)
- **How does freezing protect fruit from the cold?** (by releasing heat energy)
- **Can you think of any other situ-** ations in which the process of freezing or cooling releases heat? (Heat can be felt escaping from the back of a refrigerator or from the outdoor side of an air conditioner.)
- **Do you know why the process of freezing releases heat?** (Students probably will not know until they read the chapter; however, you can encourage them to speculate.)

Refer to the chapter opener text, and help students recognize that a

Properties of Matter

CHAPTER OBJECTIVES

After completing this chapter, you will be able to

2–1 Describe the general properties of matter.

2–1 Relate mass and inertia.

2–1 Distinguish between mass and weight.

2–1 Define and calculate density.

2–2 Classify matter based on phase.

2–2 Describe the arrangement and movement of particles in solids, liquids, and gases.

2–2 State the Gas Laws.

2–3 Identify phase changes in matter.

2–3 Interpret a phase-change diagram.

2–4 Differentiate between chemical and physical properties and changes.

2–4 Distinguish between chemical properties and chemical changes.

The day had dawned sunny and bright, although a bit chilly. But throughout the day, the temperature had steadily dropped. And now it was so cold that few of those working in the orange grove could remember a day like it. The workers talked about the unusual Florida weather, but what was really on their minds were the hundreds of orange trees whose branches were heavy with fruit not yet ripe enough for picking. Such low temperatures could wipe out the entire crop. The juice in the orange would freeze, ruining the fruit as well as the farmer's profits.

The workers knew something had to be done, and done quickly, to save the orange crop. So they lighted small fires in smokepots scattered throughout the fields. But they soon realized that the heat produced this way would never be enough to save the fruit. Suddenly, some workers raced out into the grove hauling long water hoses. Fighting time and temperature, the workers sprayed the trees with water. The water would freeze and turn into ice as the temperature continued to drop. The ice would keep the oranges warm!

With sunrise the next day, the temperature began to climb. The glistening ice that had coated the fruit trees melted away. The fruit was undamaged—cold but not frozen. The orange crop had been saved!

Does it seem strange to you that oranges can be kept warm with ice? Freezing water can sometimes do a better job of keeping things warm than fire can. As the liquid water sprayed onto the trees froze, it released heat energy. Some of this heat energy was released into the oranges, preventing them from freezing. In this chapter, you will learn more about the substances and processes in nature.

To keep oranges from being destroyed by the cold, the oranges are actually covered with water that quickly freezes. Is this science or magic? The answer lies within the pages of this chapter.

33

TEACHER DEMONSTRATION

Obtain two objects of the same size and shape but very different densities. A good choice would be a golf ball and a ping-pong ball. Display the objects.

• **How are these objects alike?** (same size, shape, and color)

• **How are they different?** (One is much heavier.)

Point out that students are describing physical characteristics of the objects. Tell students that they will be learning about other kinds of physical characteristics as they read the chapter.

Now display a container of water.

• **What do you think will happen if I place the golf ball in the water?** (It will sink.)

Place the golf ball in the water.

• **What do you think will happen if I place the ping-pong ball in the water?** (It will float.)

Place the ping-pong ball in the water.

• **Why do you think this happens?** (Possible answers: The ping-pong ball is lighter; the ping-pong ball is hollow; the ping-pong ball is less dense.)

Point out that students will be able to provide a more scientific explanation after completing this chapter.

TEACHER RESOURCES

Audiovisuals

Investigations in Science: Properties of Matter Series, film loops, BFA Educational Media

Matter and Energy: Properties of Matter, filmstrip, SVE

Matter and Its Physical Condition, film, Macmillan

Particles in Motion: States of Matter, film, SFS, National Geographic

Physical or Chemical: What Kind of Change, filmstrip, CAR

Solids, Liquids, and Gases, film, McGraw-Hill

Books

Goodstein, David L., *States of Matter*, Prentice-Hall

Solomon, J., *Structure of Matter*, Halstead

Software

Physical and Chemical Properties, Prentice-Hall

rather obvious solution to the problem of protecting the fruit did not work.

• **Why do you think the small fires in smokepots were not able to protect the fruit from the cold?** (The heat they provided was not very great, and what heat they did provide was dispersed into the atmosphere.)

• **If you had been standing in the orange grove, what would you have thought of the idea of spraying the fruit with water?** (Answers will vary; many students may feel that they would have doubted that this procedure could save the fruit.)

• **Have you ever had a problem to solve in which an unusual and unexpected solution turned out to be better than an obvious solution?** (Encourage students to share experiences involving any type of situation.)

2-1 GENERAL PROPERTIES OF MATTER

SECTION PREVIEW 2-1

In this section, students will be introduced to the general physical properties that describe all matter. They will also learn the units in which each property is measured.

Students will learn that the most important property of matter is mass. Mass is a measure of the amount of matter in an object or substance. Students will also learn the important distinction between mass and weight. Weight is the response of mass to the pull of gravity.

Students will be introduced to the idea that volume measures the amount of space taken up by matter. Then they will learn how mass and volume can be related to calculate the density of a substance.

PERFORMANCE OBJECTIVES 2-1

1. **Discuss the idea that all matter can be described by the properties of mass, weight, volume, and density.**

2. **Identify the units used to measure each of the basic properties of matter.**

3. **Compare mass and inertia.**

4. **Describe the difference between mass and weight.**

5. **Apply the ratio of mass to volume in order to measure an object's density.**

2–1 General Properties of Matter

Suppose you received a gift and wanted to tell your friend about it. Only you wanted to describe the gift without actually naming the object. What are some of the characteristics you would use?

You might start with the size and shape of the object. Next, you might describe how the object feels to your touch. Is it soft, hard, spongy, or ❶ fluffy? Is it smooth or rough? Is it solid or hollow? If it is hollow, does it contain other objects? Would the object float, sink, or perhaps even swim in water? Does it have an identifying color or odor?

The words you use to describe the object are its characteristics. All objects have certain characteristics that help you identify them. And although most of the objects around you have different characteristics, they share one important quality. They are all forms of **matter.** Matter is what the world is made of. All objects consist of matter.

Your senses of smell, sight, taste, and touch help you become familiar with the variety of matter that surrounds you. Some kinds of matter are easily recognized. Plants, animals, rocks, soil, water, glass, salt, and silver are examples of matter that are easily observed. Less easily observed, but still matter, are oxygen, carbon dioxide, nitrogen, ammonia, and air.

Figure 2–1 *What characteristics would you use to describe the various forms of matter seen in this photograph of the John Muir Trail in the High Sierra Mountains of California?* ❶

TEACHING STRATEGY 2-1

Motivation

Prepare ahead of time several brown paper bags each containing an everyday object. Objects such as a knife or a fork, a toothbrush, a sponge, a piece of fruit, and a sweater or a shirt will work well. Ask a student volunteer to take one of the bags and leave the room for a moment to determine what the object is. When the student returns, challenge him or her to describe the characteristics of the object to the class accurately enough so that the other students can guess what the object is without seeing it. The characteristics described can include size, shape, color, texture, "heaviness" or "lightness." Emphasize that the description should *not* include how the object is used—saying, for example, that a knife is used to cut food would be a dead giveaway! Repeat the activity several times using different student volunteers.

Content Development

Emphasize the idea that even the most different types of matter have certain things in common.

• **What do air and water have in common?** (Both contain oxygen and hydrogen; both take up space; both have mass and weight; both are made up of

Are these different kinds of matter similar in some ways? Is glass anything like ammonia? Do silver and oxygen have anything in common?

In order to answer these questions, you must know something about the **properties,** or characteristics, of matter. Properties describe an object. Color, odor, shape, texture, and hardness are properties of matter. They are very specific properties of matter, however. Specific properties make it easy to tell one kind of matter from another.

Some properties of matter are more general. Instead of describing the differences among forms of matter, general properties describe how all matter is the same. **General properties of matter include mass, weight, volume, and density.**

Mass

The most important general property of matter is that it has **mass.** Mass is the amount of matter in an object. The mass of an object is constant. It does not change unless some matter is either added to the object or removed from the object. This means that the mass of an object does not change when you move the object from one location to another. For example, you have the same mass whether you are on top of a mountain, at the bottom of a deep mine, or on the moon!

Scientists define mass in another way. Mass is a measure of the **inertia** (ihn-ER-shuh) of an object. Inertia is the resistance of an object to changes in its motion. Objects that have mass resist changes in their motion. Thus, objects that have mass have inertia. For example, if an object is at rest, a force must be used to make it move. If an object is moving, a force must be used to slow it down or stop it.

The more mass an object has, the greater is its inertia. The force that must be exerted to overcome that inertia is also greater. Which would be harder to pull up a hill, an empty wagon or a wagon occupied by two of your friends? Which would be harder to stop at the bottom of a hill? ❸

Mass is measured in units called grams (g) and kilograms (kg). One kilogram is equal to 1000 grams. The mass of small objects usually is expressed in grams. A nickel, for example, has a mass

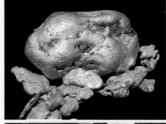

Figure 2–2 *Because their specific properties are similar, gold nuggets (top) are often confused with pyrite, or "fool's gold" (bottom), by gold prospectors. What specific properties do both minerals have in common? What general property of matter can be used to distinguish the two minerals?* ❷

SCIENCE TERMS 2-1

matter p. 34	gravity p. 36
property p. 35	volume p. 38
mass p. 35	density p. 38
inertia p. 35	specific gravity
weight p. 36	p. 40

TEACHER DEMONSTRATION

Many students have little or no idea of mass measurements of common objects. Prepare a display in which several objects or pictures of objects are mounted on a piece of posterboard or plywood. Arrange the objects in order of increasing mass. Under each object, write the value of its mass in grams. You can begin with a very small object such as a nickel (mass = 5g), then add increasingly larger objects.

ANNOTATION KEY

❶ Students should list characteristics such as color; texture; solid, liquid, or gas; hot or cold; living or nonliving; etc. (Making observations)

❷ Specific properties: Both are hard, yellow in color, found in or on the ground, have similar shapes and texture. General property: "Fool's gold" and true gold differ in density. (Making comparisons)

❸ A wagon with two people would be harder to pull up a hill and to stop at the bottom of a hill. (Applying concepts)

❶ Thinking Skill: Making observations

❷ Thinking Skill: Making generalizations

❸ Thinking Skill: Relating cause and effect

molecules; both are colorless; both are essentially tasteless.)

- **What do wood and water have in common?** (Both have mass and weight; both take up space; both have definite volume; both are made up of molecules.)

- **What do silver and air have in common?** (Both have mass and weight; both take up space; both are made up of atoms or molecules.)

Skills Development

Skills: Observing, comparing

Have students observe Figure 2-1. Ask them to name as many different types of matter as they can in the photograph. Then encourage them to compare different types of matter in terms of common properties.

Content Development

Emphasize the idea that mass is the most important property of matter, for it describes the amount of matter present in an object or substance. Ask,

- **What instrument is used to measure mass?** (balance scale)

- **In what units is mass measured?** (grams or kilograms)

- **What does it mean if one object has a mass of 5 grams and another object has a mass of 20 grams?** (More matter is present in the second object than in the first.)

HISTORICAL NOTES

In the seventeenth century, Sir Isaac Newton published a book in which he set forth his three laws of motion. The first of these laws is often called the law of inertia. In modern language, the law of inertia states that an object at rest tends to remain at rest, and an object in motion tends to keep moving in a straight line unless acted on by an unbalanced force.

BACKGROUND INFORMATION

The force of attraction between two objects is described by the law of universal gravitation: $F = Gm_1m_2/d^2$, where m_1 and m_2 are the masses of the objects in kilograms, d is the distance between the objects in meters, and G is the universal gravitational constant.

Sharpen Your Skills

Demonstrating Inertia
Skills: Observing, relating
Level: Average
Type: Hands-on
Materials: glass, playing card, coin

Students are able to demonstrate and reinforce their understanding of inertia through this simple activity. Caution students not to flick the coin in such a way that it might strike another student.

Students should be able to pull the card out fast enough so that the coin drops into the glass. Make sure they can relate this result to the concept of inertia.

When the card is pulled slowly, the coin will move along with the card and not fall into the glass.

Figure 2–3 *It may seem like magic, but it is just a demonstration of inertia. As the table is moved quickly, the dinner setting is suspended in air for an instant. What do you think probably happened seconds after this photograph was taken?* ❶

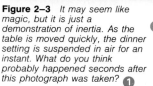

Sharpen Your Skills

Demonstrating Inertia

You can demonstrate that objects at rest tend to remain at rest by using a drinking glass, playing card, and coin.

1. Place the glass on a table.

2. Lay a flat playing card on top of the glass. Place the coin in the center of the card.

3. Using either a flicking motion or a pulling motion of your fingers, quickly remove the card so it flies out from under the coin. Can you remove the card fast enough so the coin lands in the glass? You might need to practice a few times.

How does this activity demonstrate inertia? What happens to the coin if you remove the card slowly? How does removing the card slowly demonstrate inertia?

36

---

of about 5 grams. The mass of this book is about 1700 grams, or 1.7 kilograms. The estimated mass of the sun in kilograms is 2 followed by 30 zeros!

Mass is measured on an instrument called a balance. The mass of an object is determined by comparing its mass on the balance to the known masses of standard objects.

Weight

Another general property of matter is **weight**. An object has weight because it has mass. Weight is the response of mass to the pull of **gravity**.

The force of attraction between objects is called gravity. You probably have noticed that a ball thrown up in the air soon falls to the ground. And you know that an apple that drops off a tree falls down, not up. The ball and the apple fall to the earth because of gravity, the earth's force of attraction for all objects.

All objects exert a gravitational attraction on other objects. Gravity is not a property of the earth alone. Your two hands attract each other, and you are attracted to books, chairs, and trees. But you are not pulled toward these objects as you are toward the earth because the attractions in these cases are too weak for you to notice them. What do you think makes these attractions weak but the attraction of the earth great? ❷

The earth's gravity is great because the earth has a large mass. The greater the mass of an object, the greater its gravitational force. How do you think the gravity of Jupiter compares with the gravity of the

---

2-1 (continued)

Content Development

Explain to students the concept of inertia. Have students observe Figure 2-3 and read the caption.

• **Describe the state of the table setting in the first photograph.** (The objects are at rest.)

• **What happens to the table setting when the table is first moved?** (The objects remain at rest.)

• **Why does this happen?** (Objects at rest tend to remain at rest; they resist change in their motion.)

• **What eventually causes the objects to move?** (The force of gravity pulls them to the ground.)

Stress the idea that in order for an object to change its motion, it must be acted on by a force.

Content Development

Encourage students to identify examples of inertia in everyday life. Ask,

• **What does a seat belt do for a passenger when a car stops suddenly?** (It prevents him from moving forward.)

• **Why would the passenger move forward without the restraining force of the belt?** (The passenger's inertia causes her to keep moving forward until acted on by a force.)

• **What would stop a passenger not wearing a set belt?** (the windshield of the car)

earth? How does the moon's gravity compare with the gravity of the earth or Jupiter? ❸

The pull of gravity on an object determines the object's weight. On the earth, your weight is a direct measure of the planet's force pulling you toward the center. But the pull of gravity between objects weakens as the distance between the centers of the objects increases. At a high altitude—for example at ❷ the top of a mountain—an object weighs less than it does on the surface of the earth. This is because the object is farther from the center of the earth. How would an object's weight at the bottom of a deep mine compare with its weight on the earth's surface? ❹

When an object is sent into space far from the earth, the object is said to be weightless. However, the object does not become massless. Mass does not change when location changes. No matter what happens to the force of gravity, mass remains constant. Only weight changes.

The metric unit of weight is the newton (N). The newton is used because it is a unit of force, and weight is the amount of force the earth's gravity ❸ exerts on an object. An object with a mass of 1 kilogram is pulled toward the earth with a force of 9.8 newtons. So the weight of the object is 9.8 N. An

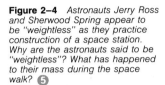

Figure 2–4 *Astronauts Jerry Ross and Sherwood Spring appear to be "weightless" as they practice construction of a space station. Why are the astronauts said to be "weightless"? What has happened to their mass during the space walk?* ❺

37

ANNOTATION KEY

❶ Objects fell to the floor due to gravity. (Applying concepts)

❷ Mass of objects, in part, determines the force of gravity. (Making inferences)

❸ Gravity of Jupiter is greater. Moon's gravity is less than that of Jupiter and earth. (Making comparisons)

❹ Weight would be greater. (Applying concepts)

❺ Because the astronauts are far away from earth's surface, where the gravitational pull is very weak, they are virtually "weightless." Mass is constant, so mass has not changed. (Relating facts)

❶ Thinking Skill: Making comparisons

❷ Thinking Skill: Relating cause and effect

❸ Thinking Skill: Making measurements

Skills Development
Skills: Making calculations, making diagrams
In order to emphasize the difference between mass and weight, have each student calculate his or her mass in kilograms and weight in Newtons (1 pound = 0.45 kg; weight in Newtons = mass × 9.8). Then have each student create a diagram to show how his or her weight would be less on the moon, but mass would remain the same. For example, a student might draw a picture of herself on earth and on the moon, with mass and weight written under each picture.

Reinforcement
Some students may continue to confuse mass and weight. To help reinforce the distinction, challenge students to find the errors in sentences such as these.

This apple weighs 200 grams. (Grams is a measure of mass, not weight.) Objects of equal mass always weigh the same. (only if they are in the same location with respect to gravity) Gravity can increase a person's mass. (Mass is constant; gravity can increase weight.)

Skills Development
Skill: Relating concepts
Have students consider the following question.
• **Why do we not feel the pull of gravity of Jupiter, when its mass is so great?** (It is too far away.)

TIE-IN/MATH

Formulas make it possible to calculate the volumes of regular solids when certain dimensions are known. Volume formulas for several common solids are given below.

Cube: $V = (side)^3$
Rectangular prism (box):
$v = length \times width \times height$
Cylinder: $V = area\ of\ base \times height$
Cone: $V = \frac{1}{3} \times area\ of$
base $\times$ height
Pyramid: $V = \frac{1}{3} \times area\ of$
base $\times$ height
Sphere: $V = \frac{4}{3}\pi \times (radius)^3$

You may want to provide students with some common objects of which they can find the volume using these formulas.

Figure 2–5 *The objects and liquids in this container have different densities. So some float while others sink. Suppose you did not know the density of each substance. How could you use this photograph to determine the relative densities of the objects and liquids?* ❸

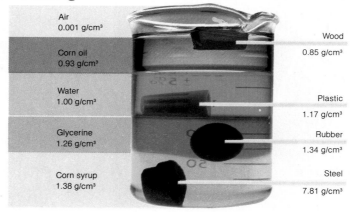

Air
0.001 g/cm³

Corn oil
0.93 g/cm³

Water
1.00 g/cm³

Glycerine
1.26 g/cm³

Corn syrup
1.38 g/cm³

Wood
0.85 g/cm³

Plastic
1.17 g/cm³

Rubber
1.34 g/cm³

Steel
7.81 g/cm³

38

object with a mass of 50 kilograms is pulled toward the earth with a force of 50×9.8, or 490 newtons. The object's weight is 490 N. What is your weight on the earth? ❶

Volume

Another important general property of matter describes the amount of space it occupies. The amount of space an object takes up is called its **volume.**

Volume is measured in liters (L), milliliters (mL), and cubic centimeters (cm³). One liter is equal to 1000 milliliters or 1000 cubic centimeters. How many milliliters are there in 3.5 liters? ❷

You now know two important general properties of matter. Matter has mass and occupies space. Using these two properties, you can now define matter in a more scientific way: Matter is anything that has mass and volume.

Density

The properties of mass and volume can be used to describe another important general property of matter called **density.** Density is the mass per unit volume of an object. Density is an important property because it allows you to compare different types of matter.

Suppose you were asked to determine whether wood or lead is heavier. You probably could not make this determination unless you knew the sizes

---

2-1 (continued)

Motivation

Bring in three similar objects of different volumes, such as a small box, a shoe box, and a very large box. Ask,
• **How are these objects similar?** (All are made up of matter; all are solids; all have mass; all can be used to store things; all are of similar shape; all are made of cardboard.)

• **How are they different?** (They are different sizes; they take up different amounts of space.)

Content Development

Explain to students that the amount of space an object takes up is called its volume. Emphasize that volume is a three-dimensional quantity. Ask,
• **What is the difference between a square and a cube?** (A square is flat while a cube has three sides.)

• **How would you measure the amount of space a square takes up?** (Find the area—side × side.)
• **How would you measure the amount of space a cube takes up?** (Find the volume—side × side × side.)
• **How would you measure the amount of space one of the boxes shown earlier takes up?** (Measure the length, width, and height, and multiply them together.)
• **What units are used to measure the**

of the pieces of wood and lead you were comparing. And even then, would it be correct to compare a small chip of lead with a baseball bat of wood?

In order to compare the masses of objects, equal volumes must be used. If you compared pieces of wood and lead that were the same size, you would find that the piece of lead has a greater mass than the piece of wood. A cubic centimeter of lead is more massive than a cubic centimeter of wood. Another way to state this is that lead has a higher density than wood. The density of a specific kind of matter is a property that helps to identify it and distinguish it from all other kinds of matter.

Since density is mass per unit volume, the following formula can be used to find the density of an object.

$$density = \frac{mass}{volume}$$ ❷

Mass usually is expressed in grams, and volume is expressed in milliliters or cubic centimeters. So density is expressed in grams per milliliter (g/mL) or grams per cubic centimeter (g/cm^3).

Sample Problem	If 96.5 grams of gold has a volume of 5 cubic centimeters, what is the density of gold?
Solution	
Step 1 Write the formula	$density = \dfrac{mass}{volume}$
Step 2 Substitute given numbers and units	$density = \dfrac{96.5 \ grams}{5 \ cubic \ centimeters}$
Step 3 Solve for unknown variable	$density = \dfrac{19.3 \ grams}{cubic \ centimeters}$

Practice Problems

❹ 1. If 96.5 g of aluminum has a volume of 35 cm^3, what is the density of aluminum? How does its density compare with the density of gold?

❺ 2. If the density of a diamond is 3.5 g/cm^3, what would be the mass of a diamond whose volume is 0.5 cm^3?

COMMON ERRORS

When calculating density, many students divide volume by mass instead of mass by volume. Remind students that a fraction bar means "divided by"—thus the bottom number must be divided into the top number. Also, stress the meaning of density—that it is a measure of mass per unit volume, not volume per unit mass.

Some students may have difficulty dividing with decimals. A quick math review with some sample problems can be given before the formula for density is introduced. If some students continue to have problems, you might try pairing them with other students who can help them learn to divide correctly.

volume of solids? (cubic meters or cubic centimeters)

• **What units are used to measure the volume of liquids?** (liters or milliliters)

• **What units are used to measure the volume of gases?** (liters or milliliters)

Content Development

Emphasize the definition of matter as anything that has mass and volume. Point out that mass and volume are

both quantities than can be measured. A particular sample of matter can be described in terms of its mass and volume.

Skills Development

Skill: Making measurements
Divide the class into small groups. Assign each group the task of measuring the volume of several objects of different sizes and shapes. Refer to the Sharpen Your Skills on page 38 for

the method of finding the volume of a solid. For objects with regular shapes, students may want to make measurements with a meter stick, then use the formulas shown in the Math Tie-In.

Content Development

Remind students of the demonstration with the ping-pong ball and golf ball. Point out that what was being shown was a difference in density.

2-2 PHASES OF MATTER

SECTION PREVIEW 2-2

In this section, students will be introduced to four phases of matter—solid, liquid, gas, and plasma. They will learn that phase is an important physical property of matter and that matter can be classified according to phase.

Students will learn the important characteristics of each phase. They will also learn how the arrangement and movement of particles is different for solids, liquids, and gases.

Students will be introduced to the special behavior of gases. They will learn how this behavior is described by Boyle's Law and Charles's Law.

PERFORMANCE OBJECTIVES 2-2

1. **Identify phase as an important physical property of matter.**
2. **Describe the four phases of matter.**
3. **Explain how the properties of solids, liquids, and gases are related to the arrangement of particles.**
4. **Describe the behavior of gases using Boyle's Law and Charles's Law.**

SCIENCE TERMS 2-2

physical property p. 40
phase p. 41
solid p. 41
crystal p. 41
crystalline solid p. 41
amorphous solid p. 42

liquid p. 42
viscosity p. 43
gas p. 43
Boyle's Law p. 45
Charles's Law p. 45
plasma p. 46

DENSITIES OF SOME COMMON SUBSTANCES

Substance	Density (g/cm³)
Air	0.0013
Gasoline	0.7
Wood (oak)	0.85
Water (ice)	0.92
Water (liquid)	1.0
Aluminum	2.7
Steel	7.8
Silver	10.5
Lead	11.3
Mercury	13.5
Gold	19.3

Figure 2–6 This chart shows the density of some common substances. Which substances will float on liquid water? Why? What will happen when a piece of lead is put in mercury? When a piece of gold is put in mercury? ④

Section Objective

To classify matter according to its phases

The density of water is 1 g/mL. An object will float in water if its density is less than the density of water. Wood floats in water because its density is about 0.8 g/cm³. What happens to a piece of lead when it is put in water? See Figure 2–6. ①

Because you know that ice floats, you should now know that it is less dense than liquid water. Actually, the density of ice is about 89 percent that of cold water. This means that only about 11 percent of a block of ice stays above the surface of the water. The rest is below the water. How does this fact explain why icebergs are so dangerous? ②

Scientists often compare the density of an object to the density of water, which is 1 g/mL. The comparison, or ratio, of the mass of a substance to the mass of an equal volume of water is called **specific gravity.** The specific gravity of water is 1. The specific gravity of gold is 19.3. What is the specific gravity of mercury? Of lead? ③

Specific gravity has no units. It is simply a number. This is because the units cancel out when the densities of the two substances are compared.

SECTION REVIEW

1. How can matter be described using two general properties?
2. What two properties of matter are related to its mass?
3. What is density? How is it calculated?
4. Each year some college students have a contest to build and race concrete boats. What advice would you give the students to make sure their boats float?

2–2 Phases of Matter

The general properties of matter such as mass, weight, volume, and density are examples of **physical properties.** Color, shape, hardness, and texture are also physical properties. Physical properties are those that can be observed without changing the identity of the substance. Wood is still wood whether it is in the form of a baseball bat or wood chips.

40

2-1 (continued)

Skills Development

Skill: Making inferences
Have students consider the following question.
• **Why is water near the bottom of the ocean colder than water near the surface?** (Cold water sinks because it is denser than warm water.)

Enrichment

Divide students into small groups. Challenge each group to create a story in which a fraud is uncovered by determining the density of a substance. For example, a person might buy a "gold" ring only to find that it is a brass ring. Have each group dramatize its story for the class.

Content Development

Because solids, liquids, and gases are familiar to students, they may feel that they "know all about them." Emphasize the scientific definition of each phase in terms of shape and volume, and also emphasize the relationship between phase and the arrangement and mobility of particles.

Section Review 2-1

1. Matter is anything that has mass and volume.
2. Inertia and weight

Figure 2–7 *As the air in these colorful balloons is heated, the balloons begin to rise (right). Is the hot air in the balloons more or less dense than the surrounding atmosphere? This iceberg floats in the water near Baffin Bay, Greenland (left). Is all of the iceberg floating on top of the water?* ❺

Ice, liquid water, and water vapor may seem very different to you. Certainly, they have different appearances and uses. But actually they are all made of exactly the same substance in different states. These states are called **phases.** Phase is an important physical property of matter. Scientists use the phases of matter to classify the various kinds of matter in the world. **Matter can exist in four phases—solid, liquid, gas, and plasma.** ❷

Solids

A pencil, a cube of sugar, a metal coin, and an ice cream cone are examples of **solids.** Because they are solids they share two important characteristics. Solids have a definite shape and a definite volume. The tiny particles that make up a solid are packed very close together, so the solid keeps its shape. The particles cannot move far out of their places, nor can they flow over or around each other. The basic movement of particles in a solid is vibration.

In many solids, the particles are arranged in a regular, repeating pattern called a **crystal** (KRIHS-tuhl). Solids made up of crystals are **crystalline solids.** Common table salt is a good example of a crystalline solid. Figure 2–8 on page 42 shows some other examples of crystalline solids. ❸

41

3. Density is mass per unit volume. Density = mass/volume.
4. The concrete boats will float only if they are less dense than water. To keep the density less than 1 g/mL (density of water), the boat's mass must be as low as possible and its volume as large as possible.

TEACHING STRATEGY 2-2
Motivation
Have students observe Figure 2-7.

- **What kind of matter is ice?** (a solid)
- **How is ice different from water?** (Water is a liquid.)
- **How is ice the same as water?** (It is really the same substance; it is made up of oxygen and hydrogen.)
- **Why is phase a physical property of matter?** (The identity of the substance remains the same.)

BACKGROUND INFORMATION

The particles of any substance are constantly in motion. The type and extent of the motion determines whether the substance is solid, liquid, or gas. Particles of a solid are in fixed positions. Their movements consist primarily of vibrations. Particles of a liquid are free to move from one place to another, but forces of attraction keep the particles close together. Particles of a gas are spread out, for there are essentially no forces of attraction between them. These particles are in constant random motion, and they collide with each other frequently.

TEACHER DEMONSTRATION

Display a candle and ask,

- **What is this candle made of?** (wax)
- **What type of matter is wax?** (a solid)

Light the candle and let it burn until the wax drips. Ask,

- **Is the wax still a solid?** (Students may answer yes or no.)

Explain that wax is what is called an amorphous solid. An amorphous solid does not hold its shape the way a crystalline solid does. Point out that students who did not think melted wax was a solid are not totally wrong, because some scientists consider amorphous solids to be slow-moving liquids.

Figure 2–8 *The regular, repeating arrangement of particles in a solid forms a crystal. Crystals have definite patterns, several of which you can see in these samples of quartz (left), wavellite (center), and chrysocolla (right). How would you describe each crystal?* **1**

1

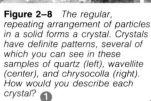

Figure 2–9 *Sealing wax is an amorphous solid. The particles making up the wax are not arranged in a rigid pattern, so they can flow around one another. Does an amorphous solid keep its shape?* **2**

42

In some solids, the particles are not arranged in a rigid way. These solids do not keep a definite shape because they are not made of crystals. Unlike most solids, the particles in these solids can slowly flow around one another. Solids that lose their shape under certain conditions are called **amorphous** (uh-MOR-fuhs) **solids.** If you have ever worked with sealing wax or silicone rubber, you are familiar with an amorphous solid.

Some scientists think of amorphous solids as slow-moving liquids. Tar, candle wax, and glass are examples. If you can look at windowpanes in very old houses, you might notice that the panes are thicker at the bottom than at the top. The glass has flowed slowly downward, just like a liquid! Glass is sometimes described as a supercooled liquid. It is formed when a material in the liquid phase is cooled to a rigid condition but no crystals form.

Liquids

The particles in a **liquid** are close together but are free to move. So a liquid has no definite shape. A liquid takes the shape of its container. A liquid in a square container is square. That same liquid in a round container is round.

Although liquids do not have a definite shape, they do have a definite volume. One liter of water in a round container or a square container is still one liter of water. If that one liter of water is poured into a two-liter bottle, it will not fill the bottle. The water does not spread out to fill the entire volume of the bottle. What would happen if you tried to pour one liter of water into a half-liter bottle? **3**

2-2 (continued)

Content Development

Emphasize the definition of a solid as a type of matter that has definite shape and volume.

Display an unbreakable solid object such as a wooden block, a plastic cup, or a pencil. Ask,

- **Can I change the shape of this object by squeezing it or pulling on it?** (no)

- **Can I make it smaller or larger without adding or subtracting matter?** (no)
- **Based on the properties of this object, what can you say about the particles of a solid?** (They are in fixed positions and they are very close together.)

Enrichment

Students may enjoy viewing crystals of familiar substances such as salt and

sugar under a microscope. Have students make a sketch of each crystal they observe and describe how various crystals are different from each other.

Content Development

Emphasize the definition of a liquid as a type of matter having definite volume but not definite shape.

Fill a beaker or other cylindrical container with water. As the students watch, pour the water into a rectan-

Even though the particles in a liquid are close together, they can flow easily around one another. Some liquids flow more easily than others, however. The resistance of a liquid to flow is called **viscosity** (vihs-кos-ih-tee). Honey has a high viscosity compared to water. If you have ever poured honey, you know it flows less easily than water. Motor oils also have a high viscosity.

Gases

A **gas** does not have a definite shape or a definite volume. A gas fills all the available space in a container, regardless of the size or the shape of the

Figure 2–10 *This figure shows how the particles of matter are arranged in a solid, a liquid, and a gas. In a solid, such as table salt (left), the particles are packed close together and cannot move far out of place. In a liquid, such as molten iron (center), the particles are close together but are free to move about or flow. In a gas, such as iodine vapor (right), the particles are free to spread out and occupy a large volume.*

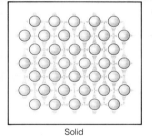

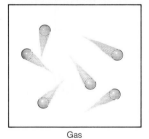

Solid   Liquid   Gas

43

Charles's Law
Skills: Relating concepts, relating cause and effect, manipulative
Level: Enriched
Type: Hands-on
Materials: balloon, string, metric tape measure, oven, freezer unit

In this activity, students obtain a better understanding of Charles's Law by observing the effects of heat and cold on the diameter of a balloon. Students should note that the balloon increases in diameter when heated and decreases in diameter when cooled. You may want to work with students when placing the balloons in the heated oven. Instruct students to use heat-resistant gloves whenever working with heated objects.

BACKGROUND INFORMATION

Because the particles of a gas are in constant motion, they have kinetic energy. Increasing the temperature of a gas makes the particles move faster, thus increasing their kinetic energy. Collisions also increase kinetic energy as faster-moving, high-energy particles transfer energy to slower-moving particles.

Charles's Law

1. Inflate a balloon, making sure it is not so large that it will break easily. Tie the end of the balloon so that air cannot escape.

2. Measure and record the diameter of the balloon.

3. Put the balloon in an oven set at a low temperature—not more than 150°F (65°C). Leave the balloon in the oven for about 15 minutes.

4. Remove the balloon and quickly measure its diameter. Record this measurement.

5. Now place the balloon in a freezer or refrigerator for 15 minutes.

6. Remove the balloon and measure and record its diameter. What happens to the size of the balloon at the higher temperature? At the lower temperature? Do your results agree with Charles's Law?

container. When air is pumped into a bicycle tire or a balloon, a large amount of gas is being squeezed into a small volume. Fortunately, the particles in a gas can be pushed close together.

The particles of a gas can also spread out to fill a large volume. The smell of apple pie baking in the oven comes to you because gases in the pie spread out to every part of the room. In fact, if allowed to, gases will expand without limit. If not for the pull of gravity, the gases making up the earth's atmosphere would soon expand into deep space! Why do you think a tiny planet like Mercury has little or no atmosphere? ❶

This behavior of gases can be explained in terms of the arrangement and movement of the particles making up the gases. The particles in a gas are spread very far apart. There is a lot of empty space between the particles. The particles also move about ❶ freely and rapidly at speeds of about 500 meters per second. Whizzing around like this, the particles are constantly hitting one another. In fact, each particle undergoes about 10 billion collisions per second! Added to that are the collisions the particles make with the walls of the container. The effect of all these collisions is an outward pressure, or push, exerted by the gas. The pressure is what makes the gas expand to fill its container. What do you think happens to a container when the pressure becomes too great? ❷

Figure 2–11 *A liquid has a definite volume but not a definite shape. It takes the shape of its container. A gas has neither a definite volume nor a definite shape. How would you describe the volume of a gas?* ❸

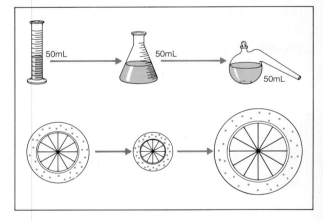

44

2-2 (continued)

Content Development

Emphasize the definition of a gas as a type of matter that has neither definite shape nor definite volume.

Display a balloon filled with air.
Ask,
- **What is inside this balloon?** (air)
- **What type of matter is air?** (a gas)
- **In what shape is the air?** (the shape of the balloon)

- **What is the volume of the air?** (the same as the volume of the balloon)
Let the air out of the balloon.
Ask,
- **What is the shape of the air now?** (Cannot really tell; it has mixed with the air that is in the shape of the room.)
- **What does this tell you about the particles of a gas?** (They spread apart easily and do not seem to hold together.)

Motivation

Have students imagine that they are standing in a crowded subway car. Suddenly someone starts pushing and shoving.
- **What do you think will happen?** (Someone may start pushing back; people will bump into other people; someone may fall down; some people will bang into the walls of the car, and so on.)
Explain that the pressure created

HELP WANTED: ARCHITECT to design high-rise housing complex planned for downtown area. College degree or extensive experience as well as state license required.

Pretend for a minute that you are about to move into a brand-new building. At first you might ask what building materials were used. Was it constructed with stone, brick, wood, or steel? Is it an attractive building?

As your moving day approaches, you may ask more complex questions about the building: "Will the living room floor be able to support a piano and a giant fishtank? Will I hear the neighbor's stereo in my room? How is the building heated and cooled?"

The person who can answer these questions is the **architect** who designed the building and selected the materials from which it was constructed.

The properties of materials are important to architects. In order to design a building that is safe, functional, and attractive, an architect must know about the strength, durability, size, and weight of building materials. An architect also must know how many people will occupy the building and what type of furniture and machines the people will bring with them. Architects constantly use their knowledge of materials in designing buildings to meet peoples' needs.

For more information about a career in architecture, write to the American Institute of Architects Information Center, 1735 New York Avenue NW, Washington, DC 20006.

BOYLE'S LAW If the volume of a gas is greatly reduced, the number of particle collisions within the gas will increase. So the pressure of the gas will increase. This relationship between volume and pressure is called **Boyle's Law.** According to Boyle's Law, the volume of a fixed amount of gas varies inversely with the pressure of the gas. An inverse proportion, or variation, means that as one factor increases, the other factor decreases. If the pressure increases, the volume decreases. If the pressure decreases, the volume increases. How can you relate Boyle's Law to what you feel when you squeeze part of an inflated balloon? ❹

CHARLES'S LAW If the temperature of a gas is changed but the pressure is kept constant, then the volume of the gas must also change in order to keep the number of particle collisions the same. This relationship between temperature and volume is called **Charles's Law.** According to Charles's Law, the volume of a fixed amount of gas varies directly with the temperature of the gas. A direct

TIE-IN/MATH

Boyle's Law and Charles's Law can be represented by proportions. Boyle's Law, which is an example of an inverse proportion, can be stated,

$$P_1V_1 = P_2V_2 \text{ or}$$
$$P_1/P_2 = V_2/V_1$$

Charles's Law, which is an example of a direct proportion, can be stated,

$$T_1V_2 = T_2V_1 \text{ or}$$
$$T_1/T_2 = V_1/V_2$$

ANNOTATION KEY

❶ Mercury has small mass, so small gravitational pull. Gravitational pull of Mercury is too small to hold down much atmosphere. (Making inferences)

❷ The container explodes. (Making predictions)

❸ A gas can be compressed into a small volume or can expand to fill all the available volume. (Interpreting illustrations)

❹ By squeezing the balloon, you decrease the volume. According to Boyle's Law, the pressure increases. You can feel this increase in pressure above and below the point at which the balloon is squeezed. (Relating observations)

❶ Thinking Skill: Relating facts

❷ Thinking Skill: Applying concepts

❸ Thinking Skill: Applying concepts

45

within the subway car when someone starts pushing is similar to the pressure created within a closed container when gas molecules collide with one another.

Content Development

Explain that anything that increases the number of particle collisions within a gas will increase the pressure.
• **Picture a street crowded with many cars. Then picture another street** with just one or two cars. On which street is there more likely to be a collision? (the crowded street) **Why?** (Each car has less space to move in.)
• **Now picture a container full of gas particles. What will happen to the number of collisions if the container becomes smaller?** (They will increase.) **Why?** (Each particle has less space to move in; particles are closer to each other and to the sides of the container.)

• **Suppose the container becomes much larger. What will happen to the number of collisions?** (They will decrease.) **Why?** (Each particle has more space to move in; particles are farther apart from each other and the sides of the container.)

Write on the chalkboard,
Volume down, pressure up
Volume up, pressure down
• **What law is represented by these relationships?** (Boyle's Law)

BACKGROUND INFORMATION

It is important when explaining Boyle's Law and Charles's Law to point out that, in order for the laws to hold true, all but two factors must remain constant. When applying Boyle's Law, pressure and volume change, but temperature remains constant. The amount of gas in the container also remains constant. When applying Charles's Law, temperature and volume change, but pressure and the amount of gas in the container remain constant.

2-2 (continued)

Content Development

Explain to students that adding heat to a gas increases the energy of the particles. Ask,

• **What do you think will happen to the motion of the particles when their energy is increased?** (They will move faster.)

• **What do you think will happen to the number of collisions between particles?** (Number of collisions will increase.)

• **What happens to the pressure of a gas as the number of particle collisions increases?** (Pressure increases.)

• **Suppose you have a gas in a closed container. You want to keep the pressure constant even though the number of particle collisions has increased. What can you do?** (Answers at first may vary. Guide students to realize that increasing the size of the container will keep the pressure constant.)

Figure 2–12 *You can see in this illustration that if the pressure of a fixed amount of gas increases, the volume of the gas decreases (top). This inverse proportion between pressure and volume is called Boyle's Law. According to Charles's Law, if the temperature of a fixed amount of gas increases, the volume of the gas increases (bottom). The relationship between temperature and volume is a direct proportion. According to Boyle's Law, what happens to the volume of a gas if the pressure doubles? According to Charles's Law, what happens to the volume of a gas if the temperature doubles?* ❶

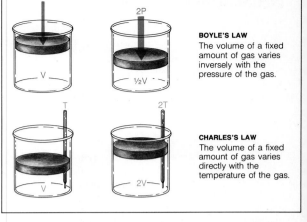

BOYLE'S LAW
The volume of a fixed amount of gas varies inversely with the pressure of the gas.

CHARLES'S LAW
The volume of a fixed amount of gas varies directly with the temperature of the gas.

proportion, or variation, means that as one factor increases, the other factor also increases. If the temperature of a gas increases, the volume increases. What do you think happens as the temperature of a gas decreases? Test your hypothesis by putting an inflated balloon in your freezer. ❷

Boyle's Law and Charles's Law together are called the Gas Laws. The Gas Laws describe the behavior of gases with changes in pressure, temperature, and volume. ❶

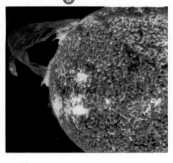

Figure 2–13 *This photograph of the sun shows the largest solar flare (upper left) ever recorded. In what phase does matter on the sun exist?* ❸

46

Plasma

The fourth phase of matter is called **plasma.** Plasma is quite rare on the earth. But the plasma phase is actually one of the most common phases in which matter is found in the universe. Stars have matter in the plasma phase.

Matter in the plasma phase is very high in energy and therefore dangerous to living things. Plasma can be made on the earth only by using equipment that produces very high energy. But the plasma cannot be contained by the walls of ordinary matter, which it would immediately destroy. Instead, magnetic fields produced by powerful magnets keep the high-energy plasma from escaping. One day, producing plasmas on the earth may meet most of our energy needs.

Explain to students that when pressure is held constant, the volume of a gas increases as temperature increases and decreases as temperature decreases.

Skills Development

Skill: Relating concepts

Have students determine which of the following statements represent an inverse relationship and which represent a direct relationship.

The greater the number of hours worked, the more money earned. (direct)

The greater a car's speed, the farther it travels in one hour. (direct)

The more hours you sleep in a day, the fewer hours you are awake. (inverse)

The more money you spend, the less you save. (inverse)

The smaller an object's mass, the greater its velocity. (inverse)

1. What are the four phases of matter?
2. What are physical properties?
3. How does a crystalline solid differ from an amorphous solid?
4. What is Boyle's Law? Charles's Law?
5. How would the volume of a gas be affected if the temperature and the pressure were both doubled?

2–3 Phase Changes

Section Objective
To identify the phase changes in matter

Ice, liquid water, and steam are all the same substance. What, then, causes the particles of a substance to be in one particular phase rather than another? The answer has to do with energy—heat energy that can cause the particles to move faster and farther apart.

A liquid tends to have more energy than that same substance in the solid phase. A gas has more energy than the solid and liquid phases of that same substance. So steam has more energy than both liquid water and ice. The greater heat content of steam is what makes a burn caused by steam more serious than a burn caused by hot water.

Because energy content is responsible for the different phases of matter, substances can be made to change phase by adding or taking away energy. The easiest way to do this is to heat or cool the substance, allowing heat energy to flow into or out of it. You are probably familiar with this idea, since you may have put liquid water in the freezer to make ice or heated liquid water on the stove and made steam. **The phase changes in matter are melting, freezing, vaporization, condensation, and sublimation.**

Changes in phase are examples of **physical changes.** A physical change is a change in which physical properties of a substance are altered but the substance remains the same kind of matter. When a tree trunk is sawed into wood chips or a sheet of paper is shredded, a physical change is taking place. In these cases, the size and shape of the substance are being changed but the identity of the substance remains the same.

Figure 2–14 *When heat is applied, ice changes to liquid water and then to water vapor. What are these two processes called?*

47

2-3 PHASE CHANGES

SECTION PREVIEW 2-3

In this section, students will be introduced to the five phase changes in matter. These are melting, freezing, vaporization, condensation, and sublimation. Students will learn that phase changes are physical changes and that the identity of the substance involved remains the same. Students will learn that phase changes are produced when energy is added to or taken away from a substance. They will discover the relationships that exist between heat, temperature, and phase change and how these relationships can be represented in a phase-change diagram.

PERFORMANCE OBJECTIVES 2-3

1. Identify the phase changes in matter.
2. Explain how adding or taking away energy will produce a phase change.
3. Discuss the relationship between heat, energy, and phase change.
4. Learn how to read and construct a phase-change diagram.

SCIENCE TERMS 2-3

physical change p. 47	vaporization p. 49
melting p. 48	evaporation p. 49
melting point p. 48	boiling p. 49
freezing p. 48	boiling point p. 49
freezing point p. 48	condensation p. 50
	sublimation p. 50

The greater the number of cars on the road, the greater the chances of an accident. (direct)
The more people who enter the contest, the less chance I have of winning. (inverse)

Section Review 2-2

1. Solid, liquid, gas, and plasma
2. Physical properties are those that can be observed without changing the identity of a substance.

3. A crystalline solid has particles arranged in a regular, repeating pattern. A crystalline solid does not lost its shape. An amorphous solid is not made of crystals. An amorphous solid can lose its shape.
4. The volume of a fixed amount of gas varies inversely with the pressure of the gas. The volume of a fixed amount of gas varies directly with the temperature of the gas.
5. Volume would remain the same.

TEACHING STRATEGY 2-3

Motivation
Have students observe Figure 2-14. Ask,
• **What phases of matter are present in this photo?** (solid, liquid, gas)
• **Is everything you see made of the same substance?** (yes) **What is the substance?** (water)
• **Do you think that other substances can exist in three different phases the way water can?** (Yes. Most substances can exist as solid, liquid, or gas.)

BACKGROUND INFORMATION

Most substances expand when heated, but water is an exception to the rule. Because the crystalline structure of ice involves large spaces between molecules, water expands as it freezes. Thus the density of ice is less than the density of liquid water. That is why ice floats in water.

TIE-IN/EARTH SCIENCE

The water cycle, which replenishes the earth's supply of fresh water, involves evaporation and condensation. Have interested students research this process and report their findings to the class.

TEACHER DEMONSTRATION

Evaporation can be used to separate dissolved solids from the liquid solvent. As a class demonstration, leave a solution of salt and water exposed to the air until the water evaporates. (This may take several days.) You may want to use ocean water if it is available in your area. Have students develop logical hypotheses regarding their observations of this demonstration.

Figure 2–15 *At Aspen, Colorado, a snow-making machine turns liquid water into snow (left). In a bakery, a loaf of bread is cut into slices by a bread slicer (right). What type of changes are these?* ❶

Figure 2–16 *The force of freezing water can cause a violent explosion. A cast-iron container about 0.6 centimeter in width is filled with water and placed in a beaker of dry ice and alcohol (top). As the water freezes and expands, a huge amount of energy is exerted against the walls of the container, causing an explosion (bottom).*

Life Science Library/Water. Photograph by Ken Kay, Time-Life Books Inc. Publisher © 1966, Time Inc.

Another example of a physical change occurs when a cube of sugar is dissolved in a glass of warm water. The sugar disappears from sight and the liquid remains clear. You might be tempted to think that somehow the sugar has changed its identity—that it is no longer sugar. But if you taste the liquid, you will know that the sugar is still there. The liquid has a sweet taste. Although the sugar has lost its white color and its original shape, it is still the same kind of matter.

Solid–Liquid Phase Changes

What happens to your ice cream pop on a hot day if you do not eat it fast enough? Right—it begins to melt. **Melting** is the change of a solid to a liquid. Melting occurs when a substance absorbs heat energy. The rigid crystal structure of the particles breaks down, and the particles are free to flow around one another.

The temperature at which a solid changes to a liquid is called the **melting point.** Most substances have a characteristic melting point. It is a physical property that helps identify the substance. The melting point of ice is 0°C. The melting point of table salt is 801°C, while that of a diamond is 3700°C.

The opposite phase change, that of a liquid to a solid, is called **freezing.** Freezing occurs when a substance loses heat energy. The temperature at which a liquid changes to a solid is called the **freezing point.** The freezing point of a substance is equal to

48

2-3 (continued)

Content Development
Ask students the following questions.
- **What are some examples of melting?** (snow melting; ice cube melting in cold drink; frozen food thawing; metal such as iron becoming molten at very high temperatures)
- **What do you think happens to the particles of a substance when the substance melts?** (They gain energy to move more freely.)
- **Where does this energy come from?** (heat)
- **What do you think will happen to the particles of a liquid when heat is removed from the liquid?** (They will lose energy and slow down; eventually the substance will freeze.)

Skills Development
Skill: Applying concepts
Have students observe Figure 2-16 and read the caption. Then have them discuss the following questions.
- **Why is it not a good idea to leave bottled beverages outdoors in cold weather?** (If the beverages freezes, the bottle may explode and shatter.)
- **What damage can be done to a car if antifreeze is not added to the water in the radiator?** (The radiator can crack as the water freezes and expands.)
- **Why do many potholes appear in**

its melting point. What is the freezing point of water? ❷

When a substance undergoes a phase change, its volume changes but its mass remains the same. As a result, the density of the substance changes. Generally, when a solid melts, its volume increases so its density decreases. The liquid phase is less dense than the solid phase. Water, however, is an exception to this general rule. Between 0° and 4°C, the density of water increases as ice melts to water. Ice is less dense than water. What everyday experiences tell you that this is true? ❸

Liquid–Gas Phase Changes

The change of a substance from a liquid to a gas is called **vaporization** (vay-puhr-ih-ZAY-shuhn). During this process, particles in a liquid absorb enough heat energy to escape from the liquid phase. Vaporization at the surface of a liquid is called **evaporation** (ih-vap-uh-RAY-shuhn).

Evaporation is sometimes thought of as a cooling process. You can better understand this if you think of perspiration on the surface of your skin. As the perspiration evaporates, it absorbs and carries away heat energy from your body. In this way, your body is cooled. Why is it important to perspire on a very hot day? ❹

If enough energy is supplied to a liquid, particles inside the liquid as well as those on the surface change to gas. These particles travel to the surface of the liquid because they are less dense than the liquid. The particles then travel into the air. This process is called **boiling.** The temperature at which a liquid boils is called the **boiling point.** The boiling point of water at the earth's surface under normal conditions is 100°C. The boiling point of table salt is 1413°C and that of a diamond is 4200°C!

The boiling point of a liquid is related to the pressure of the air above it. The gas particles that escape from the surface of the liquid must have enough "push" to equal the "push" of the air pressing down. So the lower the air pressure, the more easily the bubbles of gas can form within the liquid and then escape. Lowering the air pressure lowers the boiling point.

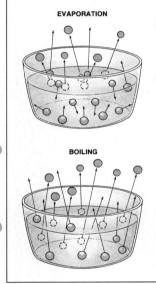

Figure 2–17 *During both evaporation (top) and boiling (bottom), particles of a liquid absorb heat energy and change from the liquid phase to the gas phase. Based on this illustration, what is the difference between evaporation and boiling?* ❺

EVAPORATION

BOILING

49

roadways during the winter? (Water gets into cracks in the pavement, then expands as it freezes, breaking up the pavement.)

Enrichment

Challenge students with this problem: You have a mixture of three liquids. Liquid A freezes at 0°C, liquid B freezes at −20°C, and liquid C freezes at −40°C. How can you separate these substances? (Possible solution: Cool the mixture to just below 0° and pour off liquids B and C. Then cool the mixture to just below −20° and pour off liquid C.)

Content Development

Ask students the following questions.
• **What are some examples of liquid changing to gas?** (water boiling; perfume evaporating; puddles drying on the sidewalk after it rains)
• **What must happen to the particles** of a liquid in order for them to change into a gas? (They must gain energy.)
• **Where does this energy come from?** (from heat)

BACKGROUND INFORMATION

A liquid boils when the vapor pressure of the liquid equals atmospheric pressure. It is the vapor pressure that gives the particles enough "push" to escape into the gas phase. As altitude increases, atmospheric pressure decreases. At high altitudes, the vapor pressure of a liquid does not need to be as high in order to equal atmospheric pressure. That is why water boils at a lower temperature on a mountain than at sea level.

FACTS AND FIGURES

The heat released by a substance as it freezes (or absorbed as it melts) is called the heat of fusion. The heat of fusion for water is 80 calories per gram.

The heat absorbed by a substance as it changes from a liquid to a gas (or released as it condenses) is called the heat of vaporization. The heat of vaporization for water is 540 calories per gram.

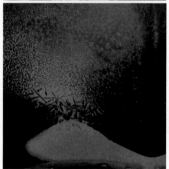

Figure 2–18 *In the cool morning air, water vapor may condense and form dew on grass. What happens to the dew by mid-afternoon?* ❶

Figure 2–19 *Certain substances such as dry ice (top) and iodine (bottom) go from the solid phase directly to the gas phase. What is this process called?* ❷

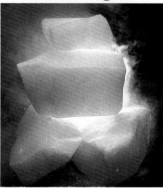

50

At high altitudes, air pressure is much lower, so the boiling point is reduced. Water will boil at a temperature lower than 100°C at high altitudes. If you could go 15 kilometers or more above the earth's surface, the pressure of the air would be so low that you could boil water at ordinary room temperature! However, this boiling water would be cool. Certainly, you would not be able to cook anything in this water, at least not for the usual amount of time. It is the heat in boiling water that cooks food, not simply the boiling process.

The opposite phase change—that of a gas to a liquid—is called **condensation** (kahn-dehn-SAY-shuhn). During condensation, a substance in the gas phase loses heat energy and changes into a liquid. Have you ever noticed that cold objects, such as glasses of iced drinks, tend to become wet on the outside? Where does this "extra" water come from? Water vapor in the surrounding air loses heat energy when it comes in contact with the cold glass. The water vapor condenses and becomes liquid drops on the glass.

Solid–Gas Phase Changes

Certain substances go from the solid phase directly to the gas phase without passing through the liquid phase. Such substances are said to sublime, and the phase change is called **sublimation** (suhb-lih-MAY-shuhn). During sublimation, the surface particles of a solid escape directly into the gas phase.

If you live in an area where winters are very cold and there is a lot of snow, you may have observed sublimation. Even when the temperature stays below the melting point of the water that makes up the snow, the fallen snow slowly disappears. But it does not leave behind puddles of water. The snow undergoes sublimation. ❷

Dry ice is a substance used to keep other substances, such as ice cream, very cold. Dry ice is solid carbon dioxide. At ordinary pressures, it cannot exist in the liquid phase. As it absorbs heat energy, it sublimes, or changes directly to a gas. By absorbing and carrying off heat energy as it changes from a solid to a gas, dry ice keeps substances that are near it cold and dry. What would happen to an ice cream cake if it were packed in regular ice rather than dry ice? ❸

Heat, Temperature, and Phase Changes

As you now know, heat plays an important role in phase changes. Heat is energy that causes the particles of matter to move faster and farther apart. As the particles move faster, they leave one phase and pass into another.

The addition of heat to a substance is usually accompanied by a rise in temperature. But if you kept a record of the temperature and the heat energy involved in changing ice to steam, you would ❸ notice several interesting things. These observations can best be explained by constructing a phase-change diagram, such as the one in Figure 2–20.

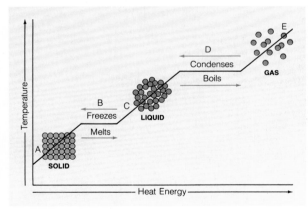

Figure 2–20 *This phase-change diagram shows what happens as a cube of ice absorbs heat energy. At which points on the diagram does the addition of heat energy cause an increase in temperature? At which points is there no temperature change with the addition of heat energy? What are these points called?* ❹

Explain that the heat energy is needed to overcome the forces holding the particles together in a solid or liquid. When the energy is being used in this way, the temperature remains unchanged.

Skills Development

Skill: Interpreting diagrams

Have students study the phase-change diagram in Figure 2-20. Ask,

• **What two factors are related in this diagram?** (addition of heat energy and temperature change)
• **According to the diagram, does adding heat always increase the temperature?** (no) **How can you tell?** (In several places the graph is flat.)
• **What is happening during the periods when temperature is not increasing?** (A phase change is occurring.)
• **Does the temperature ever decrease as heat energy is added?** (no) **How can you tell?** (The graph never slopes downward as you move from left to right.)
• **Suppose you were to remove heat energy from a substance. Would the temperature always go down?** (no) **When would it not go down?** (during a phase change)

2-3 (continued)

Reinforcement

Make sure students have grasped the relationship between energy changes and phase changes. Ask,

• **What must be added to a substance in order to make it melt?** (heat energy)
• **What must be removed in order to make it freeze?** (heat energy)
• **What will happen if you add enough heat energy to a liquid?** (It will change into a gas.)
• **What will happen if you remove enough heat energy from a vapor?** (It will change into a liquid.)

Reinforcement

Some students may have difficulty understanding why heat added to a substance during a phase change does not result in a rise in temperature. Use the following illustration.

• **Have you ever watched a car stuck in snow, mud, or sand?** The energy normally used to move the car forward is used up spinning the wheels. The car just goes deeper into the material it is stuck in. In some ways, a phase change is like that. The heat energy that normally causes a rise in temperature is busy doing something else. It is being used to break the bonds between particles. As soon as the bonds are broken and the phase change is complete, the heat energy can once again cause a rise in temperature.

Section Review 2-3

1. Melting, vaporization, and sublimation involve the absorption of heat. Freezing and condensation involve the release of heat. (Applying concepts)

The vertical, or Y, axis represents the temperature. The horizontal, or X, axis represents heat energy. The lettered line segments represent different stages in the change of ice from the solid phase to the gas phase.

In segment A, the ice cube receives heat from an outside source and the particles of the solid begin to vibrate faster. This faster vibration is indicated by a rise in temperature. Segment B shows that there is no change in temperature. But there is an increase in heat energy. Even though the ice cube is still absorbing heat, there is no accompanying rise in temperature. This is the phase change called melting. ❶ The energy the ice particles gain is used to break down the rigid solid structure of ice. The temperature does not rise during the phase change.

In segment C, the temperature once again begins to rise as heat is added. As the particles of the liquid gain energy, they continue to move faster, but not fast enough to change phase.

At the beginning of segment D, the temperature again levels off to a constant value. This value is the boiling point of water. Segment D represents the phase change called boiling. Once again, added heat energy is used to bring about a phase change. During this phase change, the forces holding the particles of the liquid together are overcome by the added heat energy and the liquid changes to a gas. Segment E represents the continued heating of the gas phase with an accompanying rise in temperature. When the gas absorbs heat, its particles move even faster, so the temperature rises.

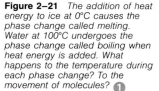

Figure 2–21 *The addition of heat energy to ice at 0°C causes the phase change called melting. Water at 100°C undergoes the phase change called boiling when heat energy is added. What happens to the temperature during each phase change? To the movement of molecules?* ❶

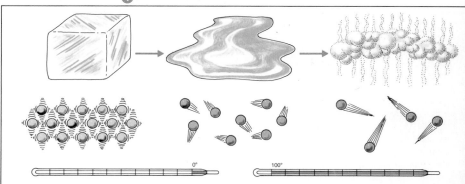

2. Evaporation is vaporization at the surface of a liquid. (Applying definitions)
3. Change of solid directly to a gas (Applying definitions)
4. Heat energy absorbed during a phase change is used to overcome forces that hold particles of the substance together. There is no increase in temperature because the particles are not moving faster. (Relating concepts)

5. Denver is at a higher altitude than Boston. Atmospheric pressure is lower in Denver than in Boston, so the boiling point is also lower. Therefore, the boiling water is not as hot, and more cooking time is required. (Applying concepts)

TEACHING STRATEGY 2-4

Motivation

Display to students a wooden splint.

This diagram clearly shows that phase changes are accompanied by increases in heat energy but not by increases in temperature. The heat energy that is absorbed is used to overcome forces that hold the particles of the substance together. Once the forces have been overcome and the substance has changed phase, added energy causes a rise in temperature.

It is important for you to remember that the gas phase consists of exactly the same particles of matter as the liquid phase and the solid phase. Phase changes produce changes in the physical properties of matter only. Regardless of its phase, it is still the same kind of matter.

SECTION REVIEW

1. What three phase changes involve the absorption of heat? What two phase changes involve the release of heat?
2. How are evaporation and boiling different?
3. What is sublimation?
4. Why does the temperature remain constant during a phase change even though the substance is absorbing heat energy?
5. In Boston, Massachusetts, it takes three minutes to soft-boil an egg. In Denver, Colorado, it takes longer. Explain why.

2–4 Chemical Properties and Changes

Section Objective

To distinguish between a chemical property and a chemical change

The properties of matter that you have learned about can be observed without changing the identity of the substance. They are physical properties. Very often the physical properties alone will enable you to tell the substances apart. You can rely on color, shape, hardness, density, odor, and the ability to dissolve in water to tell one substance from another.

But suppose you have to distinguish between two gases—oxygen and hydrogen. Both gases are colorless, odorless, and tasteless. Since they are gases, they have no definite shape or volume. And although each has a specific density, you cannot determine it easily. In this case, the physical properties are not very helpful in identifying the gases.

53

2-4 CHEMICAL CHANGES

SECTION PREVIEW 2-4

In this section, students will be introduced to the difference between physical and chemical properties of matter. They will learn that chemical properties describe the ways in which a substance can change. They will also learn that chemical properties can be useful in determining the identity of a substance.

Students will study the chemical property of flammability, which is the ability to burn. They will also study the chemical property of the ability to support burning.

Students will learn the difference between a chemical property and a chemical change. They will learn that a chemical change is the process by which a substance changes.

PERFORMANCE OBJECTIVES 2-4

1. Distinguish between physical and chemical properties of matter.
2. Explain how chemical properties are useful in identifying substances.
3. Define and discuss the chemical property of flammability.
4. Discuss the chemical property of the ability to support combustion.
5. Distinguish between a chemical property and a chemical change.

SCIENCE TERMS 2-4

chemical property p. 54
flammability p. 54
chemical change p. 54
chemical reaction p. 55

Ask,
• **What is this object made of?** (wood) Light a match and set the splint on fire. Let it burn until at least half of it has become charred, or fallen off as ash. Ask,
• **What changes do you see in the part of the splint that burned?** (The color changed to black; the burned part became brittle and easily crumbled; much of the wood seemed to disappear.)

• **Do you think that the identity of the original substance has changed?** (Answers may vary; the correct answer is yes.)
To support the idea that the substance has changed, try igniting the charred piece of wood. Ask students to consider the following question.
• **What evidence supports the idea that the charred substance is not wood?** (It does not burn the way wood does.)

Content Development
Review the idea that physical changes do not change the identity of a substance. Refer to the demonstration of the burning splint and ask,
• **Was the splint burning an example of a physical change?** (no) **Why not?** (The identity of the substance was altered.)
Emphasize that when the identity of a substance changes, the change is a chemical change.

BACKGROUND INFORMATION

The ability of hydrocarbons to burn is what makes these substances so useful as fuels. The burning of hydrocarbons, which is often called combustion, results in the production of carbon dioxide and water plus energy. Some examples of hydrocarbon fuels include gasoline, home heating oil, natural gas, and diesel fuel.

Figure 2–22 *Timber fires cause millions of dollars in damage each year. During the combustion of wood, what substance in the atmosphere combines with the wood? Is this a physical or a chemical change?* ❶

54

Fortunately, determining the physical properties is not the only way to identify a substance. Both oxygen and hydrogen can combine with other substances and take on new identities. The way in which they do this can be useful in determining the gas. The properties that describe how a substance changes into other new substances are called **chemical properties.**

Flammability (flam-uh-BIHL-ih-tee) is a chemical property. Hydrogen has the chemical property of flammability. Flammability is the ability to burn. If you were to place a glowing wooden stick into a test tube of hydrogen, you would hear a loud pop. The pop results when hydrogen combines with oxygen in the air, or burns. A new kind of matter forms as the hydrogen burns. This substance is water—a combination of hydrogen and oxygen.

The ability to support burning is another chemical property. Oxygen has the chemical property of supporting burning. But oxygen is not a flammable gas. It does not burn. So you can distinguish oxygen from hydrogen through the chemical properties of flammability and supporting burning. A glowing wooden stick placed in a test tube of oxygen will continue to burn until the oxygen is used up. In the process, oxygen combines with other substances to form new and different substances.

The changes that substances undergo when they change into new and different substances are called **chemical changes.** Chemical changes are closely related to chemical properties, but they are not the ❶ same. **A chemical property describes a substance's ability to change into a different substance; a chemical change is the process by which the substance changes.** For example, the ability of a substance to burn is a chemical property. The process of burning is a chemical change.

As you can see, physical properties are different from chemical properties because physical properties can be observed without changing the identity of the substance. Chemical properties involve a change in the identity of the substance. Physical changes do not produce a new substance. Chemical changes produce one or more new substances.

Chemical changes are taking place around you and even inside you all the time. Respiration and

---

Figure 2–23 *As the leaves change color each autumn in Vermont, this old piece of farm equipment rusts a little more (left). Fireworks dot the Houston skyline during a Fourth of July celebration (right). What three chemical changes can you identify in the photographs?* ❸

digestion are chemical changes you could not live without. Photosynthesis, or the food-making process in green plants, is a chemical change. Rusting and the changing colors of leaves in the fall are chemical changes. Can you name some other examples? ❷

Chemical changes are often called **chemical reactions.** Chemical reactions involve chemically combining different substances. The chemical reaction produces new substances with new and different physical and chemical properties. However, matter is never destroyed in a chemical reaction. The particles of one substance are rearranged to form a new substance, but the same number of particles exists before and after the reaction. ❷

SECTION REVIEW

1. How is a chemical property different from a chemical change?
2. Give an example of a chemical property and a chemical change.
3. What is the difference between a physical property and a chemical property? Between a physical change and a chemical change?
4. What is a chemical reaction?
5. Identify the following processes as either physical changes or chemical changes: boiling water, digesting food, burning coal, melting butter, tarnishing silver, baking brownies, dissolving sugar, exploding TNT.

55

BACKGROUND INFORMATION

A familiar chemical change that may be of interest to students is the tarnishing of silver. Tarnish is the result of silver reacting with sulfur to form silver sulfide. Silver can be made to tarnish by wrapping a rubber band around it—the sulfur in vulcanized rubber will react with the silver. In everyday use, silver usually comes into contact with sulfur in the form of hydrogen sulfide. Hydrogen sulfide is present in egg yolks. It is also present in small concentrations in the atmosphere.

TIE-IN/EARTH SCIENCE

The weathering of rock by carbonation is an example of a chemical change in nature. In this process, carbon dioxide in the air mixes with rain water to form carbonic acid. When the acid comes into contact with feldspars and limestone, the rock is slowly dissolved as the result of a chemical reaction.

3. leaves changing color in the fall
4. chemical weathering of rock
5. milk turning sour
6. combustion of gasoline in a car engine

Section Review 2-4

1. A chemical property describes the ability of a substance to change into another substance. A chemical change is the process by which a substance changes.
2. Flammability: burning. Combine with oxygen: rusting.
3. Unlike chemical properties, physical properties can be observed without changing the identity of the substance. Unlike chemical changes, physical changes do not produce new substances.
4. A chemical reaction is one in which two substances are chemically combined.
5. Physical change: boiling water, melting butter, dissolving sugar. Chemical change: digesting food, burning coal, tarnishing silver, baking brownies, exploding TNT.

LABORATORY INVESTIGATION
OBSERVING A CANDLE

BEFORE THE LAB

1. **Gather all materials at least one day before the investigation. If students are to work in groups, each student should have his or her own candle, but one package or box of matches per group should be sufficient.**
2. **Check the wicks of the candles to make sure that they light easily. Have a few extra candles on hand in case some candles prove hard to light or get broken.**
3. **Check fire extinguishers to make sure they are in working order and are easily accessible to students.**

PRE-LAB DISCUSSION

Review the definitions of physical and chemical properties. Review also the idea that the process by which a substance changes is called a chemical change or chemical reaction.

This investigation, although relatively simple in appearance, challenges students to "see and do" science in their daily lives. You may want to offer incentives for the most complete list of properties obtained by a lab group. The objective of this investigation is to differentiate between physical and chemical properties of matter. Students should develop a hypothesis that stresses that objective.

SKILL DEVELOPMENT

Students will use the following skills while completing this investigation.
1. Manipulative
2. Safety
3. Observing
4. Recording data
5. Inferring

Problem

How can physical and chemical properties be distinguished?

> **Materials** *(per student)*
> small candle
> glass plate or aluminum foil holder
> matches

Procedure

1. On your laboratory worksheet, prepare a data table similar to the one shown here.
2. Observe the unlighted candle for about 10 minutes. List as many physical and chemical properties as you can.
3. Carefully light the candle and continue to make your observations. Record the ob-servations in the correct columns in your data table.

	Physical properties	Chemical properties
Unlighted candle		
Lighted candle		

Observations

1. What general properties of the candle did you observe as physical properties?
2. What senses did you use when making these observations?
3. After lighting the candle, what physical changes did you observe?
4. What did you have to do to observe a chemical property of the candle?
5. What evidence of a chemical change did you observe?

Conclusions

1. Which type of property—physical or chemical—is easier to determine? Why?
2. What do you think is the basic difference between a physical property and a chemical property?
3. Can a physical property be observed without changing the substance? A chemical property?
4. What name is given to a process such as burning a candle? What is the result of such a process?

56

SAFETY TIPS

Emphasize to students that any activity involving fire must be carried out very carefully and safety goggles should be worn at all times. Remind them never to leave a burning object unattended, even "just for a minute." Point out the location of fire extinguishers, and review, if necessary, how to operate a fire extinguisher.

Caution students not to let hot wax drip onto their skin, clothing, or desk-tops. Remind students to keep unused matches away from an open flame and to extinguish thoroughly the matches they light.

CHAPTER REVIEW

SUMMARY

2-1 General Properties of Matter
❏ Mass is the amount of matter in an object.

❏ Inertia is the resistance of an object to changes in its motion. Mass is a measure of the inertia of an object.

❏ Weight is the response of mass to the pull of gravity. Gravity is the force of attraction between objects.

❏ Volume is the amount of space an object takes up.

❏ Density is the mass per unit volume of an object. Density equals mass divided by volume.

❏ The ratio of the mass of a substance to the mass of an equal volume of water is called specific gravity.

2-2 Phases of Matter
❏ A physical property can be observed without changing the identity of the substance.

❏ A solid has a definite shape and volume.

❏ A liquid has a definite volume but no definite shape. A liquid takes the shape of its container.

❏ A gas does not have a definite shape or a definite volume.

❏ Boyle's Law states that the volume of a fixed amount of gas varies inversely with the pressure of the gas. Charles's Law states that the volume of a fixed amount of gas varies directly with the temperature of the gas.

2-3 Phase Changes
❏ A physical change is a change in which physical properties of a substance are altered but the substance remains the same kind of matter. Phase changes are physical changes.

❏ Temperature does not rise during a phase change.

2-4 Chemical Properties and Changes
❏ Chemical properties describe how a substance changes into other new substances.

❏ A chemical change produces a new and different substance.

❏ A chemical reaction produces a new substance with new and different physical and chemical properties.

❏ Matter is never destroyed in a chemical reaction—the same number of particles still exist.

VOCABULARY

Define each term in a complete sentence.

amorphous solid	condensation	inertia	plasma
boiling	crystal	liquid	property
boiling point	crystalline solid	mass	solid
Boyle's Law	density	matter	specific gravity
Charles's Law	evaporation	melting	sublimation
chemical change	flammability	melting point	vaporization
chemical property	freezing	phase	viscosity
chemical reaction	freezing point	physical change	volume
	gas	physical property	weight
	gravity		

GOING FURTHER: ENRICHMENT

Part 1

To continue the study of physical and chemical properties, have students investigate the properties of sugar. In addition to observing the physical properties, they can observe a physical change by dissolving the sugar in water. Some chemical properties of sugar can be determined by burning a small amount of sugar in a flameproof dish.

Part 2

Ask students the following questions.

• **Based on your observation of the candle, what are some signs that indicate that a chemical change is taking place?** (flame, heat and light given off, smoke, burning smell)

• **Can any of these signs also indicate a physical change?** (Yes. Heat given off can be a sign of a phase change.)

• **Based on your own experience and what you've read, what are some other signs that indicate chemical change?** (substance changing color or texture; explosion; electric current generated; gas given off; new substance such as water appears)

OBSERVATIONS

1. Mass, color, volume, shape, texture, hardness, odor

2. Touch, smell, sight, hearing

3. Wax became hotter and melted.

4. Ignite the candle wick.

5. New material (smoke) was produced.

CONCLUSIONS

1. Physical, because observing physical properties of the object requires no other materials.

2. Chemical properties can be detected only through interaction with other materials.

3. Yes. No.

4. Chemical change or chemical reaction. A new substance with new and different physical and chemical properties is formed.

CHAPTER REVIEW

MULTIPLE CHOICE

1. d   3. a   5. b   7. b   9. d
2. c   4. d   6. c   8. c   10. a

COMPLETIONS

1. mass   6. viscosity
2. inertia   7. doubled
3. density   8. evaporation
4. liquid   9. sublimation
5. crystalline   10. chemical

TRUE OR FALSE

1. F volume   7. T
2. F gravity   8. F decreases
3. T   9. F remains the
4. F amorphous   same
5. T   10. T
6. F plasma

SKILL BUILDING

1a. Volume of 20-g mass is smaller. **b.** Weight of 20-g mass is smaller. **c, d, e.** melting point, density, and boiling point the same.
2a. Since the mass gives an exact relationship to the amount of product it is fairer than volume, since a product can be loosely or densely packed into the same volume package. **b.** A more accurate and scientific statement would be "I have to lose mass." Weight can be lost simply by moving farther away from the center of the earth, such as to a high mountaintop. However, this "loss of weight" would have no effect on tight-fitting clothes. **c.** The moving air from the fan aids in the evaporation of moisture (sweat) on the body. This results in a general cooling effect on the body since heat is drawn off when a liquid evaporates. **d.** Since boiling water contains less heat at high altitudes, frozen peas would, in fact, require more boiling to be heated to the same temperature as peas placed in boiling water at sea level.
3. Density equals mass over volume and is usually given in units such as g/cm^3. Since specific gravity is the ratio of the density of water to the density of another object, the units on both side of the ratio cancel out. Thus, specific gravity has no units.
4a. Phase-change diagrams should indicate that it takes more heat input to raise the temperature of cold water to its boiling point. Thus, cold water does not heat faster than hot water. **b.** Experiments should be logical and well thought out so that they do demonstrate the hypothesis. Also, students should include a control experiment and list all appropriate variables.

ESSAY

1. $0.78 \text{ g/cm}^3 \times 4.0 \text{ cm}^3 = 3.12 \text{ g}$. This object will float on water.
2. The water on the clothes freezes. Then it sublimes from the solid phase directly to the gas phase. Clothes dry as moisture is removed during sublimation.
3. Solid: definite shape, definite volume, particles tightly packed together and move through vibration. Liquid: definite shape, definite volume, particles farther apart than solids, particles flow around one another. Gas: no definite shape, particles spread to fill vol-

---

On a separate sheet of paper, write the letter of the answer that best completes each statement.

1. Which of the following is not a general property of matter?
   a. mass   b. volume   c. density   d. flammability
2. The density of an object is equal to
   a. mass/inertia.   b. mass × volume.   c. mass/volume.   d. mass × weight.
3. Matter that has a definite shape and a definite volume is
   a. solid.   b. plasma.   c. liquid.   d. gas.
4. The phase of matter in which the particles move the fastest and are farthest apart is the
   a. solid.   b. plastic.   c. liquid.   d. gas.
5. The phase change from gas to liquid is called
   a. evaporation.   b. condensation.   c. melting.   d. boiling.
6. Which of the following substances does not undergo sublimation?
   a. snow   b. iodine   c. wood   d. dry ice
7. During a phase change,
   a. heat is absorbed and the temperature rises.
   b. heat is absorbed but there is no rise in temperature.
   c. heat is given off and the temperature goes down.
   d. heat is given off and the temperature rises.
8. Which of the following is not a chemical change?
   a. burning coal   b. digesting food   c. tearing paper   d. respiration
9. Which of the following is a chemical property?
   a. inertia   b. density   c. color   d. flammability
10. Four liquids have the following densities: A = 1.0 g/mL, B = 0.8 g/mL, C = 0.6 g/mL, D = 1.2 g/mL. In what order would the liquids form layers from top to bottom if they were carefully placed in a container?
    a. C, B, A, D   b. D, A, B, C   c. A, B, C, D   d. D, C, B, A

On a separate sheet of paper, write the word or words that best complete each statement.

1. The amount of matter in an object is called _____.
2. Resistance to changes in motion is called _____.
3. Mass divided by volume is called _____.
4. Matter in the _____ phase has a definite volume but no definite shape.
5. A (An) _____ solid has a regular, repeating internal structure.
6. The resistance of a liquid to flow is called _____.
7. According to Boyle's Law, if the volume of a fixed amount of gas is halved, the pressure is _____.
8. A change in matter from the liquid phase to the gas phase at the surface of the liquid is called _____.
9. Certain substances can change from a solid directly to a gas in a phase change called _____.
10. A change that produces a new substance is called a (an) _____ change.

58

Determine whether each statement is true or false. Then on a separate sheet of paper, write "true" if it is true. If it is false, change the underlined word or words to make the statement true.

1. Some general physical properties, or characteristics, of matter include mass, weight, plasma, and density.
2. The weight of an object is determined by the pull of inertia.
3. An object with a small mass and a large volume would have a low density.
4. Crystalline solids lose their shape under certain conditions.
5. According to Charles's Law, the volume of a fixed amount of gas varies directly with the temperature of the gas.

6. The solid phase is one of the most common phases of matter in the universe.
7. When evaporation occurs, the volume of matter generally increases.
8. As the pressure of the air above a liquid decreases, the boiling point of the liquid increases.
9. During a phase change, the temperature of a substance increases.
10. A chemical change produces a new substance with new and different physical and chemical properties.

CONCEPT REVIEW: SKILL BUILDING

Use the skills you have developed in the chapter to complete each activity.

1. **Making comparisons** You are given two samples of pure copper, one with a mass of 20 grams and the other with a mass of 100 grams. Compare the two samples in terms of (a) volume, (b) weight, (c) melting point, (d) density, and (e) boiling point.
2. **Applying concepts** Explain the following statements:
   a. Selling cereal by mass rather than by volume is fairer to the consumer.
   b. "I have to lose weight" is not an accurate statement for a person to make if his or her clothes fit too tightly.
   c. You feel cooler on a hot day when you

turn on a fan even though the air being blown around is hot.
   d. Frozen peas have to be cooked for a longer time in high-altitude locations.
3. **Applying formulas** Using the formula for density, show why specific gravity is a number with no units.
4. **Making diagrams and designing experiments** A student makes the statement: "Cold water boils faster than hot water."
   a. Use a phase-change diagram to prove or disprove the statement.
   b. Describe an experiment that would prove or disprove the statement.

CONCEPT REVIEW: ESSAY

Discuss each of the following in a brief paragraph.

1. If the density of a certain plastic used to make a bracelet is 0.78 g/cm^3, what mass would a bracelet of 4 cm^3 have? Would this bracelet sink or float in water?
2. Explain how wet clothes hung on a clothesline on a very cold day dry.

3. Compare the solid, liquid, and gas phases of matter in terms of shape, volume, and arrangement and movement of particles.
4. Explain why fish are able to survive in lakes during very cold winter months when the lakes freeze.

59

ume of container, particles very far apart, particles move in a random way with rapid motion.
4. If water froze from the bottom of the lake up, the fish would die. However, since ice is less dense than liquid water, the ice rises to the top of the lake and the fish survive beneath the ice layer.

ADDITIONAL QUESTIONS AND TOPIC SUGGESTIONS

1. Ask students to design an experiment that would enable a prospector to determine whether a mineral sample was gold or "fool's gold" (iron pyrite). Students should design an experiment to find the density of the substance in order to determine its identity.
2. Have students reinforce their dia-

gram skills by making a phase-change diagram of the following data. 600 mL of water is heated from 20°C to boiling point. The heating continues for 5 more minutes until only 300 mL of water remain. During this time, the temperature does not change. Make sure students can explain why additional heating did not produce an increase in temperature (heat was used to produce phase change during this time period). Ask them to account for the "missing" 300 mL of water (evaporated during the phase change).
3. Suggest that each student select an item from the classroom and write a description of it. Have them list first its general properties and then its specific properties. You may want to assign points to students whose objects can be identified by the class using the lists of properties.
4. Have students determine the mass of several specimens. Give each group of students a balance and several different specimens. Use the same objects for each group. Compare the findings of each group and discuss the reasons for possible differences in their results.

ISSUES IN SCIENCE

The following issue can be used as a springboard for class debate or assigned as a writing homework. Many chemical changes in our environment are caused by the presence of sulfur in the atmosphere. A major source of excess sulfur in the air is pollutants from factories that burn sulfur-containing fuels. Have students research sulfur pollution and the various chemical changes caused by sulfur. Encourage them to express an opinion as to whether the chemical changes caused by sulfur are harmful, helpful, or of no consequence to living things.

Chapter 3
CLASSIFICATION OF MATTER

CHAPTER OVERVIEW

Matter is all around us. It makes up every living and nonliving thing we see or use. We are made up of matter. Matter exists in so many different forms that it is useful to classify similar kinds of matter before we try to study it.

Early scientists thought matter could be broken up into smaller and smaller pieces until the pieces were so small that they no longer could be divided. Finally, in 1808, John Dalton, an English teacher and scientist, developed a theory about the structure of atoms. Dalton's theory led the way to classifying matter by grouping substances according to particular properties or makeup. Scientists use the properties of matter to help classify matter into groups of elements, compounds, mixtures, and solutions.

Atoms are the building blocks of all matter. All of the atoms in an element are the same. Compounds are two or more elements chemically combined. Mixtures are composed of two or more elements that are not chemically combined. Solutions are a type of mixture that forms when one substance dissolves another substance.

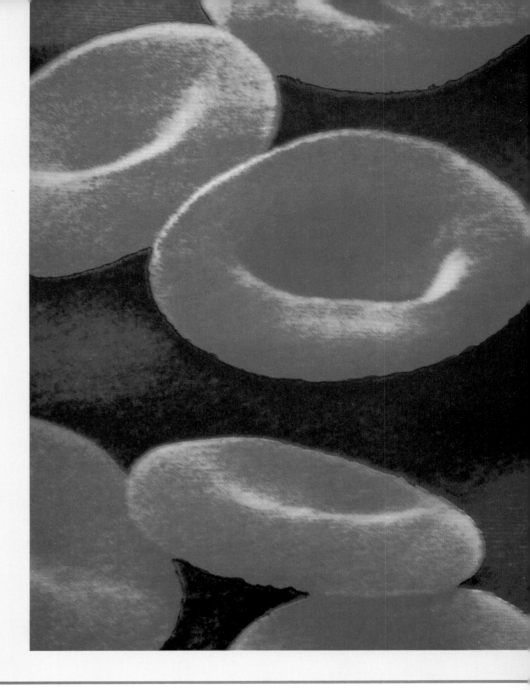

INTRODUCING CHAPTER 3

Have students examine the photo on page 60 and read the chapter introduction. Point out that the photo is a close-up of red blood cells. Ask,
- **What is blood?** (Students should know that blood is the red fluid that flows through our bodies. They may also suggest that it circulates in the heart, arteries, capillaries, and veins of the body. Blood transports nutrients to and waste products away from parts of the body.)
- **What are some of the substances that make up blood?** (Students may not be sure of their answers. Some, however, may say that blood is a combination of things.)

Point out that blood is a combination of liquid and solid substances. The liquid substance is called plasma. The solid substances are red blood cells, white blood cells, and platelets.
- **How do we identify different kinds of blood?** (Most students will say by blood type or blood group.)
- **Why do you think it is important to classify blood?** (Answers will vary, but some students may say for transfusions.)

Point out the following ideas: Nature itself is not classified. People classify things to help them learn and to organize thinking. A method of classifying often has to be changed

Classification of Matter

3

CHAPTER OBJECTIVES

After completing this chapter, you will be able to

3–1 Explain the importance of a system of classification.

3–1 Classify matter according to its makeup.

3–2 Describe the properties of mixtures.

3–2 Distinguish between homogeneous and heterogeneous mixtures.

3–2 Compare the properties of solutions with other mixtures.

3–3 Explain why elements are pure substances.

3–4 Explain why compounds are pure substances.

3–4 Discuss how chemical symbols, formulas, and balanced equations are used to describe a chemical reaction.

Have you ever thought about how important chemistry is to the healthy functioning of your body? The solids, liquids, and gases that make up your body are chemical substances—some simple and some complex. The basic processes that keep you alive—digestion, circulation, and respiration, for example—are chemical reactions. And the materials you add to your body, such as foods and medicines, are chemical substances you could not live without.

One of the most important chemical substances in the body is blood. This life stream of the human body is a unique chemical combination of liquid and solid parts. The fluid portion of blood, called plasma, accounts for about 56 percent of whole blood. Various chemical substances dissolved in water make up plasma. Suspended in the plasma are the solid parts of blood: red blood cells, white blood cells, and platelets. This amazing combination of solid and fluid substances is involved in the complex chemical reactions that keep you alive.

All the substances that make up your body—in fact, all the substances that make up the universe— can be classified into four basic categories. In this chapter, you will learn about these four categories. And you also will learn how the system of classification makes it easier for scientists, and for you, to understand the nature of matter.

These red blood cells, along with white blood cells and platelets, make up the solid part of the blood.

61

3-1 CLASSES OF MATTER

SECTION PREVIEW 3-1

Classification systems are used to organize and simplify learning and understanding. Matter is classified in a system based on the makeup or properties of the matter. Forms of matter that have identical properties throughout the substance are called homogeneous. Substances with different properties are called heterogeneous. These two subdivisions are further divided into four classes of matter: elements, compounds, mixtures, and solutions.

PERFORMANCE OBJECTIVES 3-1

1. **Explain the importance of a system of classification.**
2. **Identify substances as either homogeneous or heterogeneous.**
3. **Apply classification concepts to everyday substances.**
4. **Classify matter according to makeup.**

SCIENCE TERMS 3-1

homogeneous matter p. 63
heterogeneous matter p. 63

TEACHING STRATEGY 3-1

Motivation

Show the class a picture of a "super" cheeseburger. Discuss the ingredients in the super cheeseburger and ask questions such as the following.
• **What are the ingredients in a super cheeseburger?** (Answers will vary but will include a bun and a hamburger and ketchup, mustard, tomato, cheese, pickles, onion, mayonnaise, or lettuce.)
• **How are the ingredients alike? Different?** (Answers will vary but will probably include a reference to a type of classification such as solid, liquid, vegetable, or meat.)
• **How would different bites be alike? Different?** (Answers will vary and will probably refer to the different ingredients.)
• **Why do different parts taste, look,**

and feel different? (Each part is a different substance or thing and has different properties.)

Content Development

Tell the class to keep the super cheeseburger in mind as they read the text. Then discuss the cheeseburger ingredients again and apply the scientific classification scheme to the cheeseburger ingredients. Ask questions like the following.

• **Why do different parts taste, look, and feel different?** (They are different things made from different substances.)
• **How are the super cheeseburger ingredients alike?** (Answers will vary but should include the idea that some ingredients are solids, some liquids, some are homogeneous, some heterogeneous.)
• **Which super cheeseburger ingredients are solids?** (Answers should in-

---

3-1 Classes of Matter

Have you ever had a button, leaf, or marble collection? If so, you probably know how important it is to group, or classify, the objects in the collection. To do this, you might use characteristics such as color, size, shape, or texture. Or maybe you would classify the objects according to their uses. In any event, you would be using a classification system based on a particular property to group the objects.

Classification systems are used all the time to organize objects. Books in a library or bookstore are arranged in an organized manner. So too are clothes in a department store and food in a supermarket. Next time you are in a record store, notice how the records and tapes are organized.

In order to make the study of matter easier to understand, scientists have developed different ways to classify matter. In Chapter 2, you learned that matter exists in four phases—solid, liquid, gas, and plasma. Phases are one way to classify matter.

But classifying matter according to phases is not specific enough and can lead to confusion. One kind of substance can exist in more than one phase. Water is a good example. Water can be a solid in the form of ice, a liquid, or a gas in the form of water vapor. How would you classify water?

Figure 3-1 *Classification is as important to storekeepers as it is to scientists. How has the produce in this outdoor market been classified (left)? In what ways has the classification of yarn (right) made it easier for customers to select the yarn they need?*

62

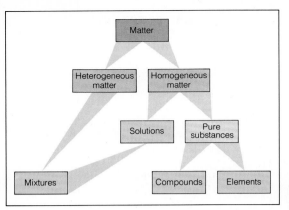

Figure 3–2 *This chart shows one way matter can be classified. In this particular classification system, what are the two main groups into which matter can be classified?* ③

Classifying matter according to phases often puts very different substances in the same group. Table salt, gold, steel, and sand are all solids. Should they be grouped together? What about water and gasoline, which are both clear liquids? How are these two liquids different? ④

In order to make the study of matter easier, scientists have used a classification system based on the makeup of matter. **According to makeup, matter exists as elements, compounds, mixtures, or solutions.**

As you read further, you will learn that some of these forms of matter have identical properties throughout, and some do not. Matter that has identical properties throughout is called **homogeneous** (hoh-muh-JEEN-ee-uhs) **matter.** All parts of homogeneous matter are alike. The properties of any one part of the matter are identical to the properties of all the other parts. Sugar, salt, water, and whipped cream are examples of homogeneous matter. What homogeneous materials can you think of?

Matter that has parts with different properties is called **heterogeneous** (heht-uhr-uh-JEEN-ee-uhs) **matter.** All parts of heterogeneous matter are not alike. The properties of any one part of the matter are different from the properties of all the other parts.

Figure 3–3 *The water droplets on this stalk of grass and the droplets of mercury are both in the liquid phase. Do you think classifying objects by phase is helpful to scientists?* ⑤

②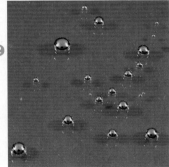

63

HISTORICAL NOTES

Explain that humans have been classifying things since time began. The ancient Greeks classified matter by physical properties. They reasoned that everything was made of the four substances earth, air, fire, and water.

In about 350 B.C., Aristotle made a simple classifying system of plants and animals. He grouped plants as herbs, shrubs, and trees. He grouped animals as water animals, land animals, and air animals. Later, the Swedish naturalist Karl von Linné (Linnaeus) developed a classification system based on the idea of species.

ANNOTATION KEY

❶ Answers will vary but should indicate a disadvantage with phase classification. (Applying concepts)

❷ Produce is classified by the type of plant from which it comes. Yarn is classified by color and texture to make it easy for customers to find the yarn they want. (Classifying objects)

❸ Heterogeneous and homogeneous matter (Interpreting illustrations)

❹ In physical properties (melting point, boiling point, density, etc.) and in chemical properties (water does not burn, while gasoline burns explosively) (Applying facts)

❺ No. Water and mercury are very different chemically, even though they are both liquids at room temperature. (Applying concepts)

❶ Thinking Skill: Observing

❷ Thinking Skill: Classifying matter

---

clude bun, meat, onion, lettuce, cheese, and other solids.)
• **Which super cheeseburger ingredients are liquids?** (Answers should include mustard, ketchup, meat juice, mayonnaise, and other liquids.)
• **Which super cheeseburger ingredients are homogeneous?** (Although students may be reluctant to predict, lead them to suggest mustard, ketchup, mayonnaise, and other homogeneous substances.)

• **Which super cheeseburger ingredients are heterogeneous?** (Students probably will suggest pickle, meat, onion, and bun.)

Skills Development
Skill: Interpreting charts
Have students observe Figure 3-2. Refer to the chart as you discuss the scientific scheme of classification.
• **What are the two major subdivisions of matter?** (heterogeneous and homogeneous)
• **What can you infer about all heterogeneous matter?** (Heterogeneous matter is always a mixture.)

3-2 MIXTURES

SECTION PREVIEW 3-2

The matter in most mixtures is heterogeneous. The substances in a heterogeneous mixture are not chemically combined. Each substance keeps its own identity and most of its own properties. A substance in a mixture can be present in any amount and can be separated.

Solutions are a special type of mixture. A solution is a homogeneous mixture that has constant makeup and properties throughout the entire solution. A solution is formed when one substance dissolves in another. Although the solution as a whole is homogeneous, each of the substances keeps its own individual properties and can be separated, as in a mixture. Solutions can be liquid, solid, or gas. All solutions have two important properties: the particles are evenly spread out and are not large enough to be seen.

PERFORMANCE OBJECTIVES 3-2

1. **Describe the properties of mixtures.**
2. **Identify relationships among mixtures.**
3. **Relate facts about mixtures.**
4. **Distinguish between homogeneous and heterogeneous mixtures.**

SCIENCE TERMS 3-2

mixture p. 65
homogeneous mixture p. 67
heterogeneous mixture p. 67
solution p. 67
alloy p. 68

Figure 3–4 *These gold nuggets from the San Francisco Mint are made of pure gold (left). The granite boulder from Mount Stuart in Washington is made of several different minerals (right). How would you classify each object?* ❷

The rock granite is heterogeneous because granite is composed of several different minerals, each having characteristic properties. Soil is heterogeneous matter, as is a super cheeseburger and cereal with raisins! Can you name some heterogeneous materials? ❶

SECTION REVIEW

1. According to makeup, what are the four classes of matter?
2. What is homogeneous matter? Heterogeneous matter?
3. Classify the following materials as either homogeneous or heterogeneous: sausage pizza; chocolate chip cookies; air inside a balloon; glass of water.
4. Why is it more useful to classify matter according to makeup rather than according to phase?
5. Most milk sold in stores is homogenized. What do you think this means?

Section Objective

To describe the properties and types of mixtures

3–2 Mixtures

Look at the piece of granite in Figure 3–4. Granite is heterogeneous matter. It is made of different minerals mixed together. You can see some ❶ of these minerals—quartz, mica, and feldspar—when you look at the granite. Sand is also heterogeneous matter. When you pick up a handful of sand,

---

3-1 (continued)

Skills Development

Skill: Classifying objects

Divide the class into groups of 4 to 6. Place ten or more items (such as typing paper, pencil, crayon, rubber ball, marble, glass, cup, manila folder, string, ribbon, rubber band, and paper clip) in a paper bag for each group. Have each group classify the items. Discuss the classification

schemes by asking questions like the following.
• **In what group did you classify the typing paper?** (Accept all answers. Some students may have classified it in "something to write on" and others in "things that can be cut."
• **In what group did you classify the rubber band?** (Accept all answers. Students may classify it into "things that hold other things," "things made of rubber," or "things that stretch.")

Continue by asking questions about how the other items were classified. Point out that things can be classified in many different ways and in many different groups or classes.

Section Review 3-1

1. Elements, compounds, mixtures, and solutions
2. Homogeneous: matter that has identical properties throughout; het-

you see dark and light grains mixed together. Granite, sand, concrete, and salad dressing are examples of matter that consist of several substances mixed together.

Matter that consists of two or more substances mixed together but not chemically combined is called a mixture. A **mixture** is a combination of substances. Each of the substances making up a mixture is a homogeneous substance. For example, granite is a mixture of minerals. It does not have the same properties throughout. But the minerals that make up granite are homogeneous substances. Every piece of quartz has the same properties as every other piece of quartz. This is true of mica and feldspar also.

Properties of Mixtures

The substances in a mixture are not chemically combined. The substances keep their separate identities and most of their own properties. When sugar ❷ and water are mixed, the water is still a colorless liquid. The sugar still keeps its property of sweetness

Figure 3–5 *Although it may look completely black, the sand on Kaimu beach in Hawaii contains some particles of white sand. What other mixtures can you identify in this photograph?* ❸

TIE-IN/ART

Paint is a familiar fluid used by artists. Paint is usually a mixture of a liquid and finely powdered pigment.

Sometimes the liquid in paint is only a wetting agent (such as water or thinner) used to make the pigment brushable. The liquid evaporates, and the dried pigment remains as a pure substance on the painted surface. Watercolors and tempera are usually mixed only with a wetting agent. Although this kind of paint sometimes *looks* homogeneous, it is really a heterogeneous mixture.

Sometimes the liquid in paint is a wetting agent plus other liquid chemicals that cause the dry paint to have a hard, shiny surface. The liquid part of the paint is usually a homogeneous solution. When the pigment is added, the paint becomes a heterogeneous mixture that can look as if it is homogeneous. An example of this kind of paint is artists' oil paints, a combination of linseed oil and solvent in solution added to a powdered pigment. When the wetting agent evaporates, the surface contains a heterogeneous mixture of pigment and a dull or shiny hardening substance.

Figure 3–6 *By combining powdered iron (top) with powdered sulfur (center), an iron-sulfur mixture is formed. What physical property of iron is being used to separate the mixture (bottom)?* ❶

even though it is dissolved in the water. Your sense of taste tells you this is so.

Substances in a mixture may change in physical appearance when they dissolve. Some physical properties of the mixture such as melting point and boiling point also may change. But the substances do not change in chemical composition. In the sugar-water mixture, the same particles of water and sugar are present after the mixing as before it. No new chemical substances have been formed.

The substances in a mixture can be present in any amount. A salt-and-pepper mixture can be one-third salt and two-thirds pepper, or one-half salt and one-half pepper. You can mix in lots of sugar or only a little in your iced tea. But in both cases, the mixture is still iced tea.

Because the substances in a mixture retain their original properties, they can be separated out by simple physical means. Look at Figure 3–6. A mixture has been made by combining powdered iron with powdered sulfur. Iron is black and sulfur is ❶ yellow. The mixture has a grayish color, although iron and sulfur particles are clearly visible. Because iron is attracted to a magnet and sulfur is not, iron can be separated from the mixture by holding a strong magnet near the mixture.

All the methods used to separate substances in a mixture are based on the physical properties of the substances making up the mixture. No chemical reactions are involved. What physical property of iron made it possible to separate it from sulfur in the iron-sulfur mixture? What are some other physical properties that might be used to separate mixtures? ❷

Types of Mixtures

Both concrete and stainless steel are mixtures. Concrete consists of pieces of rock, sand, and cement. Stainless steel is a mixture of chromium and iron. From your experience, you may know that stainless steel seems "better mixed" than concrete. You cannot see individual particles of chromium and iron in the steel, but particles of rock, sand, and cement are visible in concrete. Mixtures are classified according to how "well mixed" they are.

66

3-2 (continued)

Content Development
Point out the following.

Mixtures are two or more substances *not* chemically combined. Mixtures can be in any of the four phases—solid, liquid, gas, or plasma. Mixtures can also be combinations of different phases.

Heterogeneous mixtures *do not* have the same appearance through-

out. Heterogeneous mixtures can be in any of the four phases—solid, liquid, gas, or plasma. Heterogeneous mixtures can be combinations of different phases.

Homogeneous mixtures *seem* to have the same appearance throughout the mixture. Homogeneous mixtures can be in any of the four phases—solid, liquid, gas, or plasma. Homogeneous mixtures can be combinations of different phases.

Solutions are a special kind of homogeneous mixture that actually have the same makeup throughout the mixture. The substances in a solution are *not* chemically combined and can be separated. Solutions can be solids dissolved in liquids, liquids dissolved in liquids, gases dissolved in liquids, or gases dissolved in gases. The key to knowing that a substance is a solution is the term "dissolved."

HETEROGENEOUS MIXTURE A mixture that does not appear to be the same throughout is said to be heterogeneous. A **heterogeneous mixture** is the "least mixed" of mixtures. The particles are large enough to be seen and to separate from the mixture. Concrete is a heterogeneous mixture.

Not all heterogeneous mixtures contain solid particles. Shake up some pebbles or sand in water to make a solid-liquid mixture. This mixture is easily separated just by letting it stand. Oil and vinegar ❷ make up a liquid-liquid heterogeneous mixture. When the mixture is well shaken, large drops of oil spread throughout the vinegar. This mixture, too, will separate when allowed to stand.

HOMOGENEOUS MIXTURE A mixture that appears to be the same throughout is said to be homogeneous. A **homogeneous mixture** is "well mixed." The particles of the mixture are very small, not easily recognized, and do not settle when the mixture is allowed to stand. Stainless steel is a homogeneous mixture.

Solutions: Special Homogeneous Mixtures

A **solution** (suh-LOO-shuhn) is a type of homogeneous mixture formed when one substance dissolves in another. You might say that a solution is the "best mixed" of all mixtures. You are probably

Figure 3–7 *This gold miner in Finland is separating heavy pieces of gold from rock, sand, and dirt by shaking the mixture in a pan of water (left). The gold will settle to the bottom of the pan. Salt water is a mixture of various salts and water. When the water evaporates, deposits of salt, such as these in Mono Lake, California, are left behind (right).*

TIE-IN/LIFE and EARTH SCIENCE

The composition of mixtures is studied in all of the sciences. Life science is interested in mixtures in plants, animals, and the human body. Life scientists also study the mixtures of food that keep our body healthy and mixtures that change our environment. Earth science studies mixtures such as types of soil, layering of rocks in the earth's crust, and deposits on the ocean floor.

TIE-IN/COOKING and HOME ECONOMICS

Mixtures are easily seen in the kitchen. Every soup or stew is a mixture of various foods. When we add milk to cereal, we make a mixture. Butter and jelly on toast is a mixture.

Skills Development

Skill: Classifying matter

Have students look around the classroom and list the different mixtures they observe. (Additional mixtures might be observed at home.) Each material should be discussed and analyzed carefully to determine whether it is homogeneous, heterogeneous, a pure substance, a mixture, and/or a solution. Many substances may be listed, but the following will be helpful.

plaster: homogeneous solid mixture

tap water: homogeneous liquid mixture (contains some dirt or particles)

distilled water: homogeneous pure substance

wood: heterogeneous solid mixture

metal: homogeneous pure substance or homogeneous solution if an alloy

glass: homogeneous solid mixture

pure air: homogeneous gas solution of nitrogen, oxygen, water vapor, etc.

regular air (with dust): homogeneous mixture

slate chalkboard: homogeneous pure substance

particle chalkboard: homogeneous solid mixture

chalk: homogeneous solid mixture (possibly, but rarely, a pure substance)

pure salt water: homogeneous solution

sea water: homogeneous mixture

Figure 3–8 *This "superburger" is a delicious example of a mixture, consisting of one layer of food upon another. Toothpaste is also a mixture. It is a type of mixture known as a solution. In a solution, all of the substances are evenly spread out. What type of mixture does each substance represent?* ❶

Sharpen Your Skills

Is It a Solution?
Skills: Manipulative, inferring, observing
Level: Average
Type: Hands-on
Materials: sugar, flour, powdered drink, cornstarch, instant coffee, talcum powder, soap powder, gelatin, glass, water

In this activity, students apply their knowledge of solutions to determine which substances form solutions in water. True solutions include sugar and water, powdered drink and water, instant coffee and water, gelatin and water.

Sharpen Your Skills

Is It a Solution?

1. Obtain samples of the following substances: sugar, flour, powdered drink, cornstarch, instant coffee, talcum powder, soap powder, gelatin.

2. Keeping the materials separate, crush each material into pieces of equal size.

3. Determine how much of each substance you can dissolve in samples of a given amount of water.

Using your knowledge of the properties of solutions, determine which substances formed true solutions. Also determine which substances dissolved fastest and to the greatest extent. Report your findings in a data table.

68

familiar with many different solutions. Ocean water is one example. In this solution, different salts are dissolved in water. Another example of a solution is antifreeze. Some solutions you can drink. Lemonade and tea are good examples. One very important solution keeps you alive! Air is a solution of oxygen and other gases dissolved in nitrogen.

All solutions have two important properties. One property is that the particles in a solution are not large enough to be seen. For this reason, most solutions cannot easily be separated by simple physical means.

Another property of solutions is that the particles are evenly spread out. All parts of a solution are identical. And, as in any mixture, the substances making up a solution retain most of their original properties.

Not all solutions are liquid. Solutions can be in any of the three phases—solid, liquid, or gas. Metal solutions called **alloys** are examples of solids dissolved in solids. Gold jewelry is actually a solid solution of gold and copper. Brass is an alloy of copper and zinc. Sterling silver contains small amounts of copper in solution with silver. Stainless steel is an ❶ alloy of chromium and iron. You may find it interesting to learn about the makeup of other alloys, such as pewter, bronze, and solder. How do you think alloys are made? In Chapter 9, you will learn more about the nature of solutions.

SECTION REVIEW

1. What is a mixture? What are three properties of a mixture?
2. How is a heterogeneous mixture different from a homogeneous mixture?
3. What is a solution? What are two properties of a solution?
4. Describe how you would separate salt from water in a saltwater mixture. What physical properties of the substances are you using to separate the mixture?

3–3 Elements

In the previous sections you learned that according to its makeup, matter is classified as homogeneous or heterogeneous. And you also learned about one type of heterogeneous matter—mixtures. Now you will find out about the two types of homogeneous matter.

Homogeneous matter is also known as a **pure substance.** A pure substance is made of only one kind of material and has definite properties. A pure substance is the same throughout. All the particles in a pure substance are exactly the same. Iron, aluminum, water, sugar, and table salt are examples of pure substances. So is the oxygen you breathe. A sample taken from any of these substances is identical to any other sample taken from that substance. ②
For instance, a drop of pure water is the same—whether it comes from Arizona, Australia, or Antarctica.

Elements are the simplest pure substance. An **element** cannot be changed into simpler substances by heating or by any chemical process. The particles making up an element are in their simplest form. Suppose you melt a piece of iron by adding heat energy to it. You may think that you have changed

Figure 3–9 The molten stainless steel being poured from the vat is a solution of iron and chromium, known as an alloy. What type of mixture is stainless steel? ③

3-3 ELEMENTS

SECTION PREVIEW 3-3

Homogeneous matter is a pure substance. A pure substance is made of only one kind of matter with a definite chemical composition. A pure substance is the same throughout.

Elements are the simplest type of pure substances. An element cannot be changed into simpler substances by heating or by any chemical process. An element is made up of the same kind of atoms. An atom is the smallest particle of an element that has the properties of that element. Atoms are the basic building blocks of all matter.

PERFORMANCE OBJECTIVES 3-3

1. Explain why homogeneous matter is a pure substance.
2. Explain why elements are pure substances.
3. Define an atom as the smallest particle of an element that has the properties of the element.
4. Name 10 elements and write the chemical symbol for each.

SCIENCE TERMS 3-3

pure substance p. 69
element p. 69
atom p. 70
chemical symbol p. 70

TEACHER DEMONSTRATION

Show the class a square sheet of aluminum foil. Say that aluminum is a homogeneous pure substance. Tear the foil in half and give each half to a student. Have students repeat this procedure until each student has one small piece of foil. Have each student tear the foil into the smallest possible pieces. Tell students that if they could tear the foil into the smallest pieces that still had the properties of aluminum, each piece would be an aluminum atom.

- **Copper is an element that is a homogeneous pure substance. What would we have is we cut a copper wire into the smallest pieces that still had the properties of copper?** (Students should respond by saying copper atoms.)

TIE-IN/GOVERNMENT

Several years ago, the U.S. Postal Service started to abbreviate the names of all the states with two-letter symbols, for example TX for Texas, MA for Massachusetts, NY for New York, WI for Wisconsin, and CA for California. Have students list some of the other states and their symbols.

FACTS AND FIGURES

In the earth's crust, oceans, and atmosphere are found 92 elements. These elements are known as the "natural" elements. Only eight of these elements are found in the earth's crust. Oxygen makes up almost half and silicon about a quarter. Aluminum, iron, calcium, magnesium, sodium, and potassium make up 24 per cent. Carbon, which is fundamental to all living things, is present in less than 0.1%.

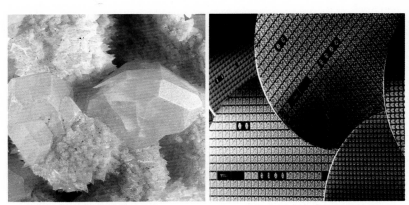

Figure 3–10 *Elements are the simplest type of pure substance. These yellow crystals from Arigento, Sicily, are made of the element sulfur (left). The computer chips are made from the element silicon (right). What other objects can you think of that are made of only one kind of element?* ❶

Figure 3–11 *In this photograph, you can see solid iodine crystals at the top of the beaker changing directly to iodine vapor. The gaseous iodine is formed by dropping the solid iodine crystals into a heated glass beaker. During this phase change has any new or simpler substance been formed?* ❷

the iron into a simpler substance. But the liquid you now have still contains only iron particles. True, the iron has changed phase—from solid to liquid. But it is still iron. No new or simpler substance has been formed.

Elements and Atoms

The smallest particle of an element that has the properties of that element is called an **atom.** An atom is the basic building block of matter. All elements are made of atoms. Atoms of the same element are alike. Atoms of different elements are different.

Scientists now know that an atom is made of even smaller particles. These particles, however, do not have the properties of the elements they make up. You will learn more about the structure of an atom in Chapter 4.

Chemical Symbols

Elements are represented by **chemical symbols.** Chemical symbols are a shorthand way of representing the elements. Each symbol consists of one or two

70

3-3 (continued)

Content Development

Point out that an element is made of only one kind of atom. Atoms from different elements are different. Like people, every element has its own special name.

- **What are some of the shorthand names (or nicknames) of your friends?** (Accept all answers.)

- **What are the real names?** (Accept all answers.)

Explain that the names of elements can be represented in a short-hand method. The shorthand name for an element is called a symbol. Lead students to infer shorthand names with the following questions.

- **What is an atom?** (An atom is the smallest particle of an element that has the properties of the element *or* Atoms are the building blocks of all

matter.)

- **What is a chemical symbol?** (a shorthand way of representing an element.)

- **If the element's name is oxygen, what logical shorthand symbol would you use?** (Students should answer O.)

- **If the element's name is nitrogen, what logical shorthand symbol would you use?** (Student should answer N.)

Point out that scientists often use the Latin name of an element to

letters, usually taken from the element's name. The symbol for the element oxygen is O. The symbol for hydrogen is H; for carbon, C. The symbol for aluminum is Al; and for chlorine, Cl. You should note that when two letters are used in a symbol, the first letter is always capitalized but the second letter is never capitalized. Two letters are needed for an element's symbol when the first letter of that element's name has already been used as the symbol for another element. For example, the symbol for carbon is C, for calcium it is Ca, and for copper it is Cu.

Scientists often use the Latin name of an element to create its symbol. The symbol for gold is Au. The Latin name for gold is *aurum*. The symbol for silver is Ag, from the Latin word *argentum*. The Latin word for iron is *ferrum*. So the symbol for this element is Fe. Mercury's symbol is Hg, from the Latin

CAREER   *Assayer*

HELP WANTED: CHEMICAL ASSAYER to determine the gold and silver content of rock samples. College degree in chemistry required. Accuracy and attention to detail essential.

For several weeks the prospectors work under the blazing sun, examining the landscape, collecting rock samples, and drilling into sun-baked hillsides. They hope to discover sites containing valuable traces of gold, silver, or other minerals.

The amounts of valuable metals in the prospectors' samples are usually so small that they can be measured only with special equipment. So after rock samples are collected from possible mining sites, they are sent to a laboratory to be tested by an **assayer** (a-SAY-er). The assayer determines the exact mineral content of the sample. The specific properties of elements allow the assayer to separate valuable metals from other elements in the sample.

Many assayers work for mining companies. Others work for the government. Some as-

sayers specialize in testing and analyzing precious metals, such as gold and silver. They may work under the direction of the U.S. Mint.

People who want to become assayers should major in chemistry in college. They should be able to concentrate on detail and work independently. To learn more about this career, write to the American Society for Metals, Chapter and Membership Development, Metals Park, OH 44073.

71

create the symbol.

Skills Development

Skill: Relating concepts

Ask students to consider the following question.

• **What are some of the things we use everyday that we cannot see?** (Accept all logical answers, but lead students to suggest that we cannot see gases such as oxygen, water vapor, carbon dioxide, and nitrogen that are in the air.)

Point out to students that we cannot see air because it is invisible. We know air is there because we can breathe it and feel it when the wind is blowing.

• **What other invisible gases do we know exist?** (Students will probably suggest the fumes from a car.)

Motivation

Discuss the following question.

• **How do we use elements in our**

lives? (Accept all logical answers.)

Have students develop lists of common elements, their symbols, and how they are used. Examples:

Cl—chlorine in bleach
Hg—mercury in a thermometer
Ne—neon in lights
Ni—nickel in coins
Cu—copper in wire
O—oxygen for torches or in a hospital
Ag—silver for jewelry
Pt—platinum for mouth braces
Au—gold for tooth repair
He—helium in balloons

Students might gather pictures of elements for a bulletin board display of items made from specific elements.

Enrichment

Some students may wish to do library research on elements found or mined in their state.

Some students could do library research to find out how elements are used to manufacture materials in their state.

3-4 COMPOUNDS

SECTION PREVIEW 3-4

An element is a pure substance made up of only one kind of atom. The name of each element can be represented by a chemical symbol. Compounds are pure substances consisting of two or more elements chemically combined in a definite composition. When two or more atoms chemically combine, a molecule is formed. A molecule can be a combination of atoms of different elements or the same element. A molecule is the smallest particle of a compound that has the properties of that compound.

Names of compounds are represented by a combination of chemical symbols that shows the number of each kind of atoms in the compound. A description of a chemical reaction using symbols and formulas is called a chemical equation.

PERFORMANCE OBJECTIVES 3-4

1. **Explain why compounds are pure substances.**
2. **Write a chemical formula for common compounds.**
3. **Explain a balanced chemical equation.**
4. **Write a balanced equation.**

SCIENCE TERMS 3-4

compound p. 73
molecule p. 73
chemical formula p. 74
subscript p. 75
chemical equation p. 76
coefficient p. 77

COMMON ELEMENTS

Name	Symbol	Name	Symbol	Name	Symbol
Aluminum	Al	Hydrogen	H	Oxygen	O
Bromine	Br	Iodine	I	Phosphorus	P
Calcium	Ca	Iron	Fe	Potassium	K
Carbon	C	Lead	Pb	Silicon	Si
Chlorine	Cl	Lithium	Li	Silver	Ag
Chromium	Cr	Magnesium	Mg	Sodium	Na
Copper	Cu	Mercury	Hg	Sulfur	S
Fluorine	F	Neon	Ne	Tin	Sn
Gold	Au	Nickel	Ni	Uranium	U
Helium	He	Nitrogen	N	Zinc	Zn

Figure 3–12 This table shows the chemical symbols for some of the most common elements. Why is Fe the symbol for iron? ❶

name *hydrargyrum*. The table in Figure 3–12 lists some common elements and their symbols.

SECTION REVIEW

1. What is a pure substance? Why are elements pure substances?
2. What is an atom? How do atoms of the same elements compare? Of different elements?
3. Write the chemical symbols for aluminum, calcium, iron, sulfur, sodium, and helium.

3–4 Compounds

The simplest type of pure substance is an element. But not all pure substances are elements. Water and table salt, for example, are pure substances. They are made of only one kind of material having definite properties. But water and table salt are not elements. They can be broken down into

72

3-3 (continued)

Section Review 3-3

1. A pure substance is made of only one kind of material having definite properties throughout. Elements are the simplest type of pure substance since they are made of only one kind of atom.
2. An atom is the smallest particle of an element that has the properties of that element. It is the basic building block of matter. Atoms of the same element are alike, while atoms of different elements are different.
4. Al, Ca, Fe, S, Na, He

TEACHING STRATEGY 3-4

Motivation

Hold up a clean, shiny, iron nail and a rusty iron nail. Conduct an open-ended discussion of the two nails.

- **How are these nails alike? Differ-ent?** (Answers will vary, but likenesses will probably include solid and iron, while differences will include shiny–dull, rusty–smooth.)
- **What is under the rust?** (Pure iron is under the rust.)
- **Which nail is a pure homogeneous element?** (The shiny iron nail is a pure homogeneous element made of iron or Fe.)
- **Which nail is a heterogeneous substance?** (The rusty nail is a hetero-

Figure 3–13 *The element sodium is often stored in kerosene because it reacts explosively with water (top). The element chlorine is a poisonous gas (center). The compound formed from sodium and chlorine, called sodium chloride, is a substance necessary for good health (bottom). What is the common name for sodium chloride?* ❷

simpler substances. Water breaks down into the elements hydrogen and oxygen. Salt breaks down into the elements sodium and chlorine. Thus water and salt, like many other pure substances, are made of more than one element.

Pure substances that are made of more than one element are called compounds. A compound is two or more elements chemically combined. Sugar is a compound made of the elements carbon, hydrogen, ❶ and oxygen. Carbon dioxide, ammonia, baking soda, and TNT are also compounds. Can you name some other familiar compounds? ❸

Unlike elements, compounds can be broken down into simpler substances. Heating is one way of separating some compounds into their elements. ❷ The compound copper sulfide can be separated into the elements copper and sulfur in this way.

Electric energy is often used to break down compounds that do not separate upon heating. By passing an electric current through water, the elements hydrogen and oxygen are obtained. What elements would you get by passing an electric current through melted salt? ❹

In general, the properties of a compound are very different from the properties of the elements in it. Salt is a white crystalline solid used to flavor food and needed for good health. But what is salt made of? One element in salt is sodium, a silvery metal that reacts explosively with water. The other element is chlorine, a poisonous greenish gas. Neither element in its pure form can be used by your body. Yet they combine to form salt, or sodium chloride, a substance you cannot and probably would not want to live without.

Compounds and Molecules

Most compounds are made of **molecules** (MAHL-uh-kyoolz). A molecule is made of two or more atoms chemically bonded together. A molecule is the

73

PURE SUBSTANCES - one kind of molecule		MIXTURES - more than one kind of molecule	
Element - one kind of atom		Heterogeneous - do not appear the same throughout	
Compound - more than one kind of atom		Homogeneous - appear the same throughout	

Figure 3–14 *Matter can be classified as either a pure substance or a mixture. Into which group does water fit? Where would you place ocean water?* ❶

smallest particle of a compound that has all the properties of that compound.

Water is a compound. A molecule of water is made up of 2 atoms of hydrogen chemically bonded to 1 atom of oxygen. One molecule of water has all the properties of a glass of water, a bucket of water, or a pool of water. If a molecule of water were broken down into atoms of its elements, would the atoms have the same properties as the molecule?

Just as all atoms of a certain element are alike, all molecules of a compound are alike. Each molecule of ammonia, for example, is like every other. Because it is made of only one kind of molecule, a compound is the same throughout. So compounds, like elements, are pure substances.

Figure 3–15 *As you can see from this diagram, molecules are made of two or more atoms chemically bonded together. Here you see a water molecule and an ammonia molecule. What are the chemical formulas for these two compounds?* ❷

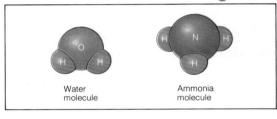

Water molecule   Ammonia molecule

Chemical Formulas

Combinations of chemical symbols are called **chemical formulas.** Most chemical formulas represent compounds. For example, ammonia is a compound made of the elements nitrogen and hydrogen, N and H. A molecule of ammonia contains

Sharpen Your Skills

Classifying Common Objects
Skills: Classifying, inferring, manipulative, observing
Level: Average–Enriched
Type: Hands-on
Materials: sugar, salt water, copper wire, taco shell, pencil eraser

In this activity, students must devise simple tests to determine whether common substances are mixtures, solutions, elements, or compounds. Check student charts to ensure accuracy. You may want to add other common materials to the list from which students choose.

Sharpen Your Skills

Classifying Common Objects

1. Obtain samples of the following materials for observation: sugar, salt water, copper wire, taco shell, pencil eraser.

2. Use simple physical tests to determine which substances are mixtures, solutions, elements, or compounds.

3. Present your observations in a chart.

3-4 (continued)

Skills Development
Skill: Interpreting illustrations
Discuss the drawings of the molecules in Figures 3-15 and 3-16. Ask questions like the following.
• **What is the formula for a molecule of water?** (H_2O)
• **How many atoms of hydrogen are in one molecule of water?** (two)
• **How many atoms of oxygen are in one molecule of water?** (one)
• **How many atoms of hydrogen are in one molecule of ammonia?** (three)
• **How many atoms of nitrogen are in one molecule of ammonia?** (one)
• **How many atoms of hydrogen occur in one hydrogen molecule?** (two)
• **How many atoms of oxygen occur in one oxygen molecule?** (two)
• **What is the formula for one molecule of oxygen?** (O_2)
• **How many atoms of nitrogen occur in one nitrogen molecule?** (two)
• **What is the formula for one molecule of hydrogen?** (H_2)
• **How many atoms of chlorine occur in one chlorine molecule?** (two)
• **What is the formula for one molecule of chlorine?** (Cl_2)

Content Development
Relate the text ideas to the shiny and rusty nails. Tell the class that Fe_2O_3 is the chemical formula for red rust.

1 atom of nitrogen and 3 atoms of hydrogen. The formula for ammonia is NH_3. The formula for rubbing alcohol is C_3H_7OH. What elements make up this compound? How about silver nitrate, $AgNO_3$? ❸

Sometimes a formula represents a molecule of an element, not a compound. For example, the symbol for the element oxygen is O. But oxygen occurs naturally as a molecule containing 2 atoms of oxygen bonded together. So the formula for a molecule of oxygen is O_2. Some other gases that exist only in pairs of atoms are hydrogen, H_2, nitrogen, N_2, fluorine, F_2, and chlorine, Cl_2. Remember that the symbols for the elements just listed are the letters only. The formulas are the letters with the small number 2 at the lower right.

When writing a chemical formula, you use the symbol of each element in the compound. You also use small numbers called **subscripts.** Subscripts are placed to the lower right of the symbols. A subscript ❷ gives the number of atoms of the element in the compound. When there is only 1 atom of an element, the subscript 1 is not written. It is understood to be 1.

Carbon dioxide is a compound of the elements carbon and oxygen. Its formula is CO_2. By looking at the formula, you can tell that every molecule is

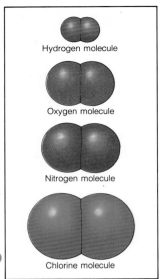

Hydrogen molecule

Oxygen molecule

Nitrogen molecule

Chlorine molecule

Figure 3–16 *Some elements are found in nature as molecules consisting of two atoms of that element. Hydrogen, oxygen, nitrogen, and chlorine are examples of such elements. What is the chemical formula for a molecule of each of these elements?* ❹

Figure 3–17 *This table shows the common properties of elements, compounds, and mixtures. Which of the three substances does not have the same properties throughout?* ❺

PROPERTIES OF ELEMENTS, COMPOUNDS, AND MIXTURES

Elements	Compounds	Mixtures
Made up of only one kind of atom	Made up of more than one kind of atom	Made up of more than one kind of molecule
Cannot be broken down by chemical means	Can be broken down by chemical means	Can be separated by physical means
Has same properties as atoms making it up	Has different properties from elements making it up	Has same properties as substances making it up
Has same properties throughout	Has same properties throughout	Has different properties throughout

BACKGROUND INFORMATION
You may wish to introduce and practice the rules for naming binary compounds.

1. A metal and a nonmetal: The name of the metal appears first and is unchanged; the name of the nonmetal follows, but its ending is changed to *-ide* (e.g., $BaCl_2$ is barium chloride).

2. Metals with more than one oxidation state and a nonmetal: A Roman numeral indicating the oxidation state of the metal is written in parentheses after the name of the metal (e.g., $FeCl_2$ is iron (II) chloride).

3. Covalent compounds made up of elements that form multiple compounds with each other: Prefixes are used before the name of the first and/or second element indicating the number of atoms of that element. The element farther to the right in the periodic table appears second and has the *-ide* ending (e.g., CO is carbon monoxide).

• **Which parts of the formula Fe_2O_3 represent a compound?** (the whole formula)
• **How many atoms of iron are in the formula Fe_2O_3?** (two)
• **How many atoms of oxygen are in the formula Fe_2O_3?** (three)
• **What happened when the iron rusted?** (A chemical reaction occurred when the iron rusted.)
• **What are the numbers 2 and 3 in the formula called?** (subscripts)
• **What does the subscript 2 in Fe_2O_3 mean?** (There are two atoms of Fe or iron in the rust compound.)
• **What does the subscript 3 in Fe_2O_3 mean?** (There are three atoms of O or oxygen in the rust compound.)
• **Which parts of the rusty nail are pure homogeneous substances?** (Fe or iron is an element and Fe_2O_3 or rust is a compound. Both Fe and Fe_2O_3 are pure homogeneous substances.)

Reinforcement
Remind students that most elements exist as single atoms. However, some elements occur naturally in pairs as a twin molecule. Examples include O_2, N_2, and Cl_2.

Write Fe_2O_3 on the chalkboard and hold up the shiny and rusty nails. Discuss the formation of the rust by asking questions like the following.
• **Where did the iron (Fe) in the rust come from?** (The iron in the rust came from the iron in the nail.)
• **Where did the oxygen (O) in the rust come from?** (The oxygen came from the air.)
• **What do you think causes iron to rust?** (Answers will vary and may include materials or processes such as water, weather, acid, other rust, or chemicals. Answers should include the fact that a chemical reaction formed the rust.)
• **Which parts of the formula Fe_2O_3 represent atoms?** (The symbols Fe and O represent atoms.)
• **Which parts of the formula Fe_2O_3 represent a rust molecule?** (The rust molecule is represented by the whole formula.)

Counting Atoms
Skill: Computational
Level: Remedial
Type: Computational

In this simple computational activity, students analyze chemical formulas for the number of atoms each contains,

$NaHCO_3$: 1 sodium, 1 hydrogen, 1 carbon, and 3 oxygen atoms

$C_2H_4O_2$: 2 carbon, 4 hydrogen, and 2 oxygen atoms

$Mg(OH)_2$: 1 magnesium, 2 oxygen, and 2 hydrogen atoms

$3H_3PO_4$: 9 hydrogen, 3 potassium, and 12 oxygen atoms

BACKGROUND INFORMATION

Oxygen is abundant in the atmosphere. Oxygen combines easily with many other elements. Many important chemical reactions involve oxygen. Burning is one of these. Rusting is a slower process that cannot take place without oxygen. The process of rusting is called oxidation.

3-4 (continued)

Motivation

Place a tablespoon of baking soda into a glass. Add a teaspoon of vinegar. Ask the class questions like the following.

• **What did you observe?** (The material fizzed.)

• **What was produced?** (A gas that bubbled.)

• **How were the starting substances different from the material that was produced?** (The starting substances were a solid (baking soda) and a liquid (vinegar). A gas was produced.)

• **What evidence do we have that this was a chemical reaction?** (Something was produced that was different.)

Counting Atoms

Calculate how many atoms of each element are present in the following compounds.

$NaHCO_3$
$C_2H_4O_2$
$Mg(OH)_2$
$3H_3PO_4$

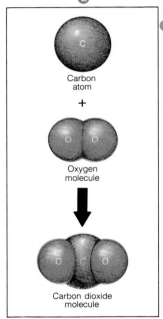

Figure 3–18 *This illustration shows the chemical reaction that occurs when carbon and oxygen combine to form carbon dioxide. What is the chemical formula for carbon dioxide?* ❷

Carbon atom

+

Oxygen molecule

Carbon dioxide molecule

Content Development

Discuss chemical equations by asking

• **What is a chemical equation?** (A chemical equation is a description of a chemical reaction using symbols and formulas).

• **What is a coefficient?** (A coefficient is a number in front of a chemical formula in a chemical equation.)

• **What does a coefficient tell you?** (A coefficient tells the number of molecules needed to balance the equation.)

made up of 1 atom of carbon, C, and 2 atoms of oxygen, O. Sulfuric acid has the formula H_2SO_4. How many hydrogen atoms, sulfur atoms, and oxygen atoms are there in a molecule of sulfuric acid? ❶

Chemical Equations

In Chapter 2 you learned that during chemical reactions, substances are changed into new and different substances through a rearrangement of their atoms. By using chemical symbols and formulas, you can describe chemical reactions.

The description of a chemical reaction using symbols and formulas is called a **chemical equation.** An equation is another example of chemical shorthand. Instead of using words to describe a chemical reaction, you can use a chemical equation.

Here is an example. When charcoal burns in a barbecue grill, carbon atoms combine with oxygen molecules in the air to form carbon dioxide:

Carbon atoms plus oxygen molecules produce carbon dioxide.

❶ By using symbols and formulas, the reaction can be written in a simpler way:

$$C + O_2 \longrightarrow CO_2$$

The symbol C represents an atom of carbon. The formula O_2 represents a molecule of oxygen. And the formula CO_2 represents a molecule of carbon dioxide. The arrow is read "yields," which is another way of saying "produces."

The chemical equation for the formation of water from the elements hydrogen and oxygen is

$$H_2 + O_2 \longrightarrow H_2O$$

Look closely at this equation. It tells you what elements are combining and what product is formed. But something is wrong. Do you know what it is? ❸

Look at the number of oxygen atoms on each side of the equation. Are they the same? On the left side of the equation there are 2 oxygen atoms. On the right side there is only 1 oxygen atom. Could 1 oxygen atom have disappeared? Scientists know that atoms are never created or destroyed in a chemical reaction. Atoms can only be rearranged. So there must be the same number of atoms of each element

Skills Development

Skill: Interpreting diagrams

Have students observe Figure 3-18. Discuss and interpret the ideas by asking the following questions.

• **How many molecules of carbon dioxide were produced by the chemical reaction?** (one)

• **How many molecules of carbon were needed to produce one molecule of carbon dioxide?** (one)

• **How many atoms of carbon were**

Figure 3–19 *During chemical reactions, substances are changed into new and different substances. The polyethylene film you see being blown into a spherical shape is the product of a complex chemical reaction (right). A more common chemical reaction occurs during cooking as eggs, butter, and other ingredients are chemically combined to make crepes (left).*

on each side of an equation. The equation must be balanced. The balanced equation for the formation of water is

$$2H_2 + O_2 \longrightarrow 2H_2O$$

Now count the atoms of each element on each side of the equation. You will find they are the same: 4 ❷ atoms of hydrogen on the left and on the right, and 2 atoms of oxygen on the left and on the right. The equation is correctly balanced.

An equation can be balanced by placing the appropriate number in front of the chemical formula. This number is called a **coefficient** (koh-uh-FIH-shuhnt). The equation now tells you that 2 molecules of hydrogen combine with 1 molecule of oxygen to produce 2 molecules of water. A balanced chemical equation is evidence of a chemical reaction.

Figure 3–20 *During the formation of water, two hydrogen molecules combine with an oxygen molecule to form two water molecules. What is the chemical equation for this reaction?* ❹

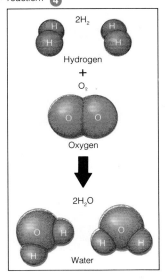

SECTION REVIEW

1. What is a compound?
2. How is a compound different from an element?
3. What is a molecule? How is a molecule of an element or compound represented?
4. What two things does a formula indicate about a compound?
5. Why must a chemical equation be balanced?
6. What three things does a chemical equation indicate about a chemical reaction?

needed to produce one molecule of carbon dioxide? (one)
• **How many atoms of oxygen were needed to produce one molecule of carbon dioxide?** (two)
• **How many molecules of oxygen were needed to produce one molecule of carbon dioxide?** (one)

Reinforcement

Have the students make a list of chemical reactions. Some students may sug-

gest that melting ice or other physical changes belong in the list. If so, review the nature of both physical and chemical changes.

Enrichment

Students may make observations of chemical changes in their everyday life and report on them to the class.

Section Review 3-4

1. A pure substance made of more than one element
2. A compound can be broken down into simpler substances.
3. Two or more atoms chemically bonded together. It is represented by a chemical formula.
4. The elements and number of atoms of each element that make up the compound
5. Atoms cannot be created or destroyed, so the same number of atoms of each element must appear on each side of an equation.
6. The substances that enter the reaction, the substances formed by the reaction, and the number of molecules of each substance

LABORATORY INVESTIGATION MAKING MODELS OF CHEMICAL REACTIONS

BEFORE THE LAB

1. **Gather all materials at least one day prior to the investigation. You should have enough supplies to meet your class needs, assuming 6 students per group.**

2. **Plan to do Part A during one class period and allow the coloring to dry overnight. Do Part B during the next class period.**

3. **Prepare each color by adding 30 mL color to 500 mL water. Orange can be made by mixing equal parts of red and yellow. Purple can be made by mixing equal parts of red and blue.**

4. **Prepare two coloring stations for each color. Each station should have marshmallows, 250 mL of color, paper towels and toothpicks on a tray. Each team will need a tray covered with waxed paper.**

5. **Prepare a place for the trays of colored marshmallows to dry overnight. If you have several sections, you may want to have each section do the coloring on a different day to be sure you have enough storage space for the marshmallows to dry.**

6. **Some students are bound to eat the marshmallows. One way of avoiding this problem is to sprinkle some powdered alum onto the marshmallows. Alum has a strong, undesirable, bitter, and mouth-puckering taste. Powdered alum is available from most grocery store spice sections and is used in canning pickles. Be sure to warn students that the marshmallows have been contaminated with alum and are *not edible* (students will find this out very fast if they taste the marshmallows).**

PRE-LAB DISCUSSION

Before doing the coloring in Part A, demonstrate how to color the marshmallows by inserting a toothpick into a marshmallow, dipping it into the color, and placing the marshmallow (with pick) onto the waxed paper to dry. Tell the teams to label their trays for easy retrieval.

Remind teams to keep each colored marshmallow separate from the others so that the colors do not mix.

Remind students to wash their hands *thoroughly* with soap to remove all traces of the alum.

Before doing Part B, tell the class that they will be making models to help them understand chemical reactions.

Making Models of Chemical Reactions

Problem

How do atoms and molecules of elements and compounds combine in chemical reactions?

Materials (per group)

toothpicks
red, yellow, green, blue, purple (red-blue), orange (yellow-red) food coloring
25 large marshmallows

Procedure

A. Making Marshmallow Atoms

1. Prepare marshmallow atoms by applying food coloring as follows:

   N (nitrogen)—red (2)
   H (hydrogen)—blue (6)
   Cu (copper)—green (4)
   O (oxygen)—yellow (6)
   K (potassium)—orange (2)
   Cl (chlorine)—purple (2)

2. Let the marshmallows dry for two hours.

B. Assembling the Marshmallow Molecules

1. Using two red marshmallows and a toothpick, make a molecule of N_2. Then make a molecule of H_2 using blue marshmallows.

2. Ammonia, NH_3, is used in cleaning solutions and fertilizers. A molecule of ammonia contains 1 nitrogen atom and 3 hydrogen atoms. Using the marshmallow molecules that you made in step 1, produce an ammonia molecule of nitrogen and hydrogen. You may use as many nitrogen and hydrogen molecules as you need to make ammonia molecules as long as you do not have any atoms left over. Note: Hydrogen and nitrogen must start out as molecules consisting of two atoms each. Now balance the equation that produces ammonia.

   $$\_\_\_ N_2 + \_\_\_ H_2 \longrightarrow \_\_\_ NH_3$$

3. Using two green marshmallows for copper and one yellow marshmallow for oxygen, prepare copper oxide, Cu_2O. Using a white marshmallow for carbon, manipulate the molecules to represent and balance this equation, which produces metallic copper.

   $$\_\_ Cu_2O + \_\_ C \rightarrow \_\_ Cu + \_\_ CO_2$$

4. Using orange for potassium, purple for chlorine, and white for oxygen, assemble potassium chlorate, $KClO_3$.

5. The decomposition of $KClO_3$ is a way to produce O_2. Take apart your $KClO_3$ to make KCl and O_2. You may need more than one molecule of $KClO_3$ to do this.

Observations

1. How many molecules of N_2 and H_2 are needed to produce two molecules of NH_3?

2. How many molecules of copper are produced from two molecules of Cu_2O?

3. How many molecules of O_2 are produced from two molecules of $KClO_3$?

Conclusions

1. Which substances that you made are elements? Which are compounds?

2. What is the difference between an atom of nitrogen and a molecule of nitrogen?

3. If you had to make five molecules of ammonia, NH_3, how many red marshmallows would you need? How many blue marshmallows?

4. What three important facts about a chemical reaction does a chemical equation provide?

5. What happens to atoms in a chemical reaction?

SKILL DEVELOPMENT

Students will use the following skills while completing this investigation.

1. Manipulative
2. Comparing
3. Relating
4. Applying
5. Inferring

SUMMARY

3–1 Classes of Matter

❏ Matter is classified according to makeup as elements, compounds, mixtures, or solutions.

❏ Homogeneous matter has identical properties throughout. Heterogeneous matter has different properties throughout.

3–2 Mixtures

❏ A mixture is composed of two or more substances mixed together but not chemically combined.

❏ The substances that make up a mixture keep their separate identities and most of their own properties.

❏ The substances in a mixture can be present in any amount.

❏ The substances in a mixture can be separated by simple physical means.

❏ A mixture that does not appear to be the same throughout is a heterogeneous mixture. It is the "least mixed" of mixtures.

❏ A mixture that appears to be the same throughout is a homogeneous mixture. It is a "well mixed" mixture.

❏ A solution is a type of homogeneous mixture formed when one substance dissolves in another. It is the "best mixed" of mixtures.

❏ The particles in a solution are not large enough to be seen. So most solutions cannot easily be separated.

❏ Alloys are metal solutions in which solids are dissolved in solids.

3–3 Elements

❏ A pure substance is homogeneous matter. It is made of only one kind of material and has definite properties.

❏ Elements are the simplest type of pure substances. They cannot be broken down into simpler substances without losing their identity.

❏ Elements are made of atoms, which are the building blocks of matter.

❏ Elements are represented by chemical symbols.

3–4 Compounds

❏ Compounds are two or more elements chemically combined.

❏ Compounds can be broken down into simpler substances.

❏ Most compounds are made of molecules. A molecule is made of two or more atoms chemically bonded together.

❏ A molecule is the smallest particle of a compound that has all the properties of that compound.

❏ A chemical formula, which is a combination of chemical symbols, usually represents a molecule of a compound. For certain elements, the chemical formula represents a molecule of the element.

❏ A subscript gives the number of atoms of the element in the compound.

❏ A chemical equation describes a chemical reaction.

VOCABULARY

Define each term in a complete sentence.

alloy	coefficient	heterogeneous mixture	mixture
atom	compound		molecule
chemical equation	element	homogeneous matter	pure substance
chemical formula	heterogeneous matter	homogeneous mixture	subscript
chemical symbol			

$$\underline{1}\ N_2 + \underline{3}\ H_2 \rightarrow \underline{2}\ NH_3$$
$$\underline{2}\ Cu_2O + 1\ C \rightarrow \underline{4}\ Cu + \underline{1}\ CO_2$$
$$\underline{2}\ KClO_3 \rightarrow \underline{2}\ KCl + \underline{3}\ O_2$$

OBSERVATIONS

1. 1 molecule of N_2 and 3 molecules of H_2
2. 4 molecules of copper
3. 3 molecules of oxygen

CONCLUSIONS

1. Elements: nitrogen, hydrogen, carbon, oxygen. Compounds: NH_3, Cu_2O, CO_2, $KClO_3$, KCl.
2. A molecule of nitrogen contains 2 atoms of the element.
3. You would need 5 red marshmallows and 15 blue marshmallows.
4. Reacting substances, products formed, and the number of atoms and molecules involved in the reaction
5. In a chemical reaction, atoms are neither created or destroyed, but they may be combined to form new products.

GOING FURTHER: ENRICHMENT

Part 1

You may want to have students construct additional models of the following molecules and then balance the equations.

$$\underline{\ \ }\ N_2 + \underline{\ \ }\ O_2 \rightarrow \underline{\ \ }\ NO$$
$$(\underline{1}\ N_2 + \underline{1}\ O_2 \rightarrow \underline{2}\ NO)$$

$$\underline{\ \ }\ KCl \rightarrow \underline{\ \ }\ K + \underline{\ \ }\ Cl_2$$
$$(\underline{2}\ KCl \rightarrow \underline{2}\ K + \underline{1}\ Cl_2)$$

$$\underline{\ \ }\ CO + \underline{\ \ }\ O_2 \rightarrow \underline{\ \ }\ CO_2$$
$$(\underline{2}\ CO + \underline{1}\ O_2 \rightarrow \underline{2}\ CO_2)$$

Part 2

Discuss how models help scientists and students to understand nature. Ask open questions like the following.

• **How do models help you understand chemical reactions?**

• **How are the marshmallow models like real atoms?**

• **How are the marshmallow models different from real atoms?**

• **What is a model?**

• **What other models are useful?**

SAFETY TIPS

Alert students that food coloring spills can cause color damage to clothing.

If you have sprinkled the marshmallows with alum, warn students that the marshmallows are *not edible* because of the alum contamination.

TEACHING STRATEGY FOR LAB PROCEDURE

1. If you have sprinkled the marshmallows with alum, be sure to warn students that the marshmallows are *not edible*.

2. After the teams have completed the investigation, share and discuss the results. Have teams take turns showing and explaining one model and the balanced equation.

CHAPTER REVIEW

MULTIPLE CHOICE

1. b **3.** d **5.** d **7.** c **9.** b
2. c **4.** b **6.** b **8.** a **10.** c

COMPLETION

1. homogeneous
2. heterogeneous
3. mixture
4. physical
5. solution
6. alloys
7. element
8. chemical symbol
9. compound
10. molecule

TRUE OR FALSE

1. F homogeneous
2. T
3. F physical
4. F heterogeneous
5. T
6. F atom
7. F chemical symbol
8. T
9. F do
10. F coefficients

SKILL BUILDING

1. Answers will vary. Sample criteria are the first letter of the name of month; number of letters in the name of a month; average temperature; hours of daylight; number of days; school and nonschool months.

2. Heterogeneous mixtures contain large clumps of particles that will not fit through the small openings of most filters. The particles in solutions are very well mixed or are mixed on the molecular level and are small enough to pass through.

3. Substances keep their own identity: you can recognize the milk, blueberries, and cereal by both sight and taste. Substances can be present in any amount; you can use varying amounts of each substance and still have a mixture of the three. Substances are easily separated according to their physical properties: you can filter the cereal flakes and berries from the milk and then pick out the berries from the flakes.

4a. Pass an electric current through water and collect the O_2 and H_2 into which it decomposes. Test each gas appropriately for identification. **b.** Evaporate the water, leaving behind the salt.

5.
  a. $2Mg + O_2 = 2MgO$
  b. $2NaCl = 2Na + Cl_2$
  c. $CH_4 + 2O_2 = CO_2 + 2H_2O$
  d. $2H_2 + O_2 = 2H_2O$

On a separate sheet of paper, write the letter of the answer that best completes each statement.

1. According to makeup, matter exists as
  a. elements, solids, metals, liquids.
  b. elements, compounds, mixtures, solutions.
  c. solids, liquids, gases, plasma.
  d. solids, compounds, mixtures, liquids.
2. Which of the following is *not* homogeneous matter?
  a. water b. carbon dioxide c. granite d. uranium
3. Matter that consists of two or more substances mixed together but not chemically combined is called a (an)
  a. element. b. compound. c. pure substance. d. mixture.
4. An example of a heterogeneous mixture is
  a. salt water. b. salad dressing. c. stainless steel. d. salt.
5. The simplest type of pure substance is a (an)
  a. compound. b. alloy. c. solution. d. element.
6. The basic building block of matter is the
  a. molecule. b. atom. c. element. d. compound.
7. The chemical symbol for helium is
  a. HE. b. H. c. He. d. h.
8. Pure substances made of more than one element are called
  a. compounds. b. mixtures. c. alloys. d. solutions.
9. The chemical formula for a molecule of nitrogen is
  a. N. b. N_2. c. N_3. d. Ni.
10. The balanced equation for the formation of water from the elements hydrogen and oxygen is
  a. $H_2 + O_2 \longrightarrow H_2O$. b. $2H_2 + 2O_2 \longrightarrow 2H_2O$.
  c. $2H_2 + O_2 \longrightarrow 2H_2O$. d. $H_2 + 2O_2 \longrightarrow 2H_2O$.

On a separate sheet of paper, write the word or words that best complete each statement.

1. Matter that has identical properties throughout is called _____.
2. Soil is an example of _____ matter.
3. Two or more substances mixed together but not chemically combined are called a (an) _____.
4. Substances making up a mixture can be separated according to _____.
5. When one substance dissolves in another, a (an) _____ is formed.
6. Bronze and pewter are solid solutions called _____.
7. A pure substance that contains only one kind of atom is a (an) _____.
8. The name of an element is represented by a (an) _____.
9. A pure substance that contains more than one element is a (an) _____.
10. The smallest particle of a substance that has all the properties of the substance is called a (an) _____.

ESSAY

1. The parts of the solution are not chemically combined. A solution is made up of two or more different kinds of particles. A solution can be separated by physical means. A solution has the same properties as its ingredients.

2a. Evaporate water **b.** Use magnet for getting iron out **c.** Float in water **d.** By size

3. The symbols and formulas are the same throughout the world. This permits scientists to communicate without misunderstanding or the need to translate symbols of one system to another.

4(a) Zn **(b)** K **(c)** Na **(d)** Mg **(e)** O **(f)** Cl **(g)** Ag **(h)** Au **(i)** C

ADDITIONAL QUESTIONS AND TOPIC SUGGESTIONS

1. What evidence can you give that water, sugar, and salt have a definite

Determine whether each statement is true or false. Then on a separate sheet of paper, write "true" if it is true. If it is false, change the underlined word or words to make the statement true.

1. Concrete is an example of <u>homogeneous</u> matter.
2. Substances in a <u>mixture</u> keep their separate identities and most of their own properties.
3. Mixtures can be separated by simple <u>chemical</u> means.
4. The "least mixed" of mixtures is a <u>homogeneous</u> mixture.
5. The "best mixed" of mixtures is a <u>solution</u>.

6. The basic building block of matter is the <u>molecule</u>.
7. The <u>chemical formula</u> for gold is Au.
8. The elements that make up table salt are <u>sodium and chlorine</u>.
9. When elements combine to form compounds, their properties <u>do not</u> change.
10. To balance a chemical equation, numbers called <u>subscripts</u> are placed in front of the appropriate chemical formulas.

Use the skills you have developed in the chapter to complete each activity.

1. **Classifying data** Develop a classification system for the months of the year. State the property or properties according to which you will classify the months. Do *not* use the four seasons. Try to make your system as useful and as specific as possible.
2. **Applying concepts** Explain why heterogeneous mixtures can be separated by filtering but solutions cannot.
3. **Relating facts** You learned that mixtures have three important properties. Using the example of breakfast cereal with milk and blueberries, illustrate each property.

4. **Designing an experiment** Describe an experiment to demonstrate that
   a. water is a compound, not an element.
   b. salt water is a solution, not a pure substance.
5. **Making calculations** Balance the following equations:
   a. $Mg + O_2 \longrightarrow MgO$
   b. $NaCl \longrightarrow Na + Cl_2$
   c. $CH_4 + O_2 \longrightarrow CO_2 + H_2O$
   d. $H_2 + O_2 \longrightarrow H_2O$

Discuss each of the following in a brief paragraph.

1. Explain why a solution is classified as a mixture instead of as a compound.
2. Describe a method of separating the following mixtures:
   a. sugar and water
   b. powdered iron and powdered aluminum
   c. wood and gold
   d. nickels and dimes

3. Explain why the system of chemical symbols and formulas is important to making the language of chemistry a universal language.
4. Write the symbols for the following elements and describe one use of each: (a) zinc, (b) potassium, (c) sodium, (d) magnesium, (e) oxygen, (f) chlorine, (g) silver, (h) gold, (i) carbon.

81

their identity, such as the formation of red iron rust from oxygen and iron (Fe_2O_3).)
4. How do molecules in a mixture differ from those in a compound? (The molecules in a mixture are as different as all of the kinds of substances that make up the mixture; the mixture is heterogeneous. The molecules in a compound are all the same; the compound is homogeneous.)
5. Classify your classmates using the following system: group—class; subdivision—girls and boys; divided into—hair color, eye color, height. How many different ways could each of your classmates be classified? Which classification is best? Why do you think so?

ISSUES IN SCIENCE

The following issues can be used as a springboard for class debate, or they can be assigned as a writing homework.
1. Some scientist think solutions should not exist in the general classification of matter. Other scientists believe that solutions are a definite part of the general classification system. What is your opinion? Explain.
2. Predict the development of classification of matter in the twenty-first century. Who do you think will undertake the investigation into new matter? What will be your role in this scientific research? How will it be important in your life?

composition? (Compounds have a definite composition. Water, sugar, and salt are compounds that have the following compositions: water is H_2O, sugar is $C_{12}H_{22}O_{11}$, and salt is NaCl. They cannot be broken down to simpler substances except by chemical means.)
2. Would the molecules of an element be the same as molecules of a compound? How would they be alike? How would they be different? (A molecule of the element iron (Fe) is a single atom. A molecule of oxygen contains two atoms of oxygen (O_2). A molecule of iron oxide (red rust) contains 2 atoms of iron and three atoms of oxygen (Fe_2O_3).
3. Define and compare "physical change" and "chemical change." (A physical change is a change in only phase or shape, such as ice changing to water to vapor, or a copper wire bending. A substance keeps its identity and composition in a physical change. In a chemical change the substance(s) lose

Unit One

DIVERSITY OF MATTER

ADVENTURES IN SCIENCE: PAUL MACCREADY AND THE RETURN OF THE PTEROSAUR

BACKGROUND INFORMATION

Paul MacCready's passion in life is problems that other people either cannot solve or have not thought about. So when the Smithsonian Institution decided that they wanted a working model of a flying Pterosaur to star in their upcoming film *On the Wing,* it is no surprise that the problem fell to him.

MacCready, a scientist and engineer who heads his own company, AreoVironment, Inc., near Pasadena, California, graduated from Yale in 1947, then received a Ph.D. in aeronautics from Cal Tech in 1952. His first area of scientific interest was meteorological research of the upper atmosphere, an endeavor that resulted in his nearly freezing to death over the Sierra Nevada Mountains while flying a sailplane at a record altitude of just under 10,000 meters. Paul MacCready is probably best known today as the "father of human-powered flight." Human-powered flight is flight that is accomplished totally by human-generated energy. In one of MacCready's planes designed for this purpose, a champion bicycle rider was hired to sit in the plane and peddle furiously to turn the propeller.

The flying Pterosaur, nicknamed QN, was the first flying machine designed to fly the way a bird flies. The model, which was constructed at MacCready's company, took two years to build and cost $700,000. Before QN crashed at Andrews Air Force Base, it had flown successfully 21 times, including at least one flight over Death Valley for the filming of *On the Wing.*

Several possible causes of the crash have been cited. MacCready himself confesses that QN had a crack in the plate that holds the head in place, and that this was a weak spot. One of the engineers noted that the tail boom, designed to provide stability on takeoff, dropped off about 10 seconds too soon. A radio control engineer felt that competing radio signals in the area may have fouled up the radio control of QN, causing the creature to crash.

Adventures in Science

Paul MacCready and the Return of the Pterosaur

Long before modern birds flew, a fearsome pterosaur with wings large enough to cover a small house soared over the earth. Sixty-five million years later, on May 17, 1986, a model of the ancient animal once again took to the sky, struggling to stay aloft. But it failed and crashed to the ground in front of hundreds of spectators.

"Now we know why pterosaurs are extinct," said the model's designer, Paul MacCready, of the flying creature he had built. MacCready accepts such mishaps as opportunities to gain insight into the dynamics of flight. Such information will help him continue to design unusual flying machines.

MacCready's model pterosaur took two years to build. The project was inspired by the discovery in 1972 of the fossilized wing bones of a pterosaur. The bone fragments were found scattered in a gully in western Texas.

SUPER "BAT"

Using these bones and other fossils, scientists put together a blueprint for the flying dinosaur, whom they affectionately named QN. QN stands for the pterosaur's scientific name, *Quetzalcoatlus northropi.*

The pterosaur's mass was about 63 kilograms, and its wings measured about 11 meters from tip to tip. With a large head, slender beak, long neck, and no tail, the pterosaur was not well adapted for flight. But most scientists agree that it did fly the ancient skies. How could it do so? Paul MacCready and his team were determined to find out.

82

TEACHING STRATEGY

Motivation

Bring in pictures and models of flying objects. Display them to the class and ask,

• **What do you think is necessary to make an object fly?** (Answers will vary. Some points to consider are shape and design of the object, the presence of wings, an engine or propeller, fuel.)

Scientists believe that the pterosaur's wings were membranous and bare—more like the wings of a bat than a bird. This means that airflow over the wings would have been smooth and efficient. The pterosaur's wings would have behaved much the same as an airplane's wings. Learning that this animal lacked a tail, MacCready theorized that QN must have been able to flap, twist, and bend its wings in order to stabilize itself while flying. MacCready also reasoned that QN must have been a very powerful flapper in order to lift its body off the ground. Once in the air, though, QN would have been able to glide on outstretched wings. Did these ideas make sense?

To find out, MacCready began the task of building a model of the pterosaur that would prove the reptile did fly. MacCready used lightweight carbon tubes for the pterosaur's hollow bones. He used tough plastic material to cover the artificial skeleton, carefully molding and shaping it over the model's wing bones. Other "scientific" material used by MacCready included rubber bands, toothpicks, and popsicle sticks. The finished product closely resembled scientists' model of a living pterosaur. With its flexible wings fully extended, the model spans 5.5 meters, or one-half the size of the original pterosaur.

BIONIC "BIRD"

Building the model was one thing, but getting it to fly was another. MacCready's model pterosaur needed a "brain." After all, the flying model had to orient itself to wind currents and respond to changing air pressure. Somehow the pterosaur had to "know" when and how to tilt and flap its wings. To direct its flight functions, MacCready tucked a tiny computer into the model's body. The computer controlled QN's 13 electric motors. MacCready also provided his bionic animal with a battery to run the motors.

In a private test conducted months before its first public flight, QN flew successfully over the Mojave Desert in California. But the May crash will send MacCready back to the drawing board to improve his model. MacCready fully believes that his model—or one like it—will one day prove that pterosaurs did fly. "Nature does nothing that is stupid," he has said. "The purpose of those huge wings is to fly." If that is indeed true, Paul MacCready will be the one to finally prove it. As for the battered QN, it is retired now and will roost permanently in the Smithsonian Institution's Air and Space Museum in Washington, DC.

Paul MacCready and his model pterosaur, QN.

Unit One

DIVERSITY OF MATTER

ISSUES IN SCIENCE: THE SPACE PROGRAM: IS IT WORTH THE COST?

BACKGROUND INFORMATION

Another aspect of this issue is not just how much money is being spent on space, but whether the space program is being run in an economically sound way. Speaking about the Space Shuttle program, a space policy expert at George Washington University says, "NASA has been having trouble making the shuttle what it claims to be—an economically viable undertaking."

Another expert at Stanford University states, "If NASA had been a bottom-line, rapacious capitalistic company, it would have pulled the plug."

Issues in Science

THE SPACE PROGRAM:

One of the great challenges that sparks scientific exploration is making the unknown known. People have always been fascinated by the unknown. The planets and their moons and the stars beyond hold mysteries, many of which if solved would unravel secrets of our own planet. Space scientists argue that such basic information could be important to our survival on Earth.

Perhaps, some people say, but we have problems on Earth that need solving too—problems such as poverty and hunger. Space exploration is simply too expensive, they say. The money could be better spent on Earth.

People in favor of the space program claim that it is not especially costly. In 1982, less than 1 percent of the U.S. federal budget was spent on space exploration. The two *Voyager* missions to Saturn cost each American about $2.00.

Another thing to remember, say those in favor of space exploration, is that money spent on space exploration is not money spent in space. The space program creates jobs on the earth. People build the spacecraft. Others monitor the spacecraft, give instructions, and collect the data sent back. If the space program were discontinued, thousands of people would be out of a job.

Of course, the space program costs money. But those in favor of continuing and expanding space technology point out an additional benefit—"spinoffs." Spinoffs are products that were invented and first used in the space program but that have turned out to have practical uses on Earth.

You may not be aware of some of the space program spinoffs, such as the shiny metallic blankets marathon runners wrap themselves in after a race. These blankets keep the runner's body from losing heat. Made of thin fabric covered with a layer of aluminum particles, these blankets were developed from space technology. The National Air and Space Administration, or NASA, used similar metallic material to bounce radio signals off the

TEACHING STRATEGY

Motivation

Begin by asking students,
• **When is the last time you considered the cost of something?** (Answers will vary.)
• **What factors were important to you?** (Possible answers include how much money was available; the quality of the product; whether one really needed the product; whether the price was fair; whether the product would "pay for itself" by saving money in other areas; whether the money could be better spent on something else.)

Content Development

Point out to students that just as it is important to consider the cost of things in our private lives, it is also important to consider the cost of government programs because, in a certain sense, we all end up paying for them. After students have read the article, list on the chalkboard some of the pros and cons of the space program. Ask,
• **Which of the arguments presented in the article do you consider the most convincing? The least convincing?** (Answers will vary.)

IS IT WORTH THE COST?

Echo I communications satellite back in 1960. Other uses for this material include packaging for frozen foods, window shades, and candy wrappers.

Fireproof fabrics developed for spacesuits are now used to make fireproof clothing and blankets. Other materials developed to stop spacecrafts from vibrating are now being used to soundproof buildings.

People who believe the space program worthwhile point to other important benefits, such as the many orbiting communications satellites that allow people to telephone all over the world. These satellites also make possible live TV transmission from one place on the earth to any other place. Satellites that orbit the earth also keep us informed of changing weather conditions. The list of practical uses of space technology is very long.

Still, many people worry about the cost of the space program. They ask, "Are we spending too much money on space? Could the money be better spent on Earth?"

Space scientists say that the cost of future space missions could be reduced. They recommend a program of 14 space missions, to be launched between 1988 and 2000. This would lower the cost of each mission. Furthermore, scientists argue, the same kind of spacecraft could be used on all the missions. This would be less expensive than building a different spacecraft for each mission.

Could space exploration lead to practical benefits on Earth? Scientists point to the many valuable spinoffs from space technology that are now used on Earth. They also say that there are many valuable natural resources in space, especially metals of all kinds. In the future, these metals may be brought back and used on Earth.

Spinoffs, space resources, and the answers to puzzling questions are all valuable "products" of space exploration. But, are they worth the money? Should the money now used in exploring space be spent instead to solve problems on Earth? What do you think?

The fireproof suit this firefighter is donning will help protect him. It is made from fabric developed for the space program. Fireproof fabric is but one of the many spinoffs from space exploration.

85

ADDITIONAL QUESTIONS AND TOPIC SUGGESTIONS

1. According to the article, what seems to be the chief reason for the space program? Do you think this reason justifies the money spent on the program? (desire to explore and understand the unknown; answers will vary)
2. Find out how government expenditures are determined. Then explain the process that would be required to make a drastic change in the amount of money spent on the space program.
3. Find out who uses and directly benefits from the space program. (the military, commercial enterprises including companies such as Western Union, scientific research projects)

CRITICAL THINKING QUESTIONS

1. One possible alternative to extensive government spending on space is to have private companies carry out various aspects of the space program. What do you think of this idea? Do you think that the money spent on space would be more justifiable if it were not coming out of taxpayers' pockets? (Answers will vary.)
2. In your opinion, what benefit of the space program would make it worth the price? (Answers will vary. There is no right or wrong answer.)
3. Agree or disagree with this statement: "All this talk of spin-offs is great, but most of these things could be invented in other ways, at a fraction of the cost. It's like saying, 'I think I'll buy a new car because I need the key chain that they're giving away free to each customer.'"

CLASS DEBATE

Have students debate this issue by simulating a television round-table discussion. Assign or have students choose roles such as the following: a NASA engineer, an astronaut, a Congressperson sponsoring a bill to cut funding for the space program, a manufacturer of communications equipment, a private citizen heading a group called "Concerned Citizens Against Space."

Unit Two
PATTERNS IN MATTER

UNIT OVERVIEW

In Unit Two, students are first introduced to the atomic nature of matter. They learn about atomic models and about subatomic particles and the forces that keep these particles together.

The students then study the development of the periodic table. They learn to use the modern periodic table of elements. They study the periodic properties of the elements and learn how the periodic table can be applied to predict properties of the elements.

Finally, students study the properties of various groups of elements. After exploring differences between metals and nonmetals, they learn about the active metals, transition metals, halogens, noble gases, and rare-earth elements.

UNIT OBJECTIVES

1. **Describe various models of the atom.**
2. **State the names and describe the properties of the three principal subatomic particles, and apply the concepts of atomic number and mass number.**
3. **Describe the four fundamental forces in nature.**
4. **Describe the development of the periodic table, and state and apply the periodic law.**
5. **Contrast metals and nonmetals.**
6. **Describe the properties of elements in groups of the periodic table.**

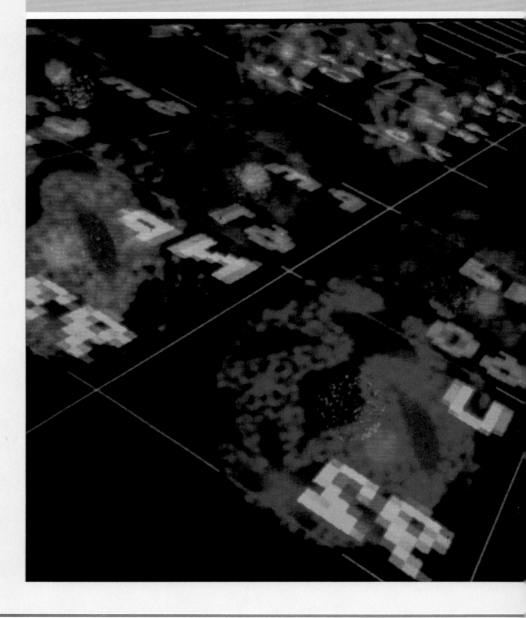

INTRODUCING UNIT TWO

Begin your teaching of the unit by having students examine the unit-opening illustration. The graphic shown was generated by a computer and represents the atoms of some of the elements in the periodic table. The different parts of the graphic were prepared separately, assembled by computer, and then "tilted" mathe-matically to provide the slanting, receding effect.

You may wish to ask students to speculate on the answers to the following questions related to the graphic.
- **What do you think the different-colored circular blotches represent?** (They represent the atoms of various elements.)
- **What do you think the blue-green smaller blotches at the center of each of the larger circles represent?** (They represent the nuclei of the atoms.)
- **What do you think the letters in the squares represent?** (They represent the chemical symbols for the elements.)
- **What do you think the numbers in the squares represent?** (They represent the atomic numbers, or numbers of protons in the nucleus, for each element.)

Now have students read the unit introduction. This material should

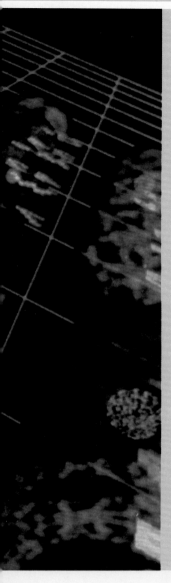

Patterns
in Matter

Dmitri Mendeleev's periodic table of the elements was proposed in 1869. The discovery of the element scandium in 1879 was just one dramatic verification of the pattern of elements predicted by Mendeleev. Others followed. More than one hundred years later, the question facing chemists and physicists was this: could the pattern be extended to create an element new to the earth? For six years, physicists at Germany's Institute for Heavy Ion Research devoted their time and efforts to finding an answer. At 4:10 P.M. on August 29, 1982, their work finally paid off. They had it—a new element! Using a particle accelerator, the team of physicists had bombarded the nucleus of an atom of the element bismuth with a nucleus of an atom of the element iron. Their hope was to get the two nuclei to combine. After ten days of experimenting, a single atom was produced. A new element, element 109, was born.

Element 109 existed for just one five-thousandth of a second. But its short life gave scientists a greater understanding of matter. As you read the chapters in this unit, you will have an opportunity to explore the nature and patterns of matter that made the short life of element 109 possible.

CHAPTERS

4 Structure of Matter

5 The Periodic Law

6 Families of Elements

This computer-generated graphic represents atoms of some elements in the periodic table. **87**

CHAPTER DESCRIPTIONS

4 Structure of Matter In Chapter 4, the development of atomic models is described. The properties of the most important subatomic particles are presented. The concepts of mass number, atomic number, atomic mass, and isotopes are introduced. Finally, the four fundamental forces are described and their role in atomic structure is analyzed.

5 The Periodic Law In Chapter 5, the development of Mendeleev's periodic table is described. The modern periodic table is contrasted with that of Mendeleev. The periodic law and periodic properties are described, as is the use of the periodic table to predict the properties of elements.

6 Families of Elements In Chapter 6, the properties of metals, nonmetals, and metalloids are contrasted. The properties of active metals and transition metals are described. Finally, the properties of halogens, noble gases, and rare-earth elements are described.

---

serve as the basis for various discussions that will better motivate students to study the chapters that follow. Here are some questions you may wish to pose to the class to initiate class discussions.

• **How is a particle accelerator able to produce changes in atoms such as those described?** (It speeds particles up, giving them the high energies that are needed to produce the changes.)

• **What does the "lifespan" of ele-ment 109 tell you about its stability?** (The short lifespan indicates great instability.)

• **Do you think that extremely short lifespans make it questionable to classify particles as new elements?** (If the lifespans are sufficiently short, it might be difficult to say whether the colliding particles truly united to form a new atom, or simply flew apart.)

• **Do you think that there is any limit to the size of nuclei that can even-tually be produced artifically?** (Answers will vary.)

• **Do you think that new elements with stable nuclei might eventually be produced?** (Some scientists do believe that this may be the case if the new nuclei contain sufficient numbers of protons and neutrons.)

Chapter 4
STRUCTURE OF MATTER

CHAPTER OVERVIEW

Anything that has mass and takes up volume is made up of matter. Since the time of the ancient Greeks, various atomic models have been proposed to account for the structure of matter. The Greek atomists believed the atom to be indivisible, as did the nineteenth-century English chemist John Dalton, who extended the atomic theory.

Through the work of later scientists, it was discovered that the atom was made up of smaller particles. J.J. Thomson discovered the negatively charged electron and proposed a "plum pudding" model of the atom. Ernest Rutherford, through his gold-foil experiments, discovered the positively charged nucleus of the atom. Niels Bohr further modified the atomic model with his theory of energy levels within the atom. His model was later refined by the modern theory of wave mechanics, which deals with the electron in terms of probable locations.

The nucleus of the atom contains positively charged protons and uncharged neutrons, each of which is thought to be made up of smaller particles, called quarks. Isotopes of an element contain an equal number of protons but different numbers of neutrons.

Four fundamental forces—electromagnetic, strong, weak, and gravity—account for the behavior of subatomic particles.

INTRODUCING CHAPTER 4

Begin this chapter by directing student's attention to the photograph on page 88. Point out that the "map" they are observing is an essential tool of scientists studying the atom. These strange markings are produced when subatomic particles such as protons are accelerated to great speeds and made to collide with one another. During the collision, energy and new particles are given off. The "map" is actually showing the collision and the emission of new particles after the collision.

Now have students read the chapter introduction. The text describes an elegant experiment being carried out deep underground. The experiment is a search for the detection of proton decay. For many years, scientists believed the proton was completely stable and could not decay. New theories, however, raise the possibility of proton decay. While discussing this experiment, try to help bring out the possible great significance of the experiments. In doing so, avoid introducing terms such as "proton" or "gluon," but do point out that the theories being tested apply to our most basic concepts regarding the structure of matter and the origins and ultimate fate of our universe.

You may wish to ask students

Structure of Matter 4

CHAPTER OBJECTIVES

After completing this chapter, you will be able to

4-1 Describe the important steps in the development of an atomic model.

4-2 Describe various models of the atom.

4-3 Classify three subatomic particles according to their location, charge, and mass.

4-3 Define the terms atomic number, isotope, mass number, and atomic mass.

4-4 Describe the four forces in nature and their relationship to atomic structure.

In James Bond movies, the science laboratory—hidden deep beneath the earth's surface—is large, comfortable, and well decorated. Thick carpeting covers the floor and lush green plants grace the corners of the room. Scientists garbed in starched white coats move about the laboratory effortlessly, gathering data from a variety of machines that buzz, blink, crackle, and hum. Before long the dramatic discovery is made. The solution to another important scientific problem is achieved!

But the world of movie thrillers is not the real world for scientists such as Ettore Fiorini, Larry Sulak, and Masatoshi Koshiba. These physicists work in tiny uncomfortable rooms with bare concrete walls and stale, hot air. Or they work in sealed plastic bubbles inside of which are six-story swimming pools containing the purest water possible. And, more importantly, they work for many years gathering data from their experiments. If they are lucky, the data may yield an answer. More often than not, the data are inconclusive and the search continues.

The question Fiorini, Sulak, and Koshiba are trying to answer has puzzled scientists for more than half a century. It has to do with whether tiny particles that make up matter disintegrate. If the physicists can determine that these particles do decay, or break down, they will be on their way to testing one of the newest and most meaningful theories of matter and energy—a theory that predicts the fate of the universe! In this chapter, you will learn about this particle and the role it plays in the structure of all forms of matter.

Using particle tracks such as these of a neutrino in a bubble chamber, scientists are attempting to test some of the most basic theories of matter and energy and to predict the fate of the universe.

89

TEACHER DEMONSTRATION

You may wish to perform the following simple demonstration to motivate students and to introduce to them the issue of the divisibility of matter, which is crucial to an understanding of this chapter. Take a sheet of paper and ask students to consider how many times it can be divided into smaller pieces. Proceed to use scissors to cut the sheet in half, then to cut one of the halves again in half, and so on, until you can no longer efficiently subdivide the paper. Ask students the following questions.

• **What might the cutting tools and method have to do with the number of subdivisions?** (They limit the practical possibility of subdivision.)

• **How many subdivisions might be possible given an ideal tool that can precisely make infinitely small cuts?** (Some students may answer that an infinite number are possible. Others may suggest that if paper is subdivided too far, it might no longer be—or have the properties of—paper, indicating a certain limit to the process. Others may go on to suggest a smallest possible particle.)

TEACHER RESOURCES

Audiovisuals

Electrons and Protons in Chemical Change, 2 filmstrips with 2 cassettes, PH Media

Matter and Molecules: Into the Atom, filmstrip with cassette, SVE

Measuring Electron Charge and Mass, 2 filmstrips with 2 cassettes, PH Media

The Nucleus: Composition, Stability, and Decay, filmstrip or slides with cassette, PH Media

Books

Bohr, Niels, *Theory and the Description of Nature.* AMS Press.

Condon, E. V., and H. Odabasi, *Atomic Structure.* Cambridge University Press.

Conn, G. K., *Atoms and Their Structure.* Cambridge University Press.

Koester, L., and A. Steyerl, *Neutron Physics.* Springer-Verlag.

Software

The Atomic Nucleus, Prentice-Hall

Atomic Structure, Prentice-Hall

• **Why must such complicated pieces of equipment and such strange conditions be needed in such experiments?** (The processes being studied occur extremely rarely, if at all, and are very difficult to observe, so experimentation must involve great precision. Detection devices must also be highly sophisticated, and care must be taken that undesirable complications, such as contamination, false recordings by instruments, and confusion created by other processes, do not interfere with the experiment or scientists' interpretation of it.)

• **How can findings that involve such tiny bits of matter reveal anything about the universe as a whole?** (The laws of nature that they may help reveal are believed to apply to matter as a whole and to govern the behavior and evolution of the universe, which is made up of these tiny particles.)

4-1 DEVELOPMENT OF AN ATOMIC MODEL

SECTION PREVIEW 4-1

In this section, students first learn that matter has mass and volume. They are then introduced to the early developments of atomic theory, which attempts to account for the structure of matter. The atomism of Democritus is used to illustrate the ancient Greek model, which proposed that the atom was indivisible. Finally, the atomism of John Dalton is discussed, and the major aspects of his atomic theory, which also assumed the atom to be indivisible, are presented.

PERFORMANCE OBJECTIVES 4-1

1. Define matter.
2. Relate indirect evidence to the steps involved in the development of a model of the atom.
3. Describe the Greek model of the atom.
4. Describe Dalton's model of the atom, and list the basic points of his atomic theory.

SCIENCE TERMS 4-1

matter p. 90   atom p. 91

TIE-IN/LITERATURE

Ask students to read a high-quality detective story, such as one of Arthur Conan Doyle's Sherlock Holmes stories (a good one to suggest is "The Speckled Band"). Have students relate the solving of the mystery to the application of scientific method.

4-1 Development of an Atomic Model

All materials are made of **matter.** Matter is anything that has mass and volume. But what is matter made of?

For thousands of years, philosophers and scientists have tried to answer this question using a variety of experiments and observations. Because the basic building blocks of matter cannot actually be seen, researchers have relied on observations of how matter behaves. Such observations are called indirect evidence. Indirect evidence about an object is evidence you get without actually seeing or touching the object. As you gather indirect evidence, you can develop a mental picture, or model. A model uses familiar ideas to explain unfamiliar facts observed in nature. A model can be changed as new information is collected. As you read further, you will learn how a model of matter was developed and changed over many years. **From the early Greek concept of the atom to the modern atomic theory, scientists have built on and modified existing models of the atom.**

The Greek Model

The search for a description of matter began with the Greek philosopher Democritus (dih-MAHK-rih-tuhs) more than 2400 years ago. He and many other philosophers had puzzled over this question: Could matter be divided into smaller and smaller

Figure 4–1 *Scientists often rely on indirect evidence to develop a model of something that cannot be observed directly. Use the two drawings in this figure to develop a model that might explain what happened during the few hours separating the two diagrams.*

90

TEACHING STRATEGY 4-1

Motivation

Begin by drawing students' attention to Figure 1-1. Ask them what has occurred during the time interval that separates what is shown in the two drawings. Relatively few students will have difficulty doing this, so most of the class should be eager to participate. Go on to call on students to explain how they are able to account for the changes shown. This can lead to a class discussion on indirect evidence that can involve examples from students' daily lives. In order to make them more aware of the role of indirect evidence, you may wish to ask them to take note of several occasions in which they make use of indirect evidence during the coming days.

Content Development

Tie the motivating discussion of indirect evidence into a scientific context, as you discuss the characteristics of the atomic models of Democritus and Dalton. Remind students of the scientific method—in particular of the role of experimentation in testing hypotheses. When you discuss the Greek model of the atom, point out that the outlook of a Greek philosopher-scientist such as Democritus was, in fact, basically nonexperimental and relied on untested speculation. Con-

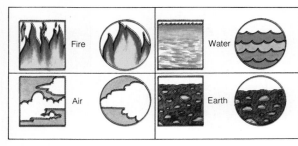

Figure 4–2 *Some ancient Greeks believed that all the matter on the earth was made of different combinations of four basic elements—fire, air, water, and earth. Which two elements do you think the Greeks believed could be combined to make steam?* ❷

pieces forever or was there a limit to the number of times a piece of matter could be divided?

After much observation and questioning, Democritus concluded that matter could not be divided into smaller and smaller pieces forever. Eventually ② the smallest possible piece would be obtained. This piece would be indivisible. Democritus named this smallest piece of matter an **atom.** The word *atom* comes from the Greek word *atomos,* meaning "not to be cut" or "indivisible."

The Greek philosophers who shared Democritus' belief about the atom were called atomists. The atomists had no way of knowing what atoms were or how they looked. But they hypothesized that atoms ③ were small, hard particles that were all made of the same material but were of different shapes and sizes. Also, they were infinite in number, always moving, and capable of joining together.

Although Democritus and the other atomists were on the right trail, the theory of atoms was ignored and forgotten. Very few people believed the idea. In fact, it took almost 2100 years before an atomic model of matter was accepted.

Dalton's Model

In the early 1800s, the English chemist John Dalton did a number of experiments that eventually led to the acceptance of the idea of atoms. Dalton had long been interested in meteorology, the study of weather. His observations about the composition of air led him to investigate the properties of gases. He discovered that gases combine as if they were made of individual particles. These particles were the atoms of Democritus.

Sharpen Your Skills

Making Indirect Observations

1. Fill two glasses almost completely full with water. Leave one glass as is. To the other glass add a piece of soap about half the size of a pea. Dissolve the soap by stirring the water.

2. Turn off all the lights in the room and make sure the room is completely dark.

3. Shine a flashlight beam horizontally from the side of the glass into the soapy water just under the surface. Repeat this procedure with the plain water. Observe and record the effect of the light beam in each glass of water.

What was the effect in the plain water? What was the effect in the soapy water? What caused the effect in the soapy water? What was the role of the glass of plain water in this activity?

91

trast this with the experimentally based science of Dalton and the other major scientists of the modern era, who not only have relied on evidence—direct and indirect—gathered through passive observation, but who also designed and actively carried out experiments to test their hypotheses. Point out that this application of the scientific method accounts for the rapid development of the atomic model over the past several centuries, as opposed to the stagnation in the development of this concept during the earlier centuries.

Reinforcement

Review the scientific method for the benefit of slower students, being sure to provide many examples. Have students identify the steps involved. Take extra care to make clear what is meant by indirect evidence, as this concept is somewhat difficult for slower students to grasp in the abstract. Once again, provide examples, making use of situations relating to the students' everyday lives.

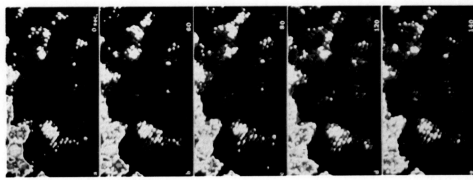

Figure 4–3 *These photographs of uranium atoms were taken by scientists at the University of Chicago. The blue spots are uranium atoms magnified more than 5 million times. The yellow areas represent a second layer of uranium atoms, and the reddish areas represent third layers. You can detect atom motion by the change in position of the colors.*

Dalton's Atomic Theory

In 1803, Dalton combined the results of his experiments with other observations about matter and proposed an atomic theory. The basic ideas of Dalton's atomic theory are as follows:

All elements are composed of atoms. Atoms are indivisible and indestructible particles.

Atoms of the same element are exactly alike.

Atoms of different elements are different.

Compounds are formed by the joining of atoms of two or more elements.

Dalton's atomic theory of matter became one of the foundations of chemistry. But like many scientific theories, Dalton's theory had to be modified as scientists gained more information about the structure of matter.

SECTION REVIEW

1. What is indirect evidence? Why is it important?
2. How did Democritus contribute to the development of an atomic model?
3. How did Dalton's atomic theory differ from the atomists' concept of the atom?
4. What type of information might scientists gather that would make it necessary to modify Dalton's atomic theory?

92

4–2 A Divisible Atom

To describe the modern atomic model

Was Dalton correct? Is an atom indivisible? In 1897, the work of the English scientist J. J. Thomson provided the first hint that an atom is made of even smaller particles. Thomson was studying the passage of an electric current through a gas. The gas gave off rays that Thomson showed were made of negatively charged particles. But Thomson knew the gas was made of uncharged atoms. So where had the negatively charged particles come from? From within the atom, Thomson concluded. A particle smaller than the atom had to exist. The atom was divisible! Thomson called the negatively charged particles "corpuscles." Today, they are known as **electrons.**

Thomson's Model

As often happens in science, Thomson's discovery of electrons created a new problem to solve. The atom was known to be neutral, or uncharged. But if electrons in the atom were negatively charged, what balanced the negative charge? Thomson's answer was that there had to be a positive charge. The atom had to contain positively charged particles to balance the negative charge of the electrons.

In all his experiments, Thomson was never able to find these positively charged particles. But he was certain they existed. So he proposed a model of the atom that is sometimes called the "plum pudding" model. Each atom was pictured as being made of a puddinglike, positively charged material. Scattered throughout this material, like plums in a pudding, were the negatively charged electrons. Figure 4–5 shows Thomson's proposed atomic model.

Rutherford's Model

Although Thomson's model was far from correct, it was an important step toward understanding the structure of the atom. The next step was taken by the British physicist Ernest Rutherford. In 1908, Rutherford devised an experiment to test Thomson's model. He fired a stream of tiny positively

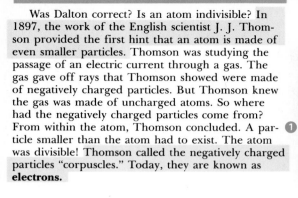

Figure 4–4 *Artist-physicist Bill Parker created this "electric art" by passing an electric current through a glass sphere containing certain gases. The light is produced when electrons in the gases absorb energy and then release it in the form of light. Who is credited with the discovery of the electron?* ❶

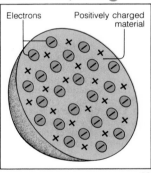

Figure 4–5 *Thomson's model of the atom pictured a "pudding" of positively charged material throughout which negatively charged electrons were scattered. What is the overall charge on this atom? How can you tell?* ❷

Electrons   Positively charged material

93

4-2 A DIVISIBLE ATOM

SECTION PREVIEW 4-2

In this section, the development of the atomic model from the late nineteenth century to the present is discussed. Thomson's discovery of the electron and of the atom's divisibility is treated, as is his "plum pudding" model, according to which the atom is made up of a thin, positively charged material that contains negatively charged electrons. Rutherford's gold-foil experiments and the discovery of the nucleus are covered next. Then Bohr's model, in which electrons exist in energy levels, is presented. Finally, the modern wave mechanics model, with its description of probable electron position, is briefly set forth.

PERFORMANCE OBJECTIVES 4-2

1. **Describe Thomson's model of the atom and the evidence that supported it.**
2. **Describe Bohr's model of the atom and the wave mechanics model of the atom.**

SCIENCE TERMS 4-2
electron p. 93
nucleus p. 94

TEACHING STRATEGY 4-2

Motivation

Review the early model of the indivisible atom and ask students to consider the difficulty of testing it experimentally, given the incredible smallness of the atom. Remind them of the role of indirect evidence in the experimentation. Then tell them that, in the case of the divisibility of atoms, such evidence is actually easy to obtain. If there is a television or computer screen handy, you may wish simply to turn it on and tell students that the light they are seeing results from the bombardment of the screen by cathode rays, which are made up of parts of atoms. Do not as yet reveal that these parts are called electrons.

HISTORICAL NOTE

The atomic models of Rutherford and Bohr, with their electrons circling a central nucleus, were influenced in this regard by their knowledge of the structure of the solar system. Powerful images (such as that of orbiting planets) developed in one area of thought have often served as a basis for constructing models in other areas. This fact stems in part from a philosophical belief, common among scientists and artists since the Renaissance, that small structures—the so called microcosm—and very large structures—the macrocosm—mirror each other.

Sharpen Your Skills

Constructing Atomic Models
Skills: Making models, manipulative
Level: Average
Type: Hands-on
Materials: string, colored pencils, cotton, cardboard or construction paper

By completing this activity, students reinforce what they have learned about atomic models. Check student models carefully for accuracy, labels, and mode of display.

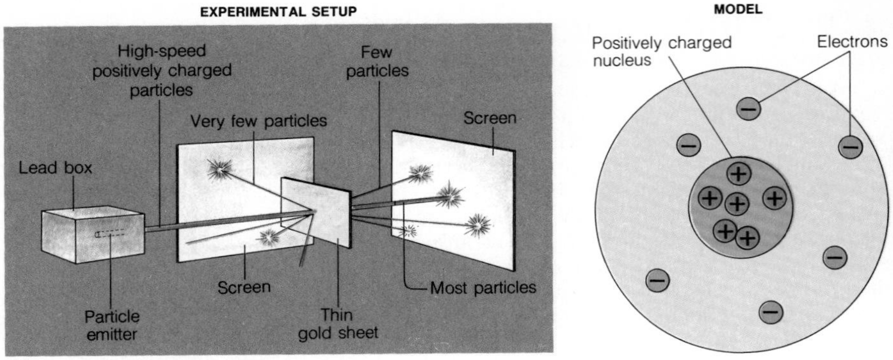

Figure 4–6 *In Rutherford's experiment, most of the positively charged particles passed right through the gold sheet (left). A few particles were slightly deflected, and a very few bounced straight back. From these observations, Rutherford concluded that the atom was mostly empty space with a dense, positively charged nucleus in the center (right).*

charged particles at a very thin sheet of gold foil. Although the gold foil was hammered very thin, it was still two thousand atoms thick! Surrounding the foil was a screen coated with a material that glowed whenever a positively charged particle hit it. Using a microscope to detect the flashes of light made by the positively charged particles as they hit the screen, Rutherford was able to prove that Thomson's model was incorrect.

If Thomson's model were correct and positive and negative particles were spread evenly throughout the atom, then all the particles that were fired would pass through the foil as easily as bullets through tissue paper. The positively charged "bullets" would be only slightly deflected by the electrons scattered throughout the puddinglike material.

What actually happened was quite a surprise to Rutherford. Most of the particles passed through the foil with *no* deflection at all. But some of the
1 particles were greatly deflected. In fact, a few bounced almost straight back from the foil, as if they had hit something solid. How was Rutherford to interpret these results?

Rutherford knew that positive charges repel other positive charges. So he proposed that an atom had a small, dense, positively charged center, which
2 he called the **nucleus** (NOO-klee-uhs; plural: nuclei, NOO-klee-igh). The nucleus is tiny compared to the atom as a whole. To get an idea of the size of the nucleus in an atom, think of a marble in a baseball stadium!

Sharpen Your Skills

Constructing Atomic Models

1. Using materials such as cardboard, construction paper, colored pencils, string, and cotton, construct models of the Thomson atom and the Rutherford atom.
2. Label the models and display them for your class. Write a brief description of the experiment that each model was based on.

4-2 (continued)

Content Development

It is important to make it clear to students that the atomic models they are studying were well supported by the experimental evidence available at the time the models were proposed. The point in presenting them is not at all to belittle the work of earlier scientists, but rather to show the logic that underlay their work and the scientific method that allowed for the replacement of each model by a more adequate one. In short, stress the nature of science as a logical and creative process rather than as an unchanging body of facts. As you deal with each model, ask students the following questions.

- **Why did Thomson (or Rutherford, etc.) propose this model? What support was there for it? How does the development of the model illustrate scientific method? Why was the model replaced by another?** (Answers will vary. The point is that each model was proposed to overcome the inadequacies of an older model. These inadequacies were revealed by experimentation, which also served to support the new model, whose inadequacies would, in time, be revealed by later experimentation. Once again, logic, scientific method, and scientific process are to be stressed.)

Rutherford reasoned that all of an atom's positively charged particles were contained in the nucleus. The negatively charged electrons were scattered outside the nucleus around the atom's edge. This arrangement meant that atoms were not a pudding filled with positively charged material, as Thomson had proposed. Atoms were mostly empty space! Although this model was useful in many ways, it did not adequately explain the arrangement of the electrons. It would be the job of future scientists to improve on Rutherford's atomic model.

The Bohr Model

Rutherford's model proposed that negatively charged electrons were held in an atom by the attraction between them and the positively charged nucleus. But where exactly were the electrons in the atom? In 1913, the Danish scientist Niels Bohr proposed an improvement to the Rutherford model that placed each electron in a specific energy level. According to Bohr's atomic model, electrons move in definite orbits around the nucleus, much like planets circle the sun. These orbits, or energy levels, are located at certain distances from the nucleus.

Figure 4–7 *If you could stand on the nucleus of an atom, the nearest electron would appear as far away as a distant star appears from the earth. How would you describe the region of an atom between the nucleus and the nearest electron?* ❶

Figure 4–8 *This atomic model shows the nucleus with its protons and neutrons. Surrounding the nucleus are rapidly moving electrons. Can scientists know with certainty where a particular electron is located in an atom?* ❷

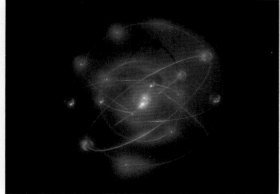

for students to grasp without going through a step-by-step discussion of what Rutherford did and what he observed.

- **What did the deflection of particles Rutherford observed indicate?** (An atom has a small, dense, positively charged center, which Rutherford called the nucleus.)

Skills Development

Skills: Developing a model, applying concepts

Ask students to construct physical models to illustrate the atomic models of Thomson and Rutherford. Encourage students to use their ingenuity in choosing materials. Display models in the classroom.

Reinforcement

Have slower students make a list of the distinguishing features of the various atomic models discussed, together with the experimental evidence that supported each feature. Help students to organize this information in table or chart form.

Enrichment

Have advanced students do library research to obtain more information on the atomic models of Thomson, Rutherford, and Bohr, and on the experimentation that revealed the inadequacies of their models. Students may wish to report their findings to their classmates.

Motivation

Point out to students that the type of tube Thomson used in his experiments is a cathode ray tube. Such tubes are still used in television sets, in which a beam of electrons is directed in such a way that it makes a bright image appear on the screen.

Content Development

Run through Rutherford's experiment very carefully with students. His experiment, which is beautifully classical in its simplicity, is often difficult

BACKGROUND INFORMATION

Wave mechanics, or quantum mechanics, is based in part on the concept formulated by Louis de Groglie that particles in motion, such as electrons, also have wavelike properties. Wave mechanics permits calculations of the probabilities that an electron in a given energy state will have certain locations or velocities at a given time. Werner Heisenberg, in his Uncertainty Principle, points out that increased precision regarding one variable, such as position, results necessarily in decreased precision regarding other variables, such as velocity. He demonstrated that, for example, exact information on the position of an electron at a given time can be obtained only by sacrificing the ability to obtain any information about the electron's velocity at the same time.

The Wave Model

Bohr's model worked well in explaining the structure and behavior of simple atoms such as hydrogen. But it did not explain more complex atoms.

Today's atomic model is based on the principles of wave mechanics. The basic ideas of wave mechanics are complicated and involve complex mathematical equations. Some of the conclusions of this theory, however, will help you understand the arrangement of electrons in an atom.

According to the theory of wave mechanics, electrons do not move about an atom in a definite path like planets about the sun. In fact, it is impossible to determine the exact location of an electron. Scientists can only predict where an electron is most likely to be found. The probable location of an electron is based on how much energy the electron has.

As you can see, the modern atomic model is based on the models of Rutherford and Bohr, and on the principles of wave mechanics. ❶ **According to the modern atomic model, an atom has a small, positively charged nucleus surrounded by a large region in which there are enough electrons to make the atom neutral.**

SECTION REVIEW

1. Describe Thomson's model of the atom.
2. How did Rutherford discover that most of the atom is empty space with a small, positively charged nucleus in the center?
3. How does the Bohr model of the atom differ from the wave model?
4. Explain why the Bohr concept of the atom is still used as a basic model, despite its shortcomings.

4–3 Subatomic Particles

When Thomson performed his experiments, he was hoping to find a single particle smaller than an atom. This task is similar to finding a particular grain of sand among the grains of sand making up all the beaches of the earth. If Thomson were alive today, he certainly would be surprised to learn that

96

4-2 (continued)

Section Review 4-2

1. Thomson proposed that the atom was made of a puddinglike, positively charged material throughout which were scattered negatively charged electrons.
2. Most of the positively charged "bullets" Rutherford fired at the sheet of gold foil passed through with no deflection. If the atom were made of a positively charged material throughout, the "bullets" should have been slightly deflected. Some of the "bullets" were greatly deflected, indicating the existence of a small, dense, positively charged center.
3. The Bohr model describes the paths of electrons as definite orbits about the nucleus. According to the wave model, the electrons do not move about the nucleus in definite paths. In fact, the exact location or path of an electron cannot be determined. Only the probability of finding an electron in a certain location can be known.
4. The Bohr model is still useful in describing the location of electrons in terms of their energy content. It also explains how an electron can remain moving in its orbit without losing energy and falling into the nucleus, collapsing the atom.

scientists know about the existence of at least two hundred different kinds of such particles! Because these particles are smaller than an atom, they are called **subatomic particles.**

At this time, you need to know about only three of these subatomic particles. **The three main subatomic particles are the proton, neutron, and electron.** As you read about these particles, note the ❷ location, mass, and charge of each. In this way, you will gain an understanding of the modern atomic theory.

The Nucleus

The nucleus is the center of the atom. Although the nucleus is about a hundred thousand times smaller than the entire atom, it accounts for 99.9 percent of the mass of an atom. Two different kinds of subatomic particles are found in the nucleus.

PROTONS One of the particles that makes up the nucleus is the **proton.** A proton is a positively charged particle. All protons are identical, regardless of the element in which they are found.

Figure 4–9 *When subatomic particles collide inside a particle accelerator, new and unusual particles may be produced. By studying the tracks made by these particles in a bubble chamber, scientists can learn more about the nature and interactions of subatomic particles.*

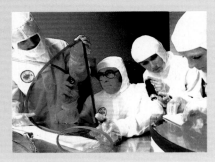
4-3 SUBATOMIC PARTICLES

SECTION PREVIEW 4-3

In this section, students obtain information on the three principal subatomic particles: the proton, the neutron, and the electron. Protons, which are positively charged, and neutrons, which are neutral, are located in the nucleus of the atom. The number of protons is called the atomic number. The total number of protons and neutrons is called the mass number. Isotopes have the same atomic number but different mass numbers. Electrons, which are negatively charged, are found outside the nucleus in the electron cloud. They are arranged in certain energy levels and cannot move from level to level without gaining or losing energy. Subatomic particles such as protons and neutrons are now generally thought to be made up of still smaller particles. These particles, which occur in groups of three, are called quarks.

PERFORMANCE OBJECTIVES 4-3

1. **Describe protons, neutrons, and electrons in terms of their masses, charges, and locations in the atom.**
2. **Define "atomic number" and "mass number."**
3. **State the difference between isotopes.**
4. **Describe the placement of electrons in the atom.**
5. **Define the term quark.**

SCIENCE TERMS 4-3

subatomic particle p. 97	mass number p. 100
proton p. 97	atomic mass p. 100
atomic mass unit p. 98	electron cloud p. 101
amu p. 98	energy level p. 101
neutron p. 98	quark p. 103
atomic number p. 99	
isotope p. 99	

TEACHING STRATEGY 4-3

Motivation

Direct students' attention to Figure 4-9. Explain to them that such photographs are used in the discovery and identification of subatomic particles. Point out the indirect nature of the evidence: only the fog—tracks left by the rapidly moving particles and not the particles themselves—is visible.

This is somewhat akin to a trail of footprints left by an intruder in a mystery story. A great deal of interpretation must be done in order to apply this indirect evidence to unravel the mystery of the identity of the intruder.

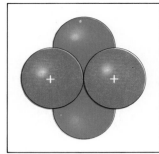

Figure 4–10 *This illustration shows the nucleus of a helium atom. The helium atom contains 2 protons and 2 neutrons. What is its atomic mass in amu's? What is its atomic number?* ❶

The mass of a subatomic particle is very small. So scientists use a special unit to measure the mass. This unit is an **atomic mass unit,** or **amu.** A proton has a mass of 1 amu. To get an idea of how small 1 amu is, imagine the number 6 followed by 23 zeros. That is how many protons it would take to equal a mass of just 1 gram!

NEUTRONS   The other particle that makes up the nucleus is the **neutron.** A neutron is an electrically neutral particle. It has no charge. Like protons, all neutrons are identical. A neutron has slightly more mass than a proton. But the mass of a neutron is still considered to be 1 amu.

Atomic Number

You learned that atoms of different elements are different. But if all protons are identical and all neutrons are identical, then what accounts for this

Figure 4–11 *The nuclei of helium, beryllium, and neon atoms all contain protons and neutrons. Yet helium, beryllium, and neon are very different elements. What accounts for this difference?* ❷

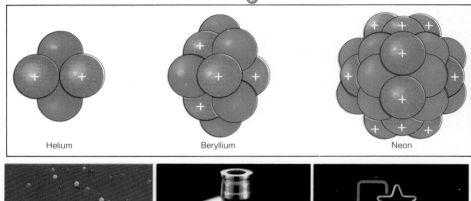

Helium   Beryllium   Neon

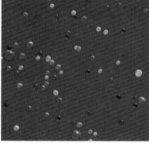

difference? The answer is that the number of protons in a nucleus determines what the element is.

The number of protons in the nucleus of an atom is called the **atomic number** of an element. The atomic number identifies the element. All hydrogen atoms—and only hydrogen atoms—have 1 proton and an atomic number of 1. Carbon atoms have 6 protons and an atomic number of 6. Oxygen has an atomic number of 8. There are 8 protons in the nucleus of every oxygen atom. How many protons does uranium, atomic number 92, have? Nitrogen, atomic number 7? ❸

Isotopes

The atomic number of an element never changes. This means that the number of protons in the nucleus of every atom of the element is always the same. This is not the case with the number of neutrons. Atoms of the same element can have different numbers of neutrons.

Atoms of the same element that have the same number of protons but different numbers of neutrons are called **isotopes** (IGH-suh-tohps). Figure 4–13 shows three isotopes of the element hydrogen. Notice that the number of protons does not change. All three isotopes of hydrogen have the same atomic number, 1. But the number of neutrons in these three isotopes is different. How many neutrons does each isotope have? Figure 4–12 shows two isotopes of the element carbon. Each isotope has 6 protons. But one isotope has 6 neutrons and the other isotope has 8 neutrons.

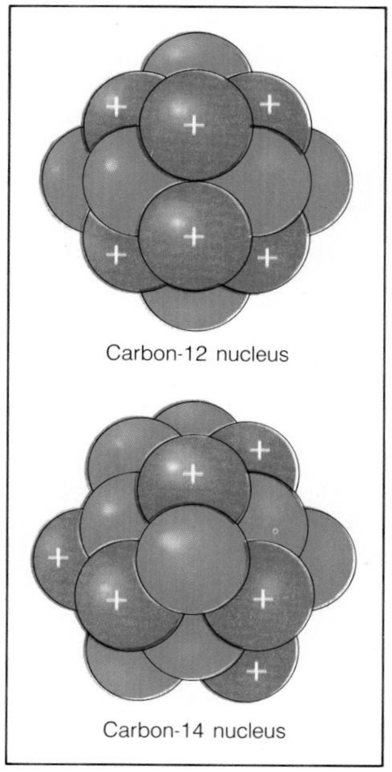

Figure 4–12 *These two isotopes of carbon have the same atomic number—6. What is the difference between the two isotopes?* ❹

Carbon-12 nucleus

Carbon-14 nucleus

Figure 4–13 *The three isotopes of hydrogen are protium, deuterium, and tritium. Which isotope contains 2 neutrons? What is the atomic number of each isotope?* ❻

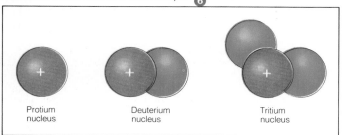

Protium nucleus

Deuterium nucleus

Tritium nucleus

99

BACKGROUND INFORMATION

Isotopes can be represented in two ways. In the first (used in the student text), the mass number is written after the name of the element, for example carbon-12, uranium-238. In the second, the mass number is written as a left superscript of the atomic symbol, and the atomic number is written as a left subscript, for example ${}^{12}_{6}C$, ${}^{238}_{92}U$.

ANNOTATION KEY

1 Uranium-235 = 143 neutrons; uranium-238 = 146 neutrons (Applying facts)

2 12.011 is closer to 12 than to 14. (Making inferences)

3 Zero (Making inferences)

4 Mass number is the number of protons plus neutrons of the most common isotope. Atomic mass is the average mass of all the naturally occurring isotopes of an element. (Applying concepts)

5 Neutron, located in the nucleus (Interpreting charts)

1 Thinking Skill: Making comparisons

2 Thinking Skill: Interpreting models

COMMON ELEMENTS

Name		Atomic Number	Mass Number
Hydrogen	H	1	1
Helium	He	2	4
Carbon	C	6	12
Nitrogen	N	7	14
Oxygen	O	8	16
Fluorine	F	9	19
Sodium	Na	11	23
Aluminum	Al	13	27
Sulfur	S	16	32
Chlorine	Cl	17	35
Calcium	Ca	20	40
Iron	Fe	26	56
Copper	Cu	29	64
Zinc	Zn	30	65
Silver	Ag	47	108
Gold	Au	79	197
Mercury	Hg	80	201
Lead	Pb	82	207

Figure 4–14 *This chart shows the symbol, atomic number, and mass number for some common elements. Why is the mass number of an element always a whole number while the atomic mass is usually not?* 4

Mass Number and Atomic Mass

All atoms have a **mass number.** The mass number of an atom is the sum of the protons and neutrons in its nucleus. The mass number of the carbon isotope with 6 neutrons is 6 (protons) + 6 (neutrons), or 12. The mass number of the carbon isotope with 8 neutrons is 6 (protons) + 8 (neutrons), or 14. To distinguish one isotope from another, the mass number is given along with the element's name. 1

Two common isotopes of the element uranium are uranium-235 and uranium-238. The atomic number, or number of protons, of uranium is 92. Since the mass number is equal to the number of protons plus the number of neutrons, the number of neutrons can easily be determined. The number of neutrons is determined by subtracting the atomic number from the mass number. How many neutrons are there in each uranium isotope? 1

Any sample of an element as it occurs in nature will contain a mixture of isotopes. As a result, the **atomic mass** of the element will be the average of the masses of all the atoms in the sample. The atomic mass of an element refers to the average mass of all the isotopes of that element as they occur in nature. For this reason, the atomic mass of an element is not usually a whole number. The atomic mass of carbon is 12.011. This number indicates that in any sample of carbon there are more atoms of carbon-12 than there are atoms of carbon-14. How do you know this to be true? 2

Electrons

Whirling around outside the nucleus are particles called electrons. An electron has a mass of 1/1836 amu and a negative charge. In a neutral atom, the number of negatively charged electrons is equal to the number of positively charged protons. What, then, is the total charge on a neutral atom? 3

As you have read, electrons do not move in fixed paths about the nucleus. In fact, the exact location of an electron cannot be known. Only the probability, or likelihood, of finding an electron in a particular region in an atom can be determined.

4-3 (continued)

Content Development

Review the concept of mass number until all students are clear about what this number signifies. Keep in mind that when students work with mass number, they often forget that this quantity is equal to the total number of protons and neutrons, not to the number of neutrons only. This error affects their calculations involving numbers of subatomic particles present.

Skills Development

Skills: Making calculations

Demonstrate for students a method that can be used to calculate the atomic mass of an element, given the atomic masses and percent natural occurrence of its isotopes. The atomic mass of each isotope is simply multiplied by the decimal form of its percent occurrence, and all the results are added. Consider as an example isotopes of a fictitious element that have the following atomic masses: 8 amu (20%), 9 amu (50%), and 10 amu (30%). The atomic mass of the element is 8 amu (0.20) + 9 amu (0.50) + 10 amu (0.30) = 9.1 amu.

Have the students apply the method to other elements, both fictitious and real. Simply provide them with the mass of each isotope and its percent occurrence (taking care that the percents add to 100 for each element).

You may also wish to have students look up in a reference the natural occurrence and masses of isotopes and verify by calculation the atomic mass of the element.

SUBATOMIC PARTICLES

Particle	Mass (amu)	Charge	Location
Proton	1	+	Nucleus
Neutron	1	Neutral	Nucleus
Electron	1/1836	–	Electron cloud

Figure 4–15 *The mass, charge, and location of the three basic subatomic particles are shown in this chart. Which subatomic particle has a neutral charge and a mass of 1 amu? Where is it located?* 5

The space in which electrons are *likely* to be found is called the **electron cloud.** The electron cloud is somewhat like the area around a beehive in which the bees move. Sometimes the electrons are near the nucleus. Sometimes they are farther away from it. In a hydrogen atom, one electron "fills" the cloud. It fills the cloud in the sense that it can be found almost anywhere within the space. 2

Although electrons whirl about the nucleus billions of times in one second, they do not do so in a random way. Each electron seems to be located in a certain area in the electron cloud. The location of an electron in the cloud depends upon how much energy the electron has.

According to modern atomic theory, electrons are arranged in **energy levels.** An energy level represents the most likely location in the electron cloud in which an electron can be found. Electrons with the lowest energy are found in the energy level closest to the nucleus. Electrons with higher energy are found in energy levels farther from the nucleus.

Each energy level within an atom can hold only a limited number of electrons. The energy level closest to the nucleus—the lowest energy level—can never hold more than 2 electrons. The second and third energy levels can each hold 8 electrons. See Figure 4–16 on page 102. The chemical properties of different elements depend on how many electrons are in the various energy levels of its atoms, or the electron arrangement of its atoms.

Sharpen Your Skills

Atomic Math

Calculate the atomic number of element X by doing the following arithmetic:

1. Multiply the atomic number of hydrogen by the number of electrons in mercury, which has an atomic number of 80.

2. Divide this number by the number of neutrons in helium, atomic number 2, mass number 4.

3. Add the number of protons in potassium, atomic number 19.

4. Add the mass number of the most common isotope of carbon.

5. Subtract the number of neutrons in sulfur, atomic number 16, mass number 32.

6. Divide by the number of electrons in boron, atomic number 5, mass number 11.

You now have the atomic number of element X. Which of the following elements is X?

fluorine: atomic number 9
neon: atomic number 10
sodium: atomic number 11

Sharpen Your Skills

Atomic Math
Skills: Making calculations, inferring
Level: Enriched
Type: Computational

This simple computational activity will reinforce students' understanding of atomic number, isotopes, and atomic mass. If students complete their calculations successfully, they will infer that atom X was sodium, atomic number 11.

TEACHER DEMONSTRATION

The concept of electron energy level is a difficult one for most students. The bookcase analogy is a useful one and can be demonstrated when the topic is introduced. If you wish, you can act it out in a sort of pantomime, asking students what you are doing. Using an empty narrow bookcase with several shelves, begin to fit books into the lowest shelf. When the shelf is full, attempt unsuccessfully to place another book onto it, and then place the book onto the second-lowest shelf, which you then fill in the same way. Do this until you have filled the three lowest shelves. Ask the following questions.

- **What am I attempting to do?** (You are attempting to fit the books into as low a position as possible.)
- **What limits my attempt?** (Each shelf can hold only a certain maximum number of books. When a shelf is filled, you must move up to a higher shelf.)

The shelves are analogous to energy levels, and the books are analogous to electrons, which tend to fill the lowest energy levels, each of which can hold only a limited number of them.

Content Development

Students sometimes get the erroneous impression that the electron cloud of an atom is actually a sort of cloudy smear in which the electrons are spread out. The "cloudlike" description of the real structure, however, relates only to the appearance of a probability diagram in which specific locations of electrons at different times are plotted simultaneously as points. The many points give an overall cloudlike appearance to the diagram.

Reinforcement

Students who might have difficulty remembering the properties and locations of the principal subatomic particles can be encouraged to construct models of the atom, with color coding for the various particles. This can be done simply by the use of colored pushpins and a corkboard disk. The model can then be used to represent different isotopes. A game can be devised in which a given student "constructs" an isotope and other students call out the numbers of subatomic particles, the atomic number, and the mass number. The game can also be run in reverse, with information on atomic number and mass number given first, and the model constructed on the information.

BACKGROUND INFORMATION

Heavier particles, which are thought to be made up of quarks, are called baryons and include protons and neutrons. Lighter particles, which are not thought to be made up of quarks, are called leptons and include electrons.

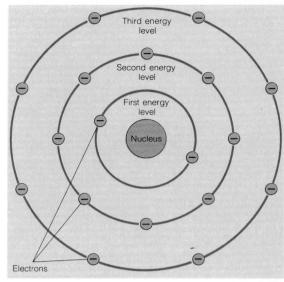

Figure 4–16 *Each energy level in an atom can hold only a certain number of electrons. How many electrons are there in the first, second, and third energy levels shown here?* ❶

Sharpen Your Skills

Probability: Finding Your Friend

The following situation might help you understand the concept of probability.

1. You are trying to locate a friend on a sunny Saturday afternoon. Although you cannot say with absolute certainty where your friend is, you can estimate the chances of finding your friend in various places. Your estimates are based on past experiences.

2. Construct a table listing at least seven possible locations for your friend. Next to each location, give the probability in percent. Remember that your total probability should equal 100 percent.

3. Would a change in the weather affect your probability determination? How about a change in the day of the week?

4. How does this activity relate to an electron's location in an atom?

102

According to modern atomic theory, electrons can move from one energy level to another. Such a move involves either the gain or the loss of energy. In order to move to a higher energy level farther from the nucleus, an electron must absorb a *specific* amount of energy. When an electron has absorbed the amount of energy required to move to a higher energy level, the electron is said to be excited. See Figure 4–17.

An electron also can lose energy and move to a lower energy level closer to the nucleus. Here again, an electron must lose a *specific* amount of energy. In addition, an electron can move to a lower energy ❶ level only if that level is not filled. For example, if the first energy level contains 2 electrons, it is filled. An electron from a higher energy level cannot move into this first energy level because the maximum number of electrons is already there. You can now understand why atoms do not collapse.

4-3 (continued)

Content Development

You may want to point out to students that the energy levels of an atom are divided into sublevels, called orbitals, which can be thought of as specific regions in which an electron is likely to be found. The first level has only one orbital, an *s* orbital, whose probability diagram is spherically symmetrical. The second and third levels each have three dumbbell-shaped *p* orbitals, as well as one *s* orbital each. At higher energy levels, orbitals designated *d* and *f* also exist. Any given orbital can hold at most two electrons, and the electrons must have opposite spin, according to the Pauli Exclusion Principle and Hund's Rule.

Enrichment

Advanced students may wish to do some basic library research on quarks and on related characteristics such as quarks' so-called "color" and "flavor." Advise them to consult up-to-date popular science magazines rather than overly difficult technical journals.

Section Review 4-3

1. Proton: nucleus, positively charged, 1 amu. Neutron: nucleus, neutral, 1 amu. Electron: electron cloud, negatively charged, 1/1836 amu.

Can the atom be "cut"? The existence of protons, neutrons, and electrons proves it can. In fact, protons and neutrons can be separated into even smaller particles. It is now believed that a new kind of particle makes up all the other known particles in the nucleus. This particle is called the **quark** (kwahrk). There are a number of different kinds of quarks. All nuclear particles are thought to be combinations of three quarks. One group of three quarks will produce a neutron. Another group of ❷ three quarks will produce a proton. If protons are accelerated so that they collide with other particles, different groups of three quarks may form. Each different group will produce a different subatomic particle.

SECTION REVIEW

1. Classify the three main subatomic particles according to location, charge, and atomic mass.
2. Why does the nucleus account for 99.9 percent of the mass of an atom?
3. What is the atomic number of an element? What is its significance?
4. Nitrogen-14 and nitrogen-15 are isotopes of the element nitrogen. Describe how atoms of these isotopes would differ from each other.
5. Why must scientists consider the concept of probability in describing the location of electrons?
6. The element sodium has only one naturally occurring isotope. How will the atomic mass of this isotope compare with the mass number?

4–4 Forces Within the Atom

What keeps an atom together? Why don't the electrons fly out of their orbits around the nucleus? Why don't the protons move away from each other? Why don't all the atoms in the universe explode?

Section Objective

To identify the four forces associated with atomic structure

Electron absorbs specific amount of energy

Electron moves to higher energy level

Electron loses specific amount of energy

Electron moves to lower energy level

FACTS AND FIGURES

According to current theory, quarks are thought to possess properties called "flavor" and "color." The six different quark flavors are up, down, strange, charm, truth, and beauty. The three colors are red, blue, and green. These names, however, do not refer to actual flavors or colors.

TEACHER DEMONSTRATION

You may wish to do a simple flame-test demonstration to illustrate energy-level changes for atoms. Dip a flame-cleaned length of nichrome of platinum wire sequentially into solutions containing ions such as Na^+, K^+, Li^+, Cu^{2+}, and Ca^{2+}, each time placing the end of the wire into a Bunsen burner flame. Clean the wire with concentrated hydrochloric acid between uses. (**Caution:** The acid is highly corrosive and also produces fumes. Conduct the demonstration in a fumehood or in a well-ventilated room.) The flame colors are produced by electrons that fall back to lower energy levels after having been excited to higher levels by the energy of the flame. The absorbed energy is released in the form of light of characteristic frequencies.

103

---

2. The nucleus contains the two particles that have an appreciable mass: proton and neutron. Electrons, found outside the nucleus, have a mass so small it is often considered zero.

3. Atomic number is the number of protons in the nucleus. The atomic number distinguishes one element from another.

4. Both atoms would have 7 protons. Nitrogen-14 would have 7 neutrons while nitrogen-15 would have 8.

5. The exact location of an electron cannot be determined. Only the probability of finding an electron in a certain location can be predicted.

6. The atomic mass would be exactly the same as the mass number since only one isotope exists. The atomic mass is an average of the masses of all naturally occurring isotopes.

4-4 FORCES WITHIN THE ATOM

SECTION PREVIEW 4-4

This section of the chapter introduces students to the four fundamental forces. These are the electromagnetic force, the strong nuclear force, the weak nuclear force, and gravity. Some physicists are attempting to account for all these forces on the basis of a single fundamental force.

PERFORMANCE OBJECTIVES 4-4

1. **List the four kinds of forces.**
2. **Describe situations in which the four kinds of forces operate.**

SCIENCE TERMS 4-4

electromagnetic force p. 104
strong force p. 104
weak force p. 105
gravity p. 105

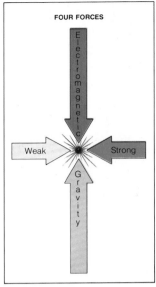

Figure 4–18 *The four known forces that govern all the interactions of matter and energy are the strong force, electromagnetic force, weak force, and gravity. Which of these four forces is the weakest?* ❶

The answers lie in the forces within the atom. **The four forces that account for the behavior of subatomic particles are the electromagnetic force, strong force, weak force, and gravity.**

The **electromagnetic force** can either attract or repel the particles on which it is acting. If the particles have the same charge, such as two protons, the electromagnetic force is a force of repulsion. If the particles have opposite charges—such as an electron and a proton—the electromagnetic force is a force of attraction.

Electrons are kept in orbit around the nucleus by the electromagnetic force. The negatively charged electrons are attracted to the positively charged nucleus.

The electromagnetic force acts in the nucleus as a force of repulsion between positively charged protons. What keeps the protons from repelling each other and causing the explosion of the atom?

The **strong force** opposes the electromagnetic force of repulsion between protons. The strong force "glues" protons together to form the nucleus. Without the strong force, there would be no atoms. The strong force works only when protons are very close together, however. Although the strong force

Figure 4–19 *The strong force opposes the electromagnetic force of repulsion between two protons (top). The strong force becomes powerful enough to overcome the repulsive force and bind protons in the nucleus only when the protons are very close together (bottom).*

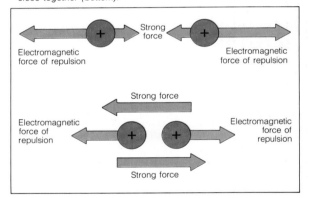

104

TEACHING STRATEGY 4-4

Motivation

Remind students of the important experiments described in the chapter introduction. Point out that the attempt to solve these basic mysteries about nature is an attempt to understand not only the nature of matter but also the forces that account for its behavior and structure. You may wish to demonstrate electromagnetic force (by using a rubbed length of glass or rubber and some bits of paper or, alternately, several magnets) and

gravitational force (simply by dropping an object to the floor).

Content Development

The subject matter dealt with in this section is not easy to comprehend. The topic of fundamental forces is therefore presented in the simplest possible form in order to give students the basic information they need to appreciate the importance of the scientific issues involved. Any deeper

treatment of the topics would result in confusion on the part of most students and would require a mathematical approach that would be far too sophisticated for most of them to grasp. You should thus endeavor to keep the focus simple and to stress the issue of basic forces and the possible large-scale consequences of the reduction of the forces to one fundamental force. In order to help do so, remind students that progress in science gen-

is the greatest of the four forces, it has a very limited range. See Figure 4–19.

The **weak force** is the key to the power of the sun. It is responsible for a process known as radioactive decay. During radioactive decay, a neutron in the nucleus changes into a proton and an electron.

The final force, **gravity,** is by far the weakest force known in nature. Yet it is probably the force most familiar to you. Gravity is the force of attraction exerted between all objects in nature. Gravity causes apples to fall from a tree and planets to remain in orbit around the sun. The effects of gravity are most easily observed in the behavior of large objects. Inside the nucleus of an atom, the effect of gravity is very small compared to the effects of the other forces. The role of gravity in the atom is not well understood.

As you can see, the four forces—electromagnetic, strong, weak, and gravity—are very different. Yet physicists have tried to develop a single principle that would account for the differences between these forces. Such a principle would explain all four forces in terms of one fundamental force and all varieties of particles in terms of one basic particle.

And that is where physicists such as Fiorini, Sulak, and Koshiba enter the picture. They are seeking to determine if the proton decays. For if all forces and particles are really the same, then the disintegration of protons in the nucleus must mean ❸ that matter is disappearing! If these physicists can discover the "death" of protons, they will be one step closer to predicting the fate of the universe.

Figure 4–20 *New stars are forming within the hydrogen and helium gas that makes up the Dumbbell Nebula. All of the natural elements heavier than hydrogen and helium are created within stars. What will be the future of these elements if the proton is found to decay?*

SECTION REVIEW

1. What four forces govern the behavior of subatomic particles?
2. Which two forces are responsible for holding the atom together?
3. In what way does the electromagnetic force differ from the other three forces?
4. Why is gravity a relatively ineffective force within the nucleus?
5. Although gravity is the weakest of the four forces within the atom, explain why it is one of the most easily observed forces in your daily life.

BACKGROUND INFORMATION

Forces can generally be though of as a measure of the ability to produce a change in the motion of an object. Force is equal to the product of the mass of the affected object and the acceleration (rate of change of velocity) produced in the object. Mathematically, this is represented as

$$F = ma$$

Forces are carried, or mediated, by particles. The electromagnetic force is carried by photons. The weak nuclear force is carried by particles called weak bosons. The strong force is believed to be carried by hypothetical particles called gluons. Gravitational force is believed to be carried by hypothetical particles called gravitons. The electromagnetic and weak forces have already successfully been combined into the so-called electro-weak force. The other forces have yet to be combined.

Combination of forces is demonstrated by interconversion between one type of particle that carries one type of force and another type of particle that carries another type of force. It is believed that in the earliest moments of time after the "big bang" in which the universe is generally thought to have begun, conditions of such high energy existed that the four forces were truly unified. At that time, neutrons and protons had not yet come into existence, and the entire universe was compacted into a tiny space.

erally involves accounting for more and more kinds of phenomena on the basis of fewer, more powerful and more comprehensive and unified theories and models.

Skills Development
Skills: Making comparisons, relating concepts, making charts
Ask interested students to create colorful charts illustrating the four forces. The charts can include creative design elements and should clearly incorporate basic information that illustrates the contrasting natures of the forces and examples of the conditions or situations under which they operate.

Section Review 4-4
1. Electromagnetic, strong, weak, and gravity
2. The strong force forms a nucleus by "gluing" protons together. The electromagnetic force keeps electrons in orbit around the nucleus.
3. The electromagnetic force is the only force that can both repulse and attract. Other forces are forces of attraction only.
4. Gravity is a force directly related to the mass of objects. Atomic particles have very small masses and thus little gravity.
5. Gravity is the force most easily observed in the behavior of large objects.

LABORATORY INVESTIGATION
SHOE-BOX ATOMS

BEFORE THE LAB
1. Obtain one shoe box for each student group, and set out the other materials needed.
2. Into each shoe box, place one or more relatively small familiar objects of the same kind, such as pencils, large nails, erasers, chalk, or large paper clips. Different boxes should contain different objects. Number each box and keep a record of what is in each. Tape the boxes securely shut.

PRE-LAB DISCUSSION
Before beginning this investigation, remind students of the important role of indirect evidence in scientific investigation. Review with them the general steps involved in scientific method, and stress the care that must be taken in formulating and testing hypotheses. Make it clear that the main point is not to determine conclusively exactly what is in the box but rather to gather indirect information about the properties of what is inside and to proceed in a scientific manner with the investigation and with the development of a reasonable model.

SKILLS DEVELOPMENT
Students will use the following skills while completing this lab investigation.
1. Manipulative
2. Observing
3. Recording data
4. Inferring
5. Concluding
6. Modeling

SAFETY TIPS
General safety procedures should be followed. Students should limit themselves to the tests suggested in the procedure. Any additional tests should be cleared with you in advance.

TEACHING STRATEGY FOR LAB PROCEDURE
Refrain from making comments on the procedures being followed (assuming they are safe and reasonably appropriate). Discourage students from calling out guesses on what is in the box or from attempting to seek hints from you.

OBSERVATIONS
1, 2, 3. All observations will depend on the items in the boxes. Observations should be checked to see if they are consistent with hidden items.

CONCLUSIONS
1. Check student sketches to see if they are logical, based on observations. Students should not be graded on whether or not they were correct but on the scientific method employed.
2. Answers will vary but will likely include responses such as smell.
3. Students should be able to give valid reasons for any differences between their original sketch and the actual contents of the box.

 LABORATORY INVESTIGATION
Shoe-Box Atoms

Problem
How can indirect evidence be used to build a model?

> **Materials** *(per group)*
> shoe box, numbered and taped shut, containing unidentified objects
> balance
> magnet
> meterstick

Procedure
1. Your teacher will give you a shoe box with an object(s) inside. Do not open or damage the box.
2. Use a magnet to determine if the contents have any magnetic properties.
3. Determine the mass of an empty shoe box. Then determine the mass of your shoe box. The difference between the two masses is the mass of the object(s) inside your shoe box.
4. By tilting the box you can determine something about the object's shape. Does it slide? (flat) Does it roll? (rounded) Does it collide inside? (more than one object)
5. Shake the box up and down to determine if the object bounces. How hard does it bounce? Does it flip?
6. For each test you perform, record your observations in a data table similar to the one shown here.

Observations
1. How many objects are in your shoe box?
2. Is the object soft? Metallic? Fragile?
3. Is the object flat or rounded?

Conclusions
1. Make a sketch of what you think is in your shoe box. Draw the objects so that they show relative sizes.
2. What other indirect evidence did you gather to help you make the drawing?
3. How does your sketch compare with the actual contents, as reported by your teacher? Make a sketch of the actual contents.
4. Describe how you can develop a model of an object without directly observing the object.

Test Performed	Results	
	Trial 1	Trial 2
Magnet brought near		
Mass of object(s) determined		
Box tilted		
Box shaken		

106

4–1 Development of an Atomic Model

❑ A model is important to scientists because it explains observed facts and can be modified.

❑ More than 2400 years ago, the Greek philosopher Democritus theorized the existence of the atom, the smallest piece of matter.

❑ John Dalton's atomic theory was based on experimental evidence about the behavior of matter. His theory stated that all matter is made of indivisible particles, or atoms.

4–2 A Divisible Atom

❑ The discovery of the electron by J. J. Thomson proved that the atom is divisible.

❑ Thomson's model pictured the atom as being made of a positively charged, puddinglike material throughout which negatively charged electrons were scattered.

❑ Rutherford's experiments with gold foil and positively charged "bullets" led him to conclude that an atom has a small, dense, positively charged nucleus surrounded by negatively charged electrons.

❑ The Bohr model of the atom pictured electrons as moving in definite orbits, or energy levels, around the nucleus.

❑ According to the theory of wave mechanics, electrons do not move about an atom in definite orbits. The exact location of an electron in an atom is impossible to determine.

4–3 Subatomic Particles

❑ Protons and neutrons are found in the nucleus. The nucleus accounts for 99.9 percent of an atom's mass.

❑ Protons have a positive charge and a mass of 1 amu.

❑ Neutrons are electrically neutral and have a mass of 1 amu.

❑ The number of protons in the nucleus of an atom is called the atomic number.

❑ Atoms of the same element that have the same number of protons but different numbers of neutrons are called isotopes.

❑ The mass number of an atom is the sum of the protons and neutrons in its nucleus.

❑ The atomic mass of an element is the average mass of all the naturally occurring isotopes of that element.

❑ Electrons have a negative charge and a mass of 1/1836 amu.

❑ Within the electron cloud, electrons are arranged in energy levels.

❑ Subatomic particles in the nucleus are made up of quarks.

4–4 Forces Within the Atom

❑ The forces that govern the behavior of subatomic particles are electromagnetic, strong, weak, and gravity.

Define each term in a complete sentence.

amu	electromagnetic force	isotope	quark
atom	electron	mass number	strong force
atomic mass	electron cloud	matter	subatomic particle
atomic mass unit	energy level	neutron	weak force
atomic number	gravity	nucleus	
		proton	

---

4. Answers will vary but should be logical and demonstrate scientific method.

GOING FURTHER: ENRICHMENT

Part 1

Ask student groups to switch boxes after they have completed their procedures and written their conclusions. Students can then attempt to evaluate critically and constructively one another's methods, reasoning, and conclusions and can debate differences in suggested models.

Part 2

Ask students to consider how the experiment might be run "in reverse." Students should choose an object (or objects) to be placed in the box and should predict which of its properties are revealed by the various tests and how clearly the properties are revealed.

Ask students to consider which objects might reveal essentially the same properties. This will help bring out the point that in many cases more than one model can effectively account for a given body of indirect evidence.

CHAPTER REVIEW

MULTIPLE CHOICE

1. b	**3.** b	**5.** d	**7.** c	**9.** d
2. c	**4.** c	**6.** a	**8.** a	**10.** a

COMPLETION

1. atoms
2. electrons
3. nucleus
4. protons
5. isotopes
6. mass number
7. electron
8. energy levels
9. quark
10. strong force

TRUE OR FALSE

1. F Democritus
2. T
3. F electrons
4. F positively
5. F nucleus
6. F neutrons
7. T
8. F mass number
9. T
10. T

SKILL BUILDING

1. The number of electrons would be equal to Z, as would the number of protons. The number of neutrons would be equal to A minus Z.

2. A helium nucleus is positively charged because it contains the positively charged protons and neutral neutrons. The mass of the helium nucleus is 4 amu since it contains two protons and two neutrons.

3. The experiment provides support for Dalton's atomic theory because it agrees with the idea that compounds are composed of the atoms of two or more elements. In this case, the compound water was broken down into the elements hydrogen and oxygen.

ESSAY

1. The atomic mass of this element would be closer to X than Y because 80 percent of the sample contains the isotope of mass number X. The atomic mass of an element is the average mass of all the naturally occurring isotopes of that element.

2. Sulfur: 2, 8, 6. Fluorine: 2, 7. Argon: 2, 8, 8. Lithium: 2, 1.

3. The electromagnetic force keeps the negatively charged electrons in orbit around the positively charged nucleus. The strong force keeps protons together to form the nucleus. The weak force is responsible for the process of radioactive decay, during which a neutron changes into a proton and an electron and produces huge amounts of energy. The role of gravity is not well understood. Its effect is very small compared to the other forces.

ADDITIONAL QUESTIONS AND TOPIC SUGGESTIONS

1. Why was Rutherford's atomic model superior to Thomson's? (It accounted for data—namely, the evidence of a positive nucleus—that could not be accounted for by and that contradicted important aspects of Thomson's model.)

2. A number of atomic models preceded the wave mechanics model. Do you think the present model is correct and will never be replaced by another? (Although the present model is superior to the earlier models and is well supported by the evidence gathered so

On a separate sheet of paper, write the letter of the answer that best completes each statement.

1. The name that Democritus gave to the smallest possible piece of matter is
   a. molecule.   b. atom.   c. electron.   d. proton.
2. Which of the following is not one of the basic ideas of Dalton's atomic theory?
   a. Compounds are formed by the joining of atoms of two or more elements.
   b. Atoms of the same element are exactly alike.
   c. Atoms of different elements are exactly alike.
   d. All elements are composed of atoms.
3. The scientist J. J. Thomson discovered the
   a. proton.   b. electron.   c. neutron.   d. nucleus.
4. Rutherford's atomic model pictured a positively charged center, or
   a. electron.   b. neutron.   c. nucleus.   d. quark.
5. Particles smaller than the atom are called
   a. molecules.   b. elements.   c. ions.   d. subatomic particles.
6. The nucleus of an atom contains
   a. protons and neutrons.   b. protons and electrons.
   c. neutrons and electrons.   d. protons, neutrons, and electrons.
7. The number of protons in an atom with an atomic number of 18 is
   a. 10.   b. 36.   c. 18.   d. 8.
8. An isotope of oxygen, atomic number 8, could have
   a. 8 protons and 10 neutrons.   b. 10 protons and 10 neutrons.
   c. 10 protons and 8 electrons.   d. 6 protons and 8 neutrons.
9. All nuclear particles are thought to be made of a combination of three
   a. electrons.   b. isotopes.   c. molecules.   d. quarks.
10. Which of the following forces within the atom is responsible for keeping electrons in orbit around the nucleus?
    a. electromagnetic   b. strong   c. weak   d. gravity

On a separate sheet of paper, write the word or words that best complete each statement.

1. Elements are composed of _____.
2. Negatively charged subatomic particles are called _____.
3. Rutherford is credited with the discovery of the _____.
4. _____ that have a positive charge and a mass of 1 amu.
5. Atoms of the same element that have the same atomic number but different atomic masses are _____.
6. An atom's _____ is the sum of the protons and neutrons in its nucleus.
7. The _____ has a negative charge and a mass almost equal to zero.
8. The negative particles in an atom are arranged in _____.
9. The _____ now thought to make up all other nuclear particles.
10. The force that holds the protons of an atom together is the _____.

108

Determine whether each statement is true or false. Then on a separate sheet of paper, write "true" if it is true. If it is false, change the underlined word or words to make the statement true.

1. The idea that matter was made of indivisible particles called atoms was proposed by <u>Aristotle</u>.
2. In the early 1800s, <u>Dalton</u> developed a theory of atomic structure that was based on chemical experiments.
3. In Thomson's experiment, the gas in the tube gave off rays that were made of negatively charged particles called <u>neutrons</u>.
4. In Rutherford's experiment, some of the positively charged "bullets" were deflected by a <u>negatively</u> charged center.
5. Most of the mass of the atom is located in the <u>electron cloud</u>.
6. Subatomic particles that have a mass of 1 amu and no electric charge are called <u>protons</u>.
7. Chlorine has an atomic number of 17. It has <u>17</u> protons in its nucleus.
8. In order to distinguish one isotope of an element from another isotope of the same element, the <u>atomic number</u> of the isotope is given with the element's name.
9. Electrons having the least amount of energy are found <u>closest to</u> the nucleus.
10. The <u>weak force</u> is responsible for a process known as radioactive decay.

Use the skills you have developed in the chapter to complete each activity.

1. **Applying definitions** If the letter Z represents the atomic number of a neutral atom and the letter A represents the mass number, explain how you could use these symbols to find the number of electrons, number of protons, number of neutrons.
2. **Applying concepts** In his experiment, Rutherford used positively charged helium nuclei as the "bullets" he fired at the gold foil. How do you account for the fact that a helium nucleus is positively charged? What is the mass of the nucleus?
3. **Relating concepts** In an experiment, a scientist passes an electric current through a container of water that has been mixed with a small amount of acid. The water seems to disappear while two cylinders on opposite sides of the container fill with gas. A simple test determines that one cylinder contains oxygen and the other contains hydrogen. How does this experiment support Dalton's atomic theory?

Discuss each of the following in a brief paragraph.

1. A certain element contains 80 percent of an isotope of mass number X and 20 percent of an isotope of mass number Y. Is the atomic mass of this element closer to X or to Y? Explain your answer.
2. Describe the electron configuration of each element based on atomic number: sulfur, 16; fluorine, 9; argon, 18; lithium, 3.
3. Describe the four forces and explain their role in the structure of an atom.

109

and might behave differently from currently known kinds of atoms.

4. Quarks have never been observed and many scientists who believe in their existence say that energy requirements for producing free observable quarks are so great that quarks will probably never be observed. Can there be good scientific reason for believing in the existence of things that may never be observed? (Some scientists would claim that belief in such perennially unobservable entities is to some extent as much philosophical as it is scientific. Others point out, as many students may, that there may be good reasons for believing in a thing, given significant indirect evidence. In the case of quarks, most scientists would agree that the evidence so far, although suggestive, is far from conclusive.)

5. Gravity, unlike electromagnetic force, is always an attractive force. Is it conceivable that there might be such a thing as repulsive gravitational force? How would such a force cause objects to behave? (It is at least conceivable that antigravity could exist, although accounting for it would require modification of present thinking regarding fundamental forces. Antigravity would act between masses to push them farther apart rather than to draw them together.)

ISSUES IN SCIENCE

The following issue can be used as a springboard for class debate, or it can be assigned as homework writing exercise.

1. Scientists tend to assume that what they learn here on earth about the basic nature of matter is applicable to matter everywhere in the universe. Is this belief justified? (This is a debatable point. There is usually an underlying assumption that the "laws" that govern nature apply everywhere, but some scientists and philosophers of science have questioned this, pointing out the limited nature of the evidence gathered so far.)

far, the history of science suggests that science is a process, and probably an unending one, rather than a set of facts. The present theoretical model will thus probably be replaced by another, given data that reveal its shortcomings and creative theory construction by scientists in the future.)

3. All elements are identified by a whole-number atomic number. It is conceivable that elements that have fractional atomic numbers exist? (Fractional atomic numbers would involve fractions of a proton, and it now seems that if a proton were to be divided the resulting particles would not really behave like fractions of a proton but would be other kinds of particles. Thus, from this point of view fractional atomic numbers seem unlikely. However, it is perhaps conceivable that atoms different in subatomic particles other than protons or neutrons might be able to exist under certain conditions

Chapter 5
THE PERIODIC LAW

CHAPTER OVERVIEW

In this chapter, students will be introduced to the periodic law, upon which is based the periodic table of the elements. Students will learn that the first periodic table was developed in the mid-1800s by Russian scientist Dmitri Mendeleev, who arranged the elements according to increasing atomic mass. Students will then learn about the modern periodic table, in which the elements are arranged according to increasing atomic number.

Students will gain an appreciation of how the periodic table is a valuable tool of chemists. They will come to understand how to read and use the table and how to determine the properties of an element according to its position in the table.

TEACHER DEMONSTRATION

Obtain samples of gold and silver jewelry, as well as samples of gold plate and silver plate. (If possible, you may want to involve a local jeweler in this demonstration.) Display the samples and have students observe them carefully. Ask,
• **What comparisons can you make between the real and the plated metals?** (Based on appearance, there may be very little difference, although sometimes plated metals look shinier than pure metals.)

INTRODUCING CHAPTER 5

To students of the twentieth century, an "exciting" event in science is probably a person walking on the moon or the discovery of life on another planet. Something as basic as the periodic table is likely to be taken for granted as "something that has always been there." Of course, this is far from the truth. The development of the periodic table was a significant breakthrough in the study of chemistry, and Mendeleev's prediction of undiscovered elements was probably as exciting in his time as some of the achievements of modern science are in our time.

In addition to introducing students to the periodic table, this chapter enables students to gain an appreciation for the history of chemistry. Beginning with the alchemists in the chapter opener and continuing through Mendeleev's work to the development of the modern periodic table, students can come to understand how the scientific method has been used and developed throughout the centuries.

Begin by directing students' attention to the drawing of the alchemists. Ask,
• **What things do you see in this picture that are different from what you would see in a modern scientific lab-**

The Periodic Law 5

CHAPTER OBJECTIVES

After completing this chapter, you will be able to

5–1 Explain how Mendeleev developed his periodic table.

5–1 Define periodic properties.

5–2 Compare the modern periodic table with Mendeleev's table.

5–2 State the periodic law.

5–3 Describe how the periodic table can be used to determine properties of the elements.

5–4 Identify some periodic properties of the elements.

Hidden away in some dark corner of a medieval castle, an alchemist peers anxiously into a huge iron pot. Strange vapors fill the room as a peculiar mixture bubbles and brews. The alchemist gently strokes a piece of gold as he tends the pot. Visions of mountains of gold crowd his mind as he dreams of becoming the richest man in the world.

Alchemists, sometimes considered to be the earliest scientists, believed they could turn common metals into gold. Hoping to profit from such discoveries, many kings and princes housed their own personal alchemists in their castles.

Many alchemists were quite clever. They learned to change the color of copper so that it looked like gold. They removed impurities from lead so that it resembled silver. But, alas, the physical appearance of the metal was the only property they managed to change! Copper was still copper and lead was still lead. No alchemist ever succeeded in changing a common metal into a precious one.

Today, scientists know what the alchemists did not: Every element is unique and has its own set of physical and chemical properties. Elements can combine with each other, but under ordinary circumstances, one element cannot change into another.

In this chapter, you will learn how the study of elements and their properties led to the development of a valuable scientific tool. You will read about a nineteenth-century Russian chemist who became very famous—not by changing lead into gold, but by performing a different kind of scientific "magic." He predicted the existence and properties of elements that had not even been discovered!

Surrounded by an odd assortment of materials and tools, the alchemist labored long hours in the hope of changing common metals into gold.

111

• **How might you test these samples to determine which is pure gold or silver and which is not?** (Possible methods include checking the density and determining how the metal reacts to air and moisture.)

Point out that some of the alchemists would coat a cheap metal with a thin layer of silver or gold, then claim that they had "changed the metal into" silver or gold. Discuss with students how the alchemists may or may not have succeeded in their deception.

TEACHER RESOURCES

Audiovisuals

Atomic Structure and the Periodic Chart: An Introduction, filmstrip or slides, PH Media

Classification of the Elements: Metals, Non-Metals, Metalloids, filmstrip or slides, PH Media

Family of Halogens, film, CRM/McGraw-Hill

The Origin of the Elements, film, CRM/McGraw-Hill

Books

Klein, M. L., and J. A. Venables, eds, *Rare Gas Solids,* Academic Press

Kuper, C. G., et al., eds, *Liquid and Solid Helium,* Halsted

Poda, J. S., *The Periodic Table: Experiments and Theory,* Halsted

Taylor, M. J., *Metal to Metal Bonded States of the Main Group Elements,* Academic Press

Software

Periodic Table, Prentice-Hall

oratory? (strange costumes, dark and cluttered environment, strange "equipment" such as big pots)

• **Do you see anything similar to what you would see in a modern scientific laboratory?** (flasks and other laboratory glassware, the use of flame to heat things, a sense of expectation and discovery)

Have students read the text on page 111. Ask,

• **What do you think the alchemists in the picture were trying to do?** (turn cheap metal into gold)

• **Did they succeed?** (no) **Why not?** (because elements cannot be changed into other elements)

• **Have you ever tried to do something only to find that it was impossible?** (Answers may be as diverse as trying to fix something irreparably broken or attempting an impossible feat such as jumping over a tall object.)

• **How did you discover that what you were trying to do was impossible?** (probably by trying to do it and failing)

• **Did you learn anything in the process?** (Answers will vary.)

Point out to students that much of the scientific process involves trial and error, and that even an apparent failure adds to the scientist's knowledge and experience. Emphasize that the alchemists, despite their strangeness, did make a contribution to early science with some of their methods, equipment, and curiosity.

5-1 DEVELOPMENT OF A PERIODIC TABLE

SECTION PREVIEW 5-1

In this section, students will trace the development of Mendeleev's periodic table. They will learn that when Mendeleev arranged the elements in order of increasing atomic mass, he found that the valence numbers always occurred in a pattern. When Mendeleev arranged the elements in rows of seven, he observed that elements in the same column all had similar physical and chemical properties.

Students will read how Mendeleev constructed a periodic table based on his belief that the properties of the elements are periodic functions of their atomic masses. Then students will discover how Mendeleev's table enabled him to predict the existence and properties of elements yet to be discovered.

PERFORMANCE OBJECTIVES 5-1

1. **Describe Mendeleev's search for a pattern among the elements.**
2. **Describe Mendeleev's observations when the elements were arranged in order of increasing atomic mass.**
3. **Describe Mendeleev's periodic table.**
4. **Explain how Mendeleev used his periodic table to predict the properties of undiscovered elements.**

SCIENCE TERMS 5-1
periodic p. 113

Figure 5–1 *Each element has its characteristic chemical and physical properties. Potassium is a soft silvery metal that reacts explosively with water (left). Aluminum, also a silvery metal, does not easily combine with oxygen in water or in the air (right). Thus, aluminum can be used in electronic devices, household items, and building materials.*

5–1 Development of a Periodic Table

Imagine that you are a detective with a great mystery to solve. You know that scattered throughout the earth are 63 unique and fascinating substances called elements. Some of the substances are rare and valuable solids; others are strange gases; still others are needed to support human life.

Your task is to track down these elements and determine how they are related. You suspect that there is a grand design, a pattern that explains everything. You want to find it. You even believe that if you can solve this mystery, you can predict the existence of elements yet to be discovered.

This story is more than a fictional detective tale. It is actually the story of the Russian chemist Dmitri Mendeleev (D'MEE-tree mehn-duh-LAY-ehf). In the mid-1800s, Mendeleev became quite famous for discovering one of the basic principles of chemistry.

Mendeleev was writing a book called *Principles of Chemistry.* He had collected thousands of facts about the 63 elements that had already been discovered. Several scientists working before Mendeleev had come to the conclusion that groups of elements had similar chemical and physical properties.

Mendeleev's hunch was that a certain pattern or order must exist among *all* the elements. He was

112

TEACHING STRATEGY 5-1

Motivation
Have students discuss the following situation.
• **Suppose you want to line up a group of people. What are some ways you can arrange them?** (Possible answers include according to height, age, and alphabetical order.)
• **Would you expect to get the same result from each method?** (no)

Have students take turns lining up members of the class according to various methods, then compare the results.

Content Development
Use the Motivation activity to lead into a discussion of the challenge that faced Mendeleev—to order the elements in a way that would reveal a pattern among them. Point out that several scientists before Mendeleev

had tried to do the same thing (see Historical Notes above). Ask,
• **Why was it important to Mendeleev to organize the elements?** (He believed that if he could order the elements correctly, elements with similar properties would be grouped together.)
• **How did Mendeleev decide to arrange the elements?** (according to increasing atomic mass)
• **What important pattern did he discover?** (that the valence numbers al-

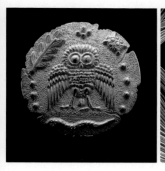

convinced that he could find a way of arranging the elements so that those with similar properties were grouped together. He set about testing his hypothesis by using the scientific method. Do you remember the basic steps of the scientific method? ❶

Mendeleev already had enough information about the elements, but he needed to organize his data. So he made a card for each of the known elements. On the card he listed the properties of that element, such as atomic mass, density, color, and melting point. He also included the element's valence, or bonding ability. The valence number indicates the number of electrons involved in bonding.

Looking for a pattern, Mendeleev decided to arrange the cards in order of increasing atomic mass. If he started with lithium, the next element would be beryllium. Then would come boron, carbon, nitrogen, oxygen, and fluorine. When the cards were arranged, Mendeleev made an important observation. ❷ The valence numbers always occurred in the pattern 1 2 3 4 3 2 1. Then Mendeleev saw something else equally remarkable. When he arranged the elements in rows of seven, they fell into columns, one under the other. All the elements in a column had the same valence! All the elements in a column showed similar chemical and physical properties!

As Mendeleev analyzed his results, he thought about the concept of **periodic** properties. When used this way, the word periodic means "repeating according to some pattern." The days of the week

Figure 5–2 *Mendeleev recognized that the properties of elements are repeated in a periodic way. Thus, certain elements have similar properties. Silver (left), gold (center), and copper (right) are all shiny hard elements that are good conductors of electricity. What are some uses of these elements?* ❷

Figure 5–3 *The periodic table was Mendeleev's greatest contribution to science—but not his only one. In 1887, Mendeleev attempted to study solar eclipses by traveling aloft in a hot air balloon. What property of elements did Mendeleev base his periodic table on?* ❸

113

HISTORICAL NOTES

Several scientists before Mendeleev attempted to order the elements according to similar properties. In 1817, German chemist Johann Dobereiner classified the elements in "triads," or groups of three elements with similar properties. Three of Dobereiner's triads include calcium, barium, strontium; chlorine, iodine, bromine; sulfur, tellurium, selenium.

In 1863, six years before Mendeleev's periodic table, English chemist John Newlands arranged the known elements according to increasing atomic mass, then created seven groups of seven elements each. He observed that every eighth element had similar properties. He called his observation the "Law of Octaves."

ANNOTATION KEY

❶ State the problem, gather information, form a hypothesis, experiment, record and analyze data, state a conclusion (Applying definitions)

❷ Jewelry, coins, decorative objects, wiring, building and machine parts (Relating facts)

❸ Atomic mass (Applying concepts)

❶ Thinking Skill: Predicting

❷ Thinking Skill: Sequencing data

---

ways occurred in the order, 1 2 3 4 3 2 1)

Explain that an element's valence number refers to the arrangement of electrons in the outermost energy level of an atom of that element. Point out that elements with similar outer energy level structures have similar properties.

Skills Development

Skill: Identifying patterns

Write the pattern 1 2 3 4 3 2 1 on the chalkboard. Ask students to describe the pattern in words. (It begins at 1, goes up to number 4, then goes back down to 1.)

Have several student volunteers come to the chalkboard and draw visual representations of the pattern. They might, for example, draw an up-and-down series of steps, or a series of

vertical lines 1–4 cm each. Ask,

• **Can you think of situations outside of chemistry in which you might find a similar pattern?** (Possible answers include a seven-note musical motif that goes up four notes, then back down; a bell-shaped curve in mathematics that shows a distribution of 1 2 3 4 3 2 1; a group of objects or people in which the first four increase in height, then the next three decrease.)

Sharpen Your Skills

Mendeleev—Chemical Superstar
Skills: Expressing an opinion, relating, applying
Level: Average
Type: Hands-on/library

This activity will help students with their vocabulary/writing comprehension skills. It will also enable them to analyze how contemporary society might evaluate the work of Mendeleev and relate his work to everyday life.

BACKGROUND INFORMATION

The six undiscovered elements whose existence and properties were predicted by Mendeleev were scandium, gallium, germanium, technetium, rhenium, and polonium.

ANNOTATION KEY

1 Every 12 months the pattern recurs (Identifying relationships)
2 It fell in the same family under silicon, element 14, in his periodic table. (Identifying relationships)
3 Repeating according to some definite pattern (Applying definitions)
1 Thinking Skill: Hypothesizing
2 Thinking Skill: Predicting
3 Thinking Skill: Applying concepts

5-1 (continued)

Reinforcement

Make sure that students understand the concept of periodicity by asking them to state in their own words what is meant by a periodic relationship among the elements. With every certain number of elements, the same properties or similar properties occur again.) Continue to reinforce the concept by having students create their own examples of a periodic relationship, such as a pattern of numbers in which the same numbers recur at regular intervals.

Sharpen Your Skills

Mendeleev—Chemical Superstar

When Mendeleev made his astonishing predictions about undiscovered elements, there was no radio, television, or newspaper and magazine coverage of the event.

1. Get together with four or five of your classmates and discuss how Mendeleev's work might be covered by the news media today.

2. Plan and stage at least two "media events" that would bring Mendeleev's discoveries to the attention of the public. For example, you might want to produce a television interview of Mendeleev or write an article that would appear in a popular science magazine.

are periodic because every seven days the pattern recurs. The notes of the musical scale are periodic, repeating a pattern with every eighth tone. Can you explain why the months of the year are periodic? (1)

Mendeleev concluded that he had found a periodic relationship among the elements. After listing each series of seven elements in order of increasing atomic mass, the same properties showed up again. Mendeleev stated that "the properties of the elements are periodic functions of their atomic masses." (1)

Mendeleev designed a periodic table in which the elements were arranged in order of increasing atomic mass. As he constructed this table, every so often he left blank spaces in order to make the known elements fit in the correct columns. Then he boldly announced that these blank spaces represented elements that had not yet been discovered. He even went so far as to predict the properties of these missing elements! He based his predictions on the properties of the elements above and below the spaces in the table. (2)

Surely enough, Mendeleev was right. Three elements discovered in his lifetime had properties

Figure 5–4 *The discovery of the element germanium in 1886 made Mendeleev the most famous chemist of the time. As you can see, his predictions about the properties of element 32, or "ekasilicon," were extremely close to the actual properties. Why do you think Mendeleev named element 32 "ekasilicon"?* (2)

MENDELEEV'S PREDICTIONS AND ACTUAL PROPERTIES OF ELEMENT 32

"Ekasilicon"		Germanium	
Date predicted	1871	Date discovered	1886
Atomic mass	72	Atomic mass	72.6
Density	5.5 g/cm³	Density	5.47 g/cm³
Bonding power	4	Bonding power	4
Color	Dark gray	Color	Grayish-white

114

Section Review 5-1

1. When the elements are arranged in order of increasing atomic mass, similar properties occur periodically.
2. Repeating according to a pattern
According to the blank spaces he left in his table to make the known elements fit in the correct columns.
4. Mendeleev knew that the problem was to find a relationship among all the elements. He had already gathered information about the elements for the purpose of writing his book. His hunch, or hypothesis, was that a pattern might be found if he arranged the elements according to atomic mass. As an experiment, he wrote the name of each element on a card and listed its properties. Then he arranged the cards in order of atomic mass. His observations were that valence numbers formed a pattern and that elements with similar properties fell into columns. He stated his con-

that agreed with those he had predicted. It is no wonder that Mendeleev became the most famous chemist of his time. Figure 5–4 shows how closely Mendeleev's predictions approached the actual properties of one of the "missing" elements.

SECTION REVIEW

1. What relationship among the elements did Mendeleev discover?
2. What is meant by the word periodic?
3. How did Mendeleev predict the existence of undiscovered elements?
4. State in your own words the way Mendeleev followed the basic steps of the scientific method.

5–2 The Modern Periodic Table

Despite the importance of Mendeleev's work, his periodic table was not perfect. When the elements are arranged in order of increasing atomic mass, several elements appear to be misplaced in terms of their properties. Mendeleev assumed that this was because the atomic masses of these elements had been incorrectly measured. Yet new measurements continued to confirm the original masses. What could be the problem?

A New Periodic Law

It was not until fifty years after Mendeleev had developed his table that the answer to the problem became apparent. It was then that the British scientist Henry Moseley determined for the first time the atomic numbers of the elements. The atomic number of an element is the number of protons contained in the nucleus of each atom of that element.

Figure 5–6 *Henry Gwyn-Jeffreys Moseley's discovery of atomic number led to a major improvement of Mendeleev's periodic table. Elements were now arranged in order of increasing atomic number. In 1915, this brilliant scientist enlisted in the English Army. Several months later, at the age of 27, Moseley was killed during the famous World War I battle of Gallipoli.*

SEPTEMBER

S	M	T	W	Th	F	S
1	2	3	4	5	6	7
8	9	10	11	12	13	14
15	16	17	18	19	20	21
22	23	24	25	26	27	28
29	30					

Figure 5–5 *The days of the month are periodic because every seven days the pattern recurs. What does periodic mean?* ③

Section Objective

To describe the design of the modern periodic table

University of Oxford, Museum of The History of Science, Courtesy AIP Niels Bohr Library.

③

115

5-2 THE MODERN PERIODIC TABLE

SECTION PREVIEW 5-2

In this section, students will discover how Mendeleev's periodic table was replaced by the modern periodic table. They will learn that in the modern periodic table, the elements are arranged according to increasing atomic number rather than increasing atomic mass.

Students will have an opportunity to observe and study the modern periodic table. They will learn that the vertical columns, which are called families or groups, consist of elements that have similar properties. They will also learn that the elements in horizontal rows, or periods, display properties that vary according to a predictable pattern.

PERFORMANCE OBJECTIVES 5-2

1. **Describe the design of the modern periodic table.**
2. **Discuss how groups, or families, contain elements with similar properties.**
3. **Explain how properties of elements vary across a horizontal row, or period.**

SCIENCE TERMS 5-2

periodic law	family p. 116
p. 116	period p. 117
group p. 116	

---

clusion in his version of the periodic law, then designed a periodic table based on his conclusions.

TEACHING STRATEGY 5-2

Motivation

Display a copy of the modern periodic table, preferably a large, wall-sized model. Point to the element sodium (Na) and explain that sodium reacts violently with water. Then move down the column to potassium (K) and explain that potassium reacts even more violently with water. Point to rubidium (Rb) and cesium (Cs) and ask,

• **What do you think will happen when these elements are brought into contact with water?** (Answers may vary. The correct answer is that they, too, will react violently with water.)

English scientist Henry Moseley determined the atomic numbers of the elements by using different metals as targets in an X-ray tube. He found that the wavelength of the X-ray was different for each element and dependent on the number of protons in the nucleus of each atom of the element.

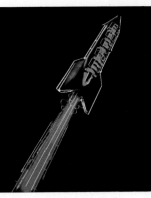

Figure 5–7 *Elements within the same family have similar properties. Both helium and neon are extremely unreactive gases. Helium is used in blimps (left), and neon is used in colored lights (right). What does unreactive mean?* ❶

ANNOTATION KEY

❶ Does not readily combine with other substances (Applying definitions)

❷ One electron in the outermost energy level (Interpreting illustrations)

❸ Metal to nonmetal; solid to liquid; very reactive to moderately reactive (Classifying)

❶ Thinking Skill: Making generalizations

❷ Thinking Skill: Classifying

❸ Thinking Skill: Identifying patterns

The discovery of atomic numbers led to an important change in Mendeleev's periodic table. It turns out that when the elements are arranged in order of *increasing atomic number*, elements with similar physical and chemical properties fall into place without exception. Thus, Mendeleev's periodic table was replaced by the modern periodic table. The **periodic law** forms the basis of the modern periodic table. ❶ **The periodic law states that the physical and chemical properties of the elements are periodic functions of their atomic numbers.**

Columns of the Table

Look at the periodic table of the elements found on pages 118–119. You will notice that the table consists of vertical columns of elements. Each column is labeled with a number and a letter. There are eight main columns of elements.

Columns of elements in the periodic table are called **groups** or **families.** Elements within the same family have similar but not identical properties. For

Lithium (Li)

Sodium (Na)

Potassium (K)

Figure 5–8 *Elements in the same family of the periodic table have similar properties. Here you see the electron arrangement of the elements lithium, sodium, and potassium. How is the electron arrangement in each element the same?* ❷

5-2 (continued)

Content Development

Review with students atomic structure. Draw a diagram on the chalkboard showing a nucleus composed of protons and neutrons surrounded by electrons. Point out that the atomic number of an element tells not only the number of protons contained in each atom of that element, but also the number of electrons.

Remind students that electrons fill the energy levels of an atom beginning with the energy level closest to the nucleus. Emphasize that the electrons in the outermost energy level are involved in bonding and determine an element's chemical properties. Help students to understand that the properties of the elements vary periodically according to atomic number because the electron configurations of the elements vary periodically according to atomic number.

Skills Development

Skill: Analyzing data

Provide students with the atomic number and atomic mass of the following pairs of elements: (a) tellurium (Te) and iodine (I); (b) cobalt (Co) and nickel (Ni); (c) argon (Ar) and potassium (K). Ask them to determine the order in which the elements in each pair would have been placed in Mendeleev's periodic table. (a) iodine, tellurium; (b) nickel, cobalt; (c) potassium, argon)

• **How are the elements in each pair ordered in the modern periodic table?** (The order of each pair is reversed.)

• **What accounts for the difference?** (Mendeleev ordered the elements according to increasing atomic mass, while the modern periodic table is ordered according to increasing atomic number.)

example, lithium (Li), sodium (Na), potassium (K), and the other members of Family IA are all soft silver-white shiny metals. They are also all highly reactive elements. Fluorine (F), chlorine (Cl), bromine (Br), and iodine (I) make up Family VIIA. These elements are also very much alike. Fluorine and chlorine are gases. Bromine is a liquid, and iodine a solid. But both bromine and iodine become gases very easily. All four elements react to form the same kinds of compounds. You will learn more about each family and its properties in Chapter 6.

Rows of the Table

Each horizontal row of elements in the periodic table is called a **period.** Unlike the elements in a family, the elements in a period are not alike in properties. In fact, the properties of the elements change greatly across any given row.

But there is a pattern to the properties of the elements as one moves across a period from left to right. The first element in a period is always a very active solid. The last element in a period is always a very inactive gas. You can see this pattern by looking at Period 4 of the periodic table. The first element, potassium (K), is an active solid. The last element, krypton (Kr), is an inactive gas.

Sharpen Your Skills

Classifying Objects

Mendeleev's table and the modern periodic table are systems of classifying the elements based on similar and different physical and chemical properties.

Choose a set of objects familiar to you, such as coins, stamps, marbles, leaves, playing cards, or jelly beans. Devise your own system of classifying the objects. Put your results in a table.

Sharpen Your Skills

Classifying Objects
Skills: Classifying, comparing, relating, applying
Level: Average
Type: Hands-on

This activity will help reinforce students' classifying skills and make them appreciate the enormous task Mendeleev undertook. Accept all logical classification systems, as no one system is more correct than another, assuming they are based on logic.

BACKGROUND INFORMATION

Until recently, groups in the modern periodic table were labeled with a Roman numeral and the capital letter A or B. Now, based on a decision made by IUPAC (International Union of Pure and Applied Chemistry), groups are label 1 through 18. Also in accordance with IUPAC, the names lanthanide and actinide have been changed to lanthanoid and actinoid.

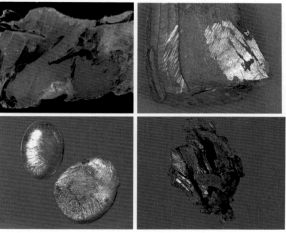

Figure 5–9 *The properties of elements in the same period are not alike. Reading from left to right are the elements potassium, calcium (top), gallium, arsenic, and bromine (bottom). In what ways do the properties change across the period?*

117

Skills Development
Skill: Relating concepts
Challenge students to explain why the order of the elements is similar, but not exactly the same, when arranged according to atomic mass instead of atomic number. (Answers may vary, but should include the idea that because protons have mass, atoms with higher atomic numbers tend also to have greater masses. However, the presence of neutrons in the nucleus of an atom can affect the mass without affecting the atomic number. Thus atomic masses do not increase in exactly the same order as atomic numbers.)

Enrichment
Have students study Figure 5-8. Then challenge them to make a similar diagram for the elements fluorine, chlorine, and bromine or beryllium, magnesium, and calcium.

HISTORICAL NOTES

A few elements, such as gold, silver, copper, and sulfur, were known in ancient times. During the Middle Ages and the Renaissance, more elements were discovered. By the time Mendeleev developed his periodic table, 63 elements were known. Today the number of natural elements totals 92, and since 1940, 17 more elements have been produced synthetically.

BACKGROUND INFORMATION

Prior to 1984, the Lanthanoid Series was called the Lanthanide Series, and the Actinoid Series was called the Actinide Series. In 1984, IUPAC mandated that the names of these series be changed to the names given on the periodic table on pages 118 and 119 and on the back endpaper of the text. These new terms were subsequently adopted by the American Chemical Society.

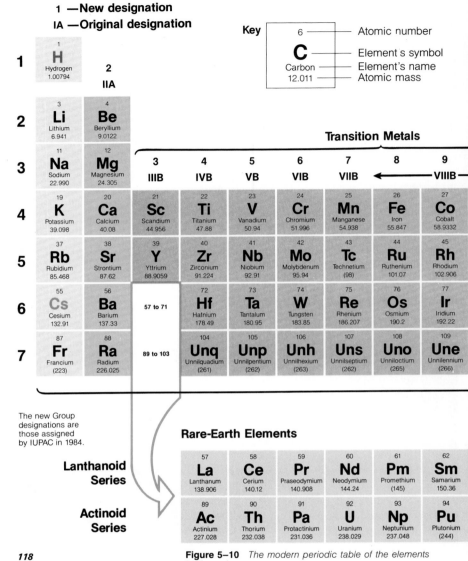

Figure 5–10 *The modern periodic table of the elements is shown here.*

118

5-2 (continued)

Content Development

Explain to students that the first 92 elements, from hydrogen to uranium, are known as natural elements. This means that they are found either free or combined in nature. These elements are sometimes referred to as the pre-Atomic Age elements. The elements beyond uranium, from number 93 to number 109, are called the *transuranium* elements. They are artificial elements produced from other elements by nuclear reactions.

Ask students to consider the production of artificial elements in light of the dreams of the alchemists. (Answers will vary.) Help students to recognize that the alchemists did believe that it was possible to change one element into another, although the techniques of nuclear physics were totally unknown to them. Also point out that the scientists of today are not particularly interested in changing base metals into gold—those scientists involved in the production of new elements tend to be primarily interested in pure research. It is an intriguing topic for discussion to consider the idea that modern science has fulfilled the alchemists' vision. It is just as valid for students to come to the conclusion that the hocus-pocus of the alchemists bears little relationship to modern nuclear science.)

Enrichment

Challenge students to consider the following question.
• **Why has it taken many, many centuries for all the natural elements to be discovered? Were not these same**

OF THE ELEMENTS

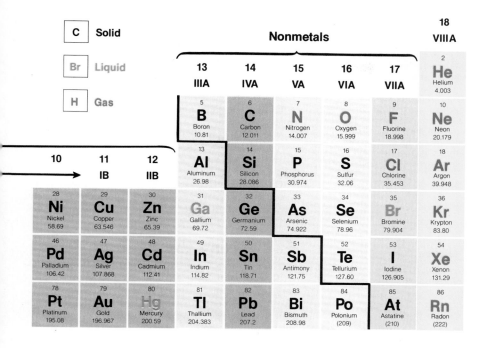

C	Solid
Br	Liquid
H	Gas

Nonmetals

Metals

The symbols shown here for elements 104-109 are being used temporarily until names for these elements can be agreed upon.

Mass numbers in parentheses are those of the most stable or common isotope.

18 VIIIA
2 **He** Helium 4.003

13 IIIA	14 IVA	15 VA	16 VIA	17 VIIA	
5 **B** Boron 10.81	6 **C** Carbon 12.011	7 **N** Nitrogen 14.007	8 **O** Oxygen 15.999	9 **F** Fluorine 18.998	10 **Ne** Neon 20.179
13 **Al** Aluminum 26.98	14 **Si** Silicon 28.086	15 **P** Phosphorus 30.974	16 **S** Sulfur 32.06	17 **Cl** Chlorine 35.453	18 **Ar** Argon 39.948

10	11 IB	12 IIB

28 **Ni** Nickel 58.69	29 **Cu** Copper 63.546	30 **Zn** Zinc 65.39	31 **Ga** Gallium 69.72	32 **Ge** Germanium 72.59	33 **As** Arsenic 74.922	34 **Se** Selenium 78.96	35 **Br** Bromine 79.904	36 **Kr** Krypton 83.80
46 **Pd** Palladium 106.42	47 **Ag** Silver 107.868	48 **Cd** Cadmium 112.41	49 **In** Indium 114.82	50 **Sn** Tin 118.71	51 **Sb** Antimony 121.75	52 **Te** Tellurium 127.60	53 **I** Iodine 126.905	54 **Xe** Xenon 131.29
78 **Pt** Platinum 195.08	79 **Au** Gold 196.967	80 **Hg** Mercury 200.59	81 **Tl** Thallium 204.383	82 **Pb** Lead 207.2	83 **Bi** Bismuth 208.98	84 **Po** Polonium (209)	85 **At** Astatine (210)	86 **Rn** Radon (222)

| 63 **Eu** Europium 151.96 | 64 **Gd** Gadolinium 157.25 | 65 **Tb** Terbium 158.925 | 66 **Dy** Dysprosium 162.50 | 67 **Ho** Holmium 164.93 | 68 **Er** Erbium 167.26 | 69 **Tm** Thulium 168.934 | 70 **Yb** Ytterbium 173.04 | 71 **Lu** Lutetium 174.967 |
| 95 **Am** Americium (243) | 96 **Cm** Curium (247) | 97 **Bk** Berkelium (247) | 98 **Cf** Californium (251) | 99 **Es** Einsteinium (252) | 100 **Fm** Fermium (257) | 101 **Md** Mendelevium (258) | 102 **No** Nobelium (259) | 103 **Lr** Lawrencium (260) |

119

HISTORICAL NOTES

In the early 1930s, a team of physicists led by Italian Enrico Fermi undertook an experimental study of atomic structure. Fermi had proclaimed that it should be possible to produce elements 93 and 94 from uranium. True to his assertion, element 93 was produced in 1940 in the laboratories of the University of California at Berkeley, and later, element 94 was produced in the same laboratories.

Between 1941 and 1961, elements 95 through 103 were produced. The production of elements 104 through 109 in the 1960s and 1970s was surrounded by controversy because both Russian and American scientists claimed to be the "discoverers" of these elements. Since the country who produces an element traditionally proposes the element's name, no names for these elements could be agreed upon. Thus IUPAC devised systematic names for the elements, which are to be used until official names can be established.

---

substances just as abundant in ancient times as they are today? (Answers may vary. An important point to consider is that many of the elements are not found free in nature; thus it is difficult to isolate them without fairly sophisticated scientific techniques. Many of the ancients believed that air, earth, and water were elements because they had no way of separating these substances into component parts.)

Skills Development
Skill: Interpreting charts
Have students observe the periodic table. Ask,
- **How are solids designated on this copy of the periodic table?** (by black lettering)
- **How are liquids designated?** (by green lettering)
- **How are gases designated?** (by red lettering)

- **How many elements are solids?** (94)
- **About what percentage of all elements does this represent?** (86%)
- **How many elements are liquids?** (4)
- **What percentage of all elements is this?** (about 4%)
- **How many elements are gases?** (11)
- **What percentage of all elements does this represent?** (about 10%)

5-3 USING THE PERIODIC TABLE

SECTION PREVIEW 5-3

In this section, students will learn how to use the periodic table. They will discover that a great deal of information can be gathered about an element by using the periodic table correctly.

Students will learn that each element is found in a separate square of the table. They will learn how to read from this square the name of the element, the chemical symbol, the atomic number, and the atomic mass.

In this section, students will become familiar with the properties of metals, nonmetals, and metalloids. They will learn how to locate these groups on the periodic table.

PERFORMANCE OBJECTIVES 5-3

1. **Read and use the periodic table.**
2. **Gather information from the element key of the periodic table.**
3. **Locate metals, nonmetals, and metalloids on the periodic table.**
4. **Discuss the properties of metals, nonmetals, and metalloids.**

SCIENCE TERMS 5-3

metal p. 121	nonmetal p. 122
ductile p. 122	metalloid p. 122
malleable p. 122	

5-2 (continued)

Reinforcement
Make sure students understand the distinction between groups and periods by asking them to complete exercises such as the following.
- **Name three elements in group 2.**
- **Name two elements in period 4.**
- **Name three elements in period 2.**
- **Name two elements in group 17.**

Section Review 5-2
1. Mendeleev arranged elements in order of increasing atomic mass. In the modern periodic table, elements are arranged in order of increasing atomic number.

Section Objective

To analyze the periodic table of elements

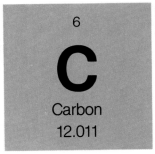

6

C

Carbon

12.011

120

---

2. Atomic number, or number of protons in the nucleus of an atom of an element
3. A vertical column of elements; a horizontal row of elements
4. Bromine

TEACHING STRATEGY 5-3

Motivation
Begin by asking students this question.

There are seven periods of elements. Look at Periods 6 and 7. You will notice that in each of these periods a row has been separated out and displayed under the main table. These two rows are part of the periodic table. They have been separated out to make the table shorter and easier to read. Elements in these two rows are rare-earth elements.

SECTION REVIEW

1. How does the arrangement of elements in the modern periodic table differ from that in Mendeleev's table?
2. What important feature of an atom did Moseley determine?
3. In the modern periodic table, what is a family? A period?
4. Chlorine is often added to swimming-pool water to kill germs. According to the periodic law, what other element might be used to do the same job?

5–3 Using the Periodic Table

The periodic table is one of the most important tools of a chemist. A great deal of information about an element can be gathered by using the periodic table correctly. As you read this section, refer often to the periodic table on pages 118–119.

Element Key

Look closely at the periodic table. Each element is found in a separate square. **Important information about an element is given in each square of the periodic table: its atomic number, chemical symbol, name, and atomic mass.**

The number at the top of each square is the *atomic number* of the element. Remember that the atomic number of an element is unique. No two elements have the same atomic number. As you look at the table, you can see that the elements are arranged in order of increasing atomic number.

Figure 5–11 *Four important facts about an element are supplied in each square of the periodic table: the symbol, name, atomic number, and atomic mass of that element.*

- **Have any of you ever been in a situation where you had to carry an ID?** (Answers may vary. Perhaps certain school activities require an ID; some students may use local recreational facilities that require an ID; students may have heard older relatives talk about using their drivers's license as an ID.)
- **What is the purpose of an ID?** (To identify a person by listing certain vital information)

HELP WANTED: MATERIALS SCIENTIST to develop new materials for use in automobile and airplane construction. College degree in chemistry or engineering required.

The airplane you see here looks as if it is flying backwards! But the plane, called the X-29, cuts through the air on its forward-swept wings with grace and speed.

Airplane designers have known since 1935 that forward-swept wings would be more aerodynamically efficient for high-speed airplanes. But early forward-swept wings made from steel tended to break off at high speeds.

Finally, in the 1970s, **materials scientists** developed a new material that makes forward-swept wings possible. They discovered that graphite, which is a form of carbon, can be sandwiched with plastic. The combination is stronger and more flexible than steel yet lighter in weight than metals.

A materials scientist works with metals, such as iron and aluminum, and with other materials, such as graphite, plastics, and ceramics. Products developed by materials scientists are all around you. The glue that holds this book together, rocket engines, and bicycle tires are just a few of the many products that materials scientists have helped to develop.

In order to join the exciting world of materials science, you should be interested in science, curious about the chemical composition of matter, and have some mechanical ability. If you would like to find out more about becoming a materials scientist, write to the American Society for Metals, Chapter and Membership Development, Metals Park, OH 44073.

Just below the atomic number, near the center of the square, is the *chemical symbol* for the element. Below the chemical symbol, the *name* of the element is spelled out. The number near the bottom of the square is the *atomic mass* of the element.

Now practice using what you have just learned. Locate the element boron in the periodic table. What is its atomic number? Its symbol? What element has the symbol Cd? What element has an atomic number of 38? What is the atomic mass of magnesium? Of bromine? ❶

Metals and Nonmetals

When you hear the word **metal,** you probably think of a familiar substance such as silver, iron, or copper. These elements are indeed metals. But substances you may not have thought of as metals— such as calcium, sodium, and potassium—are also classified as metals.

❷

TIE-IN/LANGUAGE ARTS

Many chemical symbols are based on the Latin names of the elements. For example, Pb stands for *plumbum,* which means lead, and Fe stands for *ferrum,* which means iron. Also, Na stands for *natrium,* which is Latin for sodium, and Ag stands for *argentum,* which means silver.

Sharpen Your Skills

Metals and Nonmetals
Skills: Inferring, applying, comparing, observing
Level: Enriched
Type: Hands-on

This activity will help students distinguish metals from nonmetals in a manner that is most relevant to their everyday lives. Accept all logical explanations for the differences in the number of metals and nonmetals used in the home.

• **What kind of information may be found on an ID?** (name, age, address, sex, height, weight, eye color, possibly a photo) If possible, bring in or have students bring in some samples of ID's.

Content Development
Use the Motivation discussion to lead into the idea that each square of the periodic table is like an element's ID; that is, it contains vital information that can be used to identify the element.

Reproduce on the chalkboard the enlarged element key for carbon (C) shown in the text. Ask a student volunteer to go to the chalkboard and reproduce the element key for chlorine (Cl). Use the enlarged models to point out the location of the element's name, symbol, atomic number, and atomic mass. Emphasize to students that the first letter of a chemical symbol is always capitalized, while the second letter is not.

Enrichment
Divide the class into two teams. Then divide each team in half. Give one-half of each team a set of cards marked with the atomic numbers from 1 to 18. Give the other half of each team a set of cards marked with the chemical symbols for the first 18 elements. Challenge the teams to see how quickly they can match the atomic numbers with the chemical symbols. The first team to complete the task correctly wins.

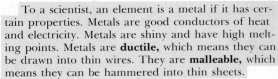

Sharpen Your Skills

The Frasch Process

Sulfur is a very important nonmetal that has many uses in today's world. Large underground deposits of sulfur are located in Louisiana and Texas. However, mining sulfur by ordinary methods is nearly impossible.

Using books and other reference materials in the library, find out about the Frasch process for removing sulfur from the ground. What properties of sulfur make this process possible? ❶

Figure 5–12 *Iodine (left) and sulfur (right) are two typical nonmetals. They are characteristically dull and brittle. Where on the periodic table are nonmetals located?* ❷

To a scientist, an element is a metal if it has certain properties. Metals are good conductors of heat and electricity. Metals are shiny and have high melting points. Metals are **ductile,** which means they can be drawn into thin wires. They are **malleable,** which means they can be hammered into thin sheets.

Of the 109 known elements, 88 are metals. If you look at the periodic table, you will see a dark, zigzag line running like steps down the right side of the table. Elements to the left of the line are metals.

Nonmetals, which are the elements to the right of the dark line, do not have the properties metals have. Nonmetals are poor conductors of heat and electricity. They usually have dull surfaces and low melting points. Those nonmetals that are solids tend to be brittle and break easily. Carbon and phosphorus are examples of nonmetals that are solids at room temperature. Bromine is a liquid nonmetal. Nonmetals that are gases include oxygen, nitrogen, and chlorine. Using the periodic table, can you name some other nonmetals? ❶

The dividing line between metals and nonmetals is not quite as definite as it appears. For along each side of the dark line are elements that have properties of both metals and nonmetals. These elements are called **metalloids** (MEHT-uhl-oidz). Metalloids may be shiny or dull. They conduct heat and electricity better than nonmetals but not as well as metals. The metalloids include boron, silicon, germanium, arsenic, antimony, tellurium, polonium, and astatine.

Figure 5-13 *Metalloids are elements that have properties of both metals and nonmetals. The metalloid silicon (left) is important in the manufacture of computer chips. Entire computer circuits can be arranged on just one silicon chip. Antimony (right), another metalloid, is used to make alloys. What are some other metalloids?* ❸

SECTION REVIEW

1. What information is given in the square that is assigned to each element?
2. What is the position on the periodic table of those elements that are called metals? Nonmetals?
3. What are some characteristic properties of metals? Of nonmetals?
4. What are metalloids?
5. Suppose that you have a sample of an unknown element. You notice that the element is shiny and that its melting point is fairly high. However, the element does not conduct heat well. Which of the following elements might the sample be—iodine, aluminum, iron, or silver? Explain your answer.

5–4 Periodic Properties of the Elements

You have learned several ways in which the periodic table provides important information about the elements. Elements in the same family, or vertical column, have similar properties. Elements on the left of the table are metals. Elements on the right are nonmetals. Metalloids, which show properties of both metals and nonmetals, are located on either side of the dark zigzag line. ❷

Section Objective

To identify periodic trends in the elements

5-4 PERIODIC PROPERTIES OF THE ELEMENTS

SECTION PREVIEW 5-4

In this section, students will become familiar with the properties of the elements that vary in a regular way from left to right across a period. These properties include electron arrangement, reactivity, atomic size, and metallic properties.

Students will discover the pattern of valence numbers that recurs in each period. They will also discover that the tendency of an element to lose or gain electrons in chemical combinations is related to its position in a period.

Students will learn that atomic size decreases as one moves across a period, and that this decrease is related to electron arrangement. Finally, students will see how elements become less metallic as one moves across a period.

PERFORMANCE OBJECTIVES 5-4

1. **Identify periodic trends in the elements.**
2. **Explain how electron arrangement changes across a period.**
3. **Explain how an element's tendency to lose or gain electrons changes across a period.**
4. **Explain how atomic size changes across a period.**
5. **Identify the change in metallic properties across a period.**

123

---

3. Good conductors of heat and electricity, shiny, high melting points, ductile, malleable; poor conductors of heat and electricity, dull surfaces, low melting points, brittle, break easily
4. Elements that have properties of both metals and nonmetals
5. The element is probably aluminum because its properties most closely resemble those given.

TEACHING STRATEGY 5-4

Motivation

Have students observe Figure 5-14.
- **What do you notice that is similar about the electron arrangement in each element?** (Each has the first two energy levels filled.)
- **What is different about the electron arrangement in each element?** (Sodium has only one electron in its outermost energy level; argon has

eight electrons.)
- **What is the valence number of sodium?** (1) **Of argon?** (0)
- **Where are these two elements located in the periodic table?** (At opposite ends of period 3; sodium is in group 1 and argon is in group 18.)
- **What might you expect would be true about the electron arrangements of the other elements in period 3?** (They would have 2 to 7 electrons in their third energy level.)

TEACHER DEMONSTRATION

Draw on the chalkboard a model of a lithium atom. Point out that the atom has three electrons, two of which are located in the first energy level. The third electron is located in the second energy level.

In a row to the right of the lithium model, draw seven more atomic models, but do not draw in the electrons. These models will be used to represent beryllium, boron, carbon, nitrogen, oxygen, fluorine, and neon. Explain to students that these elements have 4, 5, 6, 7, 8, 9, and 10 electrons, respectively.

Have student volunteers come to the chalkboard and fill in the electrons for each element. Correct any errors they might make. Then ask,
• **Based on these diagrams, how do electron arrangements vary across a period?** (Each element has one more electron in the second energy level than the previous element.)

BACKGROUND INFORMATION

The pattern of valence numbers across a period, 1 2 3 4 3 2 1 0, does not include the transition metals. These metals tend to behave somewhat differently because their inner energy levels are not completely filled. Thus transition metals are not as reactive as one might expect, given their outer energy level structure, and they often exhibit two or more valence numbers in chemical combinations. The special properties of the transition metals will be discussed further in the next chapter.

Figure 5–14 *The properties of elements vary in a regular way from left to right across a period. Sodium, an extremely reactive metal, is used in its vapor phase in street lights (right). Sodium vapor lamps provide bright-yellow light. Argon, an extremely unreactive gas, is used to make glowing works of art (left). How does the electron arrangement of each element account for its reactivity?* ❶

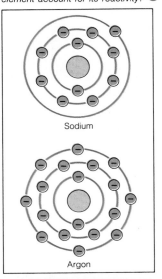

Sodium

Argon

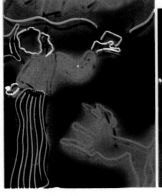

Additional information about the elements can be obtained from their location in a period, or horizontal row. **Certain properties of elements vary in a regular way from left to right across a period.** These properties include electron arrangement, reactivity, atomic size, and metallic properties.

The valence number of an element is related to the electrons in the outermost energy level of an atom of that element. It is these electrons that are involved in the chemical combining of elements to form compounds.

Starting at the left of each period, the pattern of valence numbers is 1 2 3 4 3 2 1 0. An element with a valence of 1 will gain, lose, or share 1 electron in a chemical combination. An element with a valence of 4 will gain, lose, or share 4 electrons. What is true about an element with a valence of 0? How reactive is such an element? ❷

Elements to the left in a period tend to lose electrons easily when they combine with other elements. You know that elements on the left of the table are metals. So another property of metals is that they lose electrons in chemical combinations. Elements to the right in a period tend to gain electrons easily when they combine with other elements. What kind of elements are these? ❸

The amount of energy needed to remove an electron from an atom shows a periodic increase from left to right across a period. Since atoms of elements on the left in a period tend to lose electrons, removing an electron from such an atom re-

---

5-4 (continued)

Content Development

Refer to the Motivation discussion to emphasize the configuration of electrons across a period. Point out that elements with few electrons in the outermost energy level tend to lose electrons in chemical bonds, while elements with many electrons in the outermost energy level tend to gain electrons. Review the idea that the va-

lence number of an element refers to the number of electrons that will be lost, gained, or shared when an atom of that element is involved in a chemical bond.

Stress that the valence number of group 18 elements is zero because the outermost energy level is full; thus, there is no need for these atoms to gain, lose, or share electrons.

Skills Development

Skill: Making diagrams

Have students trace on a sheet of paper the outline of the periodic table. Then have them use arrows, shading, or any other technique they wish to diagram the periodic properties of the elements. For example, to indicate the change in metallic properties, they might draw an arrow from left to right and label it "metallic properties decrease."

quires a small amount of energy. Removing an electron from an atom of an element on the right in a period requires a large amount of energy. Why? **4**

Another property of elements that varies periodically is atomic size. From left to right across a period, atomic size decreases. This decrease can be explained in terms of electron arrangement. As the atomic number increases across a period, one electron is added to each successive element. But this electron is still in the same energy level. The increase in the number of electrons in the energy level and the number of protons in the nucleus produces a stronger attraction between these oppositely charged particles. The electrons are pulled closer to the nucleus. The size of the atom decreases. Can you explain why atomic size increases from top to bottom in a family? **6**

Metallic properties of the elements are also periodic. From left to right across a period, elements become less metallic in nature.

SECTION REVIEW

1. What properties are periodic in nature?
2. What is the pattern of valences from left to right across a period?
3. How does atomic size change across a period? Down a family?
4. Why does the amount of energy needed to remove an electron from an atom decrease from top to bottom in a family?

Figure 5–15 *Metallic properties of the elements also are periodic. Chromium is a shiny hard metal often used as automobile trim (left). Bromine is a dull-brown liquid at room temperature (right). What is true about the number of electrons in the outermost energy level of atoms across a period? About the metallic properties?* **5**

Sharpen Your Skills

Predicting Formulas

Zinc (Zn), cadmium (Cd), and mercury (Hg) are in the zinc subgroup of the periodic table. Predict the formulas of the corresponding compounds of cadmium and mercury based on the fact that zinc forms the following compounds:

$ZnCl_2$ (zinc chloride)
ZnO (zinc oxide)
ZnS (zinc sulfide)
$Zn(NO_3)_2$ (zinc nitrate)

125

LABORATORY INVESTIGATION
GRAPHING TRENDS
IN THE PERIODIC TABLE

BEFORE THE LAB
Make sure you have enough graph paper and colored pencils to adequately supply each student.

PRE-LAB DISCUSSION
This lab is concerned primarily with analyzing data. It is important for students to recognize that one very effective way of analyzing data is to make a graph.

After students have read the lab, emphasize that the graphs they will be making are designed to show one variable as the function of another variable.
- **What variables are being compared in this lab?** (atomic number and atomic radius; atomic number and energy needed to remove one electron)
- **What is the independent variable in each graph?** (atomic number)
- **What is the dependent variable in each graph?** (atomic radius; energy needed to remove one electron)

SKILL DEVELOPMENT
Students will use the following skills while completing this investigation.
1. Graphing
2. Computational
3. Inferring
4. Applying
5. Predicting

TEACHING STRATEGY FOR LAB PROCEDURE
Make sure students choose reasonable intervals and adequate ranges for atomic radius and energy.

OBSERVATIONS
1. Decreases; increases
2. Increases; decreases

CONCLUSIONS
1. Atomic radius, ionization energy, electronegativity or electron affinity, number of electrons in outermost energy level
2. The atomic radius decreases across a period because the attraction between the negatively charged electrons that are added consecutively to each element and the positively charged protons that are added consecutively to each nucleus becomes greater. The atomic radius increases down a family because an additional energy level is added.
3. The energy required to remove an electron increases across a period because the electrons are more tightly held by the increased attraction of the positively charged nucleus. The energy required to remove an electron decreases down a family because the electrons are farther from the nucleus and therefore the attraction is less.

Graphing Trends in the Periodic Table

	IA	IIA	IIIA	IVA	VA	VIA	VIIA	VIIIA
2	3 **Li** 1.23 124	4 **Be** 0.89 215	5 **B** 0.80 191	6 **C** 0.77 260	7 **N** 0.70 335	8 **O** 0.66 314	9 **F** 0.64 402	10 **Ne** 0.67 497
3	11 **Na** 1.57 119	12 **Mg** 1.36 176	13 **Al** 1.25 138	14 **Si** 1.17 188	15 **P** 1.10 242	16 **S** 1.04 239	17 **Cl** 0.99 299	18 **Ar** 0.98 363
4	19 **K** 2.03 100	20 **Ca** 1.74 141						
5	37 **Rb** 2.16 96	38 **Sr** 1.91 131						
6	55 **Cs** 2.35 90	56 **Ba** 1.98 120						

8 ◄— atomic number
O ◄— symbol
0.66 ◄— atomic radius
314 ◄— energy required to remove the easiest electron

Problem
Are certain properties of elements periodic functions of their atomic numbers?

Materials (per student)
2 sheets of graph paper
2 colored pencils (different colors)
straight edge

Procedure
1. For elements 3–20, make a graph of atomic radius as a function of atomic number. Plot atomic number on the X axis and atomic radius on the Y axis. Make sure each scale is uniform and covers the range of numbers to be plotted. Label the graph. Include a title and labels for each axis.
2. For elements in Family IA, make a graph of atomic radius as a function of atomic number. On the same graph, use a different color to do the same for elements in Family IIA. Label the graph.
3. For elements 3–20, make a graph of the energy required to remove the easiest electron as a function of atomic number. Plot atomic number on the X axis and energy on the Y axis. Label the graph.
4. For elements in Family IA, make a graph of the energy required to remove the easiest electron as a function of atomic number. On the same graph, use a different color to do the same for elements in Family IIA. Label the graph.

Observations
1. What happens to the atomic radius as the atomic number increases across a period? Down a family?
2. What happens to the energy needed to remove an electron as the atomic number increases across a period? Down a family?

Conclusions
1. What properties of the elements are periodic functions of their atomic numbers?
2. Why does atomic radius change as it does?
3. Why does energy required to remove an electron change as it does?

5–1 Development of a Periodic Table

❏ Mendeleev arranged the elements in order of increasing atomic mass. All the elements in a column had the same valence and showed similar chemical and physical properties.

❏ Empty spaces in Mendeleev's periodic table proved to be undiscovered elements.

5–2 The Modern Periodic Table

❏ Moseley's discovery of atomic number altered Mendeleev's periodic table.

❏ In the modern periodic table, elements are arranged in order of increasing atomic number.

❏ The periodic law states that the physical and chemical properties of the elements are periodic functions of their atomic numbers.

❏ Vertical columns in the periodic table are called groups or families.

❏ Horizontal rows in the periodic table are called periods.

5–3 Using the Periodic Table

❏ Each element occupies one square in the table.

❏ Each square contains the element's atomic number, symbol, name, and atomic mass.

❏ The elements can be classified as metals, nonmetals, or metalloids.

❏ Metals are good conductors of heat and electricity. They are shiny and have high melting points. They are ductile and malleable.

❏ Nonmetals are poor conductors of heat and electricity. They usually have dull surfaces and low melting points. Solid nonmetals are brittle.

❏ Metalloids have properties of both metals and nonmetals.

5–4 Periodic Properties of the Elements

❏ Periodic properties of the elements include electron arrangement, reactivity, atomic size, and metallic properties.

Define each term in a complete sentence.

ductile	group	metal	nonmetal	periodic
family	malleable	metalloid	period	periodic law

On a separate sheet of paper, write the letter of the answer that best completes each statement.

1. In finding a relationship among the elements, Mendeleev
a. used the scientific method.
b. stumbled upon his discovery by accident.
c. made his discovery while looking for something else.
d. carried out many experiments to test the properties of elements.

2. In his periodic table, Mendeleev placed one element to the right of another because it had
a. similar properties to the previous element.
b. the next largest atomic number.
c. the next largest atomic mass.
d. the same valence number as the previous element.

127

GOING FURTHER: ENRICHMENT

Part 1

For elements 1 to 18 (hydrogen to argon), have students graph valence numbers (Y axis) versus atomic numbers (X axis). The result should be a sine curve ranging from 0 to 4 on the Y axis. Have students compare their graphs to those they made of atomic radius versus atomic number, and energy needed to remove one electron versus atomic number.

Part 2

Discuss with students what would happen if for one of the graphs they made during the lab, they were to substitute atomic mass for atomic number. (The results would be similar, but each curve would have a few discrepancies. Also, it would be harder to set up atomic masses in even intervals on the X-axis.)

Challenge interested students to try one of the graphs using atomic mass, then evaluate their results.

CHAPTER REVIEW

MULTIPLE CHOICE

1. a	**3.** b	**5.** b	**7.** d	**9.** a
2. c	**4.** c	**6.** b	**8.** c	**10.** b

COMPLETION

1. properties	**6.** family
2. periodic	**7.** period
3. atomic number	**8.** group
4. Mendeleev	**9.** metals
5. atomic number	**10.** metalloids

TRUE OR FALSE

1. F 63	**6.** F atomic
2. T	number
3. F periodic	**7.** T
4. F atomic mass	**8.** T
5. T	**9.** T
	10. F increases

SKILL BUILDING

1. Metals: beryllium, manganese, cadmium, platinum, lithium, chromium, mercury; Nonmetals: bromine, iodine, helium, argon; Metalloids: arsenic, astatine, germanium

2. Hydrogen, boron, sodium, sulfur, iron, copper, zinc, strontium, gold, lead

3. Students' drawing should show atomic number: 80; chemical symbol: Hg; name; Mercury; atomic mass: 201.

4. a. indium **b.** bromine **c.** germanium

5. Valence number indicates how many electrons are available for bonding. Elements with the same valence would form similar compounds because one atom of each element would "fit" with the same number of atoms of other elements. Elements with a valence of 0 would be similar in that they do not react with other elements.

6. Barium is a rather active metal; radon is an inert nonmetal. Both elements are large in atomic size, as they are near the bottom of their group. But the atomic size of radon is smaller than that of barium because it is to the right of a period while barium is to the left. The valence of barium is 2; the valence of radon is 0.

7. Students should determine that elements A, C, G, K, Q, and Y all fall into one group and elements B, F, J, P, and X all fall into another group. Period 1 includes elements A and B. Period 2

3. Moseley was able to determine each element's
a. atomic mass.   b. atomic number.   c. symbol.   d. brittleness.

4. The periodic law states that the properties of elements are periodic functions of their
a. atomic mass.   b. symbol.   c. atomic number.   d. valence.

5. The term group refers to elements
a. in the same row.
b. in the same column.
c. that were missing in Mendeleev's original table.
d. that are metalloids.

6. If a metal can be hammered or rolled into thin sheets, the metal is
a. ductile.   b. malleable.   c. brittle.   d. active.

7. A brittle element that is not a very good conductor of heat and electricity is
a. inert.   b. a metal.   c. ductile.   d. a nonmetal.

8. In the periodic table, elements known as metals are
a. in one row.   b. in one column.   c. on the left side.   d. on the right side.

9. Each period of the table begins on the left with a
a. very active metal.   b. metalloid.   c. rare-earth element.   d. nonmetal.

10. In a given period, as atomic number increases, the size of the atom
a. increases.   b. decreases.   c. stays the same.   d. equals zero.

128

CONTENT REVIEW: COMPLETION

On a separate sheet of paper, write the word or words that best complete each statement.

1. An element's _____ are those characteristics that can be used to identify the element.

2. A word that means "to repeat according to some pattern" is _____.

3. The number of protons in the nucleus of each atom of an element is called the _____ of the element.

4. The person who devised the first periodic table was _____.

5. In the modern periodic table, elements are arranged in order of increasing _____.

6. A vertical column in the periodic table is called a (an) _____ or group.

7. A horizontal row in the periodic table is called a (an) _____.

8. Elements that are found within the same _____ of the periodic table have similar properties.

9. Elements that are good conductors of heat and electricity are classified as _____.

10. Elements that have properties of both metals and nonmetals are called _____.

CONTENT REVIEW: TRUE OR FALSE

Determine whether each statement is true or false. Then on a separate sheet of paper, write "true" if it is true. If it is false, change the underlined word or words to make the statement true.

1. Mendeleev knew of <u>92</u> elements when he began work on his periodic table.

2. Mendeleev noticed a definite pattern in the <u>valence numbers</u> of the elements.

contains elements C, D, E, and F. Period 3 includes elements G, H, I, and J. Period 4 includes elements K, L, M, N, O, and P. Period 5 includes elements Q, R, S, T, U, V, W, and X. Period 6 includes elements Y and Z.

ESSAY

1. It would most resemble lead because as you extend the table with numbers greater than 106, number 114 falls in the same column as lead.

2. Copper and gold should resemble silver most closely because they are the ones directly above and below silver in the same column.

3. As Mendeleev arranged the elements in his table, he noticed that there were gaps in the table. He correctly inferred these gaps would one day be filled by yet-to-be-discovered elements.

4. Metals usually are shiny, good conductors of heat and electricity, able to be drawn into wire, and able to be

3. The word <u>ductile</u> means "repeating according to some pattern."
4. Mendeleev's periodic table was arranged in order of increasing <u>atomic number</u>.
5. Sodium, a member of Family IA, is a very <u>active</u> element.
6. The <u>atomic mass</u> is the number of protons in the nucleus of an atom.
7. High melting point is a property of <u>metals</u>.
8. <u>Nonmetals</u> are usually poor conductors of heat and electricity.
9. Elements to the left in a period tend to <u>lose</u> electrons easily.
10. From top to bottom in a given family, the atomic number increases and the size of the atom <u>decreases</u>.

CONCEPT REVIEW: SKILL BUILDING

Use the skills you have developed in the chapter to complete each activity.

1. **Classifying elements** Classify the following elements as metals, nonmetals, or metalloids: arsenic, bromine, argon, beryllium, manganese, cadmium, astatine, germanium, lithium, helium, mercury.
2. **Sequencing** Arrange the following elements in order of increasing atomic mass: sulfur, boron, copper, iron, gold, lead, sodium, hydrogen, strontium, zinc.
3. **Making a diagram** Using the element mercury, make a drawing of its square on the periodic table. Label each piece of information given.
4. **Applying concepts** Determine the identity of the following elements:
   a. This metal has a valence of 3, properties similar to aluminum, and an atomic mass slightly less than tin.
   b. This highly active element is the only liquid nonmetal. It has a valence of 1 and an atomic number of 35.
   c. This element, with a valence of 4, shows properties of metals and nonmetals and

has 32 protons in the nucleus of each atom.
5. **Applying concepts** Explain why elements with the same valence number have similar properties.
6. **Making comparisons** Compare the properties of element 56, barium, with those of element 86, radon. How do you account for the difference in properties?
7. **Applying concepts** Suppose that in another galaxy, a completely different set of elements exists. These elements, which number 26, have been assigned symbols corresponding to the letters of the alphabet by the inhabitants of the galaxy. The symbols run in order of increasing atomic number. The following elements have been found to closely resemble one another in their physical and chemical properties:

A, C, G, K, Q, and Y
B, F, J, P, and X

Develop a periodic table of these elements, using this information.

CONCEPT REVIEW: ESSAY

Discuss each of the following in a brief paragraph.

1. Suppose that element number 114 is discovered. Which known element will it most resemble? Explain your answer.
2. According to the periodic table, what two elements most resemble silver (Ag)?
3. How was Mendeleev able to tell that there were elements not yet discovered?
4. Compare the properties of metals, nonmetals, and metalloids. Use examples.
5. Why are elements with valences of 1 the most active metals or nonmetals?
6. How is the number assigned to a family related to the electron configuration of each element in that family?

129

rolled into thin sheets. Nonmetals are generally not good conductors of heat and electricity and are often brittle. Metalloids have some properties of metals and, at the same time, of nonmetals.

5. Metals with valences of 1 need to lose only 1 electron to form a stable electron configuration. This is relatively easy to do because it requires the least amount of energy. Nonmetals with valences of 1 have 7 electrons in the outermost energy level and need to gain only 1 electron to be shell complete.

6. The number assigned to a family corresponds to the number of electrons in the outermost energy level, or the number of valence electrons.

ADDITIONAL QUESTIONS AND TOPIC SUGGESTIONS

1. Based on their positions in the periodic table, compare and contrast the properties of strontium (Sr) and iodine (I). (Strontium is a metal; iodine is a nonmetal. Strontium loses electrons; iodine gains electrons in chemical combinations. Because strontium is near the beginning of period 5 and iodine is near the end, the atomic radius of strontium will be larger than the atomic radius of iodine. It would take much more energy to remove an electron from an iodine atom than from a strontium atom.)
2. Suppose the elements in the periodic table were listed alphabetically rather than according to atomic number. What problems would result? Can you think of any advantages of such an arrangement? (The table would no longer be periodic since the elements would be in no particular order according to properties. It would be impossible to determine any information about an element based on its position in the table. It would be difficult to compare one element with another. It would also be difficult to add new elements because they would have to be sandwiched into the middle of the table. The one advantage might be that it would be easy to locate an element by name.)

ISSUES IN SCIENCE

The following issues can be used as a springboard for class debate, or they can be assigned as a writing homework.
1. Henry Moseley, the scientist who first determined the atomic numbers of the elements, was drafted into the British army as a foot soldier during World War I. He was killed in battle at the age of 27. Do you feel that this loss supports the idea that scientists should not be required to participate in combat during a war or other national emergency?
2. Recently the IUPAC changed the labeling of groups in the periodic table. Find out why this change was made, then express your opinion about the desirability of the change.

Chapter 6
FAMILIES OF ELEMENTS

CHAPTER OVERVIEW

With so many elements (109), it is impractical to begin a study of each one individually. However, this chapter will enable students to become familiar with many elements and to predict properties of other elements. These predictions will be accurate because of the special grouping of elements within the periodic table.

The elements will first be broadly classified as metals or nonmetals. A more detailed presentation is then made as some metals are seen to be very active (alkali and alkaline) while others are not quite so active (transition metals). Metalloids are introduced as elements with intermediate properties of metals and nonmetals. The elements classified as nonmetals are found on the right side of the periodic table. The families of nonmetals, such as the nitrogen and the oxygen families, are presented separately. The halogens (Group VII) are the most active non-metals.

Two special classifications of elements are also highlighted. The noble gases combine with almost no other elements. The rare-earth elements are so similar to one another that they are extremely difficult to separate.

TEACHER DEMONSTRATION

The following demonstration may be used to show the differences between active and inactive metals. Prepare some dilute hydrochloric acid. Next, display some pea-sized calcium

INTRODUCING CHAPTER 6

Begin your introduction of Chapter 6 by having as many colored compounds as possible on display in the room. Have students also examine the pictorial display of the colored powders shown on page 130. Point out that the compounds shown are composed of metals bonded to nonmetals. If a periodic table is available, point to a specific colored compound and lo-cate the metal in that compound in the periodic table. For example, yellow sodium chromate has the metal sodium in it (11), the metal chromium (24), responsible for the yellow color, and the nonmetal oxygen (8). Repeat this for a few of the compounds. This will get the students initially familiar with the locations of metals and nonmetals. Ask,

• **Why do you suppose some substances have a color while others do not?** (The energy levels studied earlier are the key to this. If valence electrons can absorb some of the wavelengths of visible light, then the substance will reflect back unabsorbed colors to the observer.)

Later in the chapter students will see that a calendar and a periodic table have some similarities. Elements are grouped into columns with similar properties. Days of the week on a calendar are also grouped into columns.

Families of Elements

CHAPTER OBJECTIVES

After completing this chapter, you will be able to

6–1 Compare the properties of metals, nonmetals, and metalloids.

6–2 Name and describe the most active metals.

6–3 Describe the characteristics of the transition metals.

6–4 Explain the change in properties across the periodic table.

6–5 Describe the properties of the halogen family.

6–6 Describe the properties of the noble gases.

6–7 Identify the rare-earth elements.

The paints on this artist's palette are made from compounds called pigments. Pigments are composed of a group of elements known as transition metals.

Displaying every color of the rainbow, these finely ground particles were once valued as semiprecious stones. Traders in the ancient world carried the rarest of them across continents, hoping to bring the brightest and most exotic to the palaces of kings.

Chemists today observe these particles carefully, noting size, shape, and texture. They analyze their colors with a special instrument. Then they test the particles to see how well they can withstand exposure to heat, light, moisture, and air pollution.

Can you guess what these unique particles are? You may be surprised to know that they are *pigments*—the powderlike materials that give color to paint. When suspended in oil or other flowing substances, pigments can be splashed on canvas to capture the beauty of a sunset or to reveal the complex coloration of the human face.

A list of pigments reads like a chemistry book—zinc white, cadmium yellow, cobalt blue, iron oxide red, chromium green. All these pigments are made from a group of elements known as the transition metals. In this chapter you will read about the transition metals and about many other groups of elements. Each group has its own special set of properties and its own interesting—and sometimes surprising—practical uses.

and/or magnesium metal pieces. Also display some lead pieces and/or nickel. Have the acid poured into displayed test tubes. Announce that even though substances may be called metals they may still have different properties (i.e. the ability to react with other chemicals). Place approximately equal-sized pieces in the acids. In the tubes when a reaction takes place between calcium and magnesium, bubbles of hydrogen gas can be seen forming. The gas, an example of a nonmetal, can be identified as hydrogen by collecting it with an inverted test tube and, while keeping the tube inverted, igniting with a glowing splint. The familiar "hydrogen bark" may be heard as hydrogen combines with oxygen to make a small amount of water vapor. Meanwhile, the tubes with lead or nickel will show little or no reaction with acid. Ask students to name some other metals that might be considered active or inactive. Ask them to note where these elements appear on the periodic table.

TEACHER RESOURCES

Audiovisuals

A Look at Chemical Changes, film, CRM/McGraw-Hill

Matter and Molecules: The Matter of Elements, filmstrip, Singer Educational Division

Books

Ahrens, L. H., ed, *The Origin and Distribution of the Elements,* Pergamon

Donohue, J., *Structure of the Elements,* Wiley

Schroeder, H. A., *Elements in Living Systems,* Plenum

131

While all Mondays within a month are not identical, they do have many similarities. The same is true for Fridays, etc. Display a large calendar and discuss the thing that each Friday has in common—last day of school week, staying up later, payday for some places, etc.

Select a Saturday date on the calendar and ask students what they will be doing on that date. (Point out that the students probably have at least some idea because they can use the predictive property of the calendar without actually waiting until that Saturday to know about that specific day.)

The periodic table columns also contain a logical arrangement that allows a person to predict properties of elements by knowing their location on the table. For example, helium and neon are very unreactive elements. One might accurately predict that argon, found on the same column, may also be unreactive. This prediction can be made without actually obtaining argon to study. If the Teacher Demonstration has been done, one might predict that strontium, found in the same column as calcium and magnesium, would also react easily with acid.

• **What metals on the chart would behave like lead or nickel?** (gold, silver)

6–1 PROPERTIES OF METALS AND NONMETALS

SECTION PREVIEW 6-1

In this section, students will be shown the differences between the two broad classifications of elements: metals and nonmetals. These differences will be examined by discussing both physical and chemical properties of each type of element. The physical properties of metals result from metals having only a few valence electrons. Nonmetals, being poor conductors of heat and electricity, have more valence electrons, but tend to keep them and even attract electrons from other elements.

This section also explains, with several examples, how alloys are cooled mixtures of metals. Several elements seem to have properties of metals and nonmetals. These important elements are introduced to students as metalloids.

PERFORMANCE OBJECTIVES 6-1

1. **Describe the physical properties of metals such as heat/electrical conductivity, luster, ductility, and malleability.**
2. **Cite several examples of alloys.**
3. **Describe nonmetals as poor conducting substances that lack luster.**
4. **Distinguish metals and nonmetals from each other based on the low number of valence electrons for metals and the higher number of valence electrons in nonmetals.**
5. **Recognize that some elements, called metalloids, have some properties of metals and nonmetals.**

6–1 Properties of Metals and Nonmetals

Consider some familiar elements—gold, copper, oxygen, carbon, iron, silver, and sulfur. If you had to divide these elements into two groups based on similar properties, how would you do it?

Most likely you would classify each element as a metal or a nonmetal. For hundreds of years scientists have been able to distinguish between these two groups. **Metals and nonmetals have many easily observed physical properties that make them distinctly different from each other.** Today, chemists believe that these properties depend upon the way electrons are arranged in the atoms of the elements.

Physical Properties of Metals

The physical properties of metals make them easy to recognize. One such property is **luster,** or shininess. Most metals also allow heat and electricity to move through them easily. So metals are good conductors of heat and electricity. Metals generally have a high density. This means that they are heavy for their size. And metals usually have fairly high melting points. With these properties in mind, can you name some objects around you that are metals? ❶

There are two other physical properties that are common to many metals. Most metals are ductile—they can be drawn into thin wire. Most metals are malleable—they can be hammered into thin sheets.

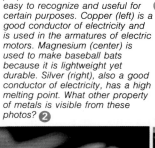

Figure 6–1 *The physical properties of metals make them easy to recognize and useful for certain purposes. Copper (left) is a good conductor of electricity and is used in the armatures of electric motors. Magnesium (center) is used to make baseball bats because it is lightweight yet durable. Silver (right), also a good conductor of electricity, has a high melting point. What other property of metals is visible from these photos?* ❷

TEACHING STRATEGY 6-1

Students should be made to feel comfortable with the terms *metal* and *nonmetal* as they apply to elements. This can best be achieved through examples. Have several examples of metals available and always point to their location in the periodic table. Discuss the properties of metals as each example of metal is observed.

Motivation

Discuss the importance of metals to health. Calcium, a very active metal, is found in our teeth and bones. Sodium is important in conducting nerve impulses. Ask,

• **What other metals are important to health?** (iron in blood, cobalt in vitamins, potassium in nerve cells) Students should also be reminded of the everyday importance of metals by looking at everything in the classroom

to notice the various metals and their forms. By noticing the chrome-plated objects, they will identify the property of luster. By noting any electrical cords or outlets, they will note the property of ductility. If they note any corrosion, they will see evidence of a chemical property of losing electrons to nonmetals.

An important aspect of a good science education is getting students to see familiar objects in new ways. Hold up

Chemical Properties of Metals

The chemical properties of metals are not quite as easy to observe as the physical properties. The chemical properties depend on the way the electrons are arranged in the atoms of the metals. An atom of a metal can have one, two, three, or four electrons in its outermost energy level. You will recall that the electrons in the outermost energy level of an atom are called valence electrons. The valence electrons in atoms of metals are rather weakly held. So metals are elements that tend to lose their outermost electrons. What happens to an atom when it loses one or more electrons? ❹

Because they tend to lose electrons, most metals will react with water or elements in the atmosphere. Such a chemical reaction often results in **corrosion** of the metal. Corrosion is the gradual wearing away of the metal due to a chemical reaction in which the metal element is changed into a metallic compound. The rusting of iron is an example of corrosion. When iron rusts, it combines with oxygen in the air to form the compound iron oxide. The tarnishing of silver is another example of corrosion. What compound is formed during tarnishing? ❺

Alloys

Sometimes two metals or a metal and a nonmetal can be mixed together in the molten, or melted, state. When the mixture cools and hardens, the result is a substance called an **alloy.** An alloy is a mixture of two elements—both metals or a metal and a nonmetal—that has the properties of a metal.

Steel, an alloy of iron and carbon, is harder and stronger than iron alone. Adding nickel or chromium to the steel makes stainless steel, an alloy that is very resistant to rusting. Brass, an alloy of copper and zinc, has properties that are very different from either of the metals from which it is made.

Physical Properties of Nonmetals

In general, the physical properties of nonmetals are just the opposite of the physical properties of metals. Nonmetals usually have no luster and are dull in appearance. Nonmetals do not conduct heat and electricity very well. Nonmetals are brittle and

COMMON ALLOYS	
Alloy	**Uses**
Alnico (Al, Ni, Co, Fe, Cu)	Magnets
Brass (Cu, Zn)	Jewelry, ornaments, musical instruments
Bronze (Cu, Sn)	Jewelry, nuts, bolts, ornaments
Gold, 14 carat (Au, Cu, Ag)	Jewelry, coins
Solder (Pb, Sn)	Electric wire, solderings, welding
Stainless steel (Fe, Cr, Ni)	Surgical instruments, cutlery, pots and pans, building materials, boats, cars
Dentist's amalgam (Hg, Ag)	Dental fillings
Wrought iron (Fe, C, Mn)	Ornaments, furniture, railings

Figure 6–2 *Some common alloys and their uses are shown in this table. Alloys are mixtures of two elements—both metals or a metal and a nonmetal. What elements make up the alloy brass? Solder? What alloy contains a solid metal combined with a liquid metal?* ❸

133

SCIENCE TERMS 6-1
luster p. 132
corrosion p. 133
alloy p. 133

FACTS AND FIGURES

The nonmetal element oxygen is the most abundant element by mass in the human body (approximately 65%). Calcium is the most abundant metal by mass at only 1.4%.

HISTORICAL NOTES

The science of obtaining metals from their "natural" impure condition is called metallurgy. This practice was established when iron was reduced from its ores to be used in tools and weapons.

ANNOTATION KEY

❶ **Answers will vary, but might include copper, silver, gold, platinum, zinc, and iron. (Classifying)**

❷ **Luster (Interpreting photographs)**

❸ **Cu, Zn; Pb, Sn; Amalgam: Ag and Hg (Interpreting charts)**

❹ **It becomes positively charged. (Applying concepts)**

❺ **Silver sulfide (Relating concepts)**

❶ **Thinking Skill: Classifying**

❷ **Thinking Skill: Applying concepts**

❸ **Thinking Skill: Applying technology**

gains electrons (nonmetals). Be sure to point out the differences between "compounds" just described and the *mixing* of metals to form alloys. Compounds have fixed or precise mass ratios. Alloys may have varying ratios of constituents. Ask,

• **Although nonmetals generally take electrons from metals, what do you suppose happens when two nonmetals combine?** (The atom with the most efficient nucleus becomes the "electron-taker," causing the other nonmetal to lose electrons. Generally, the element closer to the upper right corner of the chart has the more efficient nucleus.)

a large, clean stoppered flask. Ask students if they think the flask is empty or if it contains something. Answers will vary, but someone will likely say it contains air, which it does. This is a good starting point to explain that air is primarily made up of two nonmetals: nitrogen and oxygen. Point out that nonmetals have no observable luster and that they do not conduct electricity.

Content Development

Point out to students that even though there are more metal elements than nonmetals, most compounds in nature consist of a metal combined with a nonmetal. This point may be elaborated when it is explained that compounds usually form through sharing and/or exchanging valence electrons. This situation can best be achieved when one atom easily gives up electrons (metals) while another easily

Figure 6–3 *Nonmetals have no luster and are dull in appearance. They are not ductile or malleable. Here you see three typical nonmetals: sulfur (left), phosphorus (center), and selenium (right). What are two other properties of nonmetals?* ❶

break easily. They cannot be made into wire or hammered into thin sheets. In other words, nonmetals are not ductile or malleable. Nonmetals usually have lower densities than metals. And nonmetals generally have lower melting points.

Nonmetals are not as easy to recognize as a group as are metals. Nonmetals can be very different from one another. Bromine is a brown liquid, oxygen is a colorless gas, sulfur is a yellow solid.

Chemical Properties of Nonmetals

The chemical properties of nonmetals also tend to be opposite those of metals. Metals tend to lose electrons; nonmetals tend to gain electrons. Atoms ❶ of most nonmetals have five, six, seven, or eight electrons in their outermost energy level. Atoms with eight valence electrons have a complete outermost energy level. Atoms with five, six, or seven valence electrons gain three, two, or one electron to achieve a complete outermost energy level. Why do you think a particular nonmetal gains two electrons rather than loses six electrons? ❷

Metalloids

Some elements display properties of both metals and nonmetals. These elements are called metalloids. The word metalloid means "metallike."

All of the metalloids are solids. They look very much like metals but are not quite as shiny. Like metals, they are usually white or gray in color. For example, the metalloid silicon has a luster that makes it look like a metal.

134

Most metalloids conduct heat and electricity, but not as well as metals. Metalloids are ductile and malleable. In addition to silicon, elements that are metalloids include boron, germanium, arsenic, antimony, tellurium, and polonium.

SECTION REVIEW

1. What are some physical and chemical properties of metals? Of nonmetals?
2. What is an alloy? A metalloid?
3. Why would coating a metal object with a nonmetallic substance prevent corrosion?

6–2 Active Metals

All through history, metals such as gold, silver, iron, and copper have been valued and used. You probably are familiar with these metals. Yet there are two families of metals whose names might be unfamiliar to you. The metals in these two families are the most active metals. **The most active metals are found in Group IA and Group IIA of the periodic table.**

Alkali Metals

The elements in Group IA of the periodic table are the **alkali metals.** The members of the alkali metal family are lithium (Li), sodium (Na), potassium (K), rubidium (Rb), cesium (Cs), and francium (Fr). All six elements have the properties of metals ❷ except they are softer and less dense. The alkali metals can be cut with a knife. Because they are metals, what other physical properties do they have? ❸

The alkali metals are the most reactive of all the metals. They are so reactive, in fact, that they are always found in nature combined with other elements, never as free elements. In pure form, the alkali metals are stored under oil to keep them from reacting with oxygen or water vapor in the air. When the alkali metals do react with water, the reaction is violent. Hydrogen gas is produced, as well as extreme heat. Because of the extreme heat, the hydrogen gas can begin to burn and can possibly

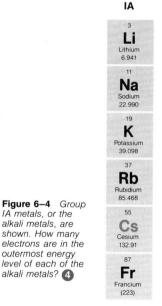

IA

❸ **Figure 6–4** *Group IA metals, or the alkali metals, are shown. How many electrons are in the outermost energy level of each of the alkali metals?* ❹

6-2 ACTIVE METALS

SECTION PREVIEW 6-2

In this section, students will be shown that the broad classification of elements called metals can actually be further divided into the subgroup "active metals." These active metals can easily be identified and located in columns I and II. These elements, alkali in Group I and alkaline in Group II, are very important to human health and are always found in nature combined with other elements.

PERFORMANCE OBJECTIVES 6-2

1. **Locate alkali and alkaline metals on the periodic table.**
2. **Describe physical and chemical properties along with practical uses of alkali and alkaline metals.**

SCIENCE TERMS 6-2
alkali metals p. 135
alkaline earth metals p. 137

flame obtained from magnesium. Or bring a camera with a flashcube attached. The flashcube can be examined before and after use through a hand lens. Thin magnesium wire is responsible for the flash. Magnesium, a very active metal, easily combines with oxygen.

If available, place a piece of lithium, a piece of sodium, and a piece of potassium each no larger than a matchhead in three separate half-filled beakers of water. Immediately cover each beaker and keep students at least ten feet away. The violent reactions of those small pieces of Group I metals show the extreme activity of these metals.

Students should then be informed that these metals are found in humans. Explain that the difference between these metals in the lab and the same metals in your body is the ionized form. The metals are so active that they easily give up one or two electrons, forming positive ions. It is the positively charged ion that is found in their bodies—not the pure, unreacted metal.

alloids used in connection with silicon to form computer chips?

Section Review 6-1
1. Metals: luster, good conductors of heat and electricity, high density, solids at room temperature (except mercury), ductile, malleable, high melting points. Nonmetals: dull, poor conductors of heat and electricity, brittle, low melting points
2. Mixture of two metals or a metal
and a nonmetal that has the properties of a metal
3. The nonmetallic coating would prevent air and water from coming in contact with metal and reacting chemically.

TEACHING STRATEGY 6-2

Motivation
Bring a Fourth of July sparkler to class and light it to show the intense

ANNOTATION KEY

1 Francium (Interpreting charts)

2 Electrons in atoms of alkali metals gain energy when heated and move to a higher energy level. When they fall back to their original position, they lose energy in the form of light. (Applying concepts)

3 Positive ions: 2+ (Relating concepts)

1 Thinking Skill: Observing

2 Thinking Skill: Applying technology

3 Thinking Skill: Classifying

4 Thinking Skill: Identifying relationships

explode. The reaction of an alkali metal with water also produces a compound known as an alkali, or a base. It is for this reason that Group IA metals are called alkali metals. You will learn more about alkalis, or bases, in Chapter 9.

The alkali metals have only one electron in their outermost energy level. This electron is easily lost. So alkali metals form positive ions. Ions are charged atoms. The tendency of alkali metals to lose their valence electron easily makes them very reactive.

1 Alkali metals can be identified by the characteristic color each produces in a flame test. See Figure 6–6. When a sample of an alkali metal is heated, some of the electrons in its atoms gain energy and move to a higher energy level. When these electrons fall back to their original position, they lose the energy in the form of light.

Although the alkali metals themselves have very few familiar uses, the compounds they form are

Figure 6–5 *This table shows some of the properties of the alkali metals and the uses of their compounds. Which alkali metal has radioactive isotopes?* 1

ALKALI METALS

Element	Properties	Uses of Compounds
Lithium (Li)	m.p. 179°C b.p. 1336°C Soft, silvery; reacts violently with water	Medicine; metallurgy
Sodium (Na)	m.p. 97.8°C b.p. 883°C Soft, silvery-white; reacts violently with water	Soap; table salt; lye
Potassium (K)	m.p. 62.5°C b.p. 758°C Soft, silvery-white; reacts violently with moisture	Fertilizer; medicine; photography
Rubidium (Rb)	m.p. 39.0°C b.p. 700°C Soft, lustrous; reacts violently with moisture	Space vehicle engines; photocells
Cesium (Cs)	m.p. 28.6°C b.p. 670°C Silvery-white, ductile; reacts with moisture	Photocells
Francium (Fr)	Extremely rare; radioactive isotopes	Not widely used

6-2 (continued)

Content Development

Have students write out the electron configuration of lithium, sodium, and potassium. Show them that in each case the alkali metals have a full, stable energy level just below the valence level. These full energy levels tend to weaken the nuclear attraction for the single valence electron. This situation causes the outer, single valence electron of this group to be easily removed by other elements. The same model applies to the alkaline metals of Group II except that the outer, valence level always forms an s^2 configuration.

• **Strontium-90 is a component in fallout. Why are scientists concerned about the appearance of strontium-90 in milk products?** (Because Sr-90 would have similar properties to calcium and could therefore be absorbed into our bones)

• **Within the following pairs of metals select the most active: Ca or Mg; Na or Rb; Ba or Cs** (Ca; Rb; Cs)

• **What would be a balanced equation for a Group I metal reacting with water?** $M + 2H_2O = 2MOH + H_2$

• **What would be the balanced equation for a Group II metal reacting with water?** $M + 2H_2O = M(OH)_2 + H_2$

Skills Development

Skill: Making predictions

• **The formula of table salt (sodium chloride) is NaCl. Using oxidation numbers predict the formula of potassium chloride and cesium chloride.** (KCl; CsCl)

Figure 6–6 *The alkali metals can be identified by flame tests. Here you see the characteristic colors produced by the elements cesium (left), rubidium (center, left), potassium (center, right), and sodium (right). What accounts for the color given off in a flame test?* ❷

some of the most important substances you use every day. Table salt, baking soda, and soap are just a few of the compounds made from the alkali metals. The properties and uses of the alkali metals and their compounds are shown in Figure 6–5. ❷

Alkaline Earth Metals

The elements in Group IIA of the periodic table are the **alkaline earth metals.** The members of the alkaline earth family are beryllium (Be), magnesium (Mg), calcium (Ca), strontium (Sr), barium (Ba), and radium (Ra). These elements, which are harder and ❸ denser than the alkali metals, also have higher melting points and boiling points. They are highly reactive, but not as reactive as the alkali metals. Like the alkali metals, the alkaline earth metals are never found free in nature.

Two of the alkaline earth metals are well known. Magnesium is often combined with aluminum to make alloys that are lightweight and strong. Magnesium compounds are used in medicines, photographic flashbulbs, and flares. Calcium is abundant in the earth in the form of marble and limestone ❹ rocks. Calcium is an essential part of the human body, especially in teeth and bones. The properties and uses of the alkaline earth metals and their compounds are shown in Figure 6–8 on page 138.

The alkaline earth metals have two electrons in their outermost energy level. Because their atomic size is smaller than that of the alkali metals, the alkaline earth metals hold their outer electrons more tightly. So although they are highly reactive, they

Figure 6–7 *Group IIA metals, or the alkaline earth metals, are shown. What type of ions do alkaline earth metals form?* ❸

IIA

4 **Be** Beryllium 9.0122
12 **Mg** Magnesium 24.305
20 **Ca** Calcium 40.08
38 **Sr** Strontium 87.62
56 **Ba** Barium 137.33
88 **Ra** Radium 226.025

137

FACTS AND FIGURES

Francium should be the most active metal on the periodic table. However, scientists estimate that currently there is less than 1 ounce of francium in the earth's crust.

TIE-IN/MEDICINE

Recently the metal lithium has been used in treatment of some manic-depressive personality disorders. Assign students to find a source, such as a psychology teacher or psychology journal, for a more detailed explanation.

Medical technologists often analyze blood samples during a hospital stay. The amount of sodium in plasma is approximately .003 g per mL.

trons. This decreased attraction makes it easier for electrons to be removed by other atoms.

- **What would you predict for the formula of calcium chloride, a material used as a drying agent?** ($CaCl_2$)

Reinforcement
If samples are available, place some sodium chloride crystals directly in a Bunsen burner flame. (Refer to flame shown in Figure 6-6). Students should note the appearance of a yellow color in the flame. Next, place a piece of glass (hold with tongs) in the same

flame. Students should also note the yellow flame produced from the glass. Many glass substances contain sodium.

Content Development
Generally, for metals, chemical activity increases from top to bottom within the chemical family. This is because the increased number of underlying energy levels between the nucleus and the valence electrons decreases the nuclear attraction for the valence elec-

Enrichment
The hardness of water actually refers to the calcium and magnesium content of the water. Assign students to find out how a water softener operates. (Sodium and potassium ions replace the calcium and magnesium ions. Sodium and potassium compounds are more soluble and consequently do not precipitate out like calcium and magnesium salts.)

FACTS AND FIGURES

Almost all of the nickel mined in the United States is found in Oregon.

BACKGROUND INFORMATION

The rusting of iron is actually the oxidation of iron. This means that in the process of rusting, iron gives up electrons to oxygen. However, rusting will not occur without moisture. One part of the iron surface acts as an anode (source of electrons) because the surface of most iron structures is not homogeneous. When the iron atoms of that area lose electrons they form iron +2. These ions travel through the moisture on the surface to an area where oxygen is found and form a Fe_2O_3 compound known as rust.

ANNOTATION KEY

❶ **The electrons are closer to the nucleus, which has a positive charge. (Relating facts)**
❷ **Calcium (Interpreting charts)**
❸ **Mercury (Interpreting charts)**
❶ **Thinking Skill: Classifying**
❷ **Thinking Skill: Applying definitions**

ALKALINE EARTH METALS

Element	Properties	Uses of Compounds
Beryllium (Be)	m.p. 1285°C b.p. 2970°C Poisonous	Radio parts; steel
Magnesium (Mg)	m.p. 650°C b.p. 1117°C Burns with very bright flame; strong but not dense	Medicine; photographic flashbulbs; auto parts; space vehicle parts; flares
Calcium (Ca)	m.p. 851°C b.p. 1487°C Silvery; important part of bones and teeth; tarnishes in moist air	Plaster and plasterboard; mortar and cement; water softeners; metal bearings
Strontium (Sr)	m.p. 774°C b.p. 1366°C Least abundant alkaline earth metal; reactive in air	Fireworks; flares
Barium (Ba)	m.p. 850°C b.p. 1537°C Extremely reactive in air	Medicine; paints; glassmaking
Radium (Ra)	m.p. (700°C) b.p. (1525°C) Silvery-white but turns black in air; radioactive	Treatment of cancer; medical research

Values in parentheses are physical properties of the most stable isotope.

Figure 6–8 *This table shows some of the properties of alkaline earth metals and the uses of their compounds. Which alkaline earth metal is essential to strong bones and teeth?* ❷

are less so than the alkali metals. Can you explain why the electrons of a smaller atom are more tightly held than the electrons of a larger atom? Alkaline earth metals form positive ions. ❶

SECTION REVIEW

1. What name is given to the elements that make up Group IA of the periodic table? Group IIA? What are the members of each group?
2. Which group is the most active? Why?
3. Why are the alkaline earth metals less reactive than the alkali metals?
4. What would be the formula for a compound formed between the element X with seven valence electrons and the alkali metal sodium? Between the element X and the alkaline earth metal calcium?

138

6-2 (continued)

Section Review 6-2

1. Alkali metals; alkaline earth metals
2. Group I, the alkali metals. They have only one electron in the outermost energy level. This electron is not held very tightly.
3. They have 2 electrons in the outermost energy level and their size is smaller, so the electrons are more tightly held.
4. NaX; CaX_2

TEACHING STRATEGY 6-3

Motivation

Display as many samples of transition metal compounds as are available. Make large name tags for each one with the transition metal component underlined. Point out that the bright colors are produced when the electrons selectively absorb certain frequencies from the visible spectrum. This would also be a good opportunity to show that different oxidation states often produce different colors, i.e. $KMnO_4$ is deep purple (Mn is in the +7 state). $MnSO_4 \cdot H_2O$ is pink (Mn is +2).

Be sure to locate or have students locate each transition metal example on the periodic table.

Content Development

Transition elements are very important to our daily lives. Make sure that students observe Figure 6-9. You may assign each student to bring to class for display an object containing an example of a transition element.

The oxidation number of an element enables correct formulas to be deduced. Point out that metals have positive oxidation numbers. Transition metals may have positive oxida-

6–3 Transition Metals

Turn to the periodic table on pages 118–119. Look between Group IIA and Group IIIA. What do you see? You should see 30 elements that do not seem to fit into any of the eight families. These elements are called the **transition metals.** Common transition elements include nickel, copper, zinc, platinum, and gold.

The transition metals have properties similar to one another and to other metals, but their properties do not fit in with those of any other family. Most transition metals are excellent conductors of heat and electricity. Most have high melting points and are hard. Unlike metals, however, some transition elements are brittle.

Transition metals are much less active than the alkali and alkaline earth metals. Many transition metals combine chemically with oxygen to form compounds called oxides. Many transition metals have more than one oxidation number. The oxidation number of an element is the number of electrons an atom of that element gains, loses, or shares when it chemically combines with another element. If an atom gains electrons, it will have a negative oxidation number. If an atom loses electrons, it will have a positive oxidation number.

Iron, for example, can have an oxidation number of 2+ or 3+. This means an atom of iron can lose either 2 or 3 electrons. Tin can have an oxidation number of 2+ or 4+. The oxidation number of manganese can range from 2+ to 7+.

Transition metals form compounds that are brightly colored. Particular compounds of the transition metals cobalt and cadmium are used as pigments in paint. Have you ever heard of cobalt blue or cadmium yellow? Transition metals have many practical uses. Figure 6–9 shows some of them.

SECTION REVIEW

1. What are the transition metals?
2. Why are the transition metals in a separate group?
3. What common metals are transition elements?
4. What are some physical and chemical properties of the transition metals?

Figure 6–9 *The transition elements have many common uses. Which transition element is liquid at room temperature?* ❸

TRANSITION ELEMENTS	
Element	**Uses**
Iron (Fe)	Manufacturing; building materials; dietary supplement
Cobalt (Co)	Magnets; heat-resistant tools
Nickel (Ni)	Coins; batteries; jewelry; plating
Copper (Cu)	Electric wiring; plumbing; motors
Silver (Ag)	Jewelry; dental fillings; mirror backing; electric conductor
Gold (Au)	Jewelry; base for money systems; coins; dentistry
Zinc (Zn)	Paints; medicines; coat metals
Cadmium (Cd)	Plating; batteries; nuclear reactors
Mercury (Hg)	Liquid in thermometers, barometers, electric switches; dentistry; paints

tion numbers. Transition metals may have more than one oxidation number because the "s" sublevel electrons may be given up along with the underlying "d" sublevel electrons. Alkali and alkaline metals only give up their "s" sublevel electrons. However, the 4s electrons in the first row of transition elements are very close in energy to the 3d sublevel electrons, so often they are lost with the 4s electrons.

Skills Development

Skill: Applying concepts

Oxygen has a typical oxidation number of −2.

- **Predict the oxidation number of the transition element in the following oxides: K_2CrO_4, $KMnO_4$, SnO_2, Fe_2O_3.** (+6, +7, +4, +3)

6-3 TRANSITION METALS

SECTION PREVIEW 6-3

In this section, students are introduced to those metals that are not quite as active as the Group I and Group II metals. The metals, called transition elements, are sometimes found in nature in their pure uncombined states. The transition metals are placed in the periodic table between groups II and III. Many of the transition elements exhibit more than one oxidation number. This means that the transition elements may combine in more than one way with the same element. For example, copper and oxygen may be in the CuO and the Cu_2O form. Transition metal compounds are often very colorful as opposed to the usually white compounds of Group I and Group II.

PERFORMANCE OBJECTIVES 6-3

1. **Locate the area of the periodic table where transition elements are found.**
2. **Identify some of the uses of transition elements.**
3. **List three properties of transition elements.**

SCIENCE TERMS 6-3

transition metal p. 139

Section Review 6-3

1. A group of 30 metals in the center of periods 4, 5, and 6, between Groups II and III, which have properties similar to one another and to the other metals.
2. Because they have properties that are not similar to those of any other family.
3. Iron, copper, zinc, silver, gold, mercury.
4. Good conductors of heat and electricity, high melting points, hard, brittle, combine with oxygen to form oxides, multiple oxidation numbers, resistant to corrosion.

6-4 FROM METALS TO NONMETALS

SECTION PREVIEW 6-4

The elements found on the right side of the periodic table are presented in a column by column format. Moving from left to right each column, or family, contains elements that are less and less metallic.

The boron family has elements that are metalloids, such as boron, and metals, such as aluminum. Moving one column to the right, the carbon family contains some very important elements. Carbon is involved with compounds that form the basis of life on this planet. Silicon and germanium are metalloids important in the computer industry. The nitrogen family members all have five valence electrons. Oxygen is found at the top of the next family. In this family, the constituents range from nonmetallic oxygen, to metalloids selenium and tellurium, to metallic polonium.

PERFORMANCE OBJECTIVES 6-4

1. **Classify elements into the appropriate element family in the periodic table.**
2. **Determine, from an element's periodic location, whether the element is a nonmetal, metalloid, or metal.**
3. **Find out the uses for many of the Group III, IV, V, and VI elements.**

SCIENCE TERMS 6-4

organic compounds p. 141

IIIA

5
B
Boron
10.81
13
Al
Aluminum
26.98
31
Ga
Gallium
69.72
49
In
Indium
114.82
81
Tl
Thallium
204.383

Figure 6–10 *Group IIIA elements are also called the boron family. What is true about the properties of these elements as you go down the group?* ❷

140

6–4 From Metals to Nonmetals

As you move from left to right across the periodic table, the properties of the elements become more nonmetallic. **It is in Groups IIIA to VIA of the periodic table that the properties of elements change from metallic to nonmetallic.** These groups include the boron family, carbon family, nitrogen family, and oxygen family.

If you look at Groups IIIA, IVA, VA, and VIA on the periodic table, you will notice that the zigzag line that divides metals and nonmetals runs right through these groups. Do you remember the name for elements on either side of this line? How many of these special elements are present in each of the four families? ❶

The Boron Family

Boron (B), the first element in the boron family, is a metalloid. Aluminum (Al), which is right beneath boron, is by its position a metalloid. But the properties of aluminum are usually those of metals. The other members of the boron family—gallium (Ga), indium (In), and thallium (Th)—are metals.

Boron, which is hard and brittle, is never found in nature in the free state. It is usually found combined with oxygen. The compound boric oxide is important in making heat-resistant glass. Boric acid is commonly used as an eyewash and antiseptic. The compound borax is useful as a cleaning agent and water softener.

Aluminum is the most abundant metal and the third most abundant element in the earth's crust. Aluminum is found as aluminum oxide in the ore called bauxite. Aluminum is extremely valuable in industry. It is light, strong, and does not tarnish in air. It is an excellent reflector of light and a good conductor of heat and electricity. Aluminum is used in pots and pans, electric wiring, airplane parts, and the manufacture of alloys. Because aluminum is very malleable, it is used to make the familiar household product aluminum foil. Can you explain why it would take a very malleable metal to make aluminum foil? ❸

TEACHING STRATEGY 6-4

Motivation

Show the diversity of some of the elements within these groups by displaying examples of elements such as nitrogen, arsenic, phosphorous and bismuth. (nonmetal, metalloid, metalloid, and metal) If samples are unavailable, begin the section by reminding students how similar the elements within the alkali group were. Then use a poster of each element in the nitrogen group with oxidation numbers, physical states, density, and uses featured. (These descriptions can be found in the Handbook of Chemistry and Physics and/or an encyclopedia.)

Content Development

As elements are found farther to the right on the periodic table, in each row the nucleus is becoming more positive and therefore able to attract new electrons. This makes the elements more nonmetallic. Within a family, from top to bottom, the nucleus also gets more positive, but the atoms are also getting larger. This increase in size makes the nucleus ineffective and therefore electrons will be removed easily—thus becoming more metallic.

Another major aspect of this section is the descriptive nature of the uses of these elements. This can be

Figure 6–11 *Aluminum, a Group IIIA metal, forms the outer walls of the World Trade Center towers in New York (left). What is the family called to which aluminum belongs? Silicon is a member of Group IVA. These silicon wafers will be used to make computer chips (right). What type of element is silicon?* ④

The Carbon Family

The carbon family includes the elements carbon (C), silicon (Si), germanium (Ge), tin (Sn), and lead (Pb). Carbon can combine with other elements in a great variety of ways. As a result, millions of carbon-containing compounds exist. Most compounds that contain carbon are called **organic compounds.** Carbon has often been called "the basis for life" because all living things contain organic compounds. You will learn more about organic compounds in Chapter 10.

Silicon is the second most abundant element in the earth's crust. Silicon is used in glass and in cement. It is also used in solar cells. Solar cells convert the energy of sunlight into electric energy.

Germanium is a metalloid used in transistors. Transistors are devices found in many electronic instruments, such as radios and televisions. Tin is a ③ metal. Tin resists rusting and corrosion, so it is used in making cans for food. The common tin can is really a steel can with a coating of tin on the inside.

The densest element in the carbon family is the metal lead. Until recently, lead was used in paints and gasoline. But because lead is poisonous, it is being removed from many compounds.

IVA

6
C
Carbon
12.011

14
Si
Silicon
28.086

32
Ge
Germanium
72.59

50
Sn
Tin
118.71

82
Pb
Lead
207.2

Figure 6–12 *The carbon family is Group IVA of the periodic table. What two elements in this family are metalloids?* ⑤

ANNOTATION KEY

1 Bismuth; oxygen (Interpreting charts)
2 Sulfur, selenium, tellurium, polonium (Identifying relationships)
3 Fluorine (Relating facts)
1 Thinking Skill: Identifying relationships
2 Thinking Skill: Identifying relationships
3 Thinking Skill: Classifying

HISTORICAL NOTES

Aluminum is plentiful and has many uses. However, it was not until the very late 1800s that aluminum could be obtained cheaply enough to be used. It was then that a young graduate student, twenty-one-year-old Charles Hall, developed a way of dissolving aluminum oxide in cryolite, then using an electric current to extract pure aluminum. The Hall process paved the way for cheap production of aluminum.

Sharpen Your Skills

Getting to Know the Elements
Skills: Observing, comparing, writing comprehension, classifying
Level: Remedial
Type: Hands-on

This activity will help students classify various elements found in their home. By writing a description of each element, students are called upon to use the information presented in the chapter and to write in a logical, orderly manner.

VA	VIA
7 **N** Nitrogen 14.007	8 **O** Oxygen 15.999
15 **P** Phosphorus 30.974	16 **S** Sulfur 32.06
33 **As** Arsenic 74.922	34 **Se** Selenium 78.96
51 **Sb** Antimony 121.75	52 **Te** Tellurium 127.60
83 **Bi** Bismuth 208.98	84 **Po** Polonium (209)

Figure 6–13 *Group VA elements are also called the nitrogen family. Which element in this family shows the most metallic properties? The oxygen family is Group VIA. Which member of this family is a gas?* 1

The Nitrogen Family

The nitrogen family consists of nitrogen (N), phosphorus (P), arsenic (As), antimony (Sb), and bismuth (Bi). Nitrogen and phosphorus are nonmetals. Arsenic is a metalloid with mostly nonmetallic properties. Antimony is a metalloid with mostly metallic properties. Bismuth is the most metallic element in the family.

1 All members of the nitrogen family have five electrons in their outermost energy level. In the heavier elements, the outermost electrons are very far from the nucleus. They are more easily lost. This ease of losing valence electrons explains why the properties shift from nonmetallic to metallic as you move down this group.

Nitrogen, the most abundant element in the earth's atmosphere, is highly stable and does not combine easily with other elements. Nitrogen is used in the production of fertilizers, explosives, drugs, and dyes. Ammonia, a compound made of nitrogen and hydrogen, is a common household cleaning agent.

Phosphorus is a nonmetal that is too active to be found free in nature. One of its main uses is in making the tips of matches. Arsenic is an important ingredient in many insecticides. Both antimony and bismuth are used in making alloys.

Sharpen Your Skills

Getting to Know the Elements

Collect examples of various elements, many of which can be found in your surroundings. Mount the elements on a piece of plywood for a permanent display. Below each element place a brief description of the element.

The Oxygen Family

2 The oxygen family includes oxygen (O), sulfur (S), selenium (Se), tellurium (Te), and polonium (Po). All these elements have six electrons in their outermost energy level. Like the nitrogen family, their properties go from nonmetallic in oxygen and sulfur to metalloid in selenium and tellurium to metallic in polonium.

Oxygen, the most abundant element in the earth's crust, is very reactive and combines with almost every other element. Oxygen is a gas. It is necessary to most forms of life. The processes of respiration in plants and animals and photosynthesis in green plants require oxygen. At elevated temperatures, oxygen combines rapidly with other substances in a process called combustion. The burning of wood is a familiar example of combustion. Oxygen itself does not burn. But it is necessary for the

6-4 (continued)

Content Development

Nitrogen does not easily combine with other elements because the nitrogen molecule N_2 is held together by a triple bond. Plants capable of breaking the triple bond are called "nitrogen fixers." Soybeans and alfalfa plants actually are host to bacteria in their roots. The bacteria are able to change the nitrogen to ammonia and help form animo acids. It is interesting that an enzyme in these bacteria is able to do, under mild field conditions, what we must use temperatures above 300°C and extreme pressures to accomplish.

Section Review 6-4

1. Boron, aluminum, gallium, indium, thallium; carbon, silicon, germanium, tin, lead
2. A compound that contains carbon
3. Nitrogen, phosphorus, arsenic, antimony, bismuth; oxygen, sulfur, selenium, tellurium, polonium
4. In each family, the heavier members have atoms with a larger radius. The outermost electrons in these heavier members are farther from the nucleus and, therefore, more easily lost. The ability to lose electrons is a property of metals.

burning of other substances. This means that oxygen supports combustion.

Sulfur, selenium, and tellurium are brittle solids at room temperature. They all combine with oxygen to form dioxides and also combine with metals and hydrogen.

Sulfur is used in the manufacture of such products as drugs, insecticides, matches, gunpowder, and rubber. Selenium is used in making red glass and enamels. Tellurium is useful in making alloys. Polonium is a very rare radioactive element.

SECTION REVIEW

1. What elements are in the boron family? The carbon family?
2. What is an organic compound?
3. What elements are in the nitrogen family? The oxygen family?
4. Why do the properties of elements in the nitrogen and oxygen families shift from nonmetallic to metallic down the group?

Figure 6–14 *This brush fire burns because of the presence of the element oxygen. Oxygen is a Group VIA nonmetal that supports combustion. What other elements belong to the oxygen family?* ❷

6–5 Halogens

Elements in Group VIIA are called **halogens** (HAL-uh-juhn). The halogens are strongly nonmetallic. They tend to gain electrons and form negative ions. **The halogens—which include the elements fluorine (F), chlorine (Cl), bromine (Br), iodine (I),** ❸ **and astatine (At)—are the most active nonmetals.** As a result, they are never found free in nature. They are always found combined in a compound.

The chemical reactivity of the halogens is due to the number of electrons in the outermost energy levels of their atoms. Each halogen atom has 7 valence electrons. Atoms of the halogens need to gain only 1 electron to fill their outermost level.

Fluorine is the most active halogen. Fluorine and chlorine are gases. Bromine is a liquid. Iodine and astatine are solids. Astatine is radioactive. See Figure 6–17 on page 144.

Like most nonmetals, halogens have low melting points and boiling points. In the gas phase, halogens exist as diatomic elements. A diatomic element always contains two atoms of that element in one

Section Objective

To describe the properties of the halogens

VIIA

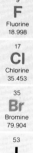

| 9 |
| F |
| Fluorine |
| 18.998 |

| 17 |
| Cl |
| Chlorine |
| 35.453 |

| 35 |
| Br |
| Bromine |
| 79.904 |

| 53 |
| I |
| Iodine |
| 126.905 |

| 85 |
| At |
| Astatine |
| (210) |

Figure 6–15 *Group VIIA elements are called the halogens. Which halogen is the most active nonmetal?* ❸

Texas Essential Elements in Section 6-5: 2A, 3A, 7B, 8A, 10

SECTION PREVIEW 6-5

The term *halogen* literally means "salt former." This section points out the characteristic of halogens of reacting easily with many metals. Group VII elements all have seven valence electrons. They typically have an efficient nucleus, small size, and therefore an ability to easily attract electrons from other atoms. In the gas phase, these elements exist as diatomic (two atoms) molecules.

PERFORMANCE OBJECTIVES 6-5

1. Locate the position of halogens on the periodic table.
2. Determine that halogens are very reactive elements that usually take electrons from metals.
3. Define halogen.
4. Identify some of the common uses of halogens.

SCIENCE TERMS 6-5

halogen p. 143

for their own electrons. Also halogens are the smallest atoms in their row on the periodic table. This small size enables them to have their positive nucleus attract new electrons.

The halogen family presents an interesting change in physical properties. Fluorine and chlorine are gases. Bromine is a liquid. And iodine and astatine are found in solid form. The molecules of the halogens all have only weak forces holding one molecule to another. However, these intermolecular forces do increase as the size of the atom increases. Ask,
• **Why does the size of the atoms increase from top to bottom within a group of elements?** (Each successive atom has added a new energy level.)
• **How does an increase in size affect the physical state of the halogens?** (Larger size tends to cause the halogens to have stronger intermolecular forces, causing a change from gas to liquid to solid.)

TEACHING STRATEGY 6-5

Motivation

One of the most common halogen compounds is table salt (NaCl). Point out to students that sodium is a silvery, soft, highly reactive metal. Chlorine is a green, poisonous gas. Yet, when they react, by exchanging a valence electron from sodium to chlorine, they form the important, stable white crystal—sodium chloride. Most chlorides between Group I metals and Group II metals have the outward appearance of sodium chloride.

Content Development

The valence level of halogens always shows the "s^2p^5" configuration. This is a very active situation because each atom now only needs one electron to obtain stability. Halogens are found in many compounds with metals because metals usually have weak attractions

TEACHER DEMONSTRATION

Solid iodine crystals may pass, with gentle heat, from the solid phase to the gaseous phase without becoming a liquid. If solid iodine is available, place a few crystals in a bottle. **CAUTION:** *Do not handle the crystals.* Place the bottle on an electric hot plate set at low heat. Soon a "purple haze" will appear in the bottle. This can be made more visible by holding a white paper behind it. When the purple haze forms, place a glass plate over the opening of the beaker and crystals will begin to condense. Remove from heat. Ask,

• **What have you just observed?** (sublimation)

TIE-IN/MEDICINE

Iodine deficiencies can cause thyroid problems, possibly goiter formation. Common table salt is frequently "iodized" by adding a small amount, approximately 0.02%, of KI.

Tincture of iodine is an antiseptic with a small amount of iodine dissolved in alcohol.

6-5 (continued)

Skills Development

Skill: Making predictions

Noting the valence electron situation for halogens and for Group I and II metals, ask students to predict the formula of lithium bromide (LiBr), potassium iodide (KI), calcium chloride ($CaCl_2$), and magnesium fluoride (MgF_2).

Reinforcement

Have students select any two halogens and write out their electronic configuration. Ask,

• **What is the valence configuration**

Figure 6–16 *Three members of the halogens, or Group VIIA elements, are shown here. Chlorine is a greenish-yellow gas (left). Bromine is a brown liquid (center), one of the few liquid elements. Iodine is a purple-black solid (right) that sublimes to produce a purple vapor. What is the most active halogen?* ❶

Figure 6–17 *Because of their chemical reactivity, the halogens have many uses.*

HALOGENS	
Element	**Uses**
Fluorine (F)	Etching glass; refrigerants; nonstick utensils; preventing tooth decay
Chlorine (Cl)	Bleaching agent; disinfectant; water purifier
Bromine (Br)	Medicine; dyes; photography
Iodine (I)	Medicine; disinfectant; dietary supplement in salt
Astatine (At)	Rare element

144

molecule. What is the formula for a molecule of fluorine? Chlorine? ❷

The halogens combine readily with metals to form a class of compounds known as salts. In fact, the word "halogen" comes from the Greek words *halos* and *genos*, which mean "salt formers." Table salt, which is sodium chloride, is one example of a salt. Perhaps you have heard of sodium fluoride, which is used to fluoridate water, or calcium chloride, which is used to melt ice on streets and sidewalks. Silver bromide, another salt, is used in photographic film.

SECTION REVIEW

1. Are the halogens strongly metallic or nonmetallic?
2. What elements make up the halogen family?
3. What does the word "halogen" mean in Greek? Why is this an appropriate name for the elements in this family?
4. Why are the halogens highly reactive?
5. What name would you give to a salt formed when chlorine reacts with zinc? When iodine reacts with potassium?

for a halogen? (seven valence electrons s^2p^5)

• **How many unpaired electrons do halogens have?** (1)

Section Review 6-5

1. Nonmetallic
2. Fluorine, chlorine, bromine, iodine, astatine
3. "Salt former." They combine readily with metals to form compounds known as salts.

4. Each halogen, with seven valence electrons, needs to gain only one electron to complete its outermost energy level.
5. Zinc chloride; potassium iodide.

TEACHING STRATEGY 6-6

Motivation

Bring a helium-filled balloon to class and suspend a message from the balloon with the school address and

6–6 Noble Gases

The six elements that make up the last family of the periodic table, or Group VIIIA, are called the **noble gases.** All the elements in this family are colorless gases that are extremely unreactive. Because they do not readily combine with other elements to form compounds, the noble gases are called **inert.**

The family of noble, or inert, gases includes helium (He), neon (Ne), argon (Ar), krypton (Kr), xenon (Xe), and radon (Rn). All the noble gases are found in small amounts in the earth's atmosphere. Argon, the most common of the noble gases, makes up about 1 percent of the atmosphere. Because they are so scarce and so unreactive, the noble gases were not discovered until the end of the nineteenth century. This was almost 50 years after Mendeleev had set up the periodic table.

The most striking property of the noble gases is their inactivity. It is only under special laboratory conditions that the noble gases can be made to combine chemically with other elements. In fact, atoms

VIIIA

2 **He** Helium 4.003
10 **Ne** Neon 20.179
18 **Ar** Argon 39.948
36 **Kr** Krypton 83.80
54 **Xe** Xenon 131.29
86 **Rn** Radon (222)

Figure 6–18 *Group VIIIA elements are known as the noble gases. Why are these gases also called inert?* ❸

Figure 6–19 *Crystals of xenon tetrafluoride such as these were first prepared in 1962 (left). Before that time, it was believed that noble gases could not take part in chemical reactions to form compounds. One of the most common uses of the noble gases is in colored lights. These tubes are filled with neon, which gives off a bright red light when electricity passes through it (right). Why are Group VIIIA gases so unreactive?* ❹

145

6-6 NOBLE GASES

SECTION PREVIEW 6-6

The far right column on the periodic table contains the noble gases. The six elements are almost totally unreactive. The inactivity of these nonmetals even extends to their inability to react with each other. Each of the elements in this group has a full valence level. This fact explains their inactivity—they are already stable in the uncombined state. The noble gases are not plentiful and are sometimes called inert.

PERFORMANCE OBJECTIVES 6-6

1. **Locate the position of the six noble gases on the periodic table of the elements.**
2. **Predict the number of valence electrons for each noble gas.**
3. **Relate the stable electronic configuration of the noble gases to their unreactivity to other elements.**
4. **List some of the typical uses of noble gases.**

SCIENCE TERMS 6-6

noble gas p. 145
inert p.145

first known compound using a noble gas.
• **Using your knowledge of attributes of reactive elements, hypothesize which noble gas was involved. Exclude radon because of difficulty of working with radioactive elements.** (Xe, because it is a very large atom that would be the most likely to lose its electrons. The compound was $XePtF_6$.)

Content Development
This would be a good opportunity to point out that many of the elements studied up to this point end out with a stable noble gas configuration when they form ions. Ask,
• **What is the electron configuration of the Cl^{-1} ion? Which noble gas configuration does this resemble?** ($1s^22s^22p^63s^23p^6$; Ar)

---

teacher's name tied to it. Ask for the balloon to be returned. After experimenting in class to see how buoyant the balloon is, release the balloon out the window to see how far it travels. This is a good example of a noble gas use and property. (low density)

Content Development
Because the activity of other elements has been explained using valence electrons and filling of energy levels, the

inactivity of this group can be easily explained by diagraming the valence configuration of the atoms. Each shows an already filled valence level. Since the valence level is full, and therefore stable, these atoms would not gain stability in combining with others, or themselves.

Skills Development
Skill: Hypothesizing
In 1962 Neils Bartlett produced the

HELP WANTED: JEWELER'S ASSISTANT willing to learn the trade of jewelry making from a busy shop owner. High school diploma or some technical training helpful, but a patient beginner with an interest in art and beauty may apply.

For thousands of years, people have adorned themselves with jewelry made from precious metals, stones, and other materials. Jewelry is admired and cherished for its beauty and value. **Jewelers** design and create stylish and attractive jewelry for their customers. They are experts in the qualities of metals and nonmetals, such as gold, silver, diamonds, and other gems.

Jewelers who own shops are usually responsible for the many facets of the jewelry business. These include designing jewelry, shaping, molding, or soldering metal pieces, cutting and setting stones, dealing with customers, and repairing broken jewelry.

Most jewelers learn their trade from more experienced jewelers or by attending technical schools, where they learn how to use jewelers' hand tools and machines. Frequently, jewelry making and repair require precise and delicate

work on small objects. So dexterity, coordination, patience, and the ability to concentrate are required to pursue a career as a jeweler. Artistic ability is also a valuable asset, especially if you would one day like to design jewelry or own your own shop.

If you would like to learn more about a career as a jeweler, contact: Jewelers of America, Time-Life Building, Suite 650, 1271 Avenue of the Americas, New York, NY 10020.

of a noble gas do not even combine with each other to form diatomic molecules.

❶ **The inactivity of the noble gases can be explained in terms of the electron configurations of their atoms.** Atoms of noble gases already have complete outermost energy levels. They do *not* need to bond to other atoms in order to fill their energy levels and achieve stability. Among the noble gases, helium has 2 valence electrons; and neon, argon, krypton, xenon, and radon each have 8 electrons.

Some common uses of the inert gases probably are quite familiar to you. You no doubt have watched a balloon filled with helium float in the air. And you have seen neon-filled, brightly colored signs above theaters, restaurants, and stores. Some of the uses of the noble gases may be less familiar to you—radon to treat cancer, argon in light bulbs, and xenon in photographic lamps.

Sharpen Your Skills

Deep-Sea Danger

One of the dangers of deep-sea diving is a condition known as "the bends." Using books and other reference materials in the library, find out what element causes the bends. Which of the noble gases can be used to help prevent the bends? Write a report in which you describe your findings.

146

SECTION REVIEW

1. Which elements make up the family of noble gases?
2. What is the most striking property of the noble gases?
3. What is another name for the noble gases? Why is this an appropriate name?
4. Why are the noble gases so unreactive?

6–7 Rare-Earth Elements

Have you ever wondered why two rows of elements stand alone at the bottom of the periodic table? The 30 elements in these two rows are called the rare-earth elements. **The rare-earth elements are so similar to one another that, in a sense, they really do belong in the same squares of the periodic table.** They have been separated out and displayed under the main table to make the table shorter and easier to read.

The first row, called the **lanthanoid series,** is made up of soft, malleable metals that have a high luster and conductivity. The primary oxidation number of the lanthanoid series is 3+. The lanthanoids are used in industry to make various alloys and high-quality glass.

The elements in the second row make up the **actinoid series.** All the actinoids are radioactive. With the exception of three elements, all the actinoids are synthetic, or made in the laboratory. Like the lanthanoids, the primary oxidation number of the actinoids is 3+. The best-known actinoid is uranium, which is used as a nuclear fuel.

SECTION REVIEW

1. Where on the periodic table are the lanthanoid series and the actinoid series located?
2. What are two uses of lanthanoids?
3. What is the best-known element in the actinoid series?
4. Based on the position of the rare-earth elements in the periodic table, what can you predict about their properties?

6-7 RARE-EARTH ELEMENTS

SECTION PREVIEW 6-7

The inclusion of this section completes an organized overview of the chemical elements. These elements are so similar within each series that they were difficult to chemically separate and could almost be treated as a family. The first of these is called the lanthanoid series. Each element has as its primary oxidation number a +3. The +3 value is also the most common oxidation number of the actinoid series. All of the actinoids are radioactive and most are man-made or synthetic.

PERFORMANCE OBJECTIVES 6-7

1. **Identify the lanthanoid series in a periodic table.**
2. **Identify the actinoid series in a periodic table.**
3. **Determine that the most common oxidation number of elements in both of these series is +3.**

SCIENCE TERMS

lanthanoid series p. 147
actinoid series p. 147

Skills Development

Skill: Identifying patterns

Ask students to predict the formula of several of the lanthanide oxides and chlorides: promethium oxide (Pm_2O_3); holmium oxide (Ho_2O_3); europium chloride ($EuCl_3$).

Section Review 6-7

1. Separated out and displayed at the bottom of the table, these 30 elements belong in rows 6 and 7.
2. Manufacture of alloys and high-quality glass
3. Uranium
4. They are metals with luster and conductivity; they have some properties in common with the transition metals; they have the same oxidation number as Sc and Y; they generally form compounds that are colored; they form positive ions; they may be radioactive.

Content Development

One of the important features of the lanthanoid and actinoid series is the high degree of similarity between the elements within the particular series. This similarity is explained by electron configuration. The lanthanide series elements begin filling of the 4f sublevel for electrons. The valence level is actually the sixth level. Because all of these elements have essentially the same $6s^2$ configuration, their properties should be very similar. The 4f sublevel is considered to be "underlying" or below the valence level and therefore to have very little direct influence on chemical behavior. The same concept is true for the actinoids, except the valence configuration is $7s^2$ and the underlying level is 5f. Since the f sublevel may contain up to 14 elements in each series, all 14 in each series act as though they could be placed in the same periodic square.

LABORATORY INVESTIGATION
FLAME TESTS

BEFORE THE LAB
1. **Gather all materials at least one day in advance. You should gather enough equipment to meet all your class needs, assuming six students per group.**
2. **Prepare an unknown solution using any element you have available that will readily form a chloride.**

PRE-LAB DISCUSSION
Before beginning this investigation, discuss with students whether they think the color produced in a flame test is a good indicator of the substances being used. Point out that it is, in fact, a good indicator, but cannot·be used to positively identify a particular substance. You may want to mention that if the light from the flame were passed through a spectroscope, the characteristic spectral lines of the substance would appear. These spectral lines are like the fingerprints of each substance and can be used to positively identify the elements in any particular compound.

Have students develop a hypothesis as to whether elements can be identified in this manner. Accept all logical hypotheses and make sure students go back to their original hypotheses once the investigation has been completed.

SKILL DEVELOPMENT
Students will use the following skills while completing this investigation.
1. Observing
2. Comparing
3. Safety
4. Manipulative
5. Inferring
6. Hypothesizing
7. Relating
8. Applying

SAFETY TIPS
Remind students about the basic rules to follow whenever working with a Bunsen burner. Make sure they wear safety goggles at all times and are prop-

erly dressed for this investigation. Also, caution them on the use of any acid, even weak hydrochloric acid, and refresh their memories as to the proper disposal of acids.

TEACHING STRATEGY FOR LAB PROCEDURE
It is essential that students carefully clean their nichrome wire loop prior to each test.

Flame Tests

Problem
Can elements be identified by using a flame test?

Materials *(per group)*
nichrome or platinum wire
cork
Bunsen burner
dilute hydrochloric acid
distilled water
8 test tubes
test tube rack
8 chloride test solutions
safety goggles

Procedure
1. Label each of the test tubes with one of the following compounds: LiCl, CaCl$_2$, KCl, CuCl$_2$, SrCl$_2$, NaCl, BaCl$_2$, unknown.
2. Pour 5 mL of each test solution in the correctly labeled test tube. Be sure to put the correct solution in each labeled test tube.
3. Push one end of a piece of nichrome or platinum wire into a cork. Then bend the other end of the wire into a tiny loop.
4. Put your safety goggles on. Clean the wire by dipping it into dilute hydrochloric acid and then into distilled water. Holding the cork, heat the wire in the blue flame of a burner until the wire is glowing and no longer colors the burner flame.
5. Dip the clean wire into the first test solution. Hold the wire at the tip of the inner cone of the burner flame. Record on a data table like the one shown here the color given to the flame.
6. Clean the wire by repeating step 4.
7. Repeat step 5 for the other six known test solutions. Remember to clean the wire after testing each solution.
8. Obtain an unknown solution from your teacher. After cleaning the wire, repeat the flame test for this compound.

Observations
1. What flame colors are produced by each compound?
2. What flame color is produced by your unknown?

Conclusions
1. Is the flame color a test for the metal or for the chloride in each compound? Explain your answer.
2. Why is it necessary to carefully clean the wire before testing each solution?
3. What metal is present in your unknown? How do you know?
4. How can you identify a metal using a flame test?
5. What do you think would happen if your test solution were a mixture of two metals? Could each metal be identified?

Compound	Color of Flame
Lithium chloride LiCl	
Calcium chloride CaCl$_2$	

OBSERVATIONS
1. LiCl: crimson; CaCl$_2$: yellow-red; KCl: violet; CuCl$_2$: blue-green; SrCl$_2$: red; NaCl: yellow; BaCl$_2$: green-yellow
2. Answers will depend on your choice of the unknown sample.

CONCLUSIONS
1. The metal because each compound contained a chloride, and the color would be the same for each if it was the

SUMMARY

6-1 Properties of Metals and Nonmetals

❏ Among the physical properties of metals are luster, good conductivity of heat and electricity, high density, high melting point, ductility, and malleability.

❏ Metals form positive ions.

❏ An alloy is a mixture of two or more metals or a metal and a nonmetal. An alloy has the properties of a metal.

❏ Nonmetals have physical properties that are, in general, just the opposite of metals.

❏ Nonmetals form negative ions.

❏ Elements with some metallic and some non-metallic properties are called metalloids.

6-2 Active Metals

❏ The metals of Group IA, called alkali metals, are very active.

❏ Group IIA metals, called alkaline earth metals, are active metals.

6-3 Transition Metals

❏ The transition metals are the three rows of elements found between Group IIA and Group IIIA of the periodic table.

❏ Transition metals have properties similar to each other, but not much like any other family.

6-4 From Metals to Nonmetals

❏ Properties of the elements change from metallic to nonmetallic in the boron, carbon, nitrogen, and oxygen families.

❏ The most abundant member of the boron family is the widely used metal aluminum.

❏ Carbon is the most important member of the carbon family because all living things contain carbon.

❏ The nitrogen and oxygen families each contain five elements whose properties range from nonmetallic to metalloid to metal.

6-5 Halogens

❏ The members of the halogen family are active, strongly nonmetallic elements that react readily with metals to form salts.

6-6 Noble Gases

❏ The noble, or inert, gases are unreactive and do not combine with other elements except under specially controlled conditions.

6-7 Rare-Earth Elements

❏ The rare-earth elements make up the two rows at the bottom of the periodic table. There are two series—the lanthanoids and the actinoids.

VOCABULARY

Define each term in a complete sentence.

actinoid series
alkali metal
alkaline earth
  metal
alloy
corrosion
halogen
inert

lanthanoid
  series
luster
noble gas
organic
  compound
transition
  metal

149

---

chloride being observed in the flame test

2. To remove any substances from prior flame tests that might contaminate your answer and provide a false color

3. Answers will vary, depending on the unknown sample chosen.

4. By its characteristic color

5. The color would be a mixture of the colors produced by each metal. No. You could not identify the two metals by a flame test alone.

GOING FURTHER: ENRICHMENT

Part 1

Provide other unknown samples of various chloride compounds and have students perform flame tests on these samples.

Part 2

If spectroscopes are available, have students observe the characteristic spectral lines produced by each chloride compound during the flame test. Have them sketch what they see. Then ask,

• **How might scientists use this method to determine the composition of distant objects such as the sun?** (By comparing the spectral lines from the sun to known spectral lines of elements on earth, scientists can determine the composition of the sun or other stars.)

CHAPTER REVIEW

MULTIPLE CHOICE

1. c	**3.** c	**5.** a	**7.** d	**9.** c
2. d	**4.** d	**6.** b	**8.** c	**10.** b

COMPLETION

1. luster
2. alloy
3. alkali metals
4. malleable
5. oxidation number
6. Oxygen
7. carbon
8. halogen
9. helium
10. radioactive

TRUE OR FALSE

1. F ductility
2. F gain
3. T
4. F alkali
5. T
6. T
7. T
8. F organic
9. T
10. T

SKILL BUILDING

1. First determine physical properties: luster, conductivity, malleability, ductility, melting point, density. Perform flame tests. (Certain metals will color the flame; nonmetals will not.) If necessary, perform simple chemical tests that can be done safely: reaction with water, reaction with hydrochloric acid.

2. The number of electrons in the outermost energy level should be: 1 for alkali metals; 2 for alkaline earth metals; 3 for boron family elements; 4 for carbon family elements; 5 for nitrogen family elements; 6 for oxygen family elements; 7 for halogens; 8 for noble gases.

3. Corrosion is the gradual wearing away of a metal due to a chemical reaction in which the metal combines with water or elements in the air to form a compound. Since metals tend to lose electrons, they are reactive enough to spontaneously undergo chemical changes such as this.

4. Elements in Group I and Group II combine readily with elements in Group VI and Group VII. Elements in Group 0 do not combine with other elements under ordinary circumstances. Transition elements have more than one oxidation number, so they can combine in several different ways. The position of an element in the periodic table is a function of its atomic number and therefore its electron configuration. Its number of valence electrons determines its combining ability.

5. a. Libr **b.** $MgCl_2$ **c.** CaO **d.** no reaction

6. Very active: fluorine, potassium, bromine; Moderately active: magnesium, calcium; Fairly inactive: mercury, gold, silver; Inert: kryton, helium

7. The noble gases are very scarce and unreactive. Because they are inert, they were not easily discovered and identified. Most of the noble gases were found by chance. And even though they are present in the atmosphere, their minute quantities made them difficult to identify.

8. Graph is a straight line that indicates the melting point decreases as the mass number increases. This is because the melting point decreases as the molecular weight increases.

CONTENT REVIEW: MULTIPLE CHOICE

On a separate sheet of paper, write the letter of the answer that best completes each statement.

1. Some metals are very heavy for their size. This property is referred to as high
   a. ductility. b. luster. c. density. d. malleability.
2. When an element combines with oxygen, the resulting compound is known as a (an)
   a. alloy. b. allotrope. c. salt. d. oxide.
3. In the periodic table, the metallic character of the elements increases as you move
   a. down and to the right. b. up and to the right.
   c. down and to the left. d. up and to the left.
4. Elements that display properties of both metals and nonmetals are called
   a. transition metals. b. alkaline earths. c. salts. d. metalloids.
5. Which of the following is an alkali metal?
   a. sodium b. gold c. neon d. chlorine
6. Which of the following is a transition metal?
   a. sodium b. gold c. neon d. chlorine
7. Which of the following is a halogen?
   a. sodium b. gold c. neon d. chlorine
8. Which of the following is a noble gas?
   a. sodium b. gold c. neon d. chlorine
9. Which element is called "the basis of life"?
   a. iron b. oxygen c. carbon d. silicon
10. When a metal combines with a halogen, the kind of compound formed is called a (an)
    a. organic compound. b. salt. c. actinoid. d. oxide.

CONTENT REVIEW: COMPLETION

On a separate sheet of paper, write the word or words that best complete each statement.

1. Metals are shiny, or have a high _____.
2. When two molten metals are mixed, the substance formed when the molten material cools and hardens is called a (an) _____.
3. The elements in Group IA are called _____.
4. If a metal is _____, it means it can be hammered into thin sheets.
5. A characteristic of transition metals is that their _____ can vary.
6. _____ is the most abundant element in the earth's crust.
7. Organic compounds are those compounds that contain the element _____.
8. In the Greek language, the word _____ means "salt former."
9. The noble gas that can make a balloon float is _____.
10. All of the actinoids are _____ elements.

CONTENT REVIEW: TRUE OR FALSE

Determine whether each statement is true or false. Then on a separate sheet of paper, write "true" if it is true. If it is false, change the underlined word or words to make the statement true.

1. The property of metals that means they can be drawn into thin wire is called <u>luster</u>.
2. Nonmetals tend to <u>lose</u> electrons.
3. In general, the <u>nonmetallic</u> character of the elements increases as you go up and to the right in the periodic table.
4. Sodium belongs to the <u>transition</u> metals.
5. Calcium is a <u>metal</u> that belongs to the alkaline earth family.

6. Gold is a <u>transition metal</u>.
7. <u>Aluminum</u> is a member of the boron family.
8. Compounds that contain carbon are known as <u>inorganic</u> compounds.
9. All members of the nitrogen family have <u>five</u> electrons in their outermost energy level.
10. The most striking property of the noble gases is their extreme <u>inactivity</u>.

CONCEPT REVIEW: SKILL BUILDING

Use the skills you have developed in the chapter to complete each activity.

1. **Designing an experiment** Describe the laboratory procedure you would follow to determine whether an unknown element is a metal or a nonmetal.
2. **Making diagrams** Draw a diagram to show the arrangement of electrons in the outermost energy level of an atom in each family of the periodic table.
3. **Applying concepts** Explain why metals are easily corroded.
4. **Applying concepts** In what ways does the position of an element in the periodic table tell you how it may combine with other elements to form compounds?
5. **Identifying patterns** Predict what will happen when the elements in each of the following pairs are brought together in a chemical reaction:

   a. lithium and bromine
   b. magnesium and chlorine
   c. calcium and oxygen
   d. potassium and neon

6. **Classifying elements** Classify each of the following elements as very active, moderately active, fairly inactive, or inert: magnesium, mercury, fluorine, krypton, helium, gold, potassium, calcium, bromine.
7. **Making inferences** Why were the noble gases difficult to discover?
8. **Making and interpreting graphs** Make a graph of melting point as a function of mass number for elements of the alkali metal family. Describe the graph. What relationship between melting point and mass number does your graph suggest?

CONCEPT REVIEW: ESSAY

Discuss each of the following in a brief paragraph.

1. Why do atoms of the alkali metals readily lose 1 electron?
2. Why do nonmetals tend to gain electrons?
3. What accounts for the extreme unreactivity of the noble gases?

4. Sodium never occurs in nature as a free element, and platinum seldom occurs in compounds. How are these observations related to the chemical properties of these two metals?

151

ESSAY

1. The alkali metals have relatively large atoms, so their one electron is far from the nucleus. Thus, it is easily lost during chemical reactions with other elements.

2. Nonmetals normally have from five to eight electrons in their outermost energy level. Those with eight already have a complete outer level. Rather than lose 5, 6, or 7 electrons, the other nonmetals tend to gain 3, 2, or 1 electron to achieve a complete outermost energy level.

3. The reason for their stability is their electron structure. Because the outer energy level of each noble gas contains eight electrons, these atoms have no tendency to gain or lose electrons in the presence of other atoms.

4. Sodium never occurs free because it is an extremely active alkali metal. Platinum, an inactive transition metal, does

ADDITIONAL QUESTIONS AND TOPIC SUGGESTIONS

1. Have your students examine several specimens of elements. Using the information in the student text, have them classify the elements into metals and nonmetals. Have them compare the differences between metals and nonmetals.
2. Have interested students prepare a class report on alchemy. Have them describe the laboratories, equipment, and accomplishments of the alchemists.
3. Have your students construct charts to show some properties of the noble gases. Have them include where these gases are found, how they are used, and how they react with other substances.
4. Have interested students prepare a class report on the halogens. Have them include the following information concerning halogens: physical and chemical characteristics, preparation, and uses.

ISSUES IN SCIENCE

The following issue can be used as a springboard for class debate or as a writing homework.

Many scientists argue that one important reason for space research is the fact that elements that are scarce on earth may be plentiful on other bodies in space such as planets and asteroids. Other scientists feel we have all of the resources of important elements that we need right here on earth. They feel the money spent on space research could be better spent searching for new deposits of vital elements. What is your opinion?

Unit Two
PATTERNS IN MATTER

ADVENTURES IN SCIENCE: STEPHEN HAWKING: CHANGING OUR VIEW OF THE UNIVERSE

BACKGROUND INFORMATION

With the Newtonian theory of gravity and Einstein's theory of general relativity, it is possible to reliably predict both the location and speed of an object in space. In the world of subatomic particles, however, things are not so easy. The quantum theory, which describes the behavior of particles that make up the atom, includes what is called an "uncertainty principle." This principle states that at a given moment, one cannot predict both the speed and location of a particle inside an atom (thus the need for an "electron cloud" to describe the location of electrons around a nucleus). Dr. Hawking, who is using the quantum theory to study black holes, says the uncertainty is especially bad there; that it is impossible to predict *either* the speed or location of a particle emitted from a black hole.

One of the factors that spurs Hawking on is the fact that connecting links between the quantum theory and every known physical field of force except gravity have been proven. Thus Hawking feels that consistency dictates a link between the quantum theory and the force of gravity.

Adventures in Science

STEPHEN HAWKING: Changing Our View of the Universe

Scientists have long struggled to find the connection between two branches of physics. One of these branches deals with the forces that rule the world of atoms and subatomic particles. The other branch deals with gravity and its role in the universe of stars and galaxies. Physicist Stephen Hawking has set himself the task of discovering the connection. Leading theoretical physicists agree that if anyone can discover a unifying principle, it will certainly be this extraordinary scientist.

Dr. Hawking's goal, as he describes it, is simple. "It is complete understanding of the universe, why it is as it is and why it exists at all." In order to achieve such an understanding, Dr. Hawking seeks to "quantize gravity." Quantizing gravity means combining the laws of gravity and the laws of quantum mechanics into a single universal law. Dr. Hawking and other theoretical physicists believe that with such a law, the behavior of all matter in the universe, and the origin of the universe as well, could be explained.

Dr. Hawking's search for a unifying theory has led him to study one of science's greatest mysteries: black holes. A black hole is an incredibly dense region in space whose gravita-

152

TEACHING STRATEGY

Motivation
Begin by asking students,
- **What is the smallest thing you can think of?** (Answers may vary. The smallest thing in the universe is actually a subatomic particle.)
- **What is the largest thing you can think of?** (Answers may vary. Probably the largest imaginable thing is the entire universe.)

Point out that two branches of physics deal with these extremes: the world of the atom and subatomic particles, and the world of the stars and galaxies.

Content Development
Have students read the article about Stephen Hawking. Ask,
- **In what way is Dr. Hawking involved in the two branches of physics we just discussed?** (He is attempting to discover a unifying principle that combines the laws of gravity with the laws of quantum mechanics.)

Stress to students the inspiring story of Dr. Hawking's success as a scientist despite his illness and physical

tional pull attracts all nearby objects, virtually "swallowing them up." A black hole is formed when a star uses up most of the nuclear fuel that has kept it burning. During most of its life as an ordinary star, its nuclear explosions exert enough outward force to balance the powerful inward force of gravity. But when the star's fuel is used up, the outward force ceases to exist. Gravity takes over and the star collapses into a tiny core of extremely dense material, possibly no bigger than the period at the end of this sentence.

Hawking has already proved that a black hole can emit a stream of electrons. Prior to this discovery, scientists believed that nothing, not even light, could escape from a black hole. So scientists have hailed Hawking's discovery as "one of the most beautiful in the history of physics."

Probing the mysteries of the universe is no ordinary feat. And Stephen Hawking is no ordinary man. Respected as one of the most brilliant physicists in the world, Hawking is also considered one of the most remarkable. For Dr. Hawking suffers from a serious disease of the nervous system that has confined him to a wheelchair, barely able to move or to speak. Although Dr. Hawking gives numerous presentations and publishes countless articles and papers, his addresses must be translated and his essays written down by other hands.

Hawking became ill during his first years at Cambridge University in England. The disease progressed quickly and left the young scholar quite despondent. He even considered giving up his research, as he thought he would not live long enough to receive his Ph.D. But in 1965, Hawking's life changed. He married Jane Wilde, a fellow student and language scholar. Suddenly life took on new meaning. "That was the turning point," he says. "It made me determined to live, and it was about that time that I began making professional progress." Hawking's health and spirits improved.

His studies continued and reached new heights of brilliance. Today, Dr. Hawking is professor of mathematics at Cambridge University and a husband and father who leads a full and active life.

Dr. Hawking believes that his illness has benefited his work. It has given him more time to think about physics. So although his body is failing him, his mind is free to soar. Considered to be one of the most brilliant physicists of all times, Dr. Hawking has taken some of the small steps that lead science to discovery and understanding. With time to ponder the questions of the universe, it is quite likely that Stephen Hawking will be successful in uniting the world of the tiniest particles with the world of stars and galaxies.

Stephen Hawking, shown here with his family, is Lucasian professor of mathematics at Cambridge University—a position once held by Isaac Newton. Hawking has received numerous prizes for his work.

153

ADDITIONAL QUESTIONS AND TOPIC SUGGESTIONS

1. What do theoretical physicists believe would be possible if a single universal law could be discovered? (They believe it would be possible to explain the behavior of all matter in the universe and the origin of the universe as well.)
2. What did Dr. Hawking prove about a black hole? How did his discovery change previous ideas about black holes? (He proved that a black hole can emit a stream of electrons. Prior to this, scientists believed that nothing, not even light, could escape from a black hole.)
3. Many handicapped persons have been extremely successful in their fields. Go to the library and research the story of such a person. Explain how his or her story compares with Dr. Hawking's story.

CRITICAL THINKING QUESTIONS

1. Why might the study of black holes be relevant to the unifying principle Dr. Hawking is looking for? (A black hole is a phenomenon that occurs in the universe when a star dies. It is caused by the force of gravity. Yet black holes also emit electrons, which are subatomic particles. These particles would obey the laws of quantum mechanics.)
2. What do you think about the idea that the behavior of the very smallest and very largest things in the universe must somehow obey the same law? Discuss your ideas in a brief paragraph.

handicaps. Point out that Dr. Hawking feels that his illness has actually enhanced his career because it has given him more time to think about physics.

Unit Two
PATTERNS IN MATTER

ISSUES IN SCIENCE: THE FIFTH FORCE: IS IT WITH US?

BACKGROUND INFORMATION

The force of attraction due to gravity that exists between objects is described by Newton's law of universal gravitation: $F = Gm_1m_2/d^2$, where m_1 and m_2 are the masses of the objects, d is the distance between them, and G is the universal gravitational constant.

Unlike gravity, hypercharge is a repelling force. The effect of hypercharge is to slow down a falling object—almost as if an unseen hand were holding it slightly back from the downward pull of the earth. Thus the greater the hypercharge, the slower the object will fall. The deceleration due to hypercharge is determined by the ratio of protons to neutrons in an atomic nucleus divided by the mass of the atom, which includes the total number of protons and neutrons plus the binding energy.

Issues in Science

THE FIFTH FORCE: IS IT WITH US?

According to legend, in the late 1500s the famous Italian scientist Galileo climbed to the top of the Leaning Tower of Pisa in Italy and dropped two cannonballs at exactly the same time. One cannonball weighed ten times as much as the other. Popular scientific theories of Galileo's day predicted that the heavier ball would land first. But both of Galileo's cannonballs hit the ground at exactly the same time!

Although this story may be only legend, Galileo's experiments did prove an important scientific fact: all falling objects, regardless of their masses, accelerate at the same rate and thus fall at the same speed in a vacuum. The force that causes falling objects to accelerate at the same rate is gravity.

Now, nearly 300 years later, a new theory is shaking the very roots of physics. Unleashing a flurry of new experiments and sharp debate, the theory suggests the existence of a new force in nature. If indeed this theory is correct, it might prove the teachings of Galileo, Newton, and even Einstein wrong, by proving that there is a force that works against gravity.

Until recently, practically all scientists would have said there is no force that works against gravity. Now, however, some scientists are not so sure. In fact, these scientists have even suggested the existence of such a force.

TEACHING STRATEGY

Motivation

Display a ball such as a tennis ball. Drop the ball from a height of several meters and ask,
• **What made the ball fall?** (You dropped it; gravity pulled it down.)
• **Suppose I dropped a much bigger ball, such as a soccer ball. How do you think the speed of its fall would com-** pare to that of the tennis ball? (It would be the same.)
• **What would happen if I dropped a marble? How would the speed of its fall compare to that of a tennis ball?** (It would be the same.)
• **Suppose I dropped a wooden ball, or an iron ball? How would its speed compare?** (It should be the same.)

Explain to students that we have been taught that all objects fall at the same rate because that is what scientists since Galileo's day have always believed. This demonstrates how difficult it is to have people accept the changing of a law or theory once it has been considered accurate for many years.

Ephraim Fischbach of the University of Washington; Daniel Sudarsky, Aaron Szafer, and Carrick Talmadge of Purdue University; and Samuel Aronson of Brookhaven National Laboratory say they have found evidence of a force that under certain circumstances works against gravity. They call it the force of hypercharge. Many other people call it "the fifth force."

Most physicists believe in the existence of four basic forces in nature. These four forces are gravity, electromagnetism, the strong nuclear force, and the weak nuclear force.

Gravity is the force of attraction between all objects in the universe. The earth and a falling apple have a gravitational attraction for each other. So they pull on each other. Because the earth is more massive, its pull on the apple is greater, and thus noticeable.

According to Dr. Fischbach, hypercharge is a relatively weak force that works against gravity when objects are within about 200 meters of each other. Since this countergravitational force is much weaker than the pull of gravity, it is hardly noticeable.

Fischbach and his associates began to suspect the existence of a fifth force when they observed some strange results in gravity experiments they performed. After reexamining the results of many previous experiments, they concluded that as the force of gravity draws two objects together, another weaker force repels the objects. This force is hypercharge.

The magnitude of the hypercharge force is in part determined by the binding energy of an atomic nucleus. Since binding energy in various atomic nuclei is not the same, atoms would differ in the amount of fifth force they generate. As a result of differences in hypercharge, all objects would not obey Galileo's theory of gravitational acceleration and would not fall to the earth at the same speed. One object would fall more slowly than another!

◀ As this juggler knows, all things that go up must come down. Or must they?

Does the fifth force exist? Several leading scientists are doubtful. Nobel prize winner Richard Feynman believes that if the force is as strong as described, "it would have had effects in other experiments. . . ." Dr. Feynman questions the validity of the tests that claim to show evidence of a new force.

Dr. Leon Lederman of Fermilab says of the fifth force, "My prediction is that the whole thing will go away."

Gravitational expert Robert Dicke of Princeton University explains, "The statistical evidence is not overwhelmingly convincing. I'd call it moderately persuasive. I put the chances of its being right at fifty percent or slightly better."

Many experiments are planned to test the theory of a fifth force. But scientists warn that it may be difficult to get valid results from the experiments.

If a fifth force exists, it will have a significant impact on the science of physics. But even with that prospect, some scientists are excited by the challenge of proving the existence of a new force. Even Nobel prize winner Dr. Sheldon Glashow of Harvard University admits, "It would be fun if it were true."

Could it be that Superman and Lois Lane have known about the fifth force all this time?

155

Content Development

Refer to the Motivation discussion and point out that new scientific instruments have been able to measure the free fall of objects in an extremely sensitive way. As a result, some scientists have come to the conclusion that all objects do not fall at the same rate, and that the differences in their speeds are due to an intriguing force called the "hypercharge force."

Emphasize to students that despite the controversy surrounding this issue, it serves as an important illustration of how scientists work. The emergence of new evidence about free fall has prompted scientists to experiment and gather more information. As a result, they will reevaluate previous conclusions and possibly draw some new conclusions.

ADDITIONAL QUESTIONS AND TOPIC SUGGESTIONS

1. At what distance from the surface of the earth would objects begin to experience the effects of the hypercharge force? (200 meters or less)
2. Object A has twice as much hypercharge as object B. Both objects are dropped from a helicopter flying 400 meters above the earth. Describe the fall of the objects. (Both objects would fall at the same rate for the first 200 meters. Then object A would begin to fall less rapidly than object B. Object B would hit the ground before object A.)
3. Why would it be difficult to test for the effects of hypercharge in an ordinary classroom or laboratory? (Objects would be affected by air friction.)

CRITICAL THINKING QUESTIONS

1. The article referred to the hypercharge force as a "new" force. Is it really new? Explain your answer. (No. If it exists at all, it will have been around as long as all other forces. It would just be newly discovered.)
2. In Unit Two Adventures in Science, you read about black holes, which occur when the force of gravity causes a star to collapse in on itself. Do you think that without the hypercharge force the earth might collapse in on itself? (There is no right or wrong answer to this question; allow students to speculate freely.)

CLASS DEBATE

As students debate this issue, they may enjoy adding a "time-machine" feature in which Sir Isaac Newton and Galileo come into the twentieth century and express their points of view.

Unit Three

INTERACTIONS OF MATTER

UNIT OVERVIEW

In Unit Three, students first explore chemical bonding. They learn about ionic, covalent, and metallic bonds, and about how to predict bond type. They are then introduced to chemical reactions and chemical equations, and to the energy associated with such reactions. The topic of reaction rate is also covered, and students apply the collision theory to explain the factors that affect rate.

Next, students learn about solutions and their properties, and about suspensions, colloids, acids, bases, and salts. They then explore the chemistry of carbon compounds. Finally, they study nuclear reactions, including transmutation, fission, and fusion. They also learn about the uses and dangers of radioactivity, and about its detection and measurement.

UNIT OBJECTIVES

1. **Explain chemical bonding, and contrast ionic, covalent, and metallic bonding.**
2. **Describe and explain the basis of chemical reactions, and interpret and balance chemical equations.**
3. **Contrast exothermic and endothermic reactions, and explain the factors that affect reaction rate.**
4. **Define solution, and classify solutions.**
5. **Describe the properties of acids and bases and the formation of salts.**
6. **Classify different carbon compounds and draw structural formulas for them.**
7. **Contrast different types of nuclear equations, and describe the detection, measurement, and uses of radioactivity.**

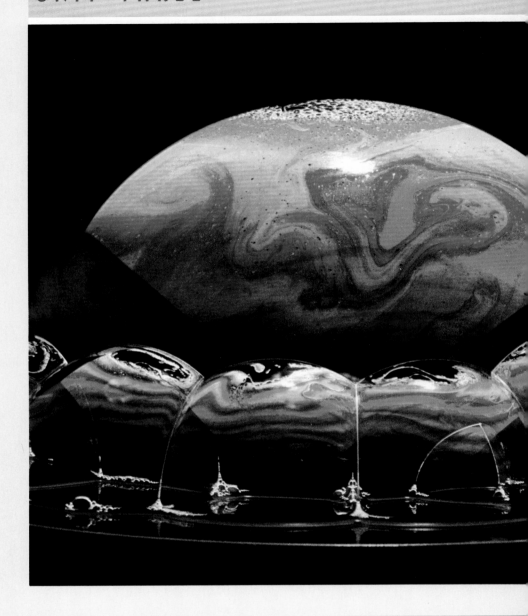

INTRODUCING UNIT THREE

Begin your teaching of the unit by having students examine the unit-opening photograph. It shows soap bubbles that have been made by flowing air into a film of soap that was produced through a saponification reaction. In such a reaction, a fat, or ester produced by combining a glycerine molecule with several long-chain fatty-acid molecules, is made to react with a strong hydroxide, such as NaOH. This forms a soap, which is essentially an organic salt containing a positive alkali metal ion and negative ion formed from a long-chain fatty-acid molecule.

You may wish to ask students to attempt to answer the following questions relating to the unit-opening photograph.

• **What, if anything, separates the contents of the attached bubbles?** (A

Interactions of Matter

See if you can solve this puzzle by determining what you would make if you performed the following steps. First, treat a fat called palmitin with an alkali such as sodium hydroxide in a process called saponification. The fat will break down to produce the substances sodium palmitate and glycerin. Discard the glycerin. Then add the sodium palmitate to a wetting compound to form a solution. Now dip a thin-sided ring, preferably one with a handle, into the liquid. Finally, apply a gentle stream of air to the film on the ring.

Here is what you actually did. When you saponified the palmitin, you made soap. Then you added it to water to make a solution. Blowing on the ring created a bubble.

Chemical reactions such as saponification may not be familiar to you. Yet chemical reactions are occurring all around you and even in your body at this very moment. As you read the chapters in this unit, you will learn about the interactions of matter that can occur in a test tube, in nature, and even inside yourself!

CHAPTERS

Saponification is the chemical process by which soap is made. As light passes through these soap bubbles, a lovely pattern of colors is produced. **157**

CHAPTER DESCRIPTIONS

7 Atoms and Bonding In Chapter 7, the basis of chemical bonding is explained. Ionic, covalent, and metallic bonding are described and contrasted. Methods for predicting bond type are also explained.

8 Chemical Reactions Chapter 8 focuses upon the nature of chemical changes. Students learn to balance chemical equations and also find out about the differences between exothermic and endothermic reactions. The chapter concludes with a discussion of reaction rate, activation energy, and collision theory.

9 Solution Chemistry Chapter 9 deals with the nature of solutions and with factors that affect rate of solution and solubility. Different types of solutions are contrasted. Finally, acid–base chemistry and pH are explored.

10 Carbon Chemistry In Chapter 10, the chemistry of carbon and organic compounds is described. Saturated and unsaturated hydrocarbons are explored. The role of several types of organic compounds in body chemistry is also treated.

11 Nuclear Chemistry Chapter 11 deals with changes in the nuclei of atoms. Radioactivity and its discovery, measurement, and uses are discussed. Transmutation and radioactive decay, as well as nuclear fission and nuclear fusion, are explained.

thin soap film separates the air trapped within the different bubbles.)
- **What colors can you see in the bubbles?** (Colors such as pink, blue, and yellow are visible.)
- **What may account for such colors? Is the soap itself permanently colored?** (The soap film does not contain pigments. The colors result mostly from the different degrees of bending different frequencies of light in the white light that enters the film. The

colors in the white light are separated out in this way.)

Next, have students read the unit introduction. This material should serve as the basis for various discussions that will better motivate students to study the chapters that follow. Here are some questions you may wish to pose to the class to stimulate class discussions.
- **What are the sources of fats that are often used to make soaps?** (The

fats used come from both animal and vegetable sources. Materials such as lard may be used. Various oils, which are liquid fats, can be used. An example is olive oil, which is used to make castile soap.)
- **Why do you think soap is useful in washing?** (Many of the materials to be washed away are greasy and not very soluble in water. Soaps have an ionic end, which is soluble in water, and a nonpolar end, which dissolves grease. The dissolved grease can then be rinsed away, together with the soap, by water.)

Chapter 7
ATOMS AND BONDING

CHAPTER OVERVIEW

In order for us to understand the reasons behind the appearance and characteristics of the substances around us, we must understand how the basic units of matter, atoms, are attached to each other. This immense task can be simplified somewhat when we notice that most "atomic attaching," or bonding, can be classified into three overall categories: ionic, covalent, and metallic. Each category describes a method by which atoms may bond to each other. By classifying a bonding arrangement you also immediately know that the substance has certain properties. Ionic: rigid, conducts electricity when melted or dissolved in water, and probably made up of a metal and a nonmetal from Group VI or VII. Covalent: Made up of elements that are somewhat similar, shares valence electrons, and frequently will be gases or liquids. Metallic: Made up of one or more types of metal atoms, conducts electricity in the solid form, and can be hammered into various shapes.

TEACHER DEMONSTRATION

To illustrate that substances bond in more than one way, use small samples of pure metals in a display, along with small samples of that same metal bonded with other elements in a compound. Some examples may be lead (metallic) and lead nitrate (ionic) or tin (metallic) and tin nitrate (ionic). Have students note the properties of each.

INTRODUCING CHAPTER 7

Begin the introduction of Chapter 7 by pointing out to students that almost all atoms are found in nature bonded, or attached, to other atoms. Using the computer-generated images of the morphine molecule, point out to students that they, like morphine, are made up of carbon, oxygen, hydrogen and nitrogen. The major chemical difference between a person and a molecule of morphine is the amount of each type of atom and the way the atoms are bonded to each other. The way atoms are bonded in a substance helps to give substances their properties. Graphite and diamonds are both made of carbon. However, due to their different bonding natures, they have drastically different properties.

• **Can you see any patterns in the arrangements of the atoms in the computer-generated image?** (The carbons all seem to be bonded to each other. Some carbons are in rings.)

• **What do you suppose holds atoms together in a chemical bond?** (Atoms tend to achieve low energy, or stable conditions, by obtaining eight valence electrons.)

• **Can you name any elements in nature that are not found in a bonded condition?** (helium, neon, argon—the noble gases in the last column on the periodic table)

Atoms and Bonding 7

CHAPTER OBJECTIVES

After completing this chapter, you will be able to

7-1 Explain chemical bonding on the basis of unfilled energy levels.

7-2 Describe the formation of ions and ionic bonds.

7-2 Relate ionic bonding to the properties of ionic compounds.

7-3 Describe the formation of covalent bonds.

7-3 Define a molecule.

7-3 Draw and interpret electron-dot diagrams.

7-4 Relate metallic bonding to the properties of metals.

7-5 Predict bond types on the basis of the positions of atoms in the periodic table.

Trapped in a tangle of twisted metal and broken glass, the driver of the mangled car cries out in pain. Within moments, the rescue squad arrives and quickly checks the driver's injuries. The emergency medical technician begins treatment by injecting the powerful pain-killing drug morphine into the victim's arm. In seconds, the drug begins to ease the pain.

At the same time, in a nearby home, a parent uses cough medicine to relieve the hacking, choking cough of a sick child. The threat of pneumonia had convinced the child's doctor that prescribing a cough medicine containing codeine was necessary. Soon the child is resting comfortably.

Although morphine and codeine are used for different purposes, they are similar in many ways. Both of these products are made from the same plant. Both are valuable drugs that ease suffering. And both can be dangerous if they are not used properly.

Morphine and codeine are similar for another reason. They are made of the same elements: carbon, oxygen, hydrogen, and nitrogen. These four elements make up many of the chemical substances found in all plants and animals, including you! If so many substances contain the same four elements, what makes them different from each other? The answer lies in the way in which these elements combine to form various substances. In this chapter you will learn how and why elements combine and what important products they form. Turn the page for a look into the world of substances and their structures.

This computer-generated photo of a morphine molecule shows the way in which carbon, oxygen, hydrogen, and nitrogen atoms combine to form this unique compound. You actually are seeing five images of the molecule. Carbon atoms are light blue; oxygen, red; hydrogen, gray; and nitrogen, dark blue.

159

The metals will not dissolve in water, but the ionic compounds will. Ask,

• **What causes the difference?** (Metallic bonding is not broken down by the positive and negative areas of water, while ionic bonding is.)

Display a pencil lead (graphite form of carbon) and a diamond. Both are pure carbon but, due to different bonding, have extremely different properties. Graphite is bonded as flat plates, which bond weakly to other flat plates. In a diamond, each carbon atom is part of a symmetrical tetrahedron. Ask,

• **How could graphite be changed into a diamond?** (Extreme pressure to get the atoms to shift positions.)

TEACHER RESOURCES

Audiovisuals

Bonding Between Atoms of Different Elements: Metals and Non-Metals–The Ionic Bond, filmstrip or slides with cassette, PH Media

Bonding Between Atoms of Different Elements: Non-Metals and Covalent Compounds, filmstrip or slides with cassette, PH Media

Bonding Between Atoms of the Same Element: Metals and the Metallic Bond, filmstrip or slides with cassette, PH Media

Bonding Between Atoms of the Same Element: Non-Metals and the Covalent Bond, filmstrip or slides with cassette, PH Media

Books

Boschke, F. L. (ed.), *Bonding and Structure,* Springer-Verlag

Gray, Harry B., *Chemical Bonds: An Introduction to Atomic and Molecular Structure,* Benjamin-Cummings

Hatfield, William E. and William E. Parker, *Symmetry in Chemical Bonding and Structure,* Merrill

Murell, John N. et al., *The Chemical Bond,* Wiley

Software

Chemical Bonding, Prentice-Hall

• **Since metals have properties that differ from nonmetals, how do you suppose their respective atoms may be bonded?** (Student answers will vary a lot at this starting point. However, they may begin here to associate the properties of a substance with a particular classification of a bonding type, such as metallic bonding.)

After this question, it would be useful to remind students of the previous information about metals and nonmetals on the periodic table. Metals tend to easily give up electrons—an important point in their bonding.

7-1 CHEMICAL BONDING

SECTION PREVIEW 7-1

In this section, the concept that all substances in the universe are made up of essentially 109 different types of elements is presented. It is the combinations and recombinations of these 109 "universal" parts that produce the many substances that we see. Of major importance is that many combinations are possible due to the mutual attraction of the outermost valence electrons in each atom to other atoms. These attractions for valence electrons usually produce a filled energy level when two or more atoms bond. It needs to be pointed out that a filled valence level means 8 electrons for elements, except for H and He.

PERFORMANCE OBJECTIVES 7-1

1. Describe chemical bonding in terms of an atom's electron arrangement.
2. Define energy level.
3. Predict which elements have stable configurations.
4. Relate valence level to atomic bonding.
5. List the maximum number of electrons in the first three energy levels.

SCIENCE TERMS 7-1
chemical bonding p. 160
valence electron p. 162

To relate electron arrangement to chemical bonding

7-1 Chemical Bonding

Every object, regardless of its size, is made up of an incredible number of tiny particles called atoms. Atoms, the basic building blocks of matter, make up all of the substances in the universe.

If you were to try to list all of these different substances, your list would probably be endless. Scientists know there are hundreds of thousands of different substances in nature. Yet there are only 109 different types of elements! How can just these 109 different elements form so many different substances?

The 109 elements are each made of specific types of atoms. Atoms of elements combine with one another to produce new and different substances called compounds. You are already familiar with several compounds: water, sodium chloride, sugar, carbon dioxide, and ammonia. Compounds contain more than one kind of atom chemically joined together.

❶ The combining of atoms of elements to form new substances is called **chemical bonding.** Chemical bonds are formed in very definite ways. The atoms combine according to certain rules. Such rules are determined by the structure of the atom.

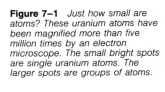

Figure 7–1 *Just how small are atoms? These uranium atoms have been magnified more than five million times by an electron microscope. The small bright spots are single uranium atoms. The larger spots are groups of atoms.*

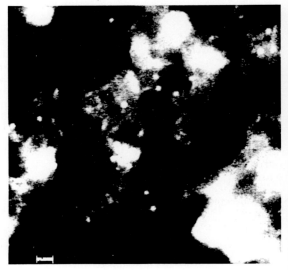

160

TEACHING STRATEGY 7-1

Motivation
Students need at this point to see that electrons in atoms do have some restrictions. They could easily be reminded of restrictions in their experiences. Have you ever flown on a large jet? Did you notice that some seating sections are reserved to two seats per aisle, while in another section four or even more seats may be in an aisle?

Another situation may be in a resort hotel that has some rooms that have occupancy for two but other rooms that may hold four or six. Energy levels in atoms are also restricted and can only hold certain numbers of electrons. Have students follow up this idea by studying and counting the electrons on each level shown in Figure 7-2. Just as seating and occupancy restrictions cannot be violated, energy level numbers cannot be exceeded.

Content Development
A major content theme in this section is the stability of an octet, or a full energy level. Ask students to suppose they were in a row boat that had a rowing capacity for 8 oarsmen. The arrangement would be 4 rows of 2 each. If there were only 7 oarsmen the boat would need one more for maximum efficiency and stability. Other boat designs may call for only two oarsmen, side by side, for stability.

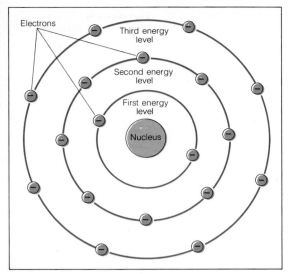

Figure 7–2 *Within the electron cloud, electrons are arranged in energy levels. Each energy level can hold only a certain number of electrons. When an energy level is holding its maximum number of electrons, it is complete. How many electrons can the first energy level hold? The second? The third?* ❶

Electrons and Energy Levels

The atom contains a positively charged center called the nucleus. Located outside the nucleus are negatively charged particles called electrons. The negative charge of the electrons balances the positive charge of the nucleus. The atom as a whole is neutral. It has no net charge.

The negatively charged electrons of an atom are attracted by the positively charged nucleus of that atom. This electron–nucleus attraction holds the atom together. The electrons, however, are not pulled into the nucleus. They remain in a region outside the nucleus called the electron cloud.

The electron cloud is made up of a number of different energy levels. Electrons within an atom are arranged in energy levels. Each energy level can hold only a certain number of electrons. The first, or innermost, energy level can hold only 2 electrons.

Figure 7–3 *An atom contains a positively charged center called the nucleus. Located outside the nucleus are negatively charged electrons. This atom shows 2 positively charged protons and 2 neutral neutrons in the nucleus. How many electrons are in this atom? What is true about the number of protons and electrons in an atom?* ❷

❷

161

TEACHER DEMONSTRATION

To illustrate a very visible example of a chemical reaction, hold up two flasks, one containing the clear solution of lead nitrate, $Pb(NO_3)_2$ (33 g/liter), the other, sodium iodide, NaI (17 g/liter). Have the students note the color (crystal clear) and the state (liquid) of the two solutions. Next, while all carefully watch, mix the two solutions. Instantly you will get a heavy yellow precipitate of PbI_2 as the double replacement reaction occurs, giving vivid evidence of the chemical change. Filtering will show the solid nature of the PbI_2 precipitate. Given the reactants, ask the students to tell about the products of the reaction. $(Pb(NO_3)_2 + 2NaI \rightarrow PbI_2 + 2NaNO_3)$

ANNOTATION KEY

❶ 2; 8; 8 (Interpreting diagrams)

❷ 2. The number of protons equals the number of electrons (Applying concepts)

❶ Thinking Skill: Relating concepts

❷ Thinking Skill: Relating facts

This analogy could be used to discuss the importance of a balanced number of electrons in energy levels.

Skills Development
Skill: Making predictions
Using an atom's position on the periodic table, have students predict the number of valence electrons. They should only do this with Groups IA, IIA, IIIA, IVA, VA, VIA, VIIA, and VIII. A pattern should be noted in

that metals usually have few valence electrons compared to nonmetals.

Students should also develop the model that only those atoms with less than a full valence level will easily bond with other atoms.

Reinforcement
Whether you are building a garage or a skyscraper, cement will be used to bond the brick together. Very different structures with very different

properties can be constructed from the same building blocks. It is simply a matter of how they are attached.

Atoms are our building blocks, and instead of glue or cement we have chemical bonds. These involve interactions of electrons. And rather than needing an additional material, such as cement, these units will be able to interlock, depending upon the numbers and locations of the electrons. These important, reactive electrons are your valence electrons. Some materials will be more or less able to form bonds based upon electron configuration, so now is a good time to glance back at Chapter 4 and review the nature and structure of atoms.

Sharpen Your Skills

A Model of Energy Levels
Skills: Making models, manipulative, diagraming, applying
Level: Remedial
Type: Hands-on
Materials: corkboard, scissors, tacks of different colors

In this activity, students reinforce their understanding of energy levels by constructing models of various atoms and their electron configurations. Check students' models carefully to ensure that they have placed the correct number of electrons in each atom's energy levels.

7-1 (continued)

Motivation

Point out that students can fill a balloon with hydrogen or helium and it will float in the air. However, as they may recall from the Hindenburg disaster, hydrogen in the presence of oxygen (in air) will burn, as it is very reactive. Helium on the other hand will not react with oxygen, nor basically with anything else, even when the energy of a spark or heat is applied. This is why helium was adopted for use in blimps.

Content Development

Because of their nonreactive nature, noble gases are used in arc welding and food processing (the metal and foods cannot oxidize) and in light bulbs to allow high temperatures to be generated without breaking down the tungsten filaments.

Figure 7–4 These balloons are filled with helium, a highly unreactive element (left). Neon gas, another unreactive element, is used in neon lights such as these (center). Argon, shown here as a laser made visible through smoke, is also highly unreactive (right). The electron configurations of each element are shown below the photographs. What is it about their electron configurations that makes these elements unreactive? ❶

Sharpen Your Skills

A Model of Energy Levels

1. Cut a thin piece of corkboard into a circle 50 cm in diameter, to represent an atom.

2. Insert a large colored pushpin or tack into the center to represent the nucleus.

3. Draw 3 concentric circles around the nucleus to represent energy levels. The inner circle should be 20 cm in diameter; the second circle, 30 cm in diameter; and the third, 40 cm in diameter.

4. Using pushpins or tacks of another color to represent electrons, construct the following atoms: hydrogen (H), helium (He), lithium (Li), fluorine (F), neon (Ne), sodium (Na), and argon (Ar).

162

The second and third energy levels can each hold 8 electrons. The electrons in the outermost energy level of an atom are called **valence electrons.**

When the outermost energy level of an atom contains the maximum number of electrons, the level is full, or complete. Atoms that have filled outermost energy levels are very stable, or unreactive. Such atoms usually do not combine with other atoms to form compounds. They do not form chemical bonds.

The atoms of elements such as helium, neon, and argon do not form chemical bonds. If you look at the periodic table on pages 118–119, you will see that these atoms are all in Family VIIIA. This family contains all the atoms that have filled outermost energy levels. Remember that if the first energy level is also the outermost, it needs only 2 electrons to make it complete. Which element in Family VIIIA has only 2 valence electrons? ❷

Electrons and Bonding

The electron arrangement of the outermost energy level of an atom determines whether or not the atom will form chemical bonds. Atoms of elements of Family VIIIA have complete outermost energy levels. These atoms generally do not form chemical bonds.

Reinforcement

• **In a bonding situation, how many more electrons would chlorine, bromine, and iodine each need to become stable? (1) How many more electrons would oxygen need to become stable? (2)**
• **How many electrons are found in an atom of sodium? How many of these are considered valence electrons?** (11, 1) This could be repeated for other elements as needed.

Enrichment

Actually, some of the noble gases have been involved in bonding. For example, xenon has formed compounds from reaction with fluorine. Assign students the task of finding out how this was done. Ask them to find out why xenon was used instead of helium.

Atoms of elements other than those of the helium family (VIIIA) do not have filled outermost energy levels. Their outermost energy level lacks one or more electrons to be complete. Some of these atoms tend to gain electrons in order to fill the outermost energy level. Fluorine, which has 7 valence electrons, gains 1 electron to fill its outer energy level. Other atoms tend to lose their valence electrons and are left with only filled energy levels. For what was the filled next-to-the-outermost energy level is now the outermost energy level. Sodium, which has 1 valence electron, loses 1 electron.

In order to achieve stability, an atom will either gain or lose electrons. In other words, an atom will bond with another atom if the bonding gives both atoms complete outermost energy levels. In the next section, you will learn how bonding takes place.

SECTION REVIEW

1. What is chemical bonding?
2. Where are the electrons that are involved in bonding located in an atom?
3. What is the maximum number of electrons that can be held in the first energy level of an atom? In the second level? In the third level?
4. Explain why elements such as krypton (Kr) and xenon (Xe) do not readily react to form compounds.

7–2 Ionic Bonds

A complete outermost energy level can be achieved by the transfer of electrons from one atom to another. Bonding that involves a transfer of electrons is called **ionic bonding.** Ionic bonding, or electron-transfer bonding, gets its name from the word **ion,** which means "charged particle." Ions are formed when ionic bonding occurs.

Because ionic bonding involves the transfer of electrons, one atom gains electrons and the other atom loses electrons. Within each atom the negative and positive charges no longer balance. The atom that has gained electrons has gained a negative

Section Objective

To describe an ionic bond

163

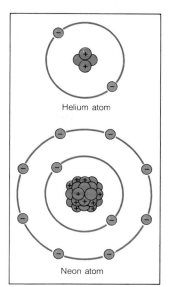

Figure 7–5 *The outermost energy level of a helium atom contains the maximum number of electrons—2. In a neon atom, the outermost energy level is the second energy level. It contains the maximum 8 electrons. What chemical property do these elements share?* ❸

7-2 IONIC BONDS

SECTION PREVIEW 7-2

In this section, students will be introduced to one of the major methods by which atoms obtain a full, stable outermost energy level. Students will become aware that some elements have only a small attraction for their valence electrons, while others have a very strong attraction for their own valence electrons. In this latter case, the atom's attraction for electrons goes beyond its own electrons, extending to the point of taking electrons from other atoms in order to fill up its outer level. This transfer of electrons will not only cause the atoms involved to now have full, stable outer energy levels, it will also cause the atoms to become charged. Students are likely to be familiar with the concept of opposites attracting, so it would seem logical that positively charged atoms, or cations, and negatively charged atoms, or anions, attract each other. Since charged atoms are called ions, this type of bonding, involving charged atoms, is called ionic bonding. In this section, students will begin to observe that Group I and Group II metals generally form ionic bonds with Group VI and Group VII nonmetals.

PERFORMANCE OBJECTIVES 7-2

1. **Predict the resulting charge on an atom when electrons are added or taken away from a specific atom.**
2. **Identify elements that have either low ionization energy or high electron affinity.**
3. **Describe the result of ionic bonding between elements as a regular pattern of ions in a crystal lattice.**

SCIENCE TERMS 7-2

ionic bonding p. 163
ion p. 164
ionization p. 165
ionization energy p. 165
electron affinity; p. 165
crystal lattice p. 166

Section Review 7-1

1. The combining of atoms of elements to form new substances
2. In the outermost energy level of the electron cloud
3. 2; 8; 8
4. These elements, which are in the last column of the periodic table, have 8 electrons in their outermost energy level and thus are stable, or unreactive.

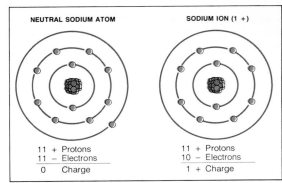

NEUTRAL FLUORINE ATOM

9 + Protons
9 − Electrons
0 Charge

NEUTRAL SODIUM ATOM

11 + Protons
11 − Electrons
0 Charge

SODIUM ION (1 +)

11 + Protons
10 − Electrons
1 + Charge

Figure 7–6 *The formation of a negative fluoride ion involves the gain of an electron by a fluorine atom. How many valence electrons does a fluorine atom have? The formation of a positive sodium ion involves the loss of an electron by a sodium atom. What is the symbol for a fluoride ion? A sodium ion?* ❶

FLUORIDE ION (1 −)

9 + Protons
10 − Electrons
1 − Charge

charge. It is a negative ion. For example, fluorine (F) has 7 valence electrons. To complete its outermost energy level, the fluorine atom gains 1 electron. In gaining 1 negatively charged electron, the fluorine atom becomes a negative ion. The symbol for the fluoride ion is F⁻.

The sodium atom (Na) has 1 valence electron. When a sodium atom loses this valence electron, it is left with an outermost energy level containing 8 electrons. In losing 1 negatively charged electron, the sodium atom becomes a positive ion. The symbol for the sodium ion is Na⁺.

In nature, it is a general rule that opposites attract. Since the two ions Na⁺ and F⁻ have opposite charges, they attract each other. The strong attraction between oppositely charged ions that have been

Figure 7–7 *The general rule that opposites attract is responsible for the formation of the ionic bond between a positive sodium ion and a negative chloride ion. Notice the transfer of an electron during the ionic bonding. What is the formula for the resulting compound?* ❷

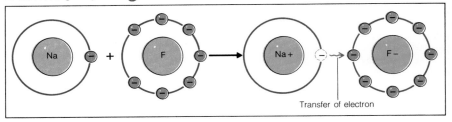

Transfer of electron

164

formed by the transfer of electrons holds the ions together in an ionic bond. The formation of the ionic bond results in the formation of the compound sodium fluoride, NaF.

Ionization Energy and Electron Affinity

In order for the outermost electron to be removed from an atom, the attraction between the negatively charged electron and the positively charged nucleus must be overcome. The process of removing an electron and forming ions is called **ionization.** Energy is needed for ionization. This energy is called **ionization energy.**

The ionization energy for atoms that have few valence electrons is low. Only a small amount of energy is needed to remove electrons from the outermost energy level. As a result, these atoms tend to lose electrons easily and to become positive ions. What elements have low ionization energies? ❸

The ionization energy for atoms with many valence electrons is very high. These atoms do not lose electrons easily. As a matter of fact, these atoms usually gain electrons. The tendency of an atom to attract electrons is called **electron affinity.** Atoms such as fluorine are said to have a high electron affinity because they attract electrons very easily. What other atoms have a high electron affinity? ❹

❷

Figure 7–8 *During ionization, an electron is removed from an atom and an ion forms. Energy is absorbed during ionization. Energy is released when an atom gains an electron and forms an ion. What is the tendency of an atom to gain electrons called?* ❺

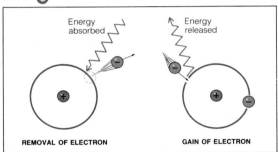

Energy absorbed

Energy released

REMOVAL OF ELECTRON

GAIN OF ELECTRON

165

Obtain a conductivity apparatus and, after exercising caution by not touching both exposed electrodes, demonstrate that salts, such as sodium chloride, calcium chloride, and magnesium chloride, contain ions. Have a beaker of distilled water to immerse electrodes in to show that pure water does not conduct electricity. Then add any of the aforementioned salts to the water. As the salt dissolves, the light will slowly light up. Repeat this demonstration with sugar and distilled water. The bulb will not light. In order for the bulb to light, an electric current must flow between the separate electrodes. Dissolved ionic substances, such as salts, provide mobile negative and positive ions. Covalent substances, such as sugar, provide no charges to complete the circuit.

Content Development

Having discussed the nature of water as a polar solvent, it is time to illustrate on the board what is happening when an ionic solid is added to water and the many partial charges that occur to isolate (dissociate) one ion from the next. The basis for the bond is simple: opposites attract. To reinforce this, be sure to have on hand some magnets with marked poles to demonstrate this. Additionally, the size of a charge is to be determined. Students have difficulty associating the loss of particles (electrons) with becoming increasingly positive. Detailed arithmetic summaries are usually the most help so that the students can see the total of positive and negative charges present and then determine whether we have a + or − excess (charge).

charged. Electrons have a negative charge. This may cause some confusion when students predict ionic charges. When an atom gains an electron it becomes negative. (Most people think of gaining something as an increase.) Be sure to remind students that electrons are negative—gaining a negative is not the same as gaining a positive.

Skills Development

Skill: Making diagrams

Have students draw out the electrons in magnesium, noting that there are 2 electrons in the valence level. Then have them draw out the electrons in energy levels for oxygen, noting 6 in the valence level. They should then deduce the formula of magnesium oxide (MgO). Repeat this for calcium oxide and calcium sulfide (CaS).

Sharpen Your Skills

Growing Crystals
Skills: Manipulative, observing, relating
Level: Average
Type: Hands-on
Materials: plastic fishing line, sea salt, beaker, hot water, stirring rod

In this activity, students grow salt crystals from a salt solution they have prepared. Students should be able to relate that the salt, when dissolved, formed ions of Na^+ and Cl^-. As the water cooled, the ions form ionic bonds and salt crystals grew on the fishing line.

ANNOTATION KEY

❶ One to one (Making calculations)
❷ Table salt (Relating facts)
❶ Thinking Skill: Making generalizations
❷ Thinking Skill: Interpreting definitions
❸ Thinking Skill: Making observations
❹ Thinking Skill: Making generalizations

Sharpen Your Skills

Growing Crystals

1. Make a small sliding loop in the end of a 10-cm length of thin plastic fishing line. Attach the loop to a small crystal of sea salt (NaCl).

2. In a beaker containing 200 mL of very hot water, dissolve by stirring as much sea salt as the water will hold.

3. Suspend the fishing line containing the loop and crystal in the beaker. Tie the other end of the line to a pencil. Lay the pencil across the top of the beaker to support the line. The crystal should be suspended about halfway down in the liquid.

4. Allow the liquid to cool slowly. Observe the growing crystals each day for 3 days. Draw what you see. Explain your observations in terms of ionic bonding.

Arrangement of Ions in Ionic Compounds

Ions of opposite charge strongly attract each other. Ions of like charge strongly repel each other. As a result, the ions in an ionic compound are arranged in a specific way. Positive ions tend to be near negative ions and farther from other positive ions.

The placement of ions in an ionic compound results in a regular, repeating arrangement called a **crystal lattice.** A crystal lattice is made up of huge numbers of ions grouped together in a regular, repeating pattern. A crystal lattice gives the compound great stability and accounts for certain physical properties. For example, ionic solids tend to have high melting points because a great deal of energy is needed to overcome the strong ion attractions within the lattice. Figure 7–9 shows the crystal lattice structure of sodium chloride.

Ionic compounds are made up of nearly endless arrays of ions. A chemical formula shows the *ratios* of ions present in the crystal lattice. For example, sodium chloride has the formula NaCl because it has one Na^+ for each Cl^- ion. What is the ratio of potassium ions to bromide ions in the ionic compound KBr? ❶

Each ionic compound has a characteristic crystal lattice arrangement. This lattice arrangement gives a

 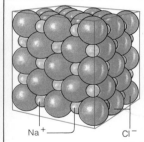

Figure 7–9 *These crystals of sodium chloride have a characteristic crystal lattice, which gives them their shape (left). In the drawing of the crystal, you can see the arrangement of the sodium and chloride ions (right). What is the common name for this crystal?* ❷

Na⁺   Cl⁻

166

7-2 (continued)

Content Development

On a chalkboard place several examples of a listing of the proton content and the electron count for neutral atoms. Then change the electron count by adding to the nonmetals and subtracting from metals. Ask students to then predict ionic charges.

Reinforcement

Some students may try to form ions on paper by adjusting the number of protons. (sodium ion formed by adding one proton, thus twelve protons and eleven electrons) Remind them that this would no longer be considered sodium because sodium may have only eleven protons. Twelve protons creates an atom of magnesium. Proton number identifies an element. Ionization is concerned only with electrons.

Content Development

• **What are the properties of metallic sodium and gaseous chlorine?** (Na is a silvery, very soft, violently reacting metal. Cl is a greenish toxic gas.)
• **How could these materials, just described, produce the white crystal we actually eat?** (The formation of ions, Na^+ and Cl^- changes their properties. Ions behave differently than pure neutral atoms.)

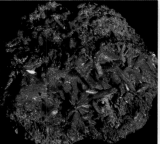

Figure 7–10 *Ionic crystals often have beautiful and unusual shapes. Here you see six-sided snowflake crystals surrounded by frost crystals (left), crystals of the mineral crocoite (center), and crystals of the mineral aragonite (right).*

particular shape to the crystals of the compound. For example, sodium chloride forms cubic crystals. Other ionic compounds form crystals of other shapes. Figure 7–10 shows some of the unusual ❸ shapes that result from ionic bonding.

SECTION REVIEW

1. What happens to electrons during ionic bonding?
2. What is an ion?
3. What is ionization energy? Electron affinity?
4. What is a crystal lattice? What holds a crystal lattice together?
5. What happens when an atom of potassium (K) bonds with an atom of iodine (I)?

7–3 Covalent Bonds

Section Objective

To describe a covalent bond

Bonding in which electrons are shared rather than transferred is called **covalent bonding.** Covalent bonding usually occurs between atoms that have high ionization energies and high electron affinities. ❹ In other words, neither atom loses electrons easily, but both atoms attract electrons.

By sharing electrons, each atom fills up its outermost energy level. So the shared electrons are in the outermost energy level of both atoms at the same time.

167

7-3 COVALENT BONDS

SECTION PREVIEW 7-3

One way for atoms to achieve the stability of a full energy level is to share their electrons with another atom. This section will show students that atoms with similar electron attracting abilities will very likely share their electrons with each other. The term *covalent* implies "cooperation among the valence electrons." A major consequence of electron sharing is the formation of molecules. Molecules will be presented as separate units of matter made up of an exact, fixed number of atoms. The molecule unit is neutral and has the properties of the substance it makes up. In the text examples, each atom obtains an octet (with the exception, of course, of hydrogen) by sharing the appropriate number of electrons.

PERFORMANCE OBJECTIVES 7-3

1. **Predict which atoms are most likely to engage in covalent bonding.**
2. **Draw formulas of molecules with the correct number of each constituent atom.**
3. **Compare and contrast the various characteristics of ionic crystals and covalent molecules.**

SCIENCE TERMS 7-3

covalent bonding p. 167
electron-dot diagram p. 168
diatomic element p. 169
molecule p. 169
network solid p. 170
polyatomic ion p. 171

Enrichment

William Bragg (1862–1942) and his son Lawrence Bragg (1890–   ) worked with X-rays and the diffraction of these rays. They showed that X-rays, when passed through crystals, would diffract and the measurement of this diffraction could be used to calculate the distance between the ions in the crystal. This technique for measuring ionic radii was similar to that used in the discovery of the bonding pattern

and double helix arrangement of the DNA molecule.

Section Review 7-2

1. Electrons are transferred from one atom to another.
2. A charged atom
3. The energy required to remove an electron from a neutral atom; the tendency of an atom to attract electrons
4. A regular, repeating arrangement of ions; the attractions between op-

positely charged ions
5. The K atom gives up an electron to the I atom, a K^+ ion and an I^- ion are formed, an ionic bond results, producing the ionic compound KI.

The idea of balancing charges in bonding ties in well with the concept of adding negative numbers in math. For example, Na_2CO_3 is a proper formula because the -2 charge on carbonate needs two $+1$ sodiums to neutralize the charge on the polyatomic ion.

HISTORICAL NOTES

Gilbert Lewis (1875–1946) published, in 1916, a paper titled "The Atom and the Molecule." It was here that the idea of sharing the electrons among the atoms of nonionic compounds was first proposed. His research on electron pairs in molecular structure gave us the concept of the covalent bond. To illustrate the arrangement, Lewis provided the idea of what are now known as "Lewis electron-dot structures," otherwise known as electron-dot formulas.

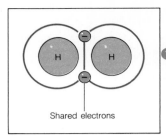

Figure 7–11 *The covalent bond between 2 atoms of hydrogen results in a molecule of hydrogen. In a covalent bond, the electrons are shared. How many valence electrons does each hydrogen atom have?* ❶

Nature of the Covalent Bond

❶ In covalent bonding, the positively charged nucleus of each atom simultaneously attracts the negatively charged electrons that are being shared. The electrons spend most of their time between the atoms. The attraction between the nucleus and shared electrons holds the atoms together.

The simplest kind of covalent bond is formed between two hydrogen atoms. Each hydrogen atom has 1 valence electron. By sharing their valence electrons, both hydrogen atoms fill their outermost energy level. Remember that the outermost energy level of a hydrogen atom is complete with 2 electrons. The two atoms are now joined in a covalent bond. See Figure 7–11.

The electron-sharing that takes place in a covalent bond can be represented by an **electron-dot diagram.** In such a diagram, the chemical symbol of an element represents the nucleus and inner energy levels of the atom. Dots surrounding the symbol represent valence electrons.

A hydrogen atom has only 1 valence electron. ❷ An electron-dot diagram of a hydrogen atom would look like this:

H •

The covalent bond between 2 hydrogen atoms shown in Figure 7–11 can be represented in an electron-dot diagram like this:

H : H

The two hydrogen atoms are sharing a pair of electrons. Each hydrogen atom achieves a complete outermost energy level. Although different colors are used here to represent different hydrogen atoms, there is really no difference between the atoms or the electrons. Color is used only to show that each hydrogen atom contributes 1 electron to the pair being shared.

Chlorine has 7 valence electrons. An electron-dot diagram of a chlorine atom looks like this:

:Cl •

168

The chlorine atom needs one more electron to complete its outermost energy level. If it bonds with another chlorine atom, the two atoms could share a pair of electrons. The electron-dot diagram for this covalent bond would look like this:

$$:\ddot{\underset{..}{Cl}}:\ddot{\underset{..}{Cl}}:$$ ❸

Covalent bonding often takes place between atoms of the same element. In addition to hydrogen and chlorine, the elements oxygen, fluorine, bromine, iodine, and nitrogen bond in this way. These elements are called **diatomic elements.** When found in nature, diatomic elements always exist as two atoms covalently bonded.

The chlorine atom, with its 7 valence electrons, can also bond covalently with an unlike atom. For example, a hydrogen atom can combine with a chlorine atom to form the compound hydrogen chloride. See Figure 7–13. The electron-dot diagram for this covalent bond is

$$H:\ddot{\underset{..}{Cl}}:$$

You can see from this electron-dot diagram that by sharing electrons each atom completes its outermost energy level.

The following electron-dot diagrams show the compounds water, H_2O, and ammonia, NH_3.

$$\underset{..}{:\underset{..}{O}:}H \qquad \overset{H}{\underset{H}{H:\overset{..}{N}:}}$$ ❹

In each compound, both kinds of atoms have completed their outermost energy levels.

Formation of Molecules

In a covalent bond, a relatively small number of atoms are involved in the sharing of electrons. The combination of atoms that results forms a separate unit rather than the large crystal lattices characteristic of ionic compounds.

The combination of atoms formed by a covalent bond is called a **molecule.** A molecule is the smallest particle of a covalently bonded substance that has all ❺

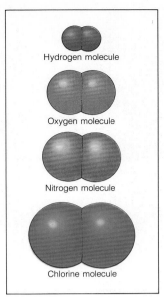

Hydrogen molecule

Oxygen molecule

Nitrogen molecule

Chlorine molecule

Figure 7–12 *Diatomic elements include hydrogen, oxygen, nitrogen, and chlorine. How many valence electrons does an atom of each element have?* ❷

Figure 7–13 *By sharing their valence electrons, hydrogen and chlorine form a molecule of the compound hydrogen chloride. What kind of bond is this?* ❸

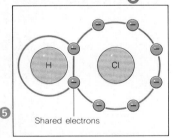

Shared electrons

169

the situation. Therefore a sharing of electrons will result. This can also be shown to fill the valence levels of both atoms. The resulting mutual attraction produces a molecule.

• **How many valence electrons does carbon have?** (4)
• **How many valence electrons does chlorine have?** (7)
• **How many more electrons does chlorine need to become stable?** (1)
• **What formula would you predict for a carbon and chlorine molecule?** (CCl_4)

This exercise points out that one carbon could share each one of its electrons with four individual chlorine atoms. Point out that covalent CCl_4 has a low boiling point—in direct contrast to ionic sodium chloride, which is difficult to melt.

HISTORICAL NOTES

Some older textbooks refer to the polyatomic ions as "radicals." This is likely due to their unusual characteristics of being covalently bonded and still maintaining a charge.

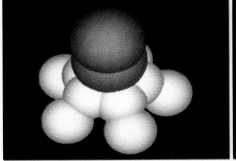

Figure 7–14 *Not all molecules are as simple as hydrogen chloride. Here you see computer images of the more complex molecules of a body fluid (left) and a virus (right).*

the properties of that substance. Molecules are represented by chemical formulas. A chemical formula contains the symbol of each element involved in the bond and subscripts that show the number of atoms of each element. When there is only 1 atom of an element, the subscript 1 is not written. It is understood to be 1. Thus, a hydrogen chloride molecule has the formula HCl. What would be the formula for a molecule that has 1 carbon (C) atom and 4 chlorine (Cl) atoms? ❶

Covalently bonded solids tend to have low melting points. Although there are attractions between the molecules of the solid, the attractions are relatively weak. So only a small amount of energy is needed to separate the molecules from one another.

Some covalent substances, however, do not have low melting points. Molecules of these substances are very large because the atoms involved continue to bond to one another. These substances are called **network solids.** Carbon in the form of graphite and silicon dioxide are examples of network solids.

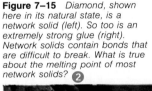

Figure 7–15 *Diamond, shown here in its natural state, is a network solid (left). So too is an extremely strong glue (right). Network solids contain bonds that are difficult to break. What is true about the melting point of most network solids?* ❷

7-3 (continued)

Motivation

Using the overhead projector, you can use a series of overlays, made by you, to illustrate the process of covalent bonding. By carefully placing electron symbols on the overlays, the bonding of methane, for example, begins with a central carbon with four valence electrons in the outer shell. Hydrogens with a single valence electron

would be attracted to these, and their sequential bonding could be illustrated by overlaying one at a time.

Skills Development
Skills: *Making diagrams, making predictions*
Using the periodic table, have students note which elements will tend to form covalent bonds. Also have them illustrate the covalent bonding within polyatomic radicals that form ions.

Skills Development
Skills: *Applying concepts, identifying relationships*
Pass out to students a page containing a blank outline of the periodic table. Have them use lines to separate the chart into columns. Using a pencil, have students shade in the area of "electron takers." (Group VI and VII) They may use some other code for "electron givers" (metals of Groups I and II). The middle part of the chart

Certain glues also form networks of atoms whose bonds are difficult to break. This accounts for the holding properties of such glues.

Polyatomic Ions

Certain ions are made up of covalently bonded atoms that tend to stay together as if they were a single atom. A group of covalently bonded atoms that acts like a single atom when combining with other atoms is called a **polyatomic ion.** Although the bonds within the polyatomic ion are covalent, the polyatomic ion usually forms ionic bonds with other atoms.

The ammonium ion, NH_4^+, is a polyatomic ion. The bonds between nitrogen and hydrogen atoms are covalent.

When the ammonium ion combines with the chloride ion, it forms an ionic bond.

SECTION REVIEW

1. What is a covalent bond?
2. What is a molecule?
3. What is a polyatomic ion?
4. What elements and how many atoms of each are represented in the following chemical formulas: Na_2CO_3, $Ca(OH)_2$, $Mg(C_2H_3O_2)_2$?

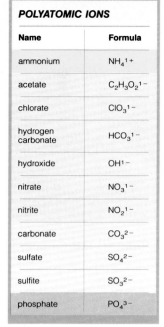

POLYATOMIC IONS

Name	Formula
ammonium	NH_4^{1+}
acetate	$C_2H_3O_2^{1-}$
chlorate	ClO_3^{1-}
hydrogen carbonate	HCO_3^{1-}
hydroxide	OH^{1-}
nitrate	NO_3^{1-}
nitrite	NO_2^{1-}
carbonate	CO_3^{2-}
sulfate	SO_4^{2-}
sulfite	SO_3^{2-}
phosphate	PO_4^{3-}

Figure 7–16 *The name and formula of some common polyatomic ions are shown here. Which polyatomic ion has a positive charge?* ❸

Figure 7–17 *A polyatomic ion is a group of covalently bonded atoms that act like a single atom when combining with other atoms.*

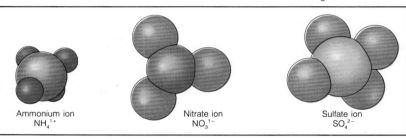

Ammonium ion
NH_4^{1+}

Nitrate ion
NO_3^{1-}

Sulfate ion
SO_4^{2-}

171

strong as ionic, intermolecular attractions causing them to be seen as liquids or low melting point solids.)

Section Review 7-3

1. A bond in which electrons are shared
2. The smallest particle of a covalently bonded substance that has all the properties of that substance
3. A group of covalently bonded atoms that acts like a single atom when combining with other atoms
4. Na_2CO_3: 2 sodium, 1 carbon, 3 oxygen
$Ca(OH)_2$: 1 calcium, 2 oxygen, 2 hydrogen
$Mg(C_2H_3O_2)_2$: 1 magnesium, 4 carbon, 6 hydrogen, 4 oxygen

can be used to show elements that may be intermediate between electron takers and givers. This may be a reference when students are asked to predict covalent or ionic bonds between elements.

Have students open their books to the chart of polyatomic ions. You name a metal and have them, as quickly as possible, deduce the formula of the metal and polyatomic ion.

Enrichment

Many times the sharing of electrons between covalently bonded atoms is unequal, such as between hydrogen and oxygen to form water.
• **What is the name of the type of bonding that still allows for electron sharing, but has unequal sharing?** (polar covalent)
• **What properties do these molecules have?** (Usually polar covalent molecules have strong, but not as

SECTION PREVIEW 7-4

Metallic bonding is still another way that some atoms are able to bond to each other. In this type of bonding, explained in this section, metals can be seen to have a weak hold on their valence electrons. While the attraction is generally weaker than the nonmetals, it is strong enough to be attractive to electrons. This situation allows the valence electrons of close by metal atoms to "wander" to neighboring atoms. This creates a type of uniform low attraction for each other's electrons in the metal crystal. This is enough to keep the metal atoms together; they are attracted to many electrons. However, the electrons feel attraction throughout the metal so they may become a mobile "sea of electrons."

PERFORMANCE OBJECTIVES 7-4

1. **Define metallic bond.**
2. **Describe the properties of metals.**
3. **Identify which elements are likely to participate in metallic bonding.**

SCIENCE TERMS 7-4

metallic bond p. 172
malleable p. 172
ductile p. 172

Figure 7–18 *The metal platinum has a very high melting point, which makes it extremely useful in heat-resistant containers. What type of bond holds platinum atoms together?* ❶

Figure 7–19 *In a metallic bond, the outer electrons of the metal atoms form a "sea of mobile electrons." What properties of metals does a metallic bond explain?* ❷

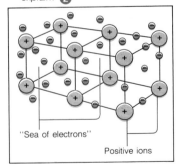

"Sea of electrons"

Positive ions

7–4 Metallic Bonds

Iron, copper, silver, and gold are familiar examples of metals. Metals are elements that tend to give up electrons easily. In metallic solids, however, only atoms of the metals are present. There are no other atoms to accept the electrons the metals give up. How, then, do the atoms of metals bond?

The atoms of metals form **metallic bonds.** In a metallic bond, the outer electrons of the atoms form a common electron cloud. This common distribution of electrons occurs throughout a metallic crystal. In a sense, the electrons become the property of all the atoms. These electrons are often described as a "sea of electrons." **The positive nuclei of atoms of metals are surrounded by free-moving, or mobile, electrons that are all attracted by the nuclei at the same time.**

The sea of mobile electrons in a metallic crystal accounts for many of the properties of metals. Metals are malleable, which means they can be hammered into thin sheets without breaking. Metals are also ductile—they can be drawn into thin wire. The flexibility of metals results from the fact that the metal ions can slide by each other and the electrons are free to flow. Yet the attractions between the ions and the electrons hold the metal together even when it is being hammered or drawn into wire.

The ability of the electrons to flow freely also accounts for the high electric conductivity of metals. Electricity flows easily through metals. What metals are good conductors of electricity? ❸

Metallic bonding also accounts for the high melting point of most metals. The attractions between the ions and the free-moving electrons are fairly strong. So a great deal of heat energy is needed to overcome the attractions and allow the metal to melt. For example, the melting point of silver is 961.9°C and of gold, 1064.4°C.

SECTION REVIEW

1. What is a metallic bond?
2. What is a malleable metal? A ductile metal?
3. How does metallic bonding account for the properties of metals?

TEACHING STRATEGY 7-4

Motivation

Have students look around the room and notice all of the objects made of metals. If you have samples of pure metals, (tin, aluminum, gold, lead) display them to students to allow them to compare forms.

Have a long piece of copper wire to display to the class. Bend the wire into various shapes while discussing the bonding properties. Bend the wire rapidly several times to cause it to break apart. Explain how the energy you are adding overcomes the attractive forces.

Content Development

Students need to realize that the bonding between atoms within metals involves a situation that allows the valence electrons to move within the crystal. Point out that the structure in Figure 7-19 uses a "freeze frame" type of picture. In reality, the electrons are continually moving.

Section Review 7-4

1. A bond in which a sea of mobile electrons surrounds the positive nuclei of the atoms
2. It can be hammered into sheets without breaking. It can be drawn into thin wire.
3. Metals tend to have high melting points and high electric conductivity, and they tend to be malleable and ductile. These properties result from the surrounding sea of electrons,

7-5 Predicting Types of Bonds

The placement in the periodic table of the elements involved in bonding often indicates whether the bond will be ionic, covalent, or metallic. Look at the periodic table on pages 118–119. Elements at the left and in the center of the periodic table are metals. These elements have metallic bonds.

Compounds formed between elements that lose electrons easily and those that gain electrons easily will have ionic bonds. You know that elements at the left and in the center of the periodic table tend to lose valence electrons easily. These elements are metals. Elements at the right tend to gain electrons readily. These elements are nonmetals. A compound formed between a metal and a nonmetal will thus have ionic bonds.

Compounds formed between elements that have similar tendencies to gain electrons will have covalent bonds. Bonds between nonmetals, which are at

❸

CAREER
Environmental Analyst

HELP WANTED: ENVIRONMENTAL ANALYST to conduct surveys of areas affected by known and unknown pollutants. Must be familiar with chemical mixtures and compounds. Advanced degree in environmental science required.

The campers pile into a van, talking excitedly about the mountain lake they will reach by evening. Finally, the van stops and the happy campers tumble out. But everyone's smile disappears at the sight and smell of dead fish on the lake's rocky shore. Many dead trees stand in the once-lush forest.

These types of destruction may be caused by pollution. Towns with problems such as these may hire an **environmental analyst** to find what is affecting the area. Environmental analysts use chemical testing of air, water, and soil to discover the causes of environmental problems.

Pollutants from industry, waste disposal, agricultural runoff, or other sources may combine chemically with natural elements. The result may be a combination of chemicals that are harmful or deadly to the environment.

After analyzing the situation, the analyst may suggest ways to control the pollution problems. Some analysts are qualified to run cleanup operations in polluted areas.

If you would like to learn more about a career as an environmental analyst, contact the Environmental Protection Agency, Public Information Center, East Tower Basement, Mail Code PM-211B, 401 M Street SW, Washington, DC 20460.

173

which holds the atoms together flexibly but strongly and permits electricity to flow freely.

TEACHING STRATEGY 7-5

Motivation
Have students on one side of the room name an element. Then the teacher names a type of bonding, covalent, ionic or metallic. Then select another student from the other side of the

room to name another element that, when matched with the first, produces the specified type of bonding.

A similar type of activity can also be done by dividing the students into two groups: generally positive oxidation number elements and generally negative oxidation number elements. Select students, one from each group, to describe the number of atoms of each to form a compound.

7-5 PREDICTING TYPES OF BONDS

SECTION PREVIEW 7-5
In this section, the writing of formulas and types of bonding are combined. Students should see that elements on the left of the periodic table give up their valence electrons when bonding. By giving up electrons, they become positively charged. This positive charge is called the oxidation number. Atoms on the right of the periodic table accept electrons to obtain an octet. This results in these atoms becoming negatively charged. This charge is also known as the oxidation number. In a correctly written formula, the oxidation numbers expressed of all atoms should equal a net total of zero.

PERFORMANCE OBJECTIVES 7-5
1. **Predict the common oxidation numbers of atoms, based on the position of that atom on the periodic table.**
2. **Predict the formation of compounds between elements and/or between elements and polyatomic ions.**

SCIENCE TERMS 7-5
oxidation number p. 175

ANNOTATION KEY
❶ Metallic bond (Applying definitions)
❷ Malleability, ductility, high melting point, electric conductivity (Relating concepts)
❸ Copper, gold, silver (Classifying metals)
❶ Thinking Skill: Making generalizations
❷ Thinking Skill: Classifying characteristics
❸ Thinking Skill: Identifying relationships

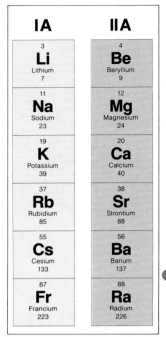

IA	IIA
3 **Li** Lithium 7	4 **Be** Beryllium 9
11 **Na** Sodium 23	12 **Mg** Magnesium 24
19 **K** Potassium 39	20 **Ca** Calcium 40
37 **Rb** Rubidium 85	38 **Sr** Strontium 88
55 **Cs** Cesium 133	56 **Ba** Barium 137
87 **Fr** Francium 223	88 **Ra** Radium 226

Figure 7–20 *The elements in Family IA and IIA are active metals. What is the oxidation number of atoms of Family IA elements? Of atoms of Family IIA elements?* ❷

the right of the periodic table, will be covalent. What type of bonding would you expect between magnesium (Mg) and fluorine (F)? Between oxygen (O) and chlorine (C1)? In a sample of zinc (Zn)? ❶

Combining Capacity of Atoms

The number of electrons in the outermost energy level of an atom, or the valence electrons, determines how an atom will combine with other atoms. If you know the number of valence electrons in an atom, you can calculate the number of electrons that atom needs to gain, lose, or share in forming a compound. The number of electrons an atom gains, loses, or shares when it forms chemical bonds is called its **oxidation number.** The oxidation number of an atom describes its combining capacity.

An atom of sodium has 1 valence electron. It loses this electron when it combines with another atom. In so doing, it forms an ion with a 1+ charge, Na^+. The oxidation number of sodium is 1+. A magnesium atom has 2 valence electrons, which it will lose when it forms a chemical bond. The magnesium ion is Mg^{2+}. The oxidation number of magnesium is 2+.

An atom of chlorine has 7 valence electrons. It will gain 1 electron when it bonds with another atom. The ion formed will have a 1− charge, Cl^-.

Figure 7–21 *This is the first photograph ever taken of atoms and their bonds. The bright round objects are single atoms. The fuzzy areas between atoms represent bonds.*

174

7-5 (continued)

Content Development
This section brings all of the concepts in the chapter together. However, this section is more than a summary of topics. The understanding of the relationship between an element's position on the periodic table and its bonding type and bonding capacity should be emphasized.

In addition to predicting the type of bonding between Mg and F, and between O and Cl, have students predict the formulas of the resulting compounds.

Have students prepare a table that shows the three types of bonding presented in the chapter. The table should also have a column showing bonding characteristics and examples.

Skills Development
Skills: Making comparisons, making predictions
Some very common substances have more than one oxidation number. To illustrate this point have students pre-

dict the formulas for iron and chloride when iron is + 2 and when iron is in the + 3 state. Do the same when copper is in the + 1 state and in the + 2 state and combined with chloride. Tin can also be a + 2 or + 4.
- **What would be the formula of the two possible chlorides of tin?** ($FeCl_2$; $FeCl_3$; CuCl; $CuCl_2$; $SnCl_2$; $SnCl_4$)
- **The following are formulas of acids containing an atom of chlorine. What is the oxidation number of**

The oxidation number of chlorine is 1−. Oxygen has 6 valence electrons. How many electrons will it gain? What is its oxidation number? ❸

Some elements have more than one oxidation number. Copper can have oxidation numbers of 1+ or 2+. Iron can have oxidation numbers of 2+ or 3+. Carbon, which has 4 valence electrons, can either lose or gain 4 electrons. Carbon can have oxidation numbers of 4+ or 4−, depending on the other atoms with which it bonds. You can determine the oxidation number of any atom by knowing the number of electrons in its outermost energy level. ❷

Using Oxidation Numbers

You can use the oxidation numbers of atoms to predict how atoms will combine and what the formula for the resulting compound will be. In order to do this, you must follow one important rule: *The sum of the oxidation numbers of the atoms in a compound must be zero.* ❸

Sodium has an oxidation number of 1+. Chlorine has an oxidation number of 1−. One atom of sodium will bond with 1 atom of chlorine to form NaCl. Magnesium has an oxidation number of 2+. When magnesium bonds with chlorine, 1 atom of magnesium must combine with 2 atoms of chlorine, since each chlorine atom has an oxidation number of 1−. In other words, 2 atoms of chlorine are needed to gain the electrons lost by 1 atom of magnesium. The compound formed, magnesium chloride, contains 2 atoms of chlorine for each atom of magnesium. Its formula is $MgCl_2$. What would be the formula for calcium bromide? For sodium oxide? Remember the rule of oxidation numbers! ❺

SECTION REVIEW

1. How can the periodic table be used to predict bond types?
2. What is an oxidation number?
3. How can the oxidation number of an atom be determined?
4. What rule of oxidation numbers must be followed in writing chemical formulas?
5. Predict the type of bond for each combination: Ca–Br, C–Cl, Ag–Ag, K–OH, SO_4^{2-}.

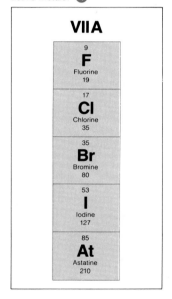

Figure 7–22 *The elements in Family VIIA are active nonmetals. What is the oxidation number of atoms of these elements? What type of bonds do these elements form when they combine with active metals?* ❹

VIIA

| 9 |
| **F** |
| Fluorine |
| 19 |

| 17 |
| **Cl** |
| Chlorine |
| 35 |

| 35 |
| **Br** |
| Bromine |
| 80 |

| 53 |
| **I** |
| Iodine |
| 127 |

| 85 |
| **At** |
| Astatine |
| 210 |

175

---

chlorine in each compound? $HClO_4$; $HClO_3$; $HClO_2$ $HClO$; HCl? (+7; +5; +3; +1; −1)

Enrichment

Have students recall the picture at the beginning of the chapter. They should now be able to explain the reasons why carbon, hydrogen, and nitrogen are covalently bonded. The morphine is a molecule instead of an ionic crystal. Have students explain why. (Since the molecule is covalent, it has no significant positive and negative areas to hold it in a rigid pattern such as a crystal.)

Section Review 7-5

1. The placement of elements in the periodic table indicates whether the bonds they form with one another will be ionic, covalent, or metallic. Ionic: metals with nonmetals; covalent: non-metals with nonmetals; metallic: atoms of the same metal.
2. The number of electrons an atom gains, loses, or shares when it forms a chemical bond
3. By the number of valence electrons in the atom
4. The sum of the oxidation numbers of the atoms in a compound must be zero.
5. Ionic, covalent, metallic, ionic, covalent

LABORATORY INVESTIGATION PROPERTIES OF IONIC AND COVALENT COMPOUNDS

BEFORE THE LAB

1. **Gather all equipment at least one day prior to the investigation. You should gather enough equipment to meet your class needs, assuming six students per group.**

PRE-LAB DISCUSSION

Before beginning this investigation, review with students the basic properties of covalent and ionic compounds. Make sure students have a clear understanding of what these terms mean. Then, after they have read through the investigation, have them prepare hypotheses as to what observations they will expect to see, based on prior knowledge. Ask students to compare their initial hypotheses to their actual observations once the lab has been completed.

SKILL DEVELOPMENT

Students will use the following skills while completing this investigation.
1. Safety
2. Manipulative
3. Observing
4. Comparing
5. Hypothesizing
6. Applying
7. Relating
8. Recording
9. Measuring

SAFETY TIPS

Remind students to wear their safety goggles during this investigation. Also have them state the basic rules to follow as related to the safety symbols found next to the procedure.

TEACHING STRATEGY FOR LAB PROCEDURE

1. No special strategy is necessary here, but you will want to circulate through the room to ensure that students have set up the investigation properly and are following all safety precautions.
2. You may find that the salt will not melt, even using a Bunsen burner. If so, have students stop trying to melt the salt after a reasonable period of time.

Properties of Ionic and Covalent Compounds

Problem

Do covalent compounds have different properties from ionic compounds?

Materials *(per group)*		
salt	glass-marking pencil	vegetable oil
sugar	light bulb	distilled water (100 mL)
4 medium-sized test tubes	light bulb socket	timer
test tube tongs	3 connecting wires	safety goggles
Bunsen burner	2 100-mL beakers	
dry-cell battery	stirring rod	

Procedure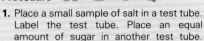

1. Place a small sample of salt in a test tube. Label the test tube. Place an equal amount of sugar in another test tube. Label that test tube.
2. Using tongs, heat the test tube of salt over the flame of the Bunsen burner. Determine how long it takes for the salt to melt. Immediately stop heating when melting begins. Record the time.
3. Repeat step 2 using the sugar.
4. Half fill a test tube with vegetable oil. Place a small sample of salt in the test tube. Shake the test tube gently for about 10 seconds. Observe the results.
5. Repeat step 4 using sugar.
6. Pour 50 mL of distilled water into a 100-mL beaker. Add some salt and stir until it is dissolved. To another 100-mL beaker add some sugar and stir until dissolved.
7. Using the beaker of salt water, set up a circuit as shown. Observe the results. Repeat the procedure using the beaker of sugar water.

Observations

1. Does the salt or the sugar take a longer time to melt?
2. Does the salt dissolve in the vegetable oil? Does the sugar?
3. Which compound is a better conductor of electricity? Explain your answer.

Conclusions

1. Which substance do you think has a higher melting point? Explain.
2. Vegetable oil is a covalent compound. If "like dissolves in like," predict the type of bonding in salt. In sugar.
3. How do the properties of each type of compound relate to their bonding?

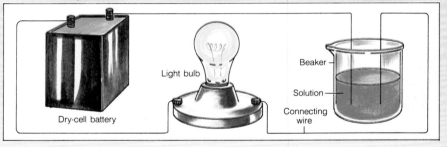

Light bulb

Dry-cell battery

Beaker

Solution

Connecting wire

The fact that they could not get it to melt is adequate for them to describe the characteristics of ionic compounds.

OBSERVATIONS

1. Salt (NOTE: Students may actually find that the salt did not melt at all if Bunsen burner temperatures were not high enough.)
2. No; yes
3. Salt is the better conductor since it forms ions when dissolved in water.

This can be inferred from the observation that the light bulb goes on.

CONCLUSIONS

1. Salt. It took longer for the salt to melt, if in fact it did melt.
2. Since salt did not dissolve in vegetable oil, it must be an ionic compound. Since sugar did dissolve, it is a covalent compound.
3. Covalent compounds generally have low melting points, dissolve in covalent

SUMMARY

7–1 Chemical Bonding

❏ Chemical bonding is the combining of elements to form new substances.

❏ The first energy level can hold a maximum of 2 electrons. The second and third energy levels can each hold 8 electrons.

❏ Electrons in the outermost energy level are called valence electrons.

❏ Bonding involves the incomplete outermost energy level of an atom.

7–2 Ionic Bonds

❏ Ionic bonding involves a transfer of electrons and a formation of ions. An ion is a charged particle.

❏ Ionization energy is the amount of energy needed to remove an electron from a neutral atom. Electron affinity is the tendency of an atom to attract electrons.

7–3 Covalent Bonds

❏ Covalent bonding involves a sharing of electrons. The shared electrons are simultaneously attracted by the nuclei of the atoms involved in the bond.

❏ Diatomic elements always exist in nature as two atoms covalently bonded.

❏ A molecule is the smallest unit of a covalently bonded substance that has all the properties of that substance.

❏ Network solids are substances whose molecules are very large because the atoms in the substance continue to bond to one another.

❏ A polyatomic ion is a group of covalently bonded atoms that acts like a single atom when combining with other atoms.

7–4 Metallic Bonds

❏ Metals are elements that tend to give up electrons easily.

❏ The basis of metallic bonding is the sea of mobile electrons that surrounds the nuclei and is simultaneously attracted by them.

❏ Metals demonstrate high electric conductivity because of the sea of mobile electrons.

7–5 Predicting Types of Bonds

❏ The position of elements in the periodic table indicates whether the bonds they form will be ionic, covalent, or metallic.

❏ The oxidation number, or combining capacity, of an atom refers to the number of electrons the atom gains, loses, or shares when it forms chemical bonds.

❏ The oxidation number of any atom can be determined by knowing the number of electrons in its outermost level.

❏ In a chemical formula, the sum of the oxidation numbers of the atoms in a compound must be zero.

VOCABULARY

Define each term in a complete sentence.

chemical bonding	ductile	ionization	oxidation number
covalent bonding	electron affinity	ionization energy	polyatomic ion
crystal lattice	electron-dot diagram	malleable	valence electron
diatomic element	ion	metallic bond	
	ionic bonding	molecule	
		network solid	

177

solvents, and do not conduct an electric current. Ionic compounds have high melting points, do not dissolve in covalent solvents, and conduct electricity when dissolved in water.

GOING FURTHER: ENRICHMENT

Part 1
Provide students with unknown compounds and have them classify the compounds according to the type of bond by conducting tests similar to those in this investigation.

Part 2
Provide students with samples of covalently bonded substances and metallic bonded substances. Have them design an experiment to compare these substances for malleability, ductility, and melting point.

CHAPTER REVIEW

MULTIPLE CHOICE

1. c	**3.** c	**5.** a	**7.** c	**9.** a
2. d	**4.** c	**6.** b	**8.** a	**10.** b

COMPLETION

1. valence electron
2. ion
3. electron affinity
4. crystal lattice
5. covalent bonding
6. diatomic
7. polyatomic ion
8. malleable
9. ionic bonds
10. oxidation number

TRUE OR FALSE

1. T
2. F   positively
3. F   lose
4. F   shared
5. T
6. F   molecule
7. T
8. T
9. T
10. F   possible

SKILL BUILDING

1. a. Ionic because Mg is a metal and Cl is a nonmetal **b.** Covalent because S and Br are both nonmetals **c.** Metallic because Na is a metal **d.** Covalent because I is a nonmetal **e.** Ionic because K is a metal and I is a nonmetal
2. a. S^{2-} **b.** Rb^{1+} **c.** Ar does not usually form ions. **d.** At^{1-} **e.** Na^{1+} **f.** Al^{3+}
3. Li: 2,1; Be: 2,2; B: 2,3; C: 2,4; N: 2,5; O: 2.6; F: 2,7; Ne: 2,8
4. Check students' drawings. The molecules of F_2 and NF_3 are both stable because the atoms they are composed of have complete outer energy levels.
5. a. K_2S **b.** LiF **c.** BaS **d.** Mg_3N_2
6. a. NH_4NO_3 **b.** $(NH_4)_2SO_4$ **c.** NH_4OH

ESSAY

1. a. Ionization energy is the energy needed to remove an electron from an atom to form an ion. Electron affinity is the tendency of an atom to attract electrons. **b.** Atoms with high electron affinity attract electrons easily; atoms with low ionization energy lose electrons easily. So when atoms with high electron affinity are combined with atoms with low ionization energy, the atoms with high electron affinity gain electrons from the atoms with low ionization energy.
2. a. A crystal lattice is a regular, repeating arrangement of ions in a compound formed by ionic bonds. This arrangement gives the compound great stability and accounts for its high melting point. The arrangement also accounts for the particular shape of the crystals of the compound. **b.** A network solid is a substance formed by covalent bonds. The molecules of the substance are large and the bonds are usually difficult to break. A network solid has a high melting point. **c.** A covalently bonded solid is formed from weak covalent bonds. Only a small amount of energy is needed to break these bonds, and so the melting point of this solid tends to be low.
3. In an ionic bond, electrons are transferred from one atom to another. In a covalent bond, electrons are shared between atoms. In a metallic bond, the outer electrons of an atom form a common electron cloud.
4. The atoms of the Family VIIIA elements have outer energy levels that are

On a separate sheet of paper, write the letter of the answer that best completes each statement.

1. Chemical bonding is the combining of elements to form new
   a. atoms.   b. energy levels.   c. substances.   d. electrons.
2. The center of an atom is called the
   a. electron.   b. energy level.   c. octet.   d. nucleus.
3. The maximum number of electrons in the second energy level is
   a. 1.   b. 2.   c. 8.   d. 18.
4. Bonding that involves a transfer of electrons is called
   a. metallic.   b. covalent.   c. ionic.   d. network.
5. Atoms that readily lose electrons have
   a. low ionization energy and low electron affinity.
   b. high ionization energy and low electron affinity.
   c. low ionization energy and high electron affinity.
   d. high ionization energy and high electron affinity.
6. Bonding that involves sharing of electrons within a molecule is called
   a. metallic bonding.   b. covalent bonding.
   c. ionic bonding.   d. crystal bonding.
7. The combination of atoms formed by covalent bonds is called a (an)
   a. element.   b. ion.   c. molecule.   d. crystal.
8. An example of a polyatomic ion is
   a. SO_4^{2-}.   b. Ca^{2-}.   c. NaCl.   d. O_2.
9. A sea of electrons is the basis of bonding in
   a. metals.   b. nonmetals.
   c. ionic substances.   d. covalent substances.
10. Bonding between atoms on the left and right sides of the periodic table tends to be
   a. covalent.   b. ionic.   c. metallic.   d. impossible.

On a separate sheet of paper, write the word or words that best complete each statement.

1. Electrons in the outermost energy level are called _____.
2. A charged particle is a (an) _____.
3. The tendency of an atom to attract electrons is called _____.
4. A regular, repeating arrangement of ions is called a (an) _____.
5. Bonding in which electrons are shared is called _____.
6. Elements that exist as two covalently bonded atoms are _____.
7. A group of covalently bonded atoms that acts like a single atom when combining is called a (an) _____.
8. Metals that can be hammered into thin sheets are said to be _____.
9. Compounds formed between metals and nonmetals will have _____ bonds.
10. The combining capacity of an atom is described by its _____.

CONTENT REVIEW: TRUE OR FALSE

Determine whether each statement is true or false. Then on a separate sheet of paper, write "true" if it is true. If it is false, change the underlined word or words to make the statement true.

1. <u>Helium</u> is an example of an element that does not tend to form chemical bonds.
2. An atom that has lost an electron is <u>negatively</u> charged.
3. Ionization energy is needed for an atom to <u>gain</u> an electron.
4. Bonding in which electrons are <u>transferred</u> is called covalent bonding.
5. <u>Bromine</u> is a diatomic element.
6. A covalent bond forms a <u>crystal</u>.
7. In a <u>metallic</u> bond, the outer electrons of the atoms form a common electron cloud.
8. A substance that can be drawn into thin wire is said to be <u>ductile</u>.
9. Compounds formed between a metal and a nonmetal will have <u>ionic</u> bonds.
10. It is <u>impossible</u> for an element to have more than one oxidation number.

CONCEPT REVIEW: SKILL BUILDING

Use the skills you have developed in the chapter to complete each activity.

1. **Making predictions** Predict the type of bond formed by each pair of atoms. Explain your answers. a. Mg and Cl b. S and Br c. Na and Na d. I and I e. Li and I
2. **Identifying patterns** Use the periodic table to predict the ion that each atom will form when bonding. a. sulfur (S) b. rubidium (Rb) c. argon (Ar) d. astatine (At) e. sodium (Na) f. aluminum (Al)
3. **Making diagrams** Draw the electron configuration for a Period 2 atom from each of the eight families of the periodic table.
4. **Drawing a conclusion** Draw an electron-dot diagram for the following molecules and explain why both molecules are stable. a. F_2 b. NF_3
5. **Making predictions** Use the periodic table to predict the formulas for the compounds formed by each of the following pairs of atoms. a. K and S b. Li and F c. Ba and S d. Mg and N
6. **Applying concepts** Predict the formulas for compounds formed by each of the following pairs of polyatomic ions. a. NH_4^+ and NO_3^- b. NH_4^+ and SO_4^{2-} c. NH_4^+ and OH^-

CONCEPT REVIEW: ESSAY

Discuss each of the following in a brief paragraph.

1. a. What is the difference between ionization energy and electron affinity? b. Why do atoms of high electron affinity tend to form ionic compounds with atoms of low ionization energy?
2. Define the following structures that result from chemical bonds. Give one physical property of each. a. crystal lattice b. network solid c. covalently bonded solid
3. List the three types of chemical bonds and explain the differences among them.
4. Explain why the elements of Family VIIIA do not tend to form chemical bonds.
5. What are four properties of metals? How does the bonding in metals account for these properties?
6. How can you use the oxidation number of an atom to predict how it will bond?

179

ADDITIONAL QUESTIONS AND TOPIC SUGGESTIONS

1. Have students prepare reports on the water molecule. Have them construct models and prepare a bulletin board display of their methods.
2. Have students construct electron-dot diagrams to figure out electron arrangement for the first 10 elements. Have them predict how these atoms will react with each other.
3. The size of an atom in relation to other atoms is a significant characteristic that becomes apparent in the study of bonding and molecule formation and should be of interest to some students. Have students locate information on sizes of atoms and ions. Have them present their findings, including charts and bulletin boards, to the class.
4. Have students make lists of molecules that are held together with covalent bonds. Have them use reference sources in the library. Have students determine the valence electrons and energy levels involved.
5. Have students use the periodic table to make lists of the elements that will form covalent bonds.
6. Have students use this book and reference material in the library to find information about the following ionic compounds: NaCl, $MgBr_2$, and KCl. Have them report on their crystal structure, electron configurations, preparation, and uses.
7. Using cardboard, construction paper, string, and colored pencils, have students construct models of NaBr, $MgCl_2$, and $AlCl_3$. Have them display their models in the classroom and compare ionic bonding with covalent bonding.

complete. This makes the atoms stable, or unreactive, and not likely to form chemical bonds.

5. Metals are both malleable and ductile. This flexibility of metals results from metallic bonding. Metal ions can slide by each other and the electrons can flow freely, while the attractions between the ions and the electrons hold the metal together. The ability of the electrons to flow freely also accounts for the high electric conductivity of metals. In addition, metals have high melting points due to the strength of the metallic bond. A great deal of heat is needed to overcome the attraction between the ions and electrons in the bond.

6. The oxidation number of an atom describes its combining capacity—how many electrons it will gain, lose, or share when bonding. From this information, the type of bond can be predicted, as well as the formula for the resulting compounds. When atoms

Chapter 8
CHEMICAL REACTIONS

CHAPTER OVERVIEW

In this chapter, students will be introduced to chemical reactions. Although some students may think that a chemical reaction is something that takes place only in a test tube in a laboratory, they will soon discover that chemical reactions take place everywhere and that many familiar processes in nature and in everyday life involve chemical reactions.

Students will learn that when a chemical reaction takes place, there is always a change in the properties and a change in the energy of the substances involved in the reaction. Students will also learn that as chemical reactions occur, bonds between atoms are broken and new bonds are formed.

Students will learn to represent chemical reactions with chemical equations. They will learn to distinguish between four general types of reactions: synthesis, decomposition, single replacement, and double replacement.

Students will be introduced to the terms endothermic, exothermic, and activation energy. They will also come to understand how the collision theory can be applied to factors that affect the rates of chemical reactions.

TEACHER DEMONSTRATION

For this demonstration you will need several flashbulbs and a camera with a flash attachment. (It is not necessary to have film in the camera.) Students should have pencil and paper to record their observations throughout the demonstration.

INTRODUCING CHAPTER 8

The restoration of the Statue of Liberty was completed in July, 1986. The restored statue was unveiled on the Fourth of July, amidst a weekend of celebration and a spectacular fireworks display. For many years funds had been collected to pay for the restoration, and numerous celebrities in the New York area had given benefit performances to "Save the Statue of Liberty."

Bronze is an alloy of copper and tin. Exposure to air and moisture had caused a patina, or thin film of corrosion, to form on the statue. The chemical reaction for this process, which involves copper, is

$$Cu + CO_2 + H_2O \rightarrow Cu(OH)_2CO_3.$$

Direct students' attention to the photograph of the Statue of Liberty. Ask,

- **Have any of you ever visited the Statue of Liberty?** (It is probable that at least a few students have; perhaps many have if you are located near New York City.) Encourage any students who have visited the Statue to share their impressions of it. It is possible that, if they were there before the restoration, they were aware of the statue's need for repair.
- **What do you think caused the changes that made it necessary to re-**

Chemical Reactions

CHAPTER OBJECTIVES

After completing this chapter, you will be able to

8–1 Describe the characteristics of chemical reactions.

8–1 Explain the basis of chemical reactions.

8–2 Interpret, write, and balance chemical equations.

8–3 Classify types of chemical reactions.

8–4 Describe the role of energy in exothermic and endothermic reactions.

8–4 Relate activation energy to chemical reactions.

8–5 Apply the collision theory to factors that affect reaction rate.

On July 4, 1986, fireworks lit up the sky in New York Harbor as the nation celebrated the one-hundredth birthday of the Statue of Liberty—symbol of freedom and brotherhood for people of all nations.

Fireworks flash brilliantly in the night sky over the dark waters of the harbor. It is Independence Day, July 4, 1986. It is a day of celebration in honor of a very special lady. She towers above the waters, the torch in her upraised hand reaching high into the sky. She is a symbol of freedom, justice, and the brotherhood of people of all nations. Her name is Liberty.

She has stood there for a century. But the passage of time had not been very kind to her. The bronze of her outer structure, once bright and gleaming, had turned a dull gray-green. And the structure that supports her had begun to weaken. What caused these changes? The answer has to do with the chemistry of atoms.

This chemistry, which damaged the Statue of Liberty, also made possible the glorious restoration of this Lady in the Harbor. And the colorful fireworks lighting up the sky in honor of her birthday are also products of the chemistry of atoms.

Chemical changes take place at all times, not just on the Fourth of July. And they take place everywhere, not just in New York Harbor. In this chapter, you will learn about the nature of these chemical changes, many of which shape the world around you.

181

Display the flashbulbs and allow students to examine the bulbs carefully. Ask,

- **What do you see inside the bulb?** (a small coil of shiny gray metal)
- **What do you think is occupying the rest of the space inside the bulb?** (Answers may vary; some students may say "nothing" or "air." The bulb actually contains oxygen.)

Place a flashbulb in the camera and set it off. Ask,

- **What did you see?** (a flash of light)

Set off several more flashbulbs and allow students to observe carefully the used bulbs. Ask,

- **What do you see inside the bulb?** (white powder)
- **How does the appearance of the bulb differ from before it was set off?** (Before the inside was clear and the coil of metal was plainly visible; now the entire bulb is clouded with white powder.)

Have students try to describe what they think happened when the bulb went off. Most will realize that a chemical reaction occurred. Point out that they will discover the nature of this reaction as they read this chapter.

TEACHER RESOURCES

Audiovisuals

Chemical Change All About Us, 16 mm film, Cor

Chemical Change and Temperature, 16 mm film, BFA

Combustion—An Introduction to Chemical Change, 16 mm film, BFA

Investigating Matter; Chemical Reaction, filmstrip with cassette, EBE

Books

Denn, Morton M., *Stability of Reaction and Transport Processes,* Prentice-Hall

Skinner, Gordon B., *Introduction to Chemical Kinetics,* Academic Press

Sykes, Peter, *The Search for Organic Reaction Pathways,* Halstead

Software

Balancing Equations, Prentice-Hall

Chemical Bonding, Prentice-Hall

Dynamic Equilibrium, Prentice-Hall

Oxidation and Reduction, Prentice-Hall

---

pair the statue? (exposure to air and water)
- **Do you think these changes were physical changes?** (no) **Why not?** (The properties of the metal changed—not only its color, but the metal in the support structure lost some of its strength.)
- **What kind of changes were these?** (chemical changes)
- **What must be done to reverse or repair a chemical change?** (There

must be another chemical change.)
- **Do any of you know what bronze is made of?** (It is an alloy of copper and tin.)

Emphasize to students that an alloy is a mixture—actually a solid solution—of two or more metals. Point out that in the corrosion of the Statue of Liberty, it was the copper that reacted with water and the atmosphere.

8-1 NATURE OF CHEMICAL REACTIONS

SECTION PREVIEW 8-1

In this section, students will be introduced to the characteristics of chemical reactions. They will learn that a chemical reaction always produces a change in the properties and a change in energy of the substances involved in the reaction.

Students will be introduced to the terms reactants and products. They will learn that substances entering a reaction are called reactants and substances produced by a chemical reaction are called products.

Students will come to understand that a chemical reaction involves the breaking and forming of chemical bonds. They will also come to recognize that the ability of a substance to combine chemically is related to the arrangement of electrons in the atoms of the substance.

PERFORMANCE OBJECTIVES 8-1

1. **Describe the characteristics of chemical reactions.**
2. **Explain that a chemical reaction is accompanied by a change in properties and a change in energy of the substances involved in the reaction.**
3. **Define the terms reactants and products.**
4. **Explain why different substances have the ability to undergo certain types of chemical reactions.**
5. **Explain how a substance's capacity to react is related to the arrangement of electrons in the outermost energy level of its atoms.**

Figure 8–1 *Rusting is a chemical reaction in which iron combines with oxygen to form the compound iron oxide (left). Rusting takes place very slowly, and only a very small amount of heat energy is given off. Fighting brush fires involves a chemical reaction in which noncombustible products are formed (right). This chemical reaction occurs rapidly. What two things always change in a chemical reaction?* ❷

8–1 Nature of Chemical Reactions

Here's a chemical puzzle for you. What do the rusting of iron, the burning of gasoline, and the cooking of sugar have in common? They are all examples of **chemical reactions.** A chemical reaction is a process in which the physical and chemical properties of the original substances change as new substances with different physical and chemical properties are formed. Can you name some other examples of chemical reactions? ❶

Characteristics of Chemical Reactions

In any chemical reaction, a new substance is formed. **When a chemical reaction takes place, there is always a change in the properties and in the energy of the substances involved in the chemical reaction.** Both the physical and chemical properties of the substances are changed.

182

TEACHING STRATEGY 8-1

Motivation

Have students review their observations of the demonstration with flashbulbs. Direct their attention to the photographs in Figure 8-2, and have them read the descriptive paragraph in the text.

• **How do your observations compare with the photographs in Figure 8-2?**

(Answers will vary, but essentially the two should be similar.)
• **Can you explain now what actually took place inside the flashbulb?** (Magnesium combined with oxygen to produce magnesium oxide.)
• **What was produced by the reaction in addition to magnesium oxide?** (energy in the form of light)

Content Development

Continue the discussion of the flashbulb demonstration.
• **What two characteristics of a chemical reaction are displayed in the popping of a flashbulb?** (change in properties of original substances and a change in energy)
• **How can you tell that the original substances have been changed into a new substance?** (The "empty space" in the bulb has been replaced by white

For example, inside a flashbulb is a small coil of shiny gray metal. This metal is magnesium. The bulb is also filled with the invisible gas oxygen. When the flashbulb is set off, the magnesium combines with the oxygen in a chemical reaction. Energy is released in the form of light, and a fine white powder is produced. You can see this powder on the inside of the bulb. The powder is magnesium oxide, a compound with physical and chemical properties very different from the elements magnesium and oxygen. So a chemical reaction has occurred.

In any chemical reaction, there are always two kinds of substances: the substances that are present before the change and the substances that are formed by the change. A substance that enters into a chemical reaction is called a **reactant** (ree-AK-tehnt). A substance that is produced by a chemical reaction is called a **product.** So a general description of a chemical reaction could be stated as reactants changing into products. In the example of the flashbulb, what are the reactants? The product? ❹

In addition to changes in properties, chemical reactions always involve a change in energy. Energy is either absorbed or released during a chemical reaction. For example, heat energy is absorbed when sugar changes into caramel. When gasoline burns, heat energy is released. Later in this chapter you

Figure 8–2 Inside this flashbulb is a thin coil of magnesium metal and the invisible gas oxygen (top). When the flashbulb is set off, a chemical reaction takes place in which the magnesium combines with oxygen to form magnesium oxide (bottom). How can you tell a chemical reaction has occurred? ❸

Figure 8–3 The ability of substances to burn fueled the Voyager 1 spacecraft on its mission to the outer planets (right). The ability of substances not to burn helped this firefighter extinguish a bog fire (left). What type of property is the ability to burn? ❺

183

SCIENCE TERMS 8-1
chemical reaction p. 182
reactant p. 183
product p. 183

ANNOTATION KEY

❶ Bleaching clothes, baking, leaves changing color, digestion, photosynthesis (Relating facts)

❷ Properties and energy of substances involved in the reaction (Identifying patterns)

❸ Formation of white powder, or magnesium oxide; release of energy in form of light (Inferring)

❹ Magnesium, oxygen; magnesium oxide (Applying concepts)

❺ Chemical property (Classifying)

❶ Thinking Skill: Hypothesizing

❷ Thinking Skill: Making generalizations

❸ Thinking Skill: Observing

❹ Thinking Skill: Applying definitions

ent? (The flashbulb reaction takes place very rapidly, with a visible energy change; rusting takes places very gradually, without an obvious change in energy. Also, the flashbulb reaction had to be "made" to happen, while the rusting happens spontaneously as a result of the iron's exposure to air and moisture.)

powder, and the shiny metal coil is no longer visible.)
Display one of the used flashbulbs and ask,
• **Can anyone think of a way besides looking at the bulb to prove that the properties of the original substances have changed?** (Try to use the flashbulb again. The fact that it will not go off a second time shows that the properties of the original substances have changed.)

Skills Development
Skills: Observing, comparing
Have students observe Figure 8-1 (left) and read the caption. Ask,
• **How is the chemical reaction shown in this photograph similar to the chemical reaction that takes place inside a flashbulb?** (Both involve a metal combining with oxygen; in both cases the properties of the metal are altered.)
• **How are the two reactions differ-**

Reinforcement
Make sure that students understand the meaning of the words *reactants* and *products*. Refer to the photograph of rusting iron and ask,
• **What are the reactants in the rusting process?** (iron and oxygen)
• **What is the product?** (iron oxide)
Point out that these words are easy to remember since reactant is similar to the word *reacts,* and product means the substance that is *produced.*

TIE-IN/EARTH SCIENCE

Figure 8-6 shows the eruption of a volcano. Volcanic eruptions are the result of chemical reactions fueled by heat from deep within the earth. Have interested students research the chemistry of volcanic eruptions and report their findings to the class.

ANNOTATION KEY

❶ Li : 1; F : 7; Ne : 8, Neon (Interpreting illustrations)
❷ Heat within the earth (Inferring)
❶ Thinking Skill: Making generalizations
❷ Thinking Skill: Identifying relationships

8-1 (continued)

Content Development

Lead into a discussion of valence electrons by reviewing the properties of noble gases. Ask,
• **Why are the noble gases so unreactive?** (The outermost energy level of electrons in a noble gas is complete.)
• **How many electrons are needed to make up a complete outermost energy level?** (Eight, unless the first energy level of the atom is also the outermost level—then only two electrons are needed.) Explain that an atom forms chemical bonds with other atoms in order to complete its outermost energy level, and that in these bonds an atom can lose, gain, or share electrons.

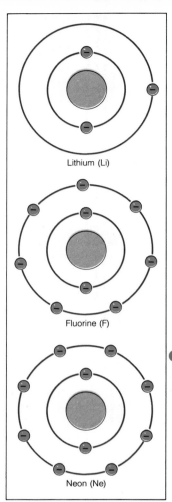

Lithium (Li)

Fluorine (F)

Neon (Ne)

Figure 8–4 *The arrangement of electrons in an atom determines the atom's ability to undergo chemical reactions. How many valence electrons does each atom shown here have? Which atom is likely to be unreactive?* ❶

184

will learn more about energy changes that accompany chemical reactions.

Capacity to React

In order for a chemical reaction to occur, the reactants must have the ability to combine with other substances to form products. What accounts for the ability of different substances to undergo certain chemical reactions? In order to answer this question, you must think back to what you learned about atoms and bonding.

Atoms contain electrons, or negatively charged particles, which are located in energy levels. The electrons in the outermost energy level of an atom are called the valence electrons. It is the valence electrons that are involved in chemical bonding. An atom forms chemical bonds with other atoms in order to complete its outermost energy level. A chemical bond can be formed by the loss or gain of electrons, which is ionic bonding. Or it can be formed by the sharing of electrons, which is covalent bonding.

The arrangement of electrons in an atom determines the bonding capacity of that atom. Bonding capacity refers to the ease with which an atom will form chemical bonds. The bonding capacity of an atom determines its chemical properties, or its ability to undergo chemical reactions.

Figure 8–5 *During a chemical reaction, bonds between atoms of the reactants are broken, atoms are rearranged, and new bonds in products are formed.*

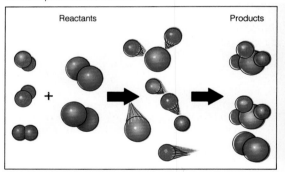

Reactants   Products

Skills Development

Skills: Observing, predicting
Have students observe the diagrams of lithium and fluorine atoms in Figure 8-4.
• **How many electrons are in the outermost energy level of lithium?** (one)
• **How many electrons are in the outermost energy level of fluorine?** (seven)
• **How would you predict that lithium would combine with another**

atom in order to fill its outermost energy level? (Answers may vary; the correct answer is that lithium would lose one electron to have a complete outer shell of two electrons.)
• **How would you predict that fluorine would bond with another atom to fill its outermost energy level?** (It would want to gain one electron.)
• **Can you make a prediction about what would happen if lithium and fluorine were combined chemically**

184

During a chemical reaction, atoms can form molecules, molecules can break apart to form atoms, or molecules can react with other molecules. In any case, new substances are produced as existing bonds are broken, atoms are rearranged, and new bonds are formed.

SECTION REVIEW

1. What is a chemical reaction?
2. What is a reactant? A product?
3. What is the relationship between the arrangement of electrons in an atom and the atom's chemical properties?

8–2 Chemical Equations

Chemical reactions involve rearrangements of atoms. In order to describe a chemical reaction, it is necessary to indicate the atoms that are involved in the reaction. One way of doing this is to use words. But describing a chemical reaction with words can be awkward. Many atoms may be involved, and the changes may be complicated.

For example, consider the flashbulb reaction described before. A word equation for this reaction would be stated: Magnesium combines with oxygen to form magnesium oxide and give off energy in the form of light. You could shorten this sentence a bit by saying: Magnesium and oxygen form magnesium oxide and light energy. ❷

Chemists have developed a more convenient way to represent a chemical reaction. Using symbols to represent elements and formulas to represent compounds, a chemical reaction can be described by a **chemical equation.** A chemical equation is an expression in which symbols and formulas are used to represent a chemical reaction.

In order to write a chemical equation, you must first write the correct chemical symbols or formulas for the reactants and products. Then you need to separate these symbols or formulas with a plus sign. A "+" sign replaces the word "and." Between the reactants and products, you need to draw an arrow.

Section Objective

To balance chemical equations

Figure 8–6 *The eruption of Mt. Ngaurahoe in New Zealand is a dramatic example of a chemical reaction. Where does the energy for this reaction come from?* ❷

185

SECTION PREVIEW 8-2

In this section students will learn how chemical equations can be used to represent chemical reactions. They will learn that elements are represented by symbols, and compounds are represented by formulas.

By the end of this section, students will be able to interpret, write, and balance chemical equations. They will also come to understand that a chemical equation illustrates the law of conservation of mass, as the number of atoms of each element remains constant.

PERFORMANCE OBJECTIVES 8-2

1. **Discuss how chemical equations are used to describe chemical reactions.**
2. **Interpret and write chemical equations.**
3. **Balance chemical equations.**
4. **Explain how a chemical equation illustrates the law of conservation of mass.**

SCIENCE TERMS 8-2

chemical equation p. 185
law of conservation of mass p. 186
coefficient p. 186

---

with each other? (They would form an ionic bond in which lithium would give up an electron to fluorine.)

Section Review 8-1
1. Process in which the physical and chemical properties of the original substances change as new substances with different physical and chemical properties are formed.
2. Substance that enters into a chemical reaction; substance that is produced by a chemical reaction
3. The arrangement of electrons in an atom determines the bonding capacity of the atom. The bonding capacity of an atom determines its chemical properties, or its ability to undergo chemical reactions.

TEACHING STRATEGY 8-2

Motivation
• Ask a student volunteer to go to the chalkboard and write in words the chemical reaction that takes place when a flashbulb is set off. (The student's choice of words may vary, but should convey that magnesium reacts with oxygen to produce magnesium oxide and energy in the form of light.)
• Ask a second volunteer to go to the chalkboard and write in words the chemical reaction that produces rust. (Iron combines with oxygen to produce iron oxide.)

Sharpen Your Skills

Mass and a Chemical Reaction
Skills: Manipulative, observing, comparing, relating, inferring, hypothesizing, measuring
Level: Average
Type: Hands-on
Materials: two unused flashbulbs, flash camera, double-pan balance

In this activity, students note that in a closed system such as the flashbulb the mass of the system does not change during the chemical reaction. This illustrates the law of conservation of mass. Students will note that a chemical reaction has occurred, based on their observations of the flashbulb before and after it has been used.

8-2 (continued)

Content Development

Use the descriptions of reactions that students wrote on the chalkboard during the Motivation to lead into a discussion of the need for a more convenient way to represent chemical reactions. Explain that chemical symbols and equations are not only easier, they also provide a standard form of expression that scientists all over the world understand.

You may find it helpful when teaching this section to have a periodic table on display, so that students can readily note the symbols for various elements.

Refer to the description of the magnesium and oxygen reaction that is on the chalkboard. Ask,

• **What two elements are the reac-** tants in this reaction? (Magnesium and oxygen)

• **What are the symbols for these elements?** (Mg and O)

Write Mg + O on the chalkboard. Ask,

• **Does the O look strange to you as a symbol for oxygen?** (It should; remind students that free oxygen is always represented as O_2, which indicates a molecule of oxygen containing two oxygen atoms.)

Rewrite on the chalkboard, Mg + O_2.

This arrow, which is read "yields," takes the place of an equal sign. It also shows the direction of the chemical change. The chemical equation for the flashbulb reaction can now be written:

$$Mg + O_2 \longrightarrow MgO + energy$$

❶ magnesium + oxygen $\longrightarrow$ magnesium oxide + energy

Conservation of Mass

Chemists have long known that atoms can be neither created nor destroyed during a chemical reaction. In other words, the number of atoms of each element must be the same before and after the chemical reaction.

If the number of atoms of each element remains the same, then mass can never change in a chemical reaction. The total mass of the reactants must equal the total mass of the products. This observation that mass remains constant in a chemical reaction is known as the **law of conservation of mass.**

Balancing Chemical Equations

The law of conservation of mass must be considered when writing a chemical equation for a chemical reaction. A chemical equation must show that atoms are neither created nor destroyed. The number of atoms of each element must be the same on both sides of the equation.

❷ **An equation in which the number of atoms of each element is the same on both sides of the equation is called a balanced chemical equation.** To balance a chemical equation, **coefficients** (koh-uh-FIHSH-uhnts) are placed in front of symbols and formulas. Coefficients are numbers that indicate how many atoms or molecules of each substance are involved in the reaction.

Let's go back to the chemical equation for the flashbulb reaction:

$$Mg + O_2 \longrightarrow MgO + energy$$

Is the law of conservation of mass observed?

How many magnesium atoms do you count on the left side of the equation? You should count 1.

Sharpen Your Skills

Mass and a Chemical Reaction

1. Place two unused flashbulbs on opposite pans of a double pan balance, or determine the mass of each flashbulb individually. The masses should be the same.

2. Put one flashbulb in a camera flash holder and flash the camera.

3. Allow the flashbulb to cool.

4. Again compare the masses of the used and unused flashbulbs.

Does the mass of the used flashbulb change? What law does this activity illustrate? What type of change has the used flashbulb undergone? How do you know?

186

Then draw an arrow and explain that the arrow means yields or produces.

• **What is the product in this reaction?** (Magnesium oxide)

• **Complete the equation by writing the formula for magnesium oxide, MgO.**

• **What does this formula tell you about the composition of a molecule of magnesium oxide?** (It contains one atom of magnesium and one atom of oxygen.)

HELP WANTED: FOOD CHEMIST to develop new food products and processing techniques. Candidates for this position should have a college degree in food science or chemistry.

If you were alive one hundred years ago, you probably would have spent much of your time growing and preparing your own food. What you did not grow or process yourself, you would have purchased fresh nearly every day. Packaged and canned foods were not common then. And there were no mechanical refrigerators.

Today, most people can reach into the refrigerator or cabinet for a snack or easy-to-prepare meal. Much of the food you eat has been processed for you by a food processing company. Almost every method of food processing involves chemical reactions. **Food chemists** use their knowledge of chemistry to develop these food processing methods.

Some food chemists develop new foods or new flavors. Others develop improved packag-

ing and storage methods for foods. Food chemists might work in the plants where food is processed. Food chemists may test samples of a product to be sure that the nutrients in the food match the nutritional information printed on the package.

If you are interested in a career as a food chemist, write to the Institute of Food Technologists, Career Guidance, Suite 300, 221 North LaSalle Street, Chicago, IL 60601.

And on the right side? You should count 1. Now try the same thing for oxygen. There are 2 oxygen atoms on the left but only 1 on the right. This cannot be correct, since atoms can be neither created nor destroyed during a chemical reaction.

To balance this equation, you must represent more than 1 atom of oxygen and more than one molecule of magnesium oxide:

$$2Mg + O_2 \longrightarrow 2MgO + energy$$

If you count atoms again, you will find 2 magnesium atoms on each side of the equation, as well as 2 oxygen atoms. The equation is balanced. It can be read: 2 atoms of magnesium combine with 1 molecule of oxygen to yield 2 molecules of magnesium oxide. Notice that when no coefficient is written, such as in front of the molecule of oxygen, the number is understood to be 1. Remember that to balance a chemical equation, you can change coefficients but never symbols or formulas.

Chemical equations are easy to write and balance. Follow the rules in Figure 8–7 and on page 188.

Figure 8–7 *These are the steps to follow in balancing a chemical equation. What law must a chemical equation obey?* ❶

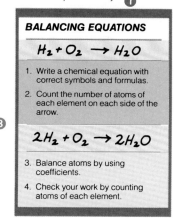

BALANCING EQUATIONS

$$H_2 + O_2 \longrightarrow H_2O$$

1. Write a chemical equation with correct symbols and formulas.
2. Count the number of atoms of each element on each side of the arrow.

❸

$$2H_2 + O_2 \longrightarrow 2H_2O$$

3. Balance atoms by using coefficients.
4. Check your work by counting atoms of each element.

BACKGROUND INFORMATION

Within chemical formulas, subscripts indicate the number of atoms of each element that are present. For example, the formula for hydrogen peroxide is H_2O_2. This means that in one molecule of hydrogen peroxide there are two hydrogen atoms and two oxygen atoms. When no subscript is present after a symbol, it is understood that one atom is present.

In a chemical equation, coefficients are used to indicate how many molecules of compounds or how many atoms of free elements take part in the reaction. By multiplying the subscripts by the coefficients, it is possible to tell how many atoms are taking part in the reaction. For example, in the reaction, $2H_2 + O_2 \longrightarrow 2H_2O$, four atoms of hydrogen react with two atoms of oxygen to produce two molecules of water, which together contain four atoms of hydrogen and two atoms of oxygen.

TIE-IN/MATH

Chemical equations can be compared to algebraic equations. In both cases, the quantity on the right side of the equation must equal the quantity on the left side. An arrow is used instead of an equal sign in a chemical equation. This is because a chemical equation describes a process in which reactants form products as atoms of matter are rearranged. Actually, a simple algebraic equation would make sense with an arrow, too. For example, $x + 3 = 5$ could also be expressed x added to 3 yields 5.

Content Development

Write on the chalkboard, "Mass remains constant in a chemical reaction." Explain that this is called the law of conservation of mass. Ask students to consider

- **How might you tell from a chemical equation if the amount of mass remains constant in a reaction?** (Answers may vary; the correct answer is that the number of atoms of each element must remain constant, even

though the atoms have been rearranged.)

Work through on the chalkboard the balancing of the magnesium oxide equation as shown in the text. Use the finished equation to point out the difference between the 2's used as coefficients and the 2 used as a subscript within the formula for oxygen.

Reinforcement

Emphasize the meaning of the equa-

tion you have just written by having students say, "Two atoms of magnesium combine with one molecule of oxygen to form two molecules of magnesium oxide."

- **How many atoms of magnesium are present on the left side of the equation?** (two) **On the right side?** (two)
- **How many atoms of oxygen are present on the left side?** (two) **On the right side?** (two)

Sharpen Your Skills

A Balancing Act
Skills: Calculating, predicting, re-
lating
Level: Enriched
Type: Computational

This activity reinforces students' ability to balance chemical equations. Students should balance the equations as follows:

1. $BaCl_2 + H_2SO_4 = BaSO_4 + 2HCl$
2. $4P + 5O_2 = P_4O_{10}$
3. $2KClO_3 = 2KCl + 3O_2$
4. $C_3H_8 + 5O_2 = 3CO_2 + 4H_2O$
5. $Cu + 2AgNO_3 = Cu(NO_3)_2 + 2Ag$

ANNOTATION KEY

❶ $2H_2 + O_2 = 2H_2O$ (Applying formulas)

❷ $Na_2S + 2AgNO_3 = 2NaNO_3 + Ag_2S$ (Applying formulas)

❶ Thinking Skill: Applying formulas

❷ Thinking Skill: Interpreting formulas

Sharpen Your Skills

Preventing a Chemical Reaction
Skills: Observing, comparing, ap-
plying, relating, hypothesizing
Level: Remedial
Type: Hands-on
Materials: two large nails, paint,
beaker, water

Students will observe in this activity that paint retards the chemical reaction that results in rust.

Sharpen Your Skills

A Balancing Act

Rewrite each of the following equations on a sheet of paper. Balance each equation, referring to the rules of balancing in Figure 8–7.

$BaCl_2 + H_2SO_4 \longrightarrow$
$\quad BaSO_4 + HCl$
$P + O \longrightarrow P_4O_{10}$
$KClO_3 \longrightarrow KCl + O_2$
$C_3H_8 + O_2 \longrightarrow CO_2 + H_2O$
$Cu + AgNO_3 \longrightarrow$
$\quad Cu(NO_3)_2 + Ag$

❶

1. Write a word equation and then a chemical equation for the reaction. Make sure the symbols and formulas for reactants and products are correct.

2. Count the number of atoms of each element on each side of the arrow. If the numbers are the same, the equation is balanced.

3. If the number of atoms of each element is not the same on both sides of the arrow, you must balance the equation by using coefficients. Put a coefficient in front of a symbol or formula so that the number of atoms of that substance is the same on both sides of the arrow. Continue this procedure until you have balanced all the atoms.

4. Check your work by counting the atoms of each element to make sure they are the same on both sides of the equation.

Sample Problem

Write a balanced equation for the reaction between nitrogen and hydrogen to form ammonia.

Solution

Step 1 Write a word equation and then a chemical equation.

Nitrogen and hydrogen form ammonia
$N_2 + H_2 \longrightarrow NH_3$

Step 2 Count the number of atoms of each element on each side of the equation.

$2 \text{ N atoms} \longrightarrow 1 \text{ N atom}$
$2 \text{ H atoms} \longrightarrow 3 \text{ H atoms}$

Step 3 Balance the equation by using coefficients.

$N_2 + 3 H_2 \longrightarrow 2 NH_3$

Step 4 Check your work by counting the atoms of each element on both sides of the equation.

$2 \text{ N atoms} \longrightarrow 2(1) = 2 \text{ N atoms}$
$3(2) = 6 \text{ H atoms} \longrightarrow 2(3) = 6 \text{ H atoms}$

Practice Problems

❶ 1. Write a balanced equation for the reaction between hydrogen and oxygen to form water.

❷ 2. Write a balanced equation for the reaction between sodium sulfide, Na_2S, and silver nitrate, $AgNO_3$, to produce sodium nitrate, $NaNO_3$, and silver sulfide, Ag_2S.

188

8-2 (continued)

Common Errors

While doing the practice problems, there are several common errors students may make. For example, many students mistakenly think that they can change subscripts as well as coefficients when balancing a chemical equation. Emphasize that a subscript is part of a formula, and that a for-

mula identifies a substance, just as a name identifies a person.

Content Development

Point out that balancing can be made easier by looking for the least common multiple of the unbalanced numbers of atoms. For example, the left side of the equation shows two hydrogen atoms, while the right side shows three hydrogen atoms. The least common multiple for these numbers is six. So

in order to balance the equation, choose coefficients that yield six atoms of hydrogen on each side.

Reinforcement

Have students write word equations for each of the following chemical equations. Make sure that they name each element and compound correctly.
(a) $2H_2 + O_2 \rightarrow 2H_2O$
(b) $4Fe + 3O_2 \rightarrow 2Fe_2O_3$
(c) $2Na + Cl_2 \rightarrow 2NaCl$

1. What is a chemical equation?
2. State the law of conservation of mass.
3. Why must a chemical equation be balanced?
4. Write a balanced chemical equation for the reaction between sodium and oxygen to form sodium oxide, Na_2O.
5. Why can't you change symbols or formulas in order to balance a chemical equation?

8–3 Types of Chemical Reactions

Section Objective

To identify the four types of chemical reactions

There are billions of different chemical reactions. In some reactions, elements combine to form compounds. In other reactions, compounds break down into elements. And in still other reactions, one element replaces another.

Chemists have identified four general types of reactions: synthesis, decomposition, single replacement, and double replacement. In each type of reaction, atoms are being rearranged and substances are being changed in a specific way.

Synthesis Reaction

In a **synthesis** (SIHN-thuh-sihs) **reaction,** two or more simple substances combine to form a new, more complex substance. For example, the reaction between sodium and chlorine to form sodium chloride is a synthesis reaction:

$$2Na + Cl_2 \longrightarrow 2NaCl$$

sodium + chlorine $\longrightarrow$ sodium chloride ❷

Reactions involving the corrosion of metals are synthesis reactions. The rusting of iron involves the chemical combination of iron with oxygen to form iron oxide. Here is the balanced equation for this reaction:

$$4Fe + 3O_2 \longrightarrow 2Fe_2O_3$$

iron + oxygen $\longrightarrow$ iron oxide

Sharpen Your Skills

Preventing a Chemical Reaction

1. Obtain two large nails. Paint one nail and let it dry. Do not paint the other nail.
2. Pour a little water into a jar or beaker.
3. Stand both nails in the container of water. Cover the container and let it stand for several days. Compare the appearance of the nails.

Describe what happens to each nail. Give a reason for your observations. Write a word equation for any reaction that has occurred.

189

8-3 TYPES OF CHEMICAL REACTIONS

SECTION PREVIEW 8-3

In this section, students will come to understand that although there are many different chemical reactions, most reactions can be classified into four general types. These types are synthesis, decomposition, single replacement, and double replacement.

Students will learn that in a synthesis reaction, two or more simple substances combine to form a new, more complex substance. Students will also learn that the opposite of a synthesis reaction is a decomposition reaction.

Students will be introduced to reactions in which atoms or groups of atoms replace each other. They will learn to distinguish between a single replacement reaction and a double replacement reaction.

PERFORMANCE OBJECTIVES 8-3

1. **Classify reactions according to general type.**
2. **Describe and cite examples of a synthesis reaction.**
3. **Describe and cite examples of a decomposition reaction.**
4. **Describe and cite examples of a single replacement reaction and a double replacement reaction.**

SCIENCE TERMS 8-3

synthesis reaction p. 189
decomposition reaction p. 190
single replacement reaction p. 190
double replacement reaction p. 191

Section Review 8-2

1. An expression in which symbols and formulas are used to represent a chemical reaction
2. The mass of reactants equals the mass of the products in a chemical reaction.
3. Atoms can never be created or destroyed in a chemical reaction. Thus, the number of atoms on both sides of a chemical equation for each element must be equal, or balanced.

4. $4Na + O_2 = 2Na_2O$
5. Symbols and formulas stand for products or reactants in a chemical equation. If you change them, then the chemical reaction being described is also changed.

TEACHING STRATEGY 8-3

Motivation

Bring in a bottle of seltzer water. Pour some seltzer into a glass and let the class observe it. Ask,

• **Do you know what chemical reaction is taking place in this seltzer water?** (Carbonic acid is breaking down to form carbon dioxide and water.)

• **What evidence do you see of this reaction?** (Bubbles of gas are moving up through the water.)

Write on the chalkboard the equation for this reaction.

$$H_2CO_3 \rightarrow H_2O + CO_2$$

TEACHER DEMONSTRATION

For this demonstration you will need a piece of zinc and a beaker of hydrochloric acid. Display the zinc, then carefully place it in the beaker.

- **Ask students to observe what takes place.** (Bubbles of gas are released.)

Write the equation for this reaction on the chalkboard.

$$Zn + 2HCl \rightarrow ZnCl_2 + H_2$$

- **What were the bubbles of gas that you saw?** (hydrogen)
- **Where did the hydrogen come from?** (from the HCl)
- **According to the equation, how did the zinc change in this reaction?** (It joined with the chlorine to produce the salt, zinc chloride.)

TIE-IN/SOCIAL STUDIES

Students may have discussed the restoration and 100th birthday of the Statue of Liberty in their social studies classes. Involve students in a class discussion about the history and significance of the Statue of Liberty.

HISTORICAL NOTES

Soda water was originally made by combining sulfuric acid with marble dust in a double-replacement reaction that produces carbonic acid and a salt. It has been reported that St. Patrick's Cathedral in New York City supplied marble chips that produced over 94 million liters of soda water.

Figure 8–8 *The tragic explosion of the Hindenburg on May 6, 1937, involved a synthesis reaction (left). Hydrogen and oxygen combined explosively to form water. A much less dramatic synthesis reaction is the corrosion of a metal such as copper, which was combined with tin to make the bronze of the Statue of Liberty (right).*

Figure 8–9 *Carbonic acid is added to liquids to give them "fizz." Carbonic acid, however, quickly decomposes into water and carbon dioxide gas. What type of a reaction is this? How do you know that a gas is produced?* ❶

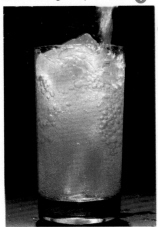

Decomposition Reaction

In a **decomposition reaction,** a complex substance breaks down into two or more simpler substances. Decomposition reactions are the reverse of synthesis reactions. When you take the cap off a bottle of soda, bubbles rise quickly to the top. Why? Carbonated beverages such as soda contain the compound carbonic acid, H_2CO_3. This compound decomposes into water and carbon dioxide gas. The CO_2 gas makes up the bubbles that are released. Here is the balanced equation for the decomposition of carbonic acid:

$$H_2CO_3 \longrightarrow H_2O + CO_2$$

carbonic acid ⟶ water + carbon dioxide

Single-Replacement Reaction

In a **single-replacement reaction,** an uncombined element replaces an element that is part of a compound. For example, the very active metal sodium must be stored in oil, not water. When it comes in contact with water, it reacts explosively. The sodium replaces the hydrogen in the water and

190

8-3 (continued)

Content Development

Refer to the equation you just wrote in the Motivation section. Ask,

- **How is this equation similar to other equations you have seen so far?** (Reactants are changing into products, as shown by formulas and an arrow.)
- **Do you notice anything different about this equation compared to others you have seen?** (So far the equations used in the text have consisted of two substances combining to form a product. In this equation, a single substance is breaking down to form two products.)

Content Development

Write on the chalkboard the examples given in the text of single replacement and double replacement reactions. Use arrows to diagram the process of one element or group of atoms replacing another.

Reinforcement

The following analogies may help students better understand the processes of single replacement and double replacement. For single replacement, draw the analogy of two people playing tennis with a third person watching on the sidelines. When one of the players gets tired, the person on the sidelines comes in and takes his or

releases lots of energy. Here is the balanced equation for the reaction of sodium with water:

$$2Na + 2H_2O \longrightarrow 2NaOH + H_2$$
$$\text{sodium + water} \longrightarrow \text{sodium hydroxide} + \text{hydrogen}$$

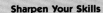

Most single-replacement reactions do not cause explosions. When a piece of zinc is placed in a beaker of hydrochloric acid, the zinc replaces the hydrogen in the acid and sets it free. Bubbles of hydrogen gas can be seen as the reaction progresses. Zinc chloride is the other product. Here is the balanced equation for this reaction:

$$Zn + 2HCl \longrightarrow ZnCl_2 + H_2$$
$$\text{zinc + hydrochloric acid} \longrightarrow \text{zinc chloride} + \text{hydrogen}$$

Double-Replacement Reaction

In a **double-replacement reaction,** different atoms in two different compounds replace each other. In other words, two compounds react to form two new compounds.

If you have ever had an upset stomach, you may have taken a medicine that contained the compound ❸ magnesium carbonate. This compound reacts with

Sharpen Your Skills

Double-Replacement Reaction

1. Place a small amount of baking soda in a glass beaker or jar.
2. Pour some vinegar on the baking soda. Observe what happens.

Baking soda is sodium hydrogen carbonate, $NaHCO_3$. Vinegar is acetic acid, $HC_2H_3O_2$. Write the chemical equation for this reaction. What gas is produced? How could you test for the presence of this gas?

Figure 8–10 *Because copper is a more active metal than silver, it can replace the silver in silver nitrate. In these four photos, you can see the gradual buildup of silver metal on the coil. What type of reaction is this? What other indication is there that a chemical change is taking place?* ❷

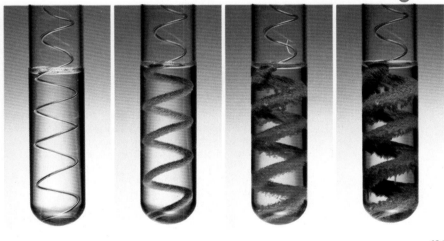

Sharpen Your Skills

**Double Replacement Reaction
Skills: Observing, manipulative, relating, inferring, predicting
Level: Average
Type: Hands-on
Materials: baking soda, glass beaker, vinegar**

Students observe a typical double replacement reaction in this activity. They will quickly observe bubbles when they place the vinegar on the baking soda. The chemical reaction should be written as follows: $NaHCO_3 + HC_2H_3O_2 = NaC_2H_3O_2 + CO_2 + H_2$. Students may suggest bubbling the gas produced through lime water to test for carbon dioxide. In this test, the lime water turns milky in the presence of carbon dioxide.

ANNOTATION KEY

❶ Decomposition; bubbles in liquid (Observing)

❷ Single replacement; liquid turns blue due to formation of copper nitrate (Applying definitions)

❶ Thinking Skill: Observing

❷ Thinking Skill: Interpreting formulas

❸ Thinking Skill: Applying technology

her place. For double replacement, explain that it is like two couples on a double date who at some point decide to switch partners!

Skills Development
Skill: Making a model
Divide the class into small groups. Challenge each group to create a dramatic presentation showing the four types of chemical reactions. For example, a group might show two or three

people getting together in a synthesis reaction, then splitting up again as the new substance decomposes.

Enrichment
Copper replaces silver in silver nitrate because copper is the more active metal. Have students use research materials in the classroom or library to find out what is meant by the activity series of metals. Based on their findings, have each group state at least two

other chemical reactions that can take place as a result of a more active metal replacing a less active one.

Motivation
Students might enjoy working in small groups to create advertisements for a stomach remedy. Challenge them to "educate the consumer" as to the chemical reaction that takes place between magnesium carbonate and hydrochloric acid.

8-4 ENERGY OF CHEMICAL REACTIONS

SECTION PREVIEW 8-4

In this section, students will learn that chemical reactions can be classified according to energy changes. They will learn that an exothermic reaction is one in which energy is released, and an endothermic reaction is one in which energy is absorbed.

Students will be introduced to the use of energy diagrams to represent the energy changes that occur during chemical reactions. They will come to understand that in an exothermic reaction, the energy of the reactants is greater than the energy of the products, while in an endothermic reaction, the energy of the products is greater than the energy of the reactants. Students will also be introduced to the term activation energy, which is the energy level that must be reached by the reactants in order for a reaction to occur.

PERFORMANCE OBJECTIVES 8-4

1. **Classify reactions according to energy changes.**
2. **Distinguish between exothermic and endothermic reactions.**
3. **Interpret an energy diagram.**
4. **Define and discuss the term activation energy.**

SCIENCE TERMS 8-4

exothermic reaction p. 193
endothermic reaction p. 194
activation energy p. 195

Figure 8–11 *Paints are chemical compounds produced by double-replacement reactions. Yellow paint contains cadmium sulfide, which gives it its characteristic color. Cadmium sulfide and hydrogen chloride are produced when cadmium chloride and hydrogen sulfide are combined. What is the balanced chemical equation for this reaction?* ❶

192

the hydrochloric acid in your stomach in the following way:

$$MgCO_3 + 2HCl \longrightarrow MgCl_2 + H_2CO_3$$
magnesium carbonate $\longrightarrow$ magnesium chloride
+ hydrochloric acid   + carbonic acid

In this double-replacement reaction, the magnesium and hydrogen replace each other, or "switch partners." One product is magnesium chloride, a harmless compound. The other product is carbonic acid. Do you remember what happens to carbonic acid? It decomposes into water and carbon dioxide. Your stomachache goes away because instead of too much acid, there is now water and carbon dioxide. You owe your relief to this double-replacement reaction:

❶ $$MgCO_3 + 2HCl \longrightarrow MgCl_2 + H_2O + CO_2$$
magnesium carbonate $\longrightarrow$ magnesium chloride
+ hydrochloric acid   + water + carbon dioxide

SECTION REVIEW

1. Name the four types of reactions.
2. What is the difference between a synthesis reaction and a decomposition reaction?
3. What is a single-replacement reaction? A double-replacement reaction?
4. What type of reaction is represented by each of the following equations:
   a. $2Na + MgF_2 \longrightarrow 2NaF + Mg$
   b. $C + O_2 \longrightarrow CO_2$
   c. $2KCl + Pb(NO_3)_2 \longrightarrow 2KNO_3 + PbCl_2$

8–4 Energy of Chemical Reactions

When chemical reactions occur, there is always a change in energy. Sometimes energy is released, or given off, as the reaction takes place. Sometimes energy is absorbed. **Based on the type of energy change involved, chemical reactions are classified ❷ as either exothermic or endothermic reactions.**

In either type of reaction, energy is neither created nor destroyed. One of two things can happen

---

Figure 8–12 *The explosion of a firecracker is an exothermic reaction (left). The cooking of pancakes is an endothermic reaction (right). What is the difference between these two types of reactions?* ❷

to the energy. It can be stored in the molecules of a reacting substance or it can be released from a reacting substance in which it was originally stored. The energy that is absorbed or released usually takes the form of heat or visible light.

Exothermic Reactions

A chemical reaction in which energy is released is an **exothermic** (ehks-uh-THER-mihk) **reaction.** ❸ A combustion reaction, or a reaction that involves burning, is an example of an exothermic reaction. For example, the combustion of methane, which occurs in a gas stove, releases a large amount of energy in the form of heat.

$$CH_4 + 2O_2 \longrightarrow CO_2 + 2H_2O + energy$$
$$methane + oxygen \longrightarrow carbon\ dioxide$$
$$+ water + energy$$

The energy that is released in an exothermic reaction was originally stored in the molecules of the reactants. The molecules of the products no longer contain this stored energy. So the energy of the products is less than the energy of the reactants. An energy diagram, such as the one in Figure 8–13, on page 194 can be used to show the energy change in an exothermic reaction. Note that the reactants are higher in energy than the products are.

193

Photosynthesis is a chemical process that requires the absorption of energy in the form of sunlight. Have students research this process and report on the endothermic reaction that requires energy from the sun.

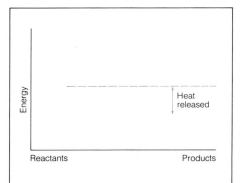

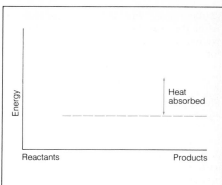

Figure 8–13 *An energy diagram for an exothermic reaction (left) indicates that heat is released during the reaction. Heat is absorbed during an endothermic reaction, as shown by its energy diagram (right). How does the heat content of products and reactants compare for each type of reaction?*

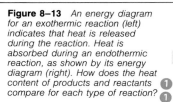

Endothermic Reactions

A chemical reaction in which energy is absorbed is an **endothermic** (ehn-duh-THER-mihk) **reaction.** The energy absorbed during an endothermic reaction is usually in the form of heat or electric energy. The decomposition of sodium chloride, or table salt, is an example of an endothermic reaction. It requires the absorption of electric energy.

$$2NaCl + energy \longrightarrow 2Na + Cl_2$$
$$sodium\ chloride + energy \longrightarrow sodium + chlorine$$

The energy that is absorbed in an endothermic reaction is now stored in the molecules of the products. So the energy of the products is more than the energy of the reactants. See Figure 8–13.

Activation Energy

The total energy released or absorbed by a chemical reaction does not tell the whole story about the energy changes involved in the reaction. In order for the reactants to form products, the molecules of the reactants must combine to form a short-lived, high-energy, extremely unstable molecule. The atoms of this molecule are then rearranged to form products. This process requires energy. The molecules of the reactants must "climb" to the top of an "energy hill" before they can form products. The energy needed to "climb" to the top

---

Kitchen Chemistry
Skills: Observing, relating, applying, inferring
Level: Average
Type: Hands-on/library

This activity will help students relate the somewhat esoteric topics in their textbook to their everyday world. Check students' charts carefully for accuracy.

Sharpen Your Skills

Kitchen Chemistry

Many interesting chemical reactions occur during various cooking processes. Observe someone preparing and cooking different kinds of food. Record your observations of the changes that take place in the properties of the food. Are the changes physical or chemical? Exothermic or endothermic? Synthesis, decomposition, or replacement?

Make a chart of your observations and conclusions. Then use books and other reference materials in the library to find out more about each of the chemical reactions you have listed.

8-4 (continued)

Enrichment

The chemical reaction that takes place inside a car battery produces electrical energy. Have students find out what this chemical reaction is, write the equation for the reaction, then draw a diagram showing what happens inside the battery.

Content Development

Direct students' attention to the decomposition reaction of NaCl shown in the text. Explain that the breaking of chemical bonds requires energy;

thus this process is endothermic. Ask,
• **What energy change would occur if the sodium and chlorine were to recombine to form sodium chloride?** (Energy would be released.) Explain that the forming of chemical bonds releases energy; thus most synthesis reactions are exothermic.

Skills Development

Skill: Interpreting diagrams
Have students study the energy

diagrams in Figure 8-13. Explain that the horizontal axis of the graph shows the passage of time as the reaction progresses.

Display the diagrams using an overhead projector. Trace with a pointer the energy path of the reactants as they change into products. Stress that energy is stored in the molecules of products and reactants. Point to Figure 13 (left) and ask,
• **In this reaction, which has more**

of the "energy hill" is called **activation energy.** After the reactants have absorbed this activation energy, they can "slide down" the energy hill to form products.

An energy diagram indicates more than whether a reaction is exothermic or endothermic. An energy diagram shows the activation energy of the reaction. Figure 8–15 shows an energy diagram for both an exothermic reaction and an endothermic reaction. ❷

All chemical reactions require activation energy. Even an exothermic reaction such as the burning of a match requires activation energy. In order to light a match, it must first be struck. The friction of match against striking pad provides the necessary activation energy.

Figure 8–14 *Even though a lighted match gives off heat and the reaction is exothermic, activation energy must first be absorbed. What provides the activation energy?* ❷

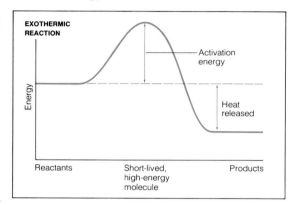

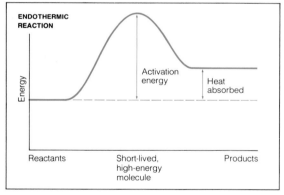

Figure 8–15 *As you can see by these energy diagrams, both an exothermic reaction and an endothermic reaction require activation energy.*

195

BACKGROUND INFORMATION

The high-energy, unstable molecule formed as reactants reach the activation energy is called an activated complex. An activated complex exists for a short time while atoms rearrange themselves. The structure of the activated complex is different from the structures of both the products and the reactants.

An activated complex is formed in the following way. Suppose particles A and B are reacting to form particles C and D. In order for the reaction to occur, A and B must collide. If they collide at just the right angle with sufficient energy, they will form an activated complex. Once this happens, two things can occur. The activated complex can break apart to form the products C and D, or the activated complex can break apart and revert back to the original reactants. Thus, simply forming an activated complex does not guarantee the formation of a product unless conditions continue to be favorable. It is rather like a basketball skimming around the rim of a basket—it has a chance to go in, but it may slide off the rim and fall back down to the ground.

stored energy—the molecules of the **reactants or the molecules of the products?** (molecules of the reactants) **How can you tell?** (The energy curve at the end of the reaction is lower than the curve at the beginning of the reaction.)

Point to Figure 8-13 (right) and ask,

• **Which molecules have the greater amount of stored energy in this reaction?** (the products) **How can you tell?** (The curve at the end of the reaction is higher than the curve at the beginning of the reaction.)

Content Development

Explain that activation energy is the energy level that must be reached in order for a reaction to occur. Emphasize that for both endothermic and exothermic reactions, the activation energy is always higher than the initial energy of the reactants.

Reinforcement

To help students better understand the concept of activation energy, have them observe an energy diagram and ask them to imagine that they are trying to roll a ball up and over the activation energy "hill." If the ball is not rolled with enough energy, it will simply slide back down. If, however, it is rolled with sufficient energy, it will crest over the hill and roll down the other side.

8-5 RATES OF CHEMICAL REACTIONS

SECTION PREVIEW 8-5

In this section, students will learn about four factors that influence rates of chemical reactions. These factors are concentration of reactants, surface area of solid reactants, temperature, and the presence of a catalyst.

Students will come to understand that all of these factors relate to molecular collisions. The theory that explains this relationship is called the collision theory.

Students will learn about the role a catalyst plays in a chemical reaction. They will come to understand that a catalyst speeds up a chemical reaction by lowering the activation energy.

PERFORMANCE OBJECTIVES 8-5

1. **Relate the collision theory to factors affecting rates of chemical reactions.**
2. **Describe how concentration of reactants affects the rate of a chemical reaction.**
3. **Describe how surface area of a solid reactant affects the rate of a chemical reaction.**
4. **Describe how temperature affects the rate of a chemical reaction.**
5. **Describe how a catalyst increases the rate of a chemical reaction.**

SCIENCE TERMS 8-5

kinetics p. 196
reaction rate p. 196
collision theory p. 197
concentration p. 197
catalyst p. 198

Section Objective

To relate the collision theory to factors affecting reaction rate.

Sharpen Your Skills

Rate of Reaction

1. Obtain two sugar cubes. Grind one of the cubes into powder.
2. Fill two clear plastic cups with warm water from the tap.
3. As close to the same time as possible, put the whole sugar cube into one cup of water and the powdered sugar into the other.
4. Stir each cup briefly every 30 seconds. Observe the time required for the complete dissolving of sugar in each cup.

How do the times compare? Which reaction rate is faster? Why? How does the collision theory help explain your observations?

196

1. What is an exothermic reaction? An endothermic reaction?
2. On which side should the energy term be written in an equation representing an endothermic reaction? In an equation representing an exothermic reaction?
3. Compare the energy content of reactants and products in an exothermic reaction. In an endothermic reaction.
4. Compare the energy diagram of an exothermic reaction requiring a large amount of activation energy with that of an exothermic reaction requiring a small amount of activation energy.

8–5 Rates of Chemical Reactions

The complete burning of a thick log can take many hours. Yet if the log is ground into very fine sawdust, the burning can take place at dangerously high speeds. In fact, if the dust is spread through the air, the burning can produce an explosion! In both these processes, the same reaction is taking place. The various substances in wood are combining with oxygen. What, then, causes the differences in reaction times?

In order to explain differences in reaction time, chemists must study **kinetics.** Kinetics is the study of **reaction rates.** The rate of a reaction is a measure of how quickly reactants turn into products. Reaction rates depend on a number of factors, which you will now read about.

Collision Theory

Chemical reactions occur when bonds between atoms are broken, the atoms are rearranged, and new bonds are formed. In order for this process to occur, activation energy must be provided. In addition, molecules of the reactants must come together to form a short-lived, high-energy molecule. These two requirements are met through collisions between the molecules of the reactants.

8-4 (continued)

Section Review 8-4

1. Exothermic: chemical reaction in which energy is released; endothermic: chemical reaction in which energy is absorbed.
2. Left, with reactants; right, with products.
3. Reactants have more energy than products. Products have more energy than reactants.

4. The top of the "energy hill" would be higher in the exothermic reaction requiring a large amount of activation energy.

TEACHING STRATEGY 8-5

Motivation

Have students consider the following situations and relate them to the collision theory.

• **Suppose you are walking around a**

department store on a day when the store is nearly empty. What are the chances of your bumping into another person? (almost no chance)

• **Suppose you are walking around the same store on a day when the store is moderately busy. What are the chances of bumping into another person?** (a reasonable chance, maybe about 50–50)

• **Now suppose the store is having a giant pre-Christmas sale on a Satur-**

The theory that relates molecular collisions to reaction rate is called the **collision theory.** According to the collision theory, reacting molecules must collide with sufficient energy if they are to form products. **The collision theory explains why the rate of a reaction is affected by four factors: concentration, surface area, temperature, and catalysts.**

Concentration

The **concentration** of a substance is a measure of the amount of that substance in a given unit of volume. A high concentration of reactants means there are a great many particles per unit volume. So there are more particles of reactants available for collisions. More collisions occur and more products are formed in a certain amount of time. What does a low concentration of reactants mean? ❶

Generally, reactants present at high concentrations react more quickly than reactants present at low concentrations. Therefore, an increase in the concentration of reactants increases the rate of a reaction. A decrease in the concentration of reactants decreases the rate of reaction. For example, a highly concentrated solution of sodium hydroxide (NaOH), or lye, will react more quickly to clear a clogged drain than will a less concentrated lye solution. Why would the rate of burning charcoal be increased by blowing air on the fire? ❷

Surface Area

When one of the reactants in a chemical reaction is a solid, the rate of reaction can be increased by breaking the solid into smaller pieces. This increases the surface area of the reactant. An increase in surface area increases the collisions between reacting molecules.

A given quantity of wood burns faster as sawdust than as logs. Sawdust has a much greater surface area exposed to air than do the logs. So oxygen molecules from the air can collide with more wood molecules per second. The reaction rate is increased. How does the collision theory account for the fact that fine crystals of table salt dissolve more quickly in water than do large crystals of rock salt? ❹

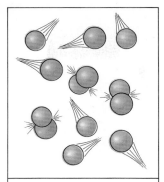
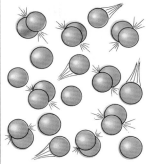

Figure 8–16 *Collisions of molecules increase when there are more molecules. The number of molecules per unit volume is called concentration. What is the relationship between concentration of reactants and reaction rate?* ❸

ANNOTATION KEY

❶ **Fewer collisions, so a slower reaction rate (Applying concepts)**

❷ **Adding more oxygen, so the concentration of reactant increases (Inferring)**

❸ **An increase in concentration of reactants increases reaction rate. A decrease in concentration decreases reaction rate. (Interpreting illustrations)**

❹ **Total surface area of fine crystals is larger and means more collisions, so rate increases. (Hypothesizing)**

❶ Thinking Skill: Applying definitions
❷ Thinking Skill: Inferring
❸ Thinking Skill: Making generalizations

197

day afternoon. You are trying to get close to the best bargain counter. What are your chances of bumping into another person? (very good chance, almost 100%)

Content Development
Review the idea that molecules are constantly in motion. Ask,
• **How is the motion of molecules related to chemical reactions?** (Molecules must collide in order to react; they could not collide if they were not moving.)
• **What condition must be met if colliding molecules are to react?** (They must collide with sufficient energy.)
• **What do you think would have to happen to the collisions in order for a chemical reaction to speed up?** (Collisions would have to happen more frequently or with greater energy.)
Explain that the four factors that affect reaction rate all affect molecular collisions, either by increasing the likelihood of collision or by increasing the energy of molecules.

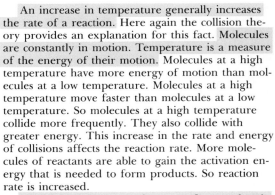

Figure 8–17 *As bellows are pumped, more oxygen is supplied to the fire and the rate of reaction increases (left). What factor affecting reaction rate is being changed here? An explosion at a grain elevator is an ever-present danger because a chemical reaction can occur almost instantaneously (right). What reaction-rate factor is responsible for such an explosion?* ❶

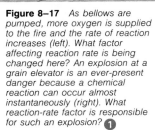

Sharpen Your Skills

Temperature and Reaction Rate

1. Fill one glass with cold water and another with hot water.

2. Drop a seltzer tablet into each glass of water and observe the reactions that occur.

Is there any noticeable difference in the two reactions? What effect, if any, does temperature have on this kind of reaction? Does this experiment prove that a difference in temperature always has the same effect?

Temperature

An increase in temperature generally increases the rate of a reaction. Here again the collision theory provides an explanation for this fact. Molecules are constantly in motion. Temperature is a measure of the energy of their motion. Molecules at a high temperature have more energy of motion than molecules at a low temperature. Molecules at a high temperature move faster than molecules at a low temperature. So molecules at a high temperature collide more frequently. They also collide with greater energy. This increase in the rate and energy of collisions affects the reaction rate. More molecules of reactants are able to gain the activation energy that is needed to form products. So reaction rate is increased.

At room temperature, the rates of many chemical reactions roughly double or triple with a rise in temperature of 10°C. How does this fact explain the use of refrigeration to keep foods from spoiling? ❷

Catalysts

Some chemical reactions take place very slowly. For such reactions, rates can be increased greatly by using a **catalyst** (KAT-uhl-ihst). A catalyst is a substance that increases the rate of a reaction but is not itself changed by the reaction.

How does a catalyst change the rate of a reaction if it is not itself changed by the reaction? The explanation again is based on the collision theory.

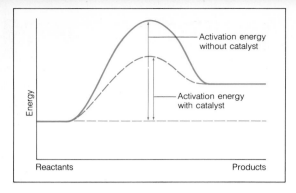

Figure 8–18 *A catalyst changes the rate of a chemical reaction without itself being changed by the reaction. According to this energy diagram, how does a catalyst affect the rate of reaction?* ❸

Reactions often involve a series of steps. A catalyst changes one or more of the steps. A catalyst produces a different, lower energy path for the reaction. In other words, it lowers the "energy hill," or ❶ activation energy. A decrease in the activation energy needed for the reaction allows more reactant molecules to form products. Collisions need not be so energetic. Therefore, more collisions are successful at producing products.

A catalyst is usually involved in one or more of the early steps in a reaction. However, the catalyst is re-formed during a later step. This explains why a catalyst is not changed by a reaction and why it does not appear as a product of a reaction it helped to speed up.

Catalysts are used in many chemical processes. They are also used in the catalytic converters that change the harmful gases produced by automobile engines into harmless ones. Some of the most important catalysts are found in your body. These bio- ❷ chemical catalysts are called enzymes. Each enzyme increases the rate of a specific reaction involved in the body's metabolism. If it were not for these enzymes, digestive processes that now take a few hours would require several weeks for completion!

SECTION REVIEW

1. What is reaction rate?
2. How is reaction rate related to collision theory?
3. Name four factors that affect reaction rate.
4. How does collision theory explain the effect of a decrease in temperature on the reaction rate?

BACKGROUND INFORMATION

The series of steps by which a chemical reaction progresses is called a reaction mechanism. A catalyst increases the speed of a reaction by changing the reaction mechanism to one that has a lower activation energy.

Sometimes it is desirable to slow down a chemical reaction. Substances added to a reaction for this purpose are called inhibitors. Like catalysts, inhibitors are not themselves changed in the reaction.

ANNOTATION KEY

❶ Concentration; surface area (Applying concepts)

❷ By decreasing temperature, decrease rate at which reactions that spoil food occur. (Relating cause and effect)

❸ Catalyst lowers the activation energy so that molecules of reactant can reach an activated complex sooner. (Interpreting diagrams)

❶ Thinking Skill: Relating cause and effect

❷ Thinking Skill: Applying technology

if these factors were not properly taken into account? (Probably the two most important factors in cooking are temperature and surface area. A recipe calls for a certain temperature to insure that the reactions do not take place too slowly or too quickly. A good example of food ruined by a too-slow cooking temperature is baking—the dough will not rise sufficiently. Surface area comes into play when a recipe calls for ingredients to be chopped, ground, or melted. An example of this is adding sugar to a recipe—if sugar cubes were added instead of granulated sugar, the finished product would probably have many lumps of unreacted sugar!

Section Review 8-5

1. How quickly products turn into reactants
2. According to the collision theory, molecules cannot react unless they collide with sufficient energy. The faster and stronger the collisions, the faster the reaction rate.
3. Temperature, catalyst, concentration, surface area
4. When temperature is decreased, molecular motion slows down. This, in turn, decreases the number of collisions and slows down the reaction rate.

LABORATORY INVESTIGATION DETERMINING REACTION RATES

BEFORE THE LAB

1. Gather all equipment at least one day prior to the investigation. Assume six students per group.
2. Prepare solutions A and B as follows. For solution A, dissolve 4.3 g potassium iodate (KIO_3) per liter of water. For every liter of solution B, make a paste of 4 g soluble starch in a small amount of water. Add paste slowly to 900 mL boiling water. Boil for several minutes and allow to cool. Just before use, add 0.2 g $Na_2S_2O_5$ and 5 mL of 1 molar H_2SO_4.

PRE-LAB DISCUSSION

Review with students the four factors that affect reaction rate. Ask,
- **Which of these factors is being tested in this lab?** (concentration)
- **What is the variable?** (the concentration of solution A)
- **Which factor is the control?** (concentration of solution B)
- **Can you offer a hypothesis about the outcome of this experiment?** (Answers may vary; the correct hypothesis is that the rate of the reaction will vary directly with the concentration of solution A.)

SKILL DEVELOPMENT

Students will use the following skills while completing this investigation.
1. Manipulative
2. Safety
3. Observing
4. Comparing
5. Hypothesizing
6. Measuring
7. Recording
8. Inferring

SAFETY TIPS

Emphasize that because solution B contains a strong acid, it must be handled carefully. Caution students to pour slowly to avoid splashing, and to wear their safety goggles throughout the investigation.

Problem

How does concentration affect reaction rate?

Materials (per group)

3 250-mL beakers
2 graduated cylinders
stopwatch or watch with a sweep
   second hand
stirring rod
distilled water at room temperature
120 mL Solution A
90 mL Solution B
safety goggles
sheet of white paper

Procedure

1. Carefully measure 60 mL of Solution A and pour it into a 250-mL beaker. Add 10 mL of distilled water and stir.
2. Carefully measure 30 mL of Solution B and pour it into a second beaker. Place the beaker of Solution B on a piece of white paper in order to see the color change more easily.
3. Add the 70 mL of Solution A water mixture to Solution B. Stir rapidly. Record the time it takes for the reaction to occur.
4. Rinse and dry the reaction beaker.
5. Repeat the procedure using the other amounts shown in the data table.

Observations

1. What visible indication is there that a chemical reaction is occurring?
2. What is the effect of adding more distilled water on the concentration of Solution A?
3. What happens to reaction time as more distilled water is added to Solution A?
4. Make a graph of your observations by plotting time along the X axis and volume of Solution A along the Y axis.

Conclusions

1. How does concentration affect reaction rate?
2. Does your graph support your answer to question 1? Explain why.
3. What would a graph look like if time were plotted along the X axis and volume of distilled water added to Solution A were plotted along the Y axis?
4. In this investigation, what is the variable? The constant?

Solution A (mL)	Distilled Water Added to Solution A (mL)	Solution B (mL)	Reaction Time (sec)
60	10	30	
40	30	30	
20	50	30	

OBSERVATIONS

1. Color change
2. Lessens concentration
3. Reaction time increases, so reaction rate decreases
4. Check students graphs. They should show a straight line going from the bottom left corner toward the top right corner.

CONCLUSIONS

1. Decreased concentration means decreased reaction rate, which would show up as increased reaction time.
2. Students' graphs should support their answer.
3. Graph would look the same.
4. Variable: concentration of A; constant: concentration of B

SUMMARY

8–1 Nature of Chemical Reactions

❏ When a chemical reaction takes place, there is always a change in the properties and in the energy of the substances.

❏ A reactant is a substance that enters into a chemical reaction. A product is a substance that is produced by a chemical reaction.

❏ An atom forms chemical bonds with other atoms in order to complete its outermost energy level. The arrangement of electrons in an atom determines the atom's bonding capacity, or its ability to undergo chemical reactions.

8–2 Chemical Equations

❏ A chemical equation is an expression in which symbols and formulas are used to represent a chemical reaction. Reactants are written to the left of the arrow in such an equation and products are written to the right.

❏ The law of conservation of mass states that matter can be neither created nor destroyed in a chemical reaction.

❏ Four basic rules should be followed in balancing equations: Write a word equation and a chemical equation, count the number of atoms of each element on each side of the arrow, use coefficients to balance the equation, check your work.

8–3 Types of Chemical Reactions

❏ In a synthesis reaction, two or more simple substances combine to form a new, more complex substance.

❏ In a decomposition reaction, a complex substance breaks down into two or more simpler substances.

❏ In a single-replacement reaction, an uncombined element replaces an element that is part of a compound.

❏ In a double-replacement reaction, different atoms in two different compounds replace each other.

8–4 Energy of Chemical Reactions

❏ When chemical reactions occur, energy can either be released or absorbed.

❏ A chemical reaction in which energy is released is called an exothermic reaction. A chemical reaction in which energy is absorbed is called an endothermic reaction.

❏ In order for reactants to form products, activation energy is needed.

8–5 Rates of Chemical Reactions

❏ The rate of a reaction is a measure of how quickly reactants turn into products.

❏ An increase in the concentration of reactants increases the rate of a reaction.

❏ An increase in the surface area of reactants increases the rate of a reaction.

❏ An increase in temperature generally increases the rate of a reaction.

❏ A catalyst is a substance that increases the rate of a reaction without itself being changed by the reaction.

VOCABULARY

Define each term in a complete sentence.

activation energy	concentration	endothermic reaction	reactant
catalyst	decomposition reaction	exothermic reaction	reaction rate
chemical equation		kinetics	single-replacement reaction
chemical reaction	double-replacement reaction	law of conservation of mass	
coefficient			synthesis reaction
collision theory		product	

201

GOING FURTHER: ENRICHMENT

Part 1

Students may find it interesting to vary the concentration of solution B rather than the concentration of solution A. Have students offer hypotheses before the investigation, then discuss the outcome.

Part 2

Have students design an experiment to test the effect of temperature on the reaction between solutions A and B. Note that it is often safer to test the effects of temperature by cooling rather than heating because some reactants can be hazardous to handle at high temperatures.

CHAPTER REVIEW

MULTIPLE CHOICE

1. d	3. a	5. b	7. c	9. c
2. d	4. d	6. b	8. c	10. c

COMPLETION

1. chemical change
2. properties/ energy
3. arrow
4. conservation of mass
5. synthesis
6. single replacement
7. exothermic
8. products
9. kinetics
10. catalyst

TRUE OR FALSE

1. F products
2. T
3. T
4. F 3
5. F decomposition
6. F synthesis
7. F less
8. T
9. F temperature
10. T

SKILL BUILDING

1. **a.** $2PbO_2 = 2PBO + O_2$
   b. $Ca + 2H_2O = Ca(OH)_2 + H_2$
   c. $Zn + S = ZnS$
   d. $BaCl_2 + Na_2SO_4 = BaSO_4 + 2NaCl$
   e. $Al + Fe_2O_3 = Al_2O_3 + 2Fe$
   f. $C_{12}H_{22}O_{11} = 12C + 11H_2O$
2. **a.** decomposition **b.** single replacement **c.** synthesis **d.** double replacement **e.** synthesis
3. Since the zinc is more reactive than iron, the zinc will react with oxygen to form zinc oxide. This then forms a coat over the iron, preventing the iron from combining with oxygen to form rust.
4. Check students diagrams carefully. They should note that both an increase in temperature or a catalyst will lower the height of the activation "energy hill."

ESSAY

1. The ease with which they form bonds with other elements, which is determined by their electron configuration.
2. Mass remains constant in a chemical reaction. That is, the mass of the products equals the mass of the reactants.
3. **a.** Increased concentration increases the rate of a reaction because there are more particles of reactants available for collisions. **b.** Increases reaction rate by lowering the activiation energy, thus allowing more reactant molecules to from products. Collisions need not be so energetic, therefore more collisions are successful informing products. **c.** Increases rate of reaction by increasing the number of collisions between reacting molecules.
4. The collisions may not be energetic enough or numerous enough.
5. **a.** Reactants have more heat content than products. **b.** Products have more heat content than reactants.

CONTENT REVIEW: MULTIPLE CHOICE

On a separate sheet of paper, write the letter of the answer that best completes each statement.

1. The substances to the left of the arrow in a chemical equation are called
   a. coefficients.   b. products.   c. subscripts.   d. reactants.
2. An atom's ability to undergo chemical reactions is determined by
   a. protons.   b. neutrons.   c. innermost electrons.   d. outermost electrons.
3. In a balanced chemical equation,
   a. atoms are conserved.   b. molecules are equal.
   c. coefficients are equal.   d. energy is not conserved.
4. Two or more simple substances combine to form a new substance in a
   a. decomposition reaction.   b. double-replacement reaction.
   c. single-replacement reaction.   d. synthesis reaction.
5. A reaction in which energy is absorbed is called
   a. exothermic.   b. endothermic.   c. analytic.   d. catalytic.
6. In an exothermic reaction, heat is
   a. absorbed.   b. released.   c. destroyed.   d. conserved.
7. The energy required for reactants to form products is called
   a. energy of motion.   b. potential energy.
   c. activation energy.   d. synthetic energy.
8. The rate of a chemical reaction can be increased by
   a. decreasing concentration.   b. decreasing temperature.
   c. increasing surface area.   d. all of the above.
9. Concentration is a measure of molecular
   a. energy.   b. speed.   c. number per unit of volume.   d. temperature.
10. Adding a catalyst to a reaction increases rate by
    a. increasing molecular motion.   b. decreasing molecular motion.
    c. lowering activation energy.   d. increasing concentration.

CONTENT REVIEW: COMPLETION

On a separate sheet of paper, write the word or words that best complete each statement.

1. In a _____ change, one kind of matter is turned into another.
2. A chemical reaction is accompanied by a change in the _____ and _____ of the substances.
3. A (An) _____ means "yields."
4. According to the law of _____, matter can be neither created nor destroyed during a chemical reaction.
5. Two or more simple substances combine to form a new, more complex substance in a (an) _____ reaction.
6. An uncombined element replaces an element that is part of a compound in a (an) _____ reaction.
7. A reaction in which energy is released is called a (an) _____ reaction.
8. In an endothermic reaction, the _____ have more energy.
9. The study of reaction rates is called _____.
10. A substance that increases the rate of a chemical reaction without itself being changed is called a (an) _____.

202

ADDITIONAL QUESTIONS AND TOPIC SUGGESTIONS

1. Explain why the container in which an exothermic reaction has taken place often feels cool. (An exothermic reaction liberates heat to the surroundings. Thus the container would feel cooler than when the reaction began.)
2. Create a model or analogy to illustrate the law of conservation of mass in

Determine whether each statement is true or false. Then on a separate sheet of paper, write "true" if it is true. If it is false, change the underlined word or words to make the statement true.

1. The substances formed as a result of a chemical reaction are called <u>reactants</u>.
2. A <u>chemical equation</u> uses symbols and formulas to represent a reaction.
3. A number written in front of a chemical symbol or formula is a (an) <u>coefficient</u>.
4. To balance the following equation, the number <u>2</u> should be placed in front of O_2: $KClO_3 \longrightarrow KCl + O_2$.
5. In a <u>synthesis</u> reaction, complex substances form simpler substances.
6. The formation of carbon dioxide during combustion of a fuel is an example of a <u>decomposition</u> reaction.
7. In an exothermic reaction, products have <u>more</u> energy than reactants.
8. The <u>collision theory</u> can be used to account for the factors that affect reaction rates.
9. <u>Concentration</u> is a measure of the energy of motion of molecules.
10. Increasing surface area <u>increases</u> reaction rate.

Use the skills you have developed in the chapter to complete each activity.

1. **Making calculations** Balance the following equations:

   a. $PbO_2 \longrightarrow PbO + O_2$
   b. $Ca + H_2O \longrightarrow Ca(OH)_2 + H_2$
   c. $Zn + S \longrightarrow ZnS$
   d. $BaCl_2 + Na_2SO_4 \longrightarrow BaSO_4 + NaCl$
   e. $Al + Fe_2O_3 \longrightarrow Al_2O_3 + Fe$
   f. $C_{12}H_{22}O_{11} \longrightarrow C + H_2O$

2. **Classifying reactions** Identify the general type of reaction represented by each equation. Explain your answers.

   a. $NiCl_2 \longrightarrow Ni + Cl_2$
   b. $MgBr_2 + 2K \longrightarrow Mg + 2KBr$

   c. $4C + 6H_2 + O_2 \longrightarrow 2C_2H_6O$
   d. $2LiI + Pb(NO_3)_2 \longrightarrow 2LiNO_3 + PbI_2$
   e. $2H_2O + O_2 \longrightarrow 2H_2O_2$

3. **Relating cause and effect** Iron is often galvanized, or covered with the more active metal zinc, in order to protect the iron from corroding. Explain why this method is effective.

4. **Developing a model** Draw an energy diagram of an exothermic reaction that has a high activation energy. On your diagram, indicate how an increase in temperature would affect the rate of this reaction. Do the same for the addition of a catalyst.

Discuss each of the following in a brief paragraph or solve completely, showing all steps.

1. Why do substances react chemically?
2. State the law of conservation of mass and explain its role in chemical reactions.
3. Use the collision theory to explain the effects on reaction rate of (a) increased concentration, (b) catalysts, and (c) increased surface area.
4. Give two reasons why collisions between molecules of reactants may *not* be effective in forming products.
5. Explain how the heat content of the products of a reaction compares with that of the reactants when the reaction is (a) exothermic or (b) endothermic.

203

ISSUES IN SCIENCE

The following issue can be used as a springboard for class debate, or it can be assigned as a homework assignment.

A tremendous amount of money was spent on the restoration of the Statue of Liberty. Much of this money was raised by a foundation comprised of private citizens who devoted a great deal of time and energy to the cause. Do you think that such a great expenditure of money and effort was worthwhile, or could it have been better spent on other things? Take a stand on this issue and present arguments to support your position.

chemical reactions. (Student answers will vary. Models should emphasize that in a chemical reaction, atoms are rearranged but never created or destroyed. A possible analogy is a collection of oranges and apples; they can be arranged in many different ways, but the number of each remains the same.)
3. Based on what you know of reaction rates, what factors might contribute to an explosive reaction? (Anything that makes the reaction happen very rapidly.

Surface area and temperature are probably the most likely causes. Also, a combination of two or more factors, such as increased temperature and increased concentration of reactants, could cause an explosive reaction.)
4. Make a diagram similar to that shown in Figure 8-5 to show the reaction between hydrogen and oxygen to form water. (Check student diagrams.)

Chapter 9
SOLUTION CHEMISTRY

CHAPTER OVERVIEW

The nature of solutions as homogeneous mixtures in which solute and solvent molecules are uniformly distributed is discussed. Solution conductivity is explained on the basis of dissociation or ionization, and the solution process is described. Next, solution types and factors affecting the rate of solution are treated. Students are then introduced to the concepts of solubility, concentration, and saturation.

Water's properties as a solvent are discussed on the basis of polarity, and freezing point depression and boiling point elevation are introduced. Then, the topic of suspensions and colloids is taken up. Finally, the nature, properties, and reactions of acids, bases, and salts are described.

TEACHER DEMONSTRATION

You may wish to perform the following demonstration in order to motivate students and to introduce them to this chapter. The demonstration illustrates the nature of solutions, the dissolving process, and differences between solvents. Set up three beakers—one containing water, one containing ethyl alcohol, and one containing toluene, an essentially nonpolar solvent. Work in a fume hood or be sure that the room is well ventilated. Drop a crystal of solid iodine into each of the three beakers, taking care not to touch the iodine with your fingers, and stir the

INTRODUCING CHAPTER 9

Begin your introduction of Chapter 9 by having students examine the photograph on page 204. Draw their attention to the various features visible in the cave scene. Ask them whether any of them have ever visited or explored a cave, and ask the students that have done so to describe what they saw.

Have students read the chapter introduction, which describes some of the processes that occurred to produce the features shown. Ask,

• **Which of the structures are stalactites?** (The elongated, iciclelike structures hanging downward from the cave ceiling are stalactites.)

• **Which of the structures are stalagmites?** (The elongated structures rising upward from the cave floor are stalagmites.)

Have students briefly describe the way in which they think such structures formed, and ask them to describe the evidence that water dripped or flowed for long periods of time within the cave. You can also ask students to do library research to determine the locations and special features of caves in your region of the country. The students can also be encouraged to do library research on the details of the physical and chemical processes

Solution Chemistry

CHAPTER OBJECTIVES

After completing this chapter, you will be able to

9–1 Define a solution and describe its properties.

9–2 Identify the factors that affect rate of solution.

9–2 Describe how temperature and pressure affect solubility.

9–2 Classify solutions.

9–3 Relate the polarity of water to its use as a solvent.

9–4 Compare suspensions and colloids.

9–5 Describe the properties of acids.

9–6 Describe the properties of bases.

9–7 Relate pH number to acid–base strength.

9–7 Describe the chemical formation of salts.

Deep within the earth, many kilometers beneath its surface, one can observe the passage of time. Tens of thousands of years are visible in the breathtaking cave formations hidden beyond the reach of all but the hardiest and most dedicated explorers. Twisting up from cave floors, flowing down from cave ceilings, and jutting out from cave walls, these chemical formations range from monumental columns to tiny crystals to wispy strands thinner than a human hair.

Such complicated cave structures take thousands of years to form. In tune with nature's rules and rhythms, water, minerals, rock, and soil interact to form the most amazing sculptures. The structure that forms depends on the amount of water in the cave and the type of minerals dissolved in it. In one of the most common processes, mineral-laden water steadily drips or flows over rock that forms the cave boundaries. Carbon dioxide dissolved in the water begins to escape. The drops, heavy with excess minerals, deposit their load onto the cave surfaces.

The familiar structures known as stalactites and stalagmites represent the buildup of billions of drops of mineral-laden water over thousands of years. Even more unusual formations can be found in the hidden passages that twist and turn within the cave. Where streams no longer flow, where water trickles through cave walls, where the bones of bats are buried, nature produces some of the rarest "art" on the earth.

But nature does not work alone. In processes familiar to any scientist, minerals continually dissolve in and escape from water. In this chapter you will learn about this process and some of its more easily observed results.

Nature's solution process has produced the stalactites, stalagmites, and other unique structures found deep within the earth.

205

liquid in each. The iodine will show only slight solubility in water, will dissolve readily in and interact with the alcohol to produce a red-brown solution, and will dissolve readily in the toluene to produce a violet solution.

TEACHER RESOURCES

Audiovisuals

Acid and Basic Solutions, filmstrip, CRM/McGraw-Hill

Acids, Bases, and Salts, 16mm film, Cor

Properties of Acids, Bases, and Salts, filmstrip, Cor

What's an Acid?, filmstrip with cassette, Silver-Burdett

Books

Bradford, Derek, *Acidity and Alkalinity,* Heinemann

Jensen, William B., *The Lewis Acid-Base Concepts: An Overview,* Wiley

Pearson, R. G. (ed.), *Hard and Soft Acids and Bases,* Academic Press

Software

Acids and Bases, Prentice-Hall

Solutions, Prentice-Hall

that occur in caves, and the amount of time required for such processes to occur to an appreciable extent.

9-1 NATURE OF SOLUTIONS

SECTION PREVIEW 9-1

In this section, students are introduced to the defining characteristics of solutions, which are homogeneous mixtures in which molecules are uniformly distributed. The solute and the solvent, the two components of a solution, are defined and distinguished, and aqueous solutions and tinctures are contrasted, as are electrolytes and nonelectrolytes. The processes of dissociation and ionization, which account for electrical conductivity, are also discussed, and, finally, an overall model of the solution process is set forth.

PERFORMANCE OBJECTIVES 9-1

1. **Define solution.**
2. **State and define the two parts that make up solutions.**
3. **Describe the conductivity of solutions.**
4. **Compare dissociation and ionization, and electrolytes and nonelectrolytes.**
5. **Describe the steps involved in the solution process.**

SCIENCE TERMS 9-1

solution p. 206	dissociation p. 208
solute p. 207	
solvent p. 207	electrolyte p. 208
aqueous solution p. 207	nonelectrolyte p. 209
tincture p. 207	ionization p. 209

Figure 9–1 *A variety of solutions is shown here. What substances make up the ice cream soda solution (top)? The brass instruments (bottom, left)? The air (bottom, right)?* ❶

9–1 Nature of Solutions

What happens when a lump of sugar is dropped into a glass of lemonade? What takes place when carbon dioxide gas is bubbled through water? And where do mothballs go when they disappear? The answer to these questions is the same: The sugar, gaseous carbon dioxide, and mothballs all dissolve in the substances in which they are mixed.

Careful examination of each of these mixtures—even under a microscope—will not reveal molecules of sugar in lemonade, carbon dioxide in water, or naphthalene in the air. But the sweet taste of lemonade tells you the sugar is there. The "fizziness" of soda water indicates the presence of carbon dioxide. And the smell of mothballs reveals the presence of naphthalene. In each of these mixtures, the molecules of one substance have become evenly distributed among the molecules of the other substance. The mixtures are homogeneous throughout. Each mixture is a **solution.**

❶ A solution is a homogeneous mixture in which one substance is dissolved in another substance. Different parts of a solution are identical. The molecules making up a solution are too small to be seen and do not settle when the solution is allowed to stand. A solution, then, is a "well-mixed" mixture.

TEACHING STRATEGY 9-1

Motivation

Ask students to state familiar examples of mixtures they believe to be solutions. You can comment on whether each is actually a solution, rather than a heterogeneous or non-solution homogeneous mixture, and ask students to describe the distinguishing physical properties of the mixtures named. If you wish, you can ask students to do library research on the nature and compositions of these mixtures.

Content Development

Contrast solutions and other kinds of mixtures, taking care to make it clear that only solutions are truly mixtures "on the molecular level"—mixtures in which molecules of the dissolved substance are not clumped together, but are surrounded by and interspersed with molecules of the substance in which they are dissolved. Also make clear the distinction between solute and solvent. Provide examples of solutions and, in each case, ask students the following.

• **Which substance is the solute and which is the solvent?** (Answers will vary, depending on the particular examples chosen.)

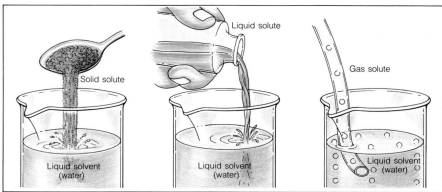

Solid solute · Liquid solute · Gas solute · Liquid solvent (water)

Figure 9–2 *A solution consists of a solute and a solvent. The most common solutions are those in which the solvent is a liquid. Here you see the three types of solutions that can be formed from a liquid solvent and a solid, a liquid, and a gas solute. What is the most common liquid solvent?* ②

Properties of Solutions

Let's go back to the glass of sweetened lemonade to discover several important properties of a solution. **A solution consists of two parts: One part is the substance being dissolved, and the other part is the substance doing the dissolving.**

In a solution, the substance that is dissolved is called the **solute** (SAHL-yoot). The substance that does the dissolving is called the **solvent** (SAHL-vuhnt). The solvent is often called the dissolving medium. In the sweetened lemonade, the solute is ② the sugar and the solvent is the lemonade. Even without the sugar, the lemonade is a solution. It is made of water and lemon juice.

The most common solutions are those in which the solvent is a liquid. The solute can be a solid, liquid, or gas. The most common solvent is water. Solutions in which the solvent is water are called **aqueous** (A-kwee-uhs) **solutions.**

When alcohol is the solvent in a solution, the solution is called a **tincture** (TIHNK-chuhr). Perhaps you are familiar with tincture of iodine, an antiseptic used to treat minor cuts and scratches. What is the solute in this solution? ③

The particles in a solution are individual atoms, ③ ions, or molecules. Because the particles are so small, they do not scatter light that passes through the solution. A liquid solution appears clear.

Most solutions cannot easily be separated by simple physical means such as filtering. However, a physical change such as evaporation or boiling can

207

BACKGROUND INFORMATION

The atoms that make up ionic substances—substances that dissociate rather than ionize in water—differ significantly (by about 1.7 or more) in their electronegativity, or ability to attract electrons. The atoms in substances that ionize, or that, in water, form true ions not originally present, differ to a lesser extent in their electronegativity, and form ions only as a result of their interaction with and attraction by water molecules.

Figure 9–3 *The particles in a solution are too small to scatter light, so a solution appears clear (top). The particles are also too small to be separated by filtering. But if the solvent evaporates, deposits of solute are left behind (bottom).*

Figure 9–4 *A solution of sugar water is a nonelectrolyte (left). A solution of potassium chloride is an electrolyte (right). What type of a compound is sugar? Potassium chloride?* ❶

208

separate the parts of many solutions. If salt water is boiled, the water will change from a liquid to a gas, leaving behind particles of salt.

Another property of a solution is that solute molecules are evenly spread among solvent molecules. All parts of a solution are uniform, or identical.

Conductivity of Solutions

An important property of a solution is whether or not it can conduct an electric current. An electric current is a flow of electrons. In order for electrons to flow through a solution, ions must be present. Ions are charged atoms. A solution that contains ions is a good conductor of electricity. A solution that does not contain ions is a nonconductor.

Pure water is a poor conductor of electric current because it does not contain ions. However, if a solute such as potassium chloride (KCl) is added to the water, the resulting aqueous solution is a good ❶conductor. The ions making up potassium chloride separate from the compound during the solution process. The separation of ions from a compound during solution is called **dissociation.** The potassium chloride dissociates in water. Potassium ions (K^+) and chloride ions (Cl^-) are free to move through the solution and conduct an electric current. Ionic compounds dissociate in solution, so they form solutions that are good conductors of electricity.

Substances that form aqueous solutions that conduct an electric current are called **electrolytes** (ih-LEHK-truh-lights). Sodium chloride and silver nitrate are examples of electrolytes. Most electrolytes are ionic compounds.

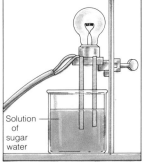
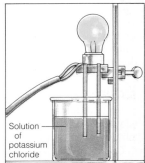

Solution of sugar water

Solution of potassium chloride

9-1 (continued)

Content Development
Make clear the distinction between electrolytes and nonelectrolytes, and between dissociation and ionization processes. Then, describe the various steps involved in the solution process. Make use of the chalkboard to illustrate them, taking time first to review briefly the difference between endo-

thermic and exothermic changes. Draw students' attention to Figure 9-5, which illustrates steps of the dissolving process.

Reinforcement
Ask slower students to construct a simple, small model of a crystal, using small Styrofoam balls and toothpicks. They can then illustrate the steps of the dissolving process, first placing the crystal model into a container and

then surrounding it with Styrofoam balls of another color that have a toothpick extending out of each of them. They can then use several of the latter balls, which represent polar molecules, to spear and pull away each of the Styrofoam balls that represent the solute. They can be encouraged to demonstrate this "solution" process in class and to explain the steps involved.

Substances whose aqueous solutions do not conduct an electric current are called **nonelectrolytes**. A solution of sugar and water does not conduct an electric current. Sugar is a nonelectrolyte, as are alcohol and benzene.

Many covalent compounds are nonelectrolytes because they do not form ions in solution. However, there are some covalent compounds that will react with certain solvents to form ions. The formation of ions from solute molecules by the action of a solvent is called **ionization** (igh-uhn-ih-ZAY-shuhn). Hydrogen chloride is a covalent compound that ionizes in water. Pure hydrogen chloride liquid is a nonelectrolyte. However, an aqueous solution of hydrogen chloride is an electrolyte. The effect of water on the hydrogen chloride molecule causes it to ionize.

A Model of the Solution Process

Although the exact way in which solutes dissolve is not completely understood, scientists have developed a model to describe a probable solution process. This model assumes that three different steps take place in the dissolving of a solid in a liquid.

In the first step, solute particles are separated from the surface of the solid solute. The attraction between solute and solvent molecules is responsible for this dissolving step. This step takes up energy. It is endothermic.

In the second step, solvent molecules are moved apart to allow solute molecules to enter the liquid surrounding the solid solute. This step, too, requires energy. It is endothermic.

In the third step, solute molecules are attracted to solvent molecules. This step gives up energy. It is exothermic. These three steps occur continuously as each surface layer of solute molecules is dissolved, leaving the next layer exposed to the solvent. Finally, all the solute molecules are distributed evenly throughout the solvent.

SECTION REVIEW

1. What is a solution? What are its two parts?
2. What is an aqueous solution? A tincture?
3. Describe three properties of a solution.
4. Compare and contrast dissociation and ionization.

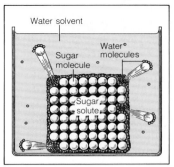

Figure 9–5 *The solution process first involves the separation of solute particles from the surface of the solid solute. Then the solute molecules enter the solution. Finally, the solute molecules are attracted to the solvent molecules.*

209

9-2 MAKING SOLUTIONS

SECTION PREVIEW 9-2

Students are introduced to the nine different solution types by phase. Factors affecting the rate of solution are then discussed. Solubility is defined and the factors affecting it are described. Concentration of solutions is taken up next, and dilute and concentrated solutions are contrasted, as are saturated, unsaturated, and supersaturated solutions.

PERFORMANCE OBJECTIVES 9-2

1. **List the nine types of solutions by phase.**
2. **State and account for factors that increase the rate of dissolving.**
3. **Define solubility and state the factors that affect it.**
4. **Define concentration and contrast concentrated and dilute solutions.**
5. **Contrast saturated, unsaturated, and supersaturated solutions.**

SCIENCE TERMS 9-2

miscible p. 210
soluble p. 211
solubility p. 211
effervescence p. 212
concentrated solution p. 212
dilute solution p. 212
concentration p. 213
saturated solution p. 213
unsaturated solution p. 214
supersaturated solution p. 214

Section Objective

To define solution properties of solubility and concentration

9–2 Making Solutions

Solutions abound in nature. The oceans, the atmosphere, even the earth's interior are solutions. Each solution has a different solute and solvent.

Types of Solutions

Matter can exist as a solid, liquid, or gas. From these three phases of matter, nine different types of solutions can be made. Figure 9–6 shows these types of solutions. ❶

The most common solutions are liquid solutions. In a liquid solution, the solvent is a liquid. The solute can be a solid, liquid, or gas. Two liquids that dissolve in each other are said to be **miscible** (MIHS-uh-buhl). Water and alcohol are miscible. Do you think oil and water are miscible? ❶

Solutions of solids dissolved in solids are called alloys. Most alloys are made of metals. Refer to Figure 6–2 on page 133 for a review of alloys.

Rate of Solution

Suppose you wanted to dissolve some sugar in a glass of water—and you wanted to do it as quickly as possible. What might you do? If your answer included stirring the solution, using granulated sugar, or heating the water, you are on the right track. ❷

Figure 9–6 *Nine different types of solutions can be made from the three phases of matter. What are solutions of solids dissolved in solids called?* ❷

TYPES OF SOLUTIONS

Solute	Solvent	Example
Gas	Gas	Air (oxygen in nitrogen)
Gas	Liquid	Soda water (carbon dioxide in water)
Gas	Solid	Charcoal gas mask (poisonous gases on carbon)
Liquid	Gas	Humid air (water in air)
Liquid	Liquid	Antifreeze (ethylene glycol in water)
Liquid	Solid	Dental filling (mercury in silver)
Solid	Gas	Soot in air (carbon in air)
Solid	Liquid	Ocean water (salt in water)
Solid	Solid	Gold jewelry (copper in gold)

TEACHING STRATEGY 9-2

Motivation

Have students carry out a simple experiment to determine the effects of various factors on the rate of solution. They should measure the time it takes for identical small sugar cubes to dissolve completely in beakers containing equal amounts of water. The sugar cube in the first beaker, which should contain cold water and which should not be stirred, will dissolve only very slowly; in fact, some sugar will remain undissolved even after several hours. The second beaker should contain water that is also cold but that is to be stirred continuously after the cube is put in. The third beaker should contain cold water that is not to be stirred; the sugar cube placed into it should first be pulverized into fine powder in a mortar and pestle. The fourth beaker, into which a whole sugar cube is to be placed, should first be heated on a hot plate to near the boiling point. Caution students about safe handling of the heat source and the hot materials.

- **What effects did the various factors have on the rate of solution?** (Stirring the water, powdering the sugar, and heating the water all increased the rate of dissolving.)

STIRRING THE SOLUTION Normally, the movement of solute molecules away from the solid solute and throughout the solvent occurs rather slowly. Stirring or shaking the solution helps move solute particles away from the solid solute faster. This brings more molecules of the solute in contact with the solvent sooner. So the solute dissolves at a faster rate.

POWDERING THE SOLID SOLUTE Solution action occurs only at the surface of the solid solute. So if the surface area of the solute is increased, the rate of solution is increased. More solute molecules are in contact with the solvent when the solid solute is ground into a fine powder. Finely powdered solids dissolve much faster than large lumps or crystals of the same substance.

HEATING THE SOLUTION If heat is applied to a solution, the molecules move faster and farther apart. As a result, the dissolving action is speeded up.

Solubility

The solubility (sahl-yoo-BIHL-uh-tee) **of a solute is a measure of how much of that solute can be dissolved in a given amount of solvent under certain conditions.** You know that table salt and sugar dissolve readily in water. These compounds are described as being very **soluble.** They have a high degree of **solubility** in water. However, only a small ❸ amount of table salt dissolves in alcohol. So the solubility of salt in alcohol is rather low. As you can see from this example, the solubility of a solute depends on the nature of the solute and the solvent.

Solubility is usually described in terms of the mass of the solute that can be dissolved in a definite amount of solvent at a specific temperature. For example, a maximum of 36 grams of table salt, or NaCl, can be dissolved in 100 grams of water at 20°C. So the solubility of NaCl at 20°C is 36 grams per 100 grams of water.

The two main factors that affect the solubility of a solute are temperature and pressure. Generally, an increase in the temperature of a solution increases the solubility of a *solid in a liquid*. The solubility of most solids is increased by raising the temperature of the solution.

Figure 9–7 *This graph shows the solubility curves of several different solutes. Which solute shows the least change in solubility with an increase in temperature?* ❸

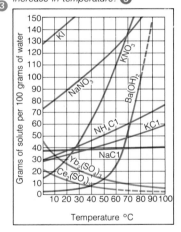

211

Solubility of a Gas in a Liquid
Skills: Manipulative, observing, comparing, relating, hypothesizing, concluding
Level: Average
Type: Hands-on
Materials: club soda in bottle, balloon, hot plate or Bunsen burner

In this activity, students investigate the properties of a gas in a liquid. Students should find that the balloon inflates when the liquid is heated. The two conditions being tested are pressure and temperature. Students should conclude that the solubility of a gas in a liquid decreases with a decrease in pressure and decreases with an increase in temperature.

ANNOTATION KEY

❶ No. (Applying definitions)
❷ Alloys (Interpreting charts)
❸ NaCl (Interpreting graphs)
❶ Thinking Skill: Classifying
❷ Thinking Skill: Hypothesizing
❸ Thinking Skill: Applying concepts

Content Development

Briefly review the phases of matter and demonstrate that there are nine solute-solvent combinations by phase. Direct students' attention to Figure 9-6, which illustrates these nine types of solutions, and ask them to name other examples of the various types.

Explain the factors affecting the rate of dissolving, pointing out the connection between temperatures and average molecular velocity.

Direct students' attention to the solubility curves shown in Figure 9-7. Be sure you make clear to students how the graph is to be interpreted and used. Ask,
• **What do you notice about most of the substances shown?** (Their solubilities increase as temperature increases.)

Content Development

Metal alloys have a great many prac-
tical uses. Many of the useful metallic materials with which students are familiar are actually alloys. For example, steel is an alloy of iron, carbon, and small amounts of other elements. Bronze is a copper–tin alloy. Brass is a copper–zinc alloy. Silver used in jewelry is a silver–copper alloy, and yellow gold used in jewelry is a gold-copper alloy. The karat numbers used in characterizing the latter actually represent the relative amounts of gold and copper present, based on the number 24: 24-karat gold, for example, is 100% gold (it contains 24 parts of gold to 0 parts of copper), 18-karat gold is 75% gold (it contains 18 parts gold to 6 parts copper; 18/24 = 0.75), and 12-karat gold is 50% gold (it contains 12 parts gold to 12 parts copper; 12/24 = 0.50).

TIE-IN/LIFE SCIENCE

The inverse dependence of gas solubility on the temperature of the liquid solvent accounts in part for the fact that tropical waters, which are at relatively high temperatures, do not support large numbers of certain types of organisms that do not thrive under conditions in which dissolved oxygen is low in concentration.

Figure 9–8 *The solubility of a gas solute in a liquid solvent depends on both the pressure and the temperature. When the cap is removed from the bottle, the solubility of the gas decreases. If the bottle is cold, the decrease in solubility is very small. If the bottle is warm, the decrease is obvious.*

Figure 9–9 *The rapid escape of gas from a liquid solution is called effervescence. What factors increase effervescence?* ❷

212

Raising the temperature of a gas-in-liquid solution decreases the solubility of the gaseous solute. Thus, the solubility of a gas decreases as the temperature of the solution increases. This is true for all gases. Perhaps you have observed this fact without actually realizing it. Have you ever let a glass of soda get warm? If so, what did you notice? The soda goes flat, or loses its fizz. Soda is given its fizz by dissolving carbon dioxide gas in soda water. As the temperature of the solution increases, the solubility of the carbon dioxide gas decreases. The gas comes out of solution, leaving the soda flat. Why do you think boiled water tastes flat? ❶

For solid and liquid solutes, increases and decreases in pressure have practically no effect on solubility. For gases dissolved in liquids, an increase in pressure increases solubility and a decrease in pressure decreases solubility. A bottle of soda fizzes when the cap is removed because molecules of carbon dioxide gas escape from solution as the pressure is decreased. The solubility of the carbon dioxide gas has been decreased by a decrease in pressure. The escape of a gas from a liquid solution is called **effervescence** (ehf-er-VEHS-uhns).

Concentration of Solutions

The concentration of a solution refers to the amount of solute dissolved in a certain amount of solvent. A solution in which a lot of solute is dissolved in a solvent is called a **concentrated solution.** A solution in which there is little solute dissolved in a solvent is called a **dilute solution.** The terms

---

9-2 (continued)

Content Development

The dependence of gas solubility on pressure is described by Henry's Law, which states that the mass of a gas dissolved in a given volume of liquid is directly proportional to the pressure of the gas. Gases that react chemically with solvents (such as ammonia in water) do not obey Henry's Law.

Skills Development
Skill: Making graphs
Permit advanced students to determine experimentally a solubility curve for one or more salts not shown in Figure 9-7. Possibilities include LiCl, NaBr, KBr, and NaI. Have the students work under your supervision and caution them about heat sources and the handling of hot solutions. They can display their graphs in the classroom and can also explain to the

class their application of scientific method to the problem they investigated.

Content Development

Describe the effect of increased temperature on gas-in-liquid solubility by pointing out that the extra energy provided by raised temperature is used by the solute molecules to overcome attractions and escape into the gas phase.

concentrated and dilute are not very precise, however. They do not indicate exactly how much solute and solvent are present.

Using the concept of solubility, the **concentration** of a solution can be expressed in another way. A solution can be described as saturated, unsaturated, or supersaturated. In order to understand these descriptions, remember that solubility measures the *maximum* amount of solute that can be dissolved in a given amount of solvent.

SATURATED SOLUTION A **saturated solution** is a solution that contains all the solute it can possibly hold at a given temperature. In a saturated solution, no more solute can be dissolved at that temperature. If more solute is added to a saturated solution, it will settle undissolved to the bottom of the solution.

In describing a saturated solution, the temperature must always be given. This is because a saturated solution at one temperature will contain a different amount of solute than will a saturated

❸ **Figure 9–10** *Many fruit juices are solutions in which a solute of fruit concentrate is dissolved in the solvent water. The concentration of such solutions is often expressed as a percent.*

CAREER   *Chemical Technician*

HELP WANTED: CHEMICAL TECHNICIAN to do laboratory work for pharmaceutical company. Background in chemistry and some technical training in laboratory work preferred. High school diploma required.

The bicycle riders jostle for good positions as they pedal toward the last sharp turn of the race. As the pack leans into the curve, a bicycle flies out from under a rider. The fallen rider scrambles out of the way.

At the first aid station it takes only minutes to apply adhesive bandages on the scrapes. But these adhesive bandages took a **chemical technician** months to test in the laboratory.

When a chemist is developing a new product such as an adhesive, a chemical technician helps test experimental formulas for that product. The chemical technician carefully follows a chemist's instructions for setting up laboratory equipment, mixing chemicals, and measuring reactions in experiments.

A chemical technician often uses computers and other instruments to collect data. Chemical technicians work in many fields, including food processing, pharmaceuticals, materials and metals industries, and electronics.

A chemical technician should have a strong interest in science and math, be able to follow instructions, and pay close attention to details. If you would like to learn more about becoming a chemical technician, write to the American Chemical Society, 1155 16th Street NW, Washington, DC 20036.

Take care to make clear the nature of concentration and the distinction between dilute and concentrated solutions. You may wish to demonstrate the preparation of such solutions.

Reinforcement
Be sure that slower students are familiar with the simple grams solute/100 grams solvent method of expressing concentration. Carry out, for their benefit, a few calculations that apply this concept. Then ask them to solve a few simple problems on their own.

Enrichment
Solution concentrations can be expressed in a number of different ways, including molarity (the number of moles of solute per liter of solution) and molality (the number of moles of solute per kilogram of solvent).

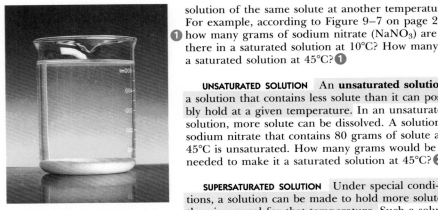

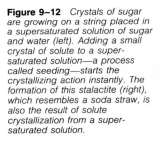

Figure 9–11 *A saturated solution contains all the solute it can possibly hold at a given temperature. Any additional solute will not dissolve but will fall to the bottom of the solution. What could be done to this solution to make the undissolved solute dissolve?* ❸

solution of the same solute at another temperature. For example, according to Figure 9–7 on page 211, ❶ how many grams of sodium nitrate ($NaNO_3$) are there in a saturated solution at 10°C? How many in a saturated solution at 45°C? ❶

UNSATURATED SOLUTION An **unsaturated solution** is a solution that contains less solute than it can possibly hold at a given temperature. In an unsaturated solution, more solute can be dissolved. A solution of sodium nitrate that contains 80 grams of solute at 45°C is unsaturated. How many grams would be needed to make it a saturated solution at 45°C? ❷

SUPERSATURATED SOLUTION Under special conditions, a solution can be made to hold more solute than is normal for that temperature. Such a solution is called a **supersaturated solution.** A supersaturated solution is unstable. If a single crystal of solute is added to a supersaturated solution, the excess solute comes out of solution and settles to the bottom. Only enough solute to make the solution saturated remains dissolved.

A supersaturated solution is prepared by allowing a saturated solution at high temperature to cool ❷ gradually and without disturbance. Although the solubility decreases with a decrease in temperature, the excess solute remains in solution. Relatively few solutes will form supersaturated solutions.

Figure 9–12 *Crystals of sugar are growing on a string placed in a supersaturated solution of sugar and water (left). Adding a small crystal of solute to a supersaturated solution—a process called seeding—starts the crystallizing action instantly. The formation of this stalactite (right), which resembles a soda straw, is also the result of solute crystallization from a supersaturated solution.*

214

9-2 (continued)

Skills Development

Skills: Making observations, making inferences, relating cause and effect
Shortly before class, prepare a saturated water solution of sodium acetate (CH_3COONa), using hot water as the solvent. Decant the saturated solution so that no undissolved crystals remain in it. Allow the solution to cool slowly.

Then add a single crystal of sodium acetate to the now-supersaturated solution. Ask,
• **What do you observe?** (Rapid precipitation occurs.)
• **How do you account for this?** (The solution must have been supersaturated.)

SECTION REVIEW 9-2
1. Stirring; powdering the solid solute; heating the solution

2. A measure of how much solute can be dissolved in a given amount of solvent under certain conditions; temperature and pressure
3. Saturated: contains all the solute it can possibly hold at a given temperature; unsaturated: contains less solute than it can possibly hold at a given temperature; supersaturated: contains more solute than is normal for that temperature
4. 85 g; about 55 g

1. What are three ways of increasing the rate of solution of a solid in a liquid?
2. What is solubility? What two factors affect the solubility of a solute?
3. Compare a saturated, unsaturated, and supersaturated solution.
4. How many grams of KNO_3 are needed to make a saturated solution at 50°C? How many grams of KNO_3 will come out of solution if the temperature drops to 20°C?

9–3 Water—The Universal Solvent

Water is the most common substance on the earth. About 70 percent of the earth's surface is covered by water, and about 65 percent of your body mass is water. Water plays an important role in dissolving a great variety of substances.

Because thousands of substances are soluble in water, water is sometimes called the universal solvent. You should remember, however, that there are certain substances that will not dissolve in water. These substances are described as **insoluble.** For example, oil and grease are insoluble in water. In order to understand why water is close to being a universal solvent, you need to know about the nature of a water molecule.

Section Objective

To relate the polarity of a water molecule to its use as a solvent

Figure 9–13 *This enormous sinkhole in Winter Park, Florida (left), was caused by the collapse of an underground cavern. The cavern originally formed by the dissolving action of water on limestone rock. The polarity of water molecules (right) explains why water is able to dissolve thousands of substances, including polar and ionic solutes. Which end of a water molecule is negative? Positive?* ❹

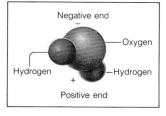

Negative end
−
Oxygen
Hydrogen
Hydrogen
+
Positive end

9-3 WATER—THE UNIVERSAL SOLVENT

SECTION PREVIEW 9-3

The polar nature of water molecules is presented as a basis for understanding water's excellent ability to act as a solvent for polar substances. The quality of water is also discussed, and hard water and soft water are contrasted. Finally, freezing point depression and boiling point elevation are discussed.

PERFORMANCE OBJECTIVES 9-3

1. State why water is often called the universal solvent.
2. Define polarity and explain the ability of water to dissolve polar substances.
3. Contrast hard and soft water.
4. Define freezing point depression and boiling point elevation and describe their applications.

SCIENCE TERMS 9-3

insoluble p. 215
polarity p. 216
polar molecule p. 216
hard water p. 217
soft water p. 217
freezing point depression p. 218
boiling point elevation p. 219

TEACHING STRATEGY 9-3

Motivation

Direct students' attention to Figure 9-13. The photograph shows a sinkhole caused by the collapse of a cavern formed by the dissolving limestone by water. Use the photograph to point out the great ability of water to act as a solvent. Ask students to offer other examples of both undesirable and de-sirable effects of the dissolving action of water.

Content Development

Review the nature of solutions as homogeneous mixtures on the molecular level. Point out that one of the most important properties of water is its ability to act as a solvent. When discussing the concept of insolubility, you should explain that, strictly speaking, there is no such thing as a truly insoluble substance. Even glass, plastics, and steel are to a measurable degree soluble in water. However, the solubilities of such substances are so very low that the substances can be considered to be insoluble for most practical purposes.

Structure of a Water Molecule

   A water molecule is the smallest particle of water that has all the properties of water. It is formed when two hydrogen atoms bond covalently with one atom of oxygen. You may remember that a covalent bond is one in which electrons are shared.

   The sharing of electrons in a water molecule is not equal, however. The oxygen atom attracts the shared electrons more strongly than the hydrogen atoms do. So the shared electrons are slightly closer to the oxygen atom than to the hydrogen atoms. The result of this unequal sharing is that the oxygen end of the water molecule has a slight negative charge and the hydrogen end has a slight positive charge. The water molecule has oppositely charged ends. These charged ends give the water molecule the property of **polarity** (poh-LAR-uh-tee).

Polar and Nonpolar Molecules

   Water is a **polar molecule.** One end of a polar molecule has a negative charge and the other end has a positive charge. **The charged ends of a polar solvent molecule such as water can separate the charged ends of a polar solute molecule.** This happens when the positive end of the solvent molecule

Figure 9–14 *Water can dissolve both polar solutes (top) and ionic solutes (bottom). What is the name given to each solution process?*

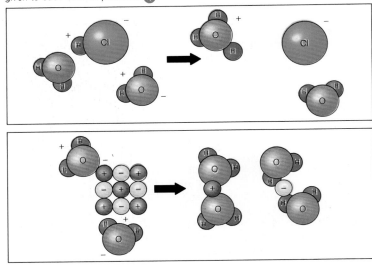

9-3 (continued)

Content Development
The rule that polar solvents tend to dissolve polar solutes and that nonpolar solvents tend to dissolve nonpolar solutes is often expressed in the form: Like dissolves like.

Motivation
Soaps and soaplike cleaning solutions used in many everyday household and industrial situations make use of the fact that the grease and dirt they remove contain nonpolar molecules and that water, the solvent that is to dissolve them, is polar. The molecules in such cleaning agents tend to be long, with a nonpolar end that dissolves grease and an ionic end that dissolves in water. The molecules in the cleaning agents thus serve to connect the grease and the water and allow the water to wash the grease away.

Content Development
First review the electron arrangement in hydrogen and oxygen and the sharing of electrons in the water molecule. The greater electromagnetivity of oxygen causes the shared negatively charged electrons to be pulled toward it, and away from the hydrogen atom, resulting in a dipole, with a partial negative charge at the oxygen end and a partial positive charge at the hydrogen end of each bond. Show students,

approaches the negative end of the solute molecule. They attract. So a force of attraction is set up between the solvent and solute molecules. This force of attraction separates the molecules of the polar solute, and the solute dissolves. See Figure 9–14.

In addition to dissolving polar solutes, water also dissolves ionic solutes, or substances made of ions. The positive end of the water molecule attracts the negative ion of the ionic solute. Likewise, the negative end of the water molecule attracts the positive ion of the solute. When the water is able to pull the solute ions out of their positions in the solute, dissolving takes place. Each ion is then surrounded by water molecules and spread evenly throughout the solution. See Figure 9–14.

Among the substances that water cannot dissolve are grease, oil, fat, and benzene. These compounds are made of nonpolar molecules, or molecules that do not have charged ends. The nonpolar molecules have no attraction for the polar water molecules. Therefore, no force is exerted. The solute molecules are not separated. Nonpolar solutes, however, dissolve readily in nonpolar solvents. *A general rule for solutions is: Like dissolves like.*

Water Quality

The taste, odor, and appearance of water determine its quality. These properties vary from area to area. The differences depend on the amount and type of material dissolved in the water.

The water you use for all sorts of purposes may come from either a groundwater or a surface source. This water may be "hard" or "soft." The hardness or softness of water depends on the source of the water and the types of rocks and soil the water comes in contact with. **Hard water** contains large amounts of dissolved metal ions, especially calcium and magnesium. Soap does not lather easily in hard water. Also, hard water causes scaly deposits to build up in hot water heaters and plumbing systems. **Soft water** does not contain these metal ions. It does not present problems with lathering soap or depositing metal ions.

Some water is softened naturally as it passes through and reacts with rock formations containing

❸ Figure 9–15 *Hard water causes scaly deposits to build up in hot water heaters and plumbing systems. This scanning electron micrograph shows crystals of calcium salts deposited when hard water evaporates or boils away. What other metal ion dissolved in water causes it to be hard?* **❷**

217

by using a molecular model, that the water molecule is angular rather than linear. Ask,
• **What is it about this shape that is important regarding the polarity of water?** (The overall polarity is possible only because of the angular shape of water, which does not allow the two H–O dipoles to cancel out, which a linear H–O–H shape would do. An overall polarity, with a partial negative charge at the oxygen side and a partial positive charge at the side of the molecule that contains the two hydrogen atoms, results.)

Reinforcement

Have slower students work with molecular models to get a better sense of the way in which water interacts with and dissolves ions and polar molecules. Have the students demonstrate the processes in class.

Sharpen Your Skills

Emulsifying Action
Skills: Relating, manipulative, observing, applying
Level: Average
Type: Hands-on
Materials: oil, vinegar, beaker, egg yolk

Students will first note that the oil and water do not dissolve in each other. Upon shaking they do dissolve, but they separate after several minutes. Adding the egg yolk makes the two liquids dissolve upon shaking. The colloid is an emulsion whose common name is mayonnaise.

9-3 (continued)

Content Development

More precisely, freezing point depression and boiling point elevation are determined by the concentration of solute particles. This concentration is expressed in terms of molality (moles solute per kilogram solvent). The equations for water solutions are

$$T_f = 1.86 \frac{°C}{molal} \times m$$

$$T_b = 0.52 \frac{°C}{molal} \times m$$

where T_f and T_b are the freezing point depression and boiling point elevation, respectively, and m is molality. If the solute is ionic, the result must be multiplied by the number of ions produced per formula unit (e.g., NaCl produces 2 ions, so the result is multiplied by 2).

Figure 9–16 The dumping of industrial wastes from a paper mill in Ontario, Canada, is one example of water pollution. What other substances carelessly dumped into water cause pollution? ❶

Figure 9–17 A solute dissolved in a liquid solvent lowers the freezing point of the solvent. Salt spread on an icy surface lowers the freezing point of the ice and causes it to melt (right). Rock salt is used in an ice cream maker to lower the freezing point of the ingredients to allow the ice cream to form at below 0°C (left). What happens to the boiling point of a solvent when a solute is added? ❷

certain minerals. These minerals remove the calcium and magnesium. Many people in areas with hard water add water softeners to their water to remove the minerals that make it hard.

Water is necessary to all life on the earth. So it is important to maintain the quality of water. Yet many of the earth's sources of fresh water are becoming polluted. Normally, water is naturally filtered through soil and sand, which helps to remove impurities. But carelessness in dumping sewage, silt, industrial wastes, and pesticides into water has caused serious problems. Water is becoming more and more polluted.

Special Properties of Solutions

Why is salt spread on roads and walkways that are icy? Why is salt added to cooking water? Why is a substance known as ethylene glycol added to the cooling systems of cars? The answers to the questions have to do with two special properties of solutions.

Experiments show that when a solute is dissolved in a liquid solvent, the freezing point of the solvent is lowered. The lowering of the freezing point is called **freezing point depression.** The addition of solute molecules interferes with the phase change of solvent molecules. So the solution can exist in the liquid phase at a lower temperature than can the pure solvent. For example, ethylene glycol, commonly known as antifreeze, is added to cooling systems to lower the freezing point of water.

Reinforcement

Sodium chloride, although inexpensive, is not a good substance to use to lower the freezing point in automobile cooling systems, partly because it promotes corrosion.

Enrichment

Some students may wish to make a study of tap water hardness in their area by comparing how easily and well soap lathers in the water versus how

the soap lathers in distilled water. They can also obtain information from their local water utility company on minerals present in water and on possible sources of pollution that may threaten the water supply in the future.

SECTION REVIEW 9-3

1. Polarity is the condition of a molecule in which it has oppositely charged

The addition of a solute to a pure liquid solvent also raises the boiling point of the solvent. This increase is called **boiling point elevation.** In this case, the addition of solute molecules interferes with the rapid evaporation, or boiling, of the solvent molecules. So the solution can exist in the liquid phase at a higher temperature than can the pure solvent. Since more energy is needed to make the solvent molecules evaporate, the boiling point increases. When salt is added to cooking water, the water will boil at a higher temperature. Although it may take a longer time to heat the water to boiling, it will take a shorter time to cook the food in that boiling water.

SECTION REVIEW

1. What is polarity? Why is water a polar molecule?
2. What is the general rule for solutions?
3. What is hard water? Soft water?
4. How does a solute affect the freezing point and boiling point of a pure solvent?
5. Of what value is antifreeze to a car's cooling system during extremely hot weather?

9–4 Suspensions and Colloids

You learned that solutions are clear, homogeneous mixtures of solute and solvent. The particles in a solution—individual atoms, ions, or molecules—are too small to be seen and do not settle out. Not all solutes dissolved in solvents form true solutions, however. Two other types of mixtures can be formed when a solute dissolves in a solvent. **The physical properties of particle size and separation of solute and solvent particles determine whether a mixture is a suspension or a colloid.** ❸

Suspensions

A **suspension** is a heterogeneous mixture in which the solute particles are larger than atoms, ions, or molecules. The particles are large enough, in fact, to be seen with or without a microscope.

219

SECTION PREVIEW 9-4

Suspensions are explained as heterogeneous mixtures in which the particles are large enough to be visible to the unaided eye. Suspensions settle out or can be filtered. Colloids, on the other hand, are homogeneous mixtures that are not true solutions, and in which particles are not visible to the unaided eye, but scatter light. Brownian motion of colloidal particles is also explained.

PERFORMANCE OBJECTIVES 9-4

1. **Describe and contrast suspensions and colloids.**

2. **Define and explain Brownian motion.**

SCIENCE TERMS 9-4

suspension p. 219
colloid p. 220
Brownian motion p. 221

• **What kind of mixture results if one material is suspended in large clumps in another material?** (The mixture is heterogeneous.)

In order to prepare them for the discussion of colloids, ask,

• **Can you imagine a situation in which one material is suspended throughout another in clumps of molecules too small to be seen? Would such a mixture be heterogeneous or homogeneous? Why?** (It would be homogeneous because it would be uniform and its components could not be picked out visually.)

• **Would it be a solution?** (No, because individual molecules would not be intermingled)

---

ends. Water is polar because one end is negatively charged (oxygen end) and the other end is positively charged (hydrogen end).
2. Like dissolves like.
3. Hard water contains large amounts of dissolved metal ions, especially calcium and magnesium. Soft water does not contain these metal ions.
4. Addition of a solute lowers the freezing point and raises the boiling point of a solvent.

5. Raises the boiling point of water in cooling system to prevent overheating

TEACHING STRATEGY 9-4

Motivation

Ask students to state the definition of a true solution (a homogeneous mixture in which molecules are completely intermingled). Then ask them the following, which prepares them for the discussion of suspensions.

Figure 9–18 *The soil and water mixture is a suspension. How can this suspension be separated?* ❷

Figure 9–19 *Fog is a type of colloid in which liquid particles are mixed in a gas (left). Whipped cream is also a colloid (center). What is the solute in whipped cream? The solvent? The constant bombardment of solute particles in a colloid enables a colloid to scatter light, so a beam of light passing through a colloid becomes visible (right).* ❸

The solute particles in a suspension are temporarily suspended, or hanging, in the solvent. The length of time during which they remain this way varies. But eventually, the particles will settle out.

If the solute particles in a suspension are very fine, they will remain suspended for a long time. They can be separated out, however, by filtering the suspension. Can particles of a true solution be separated this way? ❶

Colloids

A **colloid** (KAHL-oid) is a homogeneous mixture that is not a true solution. In a colloid, the size of the solute particles is larger than that in a solution but smaller than that in a suspension. The particles are larger than atoms, ions, or molecules but too small to be seen even with a microscope.

The solute particles in a colloid are kept permanently suspended. They are continuously bombarded by solvent molecules. This bombardment accounts for several properties of a colloid.

A colloid does not separate upon standing, as a suspension does. Because the particles are constantly bombarded, they do not have a chance to settle out. The constant bombardment of solute particles enables a colloid to scatter light. So if a beam of light is passed through a colloid, the beam becomes visible. See Figure 9–19. The white cloudy appearance of milk is due to the scattering of light in this example of a colloid. If you have ever seen a searchlight

---

9-4 (continued)

Content Development
Review the properties of solutions and focus on the issue of particle size. You may wish to prepare and show students a solution, a heterogeneous suspension (for example, fine sand in water or oil droplets in water), and a homogeneous colloid (for example, homogenized milk). Ask the students to observe the three mixtures and lead them to speculate on the nature and sizes of the particles present. You can begin to write out a list of the properties, in table form, on the chalkboard.

Content Development
The particles in colloids range from about 10^{-6} mm to about 10^{-4} mm in size. Although such particles tend to consist of clumps of molecules, in some cases they can be individual molecules if the molecules are very large, as in the case of some proteins. The scattering of light by colloids is called the Tyndall effect and results from the fact that the particles are large enough to scatter light.

There are several different classes of colloids, which differ in terms of the phases of the components. Aero-

sols are colloids in which solid or liquid particles are dispersed in a gas. If the particles are solid, the aerosol is called a smoke; if they are liquid, it is called a fog. Sols are colloids in which solid particles are dispersed in a liquid. Emulsions are colloids in which a liquid is dispersed in a liquid. Gels are colloids in which a solid is arranged in a fine network throughout a liquid. Figure 9-20 summarizes most of this information.

Motivation
Nonhomogenized milk is a heterogeneous suspension that separates spontaneously into fatty and watery components. The fat globules in such milk are large enough to separate out in this way. In the process of homogenization, milk is forced through small openings in a metal plate to break up the globules. The resulting suspended fat particles still contain clumps of molecules, but are small enough to re-

TYPES OF COLLOIDS	
Name	**Example**
Fog (liquid in gas)	Clouds
Smoke (solid in gas)	Smoke
Foam (gas in liquid)	Whipped cream
Emulsion (liquid in liquid)	Mayonnaise
Sol (solid in liquid)	Paint
Gel (liquid in solid)	Butter

sweep through the air at night, you have observed this property of colloids.

The bombardment of solute particles in a colloid can be observed under a microscope. You would not see the individual solute particles, but you would see a constant, random motion of the particles. The constant movement of colloidal particles is called **Brownian motion.**

SECTION REVIEW

1. What is a suspension? A colloid?
2. What two physical properties determine whether a mixture is a suspension or a colloid?
3. Describe three types of colloids.
4. How does a solution compare with a suspension and a colloid?

9–5 Acids

If you look in your medicine cabinet and refrigerator and on your kitchen shelves, you will find examples of a group of compounds known as **acids.** Acids are found in aspirin, vitamin C, and eyewash. Fruits such as oranges, grapes, lemons, grapefruits, and apples contain acids. Milk and tea contain acids, as do pickles, vinegar, and carbonated drinks.

Acids play an important role in the life processes that take place in your body. You could not digest food adequately if it were not for a certain acid in your stomach. Many industrial processes use acids. The manufacture of dyes, synthetic fibers, fertilizers, and explosives involves the use of acids.

Properties of Acids

As a class of compounds, all acids have certain physical and chemical properties when dissolved in water. ❸ One of the physical properties all acids share is sour taste. Lemons taste sour because they

221

main in colloidal suspension. Thus, homogenized milk is a homogeneous mixture that is not a solution, but a liquid–liquid colloid, or emulsion.

Section Review 9-4

1. A heterogeneous mixture in which the solute particles are larger than atoms, ions, or molecules; a homogeneous mixture that is not a true solution, in which the size of the solute particles is larger than that in a solution but smaller than that in a suspension
2. Whether the particles separate out upon standing; size of particles
3. Answers will vary, but any of those listed in Figure 9-20 are acceptable.
4. Particle size in a solution is that of atoms, ions, and molecules. A solution does not separate out upon standing. A solution does not show Brownian motion. A solution does not scatter light. A solution is always clear.

9-5 ACIDS

SECTION PREVIEW 9-5

The physical and chemical properties of acids are described, and the use of indicators is explained. The properties of acids are explained on the basis of the production of hydrogen ions (H^+) and hydronium ions (H_3O^+). Acid strength is discussed, and common acids are described.

PERFORMANCE OBJECTIVES 9-5

1. **State the properties of acids.**
2. **Define and describe the use of indicators.**
3. **State the names and formulas of the ions produced by acids.**
4. **Name several common acids and state their uses.**

SCIENCE TERMS 9-5

acid p. 221
indicator p. 222
hydronium ion p. 223

TEACHING STRATEGY 9-5

Motivation
Without as yet using the term *acid*, name several common acidic food substances, such as lemon juice, lime juice, vinegar, and sour cream. Ask,
• **What property do all these things have in common?** (They all have a sour taste.)

Point out that these substances also have other properties in common, such as their ability to react with certain metals, such as the aluminum of which foil is made. For this reason, they are stored in nonreactive containers. Then, point out that this similarity in properties might indicate some similarity in the molecules present. Some of the chemical substances present might belong to the same class of substances.

Figure 9–21 *Blue litmus paper turns red in an acid solution (top). Phenolphthalein, another indicator, is colorless in an acid solution (bottom).*

Sharpen Your Skills

Naming Acids

Using books and other reference materials in the library, answer these questions:

1. What is the difference between a binary acid and a ternary acid?

2. What prefix and what suffix are used with the names of all binary acids?

3. In ternary acids, what do the prefixes *hypo-* and *per-* mean? What do the suffixes *-ic* and *-ous* mean?

222

contain citric acid. Vinegar contains acetic acid. However, you should *never* use taste to identify a chemical substance. You should use other, safer properties to identify acids.

Acids affect the color of **indicators.** Indicators are compounds that show a definite color change when mixed with an acid. Litmus paper, a common indicator, changes from blue to red in an acid solution. Another indicator, phenolphthalein (fee-nohl-THAL-een), is colorless in an acid solution.

Acids react with active metals to produce hydrogen gas and a metal compound. This reaction wears away, or corrodes, the metal and produces a residue. For example, sulfuric acid in a car battery often corrodes the terminals and leaves a residue.

Another important property of acids can be identified by looking at the list of common acids in Figure 9–22. What do all these acids have in common? Acids contain hydrogen. When dissolved in water, acids ionize to produce positive hydrogen ions (H^+). A hydrogen ion is a proton. So acids are often defined as proton donors.

The hydrogen ion, or proton, produced by an acid is quickly surrounded by a water molecule. The attraction between the hydrogen ion (H^+) and the water molecule (H_2O) results in the formation of a **hydronium ion, H_3O^+.**

The definition of an acid as a proton donor helps explain why all hydrogen-containing compounds are *not* acids. Table sugar contains 22 hydrogen atoms, but it is not an acid. When dissolved in water, table sugar does not produce H^+ ions. Table sugar is not a proton donor. So it does not turn litmus paper red or phenolphthalein colorless.

Common Acids

The three most common acids in industry and the laboratory are sulfuric acid (H_2SO_4), nitric acid (HNO_3), and hydrochloric acid (HCl). These three acids are strong acids. That means they ionize to a high degree in water and produce hydrogen ions. The presence of hydrogen ions makes strong acids good electrolytes.

Acetic acid ($HC_2H_3O_2$), carbonic acid (H_2CO_3), and boric acid (H_3BO_3) are weak acids. They do not ionize to a high degree in water, so they produce

COMMON ACIDS		
Name	**Formula**	**Uses**
Strong Hydrochloric	HCl	Pickling steel Cleaning bricks and metals Digesting food
Sulfuric	H_2SO_4	Manufacturing paints, plastics, fertilizers Dehydrating agent
Nitric	HNO_3	Removing tarnish Making explosives (TNT) Making fertilizers
Weak Carbonic	H_2CO_3	Carbonating beverages
Boric	H_3BO_3	Washing eyes
Phosphoric	H_3PO_4	Making fertilizers and detergents
Acetic	$HC_2H_3O_2$	Making cellulose acetate used in fibers and films
Citric	$H_3C_6H_5O_7$	Making soft drinks

Figure 9–22 *The name, formula, and uses of some common acids are given in this table. What ion do all these acids contain?* 1

few hydrogen ions. Weak acids are poor electrolytes. Figure 9–22 lists the name, formula, and uses of some common acids. Remember to handle any acid—weak or strong—with care. 4

SECTION REVIEW

1. What are three important properties of acids?
2. Why are acids called proton donors?
3. How could you *safely* determine whether an unknown solution is an acid?

9–6 Bases

Section Objective

To identify bases

Another class of compounds that are probably quite familiar to you are **bases.** Bases are found in household products such as lye, milk of magnesia, deodorants, ammonia, and soap.

9-6 BASES

SECTION PREVIEW 9-6

The physical and chemical properties of bases are described, as are their effects on indicators. These properties are explained on the basis of the production of hydroxide (OH^-) ion. Base strength is discussed, and common bases are described.

PERFORMANCE OBJECTIVES 9-6

1. **State the properties of bases.**
2. **State the name and formula of the ion produced by bases.**
3. **Name several common bases and state their uses.**

SCIENCE TERMS 9-6

base p. 223
hydroxide ion p. 224

Enrichment

There are a number of different definitions for acids. Substances that produce H^+ ion and that have the properties ordinarily associated with acids are called Arrhenius acids. Substances that donate protons in reactions are called Bronsted–Lowry acids. Substances that accept electron pairs in reactions are called Lewis acids.

Reinforcement

Students often confuse the terms *concentrated* and *strong.* A concentrated acid suspension contains many dissolved acid molecules per unit volume. A strong acid is an acid whose molecules tend to ionize to a high degree. Thus, strong acids can exist in concentrated or in dilute solutions, as can weak acids.

Section Review 9-5

1. Turn blue litmus paper red; react with active metals to produce hydrogen gas and metal compounds; contain hydrogen and when dissolved in water produce hydrogen ions; have a sour taste
2. Acids produce hydrogen ions when they ionize. A hydrogen ion is a proton.
3. Use litmus paper or phenolphthalein.

BACKGROUND INFORMATION

You may wish to introduce and practice the rules for naming acids, bases, and salts.

1. Binary acids: The name begins with *hydro* followed by the root name of the nonmetal and ends with *-ic* (e.g., HCl is hydrochloric acid).

2. Tertiary acids: The name includes the root of the central element, an *-ic* or *-ous* ending, and sometimes a prefix.

a. least oxygen: hypo-(root) and -ous (acid)

b. next to least oxygen: (root) and -ous (acid)

c. next to most oxygen: (root) and -ic (acid)

d. most oxygen: per-(root) and -ic (acid)

3. Bases: The name begins with the element (or polyatomic ion) that appears first and ends with *hydroxide* (e.g., KOH is potassium hydroxide).

4. Salts: Names are generally formed by combining the names of the constituent ions, with the positive ion appearing first. Salts derived from binary acids end in *-ide*. Salts derived from *-ous* acids end in *-ite*; from *-ic* acids in *-ate*.

Sharpen Your Skills

Acid–Base Testing
Skills: Classifying, observing, manipulative, comparing
Level: Remedial
Type: Hands-on
Materials: red litmus paper, blue litmus paper, orange juice, milk, tea, coffee, soda, vinegar, ammonia, milk of magnesia, saliva

---

Figure 9–23 *Red litmus paper turns blue in a basic solution (top). Phenolphthalein turns bright pink (bottom).*

Properties of Bases

When dissolved in water, all bases share certain physical and chemical properties. Bases usually ❶ taste bitter and are slippery to the touch. However, bases can be poisonous and corrosive. So you should *never* use taste and touch to identify bases.

Bases turn litmus paper from red to blue and phenolphthalein to bright pink. Bases emulsify, or dissolve, fats and oils. They do this by reacting with the fat or oil to form a soap. The base ammonium hydroxide is used as a household cleaner because it "cuts" grease. The strong base sodium hydroxide, or lye, is used to clean clogged drains.

All bases contain the **hydroxide ion, OH⁻**. When dissolved in water, bases produce this ion. Because ❷ the hydroxide ion (OH^-) can combine with a hydrogen ion (H^+) and form water, a base is often defined as a proton acceptor.

Common Bases

Strong bases dissolve readily in water to produce large numbers of ions. So strong bases are good electrolytes. Examples of strong bases include

COMMON BASES		
Name	**Formula**	**Uses**
Strong Sodium hydroxide	NaOH	Making soap Drain cleaner
Potassium hydroxide	KOH	Making soft soap Battery electrolyte
Calcium hydroxide	Ca(OH)₂	Leather production Making plaster
Magnesium hydroxide	Mg(OH)₂	Laxative Antacid
Weak Ammonium hydroxide	NH₄OH	Household cleaner
Aluminum hydroxide	Al(OH)₃	Antacid Deodorant

Figure 9–24 *The name, formula, and uses of some common bases are given in this table. What ion do all these bases contain?* ❶

224

TEACHING STRATEGY 9-6

Motivation
Without as yet using the term *base*, list the names of some commonly used basic substances on the chalkboard and also have on hand solutions of some bases. Ask students what properties they think the substances may have in common and what may account for these properties. You may wish to test the solutions with indicators.

Content Development
After discussing common basic substances, point out that these substances are all classed as bases. At this point, limit yourself to a description of these substances and their uses. Once you have done so, you will be ready to go on to discuss their properties in detail, and to explore the underlying structural and compositional similarity of bases.

Skills Development
Skills: Making charts, applying definitions, making comparisons
Have students design and make charts that illustrate the differences between acids and bases, in terms of structure and properties. They may also add illustrations of their own making or cut

potassium hydroxide (KOH), sodium hydroxide (NaOH), and calcium hydroxide (Ca(OH)$_2$).

Weak bases do not produce large numbers of ions when dissolved in water. So weak bases are poor electrolytes. Ammonium hydroxide (NH$_4$OH) and aluminum hydroxide (Al(OH)$_3$) are weak bases. ❸ See Figure 9–24.

SECTION REVIEW

1. What are three important properties of bases?
2. Why are bases called proton acceptors?
3. If an electric conductivity setup were placed in the following solutions, would the light be bright or dim? NH$_4$OH, KOH, NaOH, Al(OH)$_3$

9–7 Acids and Bases in Solution: Salts

Section Objective

To describe the formation of salts

Solutions can be acidic, basic, or neutral. To measure the acidity of a solution, the **pH** scale is used. The pH of a solution is a measure of the hydronium ion (H$_3$O$^+$) concentration. Remember that the hydronium ion is formed by the attraction between a hydrogen ion (H$^+$) from an acid and a water molecule (H$_2$O). So the pH of a solution indicates how acidic the solution is.

The pH scale is a series of numbers from 0 to 14. The middle of the scale, 7, is the neutral point.

Figure 9–25 *On the pH scale, 7 is neutral, acids are between 0 and 7, bases between 7 and 14. Are you surprised to learn how many of the substances you use every day contain acids and bases? Which fruit is most acidic? What cleaner is most basic?* ❷

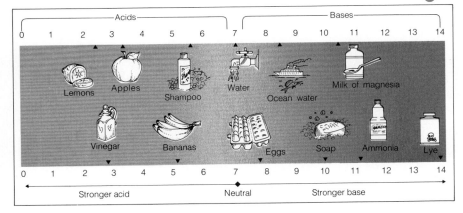

9-7 ACIDS AND BASES IN SOLUTION: SALTS

SECTION PREVIEW 9-7

The pH scale and its uses are introduced. The connection between indicators and pH is then discussed. Next, the nature of salts and their formation in neutralization reactions are discussed. Finally, precipitation is defined and explained.

PERFORMANCE OBJECTIVES 9-7

1. **Explain the nature and use of the pH scale.**
2. **Define salt.**
3. **Describe salt formation in neutralization reactions.**
4. **Define and explain precipitation.**

SCIENCE TERMS 9-7

salt p. 226
neutralization p. 227
precipitate p. 227
precipitation p. 227

from magazines that show some of the uses for acids and bases.

Enrichment
Advanced students may wish to do library research on Bronsted–Lowry acids and bases and on their reactions. They should prepare a report on the topic and present it to the class.

Section Review 9-6
1. Taste bitter; slippery to the touch; turn litmus paper from red to blue and phenolphthalein bright pink; emulsify fats and oils; contain hydroxide ion
2. When dissolved in water, the hydroxide ion of the base combines with a hydrogen ion, or proton.
3. Dim, bright, bright, dim

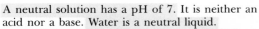

Sharpen Your Skills

A Homemade Indicator
Skills: Observing, identifying patterns, manipulative, comparing
Level: Average
Type: Hands-on
Materials: Red cabbage, boiling water, safety goggles, 5 separate containers, shampoo, grapefruit juice, clear soft drink, milk, ammonia, graduated cylinder

This activity will show to students that substances in everyday life can be used in a scientific manner. Check students' observations for each of the substances listed or substitute substances of your choice.

9-7 (continued)

Content Development

Take special care to point out that the pH scale measures the concentration of H^+ ions in solutions. The pH of a solution alone is not a direct indication of acid strength or even of acid concentration. For example, a strong acid at fairly low concentration can produce many H^+ ions and can thus have a low pH. However, with sufficient dilution, H^+ concentration falls and pH rises, even for strong acids. A weak acid at high concentration can have a low pH because, although the tendency of each molecule to ionize (that is, the strength) is low, there are many molecules present to ionize.

Make sure also that the number range of the pH scale is made clear and that students understand that solutions with high H^+ ion concentration have a low pH.

Skills Development

Skills: Making observations, developing a hypothesis
Combine, in pairs, solutions of various salts such as NaCl, NaBr, $Pb(NO_3)_2$, $Ba(NO_3)_2$, NaI, Na_2SO_4, and $CaCl_2$. Have students observe whether precipitation occurs. (In some cases, the answer may not be obvious,

Sharpen Your Skills

A Homemade Indicator

1. Shred two leaves of red cabbage and boil them in some water until the liquid gets very dark. **CAUTION:** *Wear safety goggles and use extreme care when working with heated liquids.*

2. When the liquid and shreds have cooled, squeeze all the purple juice you can from the shreds. Pour the liquid into a container.

3. Into 5 separate containers, pour about 3 to 4 mL of each of the following substances: shampoo, grapefruit juice, clear soft drink, milk, ammonia cleaner.

4. Add about 2 mL of the cabbage liquid. Stir and observe any color changes.

The cabbage liquid will turn bright red in most acids and blue-purple in most bases. Identify each substance.

Figure 9–26 *Nature has its own indicators! Hydrangeas have pink flowers in basic soil (left) and blue flowers in acidic soil (center). A common indicator used in the laboratory is pH paper (right).*

A neutral solution has a pH of 7. It is neither an acid nor a base. Water is a neutral liquid.

A solution with a pH below 7 is an acid. Strong acids have *low* pH numbers. Would hydrochloric acid have a pH closer to 2 or to 6? ❶

A solution with a pH above 7 is a base. Strong bases have *high* pH numbers. What would be the pH of NaOH? ❷

Determining Solution pH

The pH of a solution can be determined by using an indicator. You already know about two common indicators—litmus paper and phenolphthalein. Other indicators include pH paper, methyl orange, and bromthymol blue. Each indicator shows a specific color change as the pH of a solution changes. ❶

Common household materials can be used as indicators. Red cabbage juice covers the entire pH range. Grape juice is bright pink in the presence of an acid and bright yellow in the presence of a base. Even tea can serve as an indicator. Have you ever noticed how the color of tea changes when you add lemon juice? For very accurate pH measurements, a pH meter is used.

Formation of Salts

When acids react chemically with bases, they form a class of compounds called salts. A salt is a

whereas in others, such as NaI-$Pb(NO_3)_2$, the precipitation is dramatic and produces a brightly colored precipitate.) Have students draw up a chart that indicates whether precipitation occurs, and have them make hypotheses concerning the formulas of the precipitates. In some cases, by comparing data, they should be able to rule out certain possibilities and positively state which precipitate has formed. For example, the precipitate

formed by NaCl-$Pb(NO_3)_2$ must be $PbCl_2$ and not $NaNO_3$ because no precipitate forms when NaCl-$Ba(NO_3)_2$ are combined, and this combination would precipitate $NaNO_3$ if that substance were of low solubility.

Enrichment

Advanced students, especially those who already have at least a slight familiarity with the concept of logarithms, may be encouraged to do

compound formed from the positive ion of a base and the negative ion of an acid. It is a neutral substance. A salt is usually made of a metal and a nonmetal. For example, NaCl and KBr are salts. What are the names of these salts? Sometimes a salt is ❸ made of one or more polyatomic ions. NH_4Cl, $CaSO_4$, and NH_4NO_3 are such salts. Can you name these salts? ❹

The reaction of an acid with a base to produce a salt and water is called **neutralization** (noo-truhl-uh-ZAY-shuhn). In neutralization, the properties of ❷ the acid and the base are lost as two neutral substances—water and a salt—are formed.

The reaction of HCl with NaOH is a neutralization reaction. The positive hydrogen ion from the acid combines with the negative hydroxide ion from the base. This produces water. The remaining ion of the acid combines with the remaining ion of the base to form a salt.

$$H^+Cl^- + Na^+OH^- \longrightarrow H_2O + NaCl$$ ❸

Many of the salts formed by a neutralization reaction are insoluble in water. They crystallize out of solution and remain in the solid phase. An insoluble substance that crystallizes out of solution is called a **precipitate** (prih-SIHP-uh-tayt). The process by which a precipitate forms is called **precipitation.** Examples of precipitates include magnesium carbonate, silver chloride, and aluminum phosphate. Snow, rain, sleet, and hail are considered forms of precipitation because they fall out of solution. Out of what solution do they precipitate? ❻

A neutralization reaction is a double replacement reaction. And a very important one, too. For a dangerous acid can be combined with a dangerous base to form a harmless salt and neutral water.

SECTION REVIEW

1. What is pH? Describe the pH scale.
2. What is the pH of an acid? A base? A neutral solution?
3. How can the pH of a solution be determined?
4. What is neutralization? What are the products of a neutralization reaction?
5. Use an equation to show the neutralization reaction between H_2SO_4 and NaOH.

Figure 9–27 To control dangerous acid spills, these firefighters spray a blanket of base over the acid. The result is a neutral salt and water. What is this reaction called? ❺

Sharpen Your Skills

Predicting Salt Formation

Copy and complete the following table by predicting the salt formed from each acid–base combination.

	NaOH	Ca(OH)₂	NH₄OH
HCl			
HNO₃			
H₂SO₄			

227

Sharpen Your Skills

Predicting Salt Formation
Skills: Predicting, applying
Level: Enriched
Type: Computational
This activity will help reinforce the concept that salts form when an acid and a base combine. Students should arrive at the following salts: First row: NaCl, CaCl₂, NH₄Cl. Second row: NaNO₃, Ca(NO₃)₂, NH₄NO₃. Third row: Na₂SO₄, CaSO₄, (NH₄)₂SO₄.

library research on the nature of pH as $-\log[H^+]$. You can also provide sample problems for practice calculation purposes.

Content Development
A salt, such as NaCl, made from a strong acid and a strong base (in this case, HCl and NaOH) produces a neutral solution when dissolved in water. A salt, such as NH₄Cl, made from a strong acid and a weak base (HCl and NH₄OH) produces an acidic water solution, due to hydrolysis of the water (by NH₄⁺ ion, in this case, producing NH₄OH and H⁺, which makes the solution acidic). A salt, such as NaNO₂, made from a weak acid and a strong base (HNO₂ and NaOH) produces a basic water solution, due to hydrolysis of the water (by NO₂⁻ ion, in this case, producing HNO₂ and OH⁻, which makes the solution basic).

Section Review 9-7
1. The pH of a solution is a measure of the concentration of hydronium ions. The pH scale is a scale of numbers from 0 to 14 in which 7 is neutral, less than 7 is acidic, and more than 7 is basic.
2. The pH of an acid is between 0 and 7; of a base is between 7 and 14; exactly 7.
3. Use an indicator such as litmus paper, phenolphthalein, pH paper, or methyl orange. A pH meter can be used for more accurate measurement.
4. Neutralization is a chemical reaction in which an acid and a base combine to produce a salt and water.
5. $H_2SO_4 + 2NaOH = Na_2SO_4 + 2H_2O$

LABORATORY INVESTIGATION
ACIDS, BASES, AND SALTS

BEFORE THE LAB
1. **Gather all equipment at least one day prior to the investigation. You should gather enough equipment to meet your class needs, assuming up to six students per group.**
2. **Prepare dilute solutions of the acids and bases listed. Precision as to concentration is not at all crucial. Simply dilute the concentrated acids in roughly a 15 : 1 or 20 : 1 water : acid ratio, adding acid to water. Prepare the bases by weighing out roughly 50 g of each per liter of solution.**
3. **Label the bottles.**

PRE-LAB DISCUSSION
Before beginning the investigation, avoid discussing with students the general properties of acids, bases, and salts, as this is the topic they are setting out to explore. Do lead students to the hypothesis that substances that are classified in the same group, such as acids, should be expected to have certain properties in common. Then discuss the experiment in terms of scientific method, focusing students' attention on the problem, the hypothesis that they have formulated, and the variables they will manipulate in order to test the hypothesis. Also, make a point of discussing safety procedures to be followed in dealing with acids and bases.

SKILL DEVELOPMENT
Students will use the following skills while completing this investigation.
1. Safety
2. Observing
3. Comparing
4. Hypothesizing
5. Recording
6. Measuring
7. Applying
8. Relating

SAFETY TIPS
Make sure students wear safety goggles whenever working with acids or bases. Instruct students on the proper

way to handle and dispose of such chemicals. If students should spill chemicals onto their skin or clothing, wash off immediately with cold water.

TEACHING STRATEGY FOR LAB PROCEDURE
1. It is essential that students be made aware that they must clean each stirring rod between uses.

Problem
What are some properties of acids and bases? What happens when acids react with bases?

Materials *(per group)*

safety goggles   stirring rod
6 medium-sized   medicine dropper
   test tubes   evaporating dish
test tube rack   beaker
red and blue litmus paper
phenolphthalein
solutions of H_2SO_4, HCl, HNO_3
solutions of KOH, NaOH, $Ca(OH)_2$

Procedure

A. *Acids*
1. Put your safety goggles on. Over a sink, pour about 5 mL of each acid into separate test tubes. **CAUTION:** *Handle acids with extreme care. They can burn the skin.* Place the test tubes in the rack. Test the effect of each acid on litmus paper by dipping a stirring rod into the acid and then touching the rod to the litmus paper. Test each acid with both red and blue litmus paper. *Be sure to clean the rod between uses.* Record your observations.
2. Add 1 drop of phenolphthalein to each test tube. Record your observations.

B. *Bases*
1. Over a sink, pour about 5 mL of each base into separate test tubes. **CAUTION:** *Handle bases with extreme care.* Place the test tubes in the rack. Test the contents of each tube with red and blue litmus paper. Record your observations.
2. Add 1 drop of phenolphthalein to each test tube. Record your observations.
3. Place 5 mL of sodium hydroxide solution in a small beaker and add 2 drops of phenolphthalein. Record the color of the solution.

4. While slowly stirring, carefully add a few drops of hydrochloric acid until the mixture changes color. Record the color change. This point is known as the indicator endpoint. Test with blue and red litmus paper. Record your observations.
5. Carefully pour some of the mixture into a porcelain evaporating dish. Let the mixture evaporate until it is dry. How would you describe its appearance?

Observations
1. What color do acids turn litmus paper? Phenolphthalein?
2. What color do bases turn litmus paper? Phenolphthalein?
3. What happens to the color of the sodium hydroxide-phenolphthalein solution when hydrochloric acid is added?
4. Does the substance formed by the reaction of sodium hydroxide with hydrochloric acid affect litmus paper?
5. Describe the appearance of the substance that remains after evaporation. DO NOT TASTE IT. But how do you think this substance would taste?

Conclusions
1. What are some properties of acids? Of bases?
2. What type of substance is formed when an acid reacts with a base? What is the name of this reaction? What is the other product of this reaction?
3. Why does this substance have no effect on litmus paper?
4. What is meant by an indicator's endpoint?
5. Write a balanced equation for the reaction between sodium hydroxide and hydrochloric acid.

OBSERVATIONS
1. Red; colorless
2. Blue; bright pink
3. Colorless
4. No
5. White powder (NaCl); It would taste salty.

CONCLUSIONS
1. Turn litmus paper red and phenolphthalein colorless. Acids react with

SUMMARY

9–1 Nature of Solutions

❏ A solution is a homogeneous mixture in which a solute is dissolved in a solvent.

❏ A solution in which the solvent is water is an aqueous solution. A solution in which the solvent is alcohol is a tincture.

❏ An aqueous solution that conducts an electric current is called an electrolyte. A nonelectrolyte does not conduct an electric current.

9–2 Making Solutions

❏ Two liquids that dissolve in each other are said to be miscible.

❏ The rate of solution of a solid in a liquid can be increased by stirring the solution, powdering the solvent, and heating the solution.

❏ The solubility of a solute depends on the conditions of temperature and pressure.

❏ Depending upon concentration, a solution can be saturated, unsaturated, or supersaturated.

9–3 Water—The Universal Solvent

❏ The polarity of water enables it to dissolve polar solutes and ionic solutes.

❏ A rule for solutions is like dissolves like.

9–4 Suspensions and Colloids

❏ The solute particles in a suspension are large enough to be seen and to settle out upon standing.

❏ A colloid is a homogeneous mixture whose particle size is intermediate between a suspension and a solution.

9–5 Acids

❏ Acids taste sour, turn blue litmus paper red, and ionize in water to form hydrogen ions (H^+).

9–6 Bases

❏ Bases feel slippery, taste bitter, turn red litmus paper blue, and produce hydroxide ions (OH^-) in solution.

9–7 Acids and Bases in Solution: Salts

❏ The pH of a solution is a measure of the hydronium ion concentration.

❏ A neutral substance has a pH of 7. Acids have pH numbers lower than 7. Bases have pH numbers higher than 7.

❏ When an acid chemically combines with a base, the reaction is called neutralization. The products of neutralization are a salt and water.

By measuring the volume of base required to neutralize a given volume of acid, the concentration of the acid can be calculated, using the formula

$$N_{acid} = \frac{N_{base} \times V_{base}}{V_{acid}}$$

where N stands for normality, a concentration unit equal to equivalents of solute per liter of solution. In the case of a monoprotic acid, such as HCl, normality is equal to molarity, or moles of solute per liter of solution.

Part 2

Ask students to derive (but not to perform) other experiments that could be performed (such as to observe the reactions of metals with acids) to investigate other properties of acids. Ask the students in each case how the experiments and the reasoning that precede and follow them would illustrate scientific method.

VOCABULARY

Define each term in a complete sentence.

acid	concentration	indicator	precipitate	solvent
aqueous solution	dilute solution	insoluble	precipitation	supersaturated solution
base	dissociation	ionization	salt	suspension
boiling point elevation	effervescence	miscible	saturated solution	tincture
Brownian motion	electrolyte	neutralization	soft water	unsaturated solution
colloid	freezing point depression	nonelectrolyte	solubility	
concentrated solution	hard water	pH	soluble	
	hydronium ion	polar molecule	solute	
	hydroxide ion	polarity	solution	

229

bases to form neutral substances. Bases turn litmus paper blue and phenolphthalein bright pink.

2. A salt; neutralization; water
3. Both the salt and water are neutral.
4. An indicator's endpoint is the point at which a change in color indicates a neutral substance or the absence of either hydrogen or hydroxide ions in solution.
5. NaOH + HCl = NaCl + H_2O

GOING FURTHER: ENRICHMENT

Part 1

You may wish to allow interested students to perform a quantitative acid–base titration under your supervision. Provide the students with a dilute NaOH solution of known concentration, a buret, an indicator, and a dilute HCl solution of unknown (that is, unknown to the student) concentration.

CHAPTER REVIEW

MULTIPLE CHOICE

1. c	3. a	5. c	7. a	9. c
2. b	4. d	6. b	8. d	10. b

COMPLETION

1. solute
2. temperature/ pressure
3. polar
4. Brownian motion
5. indicator
6. hydronium ion
7. bitter
8. increases
9. neutralization
10. H$_2$O/KCl

TRUE OR FALSE

1. F homogeneous
2. T
3. F effervescence
4. F like
5. F hard
6. T
7. F good
8. T
9. F 7
10. T

SKILL BUILDING

1. Acid: b, d; Base: c, f; Salt: a, e

2. a. Temperature and pressure **b.** temperature **c.** As temperature increases the solubility of a gas in a liquid decreases. The soda in a warm bottle effervesces rapidly because the solubility of the carbon dioxide gas is decreased.

3. Students' experiments should be logical and well thought out. They should include a control and a variable. Students should infer that by adding more solute they can determine if the solution is saturated.

4. a. 70 g per 100 g of water **b.** 80 g **c.** about 10 g **d.** KI **e.** Ba(OH)$_2$

5. Saturated: solute falls to the bottom. Unsaturated: dissolves. Supersaturated: crystal will cause all the excess solute to precipitate out.

6. a. Crystals of ionic sodium chloride dissociate when dissolved in water. It is only when free ions are present that an electric current can be conducted. **b.** Water ionizes to produce a hydrogen ion and a hydroxide ion. In this respect, water is both a proton donor and a proton acceptor. **c.** Solution that turns red litmus paper blue is a base. A base will neutralize an acid. **d.** Antacids are generally weak bases and neutralize stomach acids by producing a harmless salt and water.

7. If such a solvent existed, there would be no possible container to hold it because the solvent would dissolve any container.

ESSAY

1. The rate of solution can be increased for a solid in a liquid by stirring, by heating, and by powdering. Best example is a cube of sugar versus powdered sugar, in hot tea versus cold tea, with stirring and without stirring.

2. Saturated means it is holding all the solute it can hold at a given temperature. But this amount may be small compared to the amount of solvent. So this solution would be saturated but dilute. If the amount necessary to make it saturated is great compared to the amount of solvent, then the solution is concentrated.

3. Hard water contains dissolved ions of calcium and magnesium. Soft water does not. Hard water does not allow soap to lather easily and creates scaly

---

CONTENT REVIEW: MULTIPLE CHOICE

On a separate sheet of paper, write the letter of the answer that best completes each statement.

1. A solution that conducts an electric current is called a(an)
  a. nonelectrolyte.   b. tincture.   c. electrolyte.   d. colloid.
2. Which process will not increase the rate of solution of a solid in a liquid?
  a. powdering the solution   b. cooling the solution
  c. heating the solution   d. stirring the solution
3. A solution that contains all the solute it can hold at a given temperature is
  a. saturated.   b. unsaturated.   c. supersaturated.   d. dissociated.
4. If the solute particles are large enough to be seen and to be filtered, the mixture is a (an)
  a. colloid.   b. true solution.   c. electrolyte.   d. suspension.
5. Which is *not* a property of a colloid?
  a. particles smaller than a suspension   b. shows Brownian motion
  c. separates upon standing   d. scatters light
6. Which of the following acids is *not* a strong acid?
  a. HCl   b. H$_2$CO$_3$ c. H$_2$SO$_4$ d. HNO$_3$
7. Bases contain which ion?
  a. OH$^-$ b. H$_3$O$^+$ c. H$^+$ d. NH$_4$$^+$
8. The pH of a strong base would be closest to
  a. 7.   b. 2.   c. 9.   d. 14.
9. When an acid combines chemically with a base, the products are
  a. a salt and hydrogen.   b. water and carbon dioxide.
  c. a salt and water.   d. a metal and a nonmetal.
10. The pH of the products formed by a neutralization reaction is
  a. 1.   b. 7.   c. 14.   d. 0.

CONTENT REVIEW: COMPLETION

On a separate sheet of paper, write the word or words that best complete each statement.

1. In a solution, the substance being dissolved is called the _____.
2. Solubility is affected by _____ and _____.
3. Because a water molecule has a positive end and a negative end, it is a (an) _____ molecule.
4. The constant movement of colloidal particles as they are bombarded by solvent molecules is called _____.
5. A compound that shows a definite color change when mixed with an acid is called a (an) _____.
6. The attraction between a hydrogen ion and a water molecule results in the formation of the _____ ion.
7. Bases have a (an) _____ taste.
8. As the pH number of an acid decreases, the strength of the acid _____.
9. The chemical reaction in which an acid combines with a base is called _____.
10. The products of the reaction between HCl and KOH are _____ and _____.

Determine whether each statement is true or false. Then on a separate sheet of paper, write "true" if it is true. If it is false, change the underlined word or words to make the statement true.

1. A solution is a <u>heterogeneous</u> mixture.
2. Two liquids that dissolve in each other are said to be <u>miscible</u>.
3. The escape of a gas from a liquid solution is called <u>ionization</u>.
4. For solutions, like dissolves <u>unlike</u>.

5. Soap does not lather easily in <u>soft</u> water.
6. Acids are often defined as <u>proton donors</u>.
7. Strong acids are <u>poor</u> electrolytes.
8. All bases contain the <u>hydroxide</u> ion.
9. A neutral solution has a pH of <u>0</u>.
10. An acid reacts with a base in <u>neutralization</u>.

CONCEPT REVIEW: SKILL BUILDING

Use the skills you have developed in the chapter to complete each activity.

1. **Classifying compounds** Identify each of the following compounds as an acid, base, or salt: a. $CaCO_3$ b. HI c. CsOH d. H_3PO_4 e. $MgSO_4$ f. $Ga(OH)_3$
2. **Applying concepts** The caps are removed from a warm bottle and a cold bottle of carbonated beverage. The soda in the cold bottle effervesces slightly. The soda in the warm bottle effervesces rapidly.
   a. What two conditions affecting solubility are present here?
   b. Which condition is the variable?
   c. Give an explanation for what happens.
3. **Designing an experiment** Describe an experiment to determine if a solution is saturated or unsaturated.
4. **Interpreting graphs** Using the solubility curves in Figure 9–7, determine the
   a. solubility of KNO_3 at 40°C.
   b. number of grams of $NaNO_3$ needed to make a saturated solution at 10°C.
   c. number of grams of NH_4Cl that settle

out when a solution is cooled from 90°C to 70°C.
   d. salt that is most soluble at 20°C.
   e. salt that is least soluble at 20°C.
5. **Identifying patterns** A crystal of solute is added to a saturated, unsaturated, and supersaturated solution. Describe what happens in each case.
6. **Making generalizations** Explain the following observations:
   a. Crystals of ionic sodium chloride will not conduct an electric current unless they are dissolved in water.
   b. Water is both an acid and a base.
   c. A given solution that turns red litmus paper blue will neutralize an acid.
   d. Antacids, such as milk of magnesia, are used to reduce excess stomach acid.
7. **Making inferences** Explain why it would be impossible for you to bring a sample of a true universal solvent to class—if indeed such a solvent existed.

CONCEPT REVIEW: ESSAY

Discuss each of the following in a brief paragraph.

1. Describe three ways in which the rate of solution of a solid in a liquid can be increased. Use a specific example.
2. Explain how a saturated solution of one solute can be concentrated and a saturated solution of a different solute can be dilute.
3. Compare the composition and effects of hard water and soft water.

231

deposits. Soft water does not.

ADDITIONAL QUESTIONS AND TOPIC SUGGESTIONS

1. Substance A, when melted, will not conduct an electric current, which indicates that it is not made up of ions. However, the same substance, when dissolved in water, produces a solution that does conduct a current. Explain

this fact. (The substance interacts with water, the solvent, reacting to form ions in a process called ionization. Thus ions carry the electric current.)
2. Refer to Figure 9-7. **a.** Which substance is the most soluble at 10°C? **b.** How many grams of $NaNO_3$ are required to make a saturated solution using 100 g of water at 20°C? **c.** How many grams of KCl will precipitate from a solution that was saturated at 100°C and that was made using 100 g

of water, if the solution is cooled to 70°C? (**a.** KI **b.** 90 g **c.** 10 g)
3. Give an example (not given in the chapter) of each of the following types of solutions. **a.** gas in liquid **b.** solid in liquid **c.** solid in solid (Answers will vary.)
4. Nitric acid, HNO_3, undergoes a reaction with barium hydroxide, $Ba(OH)_2$. Write a balanced equation for the reaction, and name the salt that is formed. What kind of reaction is this? ($2HNO_3 + Ba(OH)_2 \rightarrow 2H_2O + Ba(NO_3)_2$)

The salt is barium nitrate. The reaction is a neutralization, a kind of double replacement reaction.

ISSUES IN SCIENCE
The following issues can be used as a springboard for class debate, or they can be assigned as a writing homework.
1. Water is necessary to life on the earth. However, much of the earth's water supply is polluted or threatened with pollution. What should be done about this problem? (Answers will vary. Some students may suggest cleanup of polluted waters or tighter controls on industrial sources of pollution. Others may be concerned about the possible negative economic or productive impact of such increased controls.)
2. Acidic substances released into the atmosphere by certain industries can eventually result in acid rain, which is destructive to many plant and animal life forms. What can be done about this problem? (Answers will vary. Some students may suggest adding basic substances to bodies of water acidified by such rain, in order to neutralize the acids. Others may suggest more efficient "cleansing" of such airborne industrial wastes, or the development of other ways of disposing of them.)

Chapter 10
CARBON CHEMISTRY

CHAPTER OVERVIEW

In this chapter, students will be introduced to an important branch of science—organic chemistry. Ubiquitous carbon compounds can be found in substances from ice cream to car wax.

The presentation begins by explaining the general chemistry of the element carbon. The bonding properties of carbon are shown as the basis for organic compounds. The formulas of many organic compounds are also shown. The next section explains how carbon compounds may bond with single bonds (alkanes), double bonds (alkenes), or triple bonds (alkynes), and closed ring type compounds. Introductory naming rules (nomenclature) are also presented for organic compounds. Organic carbon compounds may also be divided into groups based on specific bonding arrangements. Highlighted are the alcohols, acids, esters, and halogenated hydrocarbons.

The final section provides an introduction to those organic compounds closely associated with living organisms. Carbohydrates, fats, oils, and proteins are defined.

INTRODUCING CHAPTER 10

The ice cream pictured in the text can be used to explain to students just how common organic chemical compounds are. Besides the flavor compounds mentioned, you should point out that the sugar in the ice cream is probably sucrose, a carbohydrate $C_{12}H_{22}O_{11}$. The fruits pictured also have organic compounds such as fats and oils. Any plastic dish or utensil is an organic polymer compound made mostly of hydrogen and carbon. In fact the paper on which the picture is printed is primarily made up of another organic polymer—cellulose.

There are millions of organic compounds already known. This chapter provides an interesting insight to the compounds formed from the Group IV element carbon. Carbon has the ability to bond with many other elements.

• **Remembering the characteristics of a chemical bond, why would carbon bond with so many elements?** (With 4 valence electrons, and being intermediate in ability to attract electrons, and being intermediate in ability to lose electrons, it could gain or lose electrons to make a stable octet.)

Carbon atoms also have a very good ability to attach themselves to other carbon atoms. This results in the formation of many different types of

Carbon Chemistry 10

CHAPTER OBJECTIVES

After completing this chapter, you will be able to

10–1 Describe the nature and properties of organic compounds.

10–1 Draw structural formulas for several simple organic compounds.

10–1 Relate the formation of isomers to the large number of organic compounds.

10–2 Distinguish between saturated and unsaturated hydrocarbons.

10–2 Identify three series of hydrocarbons.

10–3 Classify several groups of substituted hydrocarbons.

10–4 Describe the composition and uses of three types of organic compounds in the chemistry of the human body.

Banana, strawberry, pineapple, peach—what's your special flavor? How would you order your favorite ice cream sundae? Certainly not by asking for a scoop of methyl butylacetate! Yet that is exactly what you are eating when you enjoy a banana ice cream sundae.

Methyl butylacetate is the banana-flavored compound that makes banana ice cream different from strawberry or vanilla ice cream. It is one of a special group of compounds that gives flavors to food. In some cases, these compounds naturally occur in a food. So the flavoring is natural. Pineapples have their characteristic natural flavor because of the presence of ethyl butyrate. In other cases, the compounds are added to foods as artificial flavoring.

Methyl butylacetate, ethyl butyrate, and other substances similar to these belong to a much larger group of compounds known as organic compounds. The sugar and cream in the ice cream also contain organic compounds. Organic compounds are even present in the containers in which ice cream is packaged.

Perhaps you can tell already that organic compounds are important substances with a variety of uses. But what are organic compounds? In this chapter, you will learn the answer to that question. You will also learn the useful, surprising, and sometimes delicious applications of these compounds in your daily life. So just sit back and think about a nice big ethyl cinnemate sundae topped with isoamyl salicylate. . . .

These ice cream sodas and sundaes are delicious examples of the many uses of organic compounds.

233

TEACHER DEMONSTRATION

An attention-getting demonstration is the synthesis of the organic polymer compound nylon. **CAUTION:** *The compounds used are flammable and can cause eye and skin irritations. Read all labels carefully and use adequate ventilation.* Obtain two 200 to 400 mL beakers. Into beaker number one place approximately 1 g of sodium hydroxide and 75 to 100 mL of water. After this dissolves, *carefully* add about 2 g of hexane-1,6 diamine. To the second beaker add 75 to 100 mL of an organic solvent such as trichloroethane. Next place about 2 mL of decanedioyl chloride into the solvent. After the solutions are prepared, slowly layer the contents of the first beaker onto and over the contents of the second beaker. Observe two separate layers that form in the second beaker. A thin film forms where the two layers meet. The film is nylon and will continue to form in a continuous strand if slowly drawn up from the interface of the two solutions. Be sure to fully rinse the nylon with water before anyone touches the product.

TEACHER RESOURCES

Audiovisuals

Carbon and Its Compounds, 2nd ed., 16 mm film, Cor

Ecology: Air Pollution, filmstrip with cassette, LA

Ecology: Water Pollution, filmstrip with cassette, LA

The Carbon Compounds, 16 mm film, SVE

Books

Gallant, Robert and Jay M. Railey, *Physical Properties of Hydrocarbons,* vol. 2, 2nd ed., Gulf Publishing Company

Jenkins G.M. and K. Kawamura, *Polymeric Carbons—Carbon Fibre, Glass, and Charcoal,* Cambridge University Press

Sullivan, George, *Additives in Your Food,* Cornerstone

Walker, Philip L. (ed.), *Chemistry and the Physics of Carbon,* vol. 14, Dekker

complex molecules. This property is called catenation.

• **What other elements would you predict to have a strong catenation ability?** (Silicon can also catenate. Many earth substances, such as sand, clays, etc., contain silicon chains, although silicon is not nearly as effective as carbon.)

Cross-Unit Reference

After students have completed this chapter, you may want to have them skip to Chapter 27 Chemical Technology, which deals mainly with the chemistry of hydrocarbons and their many applications.

10-1 CARBON AND ITS COMPOUNDS

SECTION PREVIEW 10-1

In this section, students will find that more than 90 percent of all chemical compounds contain carbon. Historically, carbon compounds were associated with living systems, so these compounds were said to be "organic." However scientists, led by Wohler, found that organic compounds could be prepared from inorganic starting materials.

Carbon has the ability to bond with many elements and a special ability to bond with itself. The latter property is responsible for the long chainlike molecules containing many carbon atoms branching and twisting within one molecule. Many organic compounds are nonpolar gases, liquids, or low melting solids. Students will also be introduced to the concept of a structural formula. Writing a compound in this fashion shows the position of the molecule's atoms, in addition to the number of atoms. Structural formulas also enable the student to see isomers of compounds—structures with the same formula but different shapes and properties.

PERFORMANCE OBJECTIVES 10-1

1. **Explain why scientists no longer believe that organic compounds must come from living organisms.**
2. **List some carbon compounds that are not organic.**
3. **Describe the physical state of most organic compounds.**
4. **Diagram structural formulas of simple hydrocarbons.**
5. **Diagram structural isomers of a given hydrocarbon.**

SCIENCE TERMS 10-1

organic compound p. 234
organic chemistry p. 235
structural formula p. 237
isomer p. 238

What do sugar, plastic, paper, and gasoline have in common? All of these substances contain the element carbon. Carbon is present in more than 2 million known compounds, and this number is rapidly increasing. Approximately 100,000 new carbon compounds are being isolated or synthesized every year! In fact, more than 90 percent of all known compounds contain carbon!

Most compounds that contain carbon are known as organic compounds. The word *organic* means "coming from life." Because carbon-containing compounds are present in all living things, scientists once believed that **organic compounds** could be produced only by living organisms. Living things were thought to have a mysterious "vital force" that was responsible for creating carbon compounds. It was believed that the force could not be duplicated in the laboratory.

In 1828, the German chemist Friedrich Wöhler produced an organic compound called urea from two inorganic substances. Urea is a waste product produced by the human body. It was not long

Figure 10–1 *The element carbon is present in more than 2 million known compounds. Here you see two different forms of the pure element—diamond (left) and graphite (right). What branch of chemistry deals with carbon compounds?* ❶

234

Figure 10–2 *Because of the way carbon atoms combine with other carbon atoms as well as with atoms of different elements, a great variety of organic compounds exists. These include synthetic rubber for automobile tires (top left), candlewax (top right), nylon (right), and aspirin (bottom). What types of bonds can carbon atoms form with other carbon atoms?* ❷

before chemists accepted the idea that organic compounds could be prepared from materials that were never part of a living organism. What is common to all organic compounds is not that they originated in living things but that they all contain the element carbon. Today, the majority of organic compounds are synthesized in laboratories.

The branch of chemistry that deals with the study of carbon compounds is called **organic chemistry.** You should note, however, that there are some carbon compounds that are *not* considered ❷ organic compounds. The carbonates of metals, such as calcium carbonate and magnesium carbonate, are considered inorganic compounds. So are the oxides of carbon, such as carbon dioxide and carbon monoxide.

The Bonding of Carbon

Carbon's ability to combine with itself and with ❸ other elements explains why such a large number of carbon compounds exist. Carbon atoms form covalent bonds with other carbon atoms. The simplest bond involves 2 carbon atoms. The most complex involves thousands of carbon atoms. The carbon atoms can form long straight chains, branched chains, single rings, or rings joined together.

235

amount of a hydrocarbon beside the water spot. (If a hydrocarbon is unavailable, spray some rubbing alcohol, or acetone, in its place. **CAUTION:** *Avoid prolonged exposure and keep away from flames.*) The hydrocarbon compound will evaporate quickly because of its nonpolar property compared to the slowly evaporating water.

SINGLE BOND

DOUBLE BOND

TRIPLE BOND

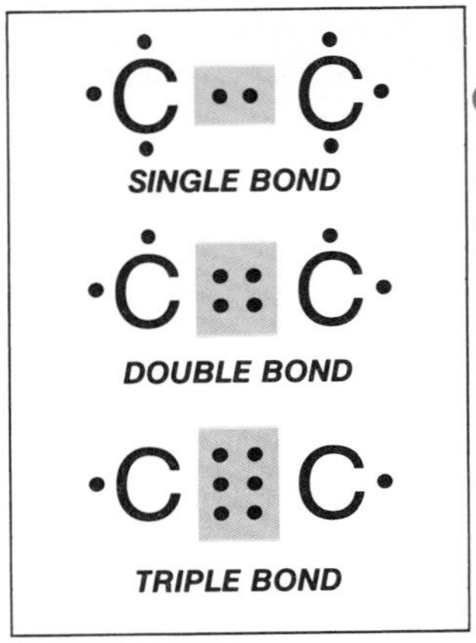

Figure 10–3 *In a single bond, one pair of electrons is shared. In a double bond, two pairs of electrons are shared. How many pairs of electrons are shared in a triple bond?* ❷

Figure 10–4 *Nonpolar organic compounds do not dissolve in polar solvents. So oil—a mixture of organic compounds—floats on water, creating this oil slick.*

The bonds between carbon atoms can be single covalent bonds, double covalent bonds, or triple covalent bonds. In a single bond, one pair of electrons is shared between 2 carbon atoms. In a double bond, two pairs of electrons are shared between 2 carbon atoms. How many pairs of electrons are shared in a triple bond? ❶

Carbon atoms also bond with many other elements. These other elements include oxygen, hydrogen, members of the nitrogen family, and the halogens. The simplest organic compounds contain just carbon and hydrogen. Because there are so many compounds of carbon and hydrogen, they form a class of organic compounds all their own. You will read about this class of compounds in the next section.

A great variety of organic compounds exist because the same atoms that bond together to form one compound may be arranged in several other ways in several other compounds. Each different arrangement of atoms represents a separate organic compound.

Properties of Organic Compounds

As you just learned, carbon compounds contain covalent bonds. These covalent bonds form molecules that are typically nonpolar, or without positive and negative ends. These two bonding characteristics determine some of the physical and chemical properties of organic compounds.

Organic compounds usually exist as gases, liquids, or low-melting solids. Organic liquids generally have strong odors and low boiling points. Another property of organic liquids is that they do not conduct an electric current. What is the name for a substance whose solution does not conduct electricity? ❸

Most organic solids have low melting points. Some even melt at temperatures slightly above room temperature. Organic compounds whose molecules are nonpolar will not dissolve in polar solvents, such as water. Oil, which is a mixture of organic compounds, floats on water because the two liquids are insoluble. In what type of solvents will most organic substances readily dissolve? ❹

10-1 (continued)

Content Development
The concept of inorganic and organic may be further explained by showing students the reaction reportedly used by Wohler. Inorganic ammonium isocyanate was heated to form "organic" urea. In this reaction $NH_4OCN \rightarrow H_2NCONH_2$. The bonding in the inorganic salt was rearranged to allow both nitrogen atoms to attach to the carbon atom. This "organic" compound made in a test tube had the same formula and properties as the waste product produced by humans.

Skills Development
Skill: Interpreting formulas
Students will be able to better interpret organic formulas if they remember that carbon forms four bonds. Using Figure 10-5 have them count the number of bonds for each carbon atom. Also show some larger organic molecules to show the four bonds of carbon.

One way to illustrate the importance of isomers to structure and properties is to use the example of straight chain pentane C_5H_{12} and neopentane $C(CH_3)_4$. The latter has a spherelike structure with four CH_3 groups extending symmetrically around the central carbon atom. Ask,

• **C_5H_{12} and $C(CH_3)_4$ both have mo-**

Structural Formulas

A molecular formula for a compound indicates what elements make up that compound and how many atoms of each element are present in a molecule. For example, the molecular formula for the organic compound ethane is C_2H_6. In every molecule of ethane, there are 2 carbon atoms and 6 hydrogen atoms.

What a molecular formula does not indicate about a molecule of a compound is how the different atoms are arranged. To do this, a **structural formula** is used. A structural formula shows the kind, number, and arrangement of atoms in a molecule. You can think of a structural formula as being a model of a molecule.

Figure 10–5 shows the structural formula for ethane and two other organic compounds—methane and propane. Note that in a structural formula, a dash (—) is used to represent the pair of shared electrons forming a covalent bond. In writing structural formulas, it is important that you remember the electron arrangement in a carbon atom.

METHANE CH_4 **ETHANE** C_2H_6 **PROPANE** C_3H_8

Carbon has 4 valence electrons, or 4 electrons in its outermost energy level. Each of these 4 electrons will form a covalent bond with an electron of another atom to produce a stable outermost level containing 8 electrons. Therefore, when structural formulas are written, there can be no dangling bonds—no dangling dashes!

Isomers

Structural formulas are very useful in organic chemistry. Knowing the arrangement of atoms in a molecule is important because several different organic compounds may have the same molecular

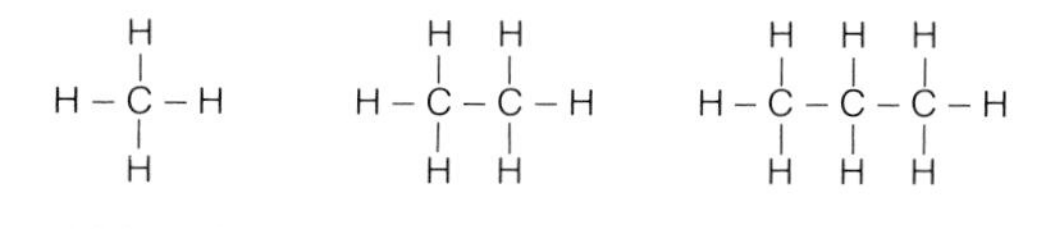

Figure 10–5 *The first three members of the alkane series are methane, ethane, and propane. Note that each carbon atom is surrounded by four dashes, corresponding to four pairs of shared electrons.*

lecular weights of 72, yet one boils at 36°C and the other at 10°C. Why are there different properties for these isomers? Observing Figure 10-7 may enable you to make some inference. (Both compounds are nonpolar. Boiling involves overcoming the attractions between molecules. $C(CH_3)_4$ has nearly spherical structure that allows only minimal area for contact with other $C(CH_3)_4$ molecules. The chain-like C_5H_{12}, however, has many places for intermolecular contact and boils at the higher temperature.)

Skills Development
Skill: Identifying patterns
Remember that carbon must have four bonds and hydrogen must have one.
• **Predict the formula of the hydrocarbon octane.** (C_8H_{18})
• **Diagram the unbranched structural formula of octane.**
• **Diagram two branched isomers of octane.**

Reinforcement
In order to emphasize the nonpolar nature of most hydrocarbons, point out that car waxes are largely high molecular weight hydrocarbons.
• **In addition to improved appearance, why do we often cover automobiles with a thin layer of wax?** (The hydrocarbons in wax keep a nonpolar layer between the metal of the automobile and the polar water in the environment.)

10-1 (continued)

Reinforcement

When dealing with isomers for the first time, students may confuse two identical structures. For example, the middle pentane isomers in Figure 10-7 could be flopped right to left, which is actually the same isomer shown in the textbook, even though the attached carbon group appears to be attached to the third carbon instead of the second. Actually the two are mirror images, not structural isomers.

Enrichment

Although the structures shown in Figures 10-5 and 10-6 indicate that the hydrocarbons are in a straight line, the actual molecular shape is twisted. For example, in Figure 10-5 propane appears to have the three carbons arranged along a 180° bond angle. The actual measured angles would show an angle of 109° from one carbon to the next resulting in a "jagged" structure. The hydrogen atoms are also 109° away from each carbon atom. This three-dimensional twisting gives the molecules several contact points to cause some weak attractions.

The 109° angle results because of an electron rearrangement with the

BUTANE
C_4H_{10}

ISOBUTANE
C_4H_{10}

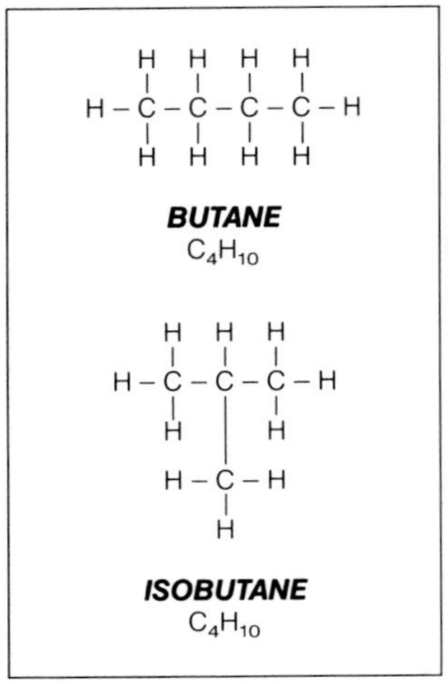

Figure 10-6 *Butane has two isomers—normal butane and isobutane. Which isomer is a branched chain?* ❷

formula. The structural formula helps to tell the compounds apart.

Compounds that have the same molecular formula but different structures are called **isomers.** Figure 10–6 shows two isomers of butane, C_4H_{10}. Notice that one isomer is a straight chain and the other isomer is a branched chain. In a branched chain, all the carbon atoms are not in a straight line. This difference in structure will account for any difference in the physical and chemical properties of these two compounds.

Figure 10–7 shows three isomers of pentane, C_5H_{12}. This time there is one straight chain and two branched chains. To see the difference between the two branched chains, count the number of carbon atoms in the straight-chain portion of each molecule. How many are there in each branched isomer? ❶

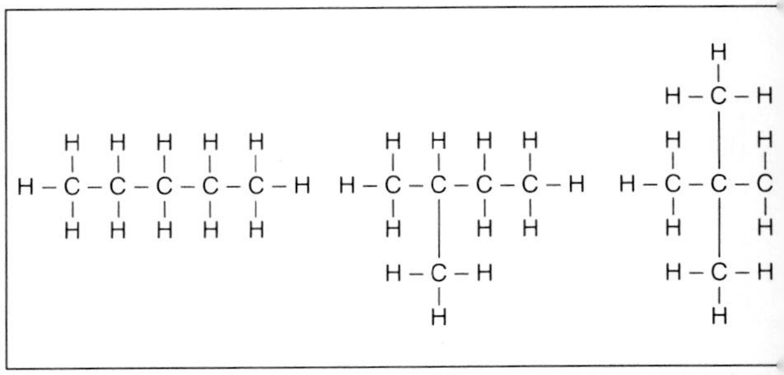

Figure 10-7 *As the number of carbon atoms increases, the number of isomers increases. How many carbon atoms are in the straight-chain portion of each pentane isomer?* ❸

What do you think happens to the number of possible isomers as the number of carbon atoms in a molecule increases? The compound whose formula is $C_{15}H_{32}$ could have more than 400 isomers!

SECTION REVIEW

1. What are organic compounds?
2. What four factors account for the abundance of carbon compounds?
3. What are three general properties of organic compounds?
4. Could two compounds have the same structural formula but different molecular formulas?

238

carbon atom. The orbitals in the s and p sublevels rearrange to form new orbitals for bonding. These new orbitals, four for carbon, are 109° apart (the shape of a tetrahedron).

Section Review 10-1

1. Compounds that contain the element carbon
2. Carbon atoms form covalent bonds with other carbon atoms. The bonds between carbon atoms can be single,

double, or triple covalent bonds. Carbon atoms bond with many other elements. The same atoms may be arranged in several different ways.
3. Gases, liquids, and low-melting solids; liquids: nonelectrolytes, strong odor, low boiling point; solids: low melting point; Most do not dissolve in water.
4. No. In order to have the same structural formula, they would have to have the same kind and number of

10–2 Hydrocarbons

Have you ever noticed a sign at a service station advertising "high octane" gasoline? Octane is a member of a large group of organic compounds known as **hydrocarbons.** A hydrocarbon is an organic compound that contains only hydrogen and carbon.

There are thousands of different hydrocarbons. Many fuels contain hydrocarbons. Natural gas and petroleum are the most abundant sources of hydrocarbons. Natural gas is mostly the hydrocarbon methane. Petroleum is a more complex mixture of hydrocarbons. The hydrocarbons in petroleum range from 1-carbon molecules to more than 50-carbon molecules. Hydrocarbons are excellent fuels because they burn in the presence of oxygen to produce heat and light.

Hydrocarbons can be classified as saturated or unsaturated depending upon the type of bonds between carbon atoms. In **saturated hydrocarbons,** all the bonds between carbon atoms are single covalent bonds. In **unsaturated hydrocarbons,** one or more of the bonds between carbon atoms is a double covalent or triple covalent bond.

Alkanes

The **alkanes** are straight-chain or branched-chain hydrocarbons in which all the bonds between carbon atoms are single covalent bonds. Alkanes are saturated hydrocarbons. All the hydrocarbons that are alkanes belong to the alkane series. The simplest ❸ member of the alkane series is methane, CH_4. Methane consists of 1 carbon atom surrounded by 4 hydrogen atoms. Why are there 4 hydrogen atoms? ❺

❼ The next simplest alkane is ethane, C_2H_6. How does the formula for ethane differ from the formula for methane? After ethane, the next member of the alkane series is propane, C_3H_8. Can you begin to see a pattern to the formulas for each successive alkane? Ethane has one more carbon atom and two more hydrogen atoms than methane. Propane has one more carbon atom and two more hydrogen atoms than ethane. Each member of the alkane series is formed by adding 1 carbon atom and 2 hydrogen atoms to the previous compound.

To classify various types of hydrocarbons

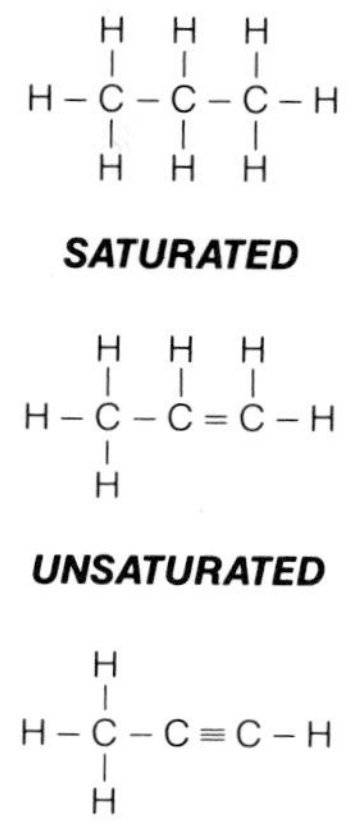

SATURATED

UNSATURATED

UNSATURATED

Figure 10-8 *Hydrocarbons can be classified as saturated or unsaturated on the basis of the type of bonds between carbon atoms. Saturated hydrocarbons contain single covalent bonds. What type of bonds do unsaturated hydrocarbons contain?* ❻

239

10-2 HYDROCARBONS

SECTION PREVIEW 10-2

In this section, students are introduced to four general classes of hydrocarbons; alkanes, alkenes, alkynes, and cyclic compounds. In each case, special properties are shown. Alkanes are "saturated," that is, the carbon atoms in the molecule contain the maximum number of bonded hydrogens. Alkenes and alkynes are "unsaturated." This term implies either a double bond (alkenes) or triple bond (alkynes) within the molecule. Cycloalkanes are carbon compounds that have closed in on themselves creating a ring. Other ring compounds have alternating double and single bonds within the ring. These are derivatives of benzene and are called aromatic compounds.

A systematic naming procedure for hydrocarbons is also presented. This organized system teaches students to name hydrocarbons based on the number of continuously bonded carbons within the compound. Figure 10-10 displays the first ten such compounds in the alkane series.

PERFORMANCE OBJECTIVES 10-2

1. **Define saturated and unsaturated hydrocarbons.**
2. **Identify the names and formulas for the first ten hydrocarbons in the alkane series.**
3. **Compare that the bonding differences between alkanes, alkenes, and alkynes lies in the appearance of single, double, and triple bonds respectively.**
4. **Explain the increased chemical activity of unsaturated hydrocarbons based on the presence of multiple bonding.**

SCIENCE TERMS 10-2

hydrocarbon p. 239	alkane p. 239
saturated hydrocarbon p. 239	alkene p. 241
	alkyne p. 242
unsaturated hydrocarbon p. 239	cycloalkane p. 243
	aromatic hydrocarbon p. 243

---

atoms. This is the only information a molecular formula gives.

TEACHING STRATEGY 10-2

Motivation

In order to get students to be more interested in saturated and unsaturated hydrocarbons bring samples, or if you prefer the labels, of margarine (several brands), different cooking oils, and shortening to class. After dis-

tributing examples around the class ask students to find and compare the amounts of saturated and unsaturated fats in each product. These values may be written on the board, with an important reminder of the *metric* values indicated. This will create a good situation with which to explain the differences in bonding between saturated and unsaturated hydrocarbons and introduce the further distinctions of alkane, alkene, and alkyne.

Figure 10-9 *Common alkanes include methane, which is also called marsh gas because it is present in swamps and marshes (left); propane, which is burned to provide heat for hot air balloons (center); and butane, which is the fuel in most lighters (right). What is the general formula for the alkanes?* ❶

The pattern that exists for the alkanes can be used to determine the formula for any member of the series. Each alkane differs from the preceding member of the series by the group CH_2. So a general formula for the alkanes can be written. That general formula is C_nH_{2n+2}. The letter n is the number of carbon atoms in the alkane. What would be the formula for a 15-carbon hydrocarbon? For a 30-carbon compound? ❷

Naming Hydrocarbons

Figure 10–10 shows the first ten members of the alkane series. Look at the names of the compounds. How is each name the same? How is each different? ❸

Often in organic chemistry, the names of the compounds in the same series will have the same ending, or suffix. Thus, the members of the alkane series all end with the suffix -ane, the same ending as in the series name. The first part of each name, or the prefix, indicates the number of carbon atoms present in the compound. The prefix *meth-* indicates 1 carbon atom. The prefix *eth-*, 2 carbon atoms, and the prefix *prop-*, 3. According to Figure 10–10, how many carbon atoms are indicated by the prefix *but-*? How many carbon atoms are in octane? As you ❹ study other hydrocarbon series, you will see that

Sharpen Your Skills

Octane Rating

1. Find out what the octane rating of gasoline means.
2. Go to a local gas station and find out the octane ratings of the different grades of gasoline being sold. Compare the prices of the different grades. Ask the station attendant to describe how each grade of gasoline performs.

②

240

10-2 (continued)

Content Development

Emphasize the requirement that hydrogen forms one bond and carbon forms four. This concept will help students see the relationship bonding has to formula. For example, draw out the changes shown in Figure 10-8 to show that forming a double bond within the saturated C_3H_8 requires that two hydrogens be removed (a process called dehydrogenation) in order for each carbon to still have four bonds. Forming a triple bond within the molecule requires that two more hydrogen atoms be removed. This still leaves each carbon with four bonds and a resulting formula of C_3H_4. The name of this compound would be propyne.

Remembering the names of the first ten alkanes is very important. Figure 10-10 gives students the list of formulas and names for the first ten. Students may be helped to remember this by having a few chairs tied together on different class days. For example, have four chairs tied together in class. Ask students to name the alkane represented and tell how many hydrogens would be needed if the four chairs were an alkane, alkene, or alkyne. On another day repeat the plan with six chairs.

ALKANE SERIES			
Name	**Formula**	**Name**	**Formula**
Methane	CH_4	Hexane	C_6H_{14}
Ethane	C_2H_6	Heptane	C_7H_{16}
Propane	C_3H_8	Octane	C_8H_{18}
Butane	C_4H_{10}	Nonane	C_9H_{20}
Pentane	C_5H_{12}	Decane	$C_{10}H_{22}$

Figure 10-10 *This table shows the names and formulas for the first ten members of the alkane series. What does the prefix* dec- *mean?* (5)

these prefixes are used again and again. It is important that you become familiar with the prefixes that mean 1 to 10 carbon atoms.

Alkenes

Hydrocarbons in which at least one pair of carbon atoms is joined by a double covalent bond are called **alkenes.** Alkenes are unsaturated hydrocarbons. The first member of the alkene series is ethene, C_2H_4. The next member of the alkene series is propene, C_3H_6. (3)

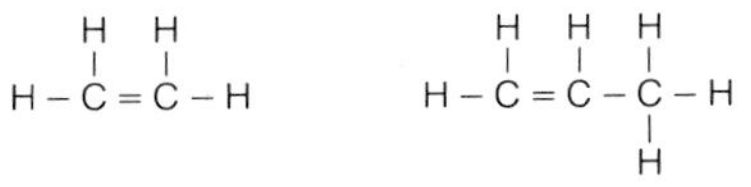

ETHENE
C_2H_4

PROPENE
C_3H_6

Figure 10-11 *The first two members of the alkene series are ethene and propene. What kind of bonds do the alkenes have?* (6)

Figure 10–12 on page 242 shows the first seven members of the alkene series. What do you notice about the name of each compound? (7)

TEACHER DEMONSTRATION

If the room is equipped with a natural gas line, light a Bunsen burner to show the property of combustion of hydrocarbons. Either write out on a chalkboard or use molecular models to show the balanced combustion reaction

$$CH_4 + 2O_2 \rightarrow 2H_2O + CO_2$$

At the same time, carefully light a propane torch and illustrate the balanced reaction

$$C_3H_8 + 5O_2 \rightarrow 4H_2O + 3CO_2$$

Also, at the same time light a disposable butane lighter and illustrate the balanced reaction

$$2C_4H_{10} + 13O_2 \rightarrow 10H_2O + 8CO_2$$

CAUTION: *As with any open flames, remove all flammable materials from the vicinity.*

This demonstration can be used to illustrate the formulas of alkanes, the property of hydrocarbon combustion, the similarity of products (carbon dioxide and water) from hydrocarbon combustion, plus other general chemistry concepts such as equation balancing.

• **What is the balanced equation that shows the combustion of octane?**
($C_8H_{18} + 8O_2 \rightarrow 8CO_2 + 9H_2$)

Motivation

The alkane series has been sometimes called the paraffin series. This term comes from Latin and literally translates as "small affinity" or "small attraction." The paraffins, alkanes, are not very chemically active. Students have likely heard of the hydrocarbon mixture called paraffin wax.

Enrichment

Changing an unsaturated substance into a saturated compound is an important industrial process called hydrogenation. The process does require energy to break the hydrogen molecule into individual atoms to react with the multiple bond in the unsaturated compound. The process, however, can be greatly speeded up with a platinum catalyst. This can be a way to change unsaturated oils into saturated shortenings.

ALKENE SERIES

Name	Formula
Ethene	C_2H_4
Propene	C_3H_6
Butene	C_4H_8
Pentene	C_5H_{10}
Hexene	C_6H_{12}
Heptene	C_7H_{14}
Octene	C_8H_{16}

Figure 10-12 *This table shows the names and formulas for the first seven members of the alkene series. What would a 9-carbon alkene be called?* ❷

Figure 10-14 *This table shows the names and formulas for the first five members of the alkyne series. What is the general formula for the alkynes?* ❹

ALKYNE SERIES

Name	Formula
Ethyne	C_2H_2
Propyne	C_3H_4
Butyne	C_4H_6
Pentyne	C_5H_8
Hexyne	C_6H_{10}

As you look at the formulas for the alkenes, you will again see a pattern in the number of carbon and hydrogen atoms added to each successive compound. The pattern is the addition of 1 carbon atom and 2 hydrogen atoms. The general formula for the alkenes is C_nH_{2n}. The letter n is the number of carbon atoms in the compound. What is the formula for an alkene with 12 carbons? With 20 carbons? ❶

In general, alkenes are more reactive than alkanes because a double bond is more easily broken than a single bond. So alkenes can react chemically by adding other atoms directly to their molecules.

Alkynes

Hydrocarbons in which at least one pair of carbon atoms is joined by a triple covalent bond are called **alkynes.** Alkynes are unsaturated hydrocarbons. The simplest alkyne is ethyne, C_2H_2, which is commonly known as acetylene. Perhaps you have heard of acetylene torches that are used in welding.

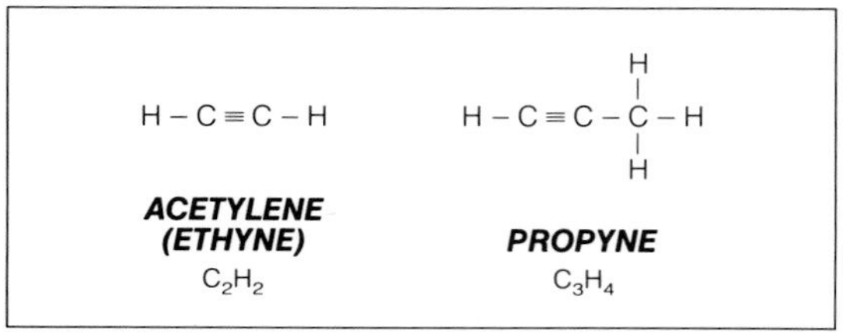

$$H-C\equiv C-H$$

ACETYLENE (ETHYNE)
C_2H_2

$$H-C\equiv C-\overset{\displaystyle H}{\underset{\displaystyle H}{C}}-H$$

PROPYNE
C_3H_4

Figure 10-13 *The simplest alkynes are ethyne and propyne. What is the common name for ethyne?* ❸

The first five members of the alkyne series are listed in Figure 10–14. Here again, each successive member of the alkyne series differs by the addition of 1 carbon atom and 2 hydrogen atoms. The general formula for the alkynes is C_nH_{2n-2}.

The alkynes are even more reactive than the alkenes. Very little energy is needed to break a triple bond. Like the alkenes, alkynes can react chemically by adding other atoms directly to their molecules. If a triple bond is broken to form a double bond, what kind of hydrocarbon will result? If the triple bond is broken to form a single bond, what kind of hydrocarbon will result? ❺

10-2 (continued)

Content Development
When atoms are double or triple bonded to each other they are held more closely together. This is because the positive nuclei are more attracted to the electron-rich area that a multiple bond provides. Other reacting atoms may also be attracted to the electron-rich area.

Benzene is usually presented as a structure with alternating double and single bonds. However, if the structure actually had some double bonds and some single bonds, the shape would be distorted because the double bonded carbon atoms would be closer together than the single bonded atoms. The structure on the right in Figure 10-16 is preferred because it represents a way of showing equal bonding between all of the carbon atoms. The actual benzene structure appears to be a result of two forms, the one on the left in the figure and another with each of the double bonds rotated to the next carbon. The result is a hybrid structure shown on the right. This phenomena is called resonance.

Skills Development
Skill: Interpreting patterns
To remember the relationship be-

Cycloalkanes and Aromatic Hydrocarbons

All the hydrocarbons you have just learned about—the alkanes, alkenes, and alkynes—are either straight-chain or branched-chain molecules. But this is not the only structure a hydrocarbon can have. Some hydrocarbons are in the shape of rings. They are often called cyclic hydrocarbons. The two main groups of cyclic hydrocarbons are the **cycloalkanes** and the **aromatic hydrocarbons.**

Cycloalkanes are saturated hydrocarbon rings. This means that they contain only single covalent bonds between carbon atoms. The simplest cycloalkane contains 3 carbon atoms. Cycloalkanes are named simply by adding the prefix *cyclo-* to the appropriate alkane name. So the simplest cycloalkane is called cyclopropane. The saturated 6-carbon cycloalkane is called cyclohexane. See Figure 10–15. What do you think the saturated 7-carbon cycloalkane is called? ❻

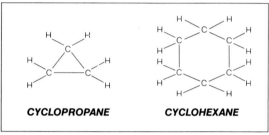

CYCLOPROPANE   CYCLOHEXANE

Figure 10-15 *Cycloalkanes are saturated hydrocarbon rings. What would the 5-carbon cycloalkane be called?* ❼

Aromatic hydrocarbons are probably the best-known class of hydrocarbons. The name of this class comes from the fact that aromatic hydrocarbons share a common physical property. These compounds have strong and often pleasant odors. ❸

The basic structure of an aromatic hydrocarbon is a ring of 6 carbon atoms joined by alternating single and double covalent bonds. This means that within the 6-carbon ring, there are 3 carbon-to-carbon single bonds and 3 carbon-to-carbon double bonds. The simplest aromatic hydrocarbon is called

243

tween multiple bonding and resulting formulas have students practice recognizing the types of compound represented by the following.

C_2H_4 (unsaturated: alkene)
CH_4 (saturated: alkane)
C_5H_8 (unsaturated: alkyne)
C_7H_{14} (unsaturated: alkene)

Enrichment
Benzene rings form the basis for many types of compounds. Moth crystals are

sold as paradichlorobenzene. Assign interested students to find the formula of this moth-killing compound ($C_6H_4Cl_2$). Another moth crystal product is naphthalene. What is its structure and formula? ($C_{10}H_8$)

10-3 SUBSTITUTED HYDROCARBONS

SECTION PREVIEW 10-3

When a hydrogen atom is removed from a hydrocarbon and substituted with another type of atom, the resulting compound is called a substituted hydrocarbon. When the substitution is done with an −OH group, the result is an alcohol. In this section, students will be shown some examples of alcohols and shown that naming of alcohols is done by placing an *ol* at the end of the hydrocarbon name.

If the substitution is based on a −COOH group, the result is an organic acid. This important group of compounds is named by adding the suffix *oic* to the root hydrocarbon name.

Another substituted hydrocarbon group presented in this section is the esters. The production of an ester is shown to be a combination of an organic acid and an alcohol.

Although there are other examples, the last substituted group in the section is the halogens. These compounds form when the active nonmetals from Group VII react with hydrocarbons.

PERFORMANCE OBJECTIVES 10-3

1. **Identify and name simple alcohol hydrocarbon derivatives.**
2. **Identify and name simple organic acid compounds.**
3. **Describe the formation of an ester compound from an organic acid and an alcohol.**
4. **List examples of halogens combining with hydrocarbons to form halogen derivatives.**

SCIENCE TERMS 10-3

substituted hydrocarbons p. 245
alcohol p. 245
hydroxyl group p. 245
denatured alcohol p. 246
organic acid p. 246

carboxyl group p. 246
ester p. 247
esterification p. 247
halogen derivative p. 247

Figure 10-16 *Benzene is an aromatic hydrocarbon with a ring structure containing 6 carbon atoms joined by alternating single and double covalent bonds (left). Benzene is used in the manufacture of explosives (right).*

BENZENE
C_6H_6

244

benzene, C_6H_6. Figure 10−16 shows the structural formula for benzene. Chemists often abbreviate this formula by drawing a hexagon with a circle in the center. Benzene is an excellent solvent for fats, oil, and rubber. It is used in the manufacture of many chemicals—including dyes, drugs, and explosives—and in the formation of synthetic materials. However, benzene is poisonous. For this reason, benzene should not be used in the school laboratory.

SECTION REVIEW

1. What are hydrocarbons?
2. Name three series of hydrocarbons.
3. What is meant by saturated and unsaturated hydrocarbons? Classify each hydrocarbon series according to these definitions.
4. What are the two groups of cyclic hydrocarbons?
5. Why is there no compound named cycloethane?

10−3 Substituted Hydrocarbons

Hydrocarbons are but one of several groups of organic compounds. Hydrocarbons contain only carbon and hydrogen atoms. But as you learned, carbon atoms form bonds with many other elements. So there are many different groups of organic

---

10-2 (continued)

Reinforcement

Some students may see the O inside the benzene ring in Figure 10-16 and mistakenly call it an oxygen atom instead of a special bonding situation.

Section Review 10-2

1. Organic compounds that contain only hydrogen and carbon

2. Alkanes, alkenes, alkynes
3. Saturated compounds have only single bonds. Alkanes are saturated hydrocarbons. Unsaturated compounds have at least one double or triple bond. Alkenes and alkynes are unsaturated hydrocarbons.
4. Cycloalkanes and aromatic hydrocarbons
5. It is impossible to form a ring out of two carbon atoms (*eth*-means "two").

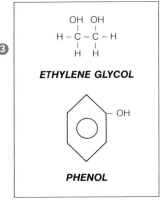

METHANOL

Figure 10-17 *Methanol, an organic alcohol (right), is used as a solvent in paints (left).*

compounds. **The important groups of organic compounds include alcohols, organic acids, esters, and halogen derivatives.** ❷

Compounds such as alcohols, organic acids, esters, and halogen derivatives are called **substituted hydrocarbons.** A substituted hydrocarbon is formed when one or more hydrogen atoms in a hydrocarbon chain or ring is replaced by a different atom or group of atoms.

Alcohols

Alcohols are substituted hydrocarbons in which one or more hydrogen atoms have been replaced by an −OH group, or **hydroxyl group.** The simplest alcohol is methanol, CH_3OH. You can see from Figure 10–17 that methanol is formed when 1 hydrogen atom in methane is replaced by the −OH group. Methanol is used to make plastics and synthetic fibers. It is also used in automobile gas tank de-icers to prevent water that has condensed in the tank from freezing. Another important use of methanol is as a solvent. Methanol, however, is very poisonous, even when used externally.

As you can tell from the name methanol, alcohols are named by adding the suffix *-ol* to the name of the corresponding hydrocarbon. When an −OH group is substituted for 1 hydrogen atom in ethane, the resulting alcohol is ethanol, C_2H_5OH. Ethanol is produced naturally by the action of yeast or bacteria on the sugar stored in grains such as corn, wheat, and barley.

Figure 10-18 *The structural formula for ethylene glycol shows how two hydrogen atoms have been replaced by two −OH groups. Phenol is an alcohol derivative of benzene. What is a common use for each of these alcohols?* ❶

ETHYLENE GLYCOL

PHENOL

245

HISTORICAL NOTES

One of the early chemical reactions scientists learned to balance was the fermentation reaction to produce the alcohol in wine.

$$C_2H_{12}O_6 \rightarrow 2CH_3CH_2OH + CO_2$$

When the percentage of alcohol becomes approximately 13 percent the yeast may die. Higher alcohol percentages for other alcoholic beverages are obtained by distilling the alcohol repeatedly.

TIE-IN/ECOLOGY

Some halogenated hydrocarbons have been proven harmful to our environment. Freon, halogenated methane CCl_2F_2, can decompose and react with ozone (O_3), converting it to molecular oxygen (O_2). The loss of ozone in our upper atmosphere means that more harmful ultraviolet rays may reach the earth's surface. Ozone screens out many of the rays.

Figure 10-19 *Formic acid, also known as methanoic acid, is the simplest organic acid. It is the acid produced by ants and is responsible for the pain caused by an ant bite. Acetic acid, the acid in vinegar, is also known as ethanoic acid. What group is characteristic of organic acids?* **1**

246

Ethanol is a good solvent for many organic compounds that do not dissolve in water. Ethanol is used in medicines. It is also the alcohol used in alcoholic beverages. In order to make ethanol available for industrial and medicinal uses only, it must be made unfit for beverage purposes. So poisonous compounds such as methanol are added to ethanol. The resulting mixture is called **denatured alcohol.**

Some alcohols have more than one –OH group. When 2 hydrogen atoms in ethane are replaced by two –OH groups, the resulting alcohol is commonly called ethylene glycol, $C_2H_4(OH)_2$. Ethylene glycol is used as a "permanent" antifreeze in automobile radiators.

When 3 hydrogen atoms in propane are replaced by three –OH groups, the resulting alcohol is called glycerol, or glycerin, $C_3H_5(OH)_3$. Glycerol, a slow-flowing liquid with a sweet taste, is used in making cellophane, soap, cosmetics, and drugs.

An alcohol can be in the form of a ring as well as a chain. When 1 hydrogen atom in a benzene ring is replaced by an –OH group, the resulting alcohol is called phenol. Phenol is used in the preparation of plastics and as a disinfectant.

Organic Acids

Organic acids are substituted hydrocarbons that contain the –COOH group, or **carboxyl group.** Figure 10–19 shows the structural formula for two common organic acids. Notice that one of the carbon–oxygen bonds in the carboxyl group is a double bond.

Organic acids are named by adding the suffix *-oic* to the name of the corresponding hydrocarbon. Most organic acids, however, have common names that are used more frequently. The simplest organic acid is methanoic acid, HCOOH. Methanoic acid is commonly called formic acid. Formic acid is found in nature in the stinging nettle plant and in certain ants. Formic acid, produced by the ant, causes the ant bite to hurt.

The acid derived from ethane is commonly called acetic acid. Acetic acid is the acid in vinegar. Vinegar contains between 4 and 6 percent acetic acid. Citric acid, which is found in citrus fruits, is a

---

10-3 (continued)

Content Development

Esterification reactions combine an acid and an alcohol. In addition to forming an ester compound, water is released. For example, the odor of oranges can be formed by combining acetic acid and octyl alcohol. Show students the equation involving structural formulas so that they can see where the water comes from.

Skills Development

Skill: Making comparisons
• **What do organic acids and organic alcohols have in common?** (Both contain –OH groups.)
• **Write out the structural formula of phenol.** (See Figure 10-18). **What would be the structural formula of benzoic acid? This substance can be used to make a food preservative.** (Check students' drawings.)
• **What is the major difference be-**

tween an acid and an alcohol? (a carbon double bonded to an oxygen)
• **Acetic acid is also known as ethanoic acid. Using Figure 10-19, write out the structural formula of ethanoic acid. Next, write out the structural formula of ethanol.** (Check students' drawings.)

Reinforcement

Ethylene glycol, antifreeze, mixes with water in a car's cooling system so easily

more complicated organic acid originally derived from the hydrocarbon propane.

Esters

If an alcohol and an organic acid are chemically combined, the resulting compound is called an **ester.** The reaction that produces an ester is called **esterification.** Esters are noted for their pleasant aromas and flavors. The substances mentioned earlier that give flavor to ice cream are esters.

Many esters occur naturally. Fruits such as strawberries, bananas, and pineapples get their sweet smell from esters. Esters can also be produced in the laboratory. Synthetic esters are used as perfume additives and artificial flavorings. ❸

Halogen Derivatives

Hydrocarbons can undergo substitution reactions in which one or more hydrogen atoms are replaced by an atom or atoms of fluorine, chlorine, bromine, or iodine. The family name for these elements is halogens. So substituted hydrocarbons that contain halogens are called **halogen derivatives.**

A variety of useful substances result from adding halogens to hydrocarbons. The compound methyl chloride, CH_3Cl, is used as a refrigerant.

Figure 10-20 *Substituted hydrocarbons known as halogen derivatives have a wide variety of uses. The rain gear these people are wearing (left) is made of polyvinyl chloride. Teflon—which is a polymer of tetrafluoroethane, $C_2H_2F_4$—is used to make tape, wire insulation, fountain pens, and a nonstick coating for cooking utensils (right).*

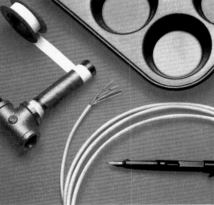

247

because the presence of the −OH group gives ethylene glycol molecules a polarity very similar to the HOH structure of water.

Enrichment

• **The odor of pineapples comes from ethyl butyerate. What acid and alcohol could be used to form this ester?** (ethyl alcohol and butyric acid)

Sharpen Your Skills

Food Additives
Skills: Expressing an opinion, comparing, applying, relating
Level: Average
Type: Hands-on/Library
Materials: food package labels

In this activity, students relate the concept of organic chemistry to their everyday lives by determining whether various food additives are organic or inorganic. They also are called upon to express an opinion on the use of additives. Most students will relate the usefulness of such additives to their potential health drawbacks.

HELP WANTED: PERFUMER to help develop new fragrances for a cosmetics and household-products manufacturer. High school diploma required. On-the-job training provided.

Think about the fragrances that greet your sense of smell every day. Think hard because you may not be fully aware of the many odors around you. For example, try to remember the fragrance of the soap or cosmetics you used today. Or the scents of foods and drinks. Imag-

ine the smell of orange juice or chocolate syrup. Think about the smell of a new car, wallet, or pair of shoes. Almost everything you buy or use has a distinct scent.

Some scents occur naturally in products, but other odors are purposely added. A person who develops scents is called a **perfumer.** Perfumers combine ingredients to make specific fragrances. Some of these ingredients—such as lemon oil—are found in nature, while others are synthetic, or artificial, ingredients.

Many of the more than 3000 ingredients used by perfumers are organic compounds. So an interest in chemistry is useful to a perfumer. Many fragrances are created by combining different ingredients until a combination with the desired fragrance is found. A perfumer may spend up to two years creating and testing one new fragrance. Read some product labels to discover items that contain fragrances created by perfumers.

If you would like information about a career as a perfumer, write to the Fragrance Foundation, 142 East 30th Street, New York, NY 10016.

Tetrachloroethane, $C_2H_2Cl_4$, which consists of 4 chlorine atoms substituted in an ethane molecule, is used in dry cleaning.

When 2 hydrogen atoms in a methane molecule are replaced by chlorine atoms, and the other 2 hydrogen atoms are replaced by fluorine atoms, a compound commonly known as Freon, CCl_2F_2, is
❶ formed. The actual name of this halogen derivative is dichlorodifluoromethane. Freon is the coolant used in many refrigerators and air conditioners.

SECTION REVIEW

1. What is a substituted hydrocarbon?
2. What is an alcohol?
3. What is an organic acid?
4. Methanol is used in car de-icers. What does this tell you about the freezing point of methanol?

10-3 (continued)

Section Review 10-3

1. A hydrocarbon in which one or more hydrogen atoms has been replaced by a different atom or group of atoms
2. A substituted hydrocarbon in which one or more hydrogen atoms has been replaced by an −OH group
3. A substituted hydrocarbon in which a hydrogen atom has been re-

placed by a −COOH group
4. The freezing point of methanol is lower than the freezing point of water.

TEACHING STRATEGY 10-4

Motivation

Ask students what they ate for breakfast. Remind students of the old adage "You are what you eat." Point out that in this section they will be able to find out exactly what this means.

• **If you had a cereal grain for break-**

fast, what did your body actually use from the cereal? (carbohydrates, proteins, and fats)

Assign students to write down or bring in the labels of any cereal from home. They should pay particular attention to the amount of protein, carbohydrate, and fats reported on the label. Then have them read the results. This introduces each topic of this section in a way relevant to student's lives.

10–4 Chemistry for Life

Have you ever thought of yourself as a chemical factory? The human body is one of the most amazing chemical factories ever created. It can produce chemicals from raw materials, start complex chemical reactions, repair and reproduce some of its own parts, and even correct its own mistakes.

What is the fuel that keeps your human chemical factory going? Nutrients contained in the foods you eat maintain the proper functioning of all the systems of the body. **The three main types of nutrients—carbohydrates, fats and oils, and proteins— are organic compounds.** ❷

Carbohydrates

Carbohydrates are organic molecules of carbon, hydrogen, and oxygen in which there are two atoms of hydrogen for every atom of oxygen. Carbohydrates are classified as **sugars** or **starches.** The simplest carbohydrate is the sugar glucose, $C_6H_{12}O_6$.

Glucose has an isomer called fructose. Fructose is found in some fruits and in honey. When a glucose

Figure 10-21 *The human body is a chemical factory that does an amazing variety of jobs. But to keep it working properly, the right nutrients must be supplied. What are these nutrients?* ❶

249

10-4 CHEMISTRY FOR LIFE

SECTION REVIEW 10-4

In this chapter-concluding section, three major nutrient groups are introduced as organic compounds. Carbohydrates are divided into two general classes, sugars and starches. Carbohydrate molecules contain carbon and two hydrogens for each oxygen. The carbohydrate compounds are our bodies' main source of energy. Fats and oils are sometimes referred to as lipids. They are also made up of carbon, hydrogen and oxygen. Lipids are esters with large molecular weight. Proteins are made up of many smaller molecules, called amino acids, linked together. Amino acids contain carbon, hydrogen, oxygen, and nitrogen. There are 22 known amino acids. Some of the amino acids also contain sulfur and phosphorus.

PERFORMANCE OBJECTIVES 10-4

1. **Name three types of organic compounds that play important roles in the human body.**

2. **Write an equation showing the breakdown of sugars in the body.**

3. **Compare carbohydrates, lipids, and proteins based on molecular bonding or composition.**

SCIENCE TERMS 10-4

carbohydrate p. 249

sugar p. 249

starch p. 249

polymer p. 250

monomer p. 250

fat p. 250

oil p. 250

lipid p. 250

protein p. 250

amino acid p. 250

Content Development

The term *carbohydrate* comes from the basic structure in those compounds. This could be presented as carbon + water. The formula of most carbohydrates shows carbon bonded to hydrogen and oxygen, which is in the two to one ratio found in water. ($C(H_2O)$)

Using the equation on page 250 show students that sugars in the body are oxidized to form energy. We obtain the carbohydrates by eating certain foods. Later, using oxygen that we have inhaled, the carbohydrate is oxidized. We then exhale the byproduct CO_2, which can be used by plants to make more carbohydrates.

Skills Development

Skill: Balancing equations
• **What is the reaction that forms sucrose?** ($C_6H_{12}O_6 + C_6H_{12}O_6 \rightarrow C_2H_{22}O_{11} + H_2O$).

Enrichment

Glucose is made up of a six-atom ring and is in the group of compounds called hexoses. Fructose is a five-atom ring and is in the group of compounds called pentoses.

TEACHER DEMONSTRATION

Students are probably familiar with starches in food products. Their awareness of starch as a polymer and their overall understanding of polymers can be increased by giving them a less abstract view. Bring several wire coat hangers to class. Explain that each hanger represents a simple sugar, or monomer. Place the monomers in a large paper sack. (You may want to label the sack "polymerization reaction" or "starch formation.") Close the paper sack and shuffle the contents vigorously. After a short time, open the sack. Carefully grab one hanger and slowly remove it. You will find several other hangers attached forming a "polymer" from the available monomers. The nylon demonstration mentioned earlier is also an example of polymer formation.

TIE-IN/HEALTH

Amino acids that cannot be manufactured by humans must be consumed in our diets. These eight amino acids are called "essential" because it is essential that we ingest them. They are isoleucine, leucine, lysine, methionine, phenylalanine, threonine, tryptophan, and valine.

Figure 10-22 *Carbohydrates are organic molecules of carbon, hydrogen, and oxygen. They are the body's main source of energy. The foods shown here (top) are rich in carbohydrates. Fats and oils are complex esters often called lipids. They too are sources of energy. The foods shown here (bottom) are rich in fats and oils.*

250

molecule is joined to a fructose molecule, the more complex sugar sucrose, $C_{12}H_{22}O_{11}$, is formed. Sucrose is common table sugar, which is also known as cane sugar.

Starches are another kind of carbohydrate. Starches are made of long chains of sugar molecules hooked together. Starch molecules are **polymers** (PAHL-ih-merz) of many simple sugars. A polymer is a giant molecule made up of smaller molecules joined together. The smaller molecules that form a polymer are called **monomers** (MAHN-uh-merz). Starch is found in foods such as bread, cereal, potatoes, pasta, and rice.

Carbohydrates are the body's main source of energy. When you eat starches and complex sugars, your body first breaks them down into simple sugars during the process of digestion. Then the simple sugars are combined with oxygen according to the following reaction:

① $$C_6H_{12}O_6 + 6O_2 \longrightarrow 6CO_2 + 6H_2O + energy$$

Fats and Oils

Like carbohydrates, **fats** and **oils** contain carbon, hydrogen, and oxygen. These molecules are large, complex esters. Fats and oils are formed from the reaction between the alcohol glycerol and organic acids called fatty acids. Fats and oils store twice as much energy as carbohydrates.

As a class of organic compounds, fats and oils are sometimes called **lipids** (LIHP-ihdz). Fats are solid at room temperature, while oils are liquid. Lipids include cooking oils, butter, and the fat in meat. Although fats and oils are high-energy nutrients, too much of these substances can be a health hazard. Unused fats are stored by the body. This increases body weight. In addition, scientific evidence indicates that eating too much saturated fat—animal fat—may contribute to heart disease.

Proteins

Proteins are used to build and repair body parts. Every living part of your body contains proteins.

10-4 (continued)

Content Development
Because fats form from a reaction between an alcohol (glycerol) and an acid (large molecular weight organic acid), they may be considered to be esters. A common fat in animals is tristearin, which is formed from stearic acid ($CH_3(CH_2)_{16}COOH$). When a fat or oil is reacted with a strong alkali such as NaOH, the product is salt of a fatty acid called a "soap." The process of soap manufacture is called saponification.

Reinforcement
• **Fats are usually obtained from animals and consist of saturated hydrocarbons. Oils are usually obtained from plants and consist of unsaturated hydrocarbons. What is the bonding difference between saturated and unsaturated hydrocarbons?** (Saturated indicates the presence of only single carbon bonds; unsaturated indicates the existence of multiple bonded carbon.)

Content Development
Proteins are formed when amino acids link together through a peptide linkage. This type of bonding results because amino acids each have an organic acid part and a nitrogen part. (Amines are organic compounds containing nitrogen.) The bond forms as the nitrogen part of one amino acid gives up a hydrogen that bonds with the −OH part of the acid, which releases water and results in the two amino acids bonding to each other. This process may be repeated to form proteins of very large molecular weight. Hemoglobin, for example, has

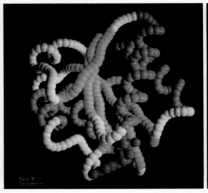

Figure 10-23 *Proteins are made of amino acids, which contain carbon, hydrogen, oxygen, and nitrogen. Most protein chains are hundreds of amino acids long. The molecular model shows the arrangement of atoms in a typical protein molecule (left). Proteins are found in foods such as meat, chicken, milk, eggs, and cheese (right).*

Blood, muscles, brain tissue, skin, and hair all contain proteins.

The raw materials used to make proteins are a special group of organic acids called **amino acids.** All amino acids contain carbon, hydrogen, oxygen, and nitrogen. Some amino acids also contain sulfur and phosphorus. There are 22 different amino acids found in nature.

Your body builds proteins by linking amino acids together. Most protein chains are hundreds of amino acid units long. Some amino acids are produced by the body itself. Others must be obtained from foods. These amino acids are called essential amino acids. Meat, fish, dairy products, and soybeans are sources of essential amino acids.

SECTION REVIEW

1. What are the three main types of organic compounds found in the human body?
2. What is a polymer? A monomer?
3. How are fats and oils formed?
4. Write a balanced equation for the reaction that produces energy from simple sugars. What waste products are given off by the body as a result of this reaction?

Sharpen Your Skills

Saturated and Unsaturated Fats

Many of the foods you eat contain saturated and unsaturated fats. Using books and other reference materials in the library, find out what is meant by the terms *saturated* and *unsaturated fats.* Find out the health risks and benefits associated with eating more of one or the other type of fat.

Make a list of foods that contain saturated fats and those that contain unsaturated fats. Analyze your daily diet for a one-week period. Indicate which types of fats you eat, how much of each you eat, and how often.

251

Sharpen Your Skills

Saturated and Unsaturated Fats
Skills: Relating, comparing, applying, drawing conclusions
Level: Enriched
Type: Hands-on/Library
This activity will help relate chemistry concepts to everyday life. Students will discover in their research that many physicians feel that people should limit their intake of saturated fats. Students will analyze their own diets and perhaps revise their eating habits based on their knowledge of organic chemistry.

---

a molecular weight near 68,000. The amino acid sequence in a protein determines the identity of that protein. Simply changing the sequence of one amino acid in a protein may change the function of the protein. Ask,
• **How many possible ways could three amino acids be linked?** (six; ABC, CAB, BAC, BCA, CAB, CBA)

Enrichment
There are 20 commonly occurring

amino acids. This represents an enormous number of possible sequences with which to form proteins.
• **How many possible arrangements can be made from 20 amino acids?** (Hint, use factorials 20! = approximately 2 followed by 18 zeros)

Cross-Unit Reference
After students complete this chapter, you may want to have them read Chapter 27 Chemical Technology.

Section Review 10-4
1. Carbohydrates, fats and oils, proteins
2. Giant molecule made up of smaller molecules, or monomers, linked together
3. By the reaction between the alcohol glycerol and a fatty acid (esterification)
4. $C_6H_{12}O_6 + 6O_2 \rightarrow 6CO_2 + 6H_2O$ + energy; carbon dioxide and water

LABORATORY INVESTIGATION PREPARING AND IDENTIFYING ESTERS

BEFORE THE LAB

1. Gather all equipment at least one day prior to the investigation. You should gather enough materials to meet your class needs, assuming six students per group.
2. If the chemicals required must be prepared, consult a physical science handbook as to the easiest way to prepare them.

PRE-LAB DISCUSSION

Before beginning this investigation, review with students the structural formulas and composition of esters. Also review the process of esterification. Suggest students formulate hypotheses as to the physical properties of esters. After completing the investigation, have students relate their original hypotheses to their observations and conclusions.

SKILL DEVELOPMENT

Students will use the following skills while completing this invesigation.
1. Safety
2. Manipulative
3. Comparing
4. Observing
5. Relating
6. Applying
7. Hypothesizing
8. Recording
9. Measuring

SAFETY TIPS

It is essential that proper safety precautions be reviewed before students actually begin this investigation. Discuss the proper use and disposal of acids with students and the need for safety goggles.

TEACHING STRATEGY FOR LAB PROCEDURE

1. Make sure students wear their safety goggles.
2. It is important that all directions be followed exactly as stated. Circulate throughout the room to ensure that directions are followed as stated and that all appropriate safety precautions are followed.
3. Help students dispose of all chemicals at the completion of the investigation.

OBSERVATIONS

1. Accept all reasonable descriptions for the odor of ethanol. Most students will say it smells like alcohol. The butyric acid may be described as smelling like rancid butter.
2. No; no; pineapple
3. Like nail polish remover
4. Wintergreen

CONCLUSIONS

1. esterification; ester
2. Fruity or flowery
3. No
4. Ethyl acetate: ethanol plus acetic acid. Smells like nail polish remover. Methyl salicylate: methanol plus salicylic acid. Smells like wintergreen.

Problem

How are esters prepared? What physical property is used to identify esters?

Materials (per group)

safety goggles   3 beakers
3 test tubes   3 glass plates
test tube holder   medicine dropper
test tube rack
hot plate and water bath (Do not use a burner for this experiment.)
5 mL concentrated sulfuric acid
5 mL methanol
10 mL ethanol
5 mL butyric acid
5 mL glacial acetic acid
1 g salicylic acid
150 mL cold distilled water

Procedure

1. Put on your safety goggles.
2. Pour about 3 mL of ethanol into a test tube. Carefully note the odor of the liquid. Add 3 mL butyric acid. Again, carefully note the odor of the liquid.
3. Over a sink, carefully add about 10 drops of sulfuric acid to the mixture in the test tube. **CAUTION:** Sulfuric acid can burn the skin.
4. Warm the mixture in a water bath for 5 to 6 minutes. **CAUTION:** Do not point the test tube toward yourself or any of your classmates.
5. Pour the contents of the test tube into a beaker containing 50 mL of cold distilled water. Cover the beaker with a glass plate and let stand for 1 to 2 minutes. Note the odor.
6. Repeat steps 2 to 5 using acetic acid instead of butyric acid. Carefully note the odors.

7. Repeat steps 2 to 5 using methanol and about 10 mL of salicylic acid. Carefully note the odors.

Observations

1. What is the odor of ethanol? Of butyric acid?
2. Does the product of the reaction between ethanol and butyric acid smell the same as ethanol? As butyric acid? Describe the odor.
3. Describe the odor of the product formed by the reaction between ethanol and acetic acid.
4. Describe the odor of the product formed by the reaction between methanol and salicylic acid.

Conclusions

1. What is the name of the reaction between an alcohol and an organic acid? What product is formed?
2. Give a general description of the odor of an ester.
3. Does an ester have the same odor as the reactants that form it?
4. You produced three esters in this experiment. These esters are ethyl acetate, methyl salicylate, and ethyl butyrate. Identify the alcohol and organic acid from which each ester is formed and describe the odor of each ester.
5. Why is methyl salicylate called oil of wintergreen?

252

CHAPTER REVIEW

10-1 Carbon and Its Compounds

❑ Most compounds that contain carbon are called organic compounds

❑ A structural formula shows the kind, number, and arrangement of atoms in a molecule.

❑ Compounds that have the same molecular formula but different structural formulas are called isomers.

10-2 Hydrocarbons

❑ Compounds that contain only hydrogen and carbon are called hydrocarbons.

❑ Saturated hydrocarbons contain only single bonds; unsaturated hydrocarbons contain at least one double or triple bond.

❑ The alkanes are saturated hydrocarbons.

❑ The alkenes are unsaturated hydrocarbons containing at least one double covalent bond.

❑ The alkynes are unsaturated hydrocarbons containing at least one triple covalent bond.

❑ Cycloalkanes are saturated cyclic hydrocarbons, or hydrocarbons with a ring structure.

❑ Aromatic hydrocarbons have a ring structure in which 6 carbon atoms are joined by alternating single and double covalent bonds.

10-3 Substituted Hydrocarbons

❑ A substituted hydrocarbon is formed when one or more hydrogen atoms is replaced by a different atom or group of atoms.

❑ Important substituted hydrocarbons include alcohols, organic acids, esters, and halogen derivatives.

❑ When an alcohol and an organic acid react chemically, an ester is formed. The reaction is called esterification.

10-4 Chemistry for Life

❑ The principal organic compounds in the human body are carbohydrates, fats and oils, and proteins. These compounds are often called nutrients.

❑ Carbohydrates are compounds of carbon, hydrogen, and oxygen. The ratio of hydrogen atoms to oxygen atoms in a carbohydrate is two to one.

❑ Fats and oils are esters formed from the alcohol glycerol and fatty acids.

❑ Proteins are formed from amino acids, which contain carbon, hydrogen, oxygen, and nitrogen. Some amino acids also contain sulfur and phosphorus.

VOCABULARY

Define each term in a complete sentence.

alcohol	denatured alcohol	monomer	starch
alkane	ester	oil	structural formula
alkene	esterification	organic acid	substituted hydrocarbon
alkyne	fat	organic chemistry	sugar
amino acid	halogen derivative	organic compound	unsaturated hydrocarbon
aromatic hydrocarbon	hydrocarbon	polymer	
carbohydrate	hydroxyl group	protein	
carboxyl group	isomer	saturated hydrocarbon	
cycloalkane	lipid		

253

Ethyl butyrate: ethanol and butyric acid. Smells like pineapple.

5. Because it smells like wintergreen

GOING FURTHER: ENRICHMENT

Part 1

Ask students to see if they can identify esters in products they have at home by comparing them to the odors they observed in this investigation. Make sure you caution students to always waft the fumes from any container toward their nose with their hands, rather than smelling directly from the container.

Part 2

Have students design an experiment to test for the presence of esters in common household products.

CHAPTER REVIEW

MULTIPLE CHOICE

1. a 3. b 5. a 7. d 9. a
2. c 4. b 6. c 8. b 10. b

COMPLETION

1. Coming from life
2. double
3. isomers
4. alkene
5. cyclo-
6. substituted hydrocarbon
7. alcohol
8. ester
9. carbohydrates
10. polymers

TRUE OR FALSE

1. F carbon
2. F structural
3. F saturated
4. T
5. T
6. F more
7. F alkynes
8. T
9. T
10. F proteins

SKILL BUILDING

1. Alkane: a; alkene: c, e; alkyne: b, f; aromatic: d
2. The number of hydrogen atoms in each series decreases by 2 because of a change in bonding from single, to double, to triple. The addition of another carbon-to-carbon bond eliminates 2 hydrogen atoms.
3. Check students' drawings.
4. Ester: a; alcohol: c; organic acid: d; halogen derivative: b
5. Check students' drawings.
6. Check students' drawings.
7. The alkene has a double bond between 2 adjacent carbon atoms, so the minimum number of carbon atoms has to be 2. The alkyne has a triple bond so the minimum number of carbon atoms has to be 20.

ESSAY

1. Carbon's ability to combine with itself in single, double, or triple covalent bonds; carbon's ability to combine with other elements; the fact that carbon compounds form isomers; they can form straight chains, branched chains, or ring structures.
2. A structural formula shows the kind, number, and arrangement of atoms in a molecule.
3. They do not ionize in water, producing an OH ion. Therefore they are not proton acceptors, or bases.
4. Not all amino acids can be produced by the body. Only through a balanced diet can these amino acids, called essential amino acids, be obtained by the body.

ADDITIONAL QUESTIONS AND TOPIC SUGGESTIONS

1. Have your students construct a number of different types of organic compounds by using black and blue construction paper and pipe cleaners. Have them cut out 30 circles, 2 cm in diameter, in each of the colors. Have your students print the symbol for each element on the proper circle. By letting the black circles indicate carbon, C, the blue circles indicate hydrogen, H, and the pipe cleaners act as bonds, have them construct structural formulas for methane, CH_4, butane, C_4H_{10}, and hexane, C_6H_{14}. Have them compare their structures with other students.

CONTENT REVIEW: MULTIPLE CHOICE

On a separate sheet of paper, write the letter of the answer that best completes each statement.

1. Organic compounds always contain
   a. carbon. b. oxygen. c. halogens. d. carboxyl groups.
2. The type of bonding found in organic compounds is
   a. metallic. b. ionic. c. covalent. d. coordinate.
3. Which of the following is *not* a property of organic compounds?
   a. nonpolar molecules b. high melting points
   c. nonelectrolytes d. generally have strong odors
4. A compound that contains only carbon and hydrogen is called a (an)
   a. isomer. b. hydrocarbon. c. carbohydrate. d. alcohol.
5. The molecular formula for methane is
   a. CH_4. b. C_4H_4. c. C_4H. d. C_2H_6.
6. The simplest aromatic hydrocarbon is
   a. cyclohexane. b. methane. c. benzene. d. phenol.
7. The –OH group is characteristic of a (an)
   a. organic acid. b. aromatic compound. c. ester. d. alcohol.
8. Compounds that often give flavor and aroma to foods are
   a. alcohols. b. esters. c. organic acids. d. aromatic compounds.
9. The human body's main source of energy is
   a. carbohydrates. b. proteins. c. fats. d. amino acids.
10. As a class of organic compounds, fats and oils are called
   a. cycloalkanes. b. lipids. c. amino acids. d. hydrocarbons.

CONTENT REVIEW: COMPLETION

On a separate sheet of paper, write the word or words that best complete each statement.

1. The word organic means _____.
2. When two pairs of electrons are shared between atoms, a (an) _____ bond is formed.
3. Compounds that have the same molecular formulas but different structural formulas are called _____.
4. Pentene is a member of the _____ series.
5. To name a saturated ring, the prefix _____ is added to the hydrocarbon name.
6. A hydrocarbon in which one or more hydrogen atoms has been replaced by a different atom or group of atoms is called a (an) _____.
7. The presence of a hydroxyl group, –OH, is characteristic of a (an) _____.
8. A compound formed from an alcohol and an organic acid is called a (an) _____.
9. Compounds that contain carbon, hydrogen, and oxygen, in which the ratio of hydrogen atoms to oxygen atoms is two to one, are called _____.
10. Giant molecules that are made of smaller molecules joined together are called _____.

254

CONTENT REVIEW: TRUE OR FALSE

Determine whether each statement is true or false. Then on a separate sheet of paper, write "true" if it is true. If it is false, change the underlined word or words to make the statement true.

1. Organic compounds contain <u>nitrogen</u>.
2. The <u>molecular</u> formula for a compound tells the kind, number, and arrangement of atoms.
3. Hydrocarbons that contain only single bonds are said to be <u>unsaturated</u>.
4. Ethane is a member of the <u>alkane</u> series.
5. The 4-carbon alkane is called <u>butane</u>.
6. A hydrocarbon containing a double bond is <u>less</u> reactive than a hydrocarbon containing a single bond.
7. Unsaturated hydrocarbons containing a triple covalent bond are called <u>alkenes</u>.
8. An organic acid is characterized by the group <u>–COOH</u>.
9. Large starch polymers are made of smaller units called <u>monomers</u> linked together.
10. <u>Fats</u> are formed from amino acids.

CONCEPT REVIEW: SKILL BUILDING

Use the skills you have developed in the chapter to complete each activity.

1. **Classifying hydrocarbons** Classify each of the following hydrocarbons as an alkane, alkene, alkyne, or aromatic compound.
   a. C_4H_{10} b. C_3H_4 c. C_2H_4
   d. C_6H_6 e. $C_{13}H_{26}$ f. $C_{42}H_{82}$
2. **Identifying patterns** Using the general formulas for the alkanes, alkenes, and alkynes, show why the number of hydrogen atoms in each series decreases by two.
3. **Making diagrams** Draw structural formulas for the following compounds.
   a. hexane c. butene
   b. cyclopentane d. propyne
4. **Classifying substituted hydrocarbons** Classify each of the following compounds as a (an) ester, alcohol, organic acid, or halogen derivative.
   a. $C_2H_5COOC_3H_7$ c. C_6H_5OH
   b. C_4H_9Cl d. C_2H_5COOH
5. **Applying definitions** Draw the structural formulas for the isomers of hexane.
6. **Making comparisons** Choose a number of carbon atoms from three to eight. Using the number you have chosen, draw the structural formulas for each of the following: the alkane, alkene, alkyne, cycloalkane, alcohol, and organic acid corresponding to that number of carbon atoms.
7. **Drawing a conclusion** Explain why the alkene series and the alkyne series begin with a 2-carbon hydrocarbon rather than a 1-carbon hydrocarbon, as the alkane series does. Use structural formulas to support your explanation.

CONCEPT REVIEW: ESSAY

Discuss each of the following in a brief paragraph.

1. Discuss four reasons why carbon compounds are so abundant.
2. Explain the importance of structural formulas in organic chemistry.
3. In Chapter 9 you learned that compounds called bases contain the hydroxide ion, OH^-. Alcohols also contain the –OH group. Why are alcohols not bases?
4. If your body contains proteins, why is it necessary to eat a balanced diet in which protein is an important nutrient?

255

tant carbohydrates that cannot be digested by humans. Have your students study cellulose, its chemical composition and properties, and determine how certain animals are able to use it as a source of food.

5. Have interested students use various reference books to look up ATP and ADP and research how they function within cells. Have them include how these chemicals bring about energy transformation and, if they can, how they can be synthesized.

6. Have your students trace the process of human digestion by consulting reference books. Have them make charts that include the name of the enzyme, where it originates in the body, the kinds of substances it works on, and the end products.

ISSUES IN SCIENCE

The following issue can be used as a springboard for class debate, or it can be assigned as a writing homework.

Many people believe life based on hydrocarbons may exist on other planets. Others disagree. Still others believe that silicon-based organisms may exist on other worlds. What is your opinion?

2. Have interested students prepare and display a collection of isomers of organic compounds. The collection should include models, diagrams, or drawings. Have the students discuss the properties of each isomer.
3. Have your students construct models of alkanes, alkenes, alkynes, and the aromatics by using black and blue construction paper and pipe cleaners. Cut approximately 50 circles that are 2 cm in diameter in each of the two colors. Have them print the symbol for hydrogen on the blue circles and the symbol for carbon on the black circles. Cut the pipe cleaners into lengths of 1 cm; these will represent the bonds between the atoms. Have your students construct structural formulas for an alkane, an alkene, an alkyne, and an aromatic. Have them compare their models with those of other members of the class.
4. Cellulose is one of the very impor-

Chapter 11
NUCLEAR CHEMISTRY

CHAPTER OVERVIEW

The discovery of radioactive elements by Becquerel and the Curies is described, as well as radioactivity in the nucleus. Transmutation of elements by means of alpha, beta, and gamma decay is discussed next, and students are introduced to the writing of nuclear equations and to the concept of half-life. Next, nuclear fission and fusion are explained.

Instruments used to detect and measure radioactivity are then described. Finally, various practical uses of radioactivity are presented.

INTRODUCING CHAPTER 11

Begin your introduction of Chapter 11 by having students examine the photograph on page 256. The photo shows a rail gun at Maxwell Laboratories in San Diego, California. The gun uses electromagnetism to accelerate objects. Ask,
• **What is the function of the various parts of the device shown in the photograph?** (Answers will vary, based upon the particular parts.)
• **The gun exerts electromagnetic forces. What is force, and how is it related to acceleration?** (Force is a push or pull that can change the rate of motion of an object. The greater the unbalanced force, the greater the resulting acceleration, by Newton's Second Law, $F = ma$, where F is force, m is mass, and a is acceleration.
• **The rail gun may be used in the fu-** ture to start certain types of nuclear reactions. What does this suggest about the energies involved in starting such reactions? (The high forces and high energies produced by the device suggest that high energies may be needed to start such reactions.)
• **What might be some of the other practical applications of such a device?** (Answers will vary.)

Nuclear Chemistry 11

CHAPTER OBJECTIVES

After completing this chapter, you will be able to

11–1 Define radioactivity.

11–1 Identify the steps leading up to the discovery of radioactivity.

11–2 Compare natural and artificial transmutation.

11–2 Describe the process and products of radioactive decay.

11–3 Describe nuclear fission and nuclear fusion.

11–4 Identify instruments that can detect and measure radioactivity.

11–5 Discuss ways in which radioactive substances can be used.

The flashing red lights and insistent loudspeakers warned all but the most essential personnel to stay away. Workers scurried to and fro, adjusting lasers and readying diagnostic sensors.

"10 . . . 9 . . . 8 . . . 7 . . . 6 . . ." The sound of the high-powered electronic equipment rose to a deafening roar.

"5 . . . 4 . . . 3 . . . 2 . . . 1 . . ." The supervisor nodded to the controller.

A powerful blast rocked the factory compound. Technicians wearing gas masks raced into the smoke-filled building. When the smoke cleared, they saw what had happened. A metal projectile no larger than an ordinary nail had been driven nearly ten centimeters into plates of thick steel.

The technicians smiled with satisfaction.

"Nice clean shot," someone observed. "We're moving right along."

It was just another day in the life of *Checmate*, a rail gun built by Maxwell Laboratories in San Diego, California. A rail gun is a powerful electromagnetic device that can accelerate objects to speeds as great as the speeds of meteors. Scientists hope that someday soon the rail gun will be used to start certain types of nuclear reactions. These reactions represent important sources of energy for the future.

Nuclear reactions were not even dreamed of until the twentieth century. But in a relatively short time, scientists have learned enough about the atom to transform ideas into applications. In this chapter, you will learn about the fascinating world of nuclear chemistry—a new frontier of modern science.

This pinpoint-sized star was created on January 13, 1986, when the world's most powerful laser, Nova, hit a tiny fuel capsule. Although the star lasted only fifty-trillionths of a second, the experiment is helping scientists better understand fusion energy.

TEACHER DEMONSTRATION

Show students photographs that illustrate very different examples of nuclear energy or processes. These can include photographs of the sun, of a nuclear power plant, of a radiation-therapy facility, of an atomic bomb detonation, and of carbon-14 fossil dating, among many other possibilities. Ask students the following.

• **What do you think each of the photos shows?** (Answers depend on the particular photographs.)

• **What do you think all these things have in common?** (They are all illustrations of nuclear processes.)

TEACHER RESOURCES
Audiovisuals

Matter and Molecules: Into the Atom, filmstrip, Singer Educational Division

Measuring Electron Charge and Mass, 2 filmstrips, PH Media

The Nucleus: Composition, Stability, and Decay, filmstrip or slides, PH Media

Books

Condon, E. V., and H. Odabasi, *Atomic Structure,* Cambridge University Press

Conn, G. K., *Atoms and Their Structure,* Cambridge University Press

Hagel, J. III, *Alternative Energy Strategies: Constraints and Opportunities,* Praeger

Software

The Atomic Nucleus, Prentice-Hall

Cross-Unit Reference

After completing this chapter, you may want to have students read the section on nuclear power in Chapter 25 Energy Resources.

11-1 RADIOACTIVE ELEMENTS

SECTION PREVIEW 11-1

Students are introduced to Becquerel's partially accidental discovery of radioactive elements. Radioactivity is explained as the release of energy and matter resulting from changes in the atomic nucleus. Nuclear binding energy and numbers of protons and neutrons in isotopes are also discussed.

PERFORMANCE OBJECTIVES 11-1

1. **Describe Becquerel's discovery of radiation.**
2. **Define radioactivity.**
3. **Define binding energy.**
4. **Compare radioactive and stable isotopes.**

SCIENCE TERMS 11-1

radiation p. 259
radioactivity p. 259
binding energy p. 260

11–1 Radioactive Elements

Have you ever looked for something and in the process discovered something quite different? One of the greatest scientific discoveries was made in this way. In 1896, the French scientist Henri Becquerel (ahn-REE bek-REL) was experimenting to see if a uranium compound gave off X-rays. Becquerel's experiments indeed provided evidence of X-rays. But they also showed something else rather exciting. Quite by accident, Becquerel discovered that the uranium compound gave off rays that had never been detected before. Little did Becquerel know then that these mysterious rays would open up a whole new world of modern science.

An Illuminating Discovery

At the time of Becquerel's work, scientists knew that certain substances glowed when exposed to sunlight. Such substances are said to be fluorescent. Becquerel wondered if in addition to glowing, fluorescent substances gave off X-rays.

To test his hypothesis, Becquerel wrapped some photographic film in lightproof paper. He placed a piece of fluorescent uranium salt on top of the film and left both out in the sun. Becquerel reasoned that if X-rays were produced by the fluorescent uranium salt, the X-rays would pass through the lightproof paper and produce an image on the film.

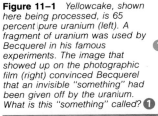

Figure 11–1 *Yellowcake, shown here being processed, is 65 percent pure uranium (left). A fragment of uranium was used by Becquerel in his famous experiments. The image that showed up on the photographic film (right) convinced Becquerel that an invisible "something" had been given off by the uranium. What is this "something" called?* ❶

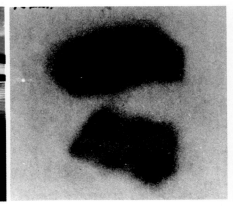

TEACHING STRATEGY 11-1

Motivation

Direct students' attention to Figure 11-1, which shows a photographic film exposed by radiation from uranium. Draw upon students' experience with cameras and film. Ask,
• **What causes film to develop images when it is exposed?** (Light causes silver bromide to decompose into black metallic silver.)

• **What is light?** (Light is a form of electromagnetic energy.)
• **What does the exposure of film by uranium demonstrate about the uranium?** (It is releasing energy.)

Content Development

As you teach students about Becquerel's discovery of radiation, ask them to point out how the discovery and the reasoning involved illustrate scientific method. Also use the occa-

sion to reveal the role that accidental factors may occasionally play in science, illustrating the fact that scientific method is not a fixed set of rules that are followed unvaryingly in all cases. Explain that imagination, creativity, and chance, as well as logic, play important roles in science.

Reinforcement

Review the steps of scientific method for the benefit of slower students.

When Becquerel developed the film, he was delighted to see an image. The image was evidence that fluorescent substances give off X-rays when exposed to sunlight. Becquerel did not test his hypothesis with just one experiment. He prepared another sample of uranium salt and left it in his desk for use the next day. Much to his disappointment, the next two days were cloudy. Impatient to get on with his work, Becquerel decided to develop the film anyway. What he saw on the film amazed him. Once again there was an image of the sample. In fact, the image on the film was just as strong and clear as the image that had been formed when the sample was exposed to sunlight.

Becquerel realized that an invisible "something" given off by the salt had gone through the light-proof paper and produced an image. In time, this invisible "something" was named **radiation.** Becquerel tested many more uranium compounds and concluded that the source of radiation was the element uranium. An element that gives off radiation is said to be **radioactive.**

Marie Curie, a Polish scientist working in France at the time of Becquerel's discovery, became very interested in Becquerel's work. She suspected that a uranium ore known as pitchblende contained other radioactive elements. She and her husband, French scientist Pierre Curie, began searching for these elements.

In 1898, the Curies discovered a new radioactive element in pitchblende. They named the element polonium in honor of Marie Curie's native Poland. Later that year, they discovered another radioactive element. They named this element radium, which means "shining element." Both polonium and radium are more radioactive than uranium. Since the Curies' discovery of polonium and radium, many other radioactive elements have been identified.

Radiation from Nuclei

Today, scientists know that it is **radioactivity** that Becquerel and the Curies had observed. **Radioactivity is the release of energy and matter that results from changes in the nucleus of an atom.**

Figure 11–2 *Marie Curie (bottom) and her husband, Pierre, were responsible for the discovery of the radioactive elements radium and polonium. Since that time, many other radioactive elements have been identified. Rectangular blocks containing radioactive cesium were the only source of illumination for this time-exposure photograph (top). The photograph was taken through a heavy glass window 1 meter thick.*

259

BACKGROUND INFORMATION

The strong nuclear force is one of the four so-called fundamental forces in nature. The other three forces are the weak nuclear force, which accounts for phenomena such as beta decay of unstable nuclei, electromagnetic force, and gravitational force. It has been hypothesized that the strong force is mediated, or carried, by a particle called the gluon. Gluons are believed to hold together quarks, which are hypothesized to make up most subatomic particles.

FACTS AND FIGURES

The ratio of neutrons to protons in stable isotopes of the elements tends to increase with increasing atomic number. The ratio tends to be close to 1 : 1 for light elements, but rises to about 1.6 : 1 for heavy elements.

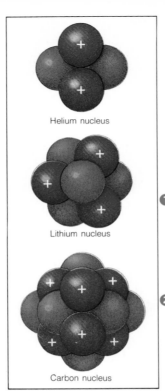

Figure 11–3 The nucleus of an atom contains positively charged protons and neutral neutrons. A helium nucleus contains 2 protons and 2 neutrons. How many protons and neutrons does a lithium nucleus contain? A carbon nucleus? ❶

Figure 11–4 Many elements have radioactive isotopes. An isotope is an atom of an element that has the same number of protons but a different number of neutrons. The number at the upper left of the symbol is the mass number. The number at the lower left is the atomic number.

260

Not all elements are radioactive. To understand why some elements are radioactive and others are not, you must understand the structure of the atom—especially the nucleus. For it is the interaction of particles and energy in the nucleus that gives rise to radioactivity.

You will recall that the nucleus of an atom contains protons and neutrons. Protons are positively charged particles. Neutrons are neutral particles. They have no charge. Protons and neutrons are held together in the nucleus by the strong force. The energy associated with the strong force is called **binding energy.** In some atoms, the binding energy is great enough to hold the nucleus together permanently. The nuclei of such atoms are said to be stable. In other atoms, the binding energy is not as great. The nucleus is not held together permanently. The nuclei of these atoms are said to be unstable. Atoms with unstable nuclei are radioactive.

Scientists believe that unstable nuclei are caused by an imbalance in the number of protons and neutrons. In a stable nucleus, the number of protons is about equal to the number of neutrons. In an unstable nucleus, however, there are either more neutrons than protons or more protons than neutrons.

Elements with atomic numbers greater than 83 are radioactive. This means that *all* isotopes of these

NONRADIOACTIVE AND RADIOACTIVE ISOTOPES OF SOME COMMON ELEMENTS

Element	Nonradioactive Isotope	Radioactive Isotope
Hydrogen	$^{1}_{1}H$	$^{3}_{1}H$
Helium	$^{4}_{2}He$	$^{6}_{2}He$
Oxygen	$^{16}_{8}O$	$^{14}_{8}O$
Potassium	$^{39}_{19}K$	$^{40}_{19}K$
Nitrogen	$^{14}_{7}N$	$^{16}_{7}N$
Lithium	$^{7}_{3}Li$	$^{8}_{3}Li$
Carbon	$^{12}_{6}C$	$^{14}_{6}C$

11-1 (continued)

Content Development

Review the nature of the neutron and the proton in terms of mass and charge. Make certain that students understand the concept of isotopes as atoms that have the same number of protons but different numbers of neutrons. Also review atomic number and mass number. Draw students' attention to Figure 11-5, which provides important information on some of the elements that have no stable isotopes.

Skills Development

Skills: Making comparisons, making graphs, interpreting graphs

Ask students to construct a graph of average mass (Y axis) versus atomic number (X axis) for the elements. The data can be obtained from any chart of the elements or periodic table. Point out that the atomic mass of an element is, numerically speaking, roughly equivalent to a weighted average, by occurrence, of the mass numbers of the isotopes of that element. Ask students to interpret the graph, which should clearly illustrate that the ratio of atomic mass to atomic number (and therefore the approximate ratios of mass number to atomic number, and of number of neutrons to number of protons), tends to increase as atomic mass increases.

RADIOACTIVE ELEMENTS

Element	Symbol	Atomic Number	Atomic Mass Number	Element	Symbol	Atomic Number	Atomic Mass Number
technetium	Tc	43	99	curium	Cm	96	247
promethium	Pm	61	145	berkelium	Bk	97	247
polonium	Po	84	209	californium	Cf	98	251
astatine	At	85	210	einsteinium	Es	99	254
radon	Rn	86	222	fermium	Fm	100	253
francium	Fr	87	223	mendelevium	Md	101	256
radium	Ra	88	226	nobelium	No	102	253
actinium	Ac	89	227	lawrencium	Lr	103	257
thorium	Th	90	232	unnilquadium	Unq	104	261
protactinium	Pa	91	231	unnilpentium	Unp	105	260
uranium	U	92	238	unnilhexium	Unh	106	263
neptunium	Np	93	237	unnilseptium	Uns	107	262
plutonium	Pu	94	244	unniloctium	Uno	108	265
americium	Am	95	243	unnilennium	Une	109	266

elements are radioactive. You will recall that isotopes are atoms of an element that have the same number of protons but different numbers of neutrons.

Many elements with atomic numbers less than 84 have at least one radioactive isotope. For example, carbon has two common isotopes—carbon-12 and carbon-14. Carbon-12, which you are familiar with as coal, graphite, and diamond, is not radioactive. Carbon-14, used in dating fossils, is radioactive. Figure 11–4 shows the radioactive and nonradioactive isotopes of some common elements. What do you notice about the numbers of protons and neutrons in the nonradioactive isotopes? In the radioactive isotopes? ❸

Figure 11–5 *The elements listed in this table are radioactive. All elements with atomic numbers greater than 83 are radioactive. What two elements with atomic numbers less than 84 are radioactive?* ❷

ANNOTATION KEY

❶ 3 protons and 4 neutrons; 6 protons and 6 neutrons (Interpreting diagrams)

❷ Technetium (Tc) 43; promethium (Pm) (Interpreting charts)

❸ Approximately equal; unequal: several more of one than the other (Interpreting diagrams)

❶ Thinking Skill: Applying concepts

❷ Thinking Skill: Making generalizations

Reinforcement

Students often are confused about mass number, which is neither atomic mass nor number of neutrons, but the total number of neutrons and protons in an atom.

Enrichment

Have interested students do library research on carbon-14 dating. Have them prepare a report on how such dating is used and on its theoretical basis. They should be encouraged to present their findings to the class.

11-2 TRANSMUTATION OF ELEMENTS

SECTION PREVIEW 11-2

Transmutation, or the change of one element into another as a result of nuclear changes, is explained. Radioactive decay processes that can produce such transmutation are then discussed. These processes include alpha decay, in which a helium nucleus is released, beta decay, in which an electron is released, and gamma decay, in which gamma rays are released. Next, artificial transmutation is explained.

The writing of nuclear reactions is taken up next. Finally, the concept of half-life is explained.

PERFORMANCE OBJECTIVES 11-2

1. **Define transmutation.**
2. **Describe and contrast alpha, beta, and gamma decay.**
3. **Read and interpret graphs illustrating decay series.**
4. **Interpret, write, and balance nuclear equations.**
5. **Explain and apply the concept of half-life.**

SCIENCE TERMS 11-2

transmutation p. 262
radioactive decay p. 262
decay series p. 262
nuclear radiation p. 262
alpha decay p. 263
beta decay p. 264
gamma decay p. 264
particle accelerator p. 265
synthetic element p. 265
transuranium element p. 265
half-life p. 266

SECTION REVIEW

1. Why were Becquerel's experiments important?
2. How did the Curies use Becquerel's discovery?
3. What is radioactivity?
4. How does the nucleus of a radioactive atom differ from the nucleus of a nonradioactive atom?
5. The nucleus of a certain atom contains 15 protons and 18 neutrons. Do you think this atom is radioactive? Explain your answer.

11–2 Transmutation of Elements

Section Objective

To describe the transmutation of elements

Transmutation is the process by which the nucleus of an atom changes so that a new element is formed. **Transmutation, the change of one element ❶ into another as a result of nuclear changes, can occur naturally or by artificial means.**

Radioactive Decay

As you read before, an unstable nucleus is radioactive. The nucleus undergoes changes that release energy and matter. As a result of the nuclear changes, a new element is formed. Natural transmutation has taken place. This form of natural transmutation is called **radioactive decay.** Radioactive decay is the spontaneous breakdown of an unstable atomic nucleus. Elements whose atoms undergo radioactive decay are called radioactive elements.

As radioactive elements decay, they change into other elements. These elements may in turn decay, forming still other elements. The spontaneous breakdown continues until a stable, nonradioactive nucleus is formed. The series of steps by which a radioactive nucleus decays into a nonradioactive ❷ nucleus is called a **decay series.** Figure 11–6 shows the decay series for uranium. What stable nucleus results from this decay series? ❶

Radioactive decay releases both particles and energy that together are known as **nuclear radiation.** The nature of the decay determines the type of radiation. There are three types of radioactive decay.

Sharpen Your Skills

What Is a Quark?

Scientists have proposed that all nuclear subatomic particles are made up of basic particles called quarks. Using books and other reference materials in the library, look up the word quark. Find out what quarks are and how they were discovered. Describe some different types of quarks and what they do. Find out what recent discoveries have been made involving quarks. Report your findings to the class.

262

11-1 (continued)

Section Review 11-1

1. Becquerel observed that something given off by uranium salt penetrated lightproof paper and produced an image on photographic film in the absence of sunlight. We now call this "something" radiation.
2. The Curies discovered two more radioactive elements in the uranium ore known as pitchblende.

3. The release of matter and energy that results from changes in the nucleus of an atom.
4. The nucleus of a radioactive element is unstable; the nucleus of a nonradioactive element is stable.
5. The atom would probably be radioactive because there are several more (3) neutrons than protons.

TEACHING STRATEGY 11-2

Motivation

Ask students to name examples of dramatic changes that matter can undergo, such as burning. Then point out that in almost all such changes, there is simply a rearrangement of atoms, but no change in the identity of atoms. Point out that it is possible for atoms themselves to change in kind, and that such change, called

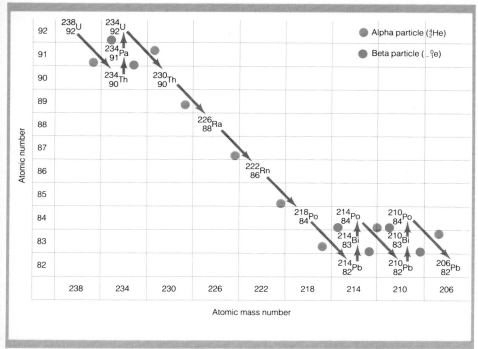

Figure 11–6 *The decay series for uranium-238 is shown in this graph. Radioactive uranium forms nonradioactive lead as a result of the decay series. What happens to the atomic mass number during a decay series? The atomic number?* ❷

ALPHA DECAY In **alpha decay,** the nucleus of a radioactive atom releases 2 protons and 2 neutrons. These 4 particles are released together and are known as an alpha particle. An alpha particle is actually the nucleus of a helium atom—2 protons and 2 neutrons.

When an atom gives off an alpha particle, it loses 2 protons. The result is a new atom with an atomic number *two less* than the original. Remember, the ❸ atomic number of an atom is the number of protons in its nucleus. An example of an element that undergoes alpha decay is uranium-238. This isotope of uranium has 92 protons and 146 neutrons. By losing an alpha particle, it changes into an atom of thorium, which has 90 protons and 144 neutrons. What do you think happens to the mass number of an atom that undergoes alpha decay? ❸

263

ANNOTATION KEY

❶ A nucleus of the element lead (Interpreting graphs)

❷ Atomic mass number decreases. Atomic number decreases (with some intermediate increases). (Interpreting graphs)

❸ It decreases by 4. (Inferring)

❶ Thinking Skill: Applying definitions

❷ Thinking Skill: Sequencing events

❸ Thinking Skill: Applying concepts

transmutation, is rarely observed under ordinary conditions.

Content Development

Explain the concept of transmutation, and point out that there are several different processes through which an element can transmute. Take extra time to explain the decay series illustrated in Figure 11-6 and make sure that students can recognize the various steps involved. Explain alpha decay as the release of an alpha particle, which contains 2 protons and 2 neutrons.

HISTORICAL NOTES

It was a goal of alchemists, early philosopher–scientists, to transmute so-called base metals into gold. The alchemists had no knowledge of the nucleus or its changes, however, and could produce only physical and chemical, rather than nuclear, changes.

ANNOTATION KEY

❶ Beta particle: gamma rays (Interpreting illustrations)

❷ A neutron in the nucleus is made up of a proton and an electron. This electron is responsible for beta decay. (Relating facts)

❶ Thinking Skill: Sequencing events

❷ Thinking Skill: Applying technology

❸ Thinking Skill: Relating concepts

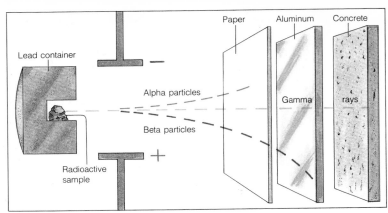

Figure 11–7 *The radiation released during radioactive decay can be separated according to charge and penetrating power. The radiation given off by a radioactive sample is passed through a magnetic field. Positively charged alpha particles are deflected toward the negative magnetic pole. Negatively charged beta particles are deflected toward the positive pole. High-energy gamma rays, which have no charge, are undeflected. Which particle is deflected the most? Which type of radiation is the most penetrating?* ❶

Figure 11–8 *Alpha and beta decay release particles as well as energy. An alpha particle is a helium nucleus. A beta particle is an electron. Where does a beta particle come from?* ❷

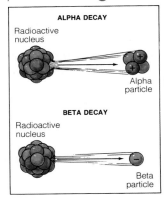

BETA DECAY During **beta decay,** a negatively charged electron, or beta particle, is released from the nucleus of an atom. Perhaps you are wondering how an electron can be in the nucleus. The answer is that a neutron is thought to be made up of a proton and an electron.

During beta decay, the neutron breaks up. The proton stays in the nucleus, but the electron is released as a beta particle. So beta decay produces a new atom with the same mass number as the original atom but with an atomic number *one higher* than the original atom. The atomic number is one higher because there is now an additional proton.

An example of an element that undergoes beta decay is carbon-14. An atom of carbon-14 has 6 protons and 8 neutrons. During beta decay it changes into an atom of nitrogen-14. An atom of nitrogen-14 has 7 protons and 7 neutrons.

GAMMA DECAY Alpha and beta decay are almost always accompanied by **gamma decay.** Gamma decay is the release of energy in the form of gamma rays. Gamma rays are electromagnetic waves of very high frequency and energy.

264

11-2 (continued)

Content Development

Explain beta and gamma decay and ask students the following questions to help reinforce what they have learned.

• **By what quantities does beta decay change an atom's atomic number and mass number?** (It increases atomic number by 1 and does not change mass number.)

• **Why is this so?** (The electron that is given off has negligible mass, and the proton formed makes up, in mass number, for the loss of the neutron that has changed. The extra proton results in increased atomic number.)

Reinforcement

Carefully explain Figure 11-7 for the benefit of slower students, pointing out that the positively charged alpha particles and negatively charged beta particles are attracted by the oppos- itely charged plates—by the negative and positive plates, respectively. Explain that the alpha particles are deflected to a lesser extent because they are much more massive (That is, they have more inertia). Encourage the students to create their own colorful charts illustrating the deflection of these particles and rays.

Figure 11-9 *Artificial transmutation of elements is done in a particle accelerator such as the one at Fermilab in Illinois. This aerial view (left) shows the outline of the underground tunnel, which is more than 6.3 kilometers long. Protons traveling through long tubes (right) will reach a final speed greater than 99.999 percent of the speed of light!*

Artificial Transmutation

One instrument in which artificial transmutation takes place is called a **particle accelerator.** By using a particle accelerator, scientists are able to bombard atomic nuclei with high-speed protons or neutrons. As the atomic nuclei are forced to absorb additional protons or neutrons, new elements are produced.

All of the elements with atomic numbers greater than 92, the atomic number of uranium, were produced by artificial transmutation. These elements are called **synthetic** or **transuranium elements.** All of the synthetic elements are radioactive.

Radioactive isotopes of natural elements can be made by using a similar technique. For example, by shooting neutrons at the nucleus of an iodine atom, scientists have been able to make I-131, a radioactive isotope of iodine. A particle accelerator can also be used to create an element from several other elements. For example, scientists can now change mercury and lead into gold.

Describing Nuclear Reactions

Nuclear reactions can be described by equations in much the same way chemical reactions can. However, the nature of the reactions is very different. The main difference between a chemical reaction and a nuclear reaction is that a chemical reaction involves an atom's electrons and a nuclear reaction involves its nucleus.

265

Content Development
There are two elements with atomic numbers less than 92 that do not occur naturally on earth. These two elements, technetium (Tc, 43) and promethium (Pm, 61), have no isotopes that are not radioactive. They have been prepared by artificial means by scientists.

Content Development
Neutrons tend to be stable in non-radioactive atoms and in radioactive atoms that do not undergo beta decay. However, outside the nucleus, free neutrons undergo beta decay. Half the neutrons in a sample of such neutrons decay in about 12 minutes.

Enrichment
During beta decay, a neutron is transformed into a proton, an electron (or beta particle), and another particle, called a neutrino. A neutrino has practically no mass and can pass through enormous amounts of matter without measureable deflection.

ANNOTATION KEY

1 $^{231}_{91}$Pa; $^{226}_{88}$Ra (Applying concepts)

2 An alpha particle has the largest mass and therefore travels at the lowest speed. (Inferring)

3 1,0 (Interpreting formulas)

4 After the second, 1/4 radioactive element, 3/4 decay element; after the third, 1/8 radioactive element, 7/8 decay element (Interpreting diagrams)

5 400,000 years; 30 hours (Interpreting charts)

6 2.5 g barium-139 and 17.5 g lanthanum-139 (Applying concepts)

① Thinking Skill: Applying formulas

② Thinking Skill: Making generalizations

③ Thinking Skill: Sequencing events

④ Thinking Skill: Applying technology

TYPES OF NUCLEAR RADIATION

Type	Atomic Mass	Atomic Number
Alpha $^4_2$He or α	4	2
Beta $^0_{-1}$e or β	0	−1
Gamma γ	0	none

Figure 11–10 *The three types of nuclear radiation are summarized in this table. How does the mass of an alpha particle relate to its speed?* **2**

Figure 11–11 *The half-life of a radioactive element is the amount of time it takes for half the atoms in a given sample of the element to decay. After the first half-life, half the atoms in the sample are the radioactive element and half are the decay element. What remains of the sample after the second half-life? After the third?* **④**

In order to write an equation for a nuclear reaction, you must first learn certain rules. Each atom of an element in the reaction is represented by the chemical symbol for that element. Two small numbers are written to the left of the symbol. The number at the upper left is the mass number of the element. The number at the lower left is the atomic number of the element. The symbol for uranium-238 would be $^{238}_{92}$U, since uranium-238 has a mass number of 238 and an atomic number of 92. How would protactinium be represented in a nuclear equation? Radium? **1**

Symbols are also used to represent alpha particles, beta particles, and neutrons. The symbol for an alpha particle is the helium nucleus, $^4_2$He. An alpha particle has a mass number of 4 and an atomic number of 2. The symbol for a beta particle, or electron, is $^0_{-1}$e. A beta particle has a mass number almost equal to 0 and an atomic number considered −1. The symbol for a neutron is $^1_0$n. What is the mass number and atomic number of a neutron? **3**

Now let's see how some of these symbols are used in a nuclear equation. Uranium-238 undergoes alpha decay to produce thorium and gamma rays.

$$^{238}_{92}\text{U} \longrightarrow {}^{234}_{90}\text{Th} + {}^4_2\text{He} + \text{gamma rays}$$

Notice that when the mass numbers on each side of the equation are added together, they equal each other. The same thing is true of the atomic numbers. You can check to see if you have written a correct nuclear equation by using this rule.

Radioactive Half-Life

The decay of radioactive elements occurs at a fixed rate. The fixed rate of decay of a radioactive element is called the **half-life.** The half-life is the amount of time it takes for half the atoms in a given sample of the element to decay. **2**

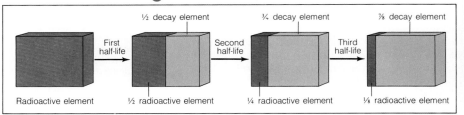

½ decay element · ¾ decay element · ⅞ decay element

Radioactive element · First half-life · ½ radioactive element · Second half-life · ¼ radioactive element · Third half-life · ⅛ radioactive element

---

11-2 (continued)

Content Development
Explain the two methods for writing chemical symbols that reveal information on the particular isotopes involved—for example, C-12 and ^{12}C. Make clear the principles that are to be used in writing and balancing nuclear equations. Also, take extra time in explaining the difficult concept of half-life, using graphs to help illustrate the quantitative aspects of the changes involved.

Skills Development
Skill: Applying concepts
Provide students with a number of examples that show nuclear equations. Ask students to state the numbers of protons and of neutrons for each isotope involved, to identify the kind of decay, and to state whether the equations are balanced. Also give them examples in which they need to balance such equations or to fill in missing subscripts, superscripts, or chemical formulas.

Reinforcement
The four subscript and superscript positions around a chemical symbol are used to reveal different information about the atoms involved. The left superscript indicates mass number (e.g., ^{35}Cl); the left subscript indicates

HALF-LIVES OF SOME RADIOACTIVE ELEMENTS

Element	Half-Life	Element	Half-Life
Bismuth-212	60.5 minutes	Polonium-215	0.0018 second
Carbon-14	5730 years	Polonium-216	0.16 second
Chlorine-36	400,000 years	Radium-226	1600 years
Cobalt-60	5.26 years	Sodium-24	15 hours
Iodine-131	8.07 days	Uranium-235	710 million years
Phosphorus-32	14.3 days	Uranium-238	4.5 billion years

Figure 11–12 *The half-lives of radioactive elements vary greatly. How long would it take a 10-gram sample of chlorine-36 to be reduced to 5 grams? How long would it take a 20-gram sample of sodium-24 to be reduced to 5 grams?* 5

The half-life of carbon-14 is 5568 years. In 5568 years, half the atoms in a given sample of carbon-14 will have decayed to another element, nitrogen-14. In another 5568 years, half the remaining carbon-14 will have decayed. At this time, one-fourth, or one-half of one-half, of the original sample will be left. One-fourth of the original sample will be carbon-14 and three-fourths will be nitrogen-14. 3

Suppose you had 20 grams of pure barium-139. Its half-life is 86 minutes. So after 86 minutes, half the atoms in the sample would have decayed into another element, lanthanum-139. You would have 10 grams of barium-139 and 10 grams of lanthanum-139. After another 86 minutes, half the atoms in the 10 grams of barium-139 would have decayed into lanthanum-139. You would have 5 grams of barium-139 and 15 grams of lanthanum-139. What will you have after the next half-life? 6

The half-lives of certain radioactive isotopes are very useful in determining the ages of rocks and fossils. Scientists can use the half-life of carbon-14 to determine the approximate age of organisms and objects less than 50,000 years old. This technique is called carbon-14 dating. Other radioactive elements, such as uranium-238, can be used to date objects many millions of years old. 4

Half-lives vary greatly from element to element. Some half-lives are only seconds while others are billions of years. For example, the half-life of rhodium-106 is 30 seconds. The half-life of uranium-238 is 4.5 billion years!

Sharpen Your Skills

A Model of Half-Life

For this activity you will need about 100 small objects of the same size, such as jellybeans, marbles, buttons, or pennies; a piece of posterboard; and tape or glue.

1. Illustrate half-life by letting each small object represent one atom. Choose the starting number carefully.
2. Display the "atoms" on the posterboard to show how the number of atoms is reduced in each half-life.
3. Decide on a half-life for your sample. Label each group of atoms with the time it has taken to reach that number, how many "atoms" remain, and which half-life is represented.

Sharpen Your Skills

A Model of Half-Life
Skills: Developing a model, calculating, relating, applying, predicting
Level: Average
Type: Hands-on/computational
Materials: 100 small objects, posterboard, tape or glue

This activity will help reinforce students' understanding of the concept of half-life. Check students' displays for accuracy and imagination. Have students who are interested see if any "real" elements have half-lives similar to the one they assigned in their model.

atomic number (e.g., $_{17}Cl$); the right superscript indicates ionic charge (e.g., Cl^-); and the right subscript indicates the number of that kind of atom present in a molecule (e.g., Cl_2).

Enrichment

Point out that there is no known way to predict whether or exactly when a given radioactive atom in a sample will decay. Half-life, which deals with such decay-time considerations, is a statistical concept and can be applied only probabilistically to large numbers of atoms in a sample. Thus, for example, if the half-life of an isotope is 1 hour, one can say that half the atoms in a sample of that isotope will have decayed by the end of an hour, but one cannot predict which of the atoms will have decayed.

11-3 HARNESSING THE NUCLEUS

SECTION PREVIEW 11-3

Nuclear fission is explained as the splitting of an atomic nucleus into two smaller nuclei of similar masses. Fission chain reactions are then discussed. Finally, nuclear fusion is explained as the joining of two atomic nuclei to form a single nucleus of greater mass. The energies involved in fission and fusion are also discussed.

PERFORMANCE OBJECTIVES 11-3

1. Describe the process of nuclear fission.
2. Trace the events in a nuclear chain reaction.
3. Describe the process of nuclear fusion.
4. Compare fission and fusion.

SCIENCE TERMS 11-3

nuclear fission p. 268
nuclear chain reaction p. 269
nuclear fusion p. 270

---

1. What is transmutation? What are the two types of transmutation?
2. What happens during radioactive decay? What are the three types of radioactive decay?
3. What is half-life?
4. The half-life of radium-222 is 38 seconds. How many grams of a 12-gram sample are left after 76 seconds? After 114 seconds? How many half-lives have occurred when 0.75 grams remain?

Section Objective

To explain how energy is released from the nucleus of an atom

11–3 Harnessing the Nucleus

Radioactive decay is one way in which energy is released from the nucleus of an atom. The amount of energy released during radioactive decay is quite small, however. For many years, scientists have known that the binding energy of a nucleus is enormous. After all, a huge quantity of energy is required to hold the protons together. If somehow the nucleus could be split apart, some of the nuclear energy would be released.

Nuclear Fission

In 1938, Italian physicist Enrico Fermi and a team of other scientists made an extremely important discovery. They found that when the nucleus of an atom of uranium-235 is struck by a neutron, it splits into two nuclei of roughly equal mass. This reaction, the first of its kind ever to be produced, is an example of **nuclear fission** (FIHSH-uhn). With the discovery of nuclear fission, Fermi made a tremendous contribution to the field of nuclear chemistry.

1 **Nuclear fission is the splitting of an atomic nucleus into two smaller nuclei of approximately equal mass.** Fission does not occur spontaneously. Elements with atomic numbers greater than 90 can be made to undergo fission. As a result of fission, a radioactive element forms a stable element.

In one typical fission reaction, a uranium-235 nucleus is bombarded by a neutron, or nuclear "bullet." The products of the reaction are a barium-141 nucleus and a krypton-92 nucleus. Three neutrons

268

11-2 (continued)

Section Review 11-2

1. The process by which the nucleus of an atom changes so that a new element is formed; natural (radioactive decay) and artificial
2. The nucleus of the atom breaks down spontaneously, giving off radiation in the form of subatomic particles and energy. Alpha decay, beta decay, gamma decay
3. The amount of time it takes for half the atoms in a sample of a radioactive element to decay
4. 3 g; 1.5 g; 4

TEACHING STRATEGY 11-3

Cross-Unit Reference

After students complete this section, you might want them to read the section on nuclear energy and power plants in Chapter 25 Energy Resources.

Motivation

Encourage students to consider examples of fission and of fusion, without as yet using these terms. For example, mention the sun and atomic detonations. Ask,

• **What kinds of changes do you think are occurring in these cases—physical, chemical, or nuclear? Why?** (Nuclear changes are occurring. This is suggested by the enormous amounts of energy involved.)

• **Where do you think this energy comes from?** (Matter is being converted into energy.)

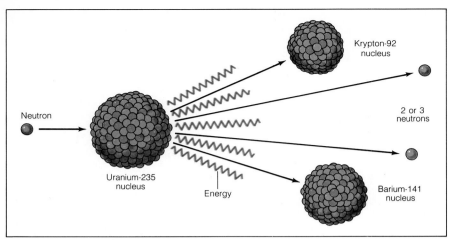

Krypton-92
nucleus

Neutron

2 or 3
neutrons

Uranium-235
nucleus

Energy

Barium-141
nucleus

are also released—the original "bullet" neutron and two neutrons from the uranium nucleus.

$$^{235}_{92}\text{U} + {}^{1}_{0}\text{n} \longrightarrow {}^{92}_{36}\text{Kr} + {}^{141}_{56}\text{Ba} + 3{}^{1}_{0}\text{n} + \text{energy}$$ ❷

The amount of energy released when a single uranium-235 nucleus splits is not very great. But the neutrons released in the first fission reaction become nuclear "bullets" capable of splitting other uranium-235 nuclei. Each uranium nucleus that is split releases three neutrons. These neutrons may then split even more uranium nuclei. The continuous series of fission reactions is called a **nuclear chain reaction.** In a nuclear chain reaction, billions of fission reactions may take place each second!

When many atomic nuclei are split in a chain reaction, huge quantities of energy are released. This energy is produced as a result of the conversion of a small amount of mass into a huge amount of energy. The total mass of the barium, krypton, and two neutrons is slightly less than the total mass of the original uranium plus the initial neutron. The missing mass has been converted into energy. An uncontrolled chain reaction produces a nuclear explosion. In Chapter 25 you will learn how scientists control fission reactions in order to produce energy for human energy needs.

Figure 11–13 *In this diagram of a chain reaction, a uranium-235 nucleus is bombarded with a neutron. The nucleus breaks up, producing a nucleus of krypton-92 and one of barium-141. Large amounts of energy as well as two additional neutrons are released. Each neutron is capable of splitting another uranium-235 nucleus. What nuclear reaction is involved in a chain reaction?* ❶

Sharpen Your Skills

Missing Mass

When a nuclear reaction takes place, the mass of the products is slightly less than the mass of the reactants. Using books and other reference materials in the library, find out what happens to this "missing mass" by looking up Einstein's famous equation or the term *mass defect.* Make a report of your findings.

269

Sharpen Your Skills

Missing Mass
Skills: Relating, applying
Level: Average
Type: Library

Through this activity, students will discover that the missing mass that follows a fusion reaction has been converted into energy. When they look into Einstein's famous equation, $E = mc^2$, they will discover that from a physicist's point of view matter and energy are interchangeable and that for situations such as fusion the law of conservation of mass must be changed to the law of conservation of mass and energy.

Content Development

Explain the concept of fission, making use of physical models to help illustrate the changes. Refer also to Figure 11-13, and explain what is shown there. Take care to analyze the nuclear equation for this uranium fission and show that the equation is balanced. Explain also that small amounts of mass are converted to large amounts of energy.

• **Do nuclear reactions obey the standard laws of conservation of mass or of energy?** (They do not, since total mass decreases and total energy increases.)

• **Does any conservation law apply?** (The total of mass and energy remains constant.)

Reinforcement

Have interested students do library research on nuclear chain reactions in nuclear power plants. Have them report to the class their findings on these reactions and on the devices involved.

Enrichment

Point out that the amount of energy produced by the conversion of mass into energy is given by Einstein's equation

$$E = mc^2$$

where E is energy in ergs, m is mass in grams, and c is the speed of light, 3×10^{10} cm/sec. The squaring of the already large c term accounts mathematically for the enormous amounts of energy produced by conversions of even small quantities of mass.

BACKGROUND INFORMATION

The overall equation for the hydrogen fusion that occurs in the sun is

$$4{}_1^1H \rightarrow {}_2^4He + 2{}_1^0e + energy$$

where ${}_1^0e$ is the symbol for a positron, or positively charged electron.

Figure 11–14 *You can get an idea of just how much energy is produced by nuclear fusion by considering that only a tiny fraction of the sun's total energy is what sustains life on the earth.*

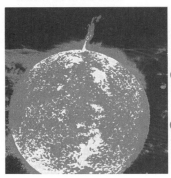

270

Nuclear Fusion

There is another kind of nuclear reaction that certain radioactive elements can undergo. Like fission, this kind of nuclear reaction produces a great deal of energy. Unlike fission, which involves the splitting of a high-mass nucleus, this reaction involves the joining of two low-mass nuclei. The reaction is called **nuclear fusion.** The word fusion means joining together. **Nuclear fusion is the joining of two atomic nuclei of smaller masses to form a single nucleus of larger mass.**

Nuclear fusion is a thermonuclear reaction. Thermo means heat. For nuclear fusion to take place, temperatures well over a million degrees Celsius must be reached. At such temperatures, the phase of matter known as plasma is formed. Plasma consists of positively charged ions, which are the nuclei of original atoms, and free electrons.

11-3 (continued)

Content Development
Explain nuclear fusion, making use of nuclear equations. Contrast fusion with fission, and describe the high-energy conditions that are necessary in order for fusion to occur. Refer students to Figure 11-15, which illustrates hydrogen fusion.

Enrichment
The sun's core is not at present hot or dense enough to produce, by fusion, elements more massive than helium. When the sun ages further, after it has become a red giant, its core will eventually contract and heat up and produce, by fusion, elements as massive as carbon. The cores of stars more massive than the sun can go on to produce elements as massive as iron. Such stars eventually explode, in a so-called supernova. In such explosions, heavy elements can form. In fact, it is believed that all the heavy elements in our solar system were produced long ago by supernovas of stars.

Interested students may wish to do library research on the nuclear chemistry of the sun and of other stars. They can prepare written reports and also colorful stellar life-cycle diagrams to be displayed in class.

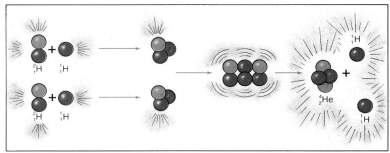

The temperature conditions required for nuclear fusion exist in the sun and other stars. In fact, it is nuclear fusion that produces the sun's energy and the energy of other stars. In the sun's core, temperatures of about 20 million degrees Celsius keep fusion going continuously. In a series of steps, hydrogen nuclei are fused into a helium-4 nucleus. See Figure 11–15.

Nuclear fusion produces a tremendous amount of energy. The energy comes from matter that is converted into energy during the reaction. In fact, the products formed by fusion have a mass that is about one percent less than the mass of the reactants. Although one percent loss of mass may seem a small amount to you, its conversion produces an enormous quantity of energy. Nuclear fusion,

Figure 11–15 *In the process of nuclear fusion that takes place in the sun, hydrogen nuclei fuse to produce helium and tremendous amounts of energy. What other products are formed by this fusion reaction?* ❶

Figure 11–16 *These laser technicians at Lawrence Livermore Laboratory are adjusting the target chamber of Nova, the device in which experimental fusion reactions are being conducted (left). Ten powerful laser beams converge simultaneously onto a small fuel pellet such as the one shown here (right). What element makes up this double-shell target?*

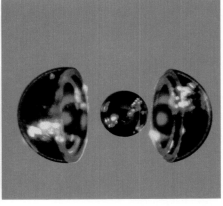

271

11-4 DETECTING AND MEASURING RADIOACTIVITY

SECTION PREVIEW 11-4

Students are introduced to various instruments that scientists use to detect and measure radioactivity. These instruments include the electroscope, the Geiger counter, the cloud chamber, and the bubble chamber.

PERFORMANCE OBJECTIVES 11-4

1. Describe the structure and use of the electroscope.
2. Describe the structure and use of the Geiger counter.
3. Describe the structure and use of the cloud chamber.
4. Describe the structure and use of the bubble chamber.

SCIENCE TERMS 11-4

electroscope p. 272
Geiger counter p. 273
cloud chamber p. 273
bubble chamber p. 273

however, is more difficult to control than nuclear fission. Scientists are continuing their search for ways to control this powerful reaction and tap a tremendous energy resource.

SECTION REVIEW

1. What is nuclear fission? Nuclear fusion?
2. How is the sun's energy produced?
3. Where does the energy produced in both fission and fusion reactions come from?
4. Compare the energy produced by fission and fusion reactions with the energy produced by radioactive decay.

11–4 Detecting and Measuring Radioactivity

Radioactivity cannot be seen or felt. Becquerel discovered radioactivity because it left marks on photographic film. Although film is still used today to detect radioactivity, scientists have more specialized instruments for this purpose. **The instruments scientists use to detect and measure radioactivity include the electroscope, Geiger counter, cloud chamber, and bubble chamber.**

Electroscope

An **electroscope** is a simple device that consists of a metal rod with two thin metal leaves at one end. If an electroscope is given a negative charge, the metal leaves separate. In this condition, the electroscope can be used to detect radioactivity.

Radioactive substances remove electrons from molecules of air. As a result, the molecules of air become positively charged ions. When a radioactive substance is brought near a negatively charged electroscope, the air molecules that have become positively charged attract the negative charge on the leaves of the electroscope. The leaves discharge, or lose their charge, and collapse. You will learn more about the electroscope when you study electricity in Chapter 19.

Section Objective

To describe various instruments that can detect and measure radioactivity

Figure 11–17 *Because radioactive substances will cause an electroscope to discharge, an electroscope can be used to detect radiation. What do radioactive substances do to molecules of air?* ❶

11-3 (continued)

Enrichment

Have advanced students consult up-to-date sources in the library to obtain information on the attempts to produce energy by nuclear fusion. They can draw diagrams of the various structures used and proposed. They should also describe the failure to produce net amounts of energy through use of such devices.

Section Review 11-3

1. The splitting of an atomic nucleus to produce two smaller nuclei of approximately equal mass; the joining of two atomic nuclei of smaller masses to produce a single nucleus of larger mass
2. In a fusion reaction involving a series of steps, four hydrogen nuclei fuse to form one helium nucleus. This reaction produces a tremendous amount of energy.

3. From the conversion of small quantities of mass into enormous quantities of energy according to Einstein's equation, $E = mc^2$
4. Radioactive decay produces small amounts of energy over a long period of time. Energy production by fission and fusion reactions is in huge amounts and usually over a short period of time. In the case of fission, the reaction can be controlled.

Geiger Counter

In 1928, Hans Geiger designed an instrument that detects and measures radioactivity. Named the **Geiger counter** in honor of its inventor, this instrument produces an electric current in the presence of a radioactive substance.

A Geiger counter consists of a tube filled with a gas such as argon or helium at reduced pressure. When radiation enters the tube through a thin window at one end, it removes electrons from the atoms of the gas. The gas atoms become positively charged ions. The electrons move through the positively charged ions to a wire in the tube, setting up an electric current. The current, which is amplified and fed into a recording or counting device, produces a flashing light and a clicking sound. The number of flashes and clicks per unit of time indicates the strength of the radiation. A counter attached to the wire is able to measure the amount of radioactivity by measuring the amount of current.

Cloud Chamber

A **cloud chamber** contains evaporated alcohol. Dry ice surrounding the chamber causes the alcohol vapor to condense. When a radioactive substance is put inside the chamber, droplets of alcohol condense around the radioactive particles. This process is similar to what happens in "cloud seeding" when rain droplets condense around particles that have been injected into the clouds. The droplets formed around the particles of radiation in a cloud chamber leave a trail that shows up along the chamber lining. An alpha particle leaves a short, fat trail while a beta particle's trail is long and thin.

Bubble Chamber

The **bubble chamber** is similar in some ways to the cloud chamber, although its construction is more complex. A bubble chamber contains a superheated liquid. A superheated liquid is hot enough to boil, but does not. Instead it remains in the liquid phase. The superheated liquid often contained in a bubble chamber is hydrogen.

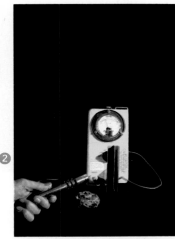

Figure 11–18 *A Geiger counter detects and measures radioactivity (top). A spiderwort plant is nature's radiation detector (bottom). The stamens of the spiderwort flower are usually blue or blue-purple. In the presence of radiation, however, the stamens turn pink.*

273

11-5 USES OF RADIOACTIVITY

SECTION PREVIEW 11-5

Various practical uses of radioisotopes are described. These uses include disease treatment, food sterilization, and use as tracers. The dangers of using, working with, or coming in contact with radioactive substances are also described.

PERFORMANCE OBJECTIVES 11-5

1. **Describe the use of radioisotopes in studying organisms.**
2. **Describe the use of radioisotopes in diagnosing and treating disease.**
3. **Describe the use of radioisotopes in sterilizing foods.**
4. **Describe the use of radioisotopes in monitoring industrial processes.**
5. **Describe the dangers associated with radioactive substances and the precautions taken to minimize the dangers.**

SCIENCE TERMS 11-5

radioisotope p. 274
tracer p. 274

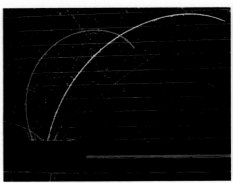

Figure 11-19 *This cloud chamber photograph (left) shows the difference between a proton (red) and an alpha particle (yellow). Which particle curves more in the chamber's magnetic field? When protons collide, a variety of other subatomic particles are produced. The tracks of these particles are shown in this bubble chamber photograph (right). By studying the tracks, scientists can learn more about the nature of subatomic particles and matter.* ❶

When radioactive particles pass through the chamber, they cause the hydrogen to boil. The boiling liquid leaves a trail of bubbles, which is used to track the radioactive particle.

SECTION REVIEW

1. Name four instruments that are used to detect radioactivity.
2. What instrument can both detect and measure radioactivity?
3. Compare a bubble chamber and a cloud chamber.

11-5 Uses of Radioactivity

Radioactive substances have many practical uses. Among the most useful radioactive substances are **radioisotopes.** Radioisotopes are artificially produced radioactive isotopes of common elements. **Radioisotopes are used to study living organisms, ❶ to diagnose and treat disease, to sterilize foods, and to monitor industrial processes.**

Radioisotopes are frequently used as **tracers.** A tracer is a radioactive element whose pathway through the steps of a chemical reaction can be followed. An example of a tracer is phosphorus-32.

The nonradioactive element phosphorus is used in small amounts by both plants and animals. If phosphorus-32 is given to an organism, the organism will use the radioactive phosphorus just as it

274

11-4 (continued)

Section Review 11-4

1. Electroscope, Geiger counter, bubble chamber, cloud chamber
2. Geiger counter
3. In both the bubble chamber and the cloud chamber, a radioactive substance leaves a trail. In the cloud chamber, the trail is droplets of condensed alcohol vapor. In the bubble chamber, the trail is bubbles from boiling liquid hydrogen.

TEACHING STRATEGY 11-5

Motivation

Ask students, before they read the section, the following questions on the uses of radioactivity. Answers to each will vary.

- **What are some of the dangers of radioactivity?**
- **Do you think radioactive substances can have any useful applications? If so, which uses?**
- **Do the potential practical uses of radioactive substances outweigh the dangers involved?**

Content Development

Describe the various uses of radioisotopes in biological science, medi-

cine, food processing, and industry. Refer to Figure 11-20 to illustrate some of these uses.

Skills Development

Skills: Applying technology, interpreting illustrations

Show students photographs in books and magazines that illustrate uses of radioisotopes. Ask,

- **What applications are being illustrated? How are the isotopes be-**

does the nonradioactive phosphorus. However, the path of the radioactive element can be traced with a Geiger counter. In this way, scientists learn a great deal about how plants and animals use phosphorus.

Tracers are extremely valuable in diagnosing diseases. Radioactive iodine, iodine-131, can be used to study the function of the thyroid gland, which absorbs iodine. Sodium-24 can be used to detect diseases of the circulatory system. Iron-59 can be used to study blood circulation.

Tracers are also valuable in industry. Leaks in pipes can be detected if some of the material flowing through the pipes is tagged with the radioisotope iodine-131.

Radioisotopes are used to treat certain diseases. When administered carefully and in the proper amounts, radiation can kill cancer cells without damaging healthy tissue. The radioisotope cobalt-60 is used extensively in cancer radiation treatments. Carbon-14 has been used to treat brain tumors.

Radioisotopes can also be used to kill bacteria that cause food to spoil. Radiation was used to preserve the food that the astronauts ate while on the moon and in orbit.

One of the difficulties in using radioactive materials is that these substances must be handled with great care. Large amounts of radiation can damage or kill living things. Marie Curie's death in 1934 was caused by too much exposure to radiation.

Today, people who work with radioactive materials take extreme precautions. They wear radiation-sensitive badges that serve as a warning of unsafe levels of radiation. Specially designed protective clothing is worn to block radiation. Scientists continue to search for greater understanding and control of radiation so that its benefits can be enjoyed without the threat of danger.

SECTION REVIEW

1. What is a radioisotope? What are its uses?
2. What is a tracer?
3. How are radioisotopes useful in treating cancer?
4. A person has a disease in which too much sodium is retained by the body. How might a tracer help to diagnose the cause of this problem?

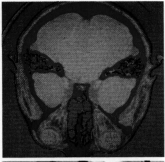

Figure 11–20 *Radioisotopes can be used as tracer elements to produce images such as this one of the brain (top). Any radioactive substance must be handled with extreme caution, as this technician is doing (bottom).*

275

TIE-IN/FOOD SCIENCE

Radioisotopes are already in common use in Europe to sterilize food. Such treated foods, including milk, can be stored for quite long periods without refrigeration, and contain no radioactive materials.

---

ing used? What dangers may be involved? (Answers depend upon the particular photographs.)

Reinforcement

For each application of radioisotopes, point out, for the benefit of slower students, the property of radioactive substances that makes the application possible. For example, the fact that radioisotopes can decay over extended periods of time and that the products

of this decay are detectable explains their use as tracers. The fact that they release large amounts of energy and highly energetic particles that can destroy living organisms accounts for their use in cancer treatment and in food sterilization.

Section Review 11-5

1. Artificially produced radioactive isotopes of common elements; study living organisms, diagnose and treat

diseases, sterilize food, monitor industrial processes
2. A radioactive element whose path through the steps of a chemical reaction can be followed
3. Administered carefully and in the proper amounts, radioisotopes can kill cancer cells without damaging healthy cells.
4. If the person is given radioactive sodium, the path of the sodium through the body can be traced. The part of the body in which too much sodium is being retained can be identified.

LABORATORY INVESTIGATION THE HALF-LIFE OF A SUGAR CUBE

BEFORE THE LAB

1. **Gather all materials at least one day prior to the investigation. You should gather enough materials to meet your class needs, assuming two to six students per group.**
2. **Test-mark a sugar cube with food coloring to make certain that the coloring does not soak through the cube and make it difficult for the marked face to be distinguished from the unmarked ones.**

PRE-LAB DISCUSSION

Before beginning the actual investigation, ask students to examine a sugar cube and count the number of faces it has (6). Then ask them to consider how likely it is for a cube, when tossed, to land with a particular face up (1 toss out of 6, assuming a regular cube and equal density throughout). Ask them to formulate a hypothesis regarding the number of tosses required in order to remove half the cubes. Review the concept of half-life and make sure that students recognize the analogy between a radioactive-decay half-life situation and the sugar-cube situation they are investigating.

SKILL DEVELOPMENT

Students will use the following skills while completing this investigation.
1. Manipulative
2. Recording
3. Applying
4. Relating
5. Graphing
6. Inferring

SAFETY TIPS

Caution students not to eat the sugar cubes.

TEACHING STRATEGY FOR LAB PROCEDURE

Caution students not to "look" while making their tosses or try to toss the cubes in such a way that the number of sides with coloring is non-randomized.

The Half-Life of a Sugar Cube

Problem

How can the half-life of a large sample of sugar cubes be determined?

Materials (per group)	
250 sugar cubes	large bowl
food coloring	medicine dropper

Procedure

1. Place a small drop of food coloring on one side of each sugar cube.
2. Put all the sugar cubes in a bowl. Then spill them on the table. Move any cubes that are on top of other cubes. Be gentle with the cubes, since they are easily broken.
3. Remove all the sugar cubes that have the colored side facing up. If you have room on the table, arrange the sugar cubes you removed in a vertical column. Put the rest of the cubes back in the bowl.
4. Repeat step 3 several more times until five or fewer sugar cubes remain.
5. On a chart similar to the one shown, record the number of tosses (times you spilled the sugar cubes), the number of sugar cubes removed each time, and the number of sugar cubes remaining. For example, suppose after the first toss you removed 40 sugar cubes. The number of tosses would be 1, the number of cubes removed would be 40, and the number of cubes remaining would be 210 (250 − 40).

Observations

1. Make a full-page graph of tosses versus cubes remaining. Place the number of tosses on the X (horizontal) axis and the number of cubes remaining on the Y (vertical) axis. Start at zero tosses with all 250 cubes remaining.

2. Determine the half-life of the decaying sugar cubes in the following way. Find the point on the graph that corresponds to one-half of the original sugar cubes (125). Move vertically down from this point until you reach the horizontal axis. Your answer will be the number of tosses.

Conclusions

1. What is the shape of your graph?
2. How many tosses are required to remove one-half of the sugar cubes?
3. How many tosses are required to remove one-fourth of the sugar cubes?
4. Assuming tosses are equal to years, what is the half-life of the sugar cubes?
5. Using your answer to question 4, how many sugar cubes should remain after 8 years? After 12 years? Do these numbers agree with your observations?
6. What factor(s) could account for differences in your observed results and those you calculated?
7. Would the determined half-life be different if you had used a larger number of sugar cubes?

Tosses	Sugar Cubes Removed	Sugar Cubes Remaining
0	0	250
1	40	210
2		
3		
4		
5		
6		

OBSERVATIONS

1. Check students' graphs to see that they fit their data.
2. Check students' determination of half-life to see that it fits their graphed data.

CONCLUSIONS

1. Students may describe their graph in words or draw the shape. The actual shape should ideally show a hyperbolic curve in the first quadrant, asymptotic with respect to the X axis.
2. Answers will vary, but should be around 4 tosses.
3. Roughly 1½ to 2 tosses should remove ¼ of the cubes.
4. 4 years
5. ¼; ⅛; Students' data should be similar, but not exactly like these ideal figures.
6. Accept all logical answers. Half-life, of course, is a statistical measurement

SUMMARY

11-1 Radioactive Elements

❑ Radioactivity was discovered accidentally by Henri Becquerel in 1896, when he observed something unusual being given off by a uranium compound.

❑ An element that gives off radiation is said to be radioactive.

❑ Radioactivity is the release of energy and matter that results from changes in the nucleus of an atom.

❑ If the binding energy—the force that holds the nucleus together—is not strong, an atom is said to be unstable. Atoms with unstable nuclei are radioactive.

11-2 Transmutation of Elements

❑ Transmutation, the process by which one element changes into another as a result of nuclear changes, can occur naturally or by artificial means.

❑ Radioactive decay is the spontaneous breakdown of an unstable atomic nucleus.

❑ The three types of radioactive decay are alpha decay, beta decay, and gamma decay.

❑ Artificial transmutation can be made to take place by bombarding atomic nuclei with high-speed subatomic particles, such as protons or neutrons, in a particle accelerator.

❑ Equations describe nuclear reactions.

❑ The decay of a radioactive element occurs at a fixed rate called the half-life.

11-3 Harnessing the Nucleus

❑ Great amounts of energy are released during fission and fusion reactions.

❑ Fission is the splitting of an atomic nucleus to form two smaller nuclei of roughly the same mass.

❑ Fusion is the joining together of two atomic nuclei to form a single nucleus of larger mass.

11-4 Detecting and Measuring Radioactivity

❑ Four devices that can detect radioactivity are the electroscope, Geiger counter, cloud chamber, and bubble chamber. The Geiger counter can also measure radioactivity.

11-5 Uses of Radioactivity

❑ Artificially produced radioactive isotopes of common elements are called radioisotopes. They can be used to diagnose and treat diseases, study plant and animal metabolism, and solve industrial problems.

❑ Radioactive isotopes whose path can be followed through the steps of a chemical reaction are called tracers.

❑ Radioactive substances must be handled carefully since large amounts of radiation can be harmful to living things.

VOCABULARY

Define each term in a complete sentence.

alpha decay	gamma decay	nuclear radiation	radioisotope
beta decay	Geiger counter	particle accelerator	synthetic element
binding energy	half-life	radioactive	tracer
bubble chamber	nuclear chain reaction	radioactive decay	transmutation
cloud chamber	nuclear fission	radioactivity	transuranium element
decay series	nuclear fusion	radiation	
electroscope			

and can never be considered an exact measurement with such small samples. As such, results from group to group, as well as from group to ideal data, will vary.

7. It should not change when more cubes are added. Students can infer this from the fact that the half-life of an element is the same regardless of how much of that element is considered.

GOING FURTHER: ENRICHMENT

Part 1

Have interested students repeat the experiment, using a larger number of sugar cubes.

Part 2

Ask students to predict the result of three experiments identical to the one just done except for the use of 4-faced (tetrahedral), 12-faced (dodecahedral), and 20-faced (icosahedral) regular solids instead of the 6-faced (cubic) regular solids.

CHAPTER REVIEW

MULTIPLE CHOICE

1. d **3.** a **5.** c **7.** b **9.** c
2. b **4.** d **6.** c **8.** d **10.** d

COMPLETION

1. Becquerel
2. radioactivity
3. binding energy
4. 83
5. alpha decay
6. particle accelerator
7. half-life
8. nuclear chain reaction
9. electroscope
10. tracer

TRUE OR FALSE

1. F polonium/radium
2. F unstable
3. T
4. T
5. T
6. F fusion
7. F cannot
8. F Geiger counter
9. T
10. T

SKILL BUILDING

1. Check student graphs. They should show a curve that falls to less than 1 gram as time increases to 120 hours.
2. 5g; 2.5 g
3. Bismuth-210, atomic number 83
4. 16,704 years
5. 1600 years
6. **a.** 2 **b.** $_{35}^{87}$Br **c.** 4
7. One of the reactants can be "tagged" with the tracer oxygen-18. The reaction products can be examined to determine where the tracer shows up—in the free oxygen or in the sugar. This can be determined by using radiation-detecting devices. Reactants and products can be compared to identify the source of the product oxygen.

ESSAY

1. Becquerel observed something unusual coming from uranium salt. He wanted to find out what was producing this "something" that we call radiation. He hypothesized that it was coming from the uranium. He tested many uranium compounds. They all produced radiation. Based on his observations, he came to the conclusion that uranium was responsible for the radiation.
2. A tube inside the Geiger counter is filled with argon gas. When a radioactive substance enters the tube, the molecules of the gas are ionized. The electrons that have been removed from the gas molecules flow through a wire, forming an electric current. The current sets off sounds and lights that announce the presence of a radioactive substance. A counter attached to a wire measures the current, which indicates the amount of radioactivity. A Geiger counter detects and measures radioactivity. The other devices only detect radioactivity.
3. During alpha decay, 2 protons and 2 neutrons are released from the nucleus of an atom. They are released together in what is called an alpha particle, which is really a helium nucleus. During beta decay, an electron, or beta particle, is released when a neutron in the nucleus splits into a proton and an electron. The proton stays in the nucleus. Gamma decay, which almost always accompanies alpha and beta decay, is the emission of high-energy rays called gamma rays.

CONTENT REVIEW: MULTIPLE CHOICE

On a separate sheet of paper, write the letter of the answer that best completes each statement.

1. In a stable nucleus, the number of neutrons is
a. about half the number of protons. b. about twice the number of protons.
c. three less than the number of protons. d. about equal to the number of protons.
2. The process that changes one element into another is called
a. alchemy. b. transmutation. c. fluorescence. d. synthesis.
3. An atom that results from alpha decay has an atomic number that is
a. two less than the original atom. b. one less than the original atom.
c. the same as the original atom. d. two more than the original atom.
4. During beta decay, which of the following is (are) released from the nucleus?
a. an electron and a proton b. an electron and a neutron
c. a neutron d. an electron
5. The radioactive isotope that enables scientists to date ancient remains is
a. iodine-131. b. phosphorus-32. c. carbon-14. d. cobalt-60.
6. An atomic nucleus splits into two smaller nuclei of roughly equal mass in
a. fusion. b. alpha decay. c. fission. d. transmutation.
7. A device in which radioactive materials leave a trail of liquid droplets is a (an)
a. bubble chamber. b. cloud chamber. c. decay chamber. d. electroscope.
8. A Geiger counter detects radioactivity when the radioactive substance
a. leaves a trail of bubbles. b. causes air molecules to become ionized.
c. causes liquid gas to boil. d. produces an electric current.
9. An artificially produced radioactive isotope of an element is called a (an)
a. synthetic isotope. b. transmutation. c. radioisotope. d. gamma isotope.
10. The radioactive isotope often used to treat cancer is
a. iodine-131. b. iron-59. c. sodium-24. d. cobalt-60.

CONTENT REVIEW: COMPLETION

On a separate sheet of paper, write the word or words that best complete each statement.

1. The scientist who discovered radiation was _____.
2. The release of energy and matter that results from changes in the nucleus of an atom is called _____.
3. In the nucleus of an atom, the energy associated with the strong force is called the _____.
4. All of the elements above atomic number _____ are radioactive.
5. Two protons and two neutrons are released from the nucleus of an atom during _____.
6. Scientists are able to bombard atomic nuclei with high speed particles in an instrument called a (an) _____.
7. The fixed rate at which a radioactive element decays is the _____.
8. A constant series of fission reactions is called a (an) _____.
9. A device that detects radioactivity by reacting to ionized air molecules is the _____.
10. A radioactive element whose path can be followed through the steps of a chemical reaction is called a (an) _____.

278

CONTENT REVIEW: TRUE OR FALSE

Determine whether each statement is true or false. Then, on a separate sheet of paper, write "true" if it is true. If it is false, change the underlined word or words to make the statement true.

1. One of the radioactive elements discovered by the Curies was <u>uranium</u>.
2. Radioactive atomic nuclei are <u>stable</u>.
3. <u>Gamma rays</u> are electromagnetic waves of very high frequency and energy.
4. All synthetic elements <u>are</u> radioactive.
5. <u>Carbon-14 dating</u> determines the age of ancient objects and organisms.
6. Two atomic nuclei join to form a single nucleus of greater mass during <u>fission</u>.
7. Radioactivity <u>can</u> be seen.
8. Gas molecules are ionized by a radioactive substance in a <u>bubble chamber</u>.
9. <u>Iodine-131</u> can be used to study the function of the thyroid gland.
10. <u>Radioisotopes</u> are used to kill bacteria.

CONCEPT REVIEW: SKILL BUILDING

Use the skills you have developed in the chapter to complete each activity.

1. **Making graphs** Sodium-24 has a half-life of 15 hours. Make a graph to show what happens to a 100-gram sample of sodium-24 over a 5-day period. Hint: Plot the time along the horizontal axis and the mass along the vertical axis.
2. **Making calculations** The half-life of cobalt-60 is 5.26 years. How many grams of a 20-gram sample of cobalt-60 remain after 10.52 years? After 15.78 years?
3. **Applying concepts** An atom of lead-210 undergoes the following decay reaction:

$$^{210}_{82}\text{Pb} \longrightarrow \text{X} + ^{0}_{-1}\text{e}$$

   What is element X? What is its mass number? Its atomic number?
4. **Analyzing data** A skeleton of an ancient fish is found to contain one-eighth the amount of carbon-14 that it contained when it was alive. How old is the skeleton?

5. **Making calculations** After 3200 years, 0.5 gram of a 2-gram sample of a radioactive element remains. What is its half-life?
6. **Applying concepts** Complete the nuclear equations. How are they related?
   a. $^{235}_{92}\text{U} + ^{1}_{0}\text{n} \longrightarrow ^{90}_{37}\text{Rb} + ^{144}_{55}\text{Cs} + ?^{1}_{0}\text{n}$
   b. $^{235}_{92}\text{U} + ^{1}_{0}\text{n} \longrightarrow ? + ^{146}_{57}\text{La} + 3^{1}_{0}\text{n}$
   c. $^{235}_{92}\text{U} + ^{1}_{0}\text{n} \longrightarrow ^{160}_{62}\text{Sm} + ^{72}_{30}\text{Zn} + ?^{1}_{0}\text{n}$
7. **Designing an experiment** In the reaction known as photosynthesis, during which green plants make food, carbon dioxide (CO_2) combines with water (H_2O) to form sugar ($C_6H_{12}O_6$) and oxygen (O_2). For a long time, scientists wondered from which compound—carbon dioxide or water—the oxygen came. Using your knowledge of radioisotopes, describe an experiment by which the origin of oxygen could be determined.

CONCEPT REVIEW: ESSAY

Discuss each of the following in a brief paragraph.

1. Describe how Becquerel's work illustrates the scientific method.
2. Describe how a Geiger counter works. How is it different from a bubble chamber, cloud chamber, and electroscope?
3. Describe the three types of radioactive decay. What is the penetrating power of each type?
4. Explain why the amount of helium in the sun is increasing.

279

3. What is the half-life of an isotope if, after 6 days, 2.0 g of an 8.0-g sample of the isotope remain? (3 days)
4. A uranium-235 nucleus can be made to undergo any of several nuclear reactions by absorbing a neutron. In one of these reactions, 2 neutrons are released, and one of the other two products is a nucleus that contains 40 protons and 57 neutrons. Write a complete nuclear equation for this reaction. Of which kind of nuclear reaction is this an example?

$\left(^{235}_{92}\text{U} + ^{1}_{0}\text{n} \rightarrow ^{97}_{40}\text{Zr} + ^{137}_{52}\text{Te} + 2^{1}_{0}\text{n}; \text{fission}\right)$

ISSUES IN SCIENCE

The following issues can be used as a springboard for class debate, or they can be assigned as a writing homework.
1. Fission reactions can be carried out in nuclear power plants to produce energy. However, there are dangers associated with such reactors. Do you think the advantages of such use outweigh the dangers and other disadvantages? (Answers will vary. Whatever their position on this issue, students should use facts to support their opinions.)
2. Radioisotopes can be used to sterilize food in order to increase its shelf life. What is your opinion on this use of such substances? (Answers will vary. Some students will point out that the food itself is not contaminated or made radioactive. Others will point out that the production, storage, and disposal of the products of these radioisotopes may present significant difficulties or dangers.)

4. The sun's energy is produced during the fusion process. In this process, hydrogen nuclei fuse to form helium nuclei. As such, each and every day, more of the hydrogen in the sun is lost and more helium is produced.

ADDITIONAL QUESTIONS AND TOPIC SUGGESTIONS

1. An atom whose nucleus contains 84 protons and 134 neutrons undergoes radioactive decay to produce an atom whose nucleus contains 82 protons and 132 neutrons. Write a nuclear equation that represents this decay, including chemical symbols. Of which kind of decay is this an example?

$\left(^{218}_{84}\text{Po} \rightarrow ^{214}_{82}\text{Pb} + ^{4}_{2}\text{He}; \text{alpha decay}\right)$

2. A radioactive isotope has a half-life of 5 minutes. Given a 100.0 g sample of this isotope, how many g of the isotope

Unit Three
INTERACTIONS OF MATTER

ADVENTURES IN SCIENCE: SHIRLEY ANN JACKSON: HELPING OTHERS THROUGH SCIENCE

BACKGROUND INFORMATION

According to the Information Division at Bell Laboratories, Dr. Shirley Ann Jackson "is as intriguing and dynamic as the microscopic particles she studies." In addition to her work at Fermilab and Bell Laboratories, Dr. Jackson served as a visiting scientist in the theoretical division at C.E.R.N. (European Organization for Nuclear Research) in Geneva, Switzerland. Dr. Jackson has written numerous articles for leading physics journals and is a frequent speaker at scientific meetings.

Although Dr. Jackson was accepted to do graduate work at Harvard, Brown, and the University of Chicago, she chose to remain at MIT, where she had completed her undergraduate studies, because she wanted to encourage the enrollment of more black students there. She continues to maintain a connection with MIT as a member of the board of trustees. Dr. Jackson is also involved in organizations dedicated to the cause of helping women gain education and employment in the sciences.

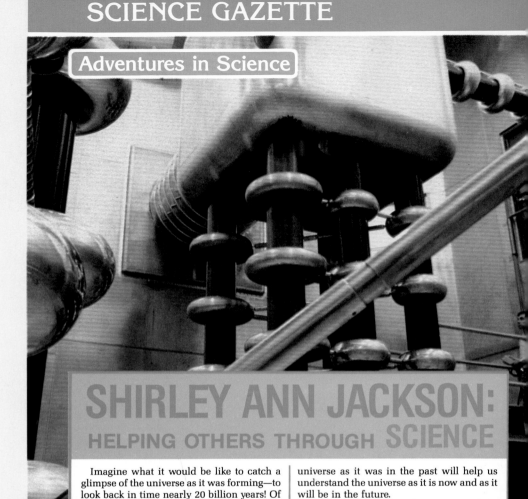

Adventures in Science

SHIRLEY ANN JACKSON:
HELPING OTHERS THROUGH SCIENCE

Imagine what it would be like to catch a glimpse of the universe as it was forming—to look back in time nearly 20 billion years! Of course, no one can really see the beginning of time. But physicists such as Shirley Ann Jackson believe that learning about the universe as it was in the past will help us understand the universe as it is now and as it will be in the future.

By unraveling some of the mysteries of the universe, Dr. Jackson hopes to fulfill a basic ambition: to enrich the lives of others and

TEACHING STRATEGY

Motivation
Bring in photographs of telephones, radios, television sets, and computers. Display the photographs and explain that much of the research that makes the production of devices such as these possible is done at a place called Bell Laboratories in Murray Hill, NJ. Point out that in this Adventure lesson, students will read about a prominent physicist at Bell Laboratories, Dr. Shirley Ann Jackson.

Content Development
Have students read the article about Dr. Jackson. Point out that, like Dr. Stephen Hawking, whom they read about in the last Adventure lesson, Dr. Jackson is an unusual person. As a black and as a woman, Dr. Jackson probably had to overcome certain obstacles in order to obtain her goal.

Explain to students that the area of physics that Dr. Jackson is currently involved in is called solid- or condensed-state physics. Solid-state physics is concerned with the physical properties of crystalline solids. Many students have probably heard the expression *solid-state* applied to various types of electronics equipment. This label refers to items based on or composed of transistors or related semiconductor devices.

make the world a better place in which to live. This contribution, Dr. Jackson believes, can be achieved through science.

Jackson was born and raised in Washington, D.C. After graduating from high school as valedictorian, she attended the Massachusetts Institute of Technology, M.I.T. There, her role as a leader in physics began to take root. Jackson became the first American black woman to receive a doctorate degree from M.I.T. She also achieved the distinction of being the first American black woman to receive a Ph.D. in physics in the United States.

After graduate school, Jackson began work as a research associate in high-energy physics at the Fermi National Accelerator Laboratory in Batavia, Illinois. This branch of physics studies the characteristics of subatomic particles—such as protons and electrons—as they interact at high energies.

Using devices at Fermilab called particle accelerators, physicists accelerate subatomic particles to speeds that approach the speed of light. The particles collide and produce new subatomic particles. By analyzing these subatomic particles, physicists are able to learn more about the structure of atoms and the nature of matter.

The experiments in which Jackson participated at Fermilab helped to prove the existence of certain subatomic particles whose identity had only been theorized. This information is important in understanding the nuclear reactions that are taking place at the center of the sun and other stars.

Jackson's research is not limited to the world of subatomic particles alone. Her work also includes the study of semiconductors—materials that conduct electricity better than insulators but not as well as metal conductors. Semiconductors have made possible the development of transistor radios, televisions, and computers.

Jackson's current work in physics at Bell Laboratories in Murray Hill, New Jersey, has brought her from the beginnings of the universe to the future of communication. This talented physicist is presently doing research in the area of optoelectronic materials. This branch of electronics—which deals with solid-state devices that produce, regulate, transmit, and detect electromagnetic radiation—is changing the way telephones, computers, radios, and televisions are made and used.

Shirley Ann Jackson, in her office at Bell Laboratories, is presently doing research in the field of optoelectronic materials used in communication devices.

Looking back on her past, Jackson feels fortunate to have been given so many opportunities at such a young age. And she is optimistic about the future. "Research is exciting," she says. Motivated by her research, Shirley Ann Jackson is happy to be performing a service to the public in the way she knows best—as a dedicated and determined scientist.

◀ **This particle-accelerator generator at Fermilab is familiar equipment to Shirley Ann Jackson.**

281

ADDITIONAL QUESTIONS AND TOPIC SUGGESTIONS

1. What aspects of the scientific method are illustrated by Dr. Jackson's work at Fermilab? (Scientists had predicted the existence of certain subatomic particles. Dr. Jackson gathered information to test this idea by carrying out experiments. When the results of these experiments were analyzed, she concluded that these particles do indeed exist.)
2. According to the article, what is Dr. Jackson's chief motivation as a scientist? Does you own attitude toward science fit in with her viewpoint? (to help other people through science; answers will vary)
3. In what ways is Dr. Jackson's story encouraging to women? To members of minorities? (first American black woman to receive doctorate from MIT)

CRITICAL THINKING QUESTIONS

1. Pure research involves the gathering of knowledge for its own sake. Applied research has practical goals in mind, often related to technology or medicine. Based on the article, which of these areas has Dr. Jackson been involved in? Explain your answer. (Both areas: work at Fermilab was probably pure research, but work at Bell Labs is applied to communications technology.)
2. Can you think of reasons why studying subatomic particles might lead to an understanding of the past and future of the universe? (One possible answer is that because atoms are the basis of all matter, they may hold the key to the changes that have taken and will take place in the universe.)

Unit Three

INTERACTIONS OF MATTER

ISSUES IN SCIENCE: FUSION ENERGY: FUTURE FUEL OR FOLLY?

BACKGROUND INFORMATION

The nuclear reaction that is currently being used to produce useful energy is fission. Nuclear fission is the splitting of an atomic nucleus into two smaller nuclei. Like fusion, this reaction is accompanied by a release of energy.

As an energy source, fusion would have an advantage over fission in that the waste materials generated by fusion stay radioactive far less long than the waste materials generated by fission. This means that fusion wastes could be disposed of more easily and would be far less harmful to people and the environment. However, fusion has the drawback of creating such intense atomic activity in the reactor that the walls of the reactor become radioactive. Also, fusion plants would be much more complex than fission plants and as much as ten times larger. As a result, fusion plants would be much more expensive to run.

Issues in Science

FUSION ENERGY: FUTURE FUEL OR FOLLY?

By the time you finish reading this sentence, more than 2 million tons of hydrogen will have exploded in the center of the sun. The energy released by the explosions provides the earth with light and heat necessary to sustain life.

The sun and other stars produce energy as a result of a process called *fusion*. The explosions in the sun are fusion reactions. Fusion is the combining of atomic nuclei of small mass to form an atomic nucleus of larger mass. In the sun, two isotopes of hydrogen—deuterium and tritium—fuse to form helium. The fusion reaction releases tremendous amounts of energy.

In the sun, fusion occurs spontaneously and uncontrollably. On the earth, this same fusion reaction produces the uncontrolled explosion associated with the hydrogen bomb. But what if fusion could be controlled? Could the energy released by the reaction help to meet the energy needs of people all over the world in a safe, efficient, and inexpensive manner?

Some scientists believe fusion power could solve the worldwide problem of shrinking energy supplies. The fuel for fusion is deuterium. Because the oceans are rich in deuterium, fuel for this process is almost limitless. A liter of ocean water contains the energy potential of 300 liters of gasoline. Fusing just 1 kilogram of deuterium could produce as much energy as burning 2000 tons of fuel oil.

If the nucleus of a deuterium atom closely approaches the nucleus of a tritium atom, the two nuclei will fuse and release energy. But deuterium and tritium have a natural, and very powerful, tendency to repel each other. It takes enormous quantities of energy to force them close enough to fuse.

The energy needed for fusion can come from heat. But the heat must be great enough to produce temperature conditions similar to those at the center of the sun. In fact, for fusion to occur deuterium and tritium nuclei must be squeezed together until they heat up to nearly 100 million degrees Celsius. So for a long time, physicists faced the problems of producing such extreme temperatures and confining the hot wisps of matter known as plasma that were produced.

In the early 1950s, Russian scientists proposed the use of magnetic fields to squeeze the hydrogen atoms together to produce the intense temperatures required for fusion. In addition, the magnetic fields could hold the plasma—something no ordinary container could do.

For the next thirty years, however, progress in fusion was slow. Then in 1983, scientists at the Princeton Plasma Physics Laboratory pro-

TEACHING STRATEGY

Motivation

Begin by asking students,

• **Have you ever had to decide whether it would be worth spending the time, energy, and money to do something?** (Most will probably say yes.)

• **Can you give some examples of such situations?** (Answers will vary.)

• **What factors eventually deter-** mined whether you decided to do a particular thing? (Answers will vary.)

• **After your decision was made, were you satisfied with the results, or did you wish you had chosen the other alternative?** (Answers will vary.)

Content Development

Use the Motivation discussion to introduce to students the idea that often in science and technology, decisions must be made as to whether a certain line of research is really worth the effort. Point out that one of the main considerations with regard to nuclear fusion is whether enough energy will ever be gotten out of fusion to justify all the energy put into making fusion happen. Scientists are currently aim-

duced the sizzling temperatures needed for a fusion reaction in their doughnut-shaped *Tokamak Fusion Test Reactor*. But this first successful test lasted only one-tenth of a second. To those scientists who support further development of nuclear fusion, even this brief test was a milestone. To those scientists who doubt the potential of fusion, this brief test was an argument against nuclear fusion.

Critics of fusion also argue that the amount of energy needed to produce the magnetic fields is much greater than the amount of energy produced by the fusion reaction.

Another argument used by critics is that not enough useful energy is produced by fusion. In recent experiments, even though temperatures of 70 million degrees were reached, the amount of heat produced could not boil a cup of water!

Another problem associated with fusion power is radioactivity. The waste products of fusion are radioactive and must be disposed of carefully. Ensuring that radiation is not released into the environment must be a primary concern of any fusion proposal.

The fusion reaction itself causes the reactor's walls to become radioactive. The walls would have to be replaced about every five years. This would be an expensive and hazardous task, and would add to the waste-disposal problem.

Fusion energy will be a costly, complex technology to develop and commercialize. Once built, however, fuel for the plants would be almost unlimited and the energy produced almost infinite. Do you think that exploring fusion power is worth the necessary time, effort, and money? Is fusion power the answer to future energy problems? Or is it just an expensive experiment?

In the laboratory, researchers are experimenting with lasers to create temperatures high enough to bring about fusion reactions between hydrogen atoms.

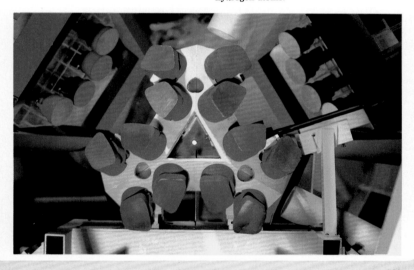

283

ing to reach the "scientific break-even" point. This is the point at which the amount of energy pumped into a reactor equals the energy produced by it.

ADDITIONAL QUESTIONS AND TOPIC SUGGESTIONS

1. What advantage does deuterium have over fuels such as gasoline and oil? (It is an unlimited resource that is easy to obtain.)
2. What have been the major difficulties encountered in making fusion reactions possible on earth? (obtaining temperatures that are high enough for fusion to occur, and then containing the matter that is produced)
3. What environmental problems are associated with fusion? (the production of radioactive wastes that must be disposed of; the possibility of radiation escaping into the environment)

CRITICAL THINKING QUESTIONS

1. Why do hydrogen nuclei repel each other? (Hydrogen nuclei contain positively charged protons, and like charges repel each other.)
2. Compare the debate surrounding nuclear fusion with the debate surrounding the value of the space program discussed in Unit One. (Answers will vary. One important difference that students should recognize is that while the space program is largely motivated by a desire to explore the unknown and gather knowledge for its own sake, fusion research is almost totally focused on meeting the need for an unlimited energy source. Thus it might be more important for fusion research to be "practical.")

CLASS DEBATE

In addition to debating the pros and cons of nuclear fusion, some students might be interested in researching and debating the advantages and disadvantages of the two techniques currently being used to produce fusion reactions. One such technique is the use of magnetic fields, which is described in the article. The other is the use of powerful lasers such as the Nova, the world's most powerful laser, which is located at Livermore Laboratory in San Francisco.

Unit Four
MOTION, FORCES, AND ENERGY

UNIT OVERVIEW

In Unit Four, students first learn about motion, frames of reference, and the difference between speed and velocity. They also explore the concepts of acceleration and momentum. Next, they study force and its relationship to motion. Newton's three laws of motion are introduced and applied, as is the concept of gravitation. Fluid forces are explored next. Archimedes' principle and Bernoulli's principle are introduced and applied.

Students then study work, power, mechanical advantage, and the nature of simple machines. Finally, they learn about the nature of energy. They are introduced to kinetic and potential energy, energy conversion, and the law of conservation of energy.

UNIT OBJECTIVES

1. **Define and do calculations involving speed, velocity, and acceleration.**
2. **Define force, and state and apply Newton's laws of motion and his law of universal gravitation.**
3. **Describe forces in fluids, and state and apply Archimedes' principle and Bernoulli's principle.**
4. **Define work and power, and describe simple machines.**
5. **Define energy, state its forms, and state and apply the law of conservation of energy.**

INTRODUCING UNIT FOUR

Begin your teaching of the unit by having students examine the unit-opening photograph, which shows the *Gossamer Albatross*, a low-mass plane flown by pedal power over the English Channel. You may wish to ask students the following questions regarding this photograph, after having them read the caption.

• **What countries are separated by the English Channel?** (England and France are separated by the English Channel.)

• **What distance does a plane have to fly in order to cross this body of water?** (At its narrowest, the English Channel is about 34 km wide.)

• **What do you notice about the plane that was used to fly this distance?** (Its wings are long, compared to the size of the compartment that holds the pilot.)

• **Why is the plane constructed in this way?** (It is easier to achieve a great deal of upward force, or lift, and the downward force, or gravity, is low because of the low mass. These factors are important because human muscle power is the only source of power for the plane's flight.)

Now have students read the unit introduction. This material should serve as the basis for various discussions that will better motivate students

Motion, Forces, and Energy

On August 23, 1977, the *Gossamer Condor,* a strange aircraft made of Styrofoam and cardboard, flew 2.2 kilometers powered by the force of human legs!

In response to an unusual challenge, Paul MacCready designed a plane that was the first to complete a human-powered flight over a short figure-eight course. MacCready knew that if he made the plane's wings as large as possible but kept its mass as small as possible, the power needed to fly the plane could be reduced. The *Gossamer Condor* had a mass of only 32 kilograms, but it had a wingspan as wide as a commercial airliner. Using only the force of his muscles, the pilot, Brian Allen, pedaled the plane around the course.

Muscle power is only one of the forces Paul MacCready understands. By reading the chapters in this unit, you too will gain an understanding of forces, motion, and energy.

Brian Allen crossed the English Channel by using the power of his muscles. This delicate looking plane, the Gossamer Albatross, *flies by pedal power—the same kind of power that moves a bicycle.* **285**

CHAPTER DESCRIPTIONS

12 Motion Chapter 12 deals with the nature of motion, frames of reference, speed, velocity, and acceleration. The concept of momentum is also introduced.

13 Forces In Chapter 13, force and its relationship to motion are discussed. Newton's three laws of motion are introduced, and gravitational force is described and related to falling motion. The concepts of weight and mass are also contrasted.

14 Forces in Fluids In Chapter 14, fluid pressure is described and related to altitude and depth. Archimedes' principle and Bernoulli's principle are introduced and applied, and the forces involved in flight are identified.

15 Work, Power, and Simple Machines Chapter 15 deals with the nature, measurement, and applications of work and power. Mechanical advantage and efficiency are introduced, and simple and compound machines are analyzed.

16 Energy In Chapter 16, energy is defined. The five forms of energy, and also kinetic and potential energy, are described. Energy conversions and the law of conservation of energy are also explained.

---

to study the chapters that follow. Here are some questions you may wish to pose to the class to initiate class discussions.

• **Do you think that there may be many practical applications of such devices?** (Answers will vary. Some students may suggest that the devices be adapted for general transportation purposes.)

• **Would you like to ride someday in such a plane? What problems or risks might you have to deal with?** (Answers will vary. Some students may point out the danger of a crash or the problem of having to continue to use one's muscles to supply power to the plane.)

Chapter 12
MOTION

CHAPTER OVERVIEW

Motion or a change in motion occurs when a force is applied to an object. Motion has two components: speed and direction. A change in motion may mean a change in an object's speed, direction, or both.

All motion is relative; that is, an object is said to be in motion only if it is changing its position with respect to a frame of reference whose position is fixed.

Speed tells us how far an object travels during every unit of time it has that speed. This implies that an object is always moving at the same speed, which is not necessarily accurate. Average speed is a more meaningful measure. Because velocity describes direction as well as speed, it gives a more complete description of motion than speed alone does.

Acceleration is the rate of change in velocity and is usually measured in M/s/s or M/s². When acceleration involves a constant change in direction toward the center of a circle but no change in speed, circular motion results. Circular motion is the result of centripetal acceleration.

All objects in motion have momentum, which is directly related to an object's mass and velocity. Momentum can be thought of as how difficult it is to stop a moving object.

INTRODUCING CHAPTER 12

Begin Chapter 12 by referring students to the chapter introduction and discussing the photograph of the ski jumper.
- **How do we know that the ski jumper is really moving?** (He constantly changes position in relation to objects around him, such as trees, people, etc.)
- **In what direction(s) is the ski jumper moving?** (He is moving both forward and downward.)
- **How did the ski jumper acquire his motion?** (He accelerated down a long, curved ramp before beginning his "jump.")
- **How is the ski jumper able to control his flight?** (As stated in the chapter introduction, through much practice and an understanding of motion)
- **If we were to carefully describe the shape of the path followed by the jumper from the time he leaves the ramp to the time he touches the ground, what would the shape be?** (It would be an arc because the jumper has both forward and downward motion during his "flight.")

286

Motion 12

CHAPTER OBJECTIVES

After completing this chapter, you will be able to

12–1 Describe a frame of reference.

12–2 Calculate speed.

12–2 Distinguish between speed and velocity.

12–3 Define and calculate acceleration and deceleration.

12–4 Describe momentum.

The eyes of the crowd are fixed on the sleek, dazzling skier as he sweeps down the ski jump track at 100 kilometers per hour. Reaching the bottom of the track, he leaps into the air. The icy wind lashes at his face. Even with goggles on, he is blinded by the glare of the snow on the mountainside below—far below.

Then, in an attempt to defy gravity, he leans forward. His body and skis take the form of an airplane wing as he rides the wind farther. Finally, his skis make contact with the snow-covered landing area. The snow flies up in his face in two streams. The sound of the cheering crowd mingles with the sound of the wind. His ride is over.

The scene is the Winter Olympics. And the ski jumper has just flown 117 meters through the air to set a new record for distance. He owes his gold medal not only to courage and years of training but also to an understanding of motion.

In this sense, ski jumping is not merely a sport. It is also a science. Learning about the science of motion may not earn you an Olympic medal, but it can be a leap into adventure and discovery.

Although this ski jumper seems to be floating in midair, his body is really in motion. You would quickly observe this fact if you were watching the ski jump from the ground below.

287

TEACHER DEMONSTRATION

Set a wind-up car in motion (or push a toy vehicle or skateboard) the longest possible distance in your classroom. Ask students to describe the motion. Then ask,

• **How do we know the vehicle was moving?** (Its position was changing relative to other objects.)

• **What caused the motion to start?** (Force applied by hand or by spring)

• **What caused the motion to stop?** (Friction; also, the spring unwinds, no additional force is applied)

• **While the object was in motion, did it move at the same velocity? Did it move in a straight line or did it curve?** (All kinds of motion may be observed at some point in the object's "run.")

Do not be concerned about students' using correct terminology at this point.

TEACHER RESOURCES

Audiovisuals

Attraction of Gravity, 16 mm film, BFA
Gravity, 4 filmstrips with 4 cassettes, PH Media
Investigations in Science: Energy and Motion, 4 filmstrips with 2 cassettes, BFA
Newton's Law of Motion, 16 mm film, SVE

Books

Casker, Barry M. and Richard J. Noer, *Revolutions in Physics,* Norton
Lightman, Alan P. et al., *Problem Book in Relativity and Gravitation,* Princeton University Press
McMullin, Ernan, *Newton on Matter and Gravity,* University of Notre Dame Press
Pick, M. et al., *Theory of the Earth's Gravity Field,* Elsevier

Software

Velocity and Acceleration, Prentice-Hall

12-1 FRAMES OF REFERENCE

SECTION PREVIEW 12-1

The motion of any object is relative and can only be described in reference to other objects. Whatever provides the basis for a particular frame of reference is assumed to have a fixed position and provides a "backdrop" against which the moving object changes position.

Students should be able to describe experiences involving the concept of frame of reference.

PERFORMANCE OBJECTIVES 12-1

1. **Explain why all motion is relative.**
2. **Describe how motion occurs with respect to a particular frame of reference.**
3. **Identify the frame of reference and the moving object in different situations.**

SCIENCE TERMS

frame of reference p. 288

Sharpen Your Skills

Frames of Reference

1. Mount a camera on a tripod or firm base.
2. Aim the camera at Polaris, the North Star.
3. Take a 15–20-minute time exposure of the stars.
4. Describe the motion you see in the photograph.

Is the motion a result of the movement of the earth or of the stars?

12–1 Frames of Reference

Is the photo in Figure 12–1 a picture of the sun setting or the earth rising? Actually, both answers could be considered correct! If you said the sun setting, you assumed the sun was moving relative to the earth. If you said the earth rising, you assumed the earth was moving relative to the sun. **The object or point from which movement is determined is called a frame of reference.** For the sunset, the **frame of reference** is the earth. It is the earth that appears to stay in place while the sun moves. What is the frame of reference for an earthrise? ❶

Suppose you are watching a car moving past you at a moderate speed. A train, moving at a greater speed, passes the car. For both movements, the earth is the frame of reference. Now suppose you are riding in the car. The car is the frame of reference. The train's speed relative to the car is greater. ❶ So the train appears to be whizzing past you as you look out the window. If the train is the frame of reference, the speed of the car relative to the train is less. So the car appears to be moving backward!

Figure 12–1 *From your frame of reference, the sun seems to be setting below the horizon in Cottonwood, Idaho. But is the sun really moving below the horizon?* ❷

TEACHING STRATEGY 12-1

Motivation

Ask students if they have ever been in a situation where they could not tell if they or some other object was moving. Have them describe the situation. Briefly outline each student's description on the board.

Content Development

For each description recorded in the previous discussion, have students describe which seemed to be the moving object, and which seemed to be the stationary object. Develop the idea that an object has motion only in relation to a frame of reference which seems to be fixed.

Skills Development

Skills: Observing, making generalizations, applying concepts

Launch a paper airplane (or have a particularly adept student do this). Ask students which way the airplane went (a) with respect to other students, (b) with respect to the launcher, and (c) with respect to the earth.

Ask students which one of the above answers "most accurately" describes the motion of the paper plane. (They are all correct and depend on the particular frame of reference being used.)

If movement is constant, it is impossible to determine whether you or another object is moving. Movement can be measured only with reference to something that is assumed to be fixed in place. Astronauts who traveled in space at 30,000 kilometers per hour were asked how it felt to move that fast. They replied that they had no sensation of movement because there was nothing nearby with which to compare their movement. Perhaps you have had a similar experience if you have ever flown in a jet plane. Did you feel that you were moving at about 800 kilometers per hour? You probably did not sense any motion because you had no other frame of reference.

The fact that movement is related to a frame of reference is often used in the movies. Sometimes the actor stays in one place and just the background moves. On the screen it looks as if the actor is moving. This is because your frame of reference is the background. What would appear to move if your frame of reference were the earth? ④

The most common frame of reference is the earth. But as you can see, there is more than one frame of reference that can be chosen. No single one is more "correct" than any other. But one or another must be used to describe movement.

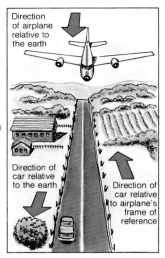

Figure 12–2 *A frame of reference must be chosen to describe how objects move in relation to one another. How would a person riding in the airplane describe the motion of the car?* ③

Figure 12–3 *Although they are traveling at more than 30,000 kilometers per hour, astronauts on the Space Shuttle feel no sensation of movement. Why do you think this is so?* ⑤

289

12-2 SPEED AND VELOCITY

SECTION PREVIEW 12-2

As an outcome of the previous section on frames of reference, motion is defined as a change in position relative to a frame of reference. The calculation of speed using the formula speed = distance/time is discussed, and the distinction made between constant and average speed. Linear motion is illustrated graphically as distance/time, with the slope of the graph related to the speed of the object. Velocity and speed are differentiated, and the rationale and method for combining velocities is discussed.

PERFORMANCE OBJECTIVES 12-2

1. **Define motion and speed.**
2. **Calculate speed using the formula speed = distance/time.**
3. **Distinguish between constant and average speed.**
4. **Represent speed graphically as distance/time.**
5. **Distinguish between speed and velocity.**

SCIENCE TERMS 12-2

motion p. 290
speed p. 291
constant speed
   p. 292

slope p. 292
average speed
   p. 293
velocity p. 293

SECTION REVIEW

1. What is a frame of reference?
2. What is the most common frame of reference?
3. Under what conditions might a car moving alongside your car appear to be moving backward?
4. Suppose you are standing on a sidewalk and your friend rides past you on her skateboard. Are you moving relative to the earth? Are you moving relative to your friend?

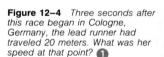

Section Objective

To define and calculate speed and velocity

12–2 Speed and Velocity

The runners are poised at the starting blocks. One hundred meters down the track, the timers ready their stopwatches. The starting gun sounds. The timers start their watches as the runners leap from their blocks. Seconds later, the winner breaks the tape and the timers check their watches.

The runners got from the starting blocks to the finish line because they moved, or changed their position. **Motion** is a change in position relative to a frame of reference. The motion of the runners was measured relative to the starting blocks. Motion is measured by distance and time. Distance is the length between two places. In the metric system, distance is measured in meters or kilometers. Time is measured in seconds or hours. In the race, the fastest runner ran 100 meters in 12 seconds.

Figure 12–4 *Three seconds after this race began in Cologne, Germany, the lead runner had traveled 20 meters. What was her speed at that point?* ❶

290

12-1 (continued)

Section Review 12-1
1. An object or point from which motion is determined
2. The earth
3. The car you are riding in is going faster than the other car and you have no other frame of reference such as houses, trees, or utility poles.
4. No; yes

TEACHING STRATEGY 12-2

Motivation
Roll a ball across a tabletop or floor at moderate speed. Ask students to carefully observe the ball and state a definition for motion. While this sounds obvious, students will probably need to be reminded about frames of reference and the need to include this in their definition. When motion has been satisfactorily defined, roll the

ball again, but faster. Ask students to observe and describe the motion of the ball. Develop the idea that an object's speed depends on both the distance it travels and the time it takes to travel that distance.

Content Development
Ask students to observe the runners in Figure 12-4.
• **What would we need to know in order to calculate the speed at which**

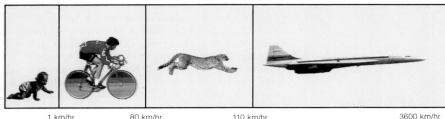

| 1 km/hr | 80 km/hr | 110 km/hr | 3600 km/hr |
| Baby crawling | Cyclist | Cheetah | Concorde SST |

Figure 12–5 *You can compare the speeds of some common objects on this scale. Where do you think your walking speed would fit?* ❷

Speed

Speed is the distance traveled by a moving object per unit of time. You can calculate the **speed** of a moving object by dividing the distance the object ❷ travels by the time it takes to travel that distance.

$$speed = \frac{distance}{time}$$

Since distance is measured in meters or kilometers and time is measured in seconds or hours, the units of speed are meters per second (m/sec) or kilometers per hour (km/hr). What was the speed of the winning runner? ❸

Sample Problem

A car travels 300 kilometers in 6 hours. What is the speed of the car?

Solution

Step 1 Write the formula

$$speed = \frac{distance}{time}$$

Step 2 Substitute given numbers and units

$$speed = \frac{300\ kilometers}{6\ hours}$$

Step 3 Solve for unknown variable

$$speed = \frac{50\ kilometers}{hour}\ or\ 50\ kilometers/hour$$

Practice Problems

1. What is the speed of a jet plane that flies 7200 km in 9 hours? ❹

2. The speed of a cruise ship is 50 km/hr. How far will the ship travel in 14 hours? ❺

291

---

each of them runs? (The distance of the race and the time it took to run that distance) Show that the relationship between speed, distance, and time may be represented mathematically as speed = distance/time. It may be helpful to point out to students that mathematically, the formula is simply a fraction. As the denominator of the fraction (time) increases, the value of the fraction (speed) decreases.

Skills Development
Skills: Applying formulas, making calculations
Have students solve the practice problems which follow the sample, then assign additional practice problems.

Common Errors
When students do the practice problems, or similar problems, stress the importance of using the correct units in their answers. A numerical answer without units is usually meaningless, and great differences in speed would be implied if the answer were in km/sec instead of km/hr.

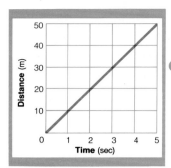

Figure 12–6 In a distance–time graph, the distance an object travels is plotted as a function of the time it takes the object to go that distance. How do you know that the object whose motion is shown here traveled at a constant speed? ❶

Figure 12–7 Study the distance–time graphs for the two lead swimmers in this race. Which graph has the steepest slope? What does that tell you about the speed of the two swimmers? ❸

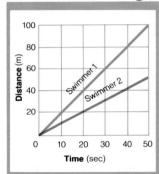

CONSTANT SPEED Figure 12–6 is a distance–time graph of a runner's motion. Distance is plotted on the vertical, or Y, axis. Time is plotted on the horizontal, or X, axis. According to the graph, how many meters did the runner travel after 1 second? ❶ You are right if you said 10 meters. The runner's speed was 10 m/sec. After 3 seconds, the runner had run 30 meters. So his speed was 30 m/3 sec = 10 m/sec. The runner's speed did not change. Speed that does not change is called **constant speed.** The speed at any particular instant can be found by dividing distance by time. Notice that a distance–time graph for constant speed is a straight line.

In Figure 12–7, the motions of two swimmers are plotted on a graph. Are the speeds of both swimmers constant? How can you tell? Now use the ❷ graph to determine if both swimmers are moving at the same speed. Swimmer 1 swims 100 meters in 50 seconds. So her speed is 100 m/50 sec = 2 m/sec. ❷ Swimmer 2 swims 50 meters in 50 seconds. Her speed is 50 m/50 sec = 1 m/sec. Swimmer 1 is the faster swimmer. If you compare the graphs of the two swimmers, you will see that the graph for swimmer 1 has a steeper, or greater, **slope.** The slope of a distance–time graph is directly related to the speed. The steeper the slope, the faster the speed.

AVERAGE SPEED The speed of a moving object is not always constant. Look at Figure 12–8. The distance–time graph describing this motion is not a straight line. According to the graph, after the first

---

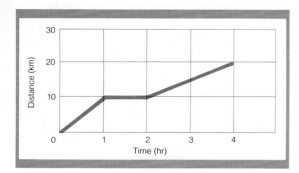

Figure 12–8 *According to this distance–time graph, how far did the object move between the first and second hour? What was the object's average speed after one hour? After two hours?* ④

hour the speed of the moving object was 10 km/hr. During the second hour, no additional distance was covered. There was no motion. What happened during the next two hours? How did the speed between hours three and four compare to the speed during the first hour? At the end of the fourth ⑤ hour, the object had gone a distance of 20 km. But as you can see, the object did not move at a constant speed.

Speed that changes is not constant speed. Dividing the total distance by the total time gives the **average speed** and not the actual speed at that instant. What is the average speed of the object in Figure 12–8?

Velocity

"The National Weather Bureau reports that Hurricane Heather is moving east at a speed of twenty kilometers per hour." A weather forecast such as this causes people to worry. But those in the potential path of a hurricane are more concerned about its direction than its speed. They want to know the **velocity** of the hurricane. **Velocity is speed in a given direction.** The speed of the hurricane is 20 km/hr. The velocity is 20 km/hr east, or 20 km/hr E. If the storm suddenly moves north, is the speed the same? Is the velocity the same? ⑥

Navigation by land, sea, or air requires precise measurements of velocity. To reach the Hawaiian Islands, a pilot must determine both the direction ③ and speed of the plane. If either measurement is wrong, the plane will not reach its destination.

ANNOTATION KEY

❶ She must compensate for the velocity of the wind, which is blowing in the opposite direction. (Applying concepts)

❷ You would move backward because the velocity of the river is greater than your velocity. (Relating facts)

❸ Final velocity (Inferring)

❹ Applying brakes on a car or bike (Relating concepts)

❶ Thinking Skill: Making generalizations

❷ Thinking Skill: Interpreting formulas

CAREER   *Air Traffic Controller*

HELP WANTED: Experienced **AIR TRAFFIC CONTROLLER** to begin work immediately at local airport. Must have controller's license. Person with pilot's license preferred but not necessary.

A blanket of fog covers the airport. Aboard a jumbo jet, the pilot studies the cockpit instruments and listens carefully to orders radioed by an **air traffic controller.** The pilot cannot see the runway. The air traffic controller sees the airplane only as a moving dot on a radar screen.

An air traffic controller has several responsibilities. These include directing arriving airplanes, departing airplanes, and airplanes that are in flight between airport destinations. A controller communicates with a pilot by radio, providing the information necessary to keep the airplane safely on its course.

An air traffic controller informs pilots of weather conditions, ground conditions, and suggested routes. The job of an air traffic controller requires a great deal of concentration, steady nerves, and efficient work habits. In order to become an air traffic controller, an applicant must pass a federal civil service exam as well as physical and psychological exams. A college degree is usually necessary.

If you would like to find out how to become an air traffic controller, write to the U.S. Government Printing Office, Library and Statutory Distribution Service, 5208 Eisenhower Avenue, Alexandria, VA 22304. Enclose a self-addressed mailing label and ask for a copy of the publication *Government Careers # GA-300-128.*

Figure 12–9 *When walking into a heavy wind, this person must increase the amount of energy she expends in order to travel at her normal walking speed. Explain why.* ❶

Suppose you are rowing a boat downstream at 16 km/hr. Would it surprise you to learn that you are actually going faster than 16 km/hr? How is this possible? The river is also moving. Since you are rowing downstream, you are going in the same direction as the river. The two velocities combine. Velocities that have the same direction combine by addition. If the velocity of the river is 10 km/hr, ❶ then you are actually moving at 16 km/hr + 10 km/hr, or 26 km/hr.

Velocities that have opposite directions combine by subtraction. If you are rowing 16 km/hr upstream, then you are actually moving at 16 km/hr − 10 km/hr, or 6 km/hr. What would happen if you were rowing at 8 km/hr upstream in the river? ❷

This idea is very important in launching rockets. Rockets are launched in the same direction as the earth rotates. The speed of the earth's rotation is about 1800 km/hr. Thus, the rocket gets an added boost of 1800 km/hr to its speed. That boost is enough to allow the rocket to escape the earth's gravitational force.

294

12-2 (continued)

Skills Development

Skills: Applying concepts, relating concepts

Have students solve additional problems involving combining velocities by addition or subtraction. Use compass points (N–S, E–W) to indicate direction.

Enrichment

For above-average students, you may want to develop the concept of velocity as a vector quantity and have students solve problems where the vectors are not parallel, using the parallelogram method. Example: A boat travels at 12 km/hr directly across a river having a current of 9 km/hr.

• **What will the boat's velocity be?** (15 km/hr)

• **Where will the boat land?** (Downstream from its intended landing place)

Section Review 12-2

1. Change in position relative to a frame of reference

2. Distance traveled by a moving object per unit of time.
Speed = distance/time

3. Total distance divided by total time

4. The steeper the slope, the faster the speed.

1. What is motion?
2. What is speed? How is it calculated?
3. What is average speed?
4. What is the relationship between steepness of the slope of a distance–time graph and speed?
5. What is velocity?
6. Draw a distance–time graph for the following motion. Starting from home, Jack walks 100 meters in 50 seconds. He stops to talk to his best friend for 100 seconds. He then turns around and sprints back home in 20 seconds. Is Jack's speed constant? What is Jack's average speed to the nearest tenth of a meter?

12–3 Acceleration

Section Objective

To define and calculate acceleration

Have you ever ridden in a roller coaster? You are pulled up to the top of the first hill at constant velocity. But as you roll down the other side, your velocity rapidly increases. At the bottom of the hill you make a sharp right turn. Then your velocity rapidly decreases as you climb the second hill. In a roller coaster ride, you experience rapid changes in velocity.

Acceleration (ak-sehl-uh-RAY-shuhn) is the rate of change in velocity. To calculate **acceleration,** divide the change in velocity by the time it takes the velocity to change. The change in velocity is the final velocity minus the original velocity.

$$\text{acceleration} = \frac{\text{final velocity} - \text{original velocity}}{\text{time}}$$ ②

The change in velocity is measured in meters per second (m/sec). The time is usually measured in seconds (sec). So acceleration is measured in m/sec divided by sec, or m/sec/sec.

A decrease in velocity is called **deceleration** (dee-sehl-uh-RAY-shuhn). Because the final velocity is less than the original velocity, deceleration has a negative value. Deceleration is sometimes called negative acceleration. When a roller coaster climbs a hill, it decelerates. Can you think of another example of deceleration? ④

Figure 12–10 *The original velocity of this roller coaster at the Arizona State Fair is 0 km/hr. The ride takes 20 seconds to complete. What other information do you need to determine its acceleration?* ③

295

12-3 ACCELERATION

SECTION PREVIEW 12-3

In this section, acceleration is defined, calculated, and represented graphically. Acceleration is the change in velocity during a given period of time. A common unit for expressing acceleration is meters/sec/sec or meters/sec². When acceleration is illustrated graphically, the result is a curved line (actually a parabola). During circular motion, an object is accelerating even though its speed is constant because its direction is continually changing. Since velocity has two components, direction and speed, a change in either component is a change in velocity, or acceleration. Centripetal acceleration is a change in velocity directed toward the center of a circle.

PERFORMANCE OBJECTIVES 12-3

1. Define acceleration and deceleration.
2. Calculate acceleration and deceleration using the formula given.
3. Interpret the distance/time graph for acceleration.
4. Describe circular motion as the result of centripetal acceleration.

SCIENCE TERMS 12-3

acceleration p. 295
deceleration p. 295
centripetal acceleration p. 298

---

5. Speed in a given direction
6. Check students' graphs carefully. They should find that Jack's speed is not constant. His average speed is 200m/170sec = 1.2 m/sec.

TEACHING STRATEGY 12-3

Motivation

Ask students to observe Figure 12-10. Ask them to describe the beginning of a roller coaster ride.

• **How does the roller coaster obtain its speed?** (It accelerates down a steep slope.) Encourage the use of the word *accelerates* instead of *speeds up*. Ask students to describe the end of the ride using the term *deceleration*.

Sample Problem

A roller coaster's velocity at the top of a hill is 10 meters/second. Two seconds later it reaches the bottom of the hill with a velocity of 26 meters/second. What is the acceleration of the roller coaster?

Solution

Step 1 Write the formula

$$acceleration = \frac{final\ velocity - original\ velocity}{time}$$

Step 2 Substitute given numbers and units

$$acceleration = \frac{26\ meters/second - 10\ meters/second}{2\ seconds}$$

$$acceleration = \frac{16\ meters/second}{2\ seconds}$$

Step 3 Solve for unknown variable

$$acceleration = 8\ meters/second/second$$

The roller coaster is increasing its velocity by 8 meters/second for every second it is moving.

Practice Problems

1. A roller coaster has a velocity of 10 m/sec at the top of a hill. Two seconds later it reaches the bottom of the hill with a velocity of 20 m/sec. What is the acceleration of the roller coaster? ❶

2. A roller coaster is moving at 25 m/sec at the bottom of a hill. Three seconds later it reaches the top of the next hill, moving at 10 m/sec. What is the deceleration of the roller coaster? ❷

Sharpen Your Skills

Sensing Motion Skills: Observing, inferring,
Level: Remedial
Type: Hands-on

Students should be able to note, even with their eyes closed, that a car has constant speed because they will feel no movement. They can sense acceleration when their body is pushed backward against the seat. They can sense deceleration when their body is thrust forward toward the dashboard. And they can sense a change in direction because they will feel movement from side to side.

Sharpen Your Skills

Sensing Motion

Next time you are riding in a car, close your eyes and determine the answers to the following questions.
  1. Can you sense constant speed? How?
  2. Can you sense acceleration? How?
  3. Can you sense deceleration? How?
  4. Can you sense change in direction? How?

296

Graphing Acceleration

The data table in Figure 12–11 is a record of a professional drag-strip race. The driver had traveled a distance of 5 meters after the first second. The distance covered in the next second was 15 meters (20 m − 5 m). By the end of four seconds, the driver had traveled 80 meters. Figure 12–11 also shows a distance–time graph of the racing car's motion. The graph is a curve rather than a straight line. A distance–time graph for acceleration is always a curve. According to the graph, how far did the driver travel in the first five seconds of the race? In the last four seconds? ❸

12-3 (continued)

Content Development
Ask students to compare Figure 12-11 to Figures 12-6 and 12-7.
• **How does the shape of the distance/time graph for acceleration differ from the graph for constant speed?** (The graph for acceleration is a curved line while the graph for constant speed is a straight line.)

Skills Development
Skills: Interpreting graphs, making predictions
• **How would the graph in Figure 12-11 be different if the object were accelerating faster?** (It would be steeper.) **Slower?** (It would be less steep.)
• **How would the graph be different if the object were decelerating?** (The graph would be a downward curve.)

Motivation
Tie a weight (about 50 g) or several iron washers to the end of a string and whirl it overhead in a circular motion at a constant speed. Ask students to describe the speed and direction of motion of the object. They should realize that while the speed of the object is constant, the direction is constantly changing. That is, instead of moving in a straight line, the object is moving inward toward the center of the circle.

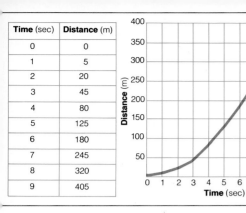

Time (sec)	Distance (m)
0	0
1	5
2	20
3	45
4	80
5	125
6	180
7	245
8	320
9	405

Figure 12–11 *The data from a professional drag race is shown on the left. A distance–time graph of the racer's motion is shown on the right. What is the acceleration of the race car? What is the shape of a distance–time graph for acceleration?* ④

Circular Motion

Acceleration is a change in velocity, and velocity expresses direction as well as speed. In circular motion the velocity is continuously changing because the direction is continuously changing. An object in circular motion is accelerating even though its speed may be constant.

The speed of the people riding the loop-the-loop in Figure 12–12 is relatively constant. But their direction is changing. So they are accelerating. They

Figure 12–12 *The gymnast on the high bar (left) and the loop-the-loop ride (right) both exhibit circular motion. The direction of the velocity is constantly changing in circular motion. What is the term for acceleration directed toward the center of a circular path?* ⑤

Content Development
Remind students that speed and direction describe an object's velocity.
- **What is true about the object's velocity when it moves in a circle—is it constant or is it changing?** (Velocity is changing because although the object's speed might be constant, its direction is constantly changing, and direction is one component of velocity.) If the object's velocity is changing, then the object must be accelerating.)

Refer students back to the definition of acceleration, if necessary.

Skills Development
Skill: Making calculations
Have students do additional practice problems using the formula.
$$\text{acceleration} = \frac{\text{final v} - \text{original v}}{\text{time}}$$

Common Errors
When doing the practice problems,

12-4 MOMENTUM

SECTION PREVIEW 12-4

The idea of momentum was first stated by Newton as an outcome of his studies of motion. The concept of momentum is one which is useful in explaining much of the behavior of matter. In this section, students are introduced to the concept of momentum as the product of mass and velocity. The law of conservation of momentum states that the total momentum in any closed system remains the same if no other forces act on the objects in the system.

PERFORMANCE OBJECTIVES 12-4

1. **Define momentum.**
2. **Calculate momentum.**
3. **Explain the law of conservation of momentum.**

SCIENCE TERMS 12-4

momentum p. 298
law of conservation of momentum
p. 299

12-3 (continued)

Section Review 12-3

1. Rate of change in velocity
2. A curve
3. Acceleration directed toward the center of circular motion
4. 20 m/sec

TEACHING STRATEGY 12-4

Motivation

Referring to the pendulum and wood block demonstration, ask students to name the factors which influence how far the wood block is moved by the swinging pendulum. Students should easily conclude that the mass and velocity of the pendulum are the two important factors. They will probably also mention the height of the pendulum as a factor, but point out that this only changes the velocity with which the pendulum strikes the block.

Content Development

Momentum may be thought of as how

Momentum

Place the following objects in the correct order from the lowest to the highest momentum. Assume that all the objects are moving at their maximum velocity.

freight train   mosquito
bullet   battleship
Space Shuttle

To relate mass and velocity to momentum

Figure 12–13 *It has been said that football is a game of momentum. What must be true of the smaller player's velocity if his momentum is great enough to stop a larger player?* ❶

---

are accelerating toward the center. Acceleration that is directed toward the center of a circular path is called **centripetal** (sehn-TRIHP-uh-tuhl) **acceleration.**

SECTION REVIEW

1. What is acceleration?
2. What is the shape of a distance–time graph for accelerated motion?
3. What is centripetal acceleration?
4. The acceleration of a freely falling body is about 10 m/sec/sec. If a ball is dropped from the top of a building, what would its velocity be after 2 seconds? Hint: What is its original velocity?

12–4 Momentum

The 100-kg fullback runs up the middle of the football field. Suddenly he collides with a 75-kg defensive back running toward him. The more massive fullback is thrown back two meters! How can a 75-kg defensive back stop a 100-kg fullback?

The answer is that the defensive back has more **momentum.** All moving objects have momentum. **Momentum is equal to the mass of an object multiplied by its velocity.**

❶   **momentum = mass × velocity**

---

difficult it is to stop a moving object. The greater the momentum, the harder it is to stop the object. Develop the idea that momentum may be expressed mathematically as the product of mass and velocity. An increase in either mass or velocity, or both, will increase momentum. The law of conservation of momentum is usually applied to objects which collide. It may be stated as: The total momentum before collision equals the total momentum after collision.

Reinforcement

Referring to the pendulum demonstration, ask students:
• **Which has the greater momentum, the heavier pendulum or the lighter one?** (The heavier one)
• **Which has the greater momentum, the faster pendulum or the slower one?** (The faster one)
Ask students to predict the effect on

Although he has less mass, the defensive back has more momentum because he is moving faster than the fullback. His greater velocity compensates for his smaller mass. If both players had the same velocity, who would have more momentum? ❷

A train has a large momentum because of its mass. A bullet has a large momentum because of its velocity. As you can see, an object's momentum depends on both its mass and its velocity. Why is it harder to stop a car moving at 100 km/hr than the same car moving at 25 km/hr? You are right if you said the car moving at 100 km/hr has more momentum and is harder to stop. This means that a car having greater momentum requires a longer distance in which to stop. The stopping distance of a car is directly related to its momentum.

Figure 12–14 *Although this bullet has a very small mass, its high speed gives it a momentum great enough to cut right through the apple.*

Conservation of Momentum

If you have ever played billiards, you know that the momentum of the moving object is transferred to the stationary object when the two objects collide. The total momentum before and after the collision is unchanged. None of the momentum is lost. The **law of conservation of momentum** states that the total momentum of any group of objects remains the same unless outside forces act on the objects. One object may lose momentum. But the momentum lost by this object is gained by another.

The momentum of a baseball bat is transferred to the ball when bat and ball meet. The more momentum the bat has, the more momentum is transferred to the ball. Why do you think a pitcher winds up before throwing the ball? In each of these situations the total momentum is conserved.

Figure 12–15 *Carol Lewis has held the American long-jump record. How does her great speed help her in the long-jump event?* ❸

SECTION REVIEW

1. What is momentum?
2. What is the law of conservation of momentum?
3. Which object has more momentum: a large cruise ship moving at 40 km/hr or a small jet plane moving at 500 km/hr? Explain your answer.
4. Using the formula for calculating momentum, determine the units of measurement.

299

LABORATORY INVESTIGATION MEASURING CONSTANT SPEED

BEFORE THE LAB

You might want to use this activity to reinforce Section 12-2, or after discussing the graph for acceleration in Section 12-3. You might also want to use it as a preparation for handling the data students might obtain in another lab activity dealing with motion and acceleration.

PRE-LAB DISCUSSION

Before beginning, review the shapes of the distance/time graphs for constant motion, no motion, and acceleration. Ask students to state a hypothesis regarding the shape of the distance/time graph for this activity.

SKILL DEVELOPMENT

Students will use the following skills while completing this investigation.
1. Observing
2. Comparing
3. Calculating
4. Hypothesizing

TEACHING STRATEGY FOR LAB PROCEDURE

Be sure that students always use the front edge of the puck as their point of measurement. If they do not, the distances between the pucks will be inaccurate.

OBSERVATIONS

Students' data table should show that distance increases constantly by about 2.1 cm for each time interval.

CONCLUSIONS

1. Straight line
2. Yes. The graph of time versus distance for constant speed is a straight line.
3. Hypothesis should have been that the graph of distance versus time is a straight line. The data will verify this hypothesis.

Measuring Constant Speed

Problem

What is the shape of a distance–time graph of constant speed?

Materials (per student)

pencil
graph paper
metric ruler

Procedure

1. The illustration on this page represents a series of flash shots taken of a dry-ice puck sliding across the floor. The time between each flash is 0.1 second. Study the illustration carefully.
2. Copy the sample data table on a piece of graph paper.
3. Position the 0-cm mark of the metric ruler on the front edge of the first puck. This position will represent distance 0.0 cm at time 0.0 second. Record this data in your data table.
4. Without moving the ruler, determine the distance of each puck from the first one.
5. Record each distance to the nearest 0.1 cm in your data table.

Observations

1. Make a distance–time graph using the data in your table. Plot the distance on the vertical, or Y, axis and the time on the horizontal, or X, axis.

Time (sec)	Distance (cm)
0.0	0.0
0.1	
0.2	
0.3	
0.4	
0.5	
0.6	

Conclusions

1. What is the shape of the graph?
2. Is the speed constant? Explain your answer.
3. Calculate the average speed.

| 0.0 sec | 0.1 sec | 0.2 sec | 0.3 sec | 0.4 sec | 0.5 sec | 0.6 sec |

GOING FURTHER: ENRICHMENT

Ask students how the series of flash shots of the puck would be different from the illustration in the book if the puck were accelerating. (The distance between the pucks would increase going across the page from left to right.)

SUMMARY

12–1 Frames of Reference

❏ A frame of reference is an object or point from which motion is determined.

❏ The earth is the most common frame of reference.

12–2 Speed and Velocity

❏ Motion is a change in position relative to a frame of reference.

❏ Speed is the distance traveled by a moving object per unit of time.

❏ Speed that does not change is called constant speed.

❏ The distance–time graph of constant speed is a straight line. The steeper the slope of the line, the greater the speed.

❏ The average speed of a moving object is the total distance divided by the total time.

❏ Velocity is speed in a given direction.

❏ Velocities that have the same direction combine by addition. Velocities that have opposite directions combine by subtraction.

12–3 Acceleration

❏ Acceleration is the rate of change in velocity. It is equal to the change in velocity divided by the time it takes to make the change.

❏ Deceleration, or negative acceleration, is a decrease in velocity.

❏ The distance–time graph for acceleration is a curve.

❏ Acceleration is a change in direction as well as in speed.

❏ Circular motion always involves acceleration because an object's direction is constantly changing. Acceleration directed toward the center of a circular path is called centripetal acceleration.

12–4 Momentum

❏ Momentum is equal to the mass of an object multiplied by its velocity.

❏ The law of conservation of momentum states that the total momentum of any group of objects remains the same if no outside forces act on the objects.

VOCABULARY

Define each term in a complete sentence.

acceleration

average speed

centripetal
  acceleration

constant
  speed

deceleration

frame of
  reference

law of
  conservation
  of momentum

momentum

motion

slope

speed

velocity

CONTENT REVIEW: MULTIPLE CHOICE

On a separate sheet of paper, write the letter of the answer that best completes each statement.

1. The most commonly used frame of reference is the
   a. sun.   b. moon.   c. earth.   d. ocean.
2. A change in position relative to a frame of reference is
   a. motion.   b. acceleration.   c. momentum.   d. direction.

301

CHAPTER REVIEW

MULTIPLE CHOICE

1. c	3. b	5. d	7. c	9. c
2. a	4. b	6. a	8. a	10. b

COMPLETION

1. earth
2. time
3. straight line
4. direction
5. addition
6. velocity
7. deceleration
8. direction
9. velocity
10. law of conservation of momentum

TRUE OR FALSE

1. T
2. F earth
3. T
4. T
5. F acceleration
6. F negative
7. T
8. T
9. F velocity
10. F conserved

SKILL BUILDING

1a. Both satellites are moving in the same direction relative to earth. The lower satellite passes the higher satellite. **b.** The lower satellite is drifting forward relative to the higher satellite. **c.** The higher satellite is drifting backward relative to the lower satellite.
2. Check student graphs carefully. They should arrive at the answer of 2 m/sec.
3. I. Constant positive acceleration
II. Constant forward velocity
III. No motion
IV. Constant backward velocity to the original starting position
4. 50 m/sec
5a. 24 kg × m/sec −8 kg × m/sec = 16 kg × m/sec
b. Both bodies will move to the right.
c. 16 kg × m/sec. The total momentum is conserved.
d. 2 m/sec
6. Because the hot escaping gases have a very high velocity (regardless of their small mass), the momentum of the rocket is great enough to lift it off the ground. As fuel is used up, the mass of the rocket decreases. This means that its velocity increases significantly while its momentum remains constant.
7. In flying from San Francisco to New York, the plane's speed would be increased by the jet stream. The two velocities combine by addition because they are in the same direction. Travel time would be less than for the reverse trip, in which the plane's speed would be decreased by the jet stream.

ESSAY

1. A passenger in the other car sees your car moving backward at 5 km/hr.
2. Yes. Acceleration is a change in speed or direction. Since the ferris wheel is moving in a circle, the direction is constantly changing.
3. 10 m/sec/sec. The graph would be a curve.
4. Momentum equals mass times velocity. The ocean liner, though moving with low velocity, has a very large mass. The bullet, though of small mass, has a very high velocity. The resulting momentum, in each case, is high.

---

3. The distance traveled by a moving object per unit of time is called
   a. acceleration. b. speed. c. momentum. d. motion.
4. Total distance divided by total time is
   a. constant speed. b. average speed. c. acceleration. d. momentum.
5. Velocity is speed and
   a. motion. b. distance. c. mass. d. direction.
6. A distance–time graph is a straight line for
   a. constant speed. b. acceleration. c. momentum. d. average speed.
7. The rate of change in velocity is called
   a. momentum. b. speed. c. acceleration. d. motion.
8. Acceleration is a change in speed or
   a. direction. b. distance. c. time. d. momentum.
9. A distance–time graph is a curve for
   a. momentum. b. speed. c. acceleration. d. velocity.
10. Momentum is mass times
    a. acceleration. b. velocity. c. motion. d. distance.

CONTENT REVIEW: COMPLETION

On a separate sheet of paper, write the word or words that best complete each statement.

1. The most commonly used frame of reference is the _____.
2. Speed is equal to distance divided by _____.
3. The distance–time graph for constant speed is a _____.
4. Velocity is speed and _____.
5. Velocities in the same direction combine by _____.
6. Acceleration is the rate of change in _____.
7. A decrease in velocity, or negative acceleration, is called _____.
8. Acceleration is a change in speed or _____.
9. Momentum is defined as mass times _____.
10. According to the _____, the total momentum of a group of objects remains the same unless outside forces act on the objects.

CONTENT REVIEW: TRUE OR FALSE

Determine whether each statement is true or false. Then on a separate sheet of paper, write "true" if it is true. If it is false, change the underlined word or words to make the statement true.

1. A <u>frame of reference</u> is a point or object from which motion is determined.
2. The <u>sun</u> is the most commonly used frame of reference.
3. The distance–time graph of <u>constant</u> speed is a straight line.
4. <u>Average</u> speed equals the total distance divided by the total time.
5. <u>Speed</u> is the rate of change in velocity.
6. Deceleration is <u>positive</u> acceleration.
7. The distance–time graph for acceleration is a <u>curve</u>.
8. <u>Centripetal</u> acceleration acts toward the center of a circular path.
9. Momentum is mass times <u>acceleration</u>.
10. Momentum is <u>lost</u> during a collision between two objects.

CONCEPT REVIEW: SKILL BUILDING

Use the skills you have developed in the chapter to complete each activity.

1. **Applying concepts** A satellite is in orbit 210 km above the earth. Another satellite orbiting at 200 km above the earth passes it. Describe the motion of the two satellites using the following frames of reference: (a) the earth (b) the higher satellite (c) the lower satellite.

2. **Making and interpreting graphs** A jogger sprints 100 meters in 12 seconds. She stops and does 20 push-ups in 88 seconds. She then jogs 1000 meters in 300 seconds. She walks another 500 meters in 400 seconds. Make a distance–time graph of her motion. What is her average speed?

3. **Interpreting graphs** Fully describe the motion at each labeled portion of the following distance–time graph.

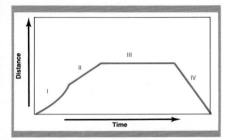

4. **Making calculations** If the acceleration of the car in Figure 12–11 is 10 m/sec/sec, what is its velocity after 5 seconds?

5. **Applying concepts**

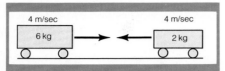

a. What is the momentum of the 6-kg cart? Of the 2-kg cart? What is the total momentum of the system?

b. If the two carts collide and stick together, what will be the direction of their motion?

c. What is the total momentum after the two carts collide? Explain your answer.

d. What is the velocity of the two carts after they collide and stick together?

6. **Relating cause and effect** Use the following information to explain the launch of a rocket: Hot gases that escape from a rocket have a very small mass but a high velocity. As fuel is used up, the mass of the rocket decreases.

7. **Identifying relationships** The jet stream is a belt of strong wind that moves west to east across the United States. Explain how the jet stream affects a plane's travel time from San Francisco to New York? From New York to San Francisco?

ISSUES IN SCIENCE

The following issue can be used as a springboard for class debate or assigned as a writing homework.

The apparent motion of the stars in the sky during the night and during the course of a year may be explained in different ways, depending on one's frame of reference. The geocentric theory—developed mainly by the astronomer Ptolemy—uses the earth as a frame of reference. The heliocentric theory—associated with the astronomer Copernicus—uses the sun as a frame of reference.

Divide the class into teams with each team researching "their" astronomer's theory and the manner in which the theory was justified based on the observations that the astronomer made. After the debate, discuss how a decision might be made as to which theory is the better one.

CONCEPT REVIEW: ESSAY

Discuss each of the following in a brief paragraph.

1. Suppose that you are sitting in a parked car. Another car passes you at a speed of 50 km/hr. Describe what a passenger in the other car sees.

2. Suppose that you are riding on a Ferris wheel moving at constant speed. Are you being accelerated? Explain your answer.

3. A drag-strip racer reaches a speed of 90 m/sec from a standing start in 9.0 sec. What is her acceleration? What would a distance–time graph of her motion look like?

4. Explain why an ocean liner slowly docking and a bullet rapidly fired both have a large momentum.

ADDITIONAL QUESTIONS AND TOPIC SUGGESTIONS

1. If the speed of light is 300,000 km/sec and it takes moonlight 1.25 seconds to reach the earth, how far away is the moon? (375,000 km)

2. A white billiard ball travels across the table and collides with a red billiard ball that is stationary. The mass of the two billiard balls is the same. After the collision, the white ball is stationary. What must be true about the motion of the red ball? (The red ball must be moving at the same speed as the white ball was moving before the collision.)

3. The winner of the 100-m dash ran the race in 9.6 seconds. The second runner ran the race in 10 seconds flat. How much farther ahead was the winner at the finish line? (4 m)

4. An object is dropped from an airplane that is flying at an altitude of

Chapter 13
FORCES

CHAPTER OVERVIEW

This chapter explores the nature of force and its relationship to energy and motion. Students will learn that a force is a push or pull that gives an object energy. This energy can set the object in motion, stop its motion, or change its motion.

While the idea of force starting motion may be familiar to students, the idea of force opposing motion is probably less familiar. Students will learn that friction is the force that opposes motion, and that there are three distinct types of frictional force.

In this chapter, students will be introduced to Newton's three laws of motion. They will also be introduced to Newton's Law of Universal Gravitation. By understanding how the force of gravity acts on an object, students will gain a clear understanding of the difference between mass and weight.

INTRODUCING CHAPTER 13

Have students observe the photograph on page 304. Help them to appreciate the awesome wonder and beauty of this picture—the idea that a few decades ago, this picture would not have even been dreamed of, let alone possible to photograph. Encourage students to imagine themselves, like the astronauts, on a trip to the moon, taking photographs in much the same way as they would take pictures on any exciting trip. Ask,
• **What type of scene on earth does this picture remind you of?** (moon coming over the horizon; sunrise)
• **What aspects of the photograph make you realize that it is not either of these things?** (The terrain is very barren, unlike anything on earth; the object rising is predominantly blue, unlike the moon and sun which appear as glowing yellow, orange, or red; the earth appears to be the object rising, rather than the land shown in the foreground.)

Use the relationship between the earth and its moon as a lead-in to a discussion about force and gravity.
• **What holds the moon in place around the earth?** (the earth's gravity)
• **Does the earth's gravity act on other objects as well?** (yes)
• **What other objects does it act on?** (everything on the earth, including

Forces

13

CHAPTER OBJECTIVES

After completing this chapter, you will be able to

13–1 Define force and describe its relationship to motion.

13–1 Compare the three types of friction.

13–2 Distinguish between balanced and unbalanced forces.

13–3 Describe Newton's three laws of motion.

13–3 Apply Newton's laws to everyday examples of motion.

13–4 Relate the force of gravity to free fall, projectile motion, and orbital motion.

13–4 Explain the relationship between gravitational force, mass, and distance.

13–5 Compare weight and mass.

Isaac Newton discovered the force that helps keep the moon in orbit around the earth. This photograph, taken by United States astronauts, shows the earth rising over the moon's horizon.

The year was 1665. Throughout London, schools and businesses had closed down. The deadly bubonic plague raged through the city, killing hundreds of people every day. Twenty-two-year-old Isaac Newton, a student and teacher at Trinity College in London, had been forced to return to his mother's farmhouse in Woolsthorpe.

As he was drinking tea in the garden at Woolsthorpe, Newton observed an apple falling from a tree. He began to wonder: Why does the apple fall vertically down to the earth? Why does it not fall sideways, or even up?

During the next year, Isaac Newton proved that the force that pulls an apple to the ground is the same force that helps keep the moon in orbit around the earth. He also was able to show that this force keeps the planets in their orbits around the sun. While Newton was making this discovery, he also was discovering the secrets of light and color, and inventing a branch of mathematics called calculus. Incredibly, Newton accomplished all this in just 18 months!

Isaac Newton is considered the founder of modern physics and "one of the greatest names in the history of human thought." Many students of his time complained that he left nothing new to be discovered! Certainly, this was not the case. You will gain an appreciation for Newton and his contribution to science as you read about his beautifully simple explanation of forces and motion: how forces determine all the motions of the earth, moon, solar system, and the entire universe.

305

TEACHER DEMONSTRATION

On a flat surface such as a table gently roll a pencil so that it moves a short distance, then stops before falling off the edge. Ask,
- **What caused the pencil to move?** (Student responses will probably include your hand, you pushed it, the force of your hand.)
- **What caused the pencil to stop?** (Student responses may include the table, it ran out of energy, you stopped pushing it, or friction.)

Now display a small rubber ball, toss it in the air, and catch it. Ask,
- **What caused the ball to go up?** (you threw it, the force of your hand and arm)
- **What caused the ball to come down?** (gravity)
- **What finally stopped the ball?** (you caught it, your hand stopped it)

TEACHER RESOURCES

Audiovisuals

Attraction of Gravity, film, BFA Educational Media

Gravity, 4 filmstrips, PH Media

Newton's Law of Motion, film, Singer Educational Media

Books

Lightman, A.P., et al, *Problem Book in Relativity and Gravitation,* Princeton University Press

McMullin, E, *Newton on Matter and Gravity,* University of Notre Dame Press

Pick, M., et al, *Theory of the Earth's Gravity Field,* Elsevier

Software

Newton's First Law, Prentice-Hall

Newton's Second Law, Prentice-Hall

Newton's Third Law, Prentice-Hall

people)
- **Is it possible to overcome the earth's gravitational force?** (yes) **How?** (in a temporary way, by tossing an object into the air or sending an airplane or space vehicle into the atmosphere; in a more permanent way by launching a rocket or spacecraft that soars beyond the earth's gravitational field.)

Direct students' attention to the text on page 305. Ask,

- **What does Newton's work have to do with gravity?** (He proved that the force that pulls objects to the ground is the same as the force that keeps the moon and the planets in place. This force is gravity.)

Emphasize to students that Newton's work began with the observation of a simple apple, and then extended to include all of the universe. Point out that part of the greatness of Newton's laws is that they have such broad

application. Emphasize also that Newton's discoveries began with the simple question, "Why does an apple fall down?" Many important scientific discoveries are made because a curious person asks, "Why?"

13-1 NATURE OF FORCES

SECTION PREVIEW 13-1

In this section, students will learn that a force is a push or a pull that gives energy to an object, causing it to start moving, stop moving, or change its motion. Students will be introduced to Aristotle's idea that it is the natural state of an object to be at rest. Then they will learn how Newton challenged this notion by proposing correctly that it is natural for an object in motion to remain in motion. Students will learn that the force that opposes motion is friction. Students will be introduced to the three types of friction: sliding, rolling, and fluid. They will learn that, although friction opposes motion, it is often a "friendly" force, for without it we could not walk, run, or power an automobile.

PERFORMANCE OBJECTIVES 13-1

1. Describe the nature of forces.
2. Explain how force is related to motion.
3. Identify friction as the force that opposes motion.
4. Name and describe the three types of frictional force.

SCIENCE TERMS 13-1

force p. 306
friction p. 307
sliding friction p. 308
rolling friction p. 308
fluid friction p. 308
lubricant p. 309

13–1 Nature of Forces

Do you play baseball or tennis? Have you raked a pile of leaves or shoveled snow off a sidewalk? Have you ever hammered a nail into a piece of wood or moved a large piece of furniture? How about something as simple as riding a bicycle, picking this book up off your desk, or opening a door? In each of these activities, a **force** is involved. You are exerting a force on an object. And although you may not know it, the object is exerting a force on you! What is force? How is it related to motion?

A force is a push or pull. A force may give energy to an object and cause it to start moving, stop moving, or change its motion. The wind pushes against you and the flag on a flagpole. A magnet pulls iron toward it. A jet engine pushes a plane forward. The moon pulls on the oceans, causing the daily tides. A nuclear explosion pushes nearby objects outward with tremendous force. A negatively charged particle and a positively charged particle are attracted to each other. In each of these examples, a force is involved. The force gives energy to an object. The energy can set the object in motion, stop its motion, or change the speed and direction of its motion.

Figure 13–1 A force is a push or pull that may give rise to motion. What force is pushing these sailboats forward (left)? Where does the force that pushes these motorcycles forward originate (right)? ❶

306

TEACHING STRATEGY 13-1

Motivation

Have students observe Figure 13-1 and Figure 13-2. Ask,
• **What types of motion do you see?** (sailboats sailing in the sea, motorcycles in a race, a sled traveling downhill, people running)
Involve students in a discussion of what produced each type of motion.

• **What is making the boats move?** (the wind blowing against the sails)
• **What causes the motorcycles to move?** (Power is generated in the engine, which then causes the wheels to push against the ground.)
• **What makes the sled travel?** (the downward pull of gravity as the sled slides down the hill)
• **What produces the motion of people running?** (Food burned as fuel gives the body energy, which enables

the muscles to move. Then the feet push against the ground.)

Content Development

Use the Motivation discussion to lead into the definition of a force. Point out to students how many times they used the words *push* and *pull* when describing how the motion in the photographs was produced. Help them to recognize that they were identifying the force needed to start the motion.

Figure 13–2 *Friction is a force that opposes the motion of an object. What type of friction is acting on the sled and speed skaters?* ❷

Friction: A Force Opposing Motion

The early Greek philosopher Aristotle believed that in order to set an object in motion and keep it moving at a constant speed, a constant force had to be applied. If the force were removed, the object would come to rest. In other words, the natural state of an object was to be at rest. For example, a horse had to pull a cart continuously to keep the cart moving. If the horse stopped pulling, the cart came to rest.

Based on many of your everyday experiences, you probably would agree with Aristotle. A ball rolled along the ground comes to rest. A sled glided along the snow eventually ends its ride. And a book pushed along a table soon stops. So it is not surprising that Aristotle's idea of constant force for constant motion lasted for almost 2000 years.

In the seventeenth century, Isaac Newton suggested a different explanation for motion. He proposed that an object in motion should move at constant velocity. No force is necessary to keep it moving in a straight line at a constant speed. If a book sliding across a table comes to rest, there must be a force acting on the book that opposes its motion. Objects do not come to rest on their own!

The force that opposes the motion of an object is called **friction** (FRIHK-shuhn). Friction is the force

❷

307

Use the following demonstration to introduce the concept of air resistance as an example of fluid friction.

Display a sheet of paper and a feather. From a standing position, release the piece of paper and let it fall to the floor. Ask,
- **Can you describe the motion of this piece of paper?** (It drifted from side to side as it fell to the floor.)
- **Did there seem to be any force resisting the fall of the paper?** (yes)
- **How could you tell?** (The paper did not fall straight down.)

Now release the feather and let it fall to the floor.
- **Can you describe the motion of the feather?** (It seemed to float in air as it slowly fell to the floor)
- **Did there seem to be any force resisting the fall of the feather?** (yes)
- **How could you tell?** (It look a long time for the feather to reach the ground.)

that brings an object to rest. When objects are in contact with each other, friction acts in a direction opposite to the motion of the moving object. The moving object slows down and finally stops.

Sliding Friction

When two solid surfaces slide over each other, **sliding friction** acts between the surfaces. When you push a chair across the floor, sliding friction opposes your motion.

The amount of sliding friction present depends on two factors: the weight of the object that is moving and the types of surfaces that the object slides across. There is more friction when a stack of cartons is pushed than when just one carton is pushed. But there is less friction opposing the motion if the cartons are pushed across a smooth floor rather than across a carpeted one.

Rolling Friction

When an object rolls over a surface, the friction produced is called **rolling friction.** Rolling friction tends to oppose motion less than sliding friction does. So wheels are often placed under objects to make it easier to move them.

Wheels and ball bearings are used to reduce friction. A train would not be able to move without wheels. And just imagine how much force would be needed if automobiles had to overcome sliding friction instead of rolling friction.

Fluid Friction

All liquids and gases are fluids. Air, water, and oil are fluids. When an object moves through a fluid, **fluid friction** opposes the motion. Air resistance is an example of fluid friction. The fall of a feather is opposed by air resistance. When you dive

Figure 13–3 *Rolling friction works for and against this skateboarder (top). The wheels make it easier for the skateboarder to move along the ground. But rolling friction will eventually cause the skateboard to stop moving. This cliff diver in Acapulco, Mexico (bottom), is also experiencing friction. What type of friction is acting on him? What is the fluid in this case?* ❶

13-1 (continued)

Content Development
Begin by involving students in a discussion about Aristotle's ideas of motion versus Newton's ideas. Ask,
- **How did Aristotle's ideas differ from Newton's ideas?** (Aristotle believed that an object's natural state is to be at rest. Newton believed that an object in motion will tend to continue in motion unless acted on by a force.)

- **How were Aristotle's ideas similar to Newton's ideas?** (Both recognized a relationship between force and motion. Both understood that there is some kind of "natural tendency" that affects an object's motion.)
- **Based on Aristotle's ideas, why must you continue to pull a wagon if you want it to move?** (Aristotle would have said that a constant force is needed to maintain constant motion.)
- **Based on Newton's ideas, why**

must you continue to pull the wagon? (to overcome the force of friction that is opposing the wagon's motion)

Reinforcement
To help students remember the three types of friction, have them cut out pictures from magazines or newspapers that show motion involving sliding friction, rolling friction, and fluid friction. Have them mount the pictures on a piece of posterboard,

from a diving board, you encounter air resistance. It is a relatively small amount of air resistance, so your motion is slowed down only a little. But the fluid resistance of the water is great enough to stop your motion before you reach the bottom of the pool.

Fluid friction usually opposes motion less than sliding friction does. Substances called **lubricants** change sliding friction to fluid friction. This reduces the friction and makes motion easier. Oil, grease, and wax are examples of lubricants.

Friction is not always an "unfriendly" force. Friction can be helpful. You often want to increase friction rather than decrease it. Tires have treads to increase the friction of the wheels on the road. Car brakes use friction to stop motion. Why do you suppose increasing friction is desirable? ❸

Without friction you could not walk. The friction between the soles of your shoes and the ground keeps you from slipping and sliding. Why do you think sand is placed on icy streets? ❹

Figure 13–4 *Friction can be a helpful force. Without friction between the tires and the track, these bikes would continue to move in a straight line instead of curving around the track. What purpose does the banking of the track serve?* ❷

SECTION REVIEW

1. What is force?
2. What is friction? What are the three types of friction?
3. What type of friction is involved in the following situations: a train moving along a track, a bird in flight, skiing, walking?

309

then label each picture according to the type of friction it represents.

Skills Development

Skill: Applying concepts

Ask students to consider the following question.

• **Sometimes the owner of an automobile will comment that something must be wrong with the car because it is making a noise that sounds like "metal on metal." In terms of frictional forces, why might this be a sign of trouble? What might be done to correct the situation?** (When two solid surfaces come in contact with each other, sliding friction results. Because this type of friction is the most opposing to motion, it can easily bring an object to a standstill, or cause a scraping sound. Sliding friction can also dissipate a lot of energy as heat, and wear away the surfaces that are rubbing together. None of these

things are good for automobile parts. What may need to be done is to replace ball bearings or repair belts or wheels, which would change the friction to rolling friction; or, add a lubricant which will change the friction to fluid friction.

Section Review 13-1

1. A push or pull that gives energy to an object, causing it to start moving, stop moving, or change its motion
2. A force opposing motion; sliding, rolling, fluid
3. Rolling, fluid, sliding, sliding

13-2 BALANCED AND UNBALANCED FORCES

SECTION PREVIEW 13-2

In this section, students will learn the difference between balanced and unbalanced forces. They will discover that balanced forces cause an object to remain at rest or move at a constant velocity, while unbalanced forces cause an object's motion to start, stop, or change.

Students will be introduced to the idea of representing forces by arrows. They will learn to add forces acting in the same direction and subtract forces acting in opposite directions. They will learn that when the combined force acting on an object is zero, the forces are balanced.

PERFORMANCE OBJECTIVES 13-2

1. **Distinguish between balanced and unbalanced forces.**

2. **Explain how equal and opposite forces cause an object to remain at rest or move at a constant velocity.**

3. **Explain how unbalanced forces change the motion of an object.**

4. **Learn to diagram forces with arrows that show the relative size and direction of each force.**

SCIENCE TERMS 13-2
balanced force p. 310
unbalanced force p. 311

Figure 13–5 *This arm-wrestling match appears to be a standoff. What must be true about the force exerted by each participant?* ❶

13–2 Balanced and Unbalanced Forces

Suppose you are arm-wrestling with a friend. You and your friend are exerting a maximum force against each other. Yet neither of you can move the other's hand. There is no change in motion. If two forces are being exerted, how can this be?

Forces that are opposite in direction and equal in size are called **balanced forces.** When forces are balanced, there is no change in motion. A book resting on a desk illustrates balanced forces. Gravity pulls the book down and the table pushes it up. The two forces are opposite and equal, so the book does not move.

A force can be represented by an arrow. The length of the arrow indicates the strength of the force. The head of the arrow indicates the direction of the force. The balanced forces exerted in the arm-wrestling contest are shown below. Notice that

the combined force is zero. Combined forces that are balanced always equal zero.

Figure 13–6 *Two forces are acting on the book. The force of gravity pulls the book down. The force of the table pushes the book up. What is true about the two forces?* ❷

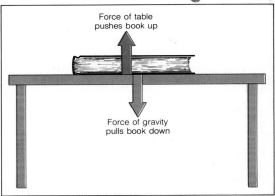

Force of table pushes book up

Force of gravity pulls book down

310

Motivation
Begin a discussion by asking students,
• **What forces are acting on you right now?** (Answers will probably vary. Some students may think that no forces are acting on them. Others may be aware of gravity pulling them down and some other force holding them up. Still others may realize that even the air in the room is exerting a slight force on them.)
• **What forces would be acting on you if you were hanging by your hands from a rope attached to the**

ceiling? (the pull of your arms and hands on the rope, the upward support of the rope, the downward pull of gravity on your body)

Content Development
Continue the discussion begun in the Motivation section by pointing out that the two situations—a student sitting at a desk and a student hanging from a rope—are not as different as they appear. In both cases, gravity is

pulling the body downward. (Of course, this pull is much more obvious to the person trying to hang onto the rope!) And in both cases, a force equal to the pull of gravity must be acting to keep the body from falling.
• **Consider the person hanging from the rope. What must be true about the upward force on the body compared to the downward force?** (The forces must be balanced.) **Why?** (The person is not falling.)

ANNOTATION KEY

❶ The force exerted by each participant is equal and opposite in direction. The combined force is zero and no motion results. (Relating cause and effect)

❷ They are equal and opposite. (Applying concepts)

❸ No one; zero (Inferring)

❹ Force between feet and ground (Relating concepts)

❶ Thinking Skill: Making predictions

❷ Thinking Skill: Making generalizations

If you were playing tug of war and the forces were balanced, who would win? The figure below shows the forces. What is the combined force? ❸

A balanced force cannot change the motion of an object. A balanced force keeps an object moving at a constant velocity. For example, a car engine continuously exerts a force against friction in order to move the car at constant velocity. The force of the engine balances the force of friction.

Unbalanced Forces

Forces that are not opposite and equal are called **unbalanced forces.** In unbalanced forces, one force is greater than the other. **While balanced forces cause no change in motion, unbalanced forces always cause a change in motion.** ❷

When two unbalanced forces are exerted in opposite directions, the combined force is the

Figure 13–7 *In this tug-of-war, forces combine in opposite directions. The rope will move in the direction of the greater force— if there is one. What other force is involved in this competition? Hint: What effect would rain have on the tug-of-war?* ❹

Sharpen Your Skills

Move That Barge

Tugboat A exerts a force of 4000 N on a barge. Tugboat B exerts a force of 8000 N in the same direction. What is the combined force on the barge? Using arrows, draw the individual and combined forces acting on the barge.

311

Sharpen Your Skills

Move That Barge
Skills: Making calculations, diagraming
Level: Remedial
Type: Computational
Materials: paper, colored pencils

This simple computational activity will help reinforce the concept of adding and subtracting forces using arrows. Students will find that the combined force on the barge is 12,000 N.

Reinforcement

It is important that students fully understand that all objects, whether at rest or in motion, are acted on by forces. (Some students may have the misconception that an object at rest has no force acting on it.) For example, everything on earth is pulled downward by the force of gravity. An object that is not falling is held in place by the upward force of the ground or other support, such as a table. The visible forces that students are probably most aware of, such as a football being kicked or a person being pushed to the ground, create a change in motion because they are unbalanced. Balanced forces are less obvious because they keep things as they are.

Content Development

Although it may be fairly obvious to students that forces are balanced when an object is at rest, it may be less obvious to them that forces are balanced when an object moves at constant velocity. To help students understand this, bring in a small toy car and demonstrate how, when given a push, the car rolls a short distance, then stops. Ask,

• **What stopped the car?** (friction)

• **What would have to be done to keep the car moving as fast as when I first pushed it?** (Something would have to continue to exert a force.)

• **What would this force have to overcome?** (The force of friction.)

Use this illustration to emphasize the idea that once an object is in motion, it can only continue in motion if the force of friction is "canceled out." This requires an equal and opposite force.

TIE-IN/MATH

Force is a vector. This means that force has both magnitude and direction. When vectors are combined, the sum or difference is called the resultant vector. Students can gain an elementary understanding of vectors by diagraming with arrows the forces acting on an object.

Sharpen Your Skills

Newton's First Law of Motion
Skills: Manipulative, observing, inferring, relating
Level: Average
Type: Hands-on
Materials: playing card, glass, coin

This activity reinforces the concept that an object at rest will remain at rest and an object in motion will remain in motion unless acted upon by an outside force (Newton's first law of motion). Students will observe that the coin falls into the glass when the playing card is flicked away. They should be able to easily relate this to Newton's first law of motion.

Figure 13–8 *When two forces are exerted in opposite directions, the combined force is the difference between the two forces (top). What is true of the combined force when two forces are exerted in the same direction (bottom)?* ❶

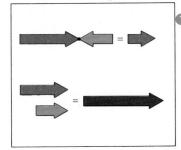

difference between the two forces. See Figure 13–8. If someone wins the arm-wrestling contest, it means there is an unbalanced force. Both arms will move in the direction of the greater force.

When two unbalanced forces are exerted in the same direction, the combined force is the sum of the two forces. See Figure 13–8. If you and your friend were pushing a car, the forces would be in the same direction. The two forces would "add together." The total force exerted by you and your friend would be greater because it would be the sum of the individual forces.

SECTION REVIEW

1. What are balanced forces?
2. What effect does a balanced force have on an object at rest? On an object in constant motion?
3. What are unbalanced forces?

13-2 (continued)

Content Development
Continue the discussion about the forces acting on a person hanging from a rope.

• **Suppose the person loosens her grip and slides down the rope. What must be true about the upward and downward forces now?** (The downward force must be greater since the body is sliding downward.)

Point out that unbalanced forces acting on an object always result in motion or a change in motion.

Skills Development
Skill: Making diagrams
Have students make arrow diagrams for the unbalanced forces described in the following situations.
(1) a tug-of-war in which one person's force is twice as great as the other person's force

(2) three people pushing a piano with equal force in the same direction
(3) a collision between a sportscar and a truck in which the truck exerts four times as much force as the sportscar

Section Review 13-2

1. Forces that are equal and opposite
2. No effect, no effect
3. Forces that are not opposite and equal
4. Changes speed and/or direction

4. What effect does an unbalanced force have on the speed and direction of an object?

5. A gorilla is playing tug of war with three monkeys. The gorilla is winning.

   a. Are the combined forces balanced or unbalanced?

   b. Draw arrows representing each monkey and the gorilla. Assume the gorilla is pulling to the right.

   c. Draw a single arrow that represents the combined forces of the three monkeys and the gorilla.

13–3 Force and Motion

During the year 1665 to 1666, Isaac Newton developed his famous three laws of motion. **The three laws of motion explain rest, constant motion, and accelerated motion, as well as how balanced and unbalanced forces act to cause these states of motion.** The importance of Newton's laws has been recognized for hundreds of years. But perhaps the significance of his contribution was best expressed by the Apollo crew as they were hurtling toward the moon. They radioed a message to mission control saying: "We would like to thank the person who made this trip possible . . . Sir Isaac Newton!"

Newton's First Law of Motion

If it were not for friction, an object set in motion would continue to move forever. Newton recognized this fact about objects in motion. He also realized that an object at rest would stay at rest unless it was acted upon by an unbalanced force. Newton called this tendency of objects to remain in motion or stay at rest **inertia** (ihn-ER-shuh).

Inertia is the property of matter that tends to resist any change in motion. The word *inertia* comes from the Latin word *iners,* which means "idle" or "lazy." Why do you think Newton used this word? ❷

The concept of inertia forms the basis for Newton's **first law of motion.** The first law of motion states that an object at rest will remain at rest, and an object in motion will remain in motion at

Sharpen Your Skills

Newton's First Law of Motion

  1. Place a playing card on top of an empty glass.

  2. Place a coin on the center of the card.

  3. Flick the card with your finger.

  What happens to the coin? Explain what you observed using Newton's first law of motion.

313

HISTORICAL NOTES

Issac Newton was born on Christmas Day, 1642. Although he lived to be 70 years old, all of his major scientific discoveries were made before the age of 45.

In his famous publication, *Principia,* Newton makes a statement worth noting:

"Nature is essentially simple. Therefore, scientists ought not to introduce more hypotheses than are needed to explain observed facts."

How elegantly Newton followed his own advice is evident in his three laws of motion. Often it takes the greatest mind to make simple the mysteries of the universe.

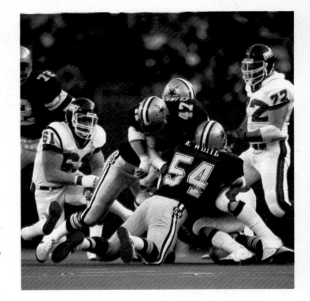

Figure 13-9 *The inertia of the running back is changed as he is brought to a sudden stop. What outside force acted on the running back to alter his inertia?* **1**

constant velocity unless an unbalanced force acts upon it. Remember that constant velocity means the same speed and the same direction. Only an unbalanced force can affect an object's state of inertia.

Imagine that you are standing in the aisle of a jumbo jet that is moving at a speed of 800 km/hr. All of a sudden you jump straight up in the air. **1** Where will you land? On the same spot from which you jumped? In front of the spot from which you jumped? Behind it?

The answer to where you would land in the jet plane is found in Newton's first law of motion. You would land on the same spot from which you jumped. You are moving at the same speed the jet plane is moving. When you leave the floor, no unbalanced force changes your forward velocity. So you must land on the same spot. The effect is the same as it would be if the jet were at rest on the runway. Where would you land if the plane accelerated while you were jumping in the air? **2**

You feel the effects of inertia every day. When you are riding in a car and it stops suddenly, you **2** keep moving forward. If you did not have a safety belt to stop you, your inertia could send you through the windshield! Perhaps you never thought

314

13-3 (continued)

Content Development

Review with students the discussion from Section 13-1 about Newton and Aristotle.

- **What did Newton believe about an object in motion at a constant velocity?** (that it would remain in motion at a constant velocity unless acted on by an unbalanced force.)

Point out that this tendency of an object to maintain its motion is called inertia. Go on to say that it is also an effect of inertia that an object at rest will stay at rest unless acted on by an unbalanced force.

- **When an object is at rest or moving at a constant velocity, are any forces acting on it?** (yes) **What kind of forces must they be?** (balanced forces) **Why?** (They are not causing a change in the object's motion.)

Emphasize that Newton's first law describes motion when balanced forces act on an object.

Content Development

It is important to emphasize that the property of inertia includes the tendency of an object to move in a straight line. Even if the velocity of an object remains the same, an unbalanced force is needed if the path of the object is to become curved. Ask,

- **Assuming the road is level in both**

314

about it in this way, but safety belts protect passengers from the effects of inertia.

When you are standing in a bus, you experience inertia in two ways. When the bus starts to move forward, what happens to you? You are thrown off balance and fall backward. Your body has inertia. It is at rest and tends to stay at rest, even though the bus is moving. When the moving bus stops, you fall forward. Even though the bus stops, you do not. You are an object in motion.

Because of inertia, a car traveling along a road will tend to move in a straight line. What happens, then, if the road curves? The driver turns the steering wheel. Because of friction between the road and the car's tires, the car will move along the curve. But the people in the car will continue to move in a straight line. As a result, they will bump into the walls of the car. You might want to observe the effects of inertia the next time you are riding in a car. Notice what happens when the car starts, stops, and changes direction. ❸

Figure 13–10 *The baseball player's inertia tends to keep him running in a straight line. Because it is hard for him to make a sharp left turn, he "rounds" the bases instead. What force enables the runner to round third base and head for home?* ❸

Newton's Second Law of Motion

Newton's first law of motion describes motion when a balanced force acts on an object. Newton also described motion when an unbalanced force acts on an object. An unbalanced force accelerates an object in the direction of that force. The larger the force is, the greater the acceleration will be. The mass of an object also determines its acceleration. If the same force is applied to a bowling ball and a tennis ball, which ball will have the greater acceleration? Why? ❺

The relationship between force, mass, and acceleration is stated in Newton's **second law of motion.**

force = mass × acceleration

When mass is in kilograms and acceleration is in meters/second/second, force is in newtons (N). One newton equals the force required to accelerate one kilogram of mass at one meter/second/second.

1 N = 1 kg × 1 m/sec/sec

Newton's second law of motion explains why a small car has better gas mileage than a large car. Suppose the acceleration of both cars is 2 m/sec/sec.

Figure 13–11 *It is easy to make this ball move with great speed after it makes contact with the racket. Although the ball has a small mass, its acceleration off the racket is great. Why?* ❹

cases, which do you think would take more effort—to pedal a bicycle in a straight line, or to pedal a bicycle around in a circle? (to pedal around in a circle) **Why?** (You must apply additional force to keep the bike on a curved path.) **What property of the bicycle are you working to overcome?** (inertia)

Reinforcement
Review the definition of acceleration as the change in velocity over time. Also review the idea that velocity tells both the speed and direction of an object. Help students to understand that when an unbalanced force acts on an object, the speed and/or direction of the object is changed. Thus we say that the object is accelerated. It is important that students realize that acceleration does not *only* mean to go faster. Acceleration can mean motion started, motion stopped, speed increased, speed decreased, or the direction of motion changed.

Enrichment
When introducing Newton's second law, you may find it helpful to also display the formula as $a = F/m$. This makes clear to students that the acceleration is directly proportional to the force and inversely proportional to the mass. It also helps them see that acceleration will change as the force/mass ratio changes. This concept can be illustrated effectively by picturing a snowball. If a person keeps adding snow to the snowball, yet each time throws it with the same force, the snowball will accelerate less each time. If, however, the snowball begins to melt, the same force applied to the snowball will cause it to accelerate more.

TEACHER DEMONSTRATION

The following demonstration will illustrate Newton's third law.

Display a medium-sized balloon and blow it up. Hold the opening of the balloon closed with your fingers for a moment. Then release your fingers and let the air rush out of the balloon. The balloon should be propelled into the air and travel a short distance before it falls to the ground. Have extra balloons available so that student volunteers can also perform the demonstration.

Figure 13–12 *One of the reasons these stock cars can accelerate around the curve is the unbalanced force of friction. In what direction does the unbalanced force of friction act?* ❶

The mass of the small car is 750 kg. The mass of the large car is 1000 kg. According to the second law of motion, the force required to accelerate the small car is 750 kg × 2 m/sec/sec, or 1500 N. The force required to accelerate the large car is 1000 kg × 2 m/sec/sec, or 2000 N. More gasoline will have to be burned in the engine of the large car to produce the additional force.

Remember that acceleration is a change in speed *or* direction. If an object is moving in a curved path, its direction is constantly changing. It is constantly accelerating. According to the second law of motion, an unbalanced force must be present when there is a change in speed or direction. Any object moving in a curved path must have an unbalanced force acting on it. The acceleration is always in the direction of the unbalanced force.

Newton's Third Law of Motion

Suppose you are an astronaut making a space-walk outside the Space Shuttle. In your excitement about your walk, you use up all the gas in your re-action jet. How do you get back to the Shuttle?

In order to save yourself, you need to know Newton's **third law of motion.** The third law of motion states that for every action, there is an equal and opposite reaction. Another way to state the ❷ third law is to say that every force must have an equal and opposite force. All forces come in pairs.

Now, back to your problem of being stranded in space. You have no walls or floor to push against.

Sharpen Your Skills

Newton's Third Law of Motion
Skills: Observing, inferring, relating
Level: Average–Enriched
Type: Hands-on
Materials: string, three rubber bands

In this activity, students demonstrate the third law of motion by observing equal and opposite reactions on the middle rubber band when they pull on the two end rubber bands. Students should be able to relate their observations to the third law of motion.

Sharpen Your Skills

Newton's Third Law of Motion

1. Tie each end of a piece of string to a separate rubber band.

2. Tie one end of a second piece of string to a third rubber band.

3. Now tie the free end of the second string to either one of the other rubber bands. You should have two rubber bands attached to a middle rubber band.

4. Pull the two end rubber bands apart and carefully observe the lengths of all three rubber bands.

Explain your observations using Newton's third law of motion.

316

13-3 (continued)

Content Development

Point out that Newton's second law explains what happens to an object when unbalanced forces act on it. Write the formula F = ma on the chalkboard. Ask,

• **What factors determine the size of the unbalanced force needed to accelerate an object?** (the mass of the object and the size of the acceleration)

• **How much more force would you need to accelerate a 4 kg object 10 m/sec/sec than to accelerate a 2 kg object the same amount?** (twice as much)

• **If a given force is applied to two objects of different mass, which object will accelerate more?** (the smaller)

• **If different size forces are applied to two objects of the same mass, which object will accelerate more?** (the one receiving the larger force)

Skills Development

Skill: Applying formulas

Have students solve the following problems using Newton's second law. Be sure to stress that the units must be Newtons, kilograms, and meters.

(1) If a 60-kg person on a 15-kg sled is pushed with a force of 300 Newtons, what will be the person's acceleration? (M = 60 + 15 = 75 kg; a = 300/75 or 4/m/sec/sec)

(2) A 50-kg skater pushed by a friend

So you throw your jet pack in the opposite direction of the Shuttle. In throwing the jet pack, you push on it and it pushes on you. The jet pack moves away from the Shuttle. You move toward safety!

Every time you walk you are using the third law of motion. As you walk, your feet push against the ground. The ground pushes against your feet with an equal and opposite force. You move forward and the earth moves in the opposite direction! Since the mass of the earth is so large, its motion is unobservable. If you were suspended a few meters above the ground, could you walk forward? ❸

The reaction engine of a rocket is another application of the third law of motion. Various fuels are burned in the engine, producing hot gases. The hot gases push against the inside tube of the rocket and escape out the bottom of the tube. As the gases move downward, the rocket moves in the opposite direction, or upward. ❸

Newton's three laws of motion can explain all aspects of an object's motion. His first law describes motion when a balanced force acts on an object. His

Figure 13–13 *Which of Newton's three laws of motion explains why the jumper lands in the water, not on the dock?* ❷

Figure 13–14 *How does Newton's third law of motion explain the movement of a water sprinkler and the launch of a rocket?* ❹

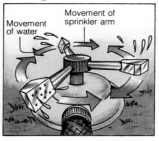

Movement of water

Movement of sprinkler arm

317

• **How did the escaping air make the balloon fly?** (by exerting a force opposite to the motion of the balloon)

• **Can you think of other objects that are moved in a similar way?** (rocket, airplane)

• **Objects on the ground are also moved according to Newton's third law. Can you explain how?** (By pushing against the ground, people can walk and run. Cars, bikes, and trucks move as their wheels push against the ground.)

• **Why is friction an important part of this process?** (Without friction, feet and wheels would just slip and slide; it would not be possible to push against the ground.)

accelerates 5 m/sec/sec. How much force did the friend apply? (250 N) (3) A bowling ball rolled with a force of 15 Newtons accelerates at a rate of 3 m/sec/sec; a second ball rolled with the same force accelerates 4 m/sec/sec. What are the masses of the two balls? (5 kg and 3.75 kg)

Enrichment

Have students work in small groups. Ask each group to make up five problems using Newton's second law. Then have groups trade problem sets and solve. Encourage students to evaluate the construction of the problems they were given to solve.

Content Development

Use the demonstration with the balloon to introduce Newton's third law. Ask,

• **What made the balloon fly in the air?** (the air rushing out of it)

Cross-Unit Reference

While discussing the nature of forces, you may wish to introduce the concept of work and its relation to force and then refer students to the discussion of work in Chapter 15.

13-4 GRAVITY

SECTION PREVIEW 13-4

In this section, students will explore the relationship between gravity and the motion of falling objects. They will learn that all objects are accelerated by gravity at the same rate, but that some objects fall more slowly than others due to air resistance.

Students will be introduced to the motion of projectiles. They will discover that the path of a projectile is determined by the forward force of its own inertia plus the downward force of gravity. Students will also learn that orbital motion results when the forward inertia of an object just balances the downward pull of gravity.

In this section, students will also be introduced to Newton's law of universal gravitation. They will learn that the forces that affect motion on earth are the same everywhere in the universe.

PERFORMANCE OBJECTIVES 13-4

1. **Relate gravity and the motion of falling objects.**
2. **Explain the effects of air resistance on falling objects.**
3. **Explain projectile motion.**
4. **Introduce Newton's law of universal gravitation.**

SCIENCE TERMS 13-4

gravity p. 318
terminal velocity p. 320
projectile p. 320
projecile motion p. 320
orbital motion p. 321
law of universal gravitation p. 321

Section Objective

To relate gravity to the motion of falling objects

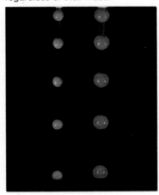

Figure 13–15 *This photograph illustrates that two objects will fall toward the earth at the same rate regardless of their mass.*

second law describes motion when an unbalanced force acts on an object. His third law explains why forces act in pairs.

SECTION REVIEW

1. State Newton's first law of motion.
2. What is inertia?
3. State Newton's second law of motion in terms of force, mass, and acceleration.
4. State Newton's third law of motion in terms of force.
5. You and a friend are pulling on opposite ends of a rope. Both of you are exerting a force of 200 N. What force is being exerted in the middle of the rope? Explain your answer.

13–4 Gravity

Legend has it that in the late 1500s, the famous Italian scientist Galileo dropped two cannonballs at exactly the same time from the top of the Leaning Tower of Pisa in Italy. One cannonball had ten times the mass of the other cannonball. According to the scientific theories of Galileo's day, the more massive ball should have landed first. But Galileo believed that the cannonballs would land at the same time. And, according to the legend, both cannonballs did land at exactly the same time! Galileo's hypothesis formed the basis of his description of the motion of falling objects.

Free Fall

All objects accelerate at the same rate, regardless of their masses. **The acceleration of a falling object is due to the force of gravity between the object and the earth.** The attractive force between all objects in the universe is called **gravity.** A pebble, a rock, and a boulder dropped from the same height at the same moment will all hit the ground at exactly the same time. And because of gravity, they will all accelerate at the same rate.

Near the surface of the earth the acceleration due to gravity (g) is 9.8 meters per second per

---

second, or 9.8 m/sec/sec. That means that for every second an object is falling, its velocity is increasing by 9.8 m/sec. Suppose an object is dropped from the top of a mountain. Its starting velocity is 0 m/sec. At the end of the first second of fall, the object has a velocity of 9.8 m/sec. After two seconds, its velocity is 19.6 m/sec. After three seconds, 29.4 m/sec. If it takes five seconds for the object to reach the ground, how fast will it be traveling? Perhaps you can now understand why even a dime can cause damage if it is dropped from a great height!

Do a leaf, a piece of paper, and a feather fall at 9.8 m/sec/sec? You have probably seen these objects fluttering through the air to the ground. Their acceleration is much less than 9.8 m/sec/sec.

As a leaf falls, air resistance opposes its downward motion. So it moves more slowly. Air resistance is a result of the force of friction. Air resistance also opposes the downward motion of a falling rock. But the shape of the leaf causes greater air resistance. If both the leaf and the rock were dropped in a vacuum, they would accelerate at 9.8 m/sec/sec.

Any falling object meets air resistance. You can think of the object as being pushed up by this opposing force of the air. As the object falls, the air resistance gradually becomes equal to the pull of gravity. The forces are then balanced. According to the first law of motion, the object continues to fall at a constant velocity. There is no further

Figure 13–16 *Although gravity pulls both a leaf and a rock toward the earth, the two objects do not accelerate at the same rate. The leaf and rock do not strike the earth at the same time. On the moon, however, they would. Why?* ❷

Figure 13–17 *The skydivers are accelerating toward the earth at the same rate. At some point, air resistance will cause them to reach terminal velocity. They will no longer accelerate but will continue to fall at a constant rate. What effect does opening a parachute have on a skydiver's fall?* ❸

319

BACKGROUND INFORMATION

It is important for students to understand that the pull of gravity on an object is directly proportional to the object's mass. That is, the greater the mass, the greater the force. If this were not so, objects of different masses would accelerate at different rates. By applying the formula F = ma, it is easy to see that, if the force due to gravity increases as mass increases, the acceleration will remain constant.

ANNOTATION KEY

❶ 49.0 m/sec/sec (Applying formulas)
❷ On the earth, air resistance keeps the leaf from accelerating at the same rate as the hammer. On the moon, which has no atmosphere and thus no air resistance, the two objects accelerate at the same rate. (Inferring)
❸ It increases air resistance, so a slower and safer terminal velocity is reached (Applying concepts)
❶ Thinking Skill: Making generalizations
❷ Thinking Skill: Making observations

chute? (A few students may have; most have probably seen pictures.)
• **Can you describe a parachute and its use?** (Answers will vary somewhat, but should include that it is a large, umbrella-shaped piece of cloth used to jump safely from an airplane.)
• **Why does a person jumping from an airplane use a parachute?** (Before studying this section, students may not know exactly why a parachute works; however, encourage them to speculate.

The correct answer is that a parachute increases air resistance so that a safer and slower terminal velocity is reached.)

Content Development

Have students read the introduction to Section 13-4. Ask,
• **Based on your own experience, would you think that falling objects accelerate at the same rate or at different rates?** (Answers may vary, but encourage students to really draw on

their own observations and not give the "textbook answer" unless they have thought it through.)
• **Based on your own experience, can you explain why early scientists believed that more massive objects accelerate faster than less massive objects?** (Guide students to understand that often lighter objects fall more slowly because of air resistance.)

BACKGROUND INFORMATION

The horizontal and vertical velocities of a projectile are independent of one another. A projectile and an object dropped straight down both accelerate at a rate of 9.8 m/sec/sec. If two objects are dropped simultaneously from the same height, and one is given a forward velocity while the other is not, both objects will still hit the ground at the same time.

13-4 (continued)

Enrichment

Challenge students to solve the following problem.
An object dropped from an airplane reaches a velocity of 200 kilometers per hour. Neglecting the effects of air resistance, how long has the object been falling? (Solution: velocity of object = 200,000/3600 m/sec = 55.6 m/sec. Time in the air = 55.6/9.8 = 5.7 sec)

Content Development

Draw on the chalkboard the path of a typical projectile (a ball thrown forward from the edge of a cliff works well). Use arrows to indicate the path of the projectile.
• **Ask students to describe the path of the object.** (The object travels out and down in a curved path.)
• **What causes the object to move in this path?** (The initial horizontal thrust of the object causes it to move forward; the force of gravity causes it to fall.)
• **What would be the path of the ob-**

320

acceleration. When a falling body no longer accelerates, it has reached its **terminal velocity.** Sky divers reach a terminal velocity of about 190 km/hr. When they reach this velocity, they stop accelerating. There is no longer any sensation of falling!

Projectile Motion

If you drop a baseball directly downward, it will accelerate at a rate of 9.8 m/sec/sec. What will be the downward acceleration of a ball that is thrown forward? The downward acceleration of the ball is still 9.8 m/sec/sec! Once you release the ball either directly downward or horizontally, the only force acting on it is gravity. Near the surface of the earth the acceleration due to gravity is 9.8 m/sec/sec.

When any object is thrown in the air, it becomes a **projectile.** A projectile moves forward due to its inertia and accelerates downward due to gravity. The path of a projectile is called **projectile motion.**

Projectile motion is always a curve. In projectile motion, gravity is an unbalanced force that changes the direction of the projectile. Gravity pulls the projectile downward as it moves forward. The combination of the two motions is a curved path. The next time you watch a display of fireworks, observe the trail left behind by the skyrockets. You will see a curved path.

Figure 13–18 *The illustration at the right shows the motion of one ball dropped straight down and two balls thrown forward. The two balls exhibit projectile motion. In what order will the three balls strike the ground? You can also see projectile motion in the trails of the fireworks.*

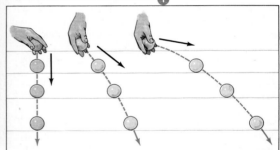

ject if there were no gravitational force? (It would move horizontally in a straight line.)
• **What would be the path of the object if it had not been thrown forward?** (It would go straight down.)

Summarize the motion of a projectile by saying: For each second a projectile travels forward, it also travels downward. This combination of forward and downward motion causes it to move in a curved path.

Orbital Motion

An object that orbits another object is in **orbital motion.** Orbital motion is the result of the combination of the object's forward inertia and the downward pull of gravity on the object. In order for a Space Shuttle to orbit the earth, it must be accelerated to a horizontal speed of 8000 m/sec. At this speed, its inertia balances the earth's pull of gravity. Inertia causes the Shuttle to move in a straight line. Gravity pulls the Shuttle toward the earth. The combination of inertia and gravity causes the Shuttle to orbit the earth. What will happen to the Shuttle as it begins to slow down? ❷

Newton's Law of Universal Gravitation

Isaac Newton was the first scientist to prove that the force pulling an apple to the ground was the same force pulling the moon toward the earth. At this time, most scientists believed that the forces on the earth were different from the forces in the rest of the universe. Newton discovered the first universal law of forces. A universal law applies to all objects in the universe.

Newton's **law of universal gravitation** states that all objects in the universe attract each other by the force of gravity. The size of the force depends on two factors: the masses of the objects and the distance between them. The moon is held in orbit around the earth by gravity. The entire solar system is held together by gravity.

There is a force of gravity between you and this book. But the book is not pulled over to you. Why? The force of gravity depends on the masses of the objects. The gravitational force between a book and you is extremely small because your mass and the book's mass are relatively small.

The force of gravity increases as the masses of the objects increase. Gravitational forces only become observable when the masses are as large as those of the planets, moon, and stars.

The force of gravity depends on the distance between the objects. The gravitational force decreases rapidly as the distance between the objects increases. The gravitational force between an apple

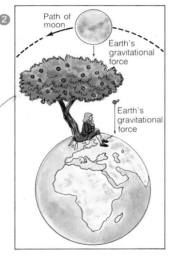

Figure 13–19 *Newton's law of universal gravitation explains why the apple falls to the ground and why the moon stays in orbit around the earth.*

Path of moon

Earth's gravitational force

Earth's gravitational force

321

13-5 WEIGHT AND MASS

SECTION PREVIEW 13-5

In this section, students will learn to distinguish between weight and mass. They will learn that weight is a measure of the force of gravity on an object, and mass is a measure of the amount of matter in an object.

Students will learn that weight changes with location, but mass never changes. They will discover that the farther an object moves from the center of the earth, the less it weighs.

In this section, students will learn to calculate weight according to the formula, weight = mass × acceleration due to gravity. They will understand that this formula is a version of Newton's second law, F = ma.

PERFORMANCE OBJECTIVES 13-5

1. **Distinguish between weight and mass.**
2. **Explain how weight changes according to location.**
3. **Calculate weight according to Newton's second law.**

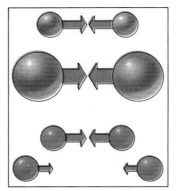

Figure 13–20 *Gravitational force between two objects depends on the masses of the objects and the distance between them. The larger arrows in the top diagram show that as mass increases, gravitational force increases. What do the arrows in the bottom diagram indicate about gravitational force and distance?* ❶

Section Objective

To distinguish between weight and mass

and the earth is 5 N on the surface of the earth. At 380,000 km—the distance to the moon—the gravitational attraction between the apple and the earth is only 0.001 N!

SECTION REVIEW

1. What is the value of the acceleration due to gravity near the surface of the earth?
2. What is terminal velocity?
3. What force acts on a projectile? What kind of path does a projectile follow?
4. What is a universal law? State Newton's law of universal gravitation.
5. What happens to the force of gravity if the mass increases? If the distance increases? Using the symbol g for force of gravity, m for mass, and d for distance, write a proportion that shows the relationship involved in Newton's law of universal gravitation.

13–5   Weight and Mass

Weight is a measure of the force of gravity on an object. Since weight is a force, its unit is the newton (N). This book weighs about 15 N. You probably weigh between 450 and 550 N.

If your weight is 500 N on the earth, would it be the same on the moon? The answer is no. The mass of the moon is much smaller than the mass of the earth. According to Newton's law of universal gravitation, a smaller mass means a smaller gravitational force. So the gravitational force on the moon is less than that on the earth. You would weigh about 80 N on the moon!

Your weight can also change on the earth. As you move farther from the center of the earth, your weight decreases. You would weigh about one newton less on a mountaintop than at sea level.

❶ Your weight varies according to the force of gravity pulling on you. And the force of gravity varies according to location. Is there less of you when you weigh less? The answer, of course, is no. You have the same amount of mass regardless of your location. Your mass is a constant value. It does not

322

13-4 (continued)

Section Review 13-4
1. 9.8 m/sec/sec
2. Speed at which air resistance equals the downward pull of gravity
3. Gravity, curved path
4. Applies to all objects in the universe. All objects attract each other with a gravitational force.
5. Increases, decreases. G is proportional to m/d.

TEACHING STRATEGY 13-5

Motivation
Display an apple and hold it in your hand. Ask,
• **What force is keeping this apple from falling?** (upward push of your hand against the apple)
• **How big must this force be?** (equal to the pull of gravity on the apple)
• **Suppose the apple were to double or triple in size. What would happen**

to the amount of force I would have to exert to hold it in my hand? (It would have to increase.)
• **What does this say about the pull of gravity on a larger apple compared to the pull on a smaller apple?** (It must be greater.)

Content Development
Use the Motivation discussion to introduce students to the definition of weight as a measure of the force of

Figure 13–21 *What effect did traveling to the moon have on the mass and weight of John Young, Apollo 16 commander?* ❷

change. Your mass is the same anywhere on the earth, on the moon, and even on Jupiter.

Before Newton's time, mass and weight were thought to be the same property. But they are not. **Weight is a measure of the force of gravity, and mass is an amount of matter.** Weight varies according to the force of gravity, and mass is a constant.

Mass and weight, however, are related. Newton's second law of motion, force = mass × acceleration, can be rewritten in terms of weight: ❷

> **weight = mass × acceleration due to gravity**
> **w = m × g**

Remember that the unit of weight is the newton and the unit of mass is the kilogram.

On the surface of the earth the acceleration due to gravity is 9.8 m/sec/sec. A 10-kg mass would weigh 10 kg × 9.8 m/sec/sec, or 98 N. If your mass is 50 kg, your weight would be 490 N. What would be the weight of a 100-kg mass? ❸

SECTION REVIEW

1. What is weight?
2. Why does an object weigh less on the moon than on the earth?
3. A 600-N astronaut is standing on an asteroid. The gravitational force of the asteroid is one-hundredth that of the earth. What is the astronaut's weight on the asteroid?

323

gravity on an object. Emphasize that the pull of gravity on an object is always proportional to the object's mass. Ask,
• **According to Newton's law of universal gravitation, what other factors besides an object's mass affect the gravitational force on that object?** (the mass of the object exerting the force and the distance between the two objects)
• **How does the mass of the moon affect the amount of gravitational force it exerts on an object?** (The mass of the moon is less than the mass of the earth, so the force of gravity exerted by the moon on an object is less than the force of gravity exerted by the earth on the same object.)
• **How does the gravitational force on an object several thousand kilometers above the earth's surface compare with the gravitational force on the same object at the earth's surface?** (An object several thousand kilometers above the earth's surface will experience much less gravitational force than an object on the earth's surface.)

Section Review 13-5
1. A measure of the force of gravity on an object
2. The mass of the moon is less than the mass of the earth, so its gravitational force is less. Since weight is a measure of the force of gravity, the object weighs less on the moon.
3. 6 N

LABORATORY INVESTIGATION
WOULD A GORILLA FALL FASTER THAN A BANANA?

BEFORE THE LAB
1. **Gather all equipment at least one day prior to the investigation. Have enough equipment to meet your class needs, assuming six students per group.**

PRE-LAB DISCUSSION
Before beginning the investigation, review with students Galileo's legendary experiment with the two cannon balls. Point out that this lab is investigating the problem, Does mass affect the rate of free fall? Ask,

• **What do you think scientists of Galileo's time would have given as a hypothesis for this experiment?** (They would have said that a heavier object falls faster than a lighter object.)

• **What hypothesis do you give for this experiment?** (Answers may vary, but most will probably say that all objects fall at the same rate.)

Continue the discussion by asking,

• **What is the variable in this experiment?** (Most students will probably answer mass.)

• **Read through the procedure carefully. Is there any other variable?** (Yes.) **What is it?** (The shape of the paper changes in step 6 of the procedure.)

Guide students to recognize that, based on the procedure of this investigation, there may be other factors besides mass that affect the rate of free fall. Encourage students to speculate as to what these factors might be, and have them offer any hypotheses they might have.

SKILL DEVELOPMENT
Students will use the following skills while completing this investigation:
1. Manipulative
2. Observing
3. Comparing
4. Recording
5. Hypothesizing
6. Relating
7. Predicting

Problem
Does mass affect the rate of free fall?

> **Materials** *(per group)*
> wood block, 10 cm × 15 cm × 2.5 cm
> Styrofoam pad, 10 cm × 15 cm × 2.5 cm
> sheet of notebook paper
> triple-beam balance

Procedure
1. Use the triple-beam balance to determine the masses of the block, Styrofoam pad, and paper. Record each mass to the nearest 0.1 gram.
2. Hold the block and foam pad horizontally at arm's length. The largest surface area of each object should be parallel to the ground.
3. Release both block and foam pad at the same time. Observe if they land at the same time or if one hits the ground before the other.
4. Repeat step 3 several times. Record your results.
5. Repeat steps 2 to 4 for the foam pad and the paper.
6. Crumple the paper into a tight ball.
7. Compare the falling rates of the crumpled paper and foam pad. Record your observations.
8. Compare the falling rates of the crumpled paper and the wood block. Record your observations.

Observations
1. Which reaches the ground first, the wood block or the foam pad?
2. Are your results the same in each trial?
3. Which reaches the ground first, the foam pad or the paper?
4. Which reaches the ground first, the foam pad or the crumpled paper? The wood block or the crumpled paper?

Conclusions
1. Galileo stated that two bodies with different masses fall at the same rate. Do your observations verify his hypothesis? Explain your answer.
2. Did crumpling the paper have any effect on its falling rate? Explain your answer.
3. Now answer this question: Would a gorilla fall faster than a banana? Explain your answer.

SAFETY TIPS
The only safety precaution to be wary of in this investigation is that students take care not to drop any object on another student's foot.

TEACHING STRATEGY FOR LAB PROCEDURE
1. When dropping the wood board and Styrofoam pad simultaneously, students should switch hands for each trial to eliminate the possible variable of one hand functioning slightly differently from the other.

2. Remind students that when dropping the wood board and foam pad, both objects must be *exactly* the same height from the ground.

3. Because several different combinations of objects are being compared, students might benefit from recording their results in a chart. The chart can be of standard design for the class, or

SUMMARY

13–1 Nature of Forces

❏ Force is a push or pull. A force may give energy to an object, setting the object in motion, stopping it, or changing its direction of motion.

❏ Friction is a force that opposes motion.

❏ The three kinds of friction are sliding, rolling, and fluid friction.

13–2 Balanced and Unbalanced Forces

❏ Balanced forces are opposite in direction and equal in size to each other.

❏ A balanced force does not change motion. A balanced force keeps an object moving at a constant velocity.

❏ Unbalanced forces cause a change in motion.

❏ Forces in the same direction are added to obtain the combined force. Forces in opposite directions are subtracted.

❏ An unbalanced force can start, stop, or change the speed or direction of motion.

13–3 Force and Motion

❏ Inertia is the tendency of matter to resist a change in motion.

❏ Newton's first law of motion states that an object at rest will remain at rest and an object in motion will remain in motion at constant velocity unless acted upon by an unbalanced force.

❏ Newton's second law of motion states that force equals mass times acceleration.

❏ Newton's third law of motion states that every action has an equal and opposite reaction. Thus, forces come in pairs.

13–4 Gravity

❏ The acceleration due to gravity at the surface of the earth is 9.8 m/sec/sec.

❏ Terminal velocity is reached when the pull of gravity equals the air resistance.

❏ The path of a projectile is a curve.

❏ Newton's law of universal gravitation states that all objects in the universe attract each other by a force of gravity.

❏ An increase in mass increases the force of gravity.

❏ An increase in distance decreases the force of gravity.

13–5 Weight and Mass

❏ Weight is a measure of the pull of gravity.

❏ Weight is a force and mass is an amount of matter. Weight varies according to the force of gravity, and mass is a constant.

❏ Weight and mass are related by the equation: $w = m \times g$

VOCABULARY

Define each term in a complete sentence.

balanced force	inertia	projectile motion	terminal velocity
first law of motion	law of universal gravitation	rolling friction	third law of motion
fluid friction	lubricant	second law of motion	unbalanced force
force	orbital motion	sliding friction	
friction	projectile		
gravity			

325

each group can create their own—the important thing is that it show clearly the results of each combination of objects.

OBSERVATIONS

1. They will reach the ground at the same time, if air resistance is similar for both.

2. Probably, but may show differences due to inability to drop both items at exactly the same time and from the exact same height.

3. Probably the foam pad, although the paper may reach the ground faster depending on size and air resistance.

4. They should reach the ground at the same time. Same time.

CONCLUSIONS

1. Some observations support the hypothesis and others do not seem to. However, when air resistance is made negligible due to crumpling of paper, the hypothesis is shown to be accurate.

2. Yes it did. It reduced air resistance so that the crumpled paper should fall at the same rate as the other objects.

3. If air resistance is not an important factor, they will fall at the same rate.

GOING FURTHER: ENRICHMENT

Part 1

Students might find it interesting to investigate the free fall of different objects made of the same material. For example, if they choose to investigate wood, they could compare a wood block, a wood board, a dowel, and a carved figurine. The investigation would work especially well if the masses of the objects were the same, so that the only variable is the shape of the object.

Part 2

The fanciful title of this lab should elicit some stimulating discussion. An interesting variation on the theme (if a bright student hasn't thought of it already) is, Which will fall faster—a live gorilla or a dead gorilla? The key factor in this distinction is that an animal that is alive can do certain things to break his fall, while a dead animal cannot (thus the expression "dead weight"). For example, ask students to consider,

● **What might happen if the gorilla were to spread himself out and arch his back like a diver? Do you think this would affect his rate of free fall?** (It probably would slow him down.)

● **How, then, might the fall of a live gorilla compare with the fall of a banana?** (The gorilla might fall more slowly.)

● **Can you think of anything else that might slow the gorilla's fall, besides his own efforts?** (the air resistance of his fur)

CHAPTER REVIEW

MULTIPLE CHOICE

1. d	**3.** b	**5.** c	**7.** c	**9.** a
2. c	**4.** a	**6.** b	**8.** b	**10.** c

COMPLETION

1. Force
2. opposes
3. lubricants
4. rolling, sliding, fluid
5. balanced
6. Inertia
7. Newton
8. terminal velocity
9. inertia; gravity
10. Weight

TRUE OR FALSE

1. T
2. T
3. F less
4. T
5. F unbalanced
6. T
7. F acceleration
8. T
9. F 9.8 m/sec/sec
10. F Weight

SKILL BUILDING

1. **a.** fluid, **b.** rolling, **c.** fluid, **d.** sliding
2. **a.** back in your hand, **b.** behind you, **c.** in front of you
3. No. The inertia of the flare will carry it forward as it drops. Students should draw a curving arc.
4. 2000N
5. **a.** south, **b.** north, **c.** north
6. Two seconds: 19.6 m/sec/sec, five seconds: 49.0 m/sec/sec, 11 seconds: 107.8 m/sec/sec

ESSAY

1. Balanced forces are opposite and equal. Unbalanced forces are not opposite and equal, and they change motion.
2. Every force must have an opposite and equal force.
3. Mass is a constant. Weight changes because of changing gravitational force. Weight equals mass times acceleration due to gravity.
4. First law describes motion when a balanced force acts on an object. Second law describes motion when an unbalanced force acts on an object. Third law explains why forces act in pairs.
5. Inertia causes the object to move in a straight line. Gravity causes the object to move downward. Combination of inertia and gravity causes the typical curving motion known as projectile motion.
6. Gravity is the same on both pieces of paper. However, crumpled paper has much less air resistance, which counteracts gravitational pull. Thus, crumpled paper will fall faster than the sheet of paper.

ADDITIONAL QUESTIONS AND TOPIC SUGGESTIONS

1. Three cars are involved in a chain collision. How will the combined force experienced by the first car compare with the combined force experienced by the last car? By the middle car? (The first car will experience a combined force forward as a result of the push from behind by cars two and three. The last car will experience only a rebound force backward as a result of its impact on the second car. The middle car will experience a combined force that will result in little or no motion forward or backward. This is because it is being

---

CONTENT REVIEW: MULTIPLE CHOICE

On a separate sheet of paper, write the letter of the answer that best completes each statement.

1. Force is
   a. a push.   b. a pull.
   c. the ability to change motion.   d. all of the above.
2. A shark swimming in the ocean illustrates which type of friction?
   a. sliding   b. rolling   c. fluid   d. stationary
3. Lubricants are used to change
   a. fluid friction to sliding friction.   b. sliding friction to fluid friction.
   c. sliding friction to rolling friction.   d. rolling friction to sliding friction.
4. The property of matter that resists a change in motion is called
   a. inertia.   b. weight.   c. gravity.   d. friction.
5. According to Newton's second law of motion, force equals mass times
   a. velocity.   b. direction.   c. acceleration.   d. weight.
6. According to Newton's third law of motion, for every force there is
   a. always a change in motion.   b. an equal and opposite force.
   c. an unbalanced force.   d. a combined force.
7. When terminal velocity is reached, the acceleration of an object is
   a. increasing.   b. decreasing.   c. zero.   d. constant.
8. When the forward inertia of a projectile balances the downward pull of gravity, the object is
   a. stationary.   b. in orbital motion.
   c. decelerating.   d. moving at constant velocity.
9. Which force explains the attraction between all objects?
   a. gravitational   b. electric   c. nuclear   d. magnetic
10. Weight equals
   a. mass.   b. acceleration due to gravity.
   c. mass times acceleration due to gravity.   d. mass times distance.

CONTENT REVIEW: COMPLETION

On a separate sheet of paper, write the word or words that best complete each statement.

1. _____ is a push or pull that gives energy to an object.
2. Friction is a force that _____ motion.
3. Substances that change sliding friction to fluid friction are called _____.
4. The types of friction are _____, _____, and _____.
5. Forces that are opposite and equal are _____.
6. _____ is the property of matter that tends to resist any change in motion.
7. A force of one _____ is needed to accelerate a mass of one kilogram one meter/second/second.
8. When a falling body no longer accelerates, it has reached its _____.
9. A projectile moves forward due to its _____ and accelerates downward due to _____.
10. _____ is a measure of the force of gravity on an object.

326

Determine whether each statement is true or false. Then on a separate sheet of paper, write "true" if it is true. If it is false, change the underlined word or words to make the statement true.

1. A <u>force</u> can set an object in motion, stop its motion, or change the speed and direction of its motion.
2. Friction is a force that always acts in a direction <u>opposite</u> to the motion of the moving object.
3. Rolling friction tends to oppose motion <u>more</u> than sliding friction does.
4. The combined force of balanced forces is <u>zero</u>.
5. Objects will remain at constant velocity unless acted upon by <u>balanced</u> forces.
6. <u>Inertia</u> is the property of matter that resists any change in motion.
7. Force equals mass times <u>velocity</u>.
8. For every action there is an equal and opposite <u>reaction</u>.
9. The acceleration due to gravity at the surface of the earth is <u>1 m/sec/sec</u>.
10. <u>Mass</u> is a measure of the force of gravity.

Use the skills you have developed in the chapter to complete each activity.

1. **Applying definitions** Identify each of the following as sliding, rolling, or fluid friction: a. sky diving; b. roller derby; c. water slide; d. stealing second base.
2. **Applying concepts** A snowmobile is pulling a sled across a frozen lake at constant velocity. You are sitting in the sled. You throw a baseball straight up in the air. Assuming there is no wind resistance, where will the ball land if a. the snowmobile continues moving at constant velocity? b. the snowmobile speeds up? c. the snowmobile stops in front of you?
3. **Applying concepts** A plane drops a flare directly over you. Does the flare hit you? Explain your answer. Draw its path.
4. **Identifying relationships** Suppose the acceleration due to gravity on a planet called Zorb is 20 m/sec/sec. What is the weight of a 100-kg Zorbian?
5. **Relating concepts** You are on ice skates facing due north on a frozen pond. You are not moving. You throw your backpack to your friend who is also on ice skates and is facing due south. Your friend catches the backpack. What is the direction of motion for a. you? b. the backpack? c. your friend?
6. **Making calculations** A heavy object is dropped from the top of a building. What is its velocity at the end of 2 seconds? At the end of 5 seconds? Just before it hits the ground after 11 seconds?

Discuss each of the following in a brief paragraph.

1. Distinguish between balanced and unbalanced forces.
2. Explain why a single force cannot exist.
3. What is the relationship between weight and mass?
4. Explain how Newton's three laws describe all aspects of an object's motion.
5. Explain why the path of a projectile is a curve. Use a diagram to illustrate your explanation.
6. Explain why a flat sheet of paper dropped from a height of 2 meters will not accelerate at the same rate as a sheet of paper crumpled into a ball.

327

pushed from behind by the last car, while also experiencing a backward rebound force as a result of its impact with the first car.)
2. Explain why force is needed to keep the planets orbiting the sun at constant velocity. Where does this force come from? (Because the planets move in a circular path rather than in a straight line, force is needed to keep them in orbit. This force comes from the gravitational pull of the sun.)

3. A golf ball dropped from the top of a tower falls for ten seconds before reaching the ground. Make a graph of the object's velocity versus time. Let the vertical axis represent velocity in meters per second, and the horizontal axis represent time in seconds. Describe the shape of your graph. (The resulting graph is a straight line with slope of 9.8.)
4. A block of wood rests on an inclined plane. When wheels are attached to the block of wood, it slides down the plane. In terms of forces and motion, explain why this happens. (Without wheels, the block of wood experiences enough sliding friction to keep it in place. That is, the frictional force between the surface of the inclined plane and the wood just balances the pull of gravity on the block of wood. When wheels are attached to the wood, the friction changes to rolling friction, which exerts less force than sliding friction. Now the pull of gravity is greater than the force of friction. As a result, the block of wood slides down the plane.)
5. A cannonball is shot from the edge of a cliff with a forward velocity of 33 m/sec. The ball takes 12 seconds to reach the ground. How far from the base of the cliff does the ball land? (Solution: The horizontal velocity of the ball is independent of its free fall. Therefore, in 12 seconds it will travel a horizontal distance of 33×12 or 396 m.

ISSUES IN SCIENCE

The following issues can be used as a springboard for class debate, or they can be assigned as a writing homework.
1. In this chapter, you read how the Apollo crew thanked Sir Issac Newton for making their journey to the moon possible. However, many people in our society do not have a great deal of enthusiasm for space travel. They feel that it costs money that could be better spent on other things, and endangers the lives of astronauts. Take a position on this issue and decide whether you would thank or criticize Newton for making a voyage to the moon possible.
2. The application of Newton's laws to space exploration illustrates how a scientist making a discovery often has no idea of how his work will eventually be applied. Some people feel that scientific research should be limited if it might lead to controversial applications. Others feel that scientists must be given total freedom in their investigations if significant scientific progress is to be made. What is your opinion?

Chapter 14
FORCES IN FLUIDS

CHAPTER OVERVIEW

Whether we realize it or not, our lives are surrounded by fluid phenomena. We live in a fluid, we swim in a fluid, and our bodies are mostly fluid. Many sports, such as golf, baseball, and racing, involve fluid forces. A dream as old as human curiosity came true in this century: By studying fluid behavior people learned to fly. Some of the most exciting technology of the day requires a study of principles that govern fluid behavior, from supersonic flight, to better designs for biking gear, to automobiles that slice through the air, to the hydraulic movements of robots.

This chapter will address the topic of fluid pressure and some phenomena it causes. It looks at Archimedes' principle and why things float and sink. The fact that fluid pressure is exerted uniformly leads to a study of hydraulics. The last topic students will be introduced to is Bernoulli's principle, which involves reduced pressures with increased velocity of the fluid. This is used to explain flight.

INTRODUCING CHAPTER 14

Begin the chapter by having students observe the photograph of the Wright brothers' plane. Students will probably be amazed at the size and scope of their plane as compared to modern jets. Ask,
• **How does the Wright brothers' plane appear similar to modern airplanes?** (Answers will vary, but should include the fact that it has wings and the same basic shape and structure as a modern plane.)
• **How is the Wright brothers' plane different from modern planes?** (Answers will vary. Students should note that the plane is quite open and there is no self-enclosed compartment for the pilot. Also, only one person could fit in it. They will also note that the plane had a small engine with a propeller, rather than jet engines. Also, the materials used by the Wright

brothers to construct their plane were quite different from those in modern airplanes.)

Now have students read the chapter introduction. Ask,
• **Why do you think the Wright brothers chose the materials they used for their plane?** (They were the only available materials that were light enough for such a small engine.)
• **Do you think a plane that only flew for 12 seconds was such a big**

Forces in Fluids 14

CHAPTER OBJECTIVES

After completing this chapter, you will be able to

14–1 Describe fluid pressure.

14–1 Relate fluid pressure to altitude and depth.

14–2 Describe Archimedes' principle in terms of buoyancy and density.

14–2 Apply Archimedes' principle to the floating and sinking of objects.

14–3 Explain how hydraulic devices operate.

14–4 Describe Bernoulli's principle.

14–4 Relate Bernoulli's principle to airplane flight.

14–4 Identify the forces involved in flight.

It is December 17, 1903. Wilbur and Orville Wright stand on a deserted beach at Kitty Hawk, North Carolina. Orville climbs into a strange-looking seat made from pieces of wood and canvas. A 12-horsepower gasoline engine is connected to two large propellers by a chain and sprocket. The Wright brothers are about to try something no one has ever succeeded in doing before. They are going to fly this machine!

They have prepared well for their attempt at flight. For the past 25 years they have studied the dynamics of air flight. They have experimented with more than 200 different wing surfaces in their homemade wind tunnel. They have observed and analyzed the flight of buzzards, carefully noting how they turn in the sky without losing balance.

Now they are finally ready. Wilbur rotates a propeller and the engine starts. Orville pulls the throttle wide open. The plane takes to the air. In a flight that lasts just 12 seconds, the plane manages to travel 36 meters. It is a small distance but a significant step in science: Human flight has become a reality!

The first flying machine was designed in the fifteenth century by Leonardo da Vinci. Why did it take so long to fly the first plane? How can a large jumbo jet weighing 3.5 million newtons fly at speeds exceeding 800 kilometers per hour? As you read this chapter, you will learn the answers.

As Wilbur Wright stood watching on the deserted beach at Kitty Hawk, North Carolina, his brother Orville took one of the most important trips in history—a 12-second, 36-meter leap toward the attainment of human flight.

329

TEACHER DEMONSTRATION

Challenge students to drink from a 10-m straw. Ask how many could? This demonstration will require a place that is 7 to 10 m high (gymnasium balcony or third floor window). Plastic or rubber tubing long enough to reach the ground (or floor) will also be needed. Drop the tubing into a jug of your favorite soft drink and students will quickly become involved in trying to suck up the drink. Make sure the end of the straw is always in the liquid and there are no air leaks. The students will find it impossible. Ask them if a vacuum pump could do it. If you are high enough (10 to 11 m) even the vacuum cannot. (Be sure to use a trap.)

• **Why can't the vacuum pump pull up the liquid?** (The air above us is not heavy enough.)

• **What would be the result if you used Mercury instead of water?** (Mercury is 13 times denser and the column would be $\frac{1}{13}$ as tall.)

TEACHER RESOURCES

Audiovisuals

Buoyancy, 16mm film, Cor
Quest for Flight, 16mm film, EBE

Books

Walker, Jearl., *The Flying Circus of Physics with Answers,* John Wiley and Sons

achievement? (Answers will vary, but most students will realize that it was an important achievement since it was the first time people had flown for even such a short time or distance.)

• **What does the flying of an airplane have to do with fluids and fluid pressure?** (Students may recall from previous chapters that air is a type of fluid. If not, remind them that air is considered a fluid. Many students mistakenly believe that only liquids are fluids.)

• **Would you consider going for a ride in a plane built in the same way as the Wright brothers' plane?** (Many students will say no, but the more adventurous might say they would enjoy such a flight.)

Point out that although the Wright brothers' plane cannot compare with modern aircraft, the principles that allowed it to fly have not changed. Then tell them that by the end of this chapter, they too will understand how a heavy airplane can lift off the ground and soar through the sky.

14-1 FLUID PRESSURE

SECTION PREVIEW 14-1

In this section, students will be introduced to the idea that air and water exert forces on objects and will look at the causes of these forces. They will be given the definition and unit for pressure and the relationship between pressure and depth. This section also discusses what happens when unequal pressures are exerted on fluids.

PERFORMANCE OBJECTIVES 14-1

1. **Explain why fluids exert forces.**
2. **Define pressure.**
3. **Explain how "suction" is created.**
4. **Give the relationship between pressure and depth.**

SCIENCE TERMS 14-1

pressure p. 330

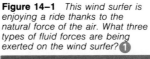
14-1 Fluid Pressure

Although you may not be aware of it, forces that exist naturally in gases and liquids affect you constantly. When you breathe, when you swim, when you drink from a straw, you are experiencing forces. As a matter of fact, you have a force approximately equal to the weight of an automobile pushing down on you right now!

In Chapter 13, you learned that fluids can produce frictional forces. But these are not the only forces caused by fluids. Fluids also push against objects. For example, water pushes against you when you swim. When you drink through a straw, air pushes against the liquid forcing it up. And at this moment, air is pushing against you with a force equal to more than 10,000 newtons!

The "push" that fluids exert on an object is called **pressure.** Perhaps you are familiar with the word pressure as it is used to describe water, air, or ❶ even blood. Scientists define pressure in a more precise way than a "push." **Pressure is a force that acts over a certain area.** In other words, pressure is force per unit area.

$$\text{pressure} = \frac{\text{force}}{\text{area}}$$

Figure 14–1 *This wind surfer is enjoying a ride thanks to the natural force of the air. What three types of fluid forces are being exerted on the wind surfer?* ❶

330

Pressure can be calculated by dividing the force exerted by a fluid by the total area over which the force acts. When force is measured in newtons (N) and area is measured in square centimeters (cm²), pressure is measured in newtons per square centimeter (N/cm²).

All liquids and gases are fluids. All fluids exert pressure. The pressure a fluid exerts is due to the fact that the fluid is made of particles that have weight and motion. The weight of the particles in a fluid causes them to push against objects.

Air, for example, exerts a pressure of 10.13 N/cm² *at sea level.* If standard air pressure is 10.13 N/cm² and your back has an area of approximately 1000 cm², then you have a force of 10,130 N pushing on your back. What keeps this force from crushing you? The fluids inside your body exert pressure, too. The air pressure outside your body is balanced by the pressure inside your body. So you do not feel 10,130 N of force.

At higher altitudes, there are fewer particles of air in a given area. So the air pressure decreases. The air pressure inside your body is now greater than the air pressure outside your body. The air rushes out of your ears and you hear a "pop." In this way, air pressure outside your body is again equal to the pressure inside your body.

Suction is a result of unequal air pressure. When you suck on a straw, you remove most of the air inside the straw. Standard air pressure, which is now greater than the air pressure inside the straw, pushes down on the surface of your drink. This pushes the drink up through the straw.

Figure 14–2 *This can was crushed because of a change in air pressure. Was the air pressure greater inside the can or outside it?* ❷

Figure 14–3 *It would be very difficult for this girl to enjoy her ice cream soda if it were not for unequal air pressure. The air pressure pushing down on the liquid outside the straw is greater than the air pressure inside the straw. The liquid is forced up the straw. What causes the air pressure inside the straw to decrease?* ❸

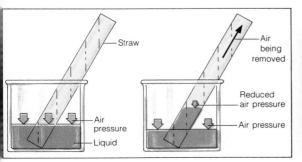

331

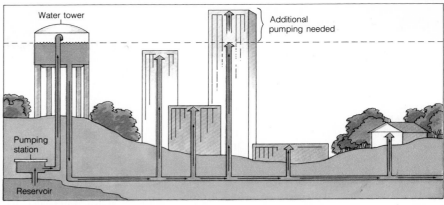

Figure 14-4 *One important application of increased fluid pressure with depth is a water tower. Notice that the tower is higher than most of the homes and buildings in the area. The weight of the water in the tower produces tremendous pressure. When the water is released from the tower, the pressure is great enough to drive the water through piping systems. What do you think must be used to pipe water through buildings higher than the tower?* ❶

The operation of a vacuum cleaner is another example of unequal air pressure. A vacuum cleaner does not suck up dirt. A fan inside the cleaner causes the air pressure inside the machine to become less than the pressure of the air outside the machine. The outside air pressure pushes the air and dirt into the vacuum cleaner.

The pressure a liquid exerts also varies with its depth. The deeper the liquid, the greater its pressure becomes. If you have ever swum to the bottom of a pool, you probably are familiar with this fact. The pressure of the water, increasing rapidly with depth, makes your ears ache. In this case, the pressure outside your body is greater than the pressure inside your body. Submarines that have descended too deep in the ocean have on occasion been crushed by the tremendous pressure. Can you explain in terms of the particles in the liquid why the pressure increases with depth? ❷

SECTION REVIEW

1. What is fluid pressure? How is it calculated?
2. What is the relationship between air pressure and altitude? Between liquid pressure and depth?
3. Explain your answers to question 2 in terms of particles of fluid.
4. Explain how a woman weighing 500 N and wearing high-heeled shoes can exert a pressure on the floor equal to about three times the pressure exerted by a 45,000-N elephant.

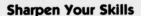

Sharpen Your Skills

Sharpen Your Skills

Air Pressure

1. Obtain an empty plastic one-liter bottle that has an air-tight top.
2. Fill the bottle one-quarter full with hot water.
3. Tightly secure the top to the bottle so that no air can enter or escape.
4. Place the bottle in a refrigerator for about five minutes. At the end of this time, record the shape of the bottle.

When the hot air in the bottle cools, the air pressure inside the bottle decreases. What causes the bottle to collapse?

332

14-1 (continued)

Content Development

You might discuss why the Hoover Dam is 200 m thick at the bottom and only a few meters thick at the top. Pressure increases with depth. Students may have experienced this in airplanes, elevators, or at the bottom of a swimming pool, as their ears feel the changes in pressure. Ask the students to stand up, bend over for one

minute, then stand up quickly. The blood pressure in their head increases when bent over because the blood column to the head is deeper. When they stand up the heart is lower than the head, the pressure in the head decreases, and they feel lightheaded. In standing, a normal adult will have 69 mm Hg pressure in the head and 194 mm Hg in the feet.

Section Review 14-1

1. Force that a fluid exerts over a certain area. Pressure equals force divided by area.
2. Air pressure decreases as altitude increases. Liquid pressure increases as depth increases.
3. There are fewer particles of fluid (air) as altitude increases. There are more particles piled up at greater depths.
4. Pressure equals force divided by area. The area of the heels of the shoes is

14–2 Buoyancy

Have you ever wondered how a submarine can sink down in the ocean and then float on the surface again? How can a steel ship weighing about five million newtons float in water? And on a more practical level, what enables you to float in a swimming pool, pond, or lake?

Fluid pressure is exerted in all directions: down, up, and to the sides. The force of a fluid that pushes an object up is called **buoyancy** (BOI-uhn-see). The upward buoyant force of a fluid opposes the downward force of gravity on an object. In other words, buoyancy acts against the weight of an object. Buoyancy makes it seem as if an object weighs less in a fluid.

The buoyant force of a fluid can be greater than, less than, or equal to the weight of an object. The size of the buoyant force determines what will happen to an object placed in a fluid. But how can the size of the buoyant force be determined?

Think for a moment of what happens when you put several ice cubes in a glass of water. The level of the water rises. The ice cubes displace, or move aside, a certain amount of water. The amount of water that is displaced has a definite weight. And the weight of the displaced water is related to the buoyant force.

Figure 14–5 *The ice cube floats in water because the buoyant force on it is equal to the weight of water it displaces (left). The same principle applies to a submarine afloat on the surface of the water (right). What principle is this?* ❸

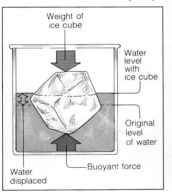

14-2 BUOYANCY

SECTION PREVIEW 14-2

Archimedes' principle is presented and used to explain floating in terms of buoyant force. It is related to ships and submarines and is stated in terms of density.

PERFORMANCE OBJECTIVES 14-2

1. **State Archimedes' principle in terms of buoyant force and also in terms of density.**
2. **Relate Archimedes' principle to why things float or sink.**

SCIENCE TERMS 14-2

buoyancy p. 333
Archimedes' principle p. 334
density p. 335

---

very small, so the force (her weight) is exerted over a very small area, causing tremendous pressure.

TEACHING STRATEGY 14-2

Motivation

Students will likely be interested in the story of Archimedes. The king had a new crown made but was suspicious that it was not pure gold. He asked Archimedes if he could determine if it was pure without harming the crown. Ask the students if they could suggest a way. While pondering the question he stepped into his bathtub, and upon noticing the water overflowing, realized the solution. He ran through the streets naked crying, "Eureka! Eureka! I have found it! I have found it!"

If the crown and a certain sized chunk of pure gold weigh the same in air but not in water, they do not have the same buoyant force, and the crown would not be pure gold. The crown was not pure gold.

Content Development

Discuss the fact that you do "lose weight" when in water. You can lift heavy objects much more easily in water. The buoyant force is subtracted from your weight to find your apparent weight.

More than 2000 years ago, the Greek scientist Archimedes discovered the exact nature of the relationship between buoyant force and the weight of the fluid displaced. This relationship, sometimes called **Archimedes' principle,** is basic to the study of the behavior of fluids. **Archimedes' principle states that the buoyant force on an object is equal to the weight of the fluid displaced by the object.**

Have you ever noticed that it is easier to lift a friend while you are both in the water? Your friend's weight seems to be much less in the water. Why? The buoyant force of the water on your friend equals the weight of the water your friend displaces. Your friend seems to weigh less because of the buoyant force of the water.

Buoyancy helps to explain why an object sinks or floats in a fluid. An object floats in a fluid because the buoyant force—the upward push—on the object is equal to or greater than the object's weight—the downward push. According to Archimedes' principle, the buoyant force is the same as the weight of the fluid displaced. So an object floats because it displaces a weight of fluid equal to or greater than its own weight.

Now, let's go back to the operation of a submarine. When a submarine is floating on the surface of the water, the weight of the water it displaces is

Figure 14–6 *This bather in the Dead Sea in Israel (left) is taking advantage of the fact that the density of salt water is greater than that of fresh water. The density of ice is slightly less than the desity of water. So a portion of this huge iceberg rises above the water's surface (right).*

14-2 (continued)

Content Development
Discuss hot air balloons in terms of density. If the balloon weighs less than the air it displaces, it floats. The density (mass/volume) of the balloon is less than the density of air. Low density means it has a big volume for little mass and thus a big buoyant force for little weight. So it floats.

Skills Development
Skill: Making comparisons
Have the class compare the weight of objects in air to their weight in water by suspending the objects from a spring scale.

Reinforcement
• **Would you weigh more or less in a vacuum? Why?** (more because the air is a fluid which buoys you up. Without the air—no buoyancy)

equal to its own weight. To make the submarine dive, special ballast tanks are flooded with water. Now the weight of the submarine is greater than the weight of the water it displaces. The submarine sinks. To resurface, air compressors force the water out of the ballast tanks. The weight of the submarine is once again less than the weight of the water it displaces. The submarine again floats.

If you place a block of wood in water, it will begin to sink. The block will continue to sink until the weight of the displaced water equals the weight of the block. At this point the block will float. If you place a block of steel in water, it will never float. The weight of the displaced water can never equal the weight of the steel block.

A steel block can never float because it weighs more than the water it displaces. Another way of saying this is that the **density** of steel is greater than the density of water. Density is the mass of a substance divided by its volume.

Archimedes' principle can now be stated in terms of density: An object will float in a fluid if the density of the object is less than the density of the fluid. The density of water is 1.0 g/cm^3. The density of wood is about 0.8 g/cm^3. Wood will float in water. The density of steel is 7.8 g/cm^3. A steel block will not float in water. The density of liquid mercury is 13.5 g/cm^3. Will a steel block float in mercury? ❶

Figure 14–7 *The density of hot air is less than the density of cold air. A hot air balloon rises as the air inside the balloon is heated. The balloon returns to the earth as the air inside it is cooled. Compare the density of the air inside the balloon to the density of the air outside the balloon during an ascent. During a descent.* ❷

335

TEACHER DEMONSTRATION
The Helium balloons suggested earlier may have lasted and could now be discussed in terms of Archimedes' principle.

To make floating objects generate more curiosity get a 1-L jar one-fourth full of corn syrup (1.38 g/cm^3) and put a piece of steel in this layer. Carefully pour in a layer of glycerol (1.26 g/cm^3) and put a rubber stopper in this layer. Continue with a layer of water, a piece of plastic, a layer of corn oil and a piece of wood.

ANNOTATION KEY
❶ Yes (Applying concepts)
❷ Ascent: density less inside the balloon; descent: density greater inside the balloon (Relating concepts)
❶ Thinking Skill: Applying concepts
❷ Thinking Skill: Relating cause and effect

Enrichment
Professional football makes use of Archimedes' principle by weighing football players in air and in water. The difference gives the buoyant force which is used to find the density of the player. The higher the density, the greater the muscle/fat ratio.

If the density of steel is 7.8 g/cm^3, how does a large cruise ship float in water? The answer is that the ship is not solid steel. The ship is built of a shell of steel that is hollow inside. Most of the ship contains air. The total density of the steel ship and air is less than the density of water. How would you describe this situation in terms of the weight of water the ship and air displace? ❶

A ship floats lower in the water when it is fully loaded. And if water leaks into the hull of a ship, the density can eventually become greater than 1 g/cm^3. What do you think will happen to the ship? ❷

Air is also a fluid. So air exerts a buoyant force. You are buoyed up by the air. The density of air, however, is only 0.00118 g/cm^3. Its buoyant force is very small. You cannot actually feel the buoyant force of the air. The density of helium gas is one-tenth the density of air. A balloon filled with helium gas will float in air. The density of carbon dioxide is almost twice the density of air. Will a balloon filled with carbon dioxide float in air? ❸

SECTION REVIEW

1. Define buoyancy.
2. State Archimedes' principle in terms of buoyancy. In terms of density.
3. The density of alcohol is 0.816 g/cm^3. The density of an ice cube is 0.917 g/cm^3. Will an ice cube float in alcohol? Explain your answer.
4. The density of ocean water is 1.02 g/cm^3. Will a boat float higher in ocean water than in fresh water? Explain your answer.

14–3 Hydraulics

At any given depth, the pressure that a fluid exerts is equal in all directions—up, down, and sideways. Look at Figure 14–8. A bottle is filled to the top with water. Water is a fluid. As you just learned, all fluids exert pressure.

What would happen to the fluid pressure if a rubber stopper were pushed down the neck of the bottle? You can see the answer in Figure 14–8. Because the water particles are already packed tightly together, they cannot move any closer than they are. The added pressure of the stopper is transmitted equally in all directions to all parts of the fluid. Why is the water pushed out the top of the bottle? ❹

Hydraulic devices use the principle that pressure is transmitted equally in all directions throughout a liquid. Hydraulic devices produce enormous forces with the application of only a very small force. The brakes on your family car operate on a hydraulic system. A small force is applied to the brake pedal and the hydraulic system stops a car weighing 10,000 N. A tractor operator uses a relatively small force to pull a handle, and a large scoop digs out several thousand newtons of soil.

How do hydraulic devices produce such enormous forces? In hydraulic devices, a force acts on a small area of liquid, producing an enormous pressure in the liquid. This original force is transmitted throughout the liquid. And at the same time, this force is multiplied into a much larger force.

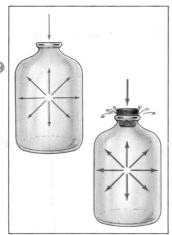

Figure 14–8 *A liquid in a confined space such as a bottle exerts pressure equally in all directions. When a stopper is pushed into the bottle, the added pressure it exerts is also transmitted equally in all directions—including up.*

14-3 HYDRAULICS

SECTION PREVIEW 14-3

This section acquaints the student with hydraulic devices and the principle on which they operate. If pressure is transmitted equally in all directions, a small force applied on a small area becomes a big force over a big area.

PERFORMANCE OBJECTIVES 14-3

1. State the principle that hydraulics is based on (Pascal's principle).
2. Explain how hydraulic devices work in terms of pressure, force, and area.

CAREER   *Tower Crane Operator*

HELP WANTED: TOWER CRANE OPERATOR for construction of a 50-story office building in midtown. High school diploma and at least three years formal training on hydraulic equipment required.

A thick slab of glass the size of a garage door is lifted by cable from the street to the top of an unfinished building. At the top, the glass is slowly moved into place between two metal tracks. One wrong move could cause the glass to shatter and endanger the people below.

The person who makes this difficult feat look easy is a **tower crane operator.** A tower crane operator must often move building materials from the street to the top of a building without actually seeing them.

A tower crane is mounted on the roof of a building. An operator controls the tower crane from a remote-control booth that is attached to the long arm of the crane. There, the operator hears instructions over a radio or watches hand signals from another worker who can see the object that is being lifted. The crane is operated

by pushing and pulling a number of buttons, levers, and pedals all at the same time. A great deal of skill is required to control the precise movements of the huge machine.

Usually, a tower crane operator has had experience running other hydraulic equipment. If you would like more information about a career as a tower crane operator, write to Associated General Contractors of America, Inc., Construction Education Services, 1957 E Street NW, Washington, DC 20036.

---

ton, output piston, input force, output force, and the small distance the desk moves for the greater distance the jack handle moves.
- **What is force like (big or small) when the area of the piston is big?** (It is big, also.)
- **What sort of devices use hydraulics?** (auto mechanic lifts, firefighter ladders, amusement park rides, etc.)

Content Development
Relate the concepts of pressure and hydraulics by asking students the following questions.
- **Would it make it easier to pull the Magdeburg hemispheres (or wet microscope slides) apart if they were held horizontally instead of vertically?** (No. Pressure is exerted in all directions equally.)
- **Would a barometer read the same if it were held in any direction?** (yes)

You could show this with an aneroid barometer.

Enrichment
Be sure to emphasize to students that energy is conserved in hydraulic devices. You only gain force at the expense of distance. At best, input force times input distance equals output force times output distance.

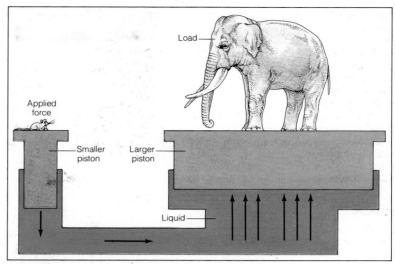

Figure 14–9 *A hydraulic lift operates on the principle that pressure is transmitted equally in all directions in a liquid. The applied force moves the smaller piston down and produces pressure in the liquid. That pressure is then exerted on every square centimeter of the larger piston. Since there are more square centimeters on the larger piston, more force is produced. The larger piston and its load move up. How do you think the distances the pistons move compare?* ❶

Look at Figure 14–9. There are two movable pistons in the same container of liquid. The piston on the left is much smaller than the piston on the right. The mouse on the smaller piston pushes on ❶ the liquid with a certain force. The force is transmitted equally throughout the liquid. The pressure of the liquid is increased equally throughout.

The pressure on the two pistons is the same. Remember that pressure is force divided by area. Is the total area of each piston the same? You are right if you answered no. The area of the larger piston is greater than the area of the smaller piston. ❷ The larger piston has more square centimeters on which force can be exerted. Since the surface area of the larger piston is larger, the force is larger.

In a hydraulic device, the pressure is the same throughout the liquid. But the surface areas of the two pistons are quite different. The piston with the larger surface area has the larger force.

338

Suppose the area of the piston on the left is 10 cm² and a force of 10 N is applied to it. The pressure that is transmitted equally throughout the liquid is 10 N divided by 10 cm², or 1 N/cm². The pressure exerted on the right piston is also 1 N/cm². If the area of the larger piston is 1000 cm², then the force must be 1000 N. The force on the larger piston is 100 times greater than the force on the smaller piston. Now do you know why a light push on the brake pedal stops a 10,000-N car? ❷

You see hydraulic devices all around you. Rescue ladders operate on hydraulic systems. Barber chairs, automobile lifts, tractors, and many amusement-park rides use hydraulic devices.

SECTION REVIEW

1. What is the effect on the pressure of a fluid if an outside pressure is applied?
2. What principle is used in the operation of hydraulic devices?
3. A 10-cm² piston exerts a pressure of 10 N/cm². What is the pressure on a 1000 cm² piston that is in the same liquid?
4. In a hydraulic lift, more force is exerted on the larger piston than is applied to the smaller piston. The larger piston can move a heavier load. Compare the distances the pistons move.

Figure 14–10 *Hydraulic devices, such as those used in a power shovel (top) and an amusement park ride (bottom), can produce enormous forces with the application of a very small force.*

14–4 Bernoulli's Principle

Section Objective

To relate Bernoulli's principle to flight

You have learned that all fluids exert pressure. Liquids and gases are fluids. Air is a gas, so it exerts pressure. The pressure of air is due to the motion of its particles and the downward pull of gravity. ❹

The Wright brothers knew that the secret to flight was the fact that air exerts pressure. They understood a principle of fluid pressure called **Bernoulli's principle,** which was first developed by the Swiss scientist Daniel Bernoulli in the eighteenth century. **Bernoulli's principle states that the pressure in a moving stream of fluid is less than the pressure in the surrounding fluid.** In other words, the faster a fluid moves, the less pressure it

14-4 BERNOULLI'S PRINCIPLE

SECTION PREVIEW 14-4

Bernoulli's principle is presented to explain flight. The terms lift, thrust, and drag are defined.

PERFORMANCE OBJECTIVES 14-4

1. State Bernoulli's principle in terms of the velocity of the fluid and the pressure of the fluid.
2. Describe how an airplane wing makes flight possible.
3. Define the forces involved in flight—lift, thrust, and drag.

SCIENCE TERMS 14-4

Bernoulli's principle p. 339
lift p. 341
thrust p. 341
drag p. 341

---

3. 10 N/cm²
4. Smaller piston moves greater distance. The distance the larger piston moves is inversely proportional to the increase in the size of the force.

TEACHING STRATEGY 14-4

Motivation

• **Why do golf balls have dimples?** (The dimples drag air in the direction they spin. As the ball moves through the air, the dimples drag air in the same direction as passing air on top, while working to slow down passing air on the bottom. This causes less pressure on top and more pressure on the bottom—or lift.)

• **Which way do they spin?** (top spins backward)

This dragging of air can be demonstrated by spinning a beach ball as you throw it. Back spin produces lift, forward spin causes it to drop faster.

One of your students may be able to demonstrate some baseball pitching techniques that produce these effects. (Aluminum foil ball does nicely.)

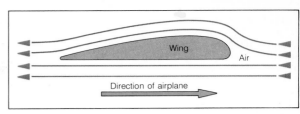

Figure 14–11 *An airplane wing is designed so that the air passing over the wing travels faster than the air passing below. Where air is flowing faster, it exerts less pressure. This is Bernoulli's principle. How does this principle account for the fact that airplanes can fly?* ❶

exerts. Try the activity on this page to convince yourself that Bernoulli was right.

   An airplane wing is shaped to take advantage of Bernoulli's principle. Look at Figure 14–11. An airplane wing is like a wedge. It is round in the front, ❶ thickest in the middle, and narrow at the back. The top of the wing bulges, but the bottom is almost perfectly flat. As a result, the top surface is longer than the bottom surface.

   As the wing moves forward, the air that moves over the top of the wing must travel a longer distance than the air that moves under the wing. But the particles of air must reach the back of the wing at the same time. Thus, the air above the wing is ❷ moving faster than the air under the wing. According to Bernoulli's principle, the pressure on top of the wing is less than the pressure under the wing. The unbalanced force pushes the wing up.

Figure 14–12 *The combined action of these four forces on an airplane enables it to take off, stay aloft, and land. Which of these four forces is the result of fluid friction?* ❷

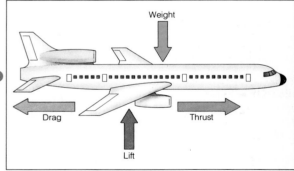

340

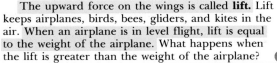

Figure 14-13 *In order to decrease drag, vehicles such as this unusual airplane (right) and this record-setting bicycle (left) have streamlined designs.*

The upward force on the wings is called **lift.** Lift keeps airplanes, birds, bees, gliders, and kites in the air. When an airplane is in level flight, lift is equal to the weight of the airplane. What happens when the lift is greater than the weight of the airplane? ❸

To move through the air, a plane must receive a forward force. This forward force is called **thrust.** The thrust is provided by either a jet engine or a propeller. An airplane also encounters fluid friction as it moves through the air. This force, which is called **drag,** tends to slow an airplane down. Drag can be reduced by making the air pass more smoothly along the airplane's surfaces. So airplanes are designed with pointed noses and thin tails. This streamlined design produces less drag.

SECTION REVIEW

1. Explain Bernoulli's principle.
2. What is lift? Thrust? Drag?
3. How does the shape of an object affect the drag on the object?
4. What lift is required to keep a jumbo jet weighing 3.5 million N in level flight?

341

moving fast and exert less pressure.)
- **In what direction do the air molecules move?** (horizontally)
- **In what direction does the pressure decrease?** (vertically)

(Both use increase in fluid velocity to produce unequal pressure and thus lift.)

Skills Development
Skills: Applying concepts, developing a model
Have students design and make a paper airplane using Bernoulli's principle (and anything else that helps). Give a prize (or other recognition) to the one that flies the farthest.

Reinforcement
Atomizers (spray bottles) use Bernoulli's principle. Put a straw in a glass of water so the end is barely above the water. Blow across the end with another straw. A fine mist is blown horizontally as water rises inside the straw.
- **What force is causing the water to rise?** (Air pressure is greater outside than in.)
- **Why is the pressure less inside the straw?** (Air molecules above it are

Section Review 14-4
1. The pressure in a moving stream of fluid is less than the pressure in the surrounding fluid.
2. Upward force on a wing; forward force; opposing force due to fluid friction
3. The more streamlined the object, the less drag. Long, tapered objects with pointed fronts allow air to flow more smoothly along their surfaces.
4. 3.5 million N

LABORATORY INVESTIGATION
A CARTESIAN DIVER

BEFORE THE LAB
1. Gather all equipment at least one day prior to the investigation.
2. One-liter plastic soft drink bottles are ideal for this investigation.
3. An alternate procedure is to use a glass bottle and a rubber stopper. When the rubber stopper is pushed down, the dropper sinks easily.
4. The key to a successful diver is that the dropper is about 95% submerged. If a squeeze does not sink the dropper, add more wire or siphon a little water up the dropper.

PRE-LAB DISCUSSION
Because of its investigative nature, let students discover as many of the principles as possible. An understanding of what pressure and density is would be helpful. Allow students to observe and make interpretations and a hypothesis as to why it works.

SKILL DEVELOPMENT
Students will use the following skills while completing this investigation.
1. Hypothesizing
2. Observing
3. Relating
4. Applying
5. Manipulative

SAFETY TIPS
Care should be taken in cutting and wrapping the wire around glass. Adding water to the dropper would serve the same purpose if you do not want students cutting the wire.

TEACHING STRATEGY FOR LAB PROCEDURE
If students are unable to make their diver work properly, suggest they add more loops of wire to the diver.

OBSERVATIONS
1. Dropper sinks.
2. Dropper rises.

A Cartesian Diver

Problem

What is the relationship between the density of an object and its buoyancy in a fluid?

Materials *(per group)*
copper wire
medicine dropper
large clear-plastic bottle with an airtight lid
glass
water

Procedure
1. Wrap several turns of wire around the middle of the medicine dropper.
2. Fill the glass with water and place the dropper in the glass. The dropper should barely float, with only the very top of it above the surface of the water.
3. If the dropper floats too high, add more turns of wire. If the dropper sinks, remove some turns of wire.

4. Completely fill the large plastic bottle with water.
5. Place the dropper in the bottle of water. The water should overflow.
6. Screw the cap tightly on the bottle. No water or air should leak out when the bottle is squeezed.
7. Squeeze the sides of the bottle. Record your observations. If the dropper does not move, take it out and add more turns of wire.
8. Release the sides of the bottle. Record your observations.

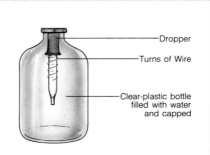

Dropper
Turns of Wire
Clear-plastic bottle filled with water and capped

Observations
1. What happens to the dropper when the sides of the bottle are squeezed?
2. What happens to the dropper when the sides of the bottle are released?

Conclusions
1. What happens to the pressure of the water when you squeeze the sides of the bottle?
2. When you squeeze the bottle, some of the water is pushed up into the dropper. Why?
3. Why does the dropper sink when you squeeze the sides of the bottle?
4. Why does the dropper rise when you release the sides of the bottle?
5. How is the density of an object related to its buoyancy in a fluid?

CONCLUSIONS
1. Pressure increases.
2. By squeezing the bottle, you are applying pressure. This pressure is felt throughout the liquid. The increased pressure forces water into the dropper.
3. The increased pressure forces water into the dropper, increasing the density of the dropper, so it sinks.
4. When you release the sides of the bottle, you decrease the pressure, so water comes out of the dropper and the density of the dropper decreases, so it rises.
5. The greater the density, the less buoyancy.

GOING FURTHER: ENRICHMENT
Part 1
Have students find the mass of the diver. Then have them put the diver in a graduated cylinder half-filled with water. Read the water level. Then push

CHAPTER REVIEW

SUMMARY

14–1 Fluid Pressure

❏ Pressure is a force that acts over a certain area.

❏ Pressure is force divided by area. A unit of pressure is newtons per square centimeter (N/cm^2).

❏ All liquids and gases are fluids. All fluids exert pressure equally in all directions.

❏ The pressure a fluid exerts is due to the fact that the fluid is made of particles that have weight and motion.

❏ Air pressure decreases as altitude increases.

❏ The pressure a liquid exerts increases as the depth of the liquid increases.

14–2 Buoyancy

❏ Buoyancy is the force caused by fluid pressure pushing upward.

❏ The buoyant force on an object is equal to the weight of the fluid displaced by the object. This relationship is Archimedes' principle.

❏ An object floats in a fluid when the buoyant force on the object is equal to or greater than the weight of the object.

❏ Density is mass divided by volume. The density of water is $1.0 \ g/cm^3$.

❏ An object will float if its density is less than the density of the fluid.

14–3 Hydraulics

❏ Pressure applied to a fluid is transmitted equally in all directions throughout the fluid.

❏ Hydraulic devices apply a small force over a small area to produce a large force over a large area.

❏ Hydraulic devices include rescue ladders, barber chairs, automobile lifts, automobile brakes, and tractors.

14–4 Bernoulli's Principle

❏ Bernoulli's principle states that the pressure in a moving stream of fluid is less than the pressure in the surrounding fluid.

❏ An airplane wing is designed to make the air move faster over the top than under the bottom. Thus, the pressure on the top of the wing is less than the pressure under the wing. The wing is pushed up against gravity.

❏ The upward force on the wing is called lift.

❏ The forward force on a plane is called thrust.

❏ Fluid friction produces drag, which opposes thrust.

VOCABULARY

Define each term in a complete sentence.

Archimedes'
  principle

Bernoulli's
  principle

buoyancy

density

drag

lift

pressure

thrust

343

---

the diver just below the water level and read the water level again. The difference is the volume of the diver.

• **How can you find the density of the diver?** (Divide mass by volume.)

• **Is its density greater or less than the density of water?** (Less, since it floats)

Part 2

Suggest students design an experiment to see if the diver acts the same when placed in alcohol and in mercury. Then have them design an experiment to see if water temperature has any effect on their original observations.

CHAPTER REVIEW

MULTIPLE CHOICE

1. b **3.** d **5.** b **7.** a **9.** d
2. c **4.** c **6.** a **8.** b **10.** c

COMPLETION

1. area
2. newton per square centimeter (N/cm^2)
3. buoyancy
4. gravity
5. weight
6. Density
7. Hydraulic
8. less
9. lift
10. drag

TRUE OR FALSE

1. F N/cm^2
2. T
3. F unequal
4. T
5. T
6. F $1.0 \ g/cm^3$
7. T
8. T
9. F slower
10. F less

SKILL BUILDING

1. Form the foil into a bowl so that its volume is maximum. The density of the foil and air will be less than the density of water. Crumple the foil into a ball and it will sink because its volume is minimum and there is very little air and its density is greater than that of water.
2. The column of water in the barometer would have to be 13.6 times the column of mercury in the barometer. This is not practical.
3. To reduce air resistance, which reduces drag
4. a. Force is doubled. **b.** Pressure remains the same.
5. Bernoulli's principle. By blowing between the papers, the air pressure between the sheets decreases. The air pressure pushing on the sheets from the other side of the paper is then greater and forces the papers together.
6. The sample of pyrite will float in mercury and the sample of gold will sink.
7. When the flaps are in the downward position, the air passing under the wing encounters increased resistance and moves slower. The air passing over the wing moves faster than the air below the wing and lift increases.
8. Since vinegar is less dense than oil, it will float on the oil. To get them to mix, even temporarily, the bottle must be shaken.

On a separate sheet of paper, write the letter of the answer that best completes each statement.

1. Force that acts over a certain area is called
  a. density. b. pressure. c. drag. d. thrust.
2. The pressure of air at sea level is
  a. zero. b. $1.0 \ g/cm^3$. c. $10.13 \ N/cm^2$. d. $1.0 \ N/cm^2$.
3. Pressure in a fluid acts
  a. upward only. b. downward only.
  c. upward and downward only. d. in all directions.
4. A submarine surfaces by
  a. increasing its density. b. taking in more water.
  c. decreasing its density. d. decreasing its drag.
5. The buoyant force of a fluid is equal to
  a. the weight of the object.
  b. the weight of the fluid displaced by the object.
  c. the pressure of the object.
  d. the volume of the fluid.
6. The relationship between buoyant force and weight of displaced fluid was stated by
  a. Archimedes. b. Bernoulli. c. Orville Wright. d. Aristotle.
7. The brake system in a car is an example of
  a. a hydraulic system. b. Bernoulli's principle.
  c. Archimedes' principle. d. density.
8. The flight of a bird is an example of
  a. a hydraulic system. b. Bernoulli's principle.
  c. Archimedes' principle. d. density.
9. The upward force on the wing of an airplane is called
  a. antithrust. b. weight. c. drag. d. lift.
10. The force on an airplane that opposes thrust is called
  a. antithrust. b. weight. c. drag. d. lift.

On a separate sheet of paper, write the word or words that best complete each statement.

1. Pressure is force per unit _____.
2. A unit of pressure is _____.
3. The force of a fluid that pushes an object up is called _____.
4. The buoyant force of a fluid opposes the downward force of _____.
5. Buoyant force on an object equals the _____ of displaced fluid.
6. _____ is measured in g/cm^3.
7. _____ devices include auto lifts and barber chairs.
8. Pressure in a moving stream of fluid is _____ than the pressure in the surrounding fluid.
9. The upward force on an airplane wing is called _____.
10. The force that opposes thrust is called _____.

344

ESSAY

1. The buoyant force of air is less than that of water.
2. Air moves faster over the top of the wing. According to Bernoulli's principle, the pressure is lower on the top of the wing. The higher pressure under the wing pushes up, giving lift to the plane.
3. Pressure in space is almost zero. The pressure inside the astronaut, because it is not balanced, would be so great as to cause the astronaut to explode.
4. Increased pressure
5. An object sinks if it is denser than the liquid it is placed in and floats if it is less dense than the liquid.
6. When you squeeze the top of a medicine dropper, you force out air and decrease the pressure inside the dropper. Air pressure on the fluid is now greater than the pressure in the dropper. The fluid is pushed into the dropper.

CONTENT REVIEW: TRUE OR FALSE

Determine whether each statement is true or false. Then on a separate sheet of paper, write "true" if it is true. If it is false, change the underlined word or words to make the statement true.

1. A unit of pressure is g/cm^3.
2. All fluids exert <u>pressure</u>.
3. Suction is a result of <u>equal</u> air pressure.
4. The upward buoyant force of a fluid opposes the <u>weight</u> of an object.
5. If the buoyant force is <u>less</u> than the weight of an object, the object sinks.

6. The density of water is <u>1.0 N</u>.
7. <u>Air</u> is a fluid.
8. Hydraulic devices use <u>fluid pressure</u>.
9. The air under the wing of a plane is moving <u>faster</u> than the air over the wing.
10. If the weight of a plane is <u>more</u> than the lift, the plane will gain altitude.

CONCEPT REVIEW: SKILL BUILDING

Use the skills you have developed in the chapter to complete each activity.

1. **Designing an experiment** Describe how you could make a sheet of aluminum foil float in water. How could you change its shape so the foil sinks?
2. **Making inferences** A barometer is a device used to measure air pressure. Explain why mercury (density 13.6 g/cm^3) is usually used in a barometer instead of water (density 1.0 g/cm^3).
3. **Identifying relationships** Airplanes are riveted together at the seams. The rivets are installed so they are even with the outside surface. Why is it important that the outside surface be so smooth?
4. **Applying concepts** Air exerts a downward force of 100,000 N on a tabletop, producing a pressure of 1000 N/cm^2.
   a. What would be the force if the tabletop were twice as large?
   b. What would be the pressure if the tabletop were twice as large?

5. **Applying concepts** A student holds two sheets of paper a few centimeters apart and lets them hang down parallel to each other. Then the student blows between the two papers. What happens to the papers? What principle is the student demonstrating? Explain your answer.
6. **Designing an experiment** The density of gold is 19.3 g/cm^3. The density of pyrite, or fool's gold, is 5.02 g/cm^3. Using mercury, density 13.6 g/cm^3, describe an experiment by which you could tell the difference between samples of the two substances.
7. **Relating concepts** Explain why an airplane gains additional lift when the flaps at the rear of the wings are in their downward position.
8. **Applying concepts** Explain why salad dressing made of oil and vinegar must be shaken before use.

CONCEPT REVIEW: ESSAY

Discuss each of the following in a brief paragraph.

1. Explain why you seem to weigh more in air than you do in water.
2. How does an airplane wing provide lift?
3. Explain why an astronaut must wear a pressurized suit in space.

4. What is the effect on a scuba diver of increasing water depth?
5. Why does an object sink or float?
6. Using the principle of fluid pressure, explain how a medicine dropper works.

345

ISSUES IN SCIENCE

The following issue can be used as a springboard for class debate or assigned as a writing homework.

Many scientists believe planes can be built that will fly at speeds much greater than modern planes. Such speeds are often referred to as hypersonic speeds. These planes might actually fly across the United States in under 20 minutes. However, the cost of developing such planes is substantial. Should the United States spend the money to develop such planes, or can the money be used for better purposes? What do you think?

ADDITIONAL QUESTIONS AND TOPIC SUGGESTIONS

1. Why does air enter your lungs when you breathe? (The air pressure is greater outside than inside.)
2. Why would expanding your chest help you float? (You would displace more water.)
3. Why can't airplanes fly in space? (There is no air to push against or create unequal pressures.)

4. Which would demonstrate a greater buoyant force, you floating in water or you floating in mercury? (same, because it is equal to your weight in both cases)

Chapter 15

WORK, POWER, AND SIMPLE MACHINES OVERVIEW

CHAPTER OVERVIEW

If we define work as the product of the force applied to an object and the distance through which the force is applied, then we can only do work when a force is applied over distance. Work does not involve time. Power is equal to the work done divided by the time it takes to do it. Both work and power can be measured.

Humans have always looked for methods to make work easier. Machines give us a mechanical advantage. Machines increase the applied force but also increase the distance over which the force must be applied. Depending on the type of machine and its efficiency, the work accomplished can be made easier.

The first use of some simple machines goes back to the Stone Age. There are six types of simple machines: the inclined plane, the wedge, the screw, the lever, the pulley, and the wheel and the axle. Combinations of these simple machines can be seen in our modern machines.

TEACHER DEMONSTRATION

Have two boards the same height as a heavy desk or table in the room. Point out to the students that the desk is heavy and picking up the end of the desk would require strength.
• **Does anyone know an easier method to lift this desk?** (Accept all answers.)

INTRODUCING CHAPTER 15

Have students observe the photograph on page 346. Read the caption. Explain that the pyramids of Egypt were made over 4600 years ago in the desert, long before we had the huge machines of today. Ask,
• **Can you infer or guess how the Egyptians moved the huge stones to the pyramid and raised them to the top?** (Accept all logical answers.)

Explain that pyramids are large structures with square bases and four smooth, triangle-shaped sides that most often come to a point. The ruins of more than 70 pyramids stand near the Nile River in Egypt. Each pyramid was built as a protective place for an Egyptian king. The Egyptians had no modern machinery or tools such as those we work with today. Point out that the Egyptians had only three simple machines to work with. Most of

the work was done by human effort.
• **What simple machines do you think they had to use?** (Accept all logical answers.)

Tell the students that the stone had to be chiseled from a limestone quarry. They cut big limestone blocks with crude chisels and saws.
• **What might a simple machine used to chisel or saw stone look like?** (Accept all logical answers.)

Explain that most of the stone

Work, Power, and Simple Machines 15

CHAPTER OBJECTIVES

After completing this chapter, you will be able to

15–1 Define work in terms of force and distance.

15–2 Describe power and its measurement.

15–3 Classify machines.

15–3 Define and calculate mechanical advantage and efficiency.

15–4 Identify the six simple machines.

15–4 Calculate mechanical advantage for each simple machine.

15–5 Describe compound machines.

The Great Pyramid of Khufu in Egypt is one of the Seven Wonders of the World. It stands over 137 meters high. Its base covers an area large enough to hold ten football fields. More than 2 million stone blocks, each weighing about 20,000 newtons, make up its structure.

The Great Pyramid, along with the many hundreds of other pyramids built by the Egyptians more than 4600 years ago, is a tribute to human effort and ingenuity. For it is exactly these two qualities that enabled the Egyptians to chisel the stone blocks from limestone quarries, to transport them to the pyramid site and to push them to the top of the magnificent structure.

The Egyptians had only three simple machines with which to work. Their only source of power was their own human effort. Several hundred thousand people toiled for twenty years to build the Great Pyramid. Today, with modern machinery, the Great Pyramid could be built with only a few hundred workers and in one-fifth the original time!

In this chapter you will learn about work, power, and simple machines. And you will gain an understanding of how machines make work easier—certainly easier than it was for the Egyptians who built the Great Pyramid.

The Great Pyramid of Khufu at Giza, Egypt, is a tribute to human effort and ingenuity. The pyramid, made of more than 2 million stone blocks, and the Sphinx, seen in front of it, were constructed with only the simplest of machines.

347

Place one board upright about 30 cm from the base of the desk. Place the second board on top of the first board, with the end of the second board under the edge of the desk. Use the second board as a lever to lift the desk.

• **Why did the boards make it easier to lift the desk?** (Accept all answers.)

Explain to the students that you used a simple machine known as a lever to help lift the desk. Repeat lifting the desk. Point out that force was pushed a long distance and the desk was lifted a short distance. The long end moved farther than the short end.

TEACHER RESOURCES

Audiovisuals

The Lever, film, BFA Educational Media

Matter and Energy: Energy, Force, and Motion, filmstrip, Singer Educational Division

Simple Machines, 6 filmstrips, Singer Educational Division

Work and Power, filmstrip, Encyclopaedia Britannica

Books

Bulliet, R. W., *The Camel and the Wheel,* Harvard University Press

Grannis, G. E., *Modern Power Mechanics,* Bobbs-Merrill

Singleton, W. T., et al., *Measurement of Man at Work,* Van Nostrand Reinhold

Software

The Lever, Prentice-Hall

came from nearby quarries, but when the supply of limestone ran out, stone was dragged many kilometers from other quarries to the pyramid site. Explain that the use of wheels or pulleys did not exist.

• **How would they get the stones to the site?** (Accept all logical answers, but lead students to suggest that people (slaves) had to physically drag or pull the stones.)

Point out that the stones were then pushed in place by using a long ramp. As each layer was finished, they lengthened and raised the ramp.

• **How would you go about lifting a stone of that size to the top of the pyramid?** (Accept all logical answers.)

Point out that with just the use of the wedge (chisel), the inclined plane (the ramp), and the lever (a lifting tool), the ancient Egyptians built these pyramids. Explain that humans creatively invented these simple machines to help make work easier. With contemporary machines, the Great Pyramid could be built in about one-fifth the time using only a few hundred workers.

SECTION PREVIEW 15-1

Work is the amount of force applied to an object times the distance the object moves in the direction of the force. If an object does not move, work is not being done. To measure work, we use the formula W (work) = F (force) × d (distance). Force is measured in newtons, and distance is measured in meters. Therefore, work is measured in newton-meter (N-m) or joule (J) units. One newton-meter is equal to one joule.

PERFORMANCE OBJECTIVES 15-1

1. **Define work in terms of force and distance.**
2. **Explain the units of force and work.**
3. **Calculate work, force, and distance using the formula W = F × d.**

SCIENCE TERMS 15-1
work p. 348
newton-meter p. 349
joule p. 349

TEACHING STRATEGY 15-1

Motivation
Have students stand along the side of the wall of the classroom. Tell them to push against the wall as hard as possible.
- **Are you doing any work?** (Accept all logical answers.)
- **Is the wall moving?** (No. The wall is in the same place.)

Point out that although the students did use energy to push against the wall, the fact that the wall *Did not move* indicates that a scientist would say no work was accomplished.)

Content Development
Explain that work is the amount of force applied to an object times the distance the object moves in the direction of the force.

Write the following on the chalkboard.

15–1 Work

A scientist defines **work** as a force acting through a distance. In order for work to be done on an object, a force must move it. If there is no movement, there is no work.

❶ Work is the product of the force applied to an object and the distance through which the force is applied. Another way of saying this is work is the amount of force applied to an object times the distance the object moves *in the direction of the force.*

❷ **work = force × distance**

As you can see from the formula, two conditions must be met in order for work to be done. One, a force must be applied. Two, the force must make an object move in the same direction as the force. If the direction of movement is *not* the same as the direction of the applied force, *no* work is done.

Suppose you push as hard as you can against a door, but the door does not move. Have you done any work? According to the two conditions, the answer is no. Although you have applied a force, there has been no movement.

Figure 15–1 *Although these lifeguards might disagree, they are not really working (left)! To a scientist, work is done when a force moves an object through a distance. The person cutting grass is working (right). Why?* ❶

348

---

work = force × distance
or,
W = F × d

Skills Development
Skill: Identifying relationships
Have students observe Figure 15-1. Read the caption to the first picture. Discuss why the lifeguards are "working" but are not "doing work."
- **What are the lifeguards doing?** (Accept all logical answers.)

- **How are the lifeguards "working"?** (Accept all logical answers.)
- **What "work" are the lifeguards doing?** (The lifeguards are not doing "work.")
- **How can you tell that the lifeguards are not doing "work"?** (The lifeguards are not applying a force over a distance.)

Read the caption to the second photograph in Figure 15-1. Discuss why work is being done.

Figure 15–2 *In order for work to be done, the applied force must make an object move in the same direction as the force. The weight lifter is applying an upward force and the barbell is moving up (left). Is he doing work? The soccer player, heading the ball in a forward direction, is making the ball move forward (right). Is he doing work?* ❷

Now suppose you are given a large box to carry. Holding the box, you walk toward the door. Have you done any work? Again the answer is no. The direction of movement is not the same as the direction of the applied force. The applied force is upward, while the direction of movement is forward. See Figure 15–3. What would you have to do with the box in order to do work? ❸

Work does not involve time. Work only involves an applied force and movement of an object in the direction of the force. You do no work if you hold or carry a box for five minutes, ten minutes, or even an hour!

Measuring Work

Remember that work equals force times distance.

$$W = F \times d$$

Force is measured in newtons and distance in meters. So the unit of work is the **newton-meter, N-m.** One newton-meter is equal to one **joule, J.** A force of one newton exerted through a distance of one meter does one newton-meter, or one joule, of work. How many newton-meters of work are done if two newtons of force are exerted through a distance of two meters? ❺

Figure 15–3 *In the scientific sense, why is no work being done in carrying the box (top)? Why is work being done in pushing the box (bottom)?* ❹

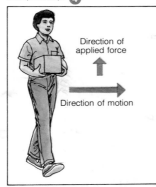

Direction of applied force

Direction of motion

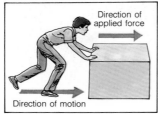

Direction of applied force

Direction of motion

• **What force is being applied to the lawnmower?** (The force of the person who is pushing)
• **In what direction is the force applied?** (The force is being applied forward to the handle or in the direction the mower and person are moving.)
• **What is true about the direction of the force and the direction of lawnmower motion?** (The movement of the mower is in the same direction as the force.)

Explain that work is being done because a force was applied that caused an object to move in the direction of the force.

Content Development

Have the students observe Figure 15-2. Read the caption. Explain that because the force moved the weights and the ball in the direction of the force, work was done.

Content Development

Explain that the amount of work done can be measured. The unit of measurement for force is called a newton and the distance moved is measured in meters. Add the following to the chalkboard formula for work.

$$\text{work} = \text{force} \times \text{distance}$$
or
$$W = F \times d$$
and
$$\text{joules} = \text{newtons} \times \text{meters}$$
$$J = N\text{-}m$$

Explain that the unit of work is called a newton-meter. The symbol for a newton-meter is N-m. Point out that one newton-meter is equal to one joule. The symbol for a joule is J.

15-2 POWER

SECTION PREVIEW 15-2

Power is the rate at which work is done. To measure power, time must be considered. The amount of work done in a unit of time is power. The unit of time is one second. Power is work (joule) divided by time (second). A joule per second is called a watt (W).

James Watt determined that a strong horse could move a 750-newton object one meter in one second. This represented power and was named horsepower (hp). Today, one horsepower is defined as the power of 745.56 watts. Although a watt is the official unit for power, we sometimes use the term horsepower when referring to the power of engines.

PERFORMANCE OBJECTIVES 15-2

1. **Describe power and its measurements.**
2. **Explain the units of power.**
3. **Calculate power, work, and time using the formula power = work/time.**

SCIENCE TERMS
power p. 350
watt p. 351
kilowatt p. 351
horsepower p. 352

15-1 (continued)

Skills Development
Skill: Making calculations
Remind students that it is very important to use the proper units. Show the class how to solve problem 1 on the chalkboard. Then, have the class complete the other problems.
1. John used a force of 300 N to push his younger brother in a wagon for 500 m. How much work did John do?
$W = F \times d$
$W = 300 \text{ N} \times 500 \text{ m}$
$W = 15,000 \text{ N-m} \times 1 \text{ J/N-m} = 15,000 \text{ J}$
2. A force of 550 N was used to move a stone 23 m. How much work was done? (12,650 J)
3. How much force was used if 13,734 J of work was done to move a box 42 m? (F = 327 N)
4. If 34,560 J of work was done with a force of 960 N, how far was the object moved? (d = 36 m)

Section Review 15-1
1. The product of the force applied to an object and the distance through which the force is applied
2. Work = Force × distance
3. Newton-meter or joule
4. The carpenter would perform

A high jumper weighs 700 newtons. What work does the jumper perform in jumping over a bar 2.0 meters high?

Solution

Step 1	Write the formula	**work = force × distance**
		W = F × d
Step 2	Substitute given numbers and units	**W = 700 newtons × 2.0 meters**
Step 3	Solve for unknown variable	**W = 1400 newton-meters or joules**

Practice Problems

❶ 1. A 900-N mountain climber scales a 100-m cliff. How much work does the climber perform?

❷ 2. A force of 200 N is required to push a lawn mower. If 4000 J of work is performed on the lawn mower, how far does it move?

SECTION REVIEW

1. What is work?
2. How are work, force, and distance related?
3. What are the units of work?
4. During a normal day's activities, would a carpenter or her supervisor be likely to perform more work? Explain your answer.

15–2 Power

The word **power** is like the word "work." It has different meanings for different people. But in science, power has a very specific meaning. Power indicates how fast work is done.

Power is the rate at which work is done, or the amount of work done per unit time. Power is equal to the work done divided by the time it takes to do it.

❶
$$\text{power} = \frac{\text{work}}{\text{time}} \quad \text{or} \quad P = \frac{W}{t}$$

350

---

more work because she would exert more force through greater distances. The supervisor moves less and exerts less force.

TEACHING STRATEGY 15-2

Motivation
Have the students observe Figure 15-4. Read the caption. Ask,
• **Which photo shows work being accomplished?** (Both pictures)

Looking at this formula, you can see why a bull-dozer has more power than a person with a shovel. The bulldozer does more work in the same amount of time. Can you explain why it takes more power to run up a flight of stairs than it takes to walk up? ❸

Measuring Power

Power is the amount of work done per unit time. Since work equals force times distance, the formula for power can also be written

$$P = \frac{F \times d}{t}$$

The unit of work is the newton-meter or joule. The unit of time is the second. So the unit of power is the newton-meter per second, N-m/sec, or the joule per second, J/sec. One joule per second is also called a **watt, W.** The watt was named for James Watt, inventor of the first practical steam engine. ❷

You are probably familiar with the watt as it is used to express electric power. Electric appliances and light bulbs are rated in watts. A 100-watt light bulb does 100 joules of work every second. Large quantities of power are measured in **kilowatts, kW.** One kilowatt equals 1000 watts. The electric company measures the electric power you use in your home in kilowatts.

Figure 15–4 *Both the man and the snowplow are doing work. But there is little doubt that the machine is doing more work in the same amount of time. So it has more power. How is power calculated?* ❹

351

Sharpen Your Skills

James Watt and the Steam Engine
Skill: Writing reports
Level: Remedial
Type: Library

This activity will introduce students to the inventor James Watt and his invention of the steam engine. Check students' reports for accuracy and the clarity of writing.

15-2 (continued)

Content Development

Power is the amount of work done per unit time. Write the following formulas on the chalkboard as you explain the relationships between work, force, distance, time, and power.
power = work/time, and
work = force × distance
power = W/t or F × d/t
watts = joule/second or newton-meter/second
W = J/s or N-m/s

Remind the class that a newton-meter is one joule and the symbol for joule is a capital J. The symbol for time in seconds is a lower case t. Power is work divided by time or joules divided by seconds (J/s). Explain that a joule per second is called a watt. The symbol for a watt is a capital W because it was named for James Watt, the inventor of the first practical steam engine.

Explain that a large amount of power is measured in kilowatt units with the symbol kW. One thousand watts is equal to one kilowatt (1000 W = 1 kW.)

Sample Problem

A crane lifts a car onto a junk pile in 10 seconds. What is the crane's power if 120,000 joules of work are performed?

Solution

Step 1   Write the formula

$$power = \frac{work}{time}$$

$$P = \frac{W}{t}$$

Step 2   Substitute given numbers and units

$$P = \frac{120,000 \text{ joules}}{10 \text{ seconds}}$$

Step 3   Solve for unknown variable

$$P = 12,000 \text{ joules per second} = 12,000 \text{ watts}$$

Practice Problems

❶ 1. A car performs 40,000 J of work in 20 sec. What is the power of the car?

❷ 2. A 750-N diver does a triple somersault off the 10-m platform. If it takes 1.5 sec to hit the water, what is the diver's power?

Sharpen Your Skills

James Watt and the Steam Engine

James Watt did not invent the steam engine. But he did build the first practical steam engine. Using books and other reference material in the library, find out more about James Watt and his work with steam engines. Your report should include information on how he improved the steam engine and how the steam engine changed the way work was done by people.

352

Horsepower

When James Watt built his steam engine in the 1760s, he wanted to use a unit of power that most people would recognize. Since the horse was the most common source of power in the eighteenth century, Watt decided to express steam-engine power in terms comparable to the power of a horse. Watt determined that a strong horse could move a 750-newton object one meter in one second. This represented power equal to 750 watts. So one **horsepower, hp,** was equal to 750 watts.

One horsepower is actually equal to 745.56 watts. Although horsepower is no longer measured in terms of an actual horse, it is used to measure the power of engines and motors. One horsepower is about the power of a small electric motor. The engine of your family car has about 100 horsepower. A diesel train engine can generate up to 10,000 horsepower. A nuclear power plant can produce 300,000 horsepower.

Skills Development

Skill: Applying formulas

Remind students that it is very important to use the proper units. Show the class how to solve problem 1 on the chalkboard. Then have the class solve the other problems.

1. What is the power of a 900-N force applied over a distance of 40 m for 45 seconds? power = work/time, and work = force × distance
power = F × d/t
power = 900 N × 40 m/45 s
power = 36,000 N-m/45 s
power = 800 N-m/s × 1 j/N-m = 800 J/s = 800 W

2. What is the power of a 300-N force applied over 20 m for 20 seconds? (power = 300 N-m/s × 1 j/N-m = 300 J/s = 300 W)

Reinforcement

Have students make up one similar problem related to work and power.

Figure 15–5 *A strong horse could lift a 750-newton object 1 meter in 1 second, or do 750 N-m of work per sec (left). A diesel train engine has about 10,000 horsepower (right). How many horses would it take to generate this power?* ③

SECTION REVIEW

1. What is power?
2. What is the relationship among power, work, and time? Among power, force, distance, and time?
3. What is a watt? A kilowatt?
4. A small motor does 4000 joules of work in 20 seconds. What is the power of the motor in watts? What is its horsepower?
5. Rate the following objects in terms of horsepower. Start with the object with the least horsepower. a. electric golf cart b. electric pencil sharpener c. aircraft carrier d. jet airplane

15–3 Machines

For centuries, people have looked for ways to make life more enjoyable. One way of doing this is to use devices that make work easier or faster. In ancient times, people fashioned stones into tools, used tree branches to pry up heavy objects, and carried the objects in carts with wheels. These devices were some of the earliest **machines.**

A machine is a device that makes work easier. A ② hammer, bicycle ramp, scissors, shovel, and doorknob are examples of machines. A machine can be used to do a variety of jobs: pump water from a well, hoist a sail, plow a field, even catch a fish!

353

15-3 MACHINES

SECTION PREVIEW 15-3

Machines make work easier or faster. Machines cannot increase the amount of work done but they can change the size and direction of the applied force. The amount of force the user puts into a machine is called effort force. Work done on a machine is called work input. Work must always be done on a machine if the machine is to do any work. The work a machine does is called work output. The work input of a machine must overcome the resistant force of the object and move it in a direction, otherwise no work is done.

Friction reduces the efficiency of a machine. The comparison of work output to work input is called the efficiency of a machine. Work output can never be greater than work input. When machines multiply the amount of effort force used, we call this the mechanical advantage of the machine.

PERFORMANCE OBJECTIVES 15-3

1. **Classify machines.**
2. **Define mechanical advantage and efficiency.**
3. **Calculate the mechanical advantage and efficiency of machines.**

SCIENCE TERMS 15-3

machine p. 353	work output
effort force p. 354	p. 355
work input p. 354	resistance dis-
effort distance	tance p. 355
p. 354	mechanical ad-
resistance force	vantage p. 355
p. 355	efficiency p. 356

Remind students to keep the units of force, distance, and time reasonable. Problems that have no specific reference to people are best. Distribute the problems for other students to solve. Discuss and modify the problems and solutions.

Section Review 15-2
1. The rate at which work is done, or the amount of work done per unit time

2. $P = W/t$ $P = (F \times d)/t$
3. 1 J/sec or 1 N-m/sec; 1000 watts
4. 200 watts; 0.27 hp
5. b, a, d, c

TEACHING STRATEGY 15-3
Students already know that work is equal to force times distance. Explain that machines are used to make work easier.

Motivation
Pound a nail securely into a block of wood.
• **Who would like to take this nail out of the wood?** (Accept one of the offers made.)

Hand one of the students the block of wood. Allow enough time for the student to suggest that a hammer or some other tool be used to remove the nail.

Humans and machines have opened the world for trade since time began. Instead of using hands or a paddle for boating, oars were installed on the sides of boats. Oars allowed the boat to move easier and faster. Wheels were used on all types of machines because of the ease in which goods could be moved. In 1865 the industrial age put machines into every aspect of life.

Have students do library research to find out about the industrial revolution. Students might use the information to give an oral report, write a paper, or make an attractive bulletin board.

TEACHER DEMONSTRATION

Attach a string or rope securely to a large, heavy box. With masking tape, mark a distance of 2 meters on the floor. Using a spring-type scale pull the box across the floor. Write the amount of force needed to pull the box on the chalkboard. Write the formula $W = f \times d$ on the chalkboard.

Have the students figure out the amount of work that was done.
- **Is there some way we could make our work easier?** (Accept all logical answers.)

Place several pencils or rollers under the box. Again pull the box with the spring scale across the floor. Record the amount of force needed to pull the box. Have the students use the formula to figure out the amount of work done with the rollers.

15-3 (continued)

Content Development
Explain that people use machines to help with work. Point out that many kinds of machines have been developed to make our work easier and/or faster.

Skills Development
Skill: Making generalizations
- **Name some machines and describe how they make work faster and/or easier.** (Accept all logical responses such as cars, planes, hammers, pliers, etc.)

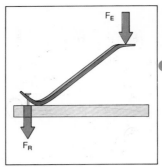

Figure 15–6 *When a machine is used, two forces always are involved. The force applied to a machine is the effort force, F_E. The force applied by the machine is the resistance force (F_R). In this diagram, what is the resistance force equal to?* ❶

Figure 15–7 *The children pushing this merry-go-round (left) are providing the effort force. What is their work called? Those enjoying the ride represent the resistance force. What is the movement of the merry-go-round called? These crew-team members are applying an effort force to the oars, which in turn are applying a resistance force (right). The resistance force propels the boats through the water.* ❷

354

Have students compile lists of the names of various simple and/or complex machines and describe how they make work faster and/or easier.

Motivation
Have the students observe Figure 15-6. Point out that a machine always involves two forces. The force applied *to* the machine is called the effort force and the force applied *by* the machine is called the resistance force.

Effort and Resistance

How do machines make work easier? You will recall that work equals force times distance. **Machines make work easier by changing the size or direction of the applied force.** Some machines make work easier by multiplying the applied force. For example, you need to exert less force to loosen a nail with a crowbar than you do to loosen it with your fingers. Other machines make work easier by redirecting the applied force. It is easier to raise a large object by pulling down on a rope attached to it than by lifting the object straight up.

There are always two forces involved in using a machine. The force that is applied *to* a machine is called the **effort force, F_E.** When you pull down on the handle of a crowbar, you are applying an effort force. As a result of the effort force, the crowbar moves. Work is done on the crowbar. Work done *on* a machine is called **work input, W_I.** Work must always be done on a machine if the machine in turn is to do any work.

Work input is equal to the effort force times the distance through which the force is applied, or the distance through which the machine moves. This distance is called the **effort distance, d_E.**

$$W_I = F_E \times d_E$$

The work input of the crowbar (W_I) is equal to the force you apply to the handle (F_E) times the distance the handle moves (d_E).

Content Development
Explain that work input is the work done *to* the machine. Work input is equal to the force of the effort times the distance the force moves. Write the following equations on the chalkboard and repeat the explanation.
Work Input = Effort Force × Effort Distance
$$W_I = F_E \times d_E$$
- **Where have we seen this formula**

When the handle of the crowbar is pushed down, the claw exerts a force on the nail. The force applied *by* the machine is called the **resistance force, F_R.** Resistance force is often equal to the weight of the object being moved. Resistance force opposes effort force.

Work done *by* a machine is called **work output, W_O.** Work output is equal to the resistance force times the distance through which the force is applied, or the distance through which the object moves. This distance is called the **resistance distance, d_R.**

$$W_O = F_R \times d_R$$

The work output of the crowbar (W_O) is equal to the force the crowbar exerts on the nail (F_R) times the distance the nail moves (d_R).

Although machines make work easier, they do *not* multiply work. Machines can only multiply force. Because machines cannot multiply work, work output can never be greater than work input.

Mechanical Advantage

The number of times a machine multiplies the effort force is called the **mechanical advantage, MA.** Mechanical advantage is equal to the resistance force divided by the effort force.

$$MA = \frac{F_R}{F_E}$$

For example, if a crowbar allows you to exert only 20 newtons of force to raise a 200-newton object, its mechanical advantage is 10. The crowbar allows you to multiply your effort force ten times. By using the crowbar, you exert a force on the nail ten times greater than the force you would exert without the crowbar. That certainly makes your work easier!

The mechanical advantage of a machine is not always greater than one. Sometimes the mechanical advantage is equal to one. According to the formula, this means the resistance force is equal to the effort force. So what is the advantage of such a machine? A machine with a mechanical advantage of one changes the direction of the effort force. It

Figure 15–8 *Machines have come a long way since ancient times, as these robots at an industrial plant illustrate. Regardless of complexity, all machines have the same purpose—to make work easier.*

Figure 15–9 *In an eggbeater, the blades turn faster than the handle. Work is transferred from the handle to the blades, but the effort force is not multiplied. It is the speed that is increased. What is the mechanical advantage of an eggbeater?* ❸

355

- **What is increased by an eggbeater machine?** (The output speed is greater than the input speed.)
- **What is decreased by an eggbeater machine?** (The output force is less than the input force.)

Skills Development
Skill: Applying formulas
Have students solve problems related to work input, work output, and mechanical advantage of machines. Have students show the equations and development of each problem on the chalkboard. Discuss the nature of the machine.

1. Effort force of 20 N and distance of 1 m. Resistance force of 50 N and distance of 0.1 m. ($W_I = 20$ N-m; $W_O = 5$ N-m; MA = 2.5)
- **What was gained by the machine?** (Mechanical advantage. The force was increased from 20 N to 50 N.)
- **What was lost by the machine?** (The distance moved was reduced from 1 m to 0.1 m. The total output work was less than the work put into the machine.)

2. Effort force of 50 N and distance of 3 m. Resistance force of 260 N and distance of 0.5 m. ($W_I = 150$ N-m; $W_O = 130$ N-m; MA = 5.2)
- **What was gained by the machine?** (Mechanical advantage. The force was increased from 50 N to 260 N.)
- **What was lost by the machine?** (The distance moved was reduced from 3 m to 0.5 m. The total output work was less than the work put into the machine.)

---

before? (Most students will remark it is the formula for work equals force times distance, or W = F × d.)

Explain that this is the "work" put into the machine or the work "input."

Content Development
Explain that work done *by* the machine is called work output. The force applied by the machine is called resistance force. The distance the object moves or the force applied is called re-

sistance distance. Work output is equal to resistance force times resistance distance. Write the following equations on the chalkboard.

Work Output = Resistance Force × Resistance distance

$$W_O = F_R \times d_R$$

Skills Development
Skill: Applying concepts
Have the students observe Figure 15-9. Read the caption. Ask,

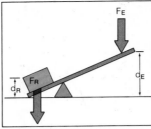

Figure 15–10 *If a machine multiplies the effort force to produce a greater resistance force, then the distance through which the effort force is applied must be greater than the distance through which the resistance force moves. In other words, to move the block, you may have to push down with less force, but you have to exert your push through a greater distance.*

does not multiply the effort force. Can you think of an example of such a machine?

Some machines have a mechanical advantage of less than one. Such a machine is used to increase the distance an object is moved or the speed with which it is moved.

Remember that work output can never be greater than work input. Even if the resistance force is greater than the effort force, which means the mechanical advantage is greater than one, work output cannot exceed work input. Something must be sacrificed. If the resistance force is greater, the distance an object is moved by this force must be smaller. Look at Figure 15–10. The effort force must travel a greater distance than the resistance force.

Efficiency

The comparison of work output to work input is called the **efficiency** of a machine. Efficiency is usually expressed as a percent. The formula for efficiency is

❶
$$\text{Efficiency} = \frac{W_O}{W_I} \times 100$$

If a machine has high efficiency, it means that much of the work input is changed to useful work output. Low efficiency means that much of the work input is lost and a great deal of useful work output does not result.

The efficiency of a machine can never be greater than 100 percent because work output can never be greater than work input. In fact, no machine is ever 100 percent efficient. The operation of any machine always involves some friction. So some of the work the machine does is used to overcome friction. As a result, work output is always less than work input. Friction reduces the efficiency of a machine.

Role of Friction

The less friction in a machine, the higher its efficiency. The most efficient machines have the smallest amount of friction. So the efficiency of a machine can be increased by reducing friction. Keeping

15-3 (continued)

Skills Development

Skill: Applying formulas
Have the class use distance to calculate the mechanical advantage of machines. You might show the first problem on the chalkboard and then have students solve the other problems.

1. What is the mechanical advantage of a machine when the input distance is 3 m and the output distance is 0.1 m?
MA = Mechanical Advantage
MA = Effort distance/Resistance distance
MA = d_E/d_R
MA = 3 m/0.1 m
MA = 30

2. What is the mechanical advantage of a machine when the input distance is 150.5 cm and the output distance is 35 cm? (MA = 4.3)

3. What is the mechanical advantage of a machine when the input distance is 12.2 cm and the output distance is 36.6 cm? (MA = 0.333)

Sharpen Your Skills

An Imaginary Machine

Write a 200-word story about a machine that does some very special job. Include the following words in your story as you describe how your machine works.

efficiency	power
effort force	resistance force
friction	work input
lubricant	work output

356

Skills Development

Skill: Applying formulas
Have the class calculate the input work, output work, mechanical advantage, and efficiency of machines. You might show the first problem on the chalkboard and then have students solve the other problems.

1. Effort force of 45 N and distance of 2 m. Resistance force of 50 N and distance of 0.4 m.
(MA = 1.11; Efficiency = 22.22%)

2. Effort force of 150 N and distance of 9 m. Resistance force of 327 N and distance of 3 m.
(MA = 2.18; Efficiency = 72.67%)

3. Effort force of 1330 N and distance of 3.2 m. Resistance force of 234 N and distance of 13.7 m.
(MA = 0.175; Efficiency = 75.32%)

• **Why would anyone want to use a machine that had a mechanical advantage of only 0.175?** (An increase in distance and speed)

a machine well lubricated and in good running order reduces friction. Oil, grease, and wax are used in many machines to reduce friction. Bearings, such as those used in bicycle wheels, reduce friction.

Efficient machines are less expensive to use. They also conserve useful energy. The efficiency of an automobile engine is only about 20 percent. In other words, only one-fifth of the work input is changed to work output. The remaining work input is represented by heat loss. Engines that have high gas mileage are more efficient than gas guzzlers. Imagine what the gas mileage would be for a car that had 90 percent efficiency!

SECTION REVIEW

1. What is a machine?
2. What is effort force? Work input? The relationship between effort force, effort distance, and work input?
3. What is resistance force? Work output? The relationship between resistance force, resistance distance, and work output?
4. What is the relationship between mechanical advantage, effort force, and resistance force?
5. What is the relationship between efficiency of a machine, work input, and work output?
6. Why would a machine with 100 percent efficiency be considered an ideal machine?

15–4   Simple Machines

Section Objective

To describe the six simple machines

The devices you think of when you hear the word "machine" are actually combinations of two or more simple machines. Simple machines do work with one movement. There are six simple machines: the inclined plane, the wedge, the screw, the lever, the pulley, and the wheel and axle. ③

Inclined Plane

Could you raise a car to a height of 10 centimeters? You could not do it by lifting the car straight up. But you could do it if you pushed the car up

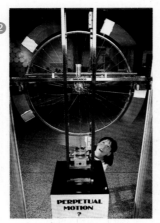

Figure 15–11   *Many attempts have been made to create a machine with 100 percent or more efficiency. So far, this has proved impossible. What force reduces the efficiency of a machine?* ①

15-4 SIMPLE MACHINES

SECTION PREVIEW 15-4

Machines are everywhere. Machines do much of the work in the world today. Many of these machines are combinations of six simple machines. These six simple machines are the inclined plane, the wedge, the screw, the lever, the pulley, and the wheel and axle. All simple machines do work with one movement. These simple machines serve any of three purposes: increasing speed, increasing force, or changing direction of a force. In this section you will investigate these machines and how they operate. The amount of work, their mechanical advantage, and their efficiency will be compared.

PERFORMANCE OBJECTIVES 15-4

1. **Identify the six simple machines.**
2. **Explain how each simple machine works.**
3. **Calculate the mechanical advantage for each simple machine.**

SCIENCE TERMS 15-4

inclined plane p. 358	effort arm p. 362
wedge p. 359	resistance arm p. 362
screw p. 360	pulley p. 363
lever p. 361	wheel p. 364
fulcrum p. 361	axle p. 364

357

Explain that if a machine were 100 percent efficient W_O would equal W_I. Point out that most machines are always less than 100 percent efficient.

Content Development
Explain that friction plays an important role in the efficiency of a machine. The most efficient machines have the smallest amount of friction.
• **How could we reduce friction in a machine?** (Accept and write all logical answers on the chalkboard. Encourage suggestions such as using grease, oil, or other lubricants that would make the parts slide easily.)

Point out that engineers are constantly experimenting to find new ways to reduce friction in machines.

Section Review 15-3
1. A device that makes work easier by changing the size or direction of an applied force

2. Force applied *to* a machine; work done *on* a machine. Work input = effort force × effort distance
3. Force applied by a machine that opposes effort force; work done *by* a machine; work output = resistance force × resistance distance
4. MA = resistance force/effort force
5. Efficiency = (work output/work input) × 100
6. Friction lowers the efficiency of a machine. Work output is always less than work input, so an actual machine cannot be 100% efficient. Only an ideal machine, which experiences no friction, can be 100% efficient.

TEACHER DEMONSTRATION

Collect one sample of each of the six simple machines. You might use the following common examples, which might be borrowed from the school custodian or advanced science teacher: inclined plane: book propped up at one end; wedge: a chisel, nail, or axe head; screw: screw or bolt; lever: crow bar, or claw end of a hammer; pulley: window shades or drapes; wheel and axle: toy car, lab cart, or AV cart.

Discuss each simple machine example. Have students point out and explain how each of the simple machines is used.

TIE-IN/FIRE DEPARTMENT

Most fire departments and rescue squads now carry a machine that is called "The Jaws of Life." When people are sealed in a car or other vehicle, the "Jaws" are used to spread or push through the metal to make an opening for escape and rescue.

a ramp. A ramp is an **inclined plane.** An inclined plane is a slanted surface used to raise an object.

When an inclined plane is used, a smaller effort force is needed to move an object. However, the object is moved through a greater distance along the inclined plane than if it were moved straight up. To raise the car 10 centimeters, you might have to push the car several meters up an inclined plane.

The mechanical advantage of an inclined plane is the length of the plane divided by its height. Suppose you needed an inclined plane 10 meters long to raise the car 10 centimeters. The mechanical ad-

Figure 15–12 *No matter how complex these combines (right) and hoisting devices (left) appear* ❶ *to be, they are actually combinations of two or more simple machines. What are the six simple machines?* ❶

Figure 15–13 *An inclined plane is a slanted surface used to raise an object (right). An inclined plane decreases the size of the effort force needed to move an object. However, the distance through which the effort force is applied is increased (left). How is the mechanical advantage of an inclined plane calculated?* ❷

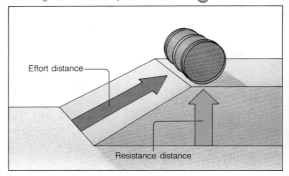

Effort distance

Resistance distance

358

axle. Explain that all machines are either simple machines, or a combination of two or more simple machines. Most machines are made from a combination of simple machines.

Motivation
Build a ramp by slanting a long board from the top of a desk or table. Attach a spring scale with a heavy string to the end of a roller skate. Pull the skate up the slanted board. Record on the

chalkboard the force needed to pull the skate.

Using the spring scale, lift the skate from the floor to the desk top. Record the force needed to lift the skate. Remind the students that work = force × distance. Explain that the slanted board is a ramp. A ramp is an inclined plane. Ask,
- **How much work was done during each trial?** (Both trials raised the skate to the same height. Therefore, the

vantage of the inclined plane would be 1000 centimeters (10 meters) divided by 10 centimeters, or 100. This means that the effort force is multiplied **❷** by 100. However, the effort distance is 100 times greater than the height to which the car is raised.

Because the length of an inclined plane can never be shorter than its height, the mechanical advantage of an inclined plane can never be less than one. This mechanical advantage, determined by dividing the length of the plane by its height, is an ideal value. Under actual circumstances, some work input is lost to friction. The friction between the object and the inclined plane has to be overcome. So the effort force in raising the car would probably be multiplied by less than 100.

Wedges and Screws

A **wedge** is an inclined plane that moves. Most wedges are made of two inclined planes. A knife, an **❸** ax, and a razor blade are examples of wedges.

A wedge is usually a piece of wood or metal that is thinner at one end. The effort force applied to the thicker end is transferred to the thinner end. As a result, a large force is exerted on a small surface.

Figure 15–14 *As a wedge is moved through the object to be cut, a small effort force is able to overcome a large resistance force (left). How can the mechanical advantage of a wedge be increased? Screws come in a variety of shapes and sizes (center, right). Which of the screws shown here has the greatest mechanical advantage?* **❸**

359

same amount of work was accomplished.)
• **Which trial used the least force?** (The trial with the inclined plane used the least force.)
• **Which trial used the force over a longer distance?** (The trial on the inclined plane)
• **What does an inclined plane do?** (An inclined plane allows work to be done with less force.)
• **What is a disadvantage of an in-** clined plane? (The force has to act over a longer distance.)

Explain to students that, neglecting friction, the same amount of work was done by lifting the skate and by pulling the skate up the inclined plane. Point out that this is true of all simple machines.

Content Development
Have these students observe Figure 15-13. Read the caption. Explain that if they needed to raise a heavy barrel onto a deck or truck, the barrel might be too heavy to lift. Several boards could serve as an inclined plane. Then the barrel could be pushed and rolled up the slanted boards. The slanted board allows a person to raise things that are normally too heavy to lift. Explain that any ramp or sloping surface is an inclined plane.
• **Why does this make the job easier?** (Accept all answers.)
• **Is the man doing less work?** (Most students should say no.)

Motivation

Give each student a large, coarsely threaded screw and a finely threaded bolt.

• **What do these have in common?** (Accept all logical answers. Most students will say the grooves.)

Explain that the simple machine, known as a screw, is another form of an inclined plane. Show students the common screw. Say a screw is a combination of a wedge and an inclined plane. Show students the bolt. Tell them that it is also an inclined plane. A screw is a coiled inclined plane that is tapered like a wedge. A bolt is only a coiled inclined plane. Have the students feel the coil of metal on the screw and bolt. Point out that this coil is called the thread.

Skills Development

Skill: Making a model

Have students cut a piece of paper diagonally across to make a triangle. Point out that the diagonal edge is an inclined plane. With a pen or marking pencil, have students mark the inclined plane edge of the paper. Tell them to tape one of the nondiagonal edges to a pencil. Then, rotate the pencil to wrap the paper around a pencil.

• **What does the inclined plane look like now?** (Accept all logical answers. Most students should suggest that the marked edge of the paper looks like the thread of a screw.)

Content Development

Explain that as in the wedge and the inclined plane, the screw multiplies the force by acting through a long distance. Point out that many automobile jacks are screws. These jacks allow people to lift heavy cars with less than normal effort. A screw uses a small force over a great distance to move a heavy force over a short distance.

Content Development

Point out that each time a screw makes one full turn, the coiled inclined plane moves a long distance while the whole screw only moves a short distance. The distance moved depends on the

distance between the threads, or the pitch.

If the distance between threads is large, then the inclined plane is steep, and one turn would move the screw forward into the wood quickly with a small mechanical advantage.

If the distance between threads is small, then the inclined plane is gentle, and one turn would move the screw through the wood slowly with a large mechanical advantage.

The wedge is moved through the material to be cut or opened up.

The longer and thinner the wedge is, the less effort force is required to overcome a large resistance force. A sharpened ax requires less effort force because the end point is thinner. When you sharpen a wedge, you are increasing its mechanical advantage by decreasing the effort force that must be applied in using it.

❶ Like the wedge, a **screw** is an inclined plane. A screw is an inclined plane wrapped around a cylinder to form a spiral. A screw rotates, and with each turn moves a certain distance up or down. A screw multiplies an effort force by acting through a long effort distance. A small effort force is needed to twist a screw into wood because of the large effort distance through which the screw is turned. The closer the threads, or ridges, of the screw, the greater the mechanical advantage of the screw.

360

Point out that when a screw has threads close together, the resistance distance is small compared to the circumference and d_E/d_R will be large. Therefore, the closer the threads of a screw are together, the greater the mechanical advantage.

Point out that when a screw has threads far apart, the resistance distance is large compared to the circumference and d_E/d_R will be smaller. Therefore, when threads are spaced

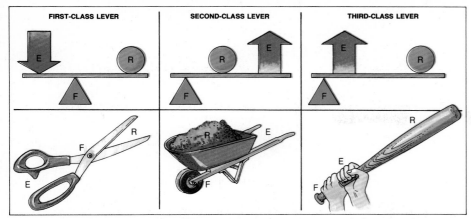

FIRST-CLASS LEVER	SECOND-CLASS LEVER	THIRD-CLASS LEVER

Figure 15–15 *The relative positions of the effort force, resistance force, and fulcrum determine the three classes of levers. Which lever multiplies effort force as well as changing its direction? Which lever multiplies the distance of the effort force?* ❶

Levers

The **lever** is a simple machine that is probably quite familiar to you. A seesaw, a shovel, a nutcracker, and a crowbar are all examples of levers. A lever is a bar that is free to pivot, or move about, a fixed point when an effort force is applied. The fixed point of the pivot is called the **fulcrum** (FUL-kruhm). When an effort force is applied to a lever, the lever moves about the fulcrum and overcomes a resistance force.

CLASSES OF LEVERS There are three classes of levers. These classes are based on the positions of the effort force, resistance force, and fulcrum. In a first-class lever, the fulcrum is between the effort force and the resistance force. See Figure 15–15. A crowbar is an example of a first-class lever. An effort force is applied to one end of the crowbar. The crowbar pivots on the fulcrum and lifts the resistance force. Pliers, scissors, and seesaws are all first-class levers. First-class levers multiply the effort force and also change its direction.

In a second-class lever, the resistance force is between the fulcrum and the effort force. See Figure 15–15. Wheelbarrows, doors, paper cutters, and

361

TIE-IN/DENTISTRY

If you look around a dental office, you will see all of the simple machines in operation. Most of the hand instruments a dentist uses are third-class levers. The polishing brush is a combination of a pulley and wheel and axle. The chair is an inclined plane. The next time you go to the dentist, try to identify some of the simple machines you see.

15-4 (continued)

Skills Development
Skill: Making a model
Have students make a fan out of a piece of paper by folding it in strips back and forth. Tell students to grasp one end of the fan. Have them cool themselves by very gently waving the fan just below their face. Point out to students that the part of the fan nearest their face is moving a greater distance than the part in their hand.

Content Development
Explain that with a third-class lever, the effort force is greater than the resistance force. A third-class lever does not multiply the force but rather, it multiplies the distance of the effort

Figure 15–16 *Sometimes a lever can have a very vital use! Where is the lever in this photograph taken at Big Bend National Park?* ❷

362

some nutcrackers are second-class levers. Second-class levers multiply the effort force, but they do not change its direction.

In a third-class lever, the effort force is between the resistance force and the fulcrum. See Figure 15–15 on page 361. A hoe, shovel, fishing pole, and your arm are examples of third-class levers.

With a third-class lever, the effort force is greater than the resistance force. A third-class lever does not multiply force. The advantage to a third-class lever is that it multiplies the distance of the effort force. The effort force needs to move through only a small distance to make the resistance force move through a large distance. Using the third-class lever in Figure 15–15 on page 361, explain how this fact applies. ❶

MECHANICAL ADVANTAGE OF A LEVER The mechanical advantage of a lever, like that of any machine, is the number of times the lever increases the effort force. It is equal to the resistance force divided by the effort force. The mechanical advantage of a lever can also be calculated by using the lengths of the effort force from the fulcrum and the resistance force from the fulcrum.

The distance from the effort force to the fulcrum is called the **effort arm.** The distance from the resistance force to the fulcrum is called the **resistance arm.** The mechanical advantage of a lever is the length of the effort arm divided by the length of the resistance arm:

❷ $$\text{mechanical advantage} = \frac{\text{effort arm length}}{\text{resistance arm length}}$$

For first- and second-class levers, the effort arm is usually greater than the resistance arm. Thus the mechanical advantage for these levers is usually greater than one. In other words, first- and second-class levers multiply the effort force.

For third-class levers, the effort arm is always less than the resistance arm. The mechanical advantage is less than one. Third-class levers do not multiply force. Third-class levers multiply distance. For example, a small movement at the handle of a shovel causes the opposite end to move in a large sweeping arc.

force. Tell the students that the effort force needs to move through only a small distance to make the resistance force move through a large distance.

Content Development
Explain that in a lever the distance from the effort force to the fulcrum is called the effort arm. The distance from the resistance force to the fulcrum is called the resistance arm.

Have students observe Figure 15-15 again. Point out the effort distance and resistance distance of the three classes of levers.

Explain that the mechanical advantage of a lever is figured by dividing the effort arm length by the resistance arm length.

Skills Development
Skill: Using a formula
Show the class how to do the first problem on the chalkboard. Then

Pulleys

If you have ever raised or lowered a window shade, you have used another simple machine called a **pulley.** A pulley is a chain, belt, or rope wrapped around a wheel. A pulley can change either the direction or the amount of an effort force.

A pulley that is attached to a wall, ceiling, or other stationary structure is called a fixed pulley. A fixed pulley cannot multiply an effort force. But it can change the direction of an effort force and make lifting an object easier. As the effort force is used to pull the rope down, the resistance force is lifted up. It is certainly easier to pull down on a rope to raise an object than it is to lift the object directly up! Because a fixed pulley does not multiply effort force, the effort force is equal to the resistance force. So the mechanical advantage of a fixed pulley is one.

A movable pulley is hung on a rope so that it moves with the effort force. A movable pulley can multiply an effort force. But a movable pulley cannot change the direction of an effort force.

Because a movable pulley multiplies effort force, its mechanical advantage is greater than one. However, the effort distance is greater than the resistance distance. For example, to lift an object one meter with a movable pulley, you might have to pull down a two-meter length of rope.

Figure 15–17 *The fixed pulley on this boat cannot multiply force. But it can change the direction of the force and thus make moving the wooden beam easier.*

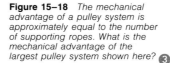

Figure 15–18 *The mechanical advantage of a pulley system is approximately equal to the number of supporting ropes. What is the mechanical advantage of the largest pulley system shown here?* ❸

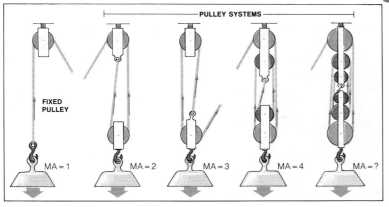

PULLEY SYSTEMS

FIXED PULLEY

MA = 1   MA = 2   MA = 3   MA = 4   MA = ?

363

(The effort force will move half as far as the resistance force.)

Motivation
• **Where is the flag on the flagpole during the day?** (At the top)
• **How did they get the flag up on the pole?** (Most students will say they pulled it up on a rope)
  Point out that the rope is connected to a pulley system.

Content Development
Explain that a pulley is a rope, chain, or belt wrapped around a wheel. A pulley can change either the direction or the amount of an effort force.

Skills Development
Skill: Designing an experiment
Divide the class into groups of three or four. Have each group collect the following items from home: metal clothes hanger, wire cutter, large empty thread spool, 2-m piece of string, and several different weights such as heavy washers or metal nuts.
  Show the class a single pulley with string. Tell students that they are to create a single pulley using a coat hanger, thread spool, and string. Allow sufficient time for the groups to create their pulley. Distribute a ruler to each group.
  Have students experiment with their pulley and weights to find out the relationship between the effort distance and the resistance distance in a single pulley system. Have students keep a written record of their results.

have the class solve the other problems.

1. What is the MA of a first-class lever that has a d_E of 100 cm and a d_R of 10 cm?
  Lever MA = d_E/d_R
  Lever MA = 100 cm/10 cm
  Lever MA = 10
• **How far will the effort force move compared to the resistance force?**
(The effort force will move 10 times farther than the resistance force.)

2. What is the MA of a second-class lever that has a d_E of 50 cm and a d_R of 25 cm? (MA = 2)
• **How far will the effort force move compared to the resistance force?** (The effort force will move twice as far as the resistance force.)
3. What is the MA of a third-class lever that has a d_E of 40 cm and a d_R of 80 cm? (MA = 0.5)
• **How far will the effort force move compared to the resistance force?**

Sharpen Your Skills

Compound Machines
Skills: Designing an experiment, applying
Level: Enriched
Type: Vocabulary/writing

This activity should only be attempted by more academic students. Most students will know of Rube Goldberg and the types of machines he has devised. You might want to assign an interested student to collect and show various "Rube Goldberg" type machines that have been illustrated in reference books. Check students' designs for originality and accuracy. Perhaps some students will actually want to construct their machine. They should confer with you first since such machines may not be safe.

15-4 (continued)

Motivation

Turn the handle of the classroom door. Ask,
- **What machine am I using?** (Most students will say the door knob.)

Point out that you just used a wheel and axle.
- **Where do we see the wheel and axle used?** (Accept all logical answers. Most students will say the car or bike wheels.)

Point out that we see and use many wheel and axle machines every day.

Content Development

Explain that the wheel and axle is a force multiplying machine. A little force applied on the steering wheel of a car will cause a large force to be transmitted to the axle.

Figure 15–19 *The block and tackle attached to the boom of the sail is an example of a pulley system. Identify the fixed and movable pulleys.*

Figure 15–20 *Each of these racers is applying an effort force to the wheel of his chair (left). Since the wheel moves through a greater distance than the axle (center), the effort force is multiplied at the axle. The same principle is responsible for the operation of a Ferris wheel (right).*

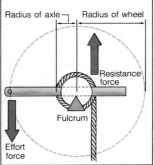

364

A greater mechanical advantage can be obtained by combining fixed and movable pulleys into a pulley system. As more pulleys are used, more sections of rope are attached to the system. Each section of rope helps to support the object. This increases the mechanical advantage. You can predict the mechanical advantage of a pulley system by counting the number of supporting sections of rope. The mechanical advantage of a pulley system is approximately equal to the number of supporting ropes. This fact is illustrated in Figure 15–19. A block and tackle is an example of a pulley system used to lift heavy machinery.

Wheel and Axle

A **wheel and axle** is a lever that rotates in a circle. A wheel and axle is made of two wheels of different sizes. The axle is the smaller wheel. The larger wheel turns about the axle. The effort force is applied to the wheel. Since the wheel is a larger circular object, it always moves through a greater distance than the axle. The effort force applied to the wheel is multiplied at the axle. Bicycles, ferris wheels, water wheels, and gears are all examples of a wheel and axle.

The mechanical advantage of a wheel and axle is similar to the mechanical advantage of a lever. The effort arm is the radius of the wheel. The radius is the distance from the center of the wheel to the edge. The resistance arm is the radius of the axle.

Point out that a screwdriver is a wheel and axle. The part gripped by the hand serves as the wheel and the shaft as the axle. The screwdriver multiplies the force that is applied.
- **Which wheel and axle machines are in our classroom?** (Accept all logical answers, but lead students to suggest the pencil sharpener, door knobs, door hinges, and any other wheel and axle machines in your room.)

Section Review 15-4

1. Inclined plane, wedge, screw, lever, pulley, wheel and axle
2. MA = length of inclined plane/ height of inclined plane
3. Almost 4
4. MA = radius of wheel/radius of axle
5. Friction of the pulleys reduces the efficiency of the machine.

The mechanical advantage of a wheel and axle is equal to the radius of the wheel divided by the radius of the axle.

SECTION REVIEW

1. Name the six simple machines.
2. How is the mechanical advantage of an inclined plane calculated? Of a lever?
3. What is the mechanical advantage of a pulley system with four supporting ropes?
4. How is the mechanical advantage of a wheel and axle calculated?
5. Why is the mechanical advantage of a movable pulley always somewhat less than the number of supporting ropes, not exactly equal to it?

15–5 Compound Machines

Section Objective

To describe compound machines

A car is not one of the six simple machines you have just learned about. The car is, however, a combination of simple machines. There are wheels and axles, a gearshift lever, a set of transmission gears, a brake lever, and a steering wheel. These are only a few of the simple machines in a car.

A car, bicycle, watch, can opener, and typewriter are examples of **compound machines.** Most of the machines you use every day are compound machines. **A compound machine is a combination of two or more simple machines.**

You are surrounded by a great variety of compound machines. How many compound machines do you have in your home? A partial list might include a washing machine, VCR, blender, sewing machine, and vacuum cleaner. Compound machines make doing work easier and more enjoyable. But remember that machines, simple or compound, cannot multiply work. You can get no more work out of a machine than you put into it!

SECTION REVIEW

1. What is a compound machine?
2. Name two different simple machines in a bicycle.

Sharpen Your Skills

Compound Machines

Design a machine that uses all six simple machines. Your machine should do something useful like wash your pet snail or scratch your back. Draw a diagram or build a model of your machine. Label each simple machine. Accompany your model with a short written explanation of what your machine does.

365

SECTION PREVIEW 15-5

Most of the machines we use are not simple machines. They are a combination of two or more simple machines called compound machines. These machines make our work easier and more enjoyable.

Machines, simple or compound, cannot multiply work. You get no more work out of a machine than you put into it.

PERFORMANCE OBJECTIVES 15-5

1. Describe compound machines.
2. Identify simple machines within a compound machine.
3. Explain the work of simple machines within a compound machine.

SCIENCE TERMS 15-5

Compound machine p. 365

• **How many simple machines do you think it takes to make a car?** (Accept all logical answers, but lead students to realize that almost every part of a car is a combination of simple machines.)

Enrichment

Have several students bring their bicycles to class. Tell the class to observe and analyze each part of the bicycle to determine what the different parts do. Then have the class label the parts to show the simple machines that are involved in the complex compound machine called a bicycle.

Section Review 15-5

1. Combination of two or more simple machines
2. Lever (brake), wheel and axle

TEACHING STRATEGY 15-5

Motivation

Show the class a hammer. Have a student demonstrate pounding a nail part way into a block of wood. Have a different student demonstrate using the hammer to pull the nail out of the wood.

• **What did the hammer do?** (Pound the nail into the wood. Remove the nail from the wood.)

• **Which simple machines are part of the hammer?** (When used to pound, the hammer is a third-class lever. When used to pull a nail, the hammer is a first-class lever.)

Content Development

Explain that a car is not a simple machine. A car has many compound machines. Each of the compound machines is made of a combination of the six simple machines.

LABORATORY INVESTIGATION MECHANICAL ADVANTAGE OF AN INCLINED PLANE

BEFORE THE LAB

1. **Gather all materials at least one day prior to the investigation. You should have enough supplies to meet your class needs, assuming three to six students per group.**

PRE-LAB DISCUSSION

Have students read the complete laboratory procedure. Discuss the procedure by asking questions similar to the following.

- **What is the purpose of the laboratory investigation?** (To find the ideal and actual mechanical advantage of an inclined plane)
- **How do we find the ideal mechanical advantage?** (Divide the length of the ramp by the height of the ramp)
- **How do we find the actual mechanical advantage?** (Divide the weight of the block by the effort force)

SKILL DEVELOPMENT

Students will use the following skills while completing this investigation.
1. Manipulative
2. Observing
3. Computational
4. Measuring
5. Recording
6. Inferring
7. Relating
8. Applying

SAFETY TIPS

Alert students to be cautious with the spring scales. Remind them that pulling too hard on the spring scale can stretch the spring and cause incorrect scale readings.

TEACHING STRATEGY FOR LAB PROCEDURE

1. Have the groups practice pulling the block up the ramp several times before reading the force. If they pull too quickly or with a jerk, the pointer will read more force than actually needed. The pull should be even and steady.
2. Have the teams follow the directions carefully as they work in the laboratory.
3. Discuss how the investigation relates to the chapter ideas by asking open questions similar to the following.
- **What does the investigation illustrate about the difference between ideal and actual mechanical advantage?** (The ideal mechanical advantage is more than the actual mechanical advantage.)
- **How could we be consistent with our measures of force?** (Repeat the activity and measure again. We could take several readings and average the results.)

Mechanical Advantage of an Inclined Plane

Problem

How are the ideal and the actual mechanical advantage of an inclined plane determined?

Materials *(per group)*

wooden ramp at least 0.80 m long
wooden block or brick
spring scale calibrated in newtons
    (0–5 N)
meterstick
2 books
string

Procedure

1. Place one end of the wooden ramp on top of the two books.
2. Measure the length and height of the ramp. Take both measurements from the bottom of the ramp, as indicated in the accompanying figure. Record each measurement to the nearest 0.1 centimeter.
3. Tie one end of a string around the block or brick. Attach the other end of the string to the spring scale. Record the weight of the block to the nearest 0.1 newton.
4. Pull the block up the ramp with the spring scale. Read the scale while pulling the block. Record this value as the effort force to the nearest 0.1 newton.

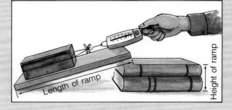

Observations

1. Calculate the work done in lifting the block without the ramp.
2. Calculate the work done in lifting the block with the ramp.
3. Calculate the ideal mechanical advantage using the formula

    IMA = length of ramp/height of ramp

4. Calculate the actual mechanical advantage using the formula

    AMA = weight of block/effort force

Length of inclined plane	cm
Height of inclined plane	cm
Weight of block	N
Effort force	N

Conclusions

1. What simple machine is the ramp? How does it make a job easier?
2. Does it require more or less force to lift the block using the ramp?
3. Is more or less work done in lifting the block when the ramp is used?
4. How does the ideal mechanical advantage compare with the actual mechanical advantage?
5. What force causes a difference in the ideal and actual mechanical advantage? How could this force be reduced?

OBSERVATIONS

1. Answers will vary, but should be the weight of the block times the height of the books.
2. Answers will vary, but should be the effort force times the height of the books.
3. Answers will vary depending on val-

SUMMARY

15–1 Work

❏ Work is the product of the force applied to an object and the distance through which the force is applied. W =F × d.

❏ The unit of work is the newton-meter or the joule.

15–2 Power

❏ Power is the rate at which work is done, or the amount of work done per unit time.

❏ Power equals work divided by time, $P = \frac{W}{t}$.

❏ The units of power are the newton-meter per second, joule per second, watt, kilowatt, and horsepower.

15–3 Machines

❏ A machine is any device that makes work easier by changing the size or direction of an applied force.

❏ Effort force is force applied to a machine.

❏ Work performed on a machine is work input.

❏ Resistance force is the force applied by a machine.

❏ Work performed by a machine is work output.

❏ Machines only multiply force, never work. Because machines cannot multiply work, work output can never be greater than work input.

❏ The number of times a machine multiplies effort force is called mechanical advantage.

❏ The efficiency of a machine is the comparison of work output to work input.

❏ Because of friction, no machine can be 100 percent efficient.

15–4 Simple Machines

❏ There are six simple machines: the inclined plane, the wedge, the screw, the lever, the pulley, and the wheel and axle.

❏ The inclined plane is a slanted surface used to raise an object.

❏ The wedge is a moving inclined plane.

❏ The screw is an inclined plane wrapped around a cylinder.

❏ The lever is a simple machine that is free to move about the fulcrum when an effort force is applied.

❏ A pulley is a chain, belt, or rope wrapped around a wheel. A fixed pulley changes the direction of an effort force. A movable pulley multiplies the effort force.

❏ A wheel and axle is a lever that rotates in a circle.

15–5 Compound Machines

❏ A compound machine is a combination of two or more simple machines.

VOCABULARY

Define each term in a complete sentence.

compound machine	inclined plane	power	watt
efficiency	joule	pulley	wedge
effort arm	kilowatt	resistance arm	wheel and axle
effort distance	lever	resistance distance	work
effort force	machine	resistance force	work input
fulcrum	mechanical advantage	screw	work output
horsepower	newton-meter		

367

two to three more times. Tell them to really aim for the best precision and accuracy possible in their measure of force by pulling with a steady pull. Have the teams calculate an average force for the trials and calculate the actual mechanical advantage again.

Have the class do the investigation with blocks that have less mass (or more mass) to find out what happens to the actual mechanical advantage.

Have the teams experiment to find ways of improving the actual mechanical advantage of the machine. Groups might try to reduce the force of friction by using wax, plastic, wax paper, rollers, or other materials on the ramp surface.

Have the teams experiment to find out what happens to the ideal and actual mechanical advantage when the ramp is either higher or lower.

---

ues for length and height of ramp, but answer should be greater than 1.
4. Answers will vary depending on the weight of the block and the effort force, but should be greater than 1 and close to the value calculated for IMA.

CONCLUSIONS

1. Ramp is an inclined plane. The inclined plane multiplies the effort force, so you need a smaller effort force to move an object.

2. Less
3. Less
4. Answers will vary, however the IMA should be greater than the AMA.
5. Friction; lubrication, which changes sliding friction to fluid or rolling friction; wheels, which change sliding friction to rolling friction

GOING FURTHER: ENRICHMENT

Have students do the investigation

CHAPTER REVIEW

MULTIPLE CHOICE

1. b	**3.** d	**5.** c	**7.** b	**9.** d
2. d	**4.** c	**6.** d	**8.** a	**10.** a

COMPLETION

1. distance
2. time
3. kilowatt
4. applied force
5. work output
6. Friction
7. inclined plane
8. wedge
9. first-class
10. wheel and axle

TRUE OR FALSE

1. T
2. F work
3. F force
4. T
5. T
6. F six
7. F inclined plane
8. T
9. T
10. F simple

SKILL BUILDING

1. a. No work, since no movement **b.** No work, since no movement **c.** No work, since no movement **d.** Work, since you are exerting a force on your pencil or pen and moving it in the same direction as the force that is applied.
2. a. 4000 N-m or 4000 j **b.** 400 watts; 500 watts **c.** .53 hp; .67 hp
3. 90% efficiency. Make it a pulley system or lubricate the pulley.
4. MA = 20
5. Set up a fixed pulley by attaching pulley to ceiling. Set up a movable pulley by attaching pulley to crate. Check students' diagrams for accuracy.
6. a. 1750 j **b.** work remains the same since same weight taken through same distance **c.** 5.83 watts **d.** 14.5 watts

ESSAY

1. No. If there is no motion, there is no work. Because the earth was supposed to be stationary, there was no motion.
2. Power is work divided by time. All the swimmers performed the same amount of work. The winner, however, performed the work in a shorter period of time.
3. No work is done because without motion there is no work.
4. They either multiply the force or distance or change the direction of the force.
5. It is a combination of several simple machines.

ADDITIONAL QUESTIONS AND TOPIC SUGGESTIONS

1. A carpenter is going to refinish a stairsteps. She must lift each step, plane it down, stain, varnish and replace each step. What are the simple machines she will need to have? (crowbar to lift: lever; plane: wedge; brush or stain and varnish: lever; nail: wedge; hammer: lever)
2. Imagine you run a machine. It seems to be getting very hot because of friction. What will you check for? (To see if the machine has enough lubricant at every joint that moves or turns. Check the ball or roller bearings.)
3. Your mother asks you to put a very heavy box onto the back of the car. What simple machine could you use

---

On a separate sheet of paper, write the letter of the answer that best completes each statement.

1. If a large force is exerted on an object, no work is performed if
   a. the object moves.   b. the object does not move.
   c. the power is too large.   d. there is no friction.
2. A unit of power is
   a. the watt.   b. the kilowatt.   c. the horsepower.   d. all of the above.
3. Machines multiply
   a. work.   b. power.   c. time.   d. force.
4. The resistance force divided by the effort force is called
   a. work.   b. power.   c. mechanical advantage.   d. efficiency.
5. The efficiency of a machine is
   a. always 100 percent.   b. always greater than 100 percent.
   c. always less than 100 percent.   d. either greater or less than 100 percent.
6. The mechanical advantage of an inclined plane is found by dividing the length of the plane by its
   a. effort force.   b. resistance force.   c. effort distance.   d. height.
7. A wheelbarrow is which type of lever?
   a. first-class   b. second-class   c. third-class   d. fourth-class
8. A movable pulley has a mechanical advantage
   a. greater than one.   b. less than one.   c. equal to one.   d. equal to zero.
9. The gears in a watch are an example of a
   a. pulley.   b. lever.   c. screw.   d. wheel and axle.
10. An example of a compound machine would be a
    a. school bus.   b. crowbar.   c. pliers.   d. ramp.

CONTENT REVIEW: COMPLETION

On a separate sheet of paper, write the word or words that best complete each statement.

1. Work equals force times _____.
2. Power is work divided by _____.
3. One _____ equals 1000 watts.
4. Machines multiply a (an) _____.
5. Work done by a machine is _____.
6. _____ reduces efficiency.
7. A ramp is a (an) _____.
8. A (An) _____ is an inclined plane that moves.
9. A scissors is a (an) _____ lever.
10. A (An) _____ is a lever that rotates in a circle.

CONTENT REVIEW: TRUE OR FALSE

Determine whether each statement is true or false. Then on a separate sheet of paper, write "true" if it is true. If it is false, change the underlined word or words to make the statement true.

1. A unit of work is the joule.
2. Power is the rate of doing motion.
3. Machines multiply work.
4. Work output is less than work input.

5. The number of times a machine multiplies <u>effort</u> force is called mechanical advantage.
6. There are <u>seven</u> simple machines.
7. A screw is a <u>lever</u> wrapped around a cylinder.
8. The fixed point at which a lever is supported is called a <u>fulcrum</u>.
9. A third-class lever multiplies <u>distance</u>.
10. A combination of <u>complex</u> machines is a compound machine.

CONCEPT REVIEW: SKILL BUILDING

Use the skills you have developed in the chapter to complete each activity.

1. **Applying definitions** For each of the following situations, determine whether work is being done. Explain each answer.
   a. You are babysitting for a friend by watching the child while it naps.
   b. A television broadcaster is reporting the news.
   c. You are doing your homework by reading this chapter.
   d. You are doing your homework by writing answers to questions.

2. **Applying formulas** Two boys each weigh 800 newtons. One boy climbs a 5.0-meter rope in 10.0 seconds. The other boy climbs the same rope in 8.0 seconds.
   a. How much work is done by each boy?
   b. What is the power in watts of each boy?
   c. What is the horsepower of each boy? Hint: 1 hp = 746 watts

3. **Applying formulas** The work output of a pulley is 900 joules. The work input is 1000 joules. What is the efficiency of the pulley? How could you increase the efficiency of the pulley?

4. **Making calculations** A water wheel is 2 meters in diameter. The axle is 10 centimeters in diameter. What is the mechanical advantage of the water wheel? Hint: Watch the units!

5. **Developing a model** Suppose you have a large crate you wish to lift off the floor. To accomplish this you have been given a pulley and some rope. The crate has a hook on it, as does the ceiling. Describe two ways in which you could use this equipment to raise the crate. Accompany each description with a diagram of the setup.

6. **Relating concepts** Suppose you live on the fifth floor of an apartment building. You have just bought a new tape deck that weighs 50 newtons. To reach your apartment, which is 35 meters up, you can climb the stairs or take an elevator.
   a. If you climb the stairs, how much work do you do?
   b. If you take the elevator, is the amount of work greater, smaller, or equal to the work done in part a?
   c. If it takes you 5 minutes to climb up the stairs, what is your power? Remember, the time unit for power is seconds.
   d. Compare your power with that of the elevator if it takes 2 minutes for the elevator to reach the fifth floor.

CONCEPT REVIEW: ESSAY

Discuss each of the following in a brief paragraph.

1. The mythical god Atlas is known for the fact that he holds up a stationary Earth. Does Atlas perform any work? Explain your answer.
2. Why does the winner in a swimming race have the most power?
3. Pushing against a wall that does not move is a form of exercise. Is work done in such a case? Explain your answer.
4. Explain how machines make work easier. Use several examples in your answer.
5. Why is a bicycle a compound machine?

369

that would aid you? Explain why you selected that machine. (Answers will vary but make sure the machine is an aid in lifting.)

ISSUES IN SCIENCE

The following issues can be used as a springboard for class debate or as a writing homework.

1. Machines have changed our ways of getting food, clothing, and shelter. Debate or describe what your life would be like today if we did not have any compound machines.

2. Some people say toy manufacturers are destroying children's imagination by having the toys operate by machine. Other people say this is stimulating the imagination because it allows the child to use a machine. What is your opinion? Explain why you believe as you do.

Chapter 16
ENERGY

CHAPTER OVERVIEW

This chapter begins with the traditional but simple definition of energy as the ability to do work. The discussion of energy is facilitated by establishing five broad categories for the forms of energy. All but one, nuclear energy, will be familiar to the students from their everyday experiences.

Kinetic energy and potential energy are defined quantitatively. Changes between kinetic and potential for an object moving up and down near earth provide a first experience of energy conversions. Energy conversions involving other forms are covered more generally. Heat engines provide further opportunities to discuss energy conversions. Tracing energy conversions through several steps emphasizes that all energy can always be accounted for during any process.

The law of conservation of energy is perhaps the most unshakable tenet of modern science. That energy can be neither created nor destroyed by ordinary means provides a major clue when scientists investigate new atomic, molecular, biological, or astronomical processes. The conservation of energy provides a bookkeeping system that guarantees a balanced budget. To account for all energy, the equivalence of mass and energy may be invoked, drawing on Einstein's famous equation $E = mc^2$.

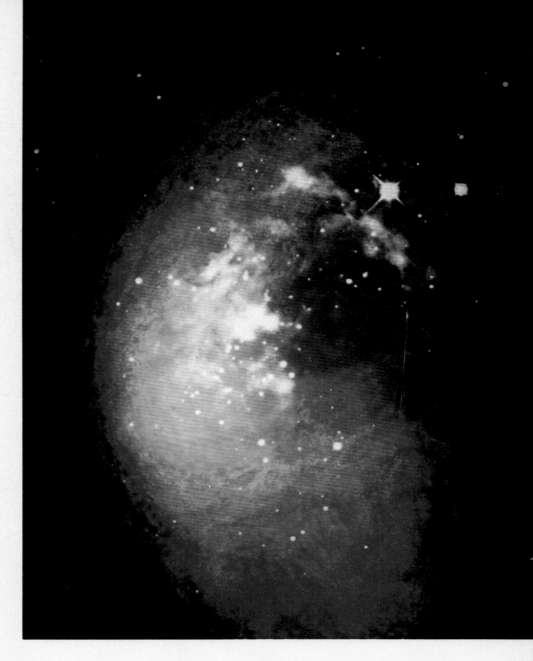

INTRODUCING CHAPTER 16

Ask your students to compare the photograph of the Orion Nebula with the sun. The sun will be described as bright, focused, and organized. As they read the text they will see that their observations are justified. The new star in Orion is not organized enough to glow brightly, but the gravitational force is beginning to fire up its furnace.

A discussion of how life on earth would be impossible without the sun as source of energy can be directed toward a discussion of the process that feeds the sun itself. Its nuclear furnace generates energy in the same manner as a hydrogen bomb—by converting matter into energy. Very high temperatures are required for this process. The high temperatures indicate the high speeds that the atomic particles obtain during the gravitational col-

lapse of a cold cloud of gas into a hot concentrated ball of fire. The high speeds allow the protons to overcome their electrical force of repulsion and fuse together to form larger atomic nuclei. The cloud brought itself together by converting gravitational potential energy into kinetic energy. The kinetic energy allowed the particles to combine and in the process release energy as a small part of each proton is converted into energy.

Energy 16

CHAPTER OBJECTIVES

After completing this chapter, you will be able to

16–1 Define energy.

16–1 Describe five forms of energy and give examples of each.

16–2 Distinguish between kinetic and potential energy.

16–2 Explain the relationship between kinetic energy, mass, and velocity.

16–2 Calculate gravitational potential energy.

16–3 Identify several energy conversions.

16–3 Describe the energy conversions that take place in heat engines.

16–4 Explain the law of conservation of energy.

From the large, cold clouds of gas and dust, small particles begin to clump together. Their own gravity and the pressure from nearby stars cause these small clumps to form a single larger mass. Like a monstrous vacuum cleaner, gravity pulls in more and more particles of dust and gas. The gravitational force becomes so enormous that the bits of matter falling faster and faster to the center begin to heat up. The internal temperature reaches fifteen million degrees. Subatomic particles called protons collide with each other at tremendous speeds. The normal electric force of repulsion between protons is overcome by the force of the particle collisions. The protons fuse together to form helium. During this process, part of the matter is transformed into energy. A star is born!

What is energy? How can energy from our sun be changed to useful energy on the earth? Can matter really be changed into energy? Is the total energy in the universe constant? As you read further, you will find answers to these questions.

The formation of the Orion Nebula is evidence of the interaction of matter and energy. This infrared map of the nebula was created by scientists to show how the nebula would appear through a large telescope sensitive to infrared.

371

TEACHER DEMONSTRATION

Since the chapter opens with a discussion of star formation, you may want a more down-to-earth demonstration. Bring in to class a number of children's toys that illustrate various forms of energy and the conversions between forms. Send two toy cars, one battery powered, one springwound or with a friction motor, across the floor. Let the class discuss why one stops first. Play with a yo-yo or large coil spring. Question the students about the temporary storage of energy. Launch a rubber-band-powered toy plane. Send a car down a hill. Almost any toys will do. Ask students to describe how each toy operates. To ultimately connect the toys to the chapter opening, ask about the source of energy. Keep pushing their sources farther back until the ultimate source of our energy is identified as the sun.

TEACHER RESOURCES

Audiovisuals

Energy—A First Film, 16 mm film, BFA

Energy Conversion and Conservation, filmstrip with cassette, Silver-Burdett

Forms of Energy, filmstrip with cassette, SVE

This World of Energy, 5 filmstrips with 5 cassettes, NGS

Books

Burberry, Peter, *Building for Energy Conservation,* Halstead

Larsen, Egon, *New Sources of Energy and Power,* Crane-Russak

Overman, Michael, *Understanding Energy,* International Publications Service

Romer, Robert H., *Energy: An Introduction to Physics,* W.H. Freeman

Software

Kinetic and Potential Energy, Prentice-Hall

• **Why does this new star not show up in ordinary photographs?** (The temperature of the star is not high enough for it to radiate in the visible portion of the electromagnetic spectrum. It only emits infrared light.)

• **Will the new star have planets?** (It is not likely that all of the gas will be drawn into the star. Small clumps may be left out and will form planets. We will not detect them since planets do not radiate enough light.)

• **How are we like a star?** (We are made out of star stuff. The heavy elements on earth were made at the same time as the elements of the sun and other stars.)

• **What force did the work to provide the initial energy for the sun?** (Gravity)

16-1 NATURE OF ENERGY

SECTION PREVIEW 16-1

Energy is defined in this section as the ability to do work. The SI unit of energy is the joule, which is also the unit of work defined in the previous chapter.

Dramatic examples of energy releases include exploding stars, erupting volcanoes, crashing waves, and lightning storms. Students will learn to classify these large energy releases as well as more everyday examples into five categories for convenient discussion. The five forms of energy are mechanical, heat, chemical, electromagnetic, and nuclear. The organization of very diverse processes into general categories enhances the idea that while energy may appear in varied forms, it is essentially the same thing: the ability to do work.

PERFORMANCE OBJECTIVES 16-1

1. **Explain how energy and work are related and why they are measured in the same units.**

2. **List the five main forms of energy and give an example of each.**

SCIENCE TERMS 16-1

energy p. 372
joule p. 372
mechanical energy p. 373
heat energy p. 373
chemical energy p. 373
electromagnetic energy p. 373
nuclear energy p. 374

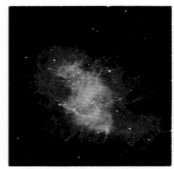

Figure 16–1 *The Crab Nebula in the constellation Taurus is the remains of a star that exploded in 1054. A supernova releases tremendous amounts of energy. What is energy?* ❶

Figure 16–2 *Energy appears in many forms. Here you see two dramatic examples of the release of energy. In what form is energy released during a lightning storm? During a volcanic eruption?* ❷

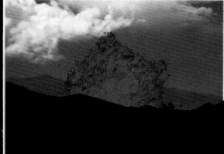

16–1 Nature of Energy

On July 4, 1054, the Chinese recorded the sudden appearance of a new star. The star shone so brightly that it could be seen even during the day. After 23 days, the distant star began to disappear. What the Chinese had observed was a supernova, an exploding star. The energy released by a supernova is capable of destroying a nearby solar system in just hours. A supernova is one of the greatest concentrations of energy in the universe.

A supernova is a very dramatic example of energy release. So, too, is a volcano. A huge amount of energy stored beneath the earth's surface is explosively released when a volcano erupts. But not all forms of energy are quite that dramatic.

You live in an ocean of energy. Energy is all around you. You hear energy as sound, see it as light, and feel it as wind. Energy creates waves on the sea, produces electricity, and keeps you warm.

What is **energy?** Energy is the ability to do work. And work involves a change in movement. Energy in its various forms is necessary for all sorts of changes. So another way of defining energy is the ability to cause change. One unit in which energy is measured is the **joule** (J).

The supernova of 1054 pushed an enormous volume of matter out into space. It did an incredible amount of work. Figure 16–1 shows the result of its great release of energy. A storm, too, releases a tremendous amount of energy. You expend energy when you turn the pages of this book.

Forms of Energy

Energy appears in many forms. All matter contains some form of energy because all matter has the ability to do work or cause change.

The five main forms of energy are mechanical, heat, chemical, electromagnetic, and nuclear. It may surprise you to learn that your body is an "energy factory" that stores and converts various forms of energy. After reading about each form of energy, see if you can describe how your "energy factory" works.

MECHANICAL ENERGY Energy associated with motion is called **mechanical energy.** Matter that is in motion has mechanical energy. Water in a waterfall has a great amount of mechanical energy. So does wind. An automobile traveling at 95 km/hr has mechanical energy. A jet plane cruising at 700 km/hr has even more! When you walk, ride a bike, or hit a ball, you use mechanical energy. As the pistons and other parts of a car engine move, mechanical energy is being used. Sound is a type of mechanical energy.

HEAT ENERGY The internal motion of particles of matter is called **heat energy.** The faster the particles move, the more heat energy is present. Rub your hands together for several seconds. Did you feel heat? You converted mechanical energy into heat energy! Heat energy often causes changes in the temperature and phase of any form of matter.

CHEMICAL ENERGY The energy that bonds atoms or ions together is called **chemical energy.** When bonds are broken, atoms are rearranged, and new bonds are formed. During this process, stored chemical energy is released. The fuel in a rocket engine has stored chemical energy. When the fuel is ignited, chemical energy is converted into heat energy.

When you start a fire in a charcoal grill, you are releasing chemical energy. When you throw a ball, you are using chemical energy stored in your muscles. This chemical energy, stored in the form of fat, comes from the food you eat.

ELECTROMAGNETIC ENERGY Moving electric charges have **electromagnetic energy.** Power lines carry

Figure 16–3 *The water cascading over these rocks has the ability to do work. Therefore, the water in a waterfall has energy. What kind of energy is it?* ❸

Figure 16–4 *This battery is made of 27 nickel–hydrogen cells. The battery produces energy as a result of chemical reactions within the cells. So the battery has stored chemical energy. To what other type of energy will the chemical energy likely be converted?* ❹

373

Figure 16–5 *Light is a form of electromagnetic energy. Each color of the rainbow (left) corresponds to a different amount of electromagnetic energy. Laser light (right) is an extremely powerful, concentrated, one-color form of electromagnetic energy.*

electromagnetic energy into your home in the form of electricity. Electric motors are driven by electromagnetic energy.

Light is another form of electromagnetic energy. Each color of light represents a different amount of electromagnetic energy. Electromagnetic energy also includes X-rays, radio waves, and laser light.

NUCLEAR ENERGY The nucleus of an atom is the source of **nuclear energy.** When a nucleus splits, nuclear energy is released in the form of heat energy and light energy. Nuclear energy is also released when lightweight nuclei collide at high speeds and fuse. The sun's energy is produced from a nuclear fusion reaction in which hydrogen nuclei fuse to form helium nuclei. Nuclear energy is the most concentrated form of energy.

SECTION REVIEW

1. What is energy?
2. Why does all matter contain energy?
3. What are the different forms of energy?
4. Copy down the first paragraph on page 371. Identify the following words or phrases in that paragraph as being one of the five forms of energy: *clump together, gravity, heat up, protons collide, electric force, protons fuse.*

Sharpen Your Skills

Forms of Energy
Skills: Classifying, applying
Level: Remedial–Average
Type: Hands-on
Materials: paper, newspapers, pen or pencil

In this activity, students are called upon to classify energy sources they read about in the newspaper into one of the five main types of energy. Students may well find that nuclear energy is the form of energy most discussed.

Sharpen Your Skills

Forms of Energy

1. Make five columns on a piece of paper.
2. Write the following headings at the top of each column: Mechanical Energy, Heat Energy, Chemical Energy, Electromagnetic Energy, and Nuclear Energy.
3. Read through a newspaper and place a check mark in the appropriate column every time a particular form of energy is mentioned.

What form of energy is most often mentioned? Would this form of energy always be the most discussed?

374

16-1 (continued)

Section Review 16-1
1. Ability to do work or cause change
2. All matter has the ability to do work. Also, matter is made of particles that are in motion, so there is always kinetic energy in matter.
3. Mechanical, heat, chemical, electromagnetic, nuclear
4. Mechanical, mechanical, heat, mechanical, electromagnetic, nuclear

TEACHING STRATEGY 16-2

As you have throughout the year, encourage your students to do the exercises that are suggested in the text. Even the simple example of a stretched rubber band can help reinforce energy concepts. If the students actually stretch rubber bands while reading, they will understand three important concepts: It takes work to stretch a rubber band; work is stored in the

rubber band; and the stretched rubber band can do work on another object. They will learn that work can be stored as potential energy and that potential energy may be released as work on another object or, of course, as the kinetic energy of a flying rubber band! Note that some work will be transformed into heat energy each time the rubber band is stretched or released. This can be detected as a change in the temperature of wide

16–2 Kinetic and Potential Energy

Stretch a rubber band between your thumb and index finger. Keep the rubber band stretched without any motion. How long can you hold it this way? After a short while you begin to sense the energy in the rubber band. Yet the rubber band is not moving! The stretched rubber band has energy *stored* in it. You cannot see this energy, but you know it is there because the stretched rubber band can do work as it returns to its normal shape. Remember that energy is the ability to do work.

The energy of motion of the stretched rubber band is temporarily being stored. Energy stored in an object due to its position is called **potential** (poh-TEHN-shul) **energy.** As the rubber band is stretched, energy is put into it. In its new position, the stretched rubber band contains potential energy.

Release your thumb and the rubber band moves. Energy that a moving object has due to its motion is called **kinetic** (kih-NEHT-ihk) **energy.** As the rubber band moves back to its normal shape, it can do work.

You just learned about five forms of energy. **The five forms of energy can be classified as potential energy (energy of position) or kinetic energy (energy of motion).** Because potential and kinetic energy most often have to do with motion, they are often treated as kinds of mechanical energy.

Kinetic Energy

Kinetic energy is energy of motion. An object that moves has kinetic energy. When you walk, run, swim, and jump, you have kinetic energy. Light and heat from the sun are examples of kinetic energy. So, too, are thunder and lightning.

The faster an object moves, the more kinetic energy it has. So kinetic energy is directly related to the velocity of an object. In baseball, a fast ball has more kinetic energy than a slow curve. You have more kinetic energy when you run than when you walk. Who has more kinetic energy, a downhill skier or a cross-country skier? ②

Figure 16–6 *This archer in the 1984 Olympic Games is making use of potential energy, or energy stored in an object because of its position. The stretched bow has the ability to do work once it is released. The more potential energy it has, the greater will be its ability to move the arrow. How did the bow get its potential energy?* ①

375

---

rubber bands if they are touched to the lips after being stretched rapidly.

Motivation

The examples of potential energy and kinetic energy that we are most familiar with are kinds of mechanical energy. Exploit this knowledge by eliciting numerous common examples. Do not dismiss examples that are not mechanical but indicate that we will concentrate on the mechanical since it is easy to calculate and visualize. Students' awareness of potential energy in nonmechanical systems can be used as you move toward a more general discussion of energy conversions.

16-2 KINETIC AND POTENTIAL ENERGY

SECTION PREVIEW 16-2

In this section, the classification of energy into five forms is refined by observing that in each of the five forms energy may become evident as energy of motion—kinetic energy, or as energy of position—potential energy.

Students should recognize that potential energy is stored energy and is the result of the work required to put the object into its position or condition. Potential energy is most evident on a human scale as gravitational or elastic. These will be emphasized over electrical, chemical or nuclear. Gravitational and elastic potential energies will be considered aspects of mechanical energy since they are closely related to kinetic energy. Gravitational potential energy is treated quantitatively as weight times height, which is the work required to lift an object at a constant speed.

Kinetic energy, the energy of motion, is calculated as one-half of the product of mass and the square of the speed, $\frac{1}{2}mv^2$. It is the work required to accelerate the object to the speed v from rest. As such it, like potential energy, is a relative measure.

PERFORMANCE OBJECTIVES 16-2

1. **Describe the two aspects of mechanical energy.**
2. **State examples of objects with kinetic and potential energies.**
3. **Calculate the kinetic energy of a given mass at a given speed.**
4. **Calculate the gravitational potential energy of a given mass at a given height.**

SCIENCE TERMS 16-2
potential energy p. 375
kinetic energy p. 375
gravitational potential energy p. 376

ANNOTATION KEY

❶ Velocity (Applying formulas)
❷ Bridge: G.P.E. = weight × height (Applying formulas)
❶ Thinking Skill: Applying formulas
❷ Thinking Skill: Making generalizations

16-2 (continued)

Content Development

Students will readily agree that a moving object has energy because it has the ability to do work on another object. Lead students toward the quantitative definition of kinetic energy by asking what characteristics of the body determine its ability to do work. Use the equation, $\frac{1}{2}mv^2 = KE$. Do the same for gravitational potential energy by suggesting that students consider the damage that various objects dropped from various heights could do to their toes. Arrive at the formula $mgh = GPE$. Use the equation with numbers. Ask,

• **What aspects of a moving body determine its ability to do work on another body?** (speed, mass)
• **What aspects of a moving body do not affect its energy?** (volume, density, shape, material, color, etc.)
• **What determines the gravitational potential energy of a body?** (The work required to lift it to its given position, that is its weight times height. Weight

is determined by the mass of the object and gravity.)

Skills Development

Skills: Applying formulas, making calculations, making graphs

Use the formula for kinetic energy to compare the kinetic energies of (a) an 80-kg man and a 40-kg boy jogging at 4 m/sec. (b) two 40-kg boys, one jogging at 4 m/sec, the other running at 8 m/sec. (c) an 80-kg man jogging at 1

Figure 16–7 *Kinetic energy is energy of motion. It is dependent on the mass and velocity of a moving object. Both Evelyn Ashford (top) and Fernando Valenzuela (bottom) are familiar with kinetic energy. Ashford uses it to get her across the finish line first. And Valenzuela puts it into his fast ball to pitch a strike.*

376

Do all objects with the same velocity have the same kinetic energy? A battleship that is moving at 40 km/hr has much more kinetic energy than a mosquito moving at the same velocity. So kinetic energy must depend on something other than just velocity. The battleship has more kinetic energy because it has greater mass. Kinetic energy depends on both mass and velocity. The mathematical relationship between kinetic energy, mass, and velocity is

$$K.E. = \frac{m \times v^2}{2}$$

According to this equation, an increase in mass or velocity will mean an increase in kinetic energy. Which of these two factors, mass or velocity, will have a greater effect on kinetic energy? ❶

Potential Energy

Potential energy is energy of position. Imagine that you are standing on the edge of a one-meter diving board. Do you think you have any energy? You probably think you do not because you are not moving. It is true that you do not have kinetic energy. But you do have potential energy. Your potential energy is due to your position above the water.

If you were standing on a three-meter diving board, you would have three times the potential energy as on the one-meter board. Energy that is dependent on height above the earth's surface is called **gravitational** (grav-ih-TAY-shuhn-uhl) **potential energy (G.P.E.).** A waterfall, suspension bridge, and wrecking ball all have a great amount of gravitational potential energy.

Weight also determines the amount of gravitational potential energy an object has. The old saying "The bigger they are, the harder they fall" is an observation of the effect of weight on gravitational potential energy. From your own experiences, you may know that gravitational potential energy is dependent on weight. You feel a lot more gravitational potential energy with a 100-newton pack on your back than you do with a 50-newton pack.

The relationship between G.P.E., weight, and height can be expressed by the following formula:

$$G.P.E. = weight \times height$$

m/sec and a 20-kg child jogging at 2 m/sec.

Observe Figure 16-7.
• **Is it possible that the second place finisher has more kinetic energy than Evelyn Ashford?** (yes, if she was moving faster when crossing the finish line)

Have students calculate their own kinetic energies after they time a walk around the room and their own potential energies after they have walked to

You can see from this formula that the greater the weight, the greater the gravitational potential energy. The higher the position above a surface, the greater the gravitational potential energy.

Figure 16–8 *Both Olympic diver Greg Louganis and the Oakland Bay Bridge have gravitational potential energy. Which has more G.P.E.?* ❷

Although potential energy is most common in mechanical energy, it does occur in the other forms of energy. A battery contains both chemical and electric potential energy. Rocket fuel contains large amounts of chemical potential energy.

SECTION REVIEW

1. What is kinetic energy? Potential energy?
2. Use the formula for kinetic energy to describe the relationship between the kinetic energy of an object, its mass, and its velocity.
3. What is gravitational potential energy? How is it calculated?
4. The gravitational potential energy of a brick at one meter is ten joules. What is the gravitational potential energy of two bricks at two meters?

16–3 Energy Conversion

Section Objective

To describe different types of energy conversion

In an amusement park in Southern California, there is a ride called Montezuma's Revenge. A car is pulled up a steep ramp and held at the top. When the car is released, it rolls backward at a terrifying velocity. After reaching the bottom of the ramp, the car does a complete loop, returning to the bottom again. Finally, the car rolls up a ramp on the opposite side and is stopped at the top.

377

16-3 ENERGY CONVERSIONS

SECTION PREVIEW 16-3

A change in the form of energy is an energy conversion. Students will read about the conversion of kinetic energy to potential energy and potential energy to kinetic energy in simple mechanical systems. They will be asked to qualitatively describe the gradual transformations of energy as an object rises and falls near the surface of the earth.

Other energy conversions such as electrical to mechanical, as in a motor, or electromagnetic to chemical, as in a photocell, are used to broaden the discussion but are not treated in detail.

Finally, heat engines are discussed and classified as internal- or external-combustion. The operation of these engines is reserved for Chapter 18.

PERFORMANCE OBJECTIVES 16-3

1. Define energy conversion.
2. Discuss the energy conversions that take place as a ball is thrown into the air.
3. List several processes that show energy conversions that do not involve gravitational potential energy.
4. Describe the energy conversion that takes place in heat engines.

SCIENCE TERMS 16-3

energy conversion p. 378
heat engine p. 381

---

the second floor of the school.

Construct a graph of the gravitational potential energy of this book as a function of the height of each of seven library shelves.

Reinforcement

Show students that the gravitational potential energy formula (weight times height) is nothing more than the definition of work: force times distance. The potential energy of an

object is determined by the work required to put the object into that position. In the case of gravitational potential energy, the force required is the opposite of the object's weight, and the distance is the height to which it was raised.

Section Review 16-2

1. Energy of motion; energy of position
2. K.E. is equal to one-half the pro-

duct of mass times the square of the velocity.

3. Potential energy due to height above the ground; P.E. = w × h
4. G.P.E. = w × h = 2w × 2h = 4 G.P.E. = 4 × 10 J = 40 J.

TEACHER DEMONSTRATION

Set up a flexible track used for toy cars to simulate a roller coaster. This will enhance the discussion of Figure 16-9. Arrange for several hills of various heights. Let the students predict locations of maximum and minimum speed before you release a car on the track. Diagram the track on the chalkboard and label it thoroughly in terms of its energy economy. Ask why no hill is higher than the initial hill.

TEACHING STRATEGY 16-3

Motivation
Refer to Montezuma's Revenge or, better yet, to a roller coaster at a local amusement park. This is bound to create excitement in your class. Students will trade stories of their favorite or most feared ride and are often able to provide surprising detail about the ride's construction and operation. Use this to your advantage, discussing the electric or pneumatic motors, or the steam engine or an old carousel; the cable, chain, or gear linking the motor to the ride; and finally the action of the ride's cars themselves. Ask for details regarding the forms of energy and the method by which work converts the energy from one form to another.

Content Development
As you begin to teach this section be sure that all examples and problems focus on the kinetic–potential energy conversion. Prepare examples that will generate data easily. Even slower students prefer a quantitative treatment since the words maximum and minimum used repeatedly may confuse them.

Figure 16–9 *What are the energy changes in this ride called?* **1**

Changes in the forms of energy are called energy conversions. One of the most common **energy conversions** involves the changing of potential energy to kinetic energy or kinetic energy to potential energy. Montezuma's Revenge is an excellent example of energy conversion.

Kinetic–Potential Energy Conversion

Kinetic energy is energy of motion. Potential energy is energy of position. These two forms of energy are continuously being converted. Looking closely at each step in Montezuma's Revenge will help you understand this energy conversion.

At the top of the ramp, the car has maximum potential energy and zero kinetic energy. Why? As **2**

Use Figure 16-10 by saying that the basketball player did 15 joules of work on the ball as he pushed it with a force of 10 Newtons through a distance of 1.5 meters. The ball has 15 joules of kinetic energy as it leaves his hand. At a point halfway up, the ball would have 7.5 J of potential energy and 7.5 J of kinetic energy for a total of 15 J. At the apex, it has 15 J of potential energy and no kinetic energy. Do this analysis at several points on

the way up and on the way down.

The actual mass of a basketball is .62 kg and it might leave a player's hand at 7 m/sec, giving it a maximum kinetic energy of 15.2 J. This would result in a maximum height of 2.5 m above his hands. Note that halfway up or down the distance, potential energy, and the kinetic energy are all half of their maximum values, while the speed would be 4.95 m/sec.

After students are secure in the

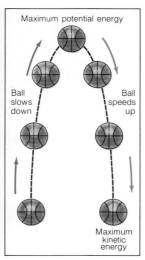

Maximum potential energy

Ball slows down

Ball speeds up

Maximum kinetic energy

Figure 16–10 *As this basketball player throws the ball in the air, various energy conversions take place. As the ball rises higher, its velocity and its kinetic energy decrease. What happens to its potential energy?* ❸

the car rolls down the ramp, its kinetic energy increases as its potential energy decreases. Energy of position is being converted to energy of motion. The potential energy increases and the kinetic energy decreases once again as the car moves up to the top of the loop. What happens as it completes the loop and returns to the bottom? In its final step, ❹ the car's kinetic energy decreases and its potential energy increases as it rolls up the ramp.

Conversions between kinetic energy and potential energy are taking place around you every day. As an example, think of tossing a ball up into the air. ❷ When you throw the ball up, you give it kinetic energy. As the ball rises, it slows down. As its velocity decreases, its kinetic energy is reduced. But during the same process of rising higher and higher from the earth, its potential energy is increasing. At the top of its path, the ball has slowed down to zero velocity and zero kinetic energy. All of its kinetic energy from the beginning of its flight has been converted to potential energy.

Then the ball begins to fall. As it gets closer to the earth's surface, its potential energy decreases. But it is speeding up at the same time. Thus, its kinetic energy is increasing. When you catch it, it has its maximum velocity and kinetic energy. The

Sharpen Your Skills

Computing Kinetic Energy

Complete the following table:

Object	Mass (kg)	Velocity (m/sec)	Kinetic energy (J)
A	1	1	
B	2	1	
C	1	2	
D	2	2	

Which has the greatest effect on the kinetic energy of a body, mass or velocity?

379

Figure 16–11 *A continuous conversion between kinetic and potential energy takes place in a pendulum. At what point is the pendulum's kinetic energy the greatest? Zero?* ❷

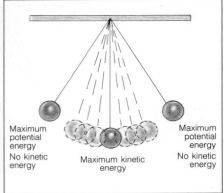

Figure 16–12 *The sun's energy is converted to heat, light, and the chemical energy stored by green plants in the form of sugars and starches.*

potential energy of the ball has changed into kinetic energy. In terms of kinetic and potential energy, what happens if the ball hits the ground and bounces back up? ❶

Figure 16–11 is a pendulum. You may have seen pendulums in large clocks. In a pendulum, there is a continuous conversion between kinetic and potential energy.

A pendulum swings in an arc. As it swings up to the top of its arc, its kinetic energy decreases and it reaches its maximum potential energy. As it then swings down, its potential energy decreases and it reaches its maximum kinetic energy. Then the pendulum gains in potential energy again as it sweeps up the opposite side. The conversion between kinetic energy and potential energy takes place over and over again. A diver springing up and down on a diving board is continuously changing potential energy to kinetic energy and kinetic energy back to potential energy.

Other Energy Conversions

Not all energy conversions involve kinetic energy and potential energy. All forms of energy can be converted to another form. For example, the sun's energy is not used merely as heat energy or light energy. It is converted to other forms of energy as well. Green plants use the energy of the sun to trigger a chemical change in which sugars and starches are made. These substances store the energy as

380

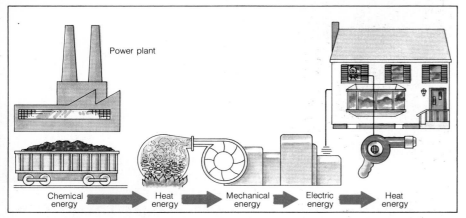

Power plant

Chemical energy → Heat energy → Mechanical energy → Electric energy → Heat energy

Figure 16–13 *A whole series of energy conversions is needed to produce the heat energy of the hair dryer. Trace the various conversions, starting with the burning of a fuel.* ③

chemical energy. In this process, then, light energy is converted to chemical energy.

In a battery, chemical energy is converted to electric energy. In a motor, electric energy is converted to mechanical energy. The mechanical energy of a waterfall is converted to electric energy in a generator.

Often a whole series of energy conversions is needed to do a particular job. The operation of a hair dryer is a good example of this. See Figure 16–13. The electric energy used by the dryer is generated from some fuel source, such as gas. The chemical energy from the fuel is released by burning it. The fuel provides heat energy, which in turn is changed to mechanical energy. This mechanical energy is used to make a generator do the work of providing the dryer with electric energy. When you turn the dryer on, the electric energy is changed back to heat energy. ②

Engines

Machines that change heat energy to mechanical energy are called **heat engines.** In a heat engine, a fuel is burned. This burning, or combustion, releases heat energy, which is then changed to mechanical energy.

Heat engines are classified according to where the fuel is burned. In an external-combustion engine, the fuel is burned outside the engine. A steam

Sharpen Your Skills

The Pendulum

1. Find a length of cord and measure off one meter. Cut the cord.

2. Tie a light mass, such as a key, to one end. Hold the other end up with one hand, so that the key is hanging.

3. Pull the key to one side. Then let the key go and observe its motion.

a. What happened to the key when you let go?

b. What do you think gave the key its energy?

c. What kind of energy did it have when it was at its highest point?

d. Where was its maximum kinetic energy?

381

Sharpen Your Skills

The Pendulum
Skills: Observing, inferring, comparing, relating
Level: Average
Type: Hands-on
Materials: cord, key

This activity will help reinforce students' understanding of the conversion of potential energy to kinetic and back again. Students should note that a. The key fell in an arc. b. Gravitational potential energy (some students may rightly point out that this energy was actually obtained by the person lifting the key). c. potential energy
d. Kinetic energy was maximum at the bottom of the arc.

Suppose you were at a second floor window and a friend on the ground was trying to throw a ball to you without aiming at the window. How should your friend toss the ball? Ideally it should stop right in front of you so that you can just grab it; at that point it would have no kinetic energy. If the ball is thrown too fast, all of its kinetic energy would not have been transformed into potential energy so that it would pass you on the way up—but you would get a second chance to catch it on the way down! This can be simulated by having the catcher stand on a table and having the thrower sit on the floor.

16-4 CONSERVATION OF ENERGY

SECTION PREVIEW 16-4

The law of conservation of energy is one of the most fundamental tenets of modern science. Based on the energy conversions studied in the previous sections, students are asked to take a large leap to the universal law that energy may neither be converted nor destroyed. Energy conversions and transfers allow for the form of energy to change—and for the exchange of energy between bodies—but the total of all energy is always the same. This, in fact, is what makes energy a useful quantity.

The law of conservation of energy is broadened to the conservation of mass–energy by reference to the equation $E = mc^2$. According to this rule, developed by Albert Einstein during his work on the theory of relativity, matter is just another form of energy. Conversions between matter and energy are permitted within the law of conservation of mass–energy.

PERFORMANCE OBJECTIVES 16-4

1. **State the law of conservation of energy.**
2. **Apply the law of conservation of energy to energy conversions within a natural process.**
3. **Explain how $E = mc^2$ broadens the law of conservation of energy to include matter.**

SCIENCE TERMS 16-4

law of conservation of energy p. 382.

engine and a steam turbine are examples of external-combustion engines.

In an internal-combustion engine, the fuel is burned inside the engine. Automobile engines are examples of internal-combustion engines. In both external- and internal-combustion engines, the first energy conversion involves the change of chemical energy to heat energy. What does the next energy conversion involve? You will learn more about the two types of heat engines in Chapter 18.

SECTION REVIEW

1. Describe the conversion between potential energy and kinetic energy as a tennis ball drops, hits the ground, and bounces back up.
2. Describe the energy conversions that take place when a flashlight is turned on.
3. What energy conversions take place in combustion engines? What is the difference between an external-combustion engine and an internal-combustion engine?
4. Identify the various energy conversions involved in the following events: An object is raised and then allowed to fall. As it hits the ground, it stops, produces a sound, and becomes warmer.

382

16–4 Conservation of Energy

You have just read of many conversions of energy: kinetic and potential in the ball, heat and chemical in fuels, heat and mechanical in engines. Perhaps you have wondered if any energy is lost during such conversions. The answer is that in spite of all the changes of form, the total amount of energy remains the same.

The law of conservation (kahn-ser-VAY-shuhn) of energy states that energy can be neither created nor destroyed by ordinary means. Energy can only be converted from one form to another. So energy conversions occur without loss or gain in energy.

The law of conservation of energy is one of the foundations of scientific thought. If energy seems to disappear, then scientists look for it. Important

---

16-3 (continued)

Section Review 16-3

1. Before the ball drops, all of its energy is potential energy. As it falls, potential energy is converted into kinetic energy. When it hits the grounds, its kinetic energy is at its maximum. Then, as it bounces up, kinetic energy is converted into potential energy.

2. Chemical energy in battery is converted into electric energy, which is then converted into electromagnetic energy (light).

3. In a combustion engine, the burning of a fuel converts chemical energy to heat energy, which is then changed to mechanical energy. In an external combustion engine, the fuel is burned outside the engine. In an internal combustion engine, fuel is burned inside the engine.

4. Kinetic energy of person raising

ball is converted into the potential energy in the raised ball. As it falls, potential energy is converted to kinetic energy. As it hits the ground, mechanical energy is converted into sound energy and heat energy.

Motivation

Use an analogy to money as an introduction to the law of conservation of energy. Our country operates on money. The government has deter-

discoveries have been made because scientists believed so strongly in the conservation of energy.

One such discovery was made by Albert Einstein in 1905. Part of his famous theory of relativity dealt with the concept that mass and energy were interchangeable. Einstein expressed this concept in the form of a mathematical equation:

$$E = mc^2$$ ❷

E is energy, m is mass, and c is the speed of light. According to this equation, the energy of any mass is equal to the product of that mass and the square of the speed of light.

With this mass–energy relationship, Einstein was saying that matter is another form of energy, or that mass and energy are two forms of the same thing and can be converted into each other. With this mass–energy relationship, Einstein modified the law of conservation of energy. He showed that if some of either matter or energy is created or destroyed, the other must make up for the change. The total amount of mass and energy is conserved.

During nuclear reactions—such as those that take place in the sun—energy and mass do not seem to be conserved. But Einstein used his famous equation to show that a loss in mass results in a gain in energy. Mass is continuously changed to energy in our sun through a process called nuclear fusion. During this process, a small loss in mass produces a huge amount of energy.

SECTION REVIEW

1. What is the law of conservation of energy? How do energy conversions support this law?
2. Explain the meaning of Einstein's equation $E = mc^2$.
3. Why does even a small loss in mass result in a tremendous gain in energy?
4. During certain nuclear reactions, a high-speed electron is ejected. The energy lost by the nucleus, however, does not equal the energy of the escaping electron. From this observation, scientists concluded that another undiscovered particle must also be ejected. They searched for more than 20 years before they found it. Why did the scientists believe another particle must exist?

Figure 16–14 The huge amount of energy produced by a hydrogen bomb is evidence of Einstein's mass–energy equation. Mass and energy are two forms of the same thing and can be converted into each other. What is the mathematical expression for this famous equation? ❷

Figure 16–15 In 1905, Albert Einstein (1879–1955) made a major contribution to science with his theory of relativity. Part of this theory states that mass and energy are interchangeable. Here you see Einstein at Oxford University, England, in 1931, where he received the honorary degree of doctor of science.

383

ANNOTATION KEY

❶ Heat energy to mechanical energy (Applying concepts)
❷ $E = mc^2$ (Applying formulas)
❶ Thinking Skill: Making generalizations
❷ Thinking Skill: Applying formulas

from observations of nature, but as a tool for learning more about nature. Since we trust the law, it provides us with clues about unexplained processes in the atom, the cell, and the universe.

Section Review 16-4

1. Energy can be neither created nor destroyed by ordinary means. Energy conversions involve changes in the forms of energy. They occur without any loss or gain of energy.
2. Energy equals the mass of an object times the square of the speed of light.
3. There is a great deal of energy locked within the nucleus of an atom. When mass changes to energy, such as during fusion on the sun, huge amounts of energy that were locked within the atom are released.
4. They believed in the law of conservation of energy. (The lost energy was finally accounted for by the discovery of an antineutrino.)

mined how much money is to be in circulation. Ask the students if all of the cash can be located. Money is continually being exchanged between various individuals but some of it does get removed from circulation when it falls behind a chair cushion or into a piggy bank. The money still exists but it is not in circulation. The discussion of energy conversions suggests that energy is a lot like money; it is all there but it is always being exchanged. The

analogy can even include conversions between various world currencies. The bouncing ball shows a conversion between two forms of energy with some energy being gradually taken out of circulation as heat energy.

Content Development

Refer to the earlier examples of energy conversions when explaining that the total energy is constant. Describe the law as not merely a conclusion

LABORATORY INVESTIGATION RELATING MASS, VELOCITY, AND KINETIC ENERGY

BEFORE THE LAB

Check that your materials are compatible with each other; while the list is simple it is easy to select items that will not work well together.

1. Are your tacks long enough so that they can be pushed in firmly, yet protrude enough to hold the rubber band? Roofing nails may be a good alternate.
2. Can the tack be pushed into the board? Waferboard or cardboard may be easier to work with especially if you want to treat it as an expendable item.
3. Are your rubber bands appropriate? Do they give enough energy to the washers? If not, use two rubber bands.
4. Glue the washers in advance.

PRE-LAB DISCUSSION

Begin by asking students to develop a logical hypothesis to the problem posed. Accept all suggestions at this point. When they have completed the investigation, ask them to check their original hypotheses and to arrive at a new one if appropriate.

Now initiate a discussion as to the control and variables used in this investigation. The control is the energy stored in a rubber band pulled back a fixed amount. Steps 4, 5, and 6 set the control. The variable is the mass launched by the rubber band. The dependent variable is the distance that the mass travels given a fixed amount of energy. Each mass receives the same kinetic energy. The larger masses will have a smaller velocity and will thus travel shorter distances.

Some students may be concerned with the use of distance traveled to represent velocity. The masses are being slowed by friction. The frictional force increases with the weight of the washers, so larger masses have proportionally larger forces slowing them down, leaving the velocity squared directly related to the stopping distance.

SKILL DEVELOPMENT

Students will use the following skills while completing this investigation.

1. Safety
2. Observing
3. Relating
4. Recording
5. Measuring
6. Inferring
7. Manipulative
8. Comparing

Problem

How does a change in mass affect the velocity of an object if its kinetic energy is constant?

Materials *(per group)*

rubber band
3 thumbtacks
12 washers glued together in groups of 2, 4, and 6
wooden board, 15 cm × 100 cm
meterstick

Procedure

1. Place three thumbtacks at one end of the wooden board, as shown in the figure. Do not push the thumbtacks all the way into the board.
2. Stretch the rubber band over the three thumbtacks to form a triangle.
3. In front of the rubber band, place two washers that have been stuck together.
4. Pull the washer and rubber band back about 2 cm, as in the figure. Release the rubber band. The washers should slide about 70 to 80 cm along the board.
5. Practice step 4 until you can make the double washer travel 70 to 80 cm each time.

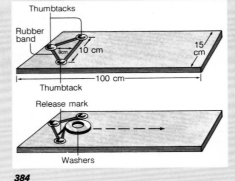

Thumbtacks
Rubber band
8cm 10 cm
15 cm
Thumbtack
100 cm
Release mark
Washers

384

6. Mark the point to which you pulled the rubber band back to obtain a distance of 70 to 80 cm. This will be your launching point for the entire experiment.
7. Launch the double washer three times. In a data table similar to the one shown here, record the distance in centimeters for each trial. Remember to use the same launching point each time.
8. Repeat step 7 for a stack of 4 washers.
9. Repeat step 7 for a stack of 6 washers.

Observations

1. Calculate the average distance traveled by 2 washers, 4 washers, and 6 washers.

Mass	Distance (cm) 1	2	3	Average Distance (cm)
2 washers				
4 washers				
6 washers				

Conclusions

1. What is the relationship between the mass, or number of washers, and the average distance traveled?
2. What kind of energy was in the washers when you held them at the launching point? How do you know?
3. After launching the washers, what kind of energy did they have?
4. You launched all the washers from the same position. Was the energy the same for each launch?
5. Assume that the farther the washers slid, the greater their initial velocity. Did the heavier group of washers move faster or slower than the lighter group?
6. If the kinetic energy is the same for each set of washers, what happens to the velocity as the mass increases?

SAFETY TIPS

The tacks may be sharp and should be counted at the end of the exercise. Keep an eye out for projectiles. While tacking the rubber bands to the boards eliminates their being fired, they could be used to launch small objects.

TEACHING STRATEGY FOR LAB PROCEDURE

In step 4 students will need to practice releasing the washers at the

CHAPTER REVIEW

SUMMARY

16–1 Nature of Energy
❏ Energy is the ability to do work.

❏ Energy appears in many forms: mechanical, heat, chemical, electromagnetic, and nuclear.

16–2 Kinetic and Potential Energy
❏ Energy stored in an object due to its position is called potential energy.

❏ Energy that a moving object has due to its motion is called kinetic energy.

❏ Kinetic energy equals one half the product of the mass times the velocity squared.

❏ Energy that is dependent on the height of an object above the earth's surface and its weight is called gravitational potential energy.

16–3 Energy Conversion
❏ Changes in the forms of energy are called energy conversions.

❏ Machines that change heat energy to mechanical energy are heat engines.

❏ In an external-combustion engine, fuel is burned outside the engine. In an internal-combustion engine, fuel is burned inside the engine.

16–4 Conservation of Energy
❏ The law of conservation of energy states that energy can be neither created nor destroyed by ordinary means.

❏ According to Einstein's equation, $E = mc^2$, matter is another form of energy.

VOCABULARY

Define each term in a complete sentence.

chemical energy	heat energy	mechanical energy
electro-magnetic energy	heat engine	nuclear energy
energy	joule	potential energy
energy conversion	kinetic energy	
gravitational potential energy	law of conservation of energy	

CONTENT REVIEW: MULTIPLE CHOICE

On a separate sheet of paper, write the letter of the answer that best completes each statement.

1. Energy is the ability to do
   a. motion.   b. power.   c. work.   d. acceleration.
2. The unit in which energy is measured is the
   a. newton.   b. joule.   c. electron.   d. dyne.
3. X-rays, lasers, and radio waves are forms of
   a. mechanical energy.   b. heat energy.
   c. electromagnetic energy.   d. nuclear energy.
4. The sun's energy source is
   a. mechanical energy.   b. electromagnetic energy.
   c. chemical energy.   d. nuclear energy.

385

---

same point. Make sure students can launch the washers so that each set of washers travels approximately the same distance.

OBSERVATIONS
1. Answers will vary, but students should note that the average distance traveled by the fewest washers will be the greatest.

CONCLUSIONS
1. The smaller the mass, the greater the distance.
2. Potential energy because they have stored energy provided by you when you moved them
3. Kinetic energy, or energy of motion
4. Yes
5. Slower
6. Decreases

GOING FURTHER: ENRICHMENT
Investigate the relationship between energy and velocity by giving one mass different amounts of energy. Ask,
• **How can you control the energy given to the mass? Where does the energy stored in the rubber band come from? Where does the energy given to the mass end up?**

CHAPTER REVIEW

MULTIPLE CHOICE

1. c   3. c   5. a   7. d   9. b
2. b   4. d   6. b   8. c   10. a

COMPLETION

1. work
2. heat
3. chemical
4. electromagnetic
5. mechanical
6. potential
7. motion
8. $m \times v^2 \div 2$
9. weight; height
10. heat-engine

TRUE OR FALSE

1. T
2. T
3. F nuclear
4. T
5. F velocity
6. F height
7. F potential
8. T
9. F mechanical
10. F law of conservation of energy

SKILL BUILDING

1. Mechanical energy is matter in motion. Sound energy is the movement of air molecules.
2. No. The bear has gravitational potential energy from the position on the ledge.
3. 500 J; 200 J; 10 J; 0 J. Graph should be a straight line.
4. Body A has less K.E. than body B. Since K.E. varies with the square of the velocity, body B will have more K.E. even though it has less mass.
5. Yes. The kinetic energy of the book was converted to heat energy.
6. Yes. The total energy was converted to heat energy due to deformation of the ball.
7. Jack and Jill have the same G.P.E. Both their masses and height were the same. The path has no effect on the energy gained or lost.
8. A. No P.E., no K.E.; B. Maximum P.E., no K.E.; C. Maximum K.E., no P.E.; D. Maximum P.E., no K.E.; E. No P.E., no K.E.

ESSAY

1. Answers will vary, but may include: automobile traveling along road, fast-moving bullet, any falling object, any ball being thrown or rolled, flowing water.
2. Kinetic energy is the energy an object has because of its motion. Potential energy is the stored energy of position.
3. Before: maximum K.E., minimum P.E.; During: maximum P.E., minimum K.E.; After: maximum K.E., minimum P.E.
4. A person bouncing on a trampoline has kinetic energy when actually moving up or down. However, at the very top of the bounce when at a momentary standstill, the person has potential energy.
5. Energy is constantly converted from one form to another, such as electric energy to heat energy in a hair dryer. However, due to the law of conservation of energy, no energy is lost or gained during such energy conversions.
6. Heat energy is converted to mechanical energy, which is converted to electromagnetic energy.

---

5. A stretched rubber band has
   a. potential energy.   b. kinetic energy.
   c. mechanical energy.   d. electromagnetic energy.
6. Energy of motion is
   a. potential energy.   b. kinetic energy.
   c. electromagnetic energy.   d. nuclear energy.
7. A 1900-kg ship traveling at 40 km/hr has kinetic energy equal to
   a. $\dfrac{1900 \times 40}{2}$.   b. $\dfrac{1900^2 \times 40}{2}$.   c. 1900×40^2.   d. $\dfrac{1900 \times 40^2}{2}$.
8. Gravitational potential energy is dependent on
   a. speed and height.   b. time and weight.
   c. weight and height.   d. acceleration and kinetic energy.
9. The energy conversions involved in heat engines are
   a. electromagnetic—mechanical—heat   b. chemical—heat—mechanical
   c. chemical—electromagnetic—heat   d. mechanical—chemical—heat
10. According to Einstein, matter is another form of
    a. energy.   b. mass.   c. time.   d. light.

CONTENT REVIEW: COMPLETION

On a separate sheet of paper, write the word or words that best complete each statement.

1. Energy is the ability to do _____.
2. The internal motion of molecules in matter is _____ energy.
3. The energy that bonds atoms or ions together is _____ energy.
4. Light is _____ energy.
5. Sound is _____ energy.
6. Energy stored in an object due to its position is called _____ energy.
7. Kinetic energy is energy of _____.
8. The equation for calculating kinetic energy is K.E. = _____.
9. Gravitational potential energy is dependent on both the _____ and _____ of an object.
10. A (An) _____ engine is a machine that changes heat energy to mechanical energy.

CONTENT REVIEW: TRUE OR FALSE

Determine whether each statement is true or false. Then on a separate sheet of paper, write "true" if it is true. If it is false, change the underlined word or words to make the statement true.

1. Energy is the ability to do <u>work</u>.
2. Gunpowder contains <u>chemical</u> energy.
3. The most concentrated form of energy is <u>mechanical</u> energy.
4. <u>Kinetic</u> energy is energy of motion.
5. In the determination of an object's kinetic energy, its <u>mass</u> has the greatest effect.
6. Gravitational potential energy depends on weight and <u>time</u>.
7. At the top of its arc, a pendulum has maximum <u>kinetic</u> energy.
8. In an external-combustion engine, the fuel is burned <u>outside</u> the engine.
9. A car engine converts chemical energy to <u>electromagnetic</u> energy.
10. Energy is neither created nor destroyed according to the <u>law of combination of matter</u>.

Use the skills you have developed in the chapter to complete each activity.

1. **Applying concepts** Sound is produced by vibrations in a medium such as air. The particles of air are first pushed together and then pulled apart. Why is sound considered a form of mechanical energy?

2. **Relating concepts** A bear in a zoo lies sleeping on a ledge. A visitor comments: "Look at that lazy bear. It has no energy at all." Do you agree? Explain your answer.

3. **Making calculations and graphs** The gravitational potential energy of a rock at 100 m is 1000 J. What is the G.P.E. at 50 m? At 20 m? At 1 m? At 0 m? Make a graph of height versus energy. What is the shape of your graph?

4. **Making comparisons** Body A has twice the mass of body B. Body B is moving twice as fast as body A. Is the kinetic energy of body A less than, equal to, or greater than body B? Explain your answer.

5. **Applying concepts** A book sliding across a desk loses all its kinetic energy and comes to rest. The book feels slightly warm. Was energy conserved? Explain your answer.

6. **Relating concepts** As a tennis ball bounces, there is a continuous conversion between kinetic and potential energy. But each bounce is lower than the previous bounce. Eventually, both the kinetic and potential energies of the ball disappear completely. Is energy conserved? Explain your answer.

7. **Applying concepts** Two cyclists are riding their bikes up a steep hill. Jill rides her bike straight up the hill. Jack rides his bike up the hill in a zigzag formation to conserve energy. Jack and Jill have identical masses. At the top of the hill does Jack have less gravitational potential energy than Jill? Explain your answer.

8. **Identifying relationships** The diagram below shows a golfer in various stages of her swing. Compare the kinetic and potential energies of the golf club at each labeled point in the complete golf swing.

Discuss each of the following in a brief paragraph.

1. List five examples of mechanical energy.
2. Compare kinetic and potential energy.
3. Describe the changes in potential and kinetic energy of a tennis ball just before, during, and just after you hit it back to your opponent with your tennis racket.
4. How does bouncing on a trampoline illustrate kinetic and potential energies?
5. Explain the following statement: "Energy can always be converted to a different form, but it is never lost."
6. Water is boiled. The resulting steam is blown against huge turbine blades. The turning blades spin in a magnetic field, producing electricity. Describe, in order, the energy conversions.

387

ADDITIONAL QUESTIONS AND TOPIC SUGGESTIONS

1. The earth travels around the sun in an elliptical orbit. The potential energy of the earth relative to the sun increases as the earth moves away from the sun. According to the law of conservation of energy, does the earth have a greater speed when it is closest or furthest from the sun?

2. Does the law of conservation of energy apply to people's bodies? The energy we require to live comes from the food that we eat. So does the energy we need to do work on things around us. What happens if a person's energy input exceeds his energy output?

3. Perpetual motion machines are said to operate forever without any additional input of energy after you get them started. Could a perpetual motion machine be used to do useful work?

4. If the law of conservation of energy means that you can't get something for nothing, why do we use simple machines?

ISSUES IN SCIENCE

The following issues can be used as a springboard for class debate, or they can be assigned as a writing homework.
1. If the law of conservation of energy is a natural law, why should we encourage people to conserve energy?
2. The sun is our ultimate source of energy. Could life on earth continue without the sun? Predict what life would be like without the sun.

Unit Four

MOTION, FORCES, AND ENERGY

ADVENTURES IN SCIENCE: DICK RUTAN AND JEANA YEAGER: MAKING AVIATION HISTORY

BACKGROUND INFORMATION

Burt Rutan's career as a designer of aircraft has a rather amusing origin. As a child, Dick Rutan liked to build model airplanes. Younger brother Burt wanted to play with the models, but Dick would not let him. So Burt decided to build his own models, and they were better than Dick's. Later on, Dick became a pilot, and Burt, the supreme model builder, became a highly innovative airplane designer.

The *Voyager* was built by a small crew of mechanics in Burt Rutan's shop in the Mojave Desert. As with most creative projects, the people involved had to work long hours—such long hours, in fact, that Rutan installed showers and laundry facilities in the shop so the staff would not have to go home!

Adventures in Science

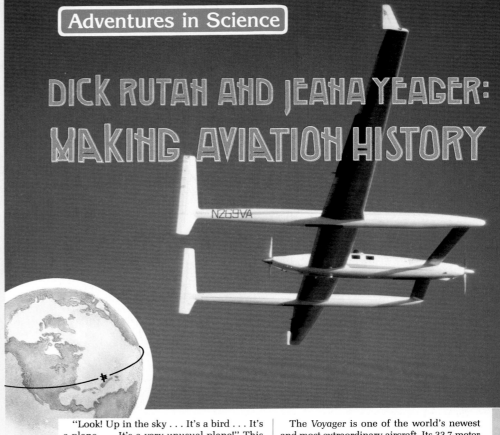

DICK RUTAN AND JEANA YEAGER: MAKING AVIATION HISTORY

"Look! Up in the sky . . . It's a bird . . . It's a plane . . . It's a very unusual plane!" This airplane, named the *Voyager*, does not look like any conventional aircraft. Its long, narrow wings are tipped with tiny upright "winglets." An extra wing streams out on either side of its nose. Two narrow fuel-filled booms suspended along either side of its body complete its design.

The *Voyager* is one of the world's newest and most extraordinary aircraft. Its 33.7-meter wingspan is greater than that of a Boeing 727. But its mass is only 8427 kilograms—just about half the mass of a small car. And although this remarkable aircraft is designed to carry up to five times its weight, it has room for only two people. But that's no surprise. For that is exactly how the *Voyager* was designed.

388

TEACHING STRATEGY

Motivation
Begin by asking students,
• **What do you think it takes to break a record—to do something better than anyone else has ever done it?** (Answers will vary. Possible answers include perseverance, skill, talent, confidence, and luck.)
• **Have you ever broken a record or won a prize for being the best at**

something? (Although it is unlikely that any have set world records, some students may have set local records in sports, performing arts, or scholastic competitions—and most have probably won races and prizes of some type.)

Encourage students to share their experiences of working to be best at something—whether they succeeded in breaking a record or not. Point out that the story they are about to read is

that of a man and woman who have broken the record for nonstop flying.

Content Development
According to Newton's second law, F = ma, the force needed to accelerate an object is directly proportional to the mass of the object. It is this law that explains why the lightweight *Voyager* needs only a fraction of the fuel required by a normal airplane.

Burt Rutan, the plane's designer, built the *Voyager* with two particular people in mind: his brother, pilot Dick Rutan, and co-pilot Jeana Yeager. Dick and Burt Rutan have been flying airplanes since they were teenagers in Dinuba, California. Dick went on to become a fighter pilot and Burt became a designer of small innovative airplanes.

When Dick returned from a tour of duty in Vietnam, he met engineer and race pilot Jeana Yeager. A spirited Texan, Yeager had grown up training horses and sky diving. Dick introduced her to the strange planes his brother had built. Soon she began breaking speed records flying them! In their quest for aviation challenges, Dick and Jeana decided to attempt a nonstop flight around the world. Burt Rutan accepted the challenge to build a plane that could make the 40,000-kilometer trip without stopping.

The *Voyager* is constructed from high-technology materials that may one day be adapted for commercial planes. Honeycombed paper is sandwiched between lightweight plastic-reinforced fibers. The combination is stronger than steel but weighs only about one-fifth as much.

The *Voyager*'s light weight allows the plane to use a fraction of the fuel a normal aircraft consumes. And that is the key to the Voyager's ability to circle the globe without stopping to refuel. According to Jeana Yeager, flying in the *Voyager* is like riding on the back of an eagle.

The *Voyager* is stable but difficult to fly. And although the plane is sleek, it is not very luxurious. Its tiny cabin has one small bunk. So one pilot can sleep while the other flies. "It is like a little cocoon home," Dick Rutan once commented.

The *Voyager* broke its first long-distance record in July 1986. Dick and Jeana flew their strange craft a distance of 18,665 kilometers without landing or refueling. Because the

For nine days, Jeana Yeager and Dick Rutan piloted their revolutionary plane *Voyager* from a tiny cockpit no larger than a telephone booth.

Voyager travels at only 130 to 160 kilometers per hour, the flight lasted nearly five days. During the flight, the pilots were treated to a spectacular view of the earth below, since the plane rarely cruises at altitudes greater than 4500 meters. Its second record-breaking flight ended on December 23, 1986, when the *Voyager* completed its nonstop trip around the world.

In addition to flying the plane and keeping it on course, the pilot on duty must keep careful track of the 5675 liters of fuel on board. The fuel is stored in fifteen different tanks inside the *Voyager*'s booms and body. As the fuel is used the remainder must be constantly shifted around to keep the plane properly balanced.

During *Voyager*'s grueling flights, for which the pilots prepare at least one month in advance, Dick and Jeana cooperate by sharing responsibility. This feeling of cooperation—combined with a love of flying, a spirit of adventure, and a dedication to science—is helping this threesome make aviation history.

389

ADDITIONAL QUESTIONS AND TOPIC SUGGESTIONS

1. Why is the *Voyager*'s fuel not stored all in one tank? (The weight of the fuel in one tank would cause the plane to become unbalanced.)
2. Would storing fuel in many tanks be as important in a regular commercial plane? Why or why not? (No. The weight of the fuel would be slight compared to the weight of the entire plane.)
3. Can you explain why small cars are more economical than larger cars? (Small, light cars require less fuel than larger, more massive cars; thus they cost less money to run.)

CRITICAL THINKING QUESTIONS

1. What disadvantages might the *Voyager* have in bad weather? (Such a lightweight plane would be buffeted about by wind more easily than a heavier plane. Also, it is possible that the effects of moisture and cold might have a greater effect on the *Voyager* than on a plane made of aluminum or steel.)
2. What contributions do you think Dick and Jeana can make to science and technology? (Answers will vary.)

Write the equation for Newton's law on the chalkboard, then ask,
• **What does it take to make an object move?** (force)
• **In an airplane, what supplies this force?** (an engine powered by fuel)
• **Do you think it would take more force to move a heavy plane or a light plane?** (a heavy plane)
• **Can you relate what you have just said to the equation on the chalkboard?** (The force needed to acceler- ate, or move, an object is directly proportional to the mass of the object.)

Unit Four

MOTION, FORCES, AND ENERGY

ISSUES IN SCIENCE: ROBOTS: DO THEY SIGNAL UNEMPLOYMENT OR AUTOMATION?

BACKGROUND INFORMATION

Many experts feel that the alternative to modernizing certain industries with robots is the collapse of the industry altogether for failing to keep pace with modern technology. Thus the ultimate loss of jobs could be far worse than the loss of jobs due to robots.

Japan uses robots more extensively in factories than the United States does. In many product areas, Japanese industries are hurting American industries by producing better products more cheaply.

Skilled machinists who have not lost their jobs to robots have complained that their jobs have become far less interesting and creative since the robots arrived. They complain that they are merely "baby sitters" for the machines. Skilled machinists also claim that the pace of their work has been thrown off by the robots—"I'm not a machine," grumbled one worker; the robot makes the pace of the work too fast, too erratic.

Some factories that have become automized by robots spend one-third of their time "down" because of glitches in the computerized robots—glitches that have to be fixed by skilled human beings.

So far, robots are quite limited in what they can do, compared to a human. One expert commented that making an "intelligent robot" is much harder than one might think; that what looks simple for a human to do is far from simple when one tries to program it into a robot's computer-brain. Right now, the thing many makers of robots are eager to do is invent a robot that can see.

Issues in Science

ROBOTS: DO THEY SIGNAL AUTOMATION OR UNEMPLOYMENT?

Sparks fly as a worker welds parts to an automobile body. Farther down the assembly line, another worker trims and grinds the weld joints. Beyond that, still another worker sprays paint on the car.

Up and down the assembly line, not a word is spoken as the workers perform their tasks. The workers do not pause, yawn, blink, or look at each other. "That's just not human," you might say. And you would be right. For these workers are robots!

Robots are becoming more and more common in assembly-line jobs. Dr. Harley Shaiken of the Massachusetts Institute of Technology has predicted that 32,000 robots may one day replace 100,000 automobile-industry workers. Is this prediction likely to come true?

ROBOT REVOLUTION

Already, more than 6000 robots are used in factories all over the United States. Every day more are being put to work. Several fully automated factories are now being tested. In such factories, all of the production and assembly is done by machines. One result of this "robot revolution" is increased unemployment in industrial regions. Workers in these areas are demanding that industry leaders slow down the switch to robots.

But, as many company executives point out, robots often perform jobs that are boring and repetitive, as well as jobs that may be hazardous to humans. For example, a robot may paint many thousands of cars and not be affected by inhaling paint fumes that may be dangerous for a human worker to inhale.

390

TEACHING STRATEGY

Motivation

Ask students to make a list of the various tasks they might perform in a typical hour of a typical school day. Be sure they include minor tasks such as sharpening a pencil, taking paper out of their notebooks, opening a book. Then ask,
• **How many of these tasks do you think could be performed just as well by a machine?** (Answers will vary.) Have students speculate as to how a machine might be "programmed" to do some of these things.

Other company executives point out that they must either use robots or lose business to companies that do. As Thomas B. Gunn of the Arthur D. Little Company puts it, "Are you going to reduce your work force by 25 percent by putting in robots, or by 100 percent by going out of business?" And James Baker of the General Electric Corporation puts it this way: "U.S. business has three choices in the 80s . . . automate, emigrate [leave], or evaporate [go out of business]."

NEW JOBS OR FEW JOBS?

Some industry experts believe that robots and computer systems will create many new jobs. "In the past," George Brosseau of the National Science Foundation explains, "whenever a new technology has been introduced, it has always generated more jobs than it has displaced. But we don't know whether that's true of robot technology. There's no question but that new jobs will be created, but will there be enough to offset the loss?" he adds.

James S. Albut of the U.S. National Bureau of Standards thinks so. "Robots can improve productivity and create many new jobs," he has written.

Others reply that although using robots may create more jobs in the long run, they cause job losses first. These people stress that it is up to government, business, and labor to teach people new skills and to find new jobs for workers who have been replaced by robots. Such efforts will ease some of the strain that accompanies the implementation of new and valuable technology.

Do you think United States companies should rapidly move ahead with the development and use of robots even at the risk of some unemployment and worker hardship? Or should the switch from human power to robot power be done slowly in order to lessen the impact on workers?

391

Content Development

Explain to students that a robot is a computerized machine designed to perform various tasks that humans perform. Point out that the use of robots in factories has created a lot of controversy because robots have taken over jobs that human beings were once paid to do.

ADDITIONAL QUESTIONS AND TOPIC SUGGESTIONS

1. Why are robots especially suited to assembly-line work? (In an assembly line, they perform the same task over and over again; thus the same set of instructions keeps them going indefinitely.)

2. According to the article, in what ways could the factory worker's life on the job become better because of robots? (Robots can take over tasks that are dangerous or unpleasant for humans to perform, thus making the worker's life safer and more enjoyable.)

CRITICAL THINKING QUESTIONS

1. One factory supervisor complained that a robot programmed to weld parts would keep right on welding even if no part was coming down the assembly line. What limitation of robots does this point out? (Robots cannot see or think. They can only carry out by rote the instructions they have been given. They cannot "reason" the way humans can.)

2. In what ways might factory managers make use of robots but at the same time not eliminate human beings from the payroll? (Answers will vary.)

CLASS DEBATE

Have students debate this issue by choosing one of the following statements to support:

(1) "Using robots is a perfect example of how business and technology have no sense of moral obligation. Progress at any price, they say. It's time somebody put people before progress."

(2) "Every technological advance has met with criticism from people who found it threatening—then those same people end up benefiting from the better life that technology provides. Where would we be today if someone had said to Tom Edison, 'You'd better slow down on those light bulbs—what will happen to the poor people who make lamp oil?'"

Unit Five
HEAT ENERGY

UNIT OVERVIEW

In Unit Five, students are introduced to heat as a form of energy. They learn about the nature of temperature as a measure of the kinetic energy of molecules. They also learn to measure heat and to relate heat transfer to phase changes. Next, they explore thermal expansion and its applications. They then study the relationships between internal energy, work, and heat.

Practical applications of heat are studied next. These include use of the principles of heat energy in heating systems, insulation, cooling systems, and heat engines.

UNIT OBJECTIVES

1. **Define temperature and contrast it with heat.**
2. **Describe the three kinds of heat transfer.**
3. **Explain thermal expansion and describe some of its practical applications.**
4. **Contrast various types of central heating systems.**
5. **Describe the practical applications of heat energy in insulation, cooling systems, and heat engines, and discuss the effects of thermal pollution.**

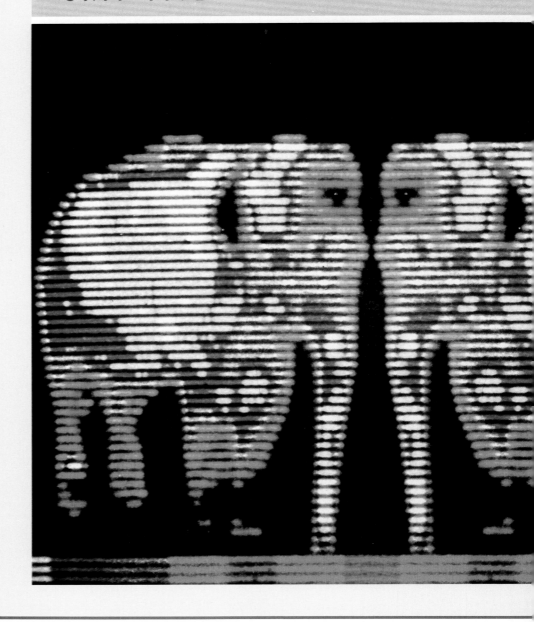

INTRODUCING UNIT FIVE

Begin your teaching of the unit by having students examine the unit-opening photograph, which shows a thermogram of two elephants. The thermogram is essentially a color-coded infrared photograph. Almost any color coding can be used. In the photograph shown, the lowest-temperature areas appear blue and the highest-temperature areas appear yellow. You may wish to ask students the following questions regarding this photograph.

• **Exactly what is it that exposes the photographic film that produces the thermogram?** (Invisible, low-frequency light called infrared light exposes the film.)
• **What is the relationship between the hotness of an object and the amount of infrared light it gives off?** (In general, the higher the temperature of the object, the more infrared light it gives off.)
• **Which parts of the elephants are coolest? Which parts are hottest?** (The blue areas are coolest; the yellow areas are hottest.)

Now have students read the unit introduction. This material should serve as the basis for various discussions that will better motivate students to study the chapters that follow.

Heat Energy

Would a technique that enabled doctors to diagnose illnesses without surgery, drugs, or harmful radiation be useful? Yes, thought Lloyd Williams and Maxwell Cade. And they knew just the method that would do it—thermography. Thermography uses the heat given off by an object to produce an image on film. The image is called a thermogram. Thermography is based on the fact that all objects, including humans, give off heat energy.

At Middlesex Hospital, London, Williams and Cade worked out the design for their Pyroscan Thermographic Camera—a camera that can photograph the patterns of heat given off from skin. The infrared camera they developed is so sensitive to heat that it can record temperature differences of only one or two degrees Celsius. Variations from normal patterns of heat emission can be used to diagnose various diseases. For example, cancerous tumors are hotter than normal body tissue. So such tumors show up on a thermogram as red areas. Arthritic joints, on the other hand, are colder and appear blue in a thermogram.

Doctors now use thermography as a painless and harmless means of diagnosing certain illnesses. The Pyroscan Thermographic Camera is an important example of the way heat is being used to make human life better and more enjoyable. By reading the chapters in this unit, you will develop a larger picture of heat energy and its many applications to everyday life.

CHAPTERS

17 Heat

18 Uses of Heat

Thermography is an important application of heat energy. This thermograph of two elephants shows the relative temperature of the elephants' skin. The hottest areas are yellow and the coolest are blue.   **393**

CHAPTER DESCRIPTIONS

17 Heat Chapter 17 deals with the nature of heat as a form of energy. Temperature is defined and the measurement of heat is explained. Heat transfer is related to phase changes. Thermal expansion is explained and its practical applications are described. Finally, internal energy, work, and heat are related.

18 Uses of Heat In Chapter 18, practical applications of heat are described. Central heating systems are contrasted. Uses of insulating materials are discussed, as are cooling systems and heat engines. Finally, the effects of thermal pollution on the environment are discussed.

• **Can you think of any dangers or disadvantages connected with the use of thermograms?** (There are no obvious dangers. Students may point out the problem of possible error or misdiagnosis, however.)

• **What nonmedical practical uses of thermogramlike infrared photography can you think of?** (Answers will vary. Some students may suggest uses in detecting areas of heat loss in buildings or in determining characteristics of different areas of the earth by means of aerial or satellite photograph.)

• **Thermograms indirectly measure temperature. Do you think that temperature and heat are the same thing?** (Answers will vary. In fact, the two quantities, although related, are different. Heat, as students will learn, is a measure of the total amount of a certain kind of energy stored in objects. Temperature is a measure of the average kinetic energy of translation of molecules.)

Chapter 17

HEAT

CHAPTER OVERVIEW

Many years ago scientists found that when work was being done on a substance, heat was produced. They also found that heat could be transferred from one substance to another. Their studies proved that heat was a form of energy. This energy was caused by the movement of molecules within the substance. This energy of motion is called kinetic energy.

When heat energy is added to a substance, the molecules move faster. When heat energy is removed from a substance, the molecules move slower. When molecules are heated, their kinetic energy increases. The faster the molecules are moving in a substance, the higher the temperature. Temperature is related to heat, but heat is not the same as temperature. Heat is a form of energy. Temperature is a measure of the average kinetic energy of the molecules in a substance.

When most substances are heated they expand. At certain temperatures substances can change phase from a solid to a liquid and then to a gas. Energy is used or given off during phase changes.

INTRODUCING CHAPTER 17

Have students observe the photograph. Point out the deep cracks in the earth's surface. Read the caption. Explain to students that most of the sun's energy strikes the earth's surface. The earth absorbs this energy and changes it to heat. Scientists have observed and recorded changes caused by heat for many centuries. At one time they thought heat flowed from place to place. Heat was thought to be an invisible weightless fluid called caloric. The theory was that heat or caloric was produced when a substance burned, and it could be transferred from one substance to another. Scientists observed that when heat was present, there was a temperature increase. Ask,
• **What do you think the temperature might be in the place in the picture?** (Accept all logical answers.)

Point out to students that high temperatures are the result of heat.
• **Have you ever been in a place that was very hot?** (Most students will respond that they have been in such a place.) Lead students into discussing the temperatures in the various places. Encourage students to discuss the vegetation in the hot places they have been.
• **What might have caused these higher temperatures?** (Accept all log-

Heat

17

CHAPTER OBJECTIVES

After completing this chapter, you will be able to

17–1 Explain how scientists discovered that heat is a form of energy.

17–2 Define temperature in terms of the kinetic energy of molecules.

17–3 Describe how heat can be measured indirectly by measuring temperature changes.

17–4 Explain how a transfer of heat energy brings about a phase change.

17–5 Explain why thermal expansion occurs.

17–5 Describe some practical applications of thermal expansion.

17–6 Relate internal energy, work, and heat.

The deep cracks in the dry, parched mud are evidence of the tremendous heat certain places, such as this Arizona canyon, experience.

395

On September 13, 1922, the temperature in El Azizia, Libya, reached 58°C—the highest temperature ever recorded on Earth! Second to this record-breaking figure was the highest temperature ever recorded in the United States. On July 10, 1913, the temperature in Death Valley, California, soared to 57°C.

Do these temperatures sound extremely hot to you? Probably so. Yet they are bone-chillingly cold compared to the temperatures experienced in some parts of the solar system. Daytime highs on the planet Mercury, for example, often reach 427°C. Temperatures on Venus are even higher. And on the surface of the sun, the average temperature is 6000°C—more than one hundred times hotter than the hottest day on Earth!

High temperatures, of course, are the result of heat. But what exactly is heat? Where does it come from? And how does it move from one place to another? Scientists who pondered these questions hundreds of years ago thought that heat was a mysterious fluid that could flow from one object to another. In this chapter, you will find out whether these scientists were correct, as well as the answers to other questions about the nature of heat.

TEACHER DEMONSTRATION

Fill a flask with cold water. Add a few drops of food coloring. Use safety gloves to insert a glass tube into a cork or rubber stopper. Press the cork into the top of the flask. The water should rise in the tube. Put a piece of tape around the tube to mark the top of the water. Discuss the demonstration.

• **What do you think will happen if heat is added to the flask?** (Some students may predict "nothing" and others may say that the water will rise in the tube.)
• **What might cause the water to rise in the tube?** (The water should expand as it is heated.)

Place a Bunsen burner or hot plate under the flask.

• **What happened?** (The water moved up the tube.)
• **Why did the water move up the tube?** (Accept all logical answers. Students might say that the heat caused the water molecules to move faster, move farther apart, and expand the liquid.)

Mark the new level of the water. Point out that when water is heated, the kinetic energy increases and expands the liquid. The demonstration illustrated a water thermometer. Temperature is measured with a thermometer. When the liquid in a thermometer becomes hotter, it rises up the tube.

TEACHER RESOURCES
Audiovisuals
Chemical Change and Temperature, 16 mm film, BFA
Heat and How We Use It, 16 mm film, EBE
Heat and Temperature, 16 mm film, Cor
Hot and Cold, 5 filmstrips, EBE

Books
Chapman, Alan J., *Heat Transfer,* 3rd ed, Macmillan
Chauliaquet, Charles et. al., *Solar Energy in Building,* Wiley
Cornwell, Keith, *The Flow of Heat,* Van Nostrand Reinhold
Parker, Philip, *Heat,* Heinemann

Software
Kinetic and Potential Energy, Prentice-Hall

ical answers.) Point out to students that physical scientists study the effects and relationship of heat and temperature on all matter.

17-1 HEAT: A FORM OF ENERGY

SECTION PREVIEW 17-1

Heat is a form of energy, and energy has the ability to do work. Count Rumford concluded that heat was produced when work was done. Therefore, energy and heat were related. He predicted that heat must be a form of energy. Later James Prescott Joule performed a series of experiments that supported the theory that motion was related to heat in the form of energy. Scientists finally concluded that the motion of molecules in matter is a result of heat energy. Heat energy is transferred in three ways: by conduction, by convection, and by radiation. Objects gain or lose heat by one or more of these three ways.

PERFORMANCE OBJECTIVES 17-1

1. **Explain how scientists discovered that heat is a form of energy.**
2. **Describe how heat energy causes molecules to move.**
3. **List examples of heat energy transfer by conduction, convection, and radiation.**

SCIENCE TERMS 17-1

heat transfer p. 397
conduction p. 397
heat conductor p. 398
insulator p. 398
convection p. 398
radiation p. 399

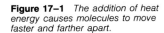

Sharpen Your Skills

The Discoveries of Rumford and Joule

The work of Count Rumford and James Prescott Joule illustrates the importance of observation and experimentation. Using books and reference materials in the library, find out more about these two scientists, their experiments, and the contributions they made toward the understanding of heat.

17-1 Heat: A Form of Energy

Have you ever toasted marshmallows over an open fire? If so, you know that the fire gives off heat. Perhaps you think that heat is some kind of substance flowing from the fire, through the air, and onto your marshmallow. Actually, that is what many eighteenth-century scientists believed. They thought that heat was an invisible, weightless fluid capable of flowing from hotter objects to colder ones. They called this substance *caloric*.

In 1798, the American scientist Benjamin Thompson, better known as Count Rumford, challenged the caloric theory. Rumford had noticed that when holes were drilled in cannon barrels, heat was produced. He devised an experiment in which he could test this observation. Holes were drilled in a cannon barrel that had been placed in a box full of water. After several hours of drilling, the water ❶ began to boil. The water boiled as long as the drilling continued. Rumford concluded that it was the drilling, not a flow of caloric, that was producing heat. Since drilling represented work being done, and energy was the ability to do work, then energy and heat must be related. Rumford concluded that heat must be a form of energy.

Molecules and Motion

Forty years after Count Rumford's experiment, British scientist James Prescott Joule investigated

Figure 17-1 *The addition of heat energy causes molecules to move faster and farther apart.*

396

TEACHING STRATEGY 17-1

Motivation

Have students observe Figure 17-1. Point out that the molecules in the jar surrounded by ice are moving *slower* than the molecules in the jar surrounded by heat. Or, the molecules in the jar surrounded by heat are moving *faster* than the molecules in the jar surrounded by ice.

Explain that if we add heat energy to a liquid, the liquid becomes a gas. The added heat energy makes the molecules in the liquid move faster and faster until the molecules are moving so fast and are so far apart that the liquid has become a gas.

Content Development

Explain that if we add heat energy to a solid, the solid becomes a liquid. The added heat energy makes the mole-

cules of the solid matter move faster and faster. Finally, molecules move very fast and spread farther. If enough heat is added, the molecules can break away from the solid matter and move about freely as in a liquid.

Skills Development

Skill: Classifying matter

• **What are some solids that we heat to make the molecules move fast enough to become a liquid?** (Students

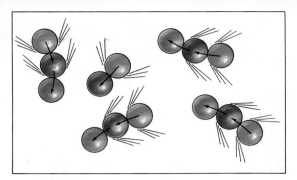

Figure 17–2 *Heat transfer by conduction involves the direct contact of molecules. As fast-moving warmer molecules collide with slow-moving cooler molecules, heat energy is transferred from the warmer to the cooler molecules. In what phases of matter can conduction take place?* ❶

the relationship between heat and motion. He performed a series of experiments that supported the idea that objects in motion produce heat. The amount of heat produced depends on the amount of motion. You have probably noticed this effect in everyday life. For example, rubbing your hands together rapidly makes them feel warmer. Sliding too ❷ quickly down a rope can produce a "rope burn." These examples show how motion produces heat.

Scientists working at the time of Joule knew that energy is needed to produce motion. They also knew that matter is made of tiny particles called molecules. Using these facts and the experiments of Rumford and Joule, scientists concluded correctly that heat is a form of energy, and that it must somehow be related to the motion of molecules.

Heat Transfer

If you hold an ice cube in your hand for several seconds, you will notice that your hand begins to ❸ feel cold and the ice cube begins to melt. You might think that cold is being transferred from the ice cube to your hand. But there is no such thing as "coldness." Cold is simply the absence of heat. The ice cube in your hand is melting because heat is being transferred from your hand to the ice cube.

The movement of heat from a warmer object to a colder one is called **heat transfer.** There are three methods of heat transfer. **Heat energy is transferred by conduction, convection, and radiation.**

CONDUCTION In **conduction** (kuhn-DUHK-shuhn), heat is transferred through a substance, or from

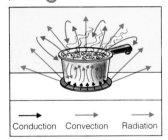

Figure 17–3 *The pot of boiling water illustrates the three methods of heat transfer—conduction (black arrows), convection (red arrows), and radiation (blue arrows). Why is the handle of the pot made of plastic?* ❷

Conduction   Convection   Radiation

molecules (the students) were to start moving? (Accept all logical answers. Students might suggest that they would "bump" against each other.)

Tell the students to move slowly and "push" against each other. Point out that as they move and "push" against each other, they are doing work. Work can only be done when energy is used.

• **If you increased your movement, what would happen?** (Some students might suggest they would get "pushed" out of the matter.)

Reinforcement

Have the students make a list of common examples of heat energy in their everyday life. They may list examples such as melting ice, thawing frozen food, boiling potatoes, cooking noodles, grilling hamburgers, toasting marshmallows, and making hot chocolate.

might be reluctant to predict, but lead them to think of common things such as butter and wax.)

Content Development

Explain that the addition of heat energy causes molecules to move faster and farther apart. The motion of molecules can also produce heat energy. Heat energy warms our houses, cooks our food, and runs our machines.

Skills Development

Skill: Developing a model
Divide the class into two groups—one group of boys and one group of girls. Have the student in each group stand as close together as possible, without holding hands or touching.

Explain that the group represents solid matter. Point out that each student in a group represents one molecule of solid matter. Ask,

• **What would happen if all of the**

ANNOTATION KEY

❶ The sun's heat energy reaches the earth
  by radiation. (Applying concepts)
❷ Plastic is an insulator. (Inferring)
❶ Thinking Skill: Applying technology
❷ Thinking Skill: Relating concepts

17-1 (continued)

Content Development

Explain to students that heat can
travel in three ways: by conduction, by
convection and by radiation.

Point out that when heat travels
by conduction, the heat energy has
been passed, or conducted, from molecule to molecule within the matter.
Conduction is the process where energy is moved from molecule to molecule by bumping or colliding. Explain
that some matter or materials conduct
heat better than others. Ask,

• **When do we want to use a good
conductor of heat?** (Accept all logical
answers. Some students might suggest
that cookware needs to be a good heat
conductor.)

Explain that in good heat conductors the molecules are very close together and transfer the heat energy
very quickly. If matter or a material
does not conduct heat very well, we
call it an insulator. In insulators the
molecules are farther apart and do
not conduct heat energy very easily.

Figure 17–4 *Heat transfer by
convection involves the motion of
molecules in currents in liquids
and gases. Heated molecules
speed up and spread out, causing
the warmer part of the liquid or
gas to become less dense than
the cooler part. The heated portion
rises, creating currents that carry
heat (left). Convection currents
near the surface of the earth
produce the distortion of objects
seen in this photograph (right).*

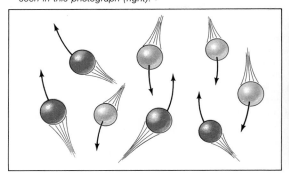

• **What are some good heat insulators?** (Accept all logical answers.
Lead the students into suggesting the
wood of pan handles, rubber used in
wet suits, wool or polyesters in quilts,
and air used in a vacuum bottle.)

Reinforcement

Gather 10 to 12 items for each student
group. Items might include a piece of
wood, a sock, an oven mitt, a hat, a
piece of heavy plastic, plastic tubing,

one substance to another, by the direct contact of
molecules. All molecules are constantly in motion.
Because they have more energy, warmer molecules
are moving faster than cooler ones.

When fast-moving warmer molecules collide with
slow-moving cooler molecules, energy is transferred
from the warmer molecules to the cooler molecules.
Now these molecules have enough energy to collide
with other slow-moving molecules. The process is
repeated over and over again. Conduction can take
place in solids, liquids, and gases because these
three phases of matter are made of molecules.

Some substances conduct heat more effectively
than other substances. These substances are called
good **heat conductors.** Silver and copper are excellent heat conductors. Copper is a popular choice for
❶ cookware because it conducts heat easily.

Substances that do not conduct heat easily are
called **insulators.** Glass, wood, plastic, and rubber
are examples of good insulating materials. Wood
and plastic handles, for example, are often used on
pots and pans. The heat from the pot or pan is not
easily conducted into your hand!

CONVECTION Heat transfer by **convection** (kuhn-
VEHK-shuhn) takes place in liquids and gases as molecules move in currents. These currents are caused
when molecules in the heated portion of a liquid or
gas speed up. As they speed up, the molecules start
to spread out. The warmer part of the liquid or gas
becomes less dense than the cooler part. That is, the
molecules in the heated part of the liquid or gas are
less closely packed. Because it is less dense than the

rubber gloves, cork tile, polyester
quilt, copper wire, iron nail, something silver, or a piece of lead.

Divide the class into groups of
four to six students. Have the groups
identify the item as a conductor or an
insulator. Students should predict that
the insulators are wood, sock, oven
mitt, hat, plastic, rubber, cork, and
polyester. Students should predict
that the conductors are copper, silver,
lead, and nail.

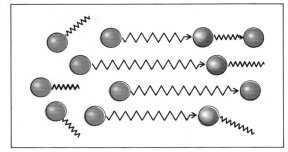

Figure 17–5 *Radiation is the transfer of heat energy in the form of invisible infrared rays. How is radiation related to the heating of the earth?* ●1

surrounding liquid or gas, the heated portion rises, creating currents that carry heat.

As warm air near the surface of the earth is heated, it becomes less dense and tends to rise. Because cooler air is denser than warmer air, it tends to sink. As the warm air rises and the cool air sinks, convection currents are formed. These currents transfer heat. The air currents in the earth's atmosphere, which contribute to our weather, are caused by convection currents.

RADIATION   When **radiation** (ray-dee-AY-shuhn) occurs, heat is transferred through space. The heat energy is in the form of invisible light known as infrared rays. Heat from the sun reaches the earth by radiation. Other familiar forms of radiation include the heat surrounding a fire or flame, the heat over a hot stove, and the heat given off by an electric heater. Now can you explain why you can toast marshmallows over a flame even if the flame does not touch the marshmallows?

SECTION REVIEW

1. How did Count Rumford's experiment support the idea that heat is a form of energy?
2. What factors caused scientists to make a connection between heat and molecular motion?
3. What type of heat transfer is illustrated by each of the following: an egg cooking in a frying pan; the roof of a house becoming hot; a warm air mass bringing a change in weather; the wire of an electric appliance becoming hot; heat from a fireplace warming a large room.

Figure 17–6 *A thermos bottle keeps liquids hot or cold by preventing heat transfer by conduction, convection, and radiation. The glass bottle reduces heat transfer by conduction. The air space between the bottles, which is a partial vacuum, prevents heat transfer by convection because there are so few air molecules to carry the heat. A silvered coating on the surface of the bottle prevents heat transfer by radiation. Why is the cap usually made of plastic?* ●2

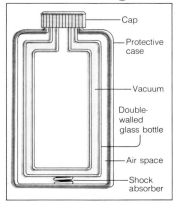

- Cap
- Protective case
- Vacuum
- Double-walled glass bottle
- Air space
- Shock absorber

399

TEACHER DEMONSTRATION

Fill a heat proof beaker with ice cubes. Discuss the ice cubes.

- **How hot are these cubes?** (Students will probably answer that the ice cubes are cold not hot.)

Point out that "cold" is the absence of heat. Place the ice-filled beaker on a hot plate. Heat the beaker until the ice cubes have melted completely. Ask,

- **What happened?** (The ice cubes melted.)
- **What caused the ice to melt?** (Students should suggest that heat from the hot plate melted the ice.)
- **How did the heat cause the ice cubes to melt?** (Accept all logical answers.)

Next, heat the water until it boils.

- **What happened?** (Students might suggest that the water boiled, changed to steam, or the water started evaporating.)
- **How did the heat get from the hot plate to the water?** (Accept all logical answers.)

Explain that when heat is moved or transferred from a warmer object to a colder object it is called heat transfer.

current. Heat is carried from places of higher temperature to places of lower temperature by the molecules of the moving liquid.

Section Review 17-1

1. As holes were drilled in a cannon barrel, heat was produced. Since drilling represented work being done, and energy was the ability to do work, then energy and heat must be related. Heat must be a form of energy.
2. Scientists knew that energy is needed to produce motion. They also knew that matter is made of tiny particles called molecules. Using these facts and the experiments of Rumford and Joule, scientists were able to relate heat and molecular motion.
3. Conduction, radiation, convection, conduction, radiation and convection

Skills Development

Skill: Relating cause and effect
Have students draw a model of what would happen if you were to heat water. Tell the students to show the flow of the water currents on their model. Ask,

- **What would happen to the water as it heated?** (Accept all logical answers. Some students might suggest the water will bubble and form convection currents.)

- **Have you ever watched pasta boil? What happens as the pasta gets softer?** (Accept all logical answers. Some students might suggest the pasta goes around as a convection current in the pan.)

Explain to students that the reason the pasta moves in circles is because the warmer water on the bottom of the pan rises to the top of the pan. Then the cooler water sinks to the bottom of the pan. This action sets up a

17-2 TEMPERATURE AND HEAT

SECTION PREVIEW 17-2

Temperature and heat are related but they are not the same. All matter is made of moving molecules. The amount of molecular motion depends on the amount of heat.

The energy of motion is called kinetic energy. The faster an object is moving, the more kinetic energy it has. Kinetic energy can be measured. Temperature is a measure of the average kinetic energy of the molecules. A thermometer is an instrument for measuring temperature. The temperature is measured in degrees Celsius or on the Kelvin scale.

PERFORMANCE OBJECTIVES 17-2

1. **Define temperature in terms of the kinetic energy of molecules.**
2. **Explain convection and conduction in terms of molecular motion.**
3. **Explain Celsius and Kelvin temperature scales.**

SCIENCE TERMS 17-2

temperature p. 400
kinetic energy p. 400
thermometer p. 401
Kelvin scale p. 401
absolute zero p. 401
Celsius p. 401

Sharpen Your Skills

Investigating Molecular Motion

1. Fill one beaker about two-thirds full with water at or near room temperature.
2. Fill a second beaker about two-thirds full with water that has been chilled by ice for several minutes. Remove the ice cubes once the water is cold.
3. Fill a third beaker about two-thirds full with hot water.
4. Use a dropper to place one drop of dark food coloring on the surface of the water in each beaker. Do not stir.
5. Describe the changes you see in each beaker of water. Note how slowly or quickly the changes occur in each beaker.

Explain your observations in terms of the effect of heat on the motion of molecules.

Figure 17-7 *Heat within the earth increases the kinetic energy of water molecules so that they escape from the earth as an eruption of hot water and steam. How does this photograph of Old Faithful Geyser in Yellowstone National Park, Wyoming, illustrate the relationship between heat and temperature?* ②

400

17–2 Temperature and Heat

If a weather forecast predicts temperatures between 30°C and 35°C, you know you can expect a hot day. You may think that **temperature** is a measure of heat, but it is not. Temperature and heat are related, but they are not the same thing. In order to understand the relationship between heat and temperature, you need to understand how energy and the motion of molecules are related.

Kinetic Energy

Energy of motion is called **kinetic energy.** The faster an object is moving, the more kinetic energy it has. Like all objects, molecules have kinetic energy because of their motion. When molecules are heated, their kinetic energy increases.

Temperature is a measure of the average kinetic energy of molecules. The higher the temperature of a substance, the faster the molecules in that substance are moving, on the average. Likewise, a lower temperature indicates the molecules are moving more slowly. In which pot of water would most of the molecules be moving faster, a pot at 90°C or one at 70°C? ①

TEACHING STRATEGY 17-2

Point out that when heat is transferred by convection, conduction or radiation, the molecules in a substance speed up.

Motivation

Have students observe Figure 17-7. Read the caption and discuss the ideas using some of the following questions.
• **Why do you think that Old Faithful erupts so violently?** (Accept all logical answers. Some students may predict it is the heating of the molecules of water.)

Point out that Old Faithful erupts on the average of every 30 to 90 minutes.
• **Why do you think Old Faithful erupts on an irregular schedule?** (Accept all logical answers.)

Explain that when the geyser erupts, hot water and steam escape from inside the earth. The loss of hot water and steam is a loss of heat energy. The water and steam are cooled by the air. Most of the cooled steam

and hot water return to the earth. This water has less kinetic energy and must be reheated to gain enough kinetic energy to erupt again.

Content Development

Point out that the faster the molecules are moving, the more kinetic energy a substance has. And the more kinetic energy a substance has, the higher the temperature of that substance.

Measuring Temperature

A **thermometer** is an instrument for measuring temperature. Most common thermometers consist of a very thin tube filled with liquid, which is usually alcohol or mercury. As the liquid in the thermometer gets warmer, the molecules move faster and farther apart. The liquid expands and rises in the tube. The reverse happens as the liquid cools. The molecules move more slowly and closer together. The liquid contracts and drops in the tube. ❷

Along the tube of a thermometer is a set of numerals, called a scale, that allows you to read the temperature. The scale of a thermometer shows the temperature in degrees **Celsius (C).** The degree Celsius is the metric unit most often used to measure temperature. Water freezes at 0°C and boils at 100°C at sea level.

Another metric temperature scale often used by scientists is the **Kelvin scale.** On this scale, temperatures are measured in units called kelvins (K). You can convert Celsius degrees to kelvins simply by adding 273° to the Celsius temperature. For example, if a thermometer reads 10°C, the same temperature on the Kelvin scale would be 283°K (273 + 10). A temperature of −5°C would be equivalent to 268°K (273 + −5). What is the freezing point of water on the Kelvin scale? The boiling point? ❺

One reason the Kelvin scale is useful is that its lowest reading, 0°K, is the lowest possible temperature that anything can reach. Often referred to as **absolute zero,** it is the temperature at which all molecular motion stops. What is the value of absolute zero on the Celsius scale? ❻

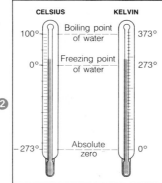

Figure 17–8 *A comparison of the Celsius and Kelvin temperature scales is shown here. What is the boiling point of water on the Kelvin scale? The freezing point?* ❸

Figure 17–9 *At a temperature of −195.8°C, nitrogen gas becomes a liquid. A banana dipped in liquid nitrogen becomes so frozen it can be used to hammer a nail into a block of wood. What is the equivalent temperature on the Kelvin scale?* ❹

401

SECTION REVIEW

1. What is temperature?
2. How does a thermometer measure temperature?
3. What is the most common scale for a scientific thermometer?
4. How would you convert a temperature in kelvins to degrees Celsius?
5. What must be true about the kinetic energy of molecules at 0°K? Can matter actually reach this temperature?

cookie baking, people walking, and many others. Discuss student examples.

Section Review 17-2

1. A measure of the average kinetic energy of molecules
2. The liquid in the tube of the thermometer expands as it becomes warmer and contracts as it becomes cooler.
3. Celsius scale
4. Subtract 273
5. The kinetic energy must be zero. Matter cannot reach absolute zero because molecules are always in motion. Once molecules cease to move, they are no longer molecules.

Skills Development

Skill: Designing an experiment
Divide the students into pairs. Designate each person as either A or B. Have the A student feel the B student's hands. Then, tell the B students to do something to raise the amount of kinetic energy in their hands.
• **What would be a way to raise the kinetic energy in your hands?** (Accept all logical answers.)
    Have students try their ideas. If

the students do not think of rubbing or clapping their hands together, suggest they try these methods to raise the kinetic energy. Have the A student feel the B student's hands after each try. Discuss the students' experiments.

Reinforcement

Have students make a list of common examples of kinetic energy in their everyday life. Students might list a moving vehicle, boiling liquid, a

17-3 MEASURING HEAT

SECTION PREVIEW 17-3

Heat can only be measured by indirect methods. An increase in temperature indicates an increase in molecular motion and an increase in heat. A decrease in temperature indicates a decrease in molecular motion and a decrease in heat. Heat is measured in units called calories. Temperature is measured in units called degrees. The temperature and amount of heat in a substance are related, but temperature is not the same as heat.

Substances absorb heat energy differently. The ability of a substance to absorb heat energy is called its specific heat. The specific heat of a substance is the number of calories needed to raise the temperature of one gram of the substance one degree Celsius. Different substances have different specific heat values.

PERFORMANCE OBJECTIVES 17-3

1. **Describe how heat can be measured indirectly by measuring temperature changes.**
2. **Explain the difference between a measure of temperature and the amount of heat in a substance.**
3. **Calculate heat changes (in calories) using specific heat values.**

SCIENCE TERMS 17-3

calorie p. 402
specific heat p. 403
calorimeter p. 404

17–3 Measuring Heat

You know from cooking soup or boiling water that heat energy must be added to a substance in order to raise its temperature. Heat is needed to set molecules in motion. And temperature is a measure of that motion.

Heat cannot be measured directly. But changes in temperature provide an indirect measurement of heat. **An increase in temperature indicates the addition of heat; a decrease in temperature represents the removal of heat.**

One unit used to measure heat is the **calorie.** One calorie is defined as the amount of heat needed to raise the temperature of one gram of liquid water one degree Celsius. For example, to raise the temperature of one gram of water from 7°C to 8°C or from 33°C to 34°C, one calorie of heat is needed. Another unit used to measure heat is the joule.

The amount of heat needed for a given temperature change depends on the mass of the water being heated. For example, twenty calories will raise the temperature of one gram of water twenty degrees. But the same number of calories will raise the temperature of ten grams of water only two degrees.

Figure 17–10 *Although heat cannot be measured directly, a change in temperature provides an indirect measurement of heat. Higher temperatures indicate more heat (left). Lower temperatures indicate an absence of heat (right).*

402

Motivation

Light a candle. Ask,
- **What happens when the candle burns?** (The burning candle produces a flame and heat.)
- **What happens to the heat produced?** (The heat from the candle flame warms the air.)

Explain that the burning candle is causing the molecules in the air to move faster, thus producing an increase in air temperature. The longer the candle burns, the longer heat will be added to the air and the temperature increase will be greater.

- **What will happen to the temperature of the candle flame after burning for several minutes?** (Accept all logical answers but lead students to determine that the flame of the candle is constantly at the same temperature.)

Content Development

Have students observe Figure 17-10 and read the caption.
- **How are these pictures related?** (Students will probably say that they are not related. One picture was taken in summer and the other picture was taken in winter.)
- **Which picture shows the coolest temperature?** (Students should answer that the photograph on the right shows the coolest temperature.)

Specific Heat Capacity

Mass is not the only factor that determines temperature change. The same amount of heat will produce a different temperature change in different substances even if their masses are the same. Some substances absorb heat energy more easily than other substances.

The ability of a substance to absorb heat energy is called its **specific heat.** The specific heat of a substance is the number of calories needed to raise the temperature of one gram of that substance one Celsius degree. The specific heat of water is 1.0 calorie per gram Celsius degree. Figure 17–11 shows the specific heat values of other substances.

Calculating Heat Energy

Specific heat can be used to calculate the amount of heat energy gained or lost by a substance. The heat gained or lost by the substance is equal to the product of its mass (m) times its change in temperature (ΔT) times its specific heat (s.h.).

Heat gained or lost = mass × change in temperature × specific heat ❷
= m × ΔT × s.h.

TABLE OF SPECIFIC HEATS

Substance	Specific Heat (cal/g·C°)
Air	.25
Aluminum	.22
Copper	.09
Glass	.20
Ice (−20°C to 0°C)	.50
Mercury	.03
Ocean water	.93
Water	1.00
Wood	.42

Figure 17–11 *According to this table, which heats up more quickly, aluminum or mercury?* ❶

Sample Problem

How much heat is needed to raise the temperature of 4 grams of aluminum 5C°?

Solution

Step 1	Write the formula	**Heat gained = m × ΔT × s.h.**
Step 2	Substitute given numbers and units	**Heat gained = 4 grams × 5C° × 0.22 calories per gram Celsius degree**
Step 3	Solve for unknown variable	**Heat gained = 4.4 calories**

Practice Problems

❷ 1. Calculate the heat lost by 10 g of copper if it is cooled from 35°C to 21°C.

❸ 2. Ten g of a certain substance gained 16.5 cal of heat when the temperature increased from 70°C to 85°C. What is the specific heat of the substance?

403

Reinforcement

Reinforce the ideas that an increase in temperature indicates the addition of heat and a decrease in temperature represents the removal of heat. Ask students to apply these concepts to the following real life situations.

• **What happens to the temperature and heat when water freezes to ice?** (The decrease in temperature represents the removal of heat.)

• **What happens to the temperature and heat when sleet changes to water?** (The increase in temperature indicates the addition of heat.)

• **What happens to the temperature and heat when frozen turkey becomes cooked turkey?** (The increase in temperature indicates the addition of heat.)

• **What happens to the temperature and heat when liquid fuel burns?** (The increase in temperature indicates the addition of heat.)

• **What happens to the temperature and heat when water changes to boiling water?** (The increase in temperature indicates the addition of heat.)

• **What happens to the temperature and heat when summer changes to winter?** (The decrease in temperature could represent a loss of heat. Or, the decrease in temperature could be caused by the fact that less heat is added during the winter.)

• **What happens to the temperature and heat when a flame in a fireplace continues to burn?** (The temperature of the flame remains constant. Heat is added by burning, but the same amount of heat is transferred to the air. The temperature and heat in the air is increased.)

Skills Development

Skill: Applying concepts

Explain that temperature is a measure of how *fast* the molecules in the substance are moving. Temperature is a measure of the *average* kinetic molecular motion in a substance.

• **In which of the scenes pictured in Figure 17-10 would you predict the molecules have the greatest motion?** (Accept all logical answers. Students should reply that the molecules on the left would be moving faster than the molecules on the right.)

• **Why?** (Students should predict the scene showing the warmest temperature would have the most heat. Therefore the molecules should be moving faster.)

Point out that an increase in temperature indicates the addition of heat and a decrease in temperature indicates the removal of heat.

17-4 HEAT AND PHASE CHANGES

SECTION PREVIEW 17-4

Matter exists as a solid, a liquid, or a gas. We can cause a change of state by adding or subtracting heat. A physical change of matter is called a phase change. When matter changes from solid to liquid, liquid to gas, liquid to solid, gas to liquid, solid to gas, or gas to solid, a phase change has taken place. A change in phase requires a gain or loss of heat energy.

The amount of heat required to change a substance from the solid phase to a liquid phase is called the heat of fusion. The amount of heat required to change a substance from the liquid phase to the gas phase is called the heat of vaporization.

PERFORMANCE OBJECTIVES 17-4

1. **Explain how a transfer of energy brings about a phase change.**
2. **Describe a phase change from a solid to a liquid using heat of fusion.**
3. **Describe a phase change from a liquid to a gas using heat of vaporization.**
4. **Calculate the heat energy needed for changing ice to liquid water and liquid water to gas.**

SCIENCE TERMS 17-4

phase change p. 404
heat of fusion p. 405
heat of vaporization p. 405
melting point p. 405
freezing point p. 406
boiling point p. 406

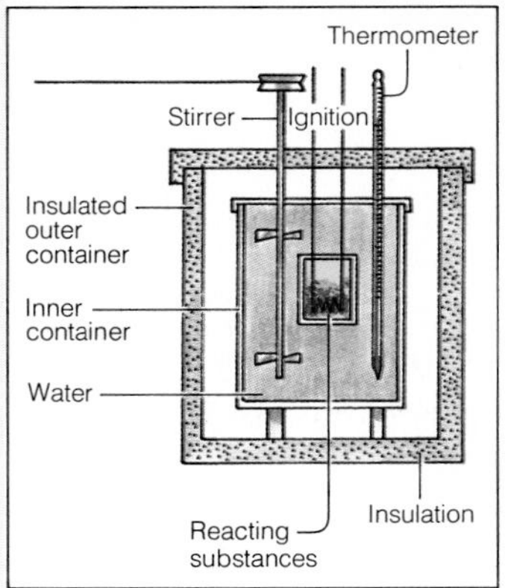

Figure 17–12 *The calorimeter is a device used to measure the heat given off during a chemical reaction. What principle of heat transfer is the basis of operation of the calorimeter?* ❶

The Calorimeter

Within a closed system, the heat lost by one substance must equal the heat gained by another substance. A device that makes use of this principle is a **calorimeter** (kal-uh-RIHM-uh-ter).

A calorimeter is used to measure the heat given off in chemical reactions. Figure 17–12 shows the construction of a calorimeter. An insulated outer container filled with water surrounds an inner container in which a chemical reaction takes place. Since the heat given off by the reacting substances equals the heat gained by the water, the heat of the chemical reaction can be calculated. The temperature change, mass, and specific heat of the water must be known in order to make the calculation. For example, suppose the surrounding water has a mass of 300 grams. If the temperature of the water increases 5C°, then the heat given off by the chemical reaction is equal to $300 \times 5 \times 1$, or 1500 calories. How much heat would be given off by a chemical reaction that raised the temperature of 150 grams of water 10C°? ❷

SECTION REVIEW

1. How can heat be measured?
2. What unit is used to measure heat?
3. What is specific heat?
4. Which would require more heat energy: bringing 100 grams of water at 40°C to the boiling point or raising the temperature of 1000 grams of water from 80°C to 90°C?

Section Objective

To relate phase changes and heat energy

17–4 Heat and Phase Changes

Have you ever watched an ice cube melt in a glass of water? Heat is being transferred from the water to the ice. As the ice absorbs the heat, it melts, or changes into a liquid. Eventually all the ice will change into liquid water.

The physical change of matter from the solid phase to the liquid phase is called a **phase change.** There are several different phase changes. Phase changes occur when a solid becomes a liquid, which

404

17-3 (continued)

Section Review 17-3

1. By measuring temperature changes. For a given substance, a certain amount of heat will raise the temperature of 1 g of that substance 1°C.
2. Calorie
3. The amount of heat needed to raise the temperature of 1 g of a substance 1°C

4. Raising the temperature of 1000 g of water 10°C

TEACHING STRATEGY 17-4

Motivation

Have the students make a list of appliances or commonly used items that use the principle of phase change. Students might suggest items such as a refrigerator, a humidifier, or an air conditioner.

Content Development

Point out that the amount of heat required to change a substance from the solid phase to the liquid phase is called the heat of fusion. Explain that *fusion* is simply a scientific word for "liquefying", "to make liquid", or "to melt". As more heat is applied to a solid the molecules begin to move faster and faster. At a certain point the molecules of the solid break apart and form into a liquid. At that point of breaking

Figure 17–13 This observatory at Mt. Washington, New Hampshire, dramatically shows one important phase change—freezing. Does heat energy of a substance increase or decrease during freezing? ❸

is called melting, and when a liquid becomes a solid, which is called freezing. The change of a liquid to a gas, or vaporization, and the change of a gas to a liquid, or condensation, are also phase changes.

A change in phase requires a change in heat energy. When ice melts and changes into water, energy in the form of heat is being absorbed by the ice. The energy is needed to overcome the forces of attraction that hold the water molecules together in the solid phase. Where do you think this heat energy is coming from? ❹

The amount of heat needed to change one gram of a substance from the solid phase to the liquid phase is called **heat of fusion.** The heat of fusion for ice is 80 calories per gram, 80 cal/g. In order to melt one gram of ice, 80 calories of heat is needed. What do you think happens when one gram of liquid water changes into ice? You are right if you said 80 calories of heat are lost by the one gram of liquid water as it freezes into ice.

The amount of heat needed to change one gram of a substance from the liquid phase to the gas phase is called the **heat of vaporization.** The heat of vaporization for water is 540 calories per gram, 540 cal/g. How much heat is needed to change ten grams of water to steam? How much heat is given off if ten grams of steam condensed into water?

In order for a substance to undergo a phase change, the substance must be at a certain temperature. The temperature at which a substance changes from the solid phase to the liquid phase is called its **melting point.** The temperature at which a substance changes from the liquid phase to the solid

Figure 17–14 Here you can see water in its three phases—solid, liquid, and gas. In order to produce a phase change, heat energy must be added or removed. What phase changes involve the addition of heat? The removal? ❺

405

apart, a certain amount of heat has been applied to that solid. The amount of heat required to change 1 g of the solid substance to 1 g of the liquid substance, without changing the temperature, is called the heat of fusion. The heat of fusion for water is 80 cal/g. This means that it takes 80 calories of heat energy to change 1 g of 0°C *solid* ice to 0°C liquid water.

Skills Development
Skill: Making calculations
Have students calculate how much energy is required to change 250 g of solid ice at 0°C to liquid water at 0°C.
Heat = 250 g × 80 cal/g
Heat = 20,000 cal

17-4 (continued)

Content Development

Point out to students that when a liquid loses heat energy, it will form into a solid. The amount of heat loss needed to change a substance from the liquid phase to the solid phase is called heat of solidification. The heat of solidification is equal to the heat of fusion for the same substance. Thus the heat of solidification for water is 80 cal/g. The heat of vaporization is different for each substance.

Content Development

Explain that at a certain temperature the molecules of a liquid break apart and form into a gas. At that point of breaking apart, a certain amount of heat has been applied to that liquid. The amount of heat required to change 1 g of liquid to 1 g of vapor, at the same temperature, is called heat of vaporization. The heat of vaporization for water is 540 cal/g. This means that it takes 540 cal of heat energy to change 1 g of 100°C *liquid* water to 100°C water vapor. The heat of vaporization is different for each substance.

Motivation

Place an ice cream cone in an ice cream cone holder or small glass. Put a piece of paper towel or plate under the glass to catch any drippings. Ask,
• **How long do you think the ice**

phase is called its **freezing point.** And the temperature at which a substance changes from the liquid phase to the gas phase is called its **boiling point.**

During a phase change, there is a change in heat energy but no change in temperature. Forces of attraction between molecules are overcome, but the average kinetic energy of the molecules remains the same. Once the melting point or boiling point of a substance has been reached, adding or removing heat will result in more of the substance changing phase, not in a change in temperature. Only after the phase change has been completed will a change in heat energy produce a temperature change.

A graph that shows how heat energy, temperature change, and phase change are related for water is called a phase-change diagram or a heating curve. See Figure 17–15. In this diagram, you can see that ice is being heated from below 0°C to its melting point. There is a temperature change. For every degree Celsius that the temperature rises, 0.5 cal/g of heat is required. At 0°C, the ice undergoes a phase change. There is no change in temperature

cream will stay frozen? (Accept all logical answers.)
• **What is going to happen to the ice cream?** (Most students will predict it will melt.)

Content Development

Explain that when matter changes from a solid to a liquid, it melts. The temperature at which a substance changes from a solid to a liquid is called its melting point. The heat

needed to melt ice from 0°C to water at 0°C is 80 cal/g, the same as the heat of fusion of ice.

Skills Development
Skill: Making calculations
Tell the class that ice cream is mostly water. Have students calculate how much energy is required to melt a 90-g single dip of ice cream at 0°C to liquid at 0°C.
Heat = 90 g × 80 cal/g

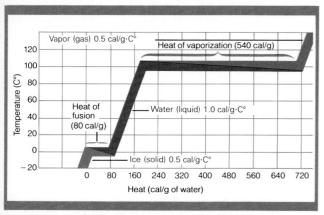

Figure 17–15 *A heating curve, or phase-change diagram, illustrates the fact that during a phase change, the addition of heat produces no change in temperature. According to the diagram, how many calories per gram are required for ice to melt? For water to vaporize?* ❶

during a phase change. How many calories per gram are required for this phase change? ❷

Any heat now added to the water will cause a steady increase in temperature until 100°C is reached. Then the temperature will remain at 100°C while the liquid water changes to steam. Once the phase change is complete, the temperature will begin to rise again as additional heat is added to the steam. For one gram of ice at 0°C, how many calories are needed to change it to one gram of steam at 100°C? ❸

SECTION REVIEW

1. What is necessary for a phase change to occur?
2. What is the term used to describe the amount of heat needed to change one gram of a substance from the solid phase to the liquid phase? From the liquid phase to the gas phase?
3. What happens to temperature during a phase change? To heat energy?
4. Compare the amount of heat released when 54 grams of water freezes to ice, with the amount of heat released when 8 grams of steam condenses to water.

17-5 THERMAL EXPANSION

SECTION PREVIEW 17-5

Most substances—solids, liquids, and gases—expand when their temperature is increased. When substances are heated, the molecules move faster and spread farther apart so that the substances become larger, or expand. The rate of expansion is different for solids, liquids, and gases.

In solids, the molecules are very close together, so solids expand the least. In liquids, the molecules move about easily and are farther apart, so liquids expand more than solids. In gases, the molecules move about very quickly and are very far apart, so gases expand the most.

The rate of expansion differs for different solids. Because the molecules of all solids at the same temperature move differently, some solids expand more than others.

PERFORMANCE OBJECTIVES 17-5

1. **Explain why thermal expansion occurs.**
2. **Describe some practical applications of thermal expansion.**

SCIENCE TERMS 17-5

thermal expansion p. 408
thermostat p. 409
bimetallic strip p. 409

TEACHING STRATEGY 17-5

Motivation

Stretch a 1-m long piece of copper wire between two ring stands or other supports. Hang a weight, such as a metal washer, from the middle of the wire. Measure the vertical distance of the weight from the table top. Heat the full length of the copper wire with a Bunsen burner (or several candles). Remeasure the vertical distance from the weight to the table top. Ask,
• **What happened?** (The weight moved closer to the table, or the wire expanded.) Rub an ice cube along the wire.

• **What happened?** (The weight raised.)
• **What caused the wire to expand and contract?** (Accept all logical answers, but lead students to suggest that the addition and removal of heat caused the changes.)

Point out to students that the weight was close to the table *only* when the wire was heated. Explain that most solid substances expand when heated and contract when cooled.

17-5 Thermal Expansion

Have you ever wondered why sidewalks have cracks between the squares of concrete? The reason is that concrete expands in hot weather. Without the cracks, the surface of the sidewalk would buckle. Spaces are left in bridge roadways and between railroad tracks for the same reason.

The liquid in a thermometer expands when it is heated. A tightly closed bottle of carbonated soda left out in the sun may explode or at least bubble over in a fizzy mess when opened. Automobile and bicycle tires tend to look "higher" in warm weather than in cold weather. All of these examples illustrate **thermal expansion.** Thermal expansion is the expansion of a substance due to heat. **① Most substances—solids, liquids, and gases—expand when their temperature is increased.**

Expansion in Solids

A molecular model can help to explain why solids expand when heated. The molecules in a solid are arranged in fixed positions about which they vibrate. As heat energy is added to the solid, the kinetic energy of the molecules increases and their vibrations speed up. The molecules move farther away from their fixed positions and farther away from each other. This separation of molecules causes the solid to expand.

Figure 17–16 *Thermal expansion is the expansion of a substance due to heat. Solids expand when heated, so expansion links are provided in bridge surfaces (left). When the temperature is low, the gap between the metal links is large. When the temperature is high, the gap is smaller. As the soda water in this bottle warms, the gas molecules move faster (right). They eventually come out of solution as bubbles, or fizz.*

Content Development

Point out that solids, liquids, and gases expand differently, such as
1. In solids the molecules are very close together and seem to vibrate rather than move, so solids expand and contract the least.
2. The molecules in liquids move about quite easily and are farther apart, so liquids can expand and contract more than solids.
3. The molecules in gases move about

Expansion in Liquids

The molecules in a liquid also experience an increase in kinetic energy when heated. As the molecules begin to move faster, they move farther apart. So most liquids expand when heated.

There is one exception to this rule, however. Between the temperatures of 4°C and 0°C, water expands as it cools. Because of this expansion, the volume of water increases as it cools. As the volume increases, the density decreases.

Ice is less dense than liquid water. You can see evidence of this when you look at ice cubes floating in a glass of water or chunks of ice floating on top of a pond. What would be the effect on life on the earth if ice were more dense than liquid water? ❶

Expansion in Gases

As the temperature of a gas increases, the molecules move faster and faster. They begin to collide with each other and with the sides of their container. Since the molecules in a gas have considerable freedom of motion, thermal expansion in a gas can be quite dramatic. Many explosions are caused when a tightly closed container of gas becomes too hot. Why should you never heat a gas in a closed container? ❸

Applications of Thermal Expansion

The principle of thermal expansion can be useful in constructing heat-regulating devices. These devices make use of the fact that different solids expand at different rates.

A device that helps control temperature in an indoor area or in an appliance is called a **thermostat** (THER-muh-stat). The switch in a thermostat is a **bimetallic strip,** which consists of two different metals joined together. These two metals have different rates of expansion. When heated or cooled, one of the metals expands or contracts faster than the other, causing the strip to bend. The metal that expands more forms the outside of the curve of the bimetallic strip. The bending and unbending of the bimetallic strip opens and closes an electric circuit ❷

Figure 17–17 *Because water expands between 4°C and 0°C, the density of ice is less than the density of water. This fact explains why ice floats. What must be true of the volume of water during this temperature interval?* ❷

the warm water will cause the outside glass to expand.)
• **Why do sections of steel railroad tracks and concrete highways have spaces between the sections?** (To allow for expansion during the hot summer months.)

Skills Development

Skill: Making predictions
Cut some aluminum foil backed wrapping paper into a strip about 1 cm wide and 3 cm long. Show the students the foil strip. Ask students to write a prediction and explanation of how a warmed strip should bend if
• **aluminum expanded more than paper?** (If aluminum expanded more than paper, the heated strip should bend toward the paper because the aluminum would get longer than the paper.)
• **paper expanded more than aluminum?** (If paper expanded more than aluminum, the heated strip should bend toward the paper.)

very quickly and easily, so gases expand the most.

Enrichment

Have students write an explanation of possible ways that the expansion and/or contraction of substances could be used to solve or explain the following problems or situations.
• **A metal cover is stuck tight on a glass ketchup bottle. How could you use the expansion and/or contraction** of substances to remove the cover? (Hot water will make the metal cover expand more than the bottle. Then the lid can be unscrewed.)
• **Two glasses are stuck together, one inside the other. How could you use the expansion and/or contraction of substances to separate the glasses?** (Pour cold water into the inside glass as you let warm water run over the outside glass. The cold water will cause the inside glass to contract and

17-6 HEAT AND INTERNAL ENERGY

SECTION PREVIEW 17-6

The relationship between heat, motion, and work helps scientists understand that heat is a form of energy. The temperature of a substance can be increased by placing it in contact with a second substance at a higher temperature, or by doing work on the substance. Energy rather than heat is contained in substances. The energy contained in a substance is called internal energy.

PERFORMANCE OBJECTIVES 17-6

1. **Relate internal energy, work, and heat.**
2. **Explain the internal energy of a substance.**
3. **Describe how the internal energy of a substance can be changed.**

SCIENCE TERMS 17-6

internal energy p. 411

Figure 17–18 *Because the two heated metals making up the bimetallic strip expand at different rates, the strip bends (left). A bimetallic strip is an important part of a thermostat (right). When the temperature gets too cold, the bimetallic strip uncoils. This action causes a drop of mercury to close a switch and start the heating system. When the temperature reaches the desired level, the strip coils up, the mercury opens the switch, and the heat goes off. On what principle is the operation of a bimetallic strip based?* ❷

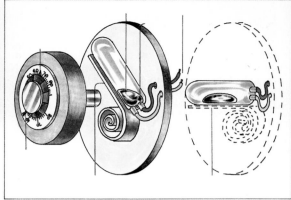

that controls the heating or cooling device. Thermostats can be found in air conditioners, electric blankets, refrigerators, and home heating systems. What are other uses for thermostats? ❶

SECTION REVIEW

1. What is meant by thermal expansion?
2. What happens to the molecules of a substance when the substance is heated?
3. How does a bimetallic strip make use of the principle of thermal expansion?
4. Using the formula for density, show why an ice cube floats in water.

17–6 Heat and Internal Energy

Count Rumford observed that heat was produced when holes were drilled in cannon barrels. James Prescott Joule observed that objects in motion produce heat. In both cases, work was being done. You may think of work as washing dishes, babysitting, or doing homework. But when scientists speak of work, they are referring to a force acting on an object and causing it to move.

Objects in motion have kinetic energy. The molecules of any substance have kinetic energy because they are always moving. Adding heat to a substance may increase the average kinetic energy of the molecules and cause a rise in temperature. Doing work

410

Figure 17–19 *These runners in the 1984 Olympic Games have a great deal of kinetic energy, or energy of motion. Therefore, they have the ability to do work. The work they do involves exerting a force to move their bodies a certain distance. As a result of this work, their body temperatures increase. What then is true of their internal energy?* ❸

on a substance also may cause a rise in temperature. The relationship between heat, motion, and work helped scientists to understand that heat is a form of energy.

Although heat can be transferred from one substance to another, a substance cannot really contain heat. Heat contained by a substance is actually energy. **Energy contained in a substance is called internal energy.** ❶ A change in temperature indicates a change in **internal energy.** When a substance receives heat or has work done on it, it gains internal energy. When a substance gives off heat or does work, it loses some of its internal energy.

SECTION REVIEW

1. What is internal energy?
2. Do work and heat have similar effects on a substance? Explain your answer.
3. A nail hit with a hammer becomes hot. When placed in a glass of water, the nail quickly becomes cool. In terms of work, heat, and energy, describe what happens to the nail.

Sharpen Your Skills

Associating Meanings

Sometimes words that have a scientific meaning also have another, more common meaning. Very often the two meanings are related. This relationship can help you remember the scientific definition.

Look up the meaning of each underlined word in the following terms. Then write one sentence that tells how the word's general meaning relates to its scientific meaning.

absolute zero
internal energy
kinetic energy
specific heat
thermal expansion

411

molecules vibrating. How do you know that the molecules are vibrating? (The molecules in all matter have kinetic energy and vibrate or move.)

Content Development
Explain that when heat is added to a substance, the internal energy is increased. (An increase in internal energy can be determined by measuring the temperature change and applying the formula for specific heat.)

Content Development
Explain that when a substance is hit by something, the kinetic motion of the hitting object is transferred to the molecules of the substance that is hit.

Section Review 17-6
1. Energy contained in a substance
2. Yes. Both work and heat can cause an increase in internal energy, as well as a rise in temperature.
3. The hammer does work on the nail, increasing its internal energy. This is indicated by a rise in temperature. When the nail is placed in water, it gives off heat to the water and loses internal energy as it cools.

marbles have now? (The marbles still have kinetic energy.)
• **How can you tell that the marbles have kinetic energy?** (I can hear them moving.)

Reinforcement
Place a single marble on a table. Tell the class to observe the motionless marble as you discuss the ideas using questions similar to the following.
• **What kind of energy does this**

marble have? (Accept all logical answers.)
• **What are the molecules in the marble doing?** (The molecules in the marble are vibrating.)
• **What kind of energy do the vibrating molecules in the marble have?** (The vibrating molecules in the marble have kinetic energy.)
• **Can you see or hear the marble molecules vibrating?** (No!)
• **You cannot see or hear the marble**

LABORATORY INVESTIGATION TEMPERATURES OF MIXTURES

BEFORE THE LAB

1. **Gather all materials at least one day prior to the investigation. You should have enough supplies to meet your class needs, assuming six students per group.**
2. **In addition to the materials listed, be sure to have a beaker forceps (tongs) available for each team.**

PRE-LAB DISCUSSION

Have students read the complete laboratory procedure. Discuss the procedure by asking questions similar to the following.

- **What is the purpose of the laboratory investigation?** (To find the final temperatures of mixtures of different amounts of hot and cold water)
- **Why is it important to use forceps (tongs) to lift the beaker of 75° water?** (The hot water could burn our fingers.)
- **How much hot water and cold water should we use for the first trial?** (We should use 40 mL of hot water and 40 mL of cold water for the first trial.)
- **How much hot water and cold water should we use for the second trial?** (We should use 80 mL of hot water and 40 mL of cold water for the second trial.)
- **How much hot water and cold water should we use for the third trial?** (We should use 40 mL of hot water and 80 mL of cold water for the third trial.)

Tell the class to record the water temperatures to the nearest half or whole degree Celsius.

Have students develop possible hypotheses to the problem they will be investigating. Alert them that they will not be graded on their hypothesis, but that they should check their initial hypothesis and their experimental data once the investigation has been completed.

SKILL DEVELOPMENT

Students will use the following skills while completing this investigation.
1. Manipulative
2. Measuring
3. Observing
4. Comparing
5. Predicting
6. Safety
7. Recording

SAFETY TIPS

Alert students to be cautious while using the hot plate and hot water. Remind students to use a beaker forceps to lift the beaker of 75°C hot water.

Temperatures of Mixtures

Problem

When hot and cold water are mixed together, what will be the temperature of the mixture?

Materials *(per group)*

3 Styrofoam cups	stirring rod
2 250-mL beakers	several ice cubes
thermometer	hot plate
2 100-mL graduated cylinders	

Procedure

1. Place the ice cubes in one beaker and fill the beaker about two-thirds full with water. Cool the water until the temperature is 10°C or lower.
2. Fill the other beaker about two-thirds full with water and heat the beaker until the temperature is at least 75°C. Do *not* boil the water.
3. Line up the three Styrofoam cups. Place 40 mL of cold water in the first cup. Be sure that *no ice* is in the water. Place 40 mL of hot water in the second cup.
4. Measure and record the temperature of the water in each cup.
5. Pour the samples of hot and cold water into the third cup and stir. Measure and record the temperature of the mixture.
6. Pour out the water in each Styrofoam cup, but save the cups for the next steps.
7. Repeat steps 3 to 6 using 80 mL of hot water and 40 mL of cold water.
8. Repeat steps 3 to 6 using 40 mL of hot water and 80 mL of cold water.
9. For each trial, record your results in a data table similar to the one shown here.

Observations

1. For each trial, was the temperature of the mixture closer to the temperature of the hotter sample or the colder sample? How much closer?

Conclusions

1. What explanation can you offer for your observations in each trial?
2. When hot and cold water are mixed together, what is one factor that determines the temperature of the mixture?
3. What types of heat transfer are involved when the mixture is made?
4. What sources of error are present in this experiment?
5. What would you predict the approximate temperature of a mixture to be if 20 mL of water at 10°C are mixed with 100 mL of water at 80°C?

Trial	Cold Water		Hot Water		Mixture	
	Volume	*Temperature*	*Volume*	*Temperature*	*Volume*	*Temperature*
I						
II						
III						

TEACHING STRATEGY FOR LAB PROCEDURE

1. You might ask the teams to write down what they *guess* the final temperature will be for the first trial *before* they do the activity. Then, before the teams do the second and third trials they have some evidence to make a reasonable estimate or prediction of the final temperature.
2. Have the teams follow the directions carefully as they work in the laboratory.

SUMMARY

17-1 Heat: A Form of Energy

❑ The experiments of Rumford led to the conclusion that heat is a form of energy. The experiments of Joule led to the conclusion that objects in motion produce heat.

❑ Heat is a form of energy related to the motion of molecules.

❑ The three types of heat transfer are conduction, convection, and radiation.

❑ Substances that conduct heat effectively are called heat conductors. Substances that do not conduct heat easily are called insulators.

17-2 Temperature and Heat

❑ Kinetic energy is energy of motion.

❑ Temperature is the measure of the average kinetic energy of molecules.

❑ The degree Celsius is the metric unit most often used to measure temperature.

17-3 Measuring Heat

❑ Heat can be measured indirectly by measuring changes in temperature.

❑ A calorie is the amount of heat needed to raise the temperature of one gram of liquid water one degree Celsius.

❑ The ability of a substance to absorb heat energy is called its specific heat.

❑ Heat gained or lost = mass × change in temperature × specific heat (m × ΔT × s.h.).

17-4 Heat and Phase Changes

❑ A phase change requires a gain or loss of heat energy.

❑ The amount of heat needed to change a substance from the solid phase to the liquid phase is called heat of fusion.

❑ The amount of heat needed to change a substance from the liquid phase to the gas phase is called heat of vaporization.

❑ During a phase change, there is a change in heat energy but not in temperature.

17-5 Thermal Expansion

❑ Thermal expansion, the expansion of a substance due to heat, can be explained in terms of the kinetic energy of molecules.

❑ Most substances expand when heated.

❑ Between 4°C and 0°C, water expands as it cools. Ice is less dense than liquid water.

17-6 Heat and Internal Energy

❑ Adding heat to a substance increases the average kinetic energy of the molecules and may cause a rise in temperature.

❑ Energy contained in a substance is called internal energy. A rise in temperature indicates an increase in internal energy.

❑ When a substance has work done on it, it gains internal energy. When a substance does work, it loses internal energy.

VOCABULARY

Define each term in a complete sentence.

absolute zero	convection	insulator	specific heat
bimetallic strip	freezing point	internal energy	temperature
boiling point	heat conductor	Kelvin scale	thermal expansion
calorie	heat of fusion	kinetic energy	thermometer
calorimeter	heat of	melting point	thermostat
Celsius	vaporization	phase change	
conduction	heat transfer	radiation	

413

---

trial: mixture temperature should be significantly closer to the temperature of the hot water. Third trial: mixture temperature should be significantly closer to the temperature of the cold water.

CONCLUSIONS

1. The temperature of the mixture is closer to the temperature of the sample with greater mass.
2. The temperature of the mixture will depend upon the relative masses of the hot and cold water.
3. Conduction and convection
4. Heat lost to the surrounding air; allowing too much time to elapse between measuring; measuring temperature incorrectly; leaving water in the graduated cylinder when transferring water to the cups; not stirring the mixture enough
5. Between 65°C and 70°C

GOING FURTHER: ENRICHMENT

You may want to have students do an experiment to find the final temperature of a mixture of ice and hot water. Start with specific amounts of ice and water (measured to the nearest gram). Remind students that heat gained is always equal to heat lost. After the final temperature is found, students can calculate the heat gained and lost by the ice and water, and then calculate the heat of fusion.

---

3. After the teams have completed the investigation, you might ask several teams to record their results on the chalkboard. Discuss the similarities and differences in the team results. Lead the class to suggest *logical* cause-and-effect explanations for any differences.
4. Discuss how the investigation relates to the chapter ideas by asking open questions similar to the following.

• **How does the investigation illustrate that heat and temperature are related?**

• **What happened to the kinetic energy of both the hot and cold water during the investigation?**

• **How could you determine the amount of heat (calories) gained by the cold water and lost by the hot water?** (Use the formula for specific heat.)

OBSERVATIONS

1. First trial: mixture temperature should be approximately halfway between the sample temperatures. Second

CHAPTER REVIEW

MULTIPLE CHOICE

1. a   3. b   5. a   7. c   9. b
2. d   4. b   6. d   8. d   10. a

COMPLETION

1. convection
2. Insulators
3. kinetic energy
4. 273°
5. absolute zero
6. specific heat
7. 21,600
8. thermal expansion
9. thermostat
10. internal energy

TRUE OR FALSE

1. F heat
2. T
3. F kinetic energy
4. T
5. F indirectly
6. F heat of vaporization
7. F the same as
8. F increases
9. T
10. T

SKILL BUILDING

1. The ice cube would absorb 800 cal and become water at 0°C. One thousand calories of heat would then be used to raise the temperature of the water 100°C. This leaves 3200 cal of heat, which is enough to accomplish the phase change to steam of only about 6 g of water.
2. 4500 calories = 4.5 kilocalories
3. Conduction: Heat moves directly from one molecule to another in solids, liquids, and gases. Convection: Heat moves in currents caused by unequal heating of liquids and gases. Radiation: Heat moves as invisible infrared rays, primarily through gases and a vacuum.
4. Friction causes the tires to heat, which causes the molecules to move faster and collide with the walls of the tires more frequently. More frequent collisions cause an increase in pressure.
5. a. C   b. A and B   c. A is 2 times faster than C   d. Kinetic energy of B is two times greater than A.   e. B = C

ESSAY

1. Although the metal of the cannon was in contact with the surrounding water, no heat was produced until the work of drilling began. Once the water began to boil, it would not continue unless the drilling continued—even though the water was still in contact with the metal.

2. When it becomes warmer, the liquid in the tube of the thermometer expands because the molecules are moving faster and farther apart. When the liquid becomes cooler, it contracts as the molecules slow down and come closer together.
3. The heat energy going into the substance during a phase change is being used to break down the molecular attraction within the substance; thus there is no energy available to increase the molecules' kinetic energy, which would increase the temperature.
4. Heat is a form of energy. Energy is the ability to do work. When work is done on a substance, the internal energy of the substance is increased. When heat is added to a substance, the internal energy of the substance is also increased. Giving off energy or doing work causes a substance to lose some of its internal energy.
5. Heat is a form of energy related to

Determine whether each statement is true or false. Then on a separate sheet of paper, write "true" if it is true. If it is false, change the underlined word or words to make the statement true.

1. When an ice cube melts, <u>coldness</u> is being transferred.
2. Heat energy from the sun reaches the earth as invisible light called <u>infrared</u>.
3. Temperature is a measure of the average <u>heat energy</u> of molecules.
4. The higher the temperature, the <u>faster</u> the molecules in a substance are moving.
5. Heat can be measured <u>directly</u>.
6. The heat needed to change 1 gram of ice to 1 gram of water is called the <u>heat of fusion</u>.
7. The amount of heat needed to change one gram of water to steam is <u>540 cal/g</u>.
8. If water cools from 3°C to 1°C, its volume <u>decreases</u>.
9. Ice is <u>less</u> dense than liquid water.
10. When an object does work, it <u>loses</u> some of its internal energy.

CONCEPT REVIEW: SKILL BUILDING

Use the skills you have developed in the chapter to complete each activity.

1. **Interpreting diagrams** Use the heating curve in Figure 17–15 to help you describe what would happen to a 10-gram ice cube at 0°C if it were to gain 5000 calories of heat.
2. **Analyzing data** A chemical reaction takes place in a calorimeter. The following data are obtained:

mass of water	300 g
initial temperature of water	25°C
final temperature of water	40°C

   What is the heat in kilocalories released by the reaction? A kilocalorie is 1000 calories.
3. **Making comparisons** Compare the three methods of heat transfer in terms of how heat moves and in what kinds of substances the transfer takes place.
4. **Applying concepts** Explain why the air pressure in car tires is different after the car has been driven awhile?

5. **Interpreting diagrams**

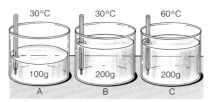

a. Which container(s) has(have) the greatest heat content?
b. In which containers is the motion of molecules the same?
c. Compare the molecular motion in containers A and C.
d. Compare the kinetic energy of containers A and B.
e. Which container needs the greatest number of calories to change the temperature by one Celsius degree?

CONCEPT REVIEW: ESSAY

Discuss each of the following in a brief paragraph.

1. Explain how Count Rumford's experiment disputed the caloric theory.
2. Explain how a thermometer makes use of the property of thermal expansion.
3. Why is there no temperature change during a phase change?
4. How are work, heat, and energy related?
5. Compare temperature and heat.

415

the kinetic energy of molecules. Temperature is a measure of the average kinetic energy of molecules. Temperature is not a measure of heat. But temperature indirectly measures changes in heat energy.

ADDITIONAL QUESTIONS AND TOPIC SUGGESTIONS

1. An ice cube with a mass of 100 g is taken from a refrigerator with a temperature of −10°C. The ice was placed into a glass of water that had a temperature of 0°C. If no heat is gained or lost from the surroundings, what will happen to the ice and water? (The freezing point of water is 0°C. It takes

80 cal of heat energy to freeze water to ice. The ice cube has 100 g × 10°C × 1 cal/gC° or 1000 cal that it can lose in warming to 0°C. This heat loss by the water could change 1000/80 or 12.5 g of water to ice. Therefore the final mixture should contain 112.5 g of ice floating in water, all at 0°C.)

2. How much heat is required to convert 1 g of ice at −10°C to vapor at 100°C?
(Heat to raise ice to 0°C:
Heat = mass × temp. change × sp. heat
Heat = 1 g × 10°C × 1 cal/gC°
Heat = 10 cal)
(Heat to raise ice to water:
Heat = mass × 80 cal/gC°
Heat = 1 × 80 cal/gC°
Heat = 80 cal)
(Heat to raise 0°C water to 100°C water:
Heat = mass × temp. change × sp. heat
Heat = 1 g × 100°C × 1 cal/gC°
Heat = 100 cal)
(Heat to change 100°C liquid water to 100°C vapor:
Heat = mass × 540 cal/gC°
Heat = 1 × 540 cal/gC°
Heat = 540 cal)
(The total would be
10 + 80 + 100 + 540, or 730 calories.)

3. Ice cubes at 0°C are dropped into a beaker of water at 0°C. What is observed about the temperature? What will happen? (Nothing should happen to the temperature, or the temperature will stay at 0°C. The ice and water were at the same temperature. Therefore the ice should not melt and the water should not freeze.)

ISSUES IN SCIENCE

The following issue can be used as a springboard for class debate, or it can be assigned as a homework writing assignment.

Many people think the new digital thermometer is more accurate and better than the older mercury thermometer. What is your opinion and why? Which kind of thermometer should most families use? What are the advantages and disadvantages of each kind of thermometer?

Chapter 18
USES OF HEAT

CHAPTER OVERVIEW

Heat has many uses in modern society. We heat our homes and buildings by using heat in different types of heating systems. We have learned to control and contain heat by insulating. We known how to remove heat to cool buildings.

Modern industry relies on converting fuel into heat energy and then to mechanical energy that will do work. Our internal and external combustion engines are based on this heat energy conversion.

The huge use of heat by modern society is causing thermal pollution. We must learn more about the effects of heat on our everyday life. We must also learn how to conserve and reuse heat energy once it is released from fuels. If our society is to continue to grow, we need to learn how to control or reduce the adverse effects of thermal pollution.

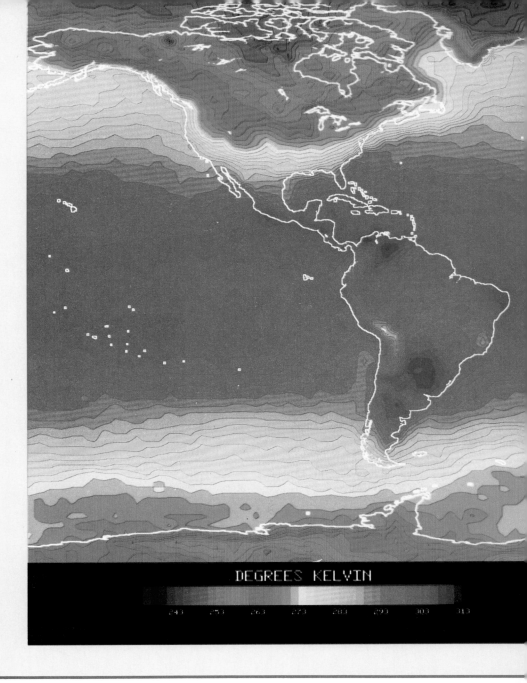

DEGREES KELVIN

Introducing Chapter 18

Have students observe the photograph on page 416. Read the caption. Point out that the first Seasat satellite was successfully orbited by NASA on June 26, 1978. Explain that satellites often house many instruments that perform compatible experiments. The Seasat series of satellites provides more than 100 photos each day. In addition to the photographic capability,

Seasat carries sensors to obtain information on the heat balance in the earth/atmosphere system.

Have students correlate the temperatures on the Kelvin scale to the land and sea mass shown in the photograph by asking questions such as the following.
- **Where is the coldest spot on the map?** (Accept all logical answers.)
- **Where is the hottest spot on the map?** (Accept all logical answers.)

Have students discuss the temperature ranges shown on the map. Explain that scientists have reported that the temperature of the earth is gradually rising.
- **How do you think a Seasat temperature map will look if the data is taken ten years from now?** (Accept all logical answers.)
- **How do you think this extra heat will affect the earth?** (Accept all logical answers. Lead students to suggest

Uses of Heat 18

CHAPTER OBJECTIVES

After completing this chapter, you will be able to

18–1 Distinguish among various types of central heating systems.

18–2 Explain how insulation prevents heat loss.

18–3 Describe the operation of a cooling system.

18–4 Explain how heat engines convert heat energy into mechanical energy.

18–5 Define thermal pollution and discuss its effects on the environment.

The year is 2064. Across the Midwest, an area once called the "Breadbasket of the Nation" is covered with desert sand. In Arizona, broad-leafed evergreen trees form a continuous canopy over a region that receives an average rainfall of 260 centimeters per year.

The eastern half of New York is under water. Evening weather reports include a "glacier watch," warning citizens of northeastern seaport towns to beware of rising tides due to the melting of polar icecaps.

This scene may sound unbelievable, but it is within the realm of possibility. Scientists report that the temperature of the earth is gradually rising due to the "greenhouse effect." The greenhouse effect occurs when ultraviolet rays from the sun are absorbed by the earth, and in turn the earth radiates infrared rays back into the atmosphere. A cloud of carbon dioxide and other gases in the atmosphere absorbs the infrared rays. The infrared rays are trapped in the atmosphere. The result is a kind of "thermal blanket" wrapped around the earth.

Perhaps you are aware that heat may affect your life dramatically in the future. But did you know that heat also plays an important role in your daily life right now? In this chapter you will learn how heat is obtained, used, and controlled. As to whether predictions based on the greenhouse effect will come true, you'll just have to stick around until 2064 to find out!

This satellite map, taken by the Seasat satellite, shows average sea and land surface temperature all over the world. If the temperature of the earth continues to rise, a future map will have a decidedly different appearance.

417

TEACHER DEMONSTRATION

Show the class an assortment of objects, such as an ice cube, a lighted candle, a thermometer, a toy car (or picture of a car, bus, or truck), a picture of a house, and a picture of a factory. Use open-ended questions to lead students to the idea that heat has many applications and uses. Ask questions such as the following.

- **How are these objects related?** (Accept all logical answers.)
- **What do these things have to do with heat and energy?** (Accept all logical answers.)
- **Which thing(s) use(s) fuel to do work?** (Accept all logical answers.)
- **Which things have some heat energy?** (Accept all logical answers. All of the objects and pictures have mass and heat energy.)

TEACHER RESOURCES
Audiovisuals
Heat and How We Use It, film, Encyclopaedia Britannica
Heat and Temperature, film, Coronet
Hot and Cold, 5 filmstrips, Encyclopaedia Britannica

Books
Chapman, A. J. *Heat Transfer,* Macmillan
Cornwall, K. *The Flow of Heat,* Van Nostrand Reinhold
Parker, P. *Heat,* Heinemann

that land areas could decrease and sea areas could increase.)

Have students read the material on page 417, which accompanies the opening photograph. Point out and discuss the importance of heat and heat energy in our daily lives.

18-1 HEATING SYSTEMS

SECTION PREVIEW 18-1

Most buildings in the United States have central heating systems. This means that heat is generated for an entire building or group of buildings from one central location. Central heating systems are divided into two main groups: indirect and direct heating systems.

The indirect system circulates hot water or steam through pipes that lead to convectors or radiators. Hot water and steam heating are two examples of indirect heating systems.

The direct system circulates warm air throughout the area being heated. Warm air heating, the heat pump, and solar heating are examples of direct heating systems.

PERFORMANCE OBJECTIVES 18-1

1. **Describe the differences between direct and indirect heating systems.**
2. **Explain the similarities and differences between hot water and steam heating systems.**
3. **Explain the kinds of heat transfer in each type of heating system.**

SCIENCE TERMS 18-1

central heating system p. 418
hot water system p. 418
steam heating system p. 419
radiant hot water system p. 419
radiant electric system p. 419
warm air system p. 420
heat pump system p. 420
solar heating system p. 421
active solar heating p. 421
passive solar heating p. 421

18-1 Heating Systems

If you have ever been in a building that is too hot or too cold, you know the importance of a good heating system. Most buildings and residences in the United States have **central heating systems** that provide comfortable environments for daily activities. **A central heating system generates heat for an entire building or group of buildings from one central location.** Then the heat is delivered where it is needed.

Based on the way that heat is delivered, central heating systems are divided into two main groups: direct systems and indirect systems. A direct system circulates warm air throughout the area being heated. An indirect system circulates hot water or steam through pipes that lead to convectors or radiators. The convectors or radiators give off the heat.

Although there are different types of central heating systems, all require a source of heat, such as electricity or the burning of a fuel. All central heating systems also have automatic controls. These controls regulate the temperature of the area to be heated, turn off the system if any part of it becomes dangerously overheated, and prevent the system from starting if conditions are unsafe.

Figure 18-1 *For cave dwellers, a fire represented a central heating system (right). Modern central heating systems are considerably more complex. A technician in this steam boiler control room coordinates the delivery of heat to an entire building (left). Would this central heating system be a direct or indirect system?* ❶

Hot Water Heating

A **hot water system** consists of a network of pipes and convectors connected to a hot water heater. Fuel burned in the hot water heater raises

---

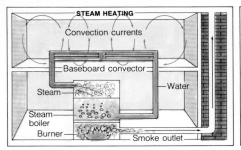
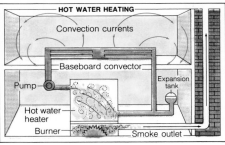

the temperature of the water to about 82°C. Then the water is pumped through pipes to a convector in each room. The water heats the convector. The heat given off by the convector is circulated throughout the room by convection currents. Once the water has lost its heat, it returns to the hot water heater by another pipe.

Figure 18–2 *A hot water heating system (left) and a steam heating system (right) are two common central heating systems that are quite similar. What is the major difference between the two systems?* ❷

Steam Heating

A **steam heating system** is similar to a hot water system except that the water is changed to steam in a boiler. The steam is then forced through pipes to the convectors, where it gives off heat to the room. ❷ In giving off heat, the steam condenses, or changes from the gas phase to the liquid phase. The condensed steam, or water, flows back to the boiler.

Radiant Hot Water Heating

In a **radiant hot water system,** water is heated in a hot water heater and then transferred to a continuous coil of pipe in the floor of each room. As heat radiates from the pipe, a nearly uniform temperature is maintained from floor to ceiling. This means that the temperature difference between the floor and the ceiling is limited to only a few degrees. Can you think of a reason why radiant hot water heating provides a more even temperature than steam heating or hot water heating? ❸

Radiant Electric Heating

The source of heat for a **radiant electric system** is electricity. As electricity passes through wires or cables that resist the current, heat is produced.

the steam pressure pushes the steam through pipes. Ask,

• **What happens as the water or steam loses its heat?** (Accept all logical answers. Lead students to suggest that hot water will cool and then flow back to the boiler. Steam will cool, condense to water, and the water then flows back to the boiler.)

Skills Development
Skill: Making comparisons
Have students observe Figure 18-2. Tell students to compare the two systems. Ask,

• **Which indirect heating system uses a pump?** (A hot water heating system can use a pump.)

• **What causes the steam to move in a steam heating system?** (The pressure of the steam in the boiler forces the steam through the pipes.)

• **Which indirect heating system has an expansion tank?** (A steam system has an expansion tank.)

• **How are hot water and steam systems similar?** (Both hot water and steam systems have a boiler and distribute the heat to the rooms by pipes and to the air by convectors.)

TEACHER DEMONSTRATION

Light a candle and hold a block of paraffin wax along the side of the flame.
- **What is causing the paraffin to melt?** (Most of the students will answer the heat of the flame.)

Explain that the heat melts only the side of the paraffin that is near it. This higher temperature near the paraffin is due to radiation. Point out that the heat above the candle is due to convection currents.
- **How could we use this heat to warm this room?** (Accept all logical answers.)

HISTORICAL NOTES

The first heating system from a central station was installed in Lockport, New York, in 1877, by Birdsall Holly. He dug a trench 30.5 meters long and ran a pipe from the central station to his house. He later developed the Holly Steam Combination Company, Ltd. in Lockport.

18-1 (continued)

Content Development
Explain that in a warm air system the furnace is surrounded by a brick or iron jacket filled with air. The furnace heats the air, which is pumped by a fan and circulated to the rooms through pipes to the registers (convectors).

Skills Development
Skill: Applying concepts
- **What happens when the warm air reaches the room?** (Most students will say it circulates in a convection current and then cools down.)
- **What happens to the air after it cools?** (Accept all logical answers. Lead students to understand that cool air is denser than warm air and will sink to the floor. The cooled air is then pumped back to the furnace.)

Content Development
Point out to students that the heat pump system gets its heat from the earth. Explain that an electric motor

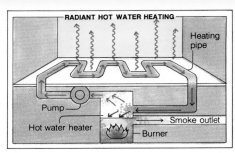

Figure 18–3 *In these central systems, heat is transferred by radiation. The source of heat in a radiant hot water system (left) is hot water. In a radiant electric system (right), the source of heat is electricity. What is radiation?* ❶

Figure 18–4 *In a warm air system (left), hot air from a furnace is forced through pipelike connections called ducts to vents. How is heat transferred in this system? A heat pump system (right) takes heat from the outside and brings it inside—even in cold weather! What two phase changes are involved in this heating system?* ❷

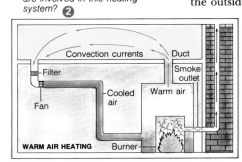

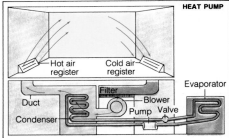

These wires or cables can be installed in the ceiling, floor, baseboards, or walls of a room. The heat produced is radiated to all parts of the room. A thermostat, often installed in each room or local area, controls the amount of heat produced by the wires or cables.

Warm Air Heating

A **warm air system** consists of a furnace, a blower, pipelike connections called ducts, and vents that open into each room being heated. The furnace heats the air, which is then forced by the blower through the ducts to the vents. Convection currents keep the warm air moving as it transfers its heat to the surrounding air. Cool air returns to the furnace by another duct. As the air circulates, filters remove dust particles.

Heat Pump

A **heat pump system** is based on the principle that the earth or outside air contains heat that can be used to heat an area—even in cold weather! What a heat pump actually does is take heat from the outside air and bring it inside.

makes a liquid flow through long pipes under the ground outside the building. The flowing liquid takes heat from the earth and brings it back into the building.

Skills Development
Skill: Using a model
Have students observe Figure 18-4. Compare and discuss the advantages and disadvantages of the warm air and the heat pump systems of heating.

You might use some of the following questions.
- **What are some advantages of warm air heating systems?** (Accept all logical answers. Students might include the lower initial costs of a warm air system.)
- **What are some disadvantages of warm air heating systems?** (Accept all logical answers. Students might include the problems of cold drafts or soot.)

A heat pump circulates a liquid that evaporates at a low temperature through a coil *outside* the building. As the liquid passes through the coil, it picks up heat from the air or the ground. When the liquid gains enough heat, it becomes a vapor. The vapor travels into a compressor, where an increase in pressure raises its temperature. The hot vapor then passes to a coil *inside* the building where it heats the air. The warm air is forced through ducts and circulated through each room just as in a warm air system.

Once the hot vapor has given off its heat, it condenses into a hot liquid. The hot liquid is then cooled as it passes through a pressure-reducing valve. Finally, the cooled liquid is pumped into the outdoor coil to begin the process all over again. Can you see some disadvantages in this type of heating system? ❸

Solar Heating

A **solar heating system** uses the energy of the sun to produce heat. There are two basic types of solar heating systems: **active solar heating** and **passive solar heating.**

An active solar system includes a device for collecting solar energy—called a solar collector—a place to store the heat, and a means for circulating the heat throughout the building.

Figure 18–5 shows a typical active solar heating system. The solar collector consists of a metal plate painted black on the side that faces the sun. Black absorbs sunlight better than any other color. The sunlight that is absorbed by the plate heats it. On the back of the plate is a series of metal tubing. Water, or some other liquid, circulates through the tubing. The tubing is covered by glass or clear plastic to keep it from losing heat.

As sunlight strikes the collector, it is absorbed. The heat absorbed by the collector is transferred to the water. The heated water flows through a tube to a storage tank. Here the heat from the water in the tube is transferred to the water in the tank by a heat exchanger in the tank. The hot water circulates through pipes to heat the house or to heat air blown into the house. In the meantime, a pump

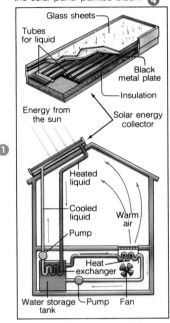

Figure 18–5 *Water in the solar panel of this active solar system (top) is heated by the sun and piped to a storage tank. Here it heats water in the water tank. This heated water then circulates through pipes to heat the house (bottom). Why is the metal plate in the solar panel painted black?* ❹

421

means "without force." Passive solar systems consist of collectors that collect radiant energy from the sun, change it to heat, and use the heat directly.

• **What do you think *active* means in regard to solar heating?** (Accept all logical answers.)

Point out that active means "moving with force." An active solar heating system is something like a heat pump. But, an active solar system receives heat from our sun rather than the earth. Explain that in an active solar heating system, the collector is usually a black plate. On the back of the plate, a liquid runs through tubes. The sun heats the plate, the plate heats the tubes, and the tubes heat the liquid. The liquid is then pumped to a storage tank. When heat is needed, the warm liquid is circulated to heat the building. Sometimes the heated water is circulated to convectors as in a hot water system. Sometimes the liquid heats air and the heated air is circulated as in a warm air system. A pump then circulates the cooled liquid back to the collector to be reheated.

Reinforcement

Have students read, write reports, and discuss the advantages and disadvantages of using heat pumps or solar systems as compared to the "conventional" warm air, warm water, steam, or radiant heating systems.

• **What are some advantages of warm heat pump systems?** (Accept all logical answers. Students might include the conservation of fossil fuels or low cost of operation.)

• **What are some disadvantages of heat pump systems?** (Accept all logical answers. Students might include the high initial cost, or that they question whether the heat pump *really* works.)

Content Development

Explain that in some parts of the country the sun is used to furnish all or part of the energy needed to heat homes and buildings. This is called a solar heating system. The two types of solar heating systems are called active and passive.

• **What do you think the word *passive* means in this case?** (Accept all logical answers.)

Point out that the word *passive*

18-1 (continued)

Section Review 18-1

1. A central heating system generates heat for a building or a group of buildings in one central place.

2. Hot water system: water is heated in a hot water heater, then circulated through pipes to convectors. Heat is given off by hot water. Steam system: water is heated to steam in a boiler, then the steam is forced through pipes to convectors. Heat is given off as the steam condenses.

3. Electricity passes through wires that resist the flow of current, producing heat that radiates into the room. It requires no combustion of fuel in the building being heated.

4. A passive solar system uses solar energy directly to heat an area. An active solar system collects, stores, transfers, and circulates the heat energy from the sun.

5. Heat flowing from a warmer substance to a cooler substance causes the liquid refrigerant to gain heat from the outside air or ground. A continued transfer of heat causes the liq-

Figure 18–6 *The solar furnace at Odeille, France (left), uses hundreds of movable mirrors to focus the direct rays of the sun onto an enormous mirror. The curved mirror reflects the rays onto a single point, producing temperatures of more than 3800°C. The front side of this solar house is all windows so that the greatest amount of sunlight can be collected (right).*

Figure 18–7 *This building uses a unique central heating system. Water used to cool the computers is circulated throughout the building. Because the water has absorbed heat from the computers, it can be used to heat the building's interior.*

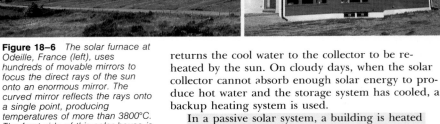

422

returns the cool water to the collector to be reheated by the sun. On cloudy days, when the solar collector cannot absorb enough solar energy to produce hot water and the storage system has cooled, a backup heating system is used.

In a passive solar system, a building is heated directly by the rays of the sun. To get the most heat from a passive solar system, the building must be designed with the placement, size, and orientation of windows in mind. Figure 18–6 shows a building designed for passive solar heating.

Because of the variations in the amount of solar energy received at a particular location, passive solar systems are usually not the only source of heat for a building. A backup heating system usually must be used with a passive solar system. A backup system provides heat when sunlight is not available or when the heat collected during the day is not enough for a cold night. What conditions do you think affect the amount of solar energy a location receives? ❶

SECTION REVIEW

1. What is a central heating system?
2. How does a steam heating system differ from a hot water system?
3. Describe how a radiant electric system produces heat. Why is it different from other central heating systems?
4. What is the basic difference between an active solar system and a passive solar system?
5. Describe the heat transfers involved in a heat pump system.

---

uid to change phase and become a vapor. As the vapor passes through the inside coil, heat flows from the hot vapor to the cooler air. This loss of heat energy causes the vapor to condense into a liquid.

TEACHING STRATEGY 18-2

Motivation

Take a sample of insulating material, such as fiberglass, and wrap it around

one end of a short metal rod. Place the other end of the rod into the flame of a Bunsen burner or alcohol lamp. (The fiberglass insulating material will prevent the heat from passing out of the metal rod and to your hand.) Ask,

• **What can you tell us about metals and heat conduction?** (Most students will remember from Chapter 17 that metals are good heat conductors.)

18–2 Insulation

Once heat is brought into a room or building, it will quickly begin to escape if the area lacks proper **insulation.** Insulation materials reduce heat transfer because they are poor conductors of heat. **Insulation prevents heat loss by reducing the transfer of heat that occurs by conduction and convection.**

A common insulating material is **fiberglass.** Fiberglass consists of long, thin strands of glass packed together. In between the strands are air spaces. Glass is a poor conductor of heat. So is the air that is trapped between the fibers.

Insulating materials are packed beneath roofs and in the outside walls of buildings. Insulation can also be used around doors and windows. This type of insulation is called weather stripping. Weather stripping prevents heat loss by closing up spaces through which heat is transferred by convection. Double-pane window glass is another effective insulator. The air trapped between the panes of glass does not conduct heat well. And the air space is so small that convection cannot take place either.

Figure 18–8 *The long, shaggy hair of a musk ox provides insulation from the cold Arctic winter. During the fall, the ox grows an inner matting of hair, which combined with the outer coat gives a double blanket of protection.*

Figure 18–9 *Invisible heat energy, or infrared energy, can be "seen" by using a device called a thermograph. This thermogram, or heat picture, reveals heat loss from a house. Generally, the lighter and brighter the color, the greater the heat loss. How can a thermogram be useful to homeowners?* ②

423

18-2 INSULATION

SECTION PREVIEW 18-2

Insulation prevents heat loss by reducing the transfer of heat that occurs by conduction and convection. Insulating materials can be used in the walls and under the roofs of buildings. Storm windows, when placed over regular windows, create insulating air spaces between the two glass surfaces. Weatherstripping or special materials can be placed around windows and doors, slowing heat transfer (heat escape) through cracks that might be present.

PERFORMANCE OBJECTIVES 18-2

1. Describe how insulation, weatherstripping, and storm windows reduce heat transfer.

2. Explain how insulation prevents heat transfer out of a building during winter.

3. Describe how insulation prevents heat transfer into a building during summer.

SCIENCE TERMS 18-2

insulation p. 423
fiberglass p. 423

---

down, but not completely *stop* heat loss.

Skills Development
Skill: Applying technology
• **What if you lived in a very hot climate? What would you do to slow down heat transfer *into* your house?** (Accept all logical answers such as insulating the roof and walls.) (NOTE: Air conditioning only cools a house, it does not slow down or prevent heat transfer *into* the house.)
• **What if you lived in a very cold climate? What would you do to slow down energy transfer *out* of your house?** (Accept all logical answers such as insulating the roof and walls.) (NOTE: Heating systems only warm houses, they do not slow down or prevent heat transfer *out* of the house.)

• **Why isn't the heat burning my hand?** (Accept all logical answers.)

Content Development
Explain that insulators, such as fiberglass and other loose materials, prevent heat from moving easily from one place to another. The fluffier an insulating material is, the more air spaces or pockets the material has. Point out that air is an *excellent* heat insulator. The many air spaces in

good heat insulators prevent heat from being conducted away.

Content Development
Point out that there are two main ways in which heat is lost from houses. Heat is conducted through the windows, walls, and roof. Heat convection currents transfer heat away through any cracks around doors and windows. Heat is also radiated through the windows. Explain that insulation can slow

18-3 COOLING SYSTEMS

SECTION PREVIEW 18-3

Most cooling systems work on the principle of evaporation. Cooling systems remove heat energy from a room, building, or other space. Refrigerators and freezers cool by taking heat away from the material inside the unit.

Air conditioning systems do four things: cool the temperature, lower the humidity, remove stale air and dust, and add fresh air.

Cooling systems are a special form of heat exchanger. Cooling systems *use* the heat energy of evaporization to cool the inside of the container. The evaporated gas is then pumped to the outside compressor where energy is *released* during condensation and blown away by the fan.

PERFORMANCE OBJECTIVES 18-3

1. **Describe the operation of a cooling system.**
2. **Describe how the heat of evaporization and heat of condensation are used to cool a refrigerator.**

SCIENCE TERMS 18-3

storage tank p. 424
freezer unit p. 424
compressor p. 424
condenser coil p. 424
refrigerant p. 424
Freon p. 424

Figure 18–10 *Believe it or not, blocks of ice can be used to insulate a home, as this Eskimo of the Arctic Circle well knows. How is an igloo insulated?* ❶

A well-insulated building works as well in hot weather as it does in cold weather. In hot weather, the insulation keeps heat out. The building is kept relatively cool as heat from the outside air is prevented from entering by either conduction or convection. ❶

SECTION REVIEW

1. What is insulation? What is its purpose?
2. How does fiberglass prevent heat loss?
3. Why is good insulation important in both hot and cold weather?
4. Explain why insulation prevents heat transfer by both conduction and convection.
5. The cardboard used for a pizza box is naturally brown in color. Explain why companies spend extra money to dye these boxes white. What else might be done to the boxes to make them more effective insulators?

Section Objective

To describe the operation of a cooling system

Sharpen Your Skills

Evaporation and Cooling

1. Place a drop of water on the back of your hand. Observe how your hand feels as the drop of water evaporates.
2. Repeat step 1 but this time use a drop of rubbing alcohol. Is there any difference in the rate of evaporation?
3. Fasten a small piece of wet cotton around the bulb of a thermometer. Fan it with a sheet of cardboard. What happens to the level of mercury in the thermometer?

424

18–3 Cooling Systems

Have you ever stepped out of a swimming pool and felt a chill—even though you were warm before you got wet? This cooling effect is due to evaporation. As the water molecules on your skin absorb heat from your body, they change from the liquid phase to the gas phase. This absorption of heat leaves your body temperature lower than before. Evaporation is a cooling process.

The process of evaporation is used by cooling systems to remove heat energy from a room, building, or other space. Refrigerators, air conditioners, and dehumidifiers all contain **cooling systems.**

A cooling system consists of four basic parts: a **storage tank, freezer unit, compressor,** and **condenser coils.** A cooling system also includes a **refrigerant.** A refrigerant is the liquid that is to be evaporated. A refrigerant evaporates at a low temperature. Many cooling systems use **Freon** (FREE-ahn) as the refrigerant. Another common refrigerant is ammonia.

18-2 (continued)

Section Review 18-2

1. A material that conducts heat poorly; to prevent heat loss by reducing the transfer of heat by conduction and convection
2. Thin strands of glass are packed with air between them. Glass is a poor conductor of heat, as is the air trapped between the fibers.
3. In hot weather, it keeps heat out of a building. In cold weather, it keeps heat in.
4. Conduction is prevented because the materials are poor conductors of heat. Convection is prevented because the air spaces in the insulating materials are so small.
5. The darker-colored box is a poorer conductor of heat than a white box. As such, the pizza stays warmer longer. Adding a piece of aluminum foil on top of the pizza will also help.

TEACHING STRATEGY 18-3

Motivation

Explain that all cooling systems use evaporation as part of the cooling process. Point out that before we had refrigeration units, people kept food cool by wrapping it in wet leather or fabric. If possible, show students a canvas or leather evaporative water cooling bag. These bags are still used in desert areas.

Figure 18–11 shows a typical refrigerator system. Liquid Freon in the storage tank is pumped to the freezer unit. As the liquid refrigerant evaporates here, it absorbs heat from the freezer compartment. So the inside of the refrigerator becomes cool. The Freon vapor then flows to a compressor, where the pressure of the gas is increased. The hot gaseous Freon next passes through the condenser coils, where it loses its heat and changes back into a liquid. The liquid Freon then returns to the storage tank and the process begins again.

The heat removed from the freezer compartment of a refrigerator is radiated from the condenser coils to the outside air. The condenser coils are often found on the back surface of a refrigerator. Fans are sometimes used to help blow away the air that is heated by the coils, which can become quite warm. So you must be careful not to touch these coils. Although it might sound strange, you could burn yourself on the refrigerator!

SECTION REVIEW

1. How does a cooling system use evaporation?
2. What are the basic parts of a cooling system?
3. What is a refrigerant?
4. Why is it unwise to try to cool a room by opening the door of the refrigerator?

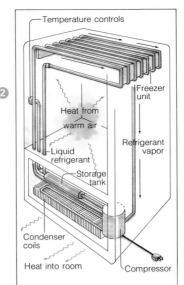

Figure 18–11 *In this diagram, you can see how the basic parts of a refrigerator work as a cooling system. What phase change takes place in the freezer unit? In the condenser coils?* ❷

18–4 Heat Engines

Section Objective

To explain how heat engines use heat energy to do work

In Chapter 17, you learned that the experiments of Rumford and Joule showed that work produces heat. **Heat engines** make use of the reverse process. **Heat engines are machines that convert heat energy into mechanical energy in order to do work.**

All heat engines involve **combustion.** Combustion is the burning of a fuel. During combustion, a fuel is heated to a temperature at which it combines with oxygen in the air and gives off heat. Heat engines are classified into two main types according to where combustion takes place.

425

ANNOTATION KEY

❶ The ice prevents heat transfer by conduction. (Applying concepts)
❷ Evaporation, condensation (Interpreting illustrations)
❶ Thinking Skill: Relating Concepts
❷ Thinking Skill: Applying technology

Content Development

Have students observe Figure 18-11. Read the caption. Explain that a refrigerator cools by taking heat away from materials. The refrigerator has a pipe filled with a gas called Freon. A motor runs a compressor, which takes heat away from the Freon until it becomes a liquid. The liquid Freon then flows to the ice compartment or freezing unit where it again becomes a gas.

Content Development

Explain that when a liquid evaporates, it *uses* heat from inside the refrigerator. The Freon gas then continues to the compressor, where the pressure forces it to change to a liquid by condensing. During condensation, heat energy is *released* and is blown away by a fan.

SECTION REVIEW 18-3

1. Liquid refrigerant passes through the freezer unit where is absorbs and evaporates into a vapor. Evaporation removes heat from the freezing compartment, causing it to become cold.
2. Storage tank, freezer unit, compressor, condenser coil
3. Liquid that evaporates at a low temperature and is used in a cooling system
4. A refrigerator transfers heat into the room. By opening the refrigerator door, more heat from the room flows into the freezing compartment. The refrigerator must now work harder to cool itself, releasing more heat back into the room.

18-4 HEAT ENGINES

SECTION PREVIEW 18-4

Heat engines are machines that convert heat energy into mechanical energy that can do work. Heat engines are classified into two types: the external-combustion engine and the internal-combustion engine.

In the external-combustion engine, fuel is burned outside of the engine. The steam engine is an example of an external-combustion engine. In a steam engine, steam is produced by making water boil in a boiler that is *outside* the engine. The boiling water expands to steam, which provides the energy to operate the engine.

In the internal-combustion engine, fuel is burned inside of the cylinder of the engine. When the fuel burns, the heat produced expands the gases and forces a piston to move.

PERFORMANCE OBJECTIVES 18-4

1. **Explain how heat engines convert heat energy into mechanical energy.**
2. **Classify the two main types of heat engines.**
3. **Identify the sequence of events in a four-stroke gasoline engine.**

SCIENCE TERMS 18-4

heat engine p. 425
combustion p. 425
external-combustion engine p. 426
piston p. 426
cylinder p. 426
turbine p. 426
internal-combustion engine p. 426
carburetor p. 426
intake valve p. 426
intake stroke p. 426
spark plug p. 427
compression stroke p. 427
power stroke p. 427
exhaust stroke p. 427
exhaust valve p. 427
diesel engine p. 427

Sharpen Your Skills

Technology and Social Change

It has been said that the Industrial Revolution of the nineteenth century was powered by the steam engine.

Using books and other reference materials in the library, find out how the Industrial Revolution changed American society. What was the role of the steam engine in this revolution? Discuss your findings with your class.

Can you name some technological advances that have changed modern society? How have they changed it?

Figure 18–12 *The paddle wheels of this steamship are driven by an external-combustion engine (top). The operation of an external-combustion engine converts heat energy into mechanical energy (bottom).*

External-Combustion Engine

In an **external-combustion engine,** fuel is burned outside the engine. The steam engine is an external-combustion engine. Steam is heated in a boiler outside the engine and then passed through a valve into the engine. In early steam engines, the steam pushed against a metal plate called a **piston,** which moved back and forth in a tube called a **cylinder.** The movement of the piston passed mechanical energy to a connecting rod, which then did some kind of work, such as turning the wheels of a train or the propellers of a steamship.

Modern steam engines usually do not use a piston and cylinder. Instead, steam under great pressure is passed through holes onto paddle wheels called **turbines.** The turbines, rotating like high-speed windmills, produce mechanical energy. A steam turbine is more efficient than a piston and cylinder because it wastes less energy.

Internal-Combustion Engine

When the burning of fuel takes place inside an engine, the engine is called an **internal-combustion engine.** A familiar type of internal-combustion engine is the gasoline engine, which powers most cars.

A gasoline engine is a four-stroke engine. In the first stroke, gasoline is turned into a vapor and mixed with air in the **carburetor** (KAHR-ber-ay-ter). The mixture is then transferred through the **intake valve** to a cylinder. This process is the **intake stroke.**

Inside the cylinder is a piston. As the piston moves to the top of the cylinder, the gaseous mixture is compressed, or pushed together. The mixture

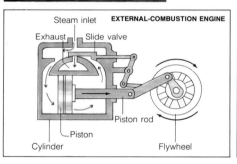

EXTERNAL-COMBUSTION ENGINE

Steam inlet
Exhaust
Slide valve
Piston
Cylinder
Piston rod
Flywheel

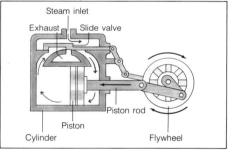

Steam inlet
Exhaust
Slide valve
Piston
Cylinder
Piston rod
Flywheel

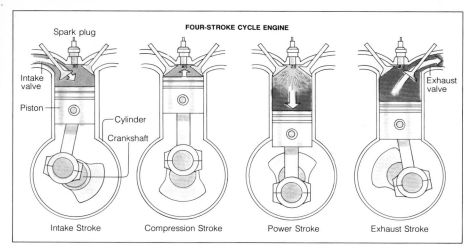

FOUR-STROKE CYCLE ENGINE

Spark plug

Intake valve

Piston

Cylinder

Crankshaft

Exhaust valve

Intake Stroke   Compression Stroke   Power Stroke   Exhaust Stroke

is reduced to one-seventh of its original volume. A **spark plug** produces an electric spark that ignites the fuel at just the right moment in the four-stroke cycle. This process is the **compression stroke.**

The explosion of hot gases increases the volume of the mixture and forces the piston back down in what is called the **power stroke.** At this point, energy is transferred from the piston to the wheels of the car by a series of shafts and gears.

Finally, the piston moves to the top of the cylinder to expel gases through the **exhaust valve.** This process is called the **exhaust stroke.** As the piston falls back down, more gas and air from the carburetor enter the cylinder to begin the four-stroke cycle again. A fixed amount of gasoline is used up in each cycle, and waste products are given off as exhaust at the end of each cycle. Figure 18–13 shows the four strokes that make up each cycle.

A **diesel engine,** like a gasoline engine, is an internal-combustion engine. But in a diesel engine, only air is taken in during the intake stroke. At the end of the compression stroke, a measured amount of fuel is injected into the compressed air in the cylinder. The compression of the gas raises its temperature high enough so that the fuel ignites spontaneously. For this reason, a diesel engine does not have spark plugs. Can you explain why a diesel engine might more correctly be called a compression–ignition engine? ❷

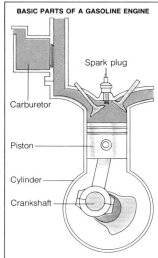

BASIC PARTS OF A GASOLINE ENGINE

Spark plug

Carburetor

Piston

Cylinder

Crankshaft

Figure 18–13 *A gasoline engine is a four-stroke internal-combustion engine. Here you see the* ❷ *processes involved in each stroke. During which stroke is energy transferred from the piston to the wheels of the car?* ❶

427

ANNOTATION KEY

❶ **Power stroke (Interpreting diagrams)**

❷ **The compression of the gases raises the temperature high enough so that the fuel ignites spontaneously. (Relating concepts)**

❶ **Thinking Skill: Sequencing events**

❷ **Thinking Skill: Applying technology**

similar to the following.
• **What happens during the intake stroke?** (The exhaust valve is closed and the intake valve is opened. The piston is pulled down by the crankshaft. The mixture of gasoline vapor and air from the carburetor enters the chamber through the intake valve.)
• **What happens during the compression stroke?** (The exhaust valve remains closed. The intake valve closes. The piston is pushed up the cylinder by the crankshaft. The piston compresses the vapor into a very small volume.)
• **What happens during the power stroke?** (The intake and exhaust valve remain closed. High voltage electricity is sent to the spark plug. The spark ignites the vapor. The exploding vapor expands rapidly and pushes the piston down the cylinder. The downward motion of the piston turns the crankshaft.)
• **What happens during the exhaust stroke?** (The intake valve remains

• **What kind of engine made the vehicle move?** (Most students will probably reply "gasoline." However, some may have traveled in a vehicle powered by a diesel engine and some by electric railroad.) Point out that gasoline and diesel engines are called internal-combustion engines.

Content Development
Explain that during combustion the oxidation must be fast enough to produce both heat and light. Point out that heat engines are divided into two main types according to where the combustion takes place. Heat engines are machines that convert heat energy into mechanical energy to do work.

Skills Development
Skill: Sequencing events
Interpret and discuss each of the four strokes of the cycle shown in Figure 18-13 (top diagram). Ask questions

18-5 THERMAL POLLUTION

SECTION PREVIEW 18-5

Thermal pollution occurs when waste heat damages the environment by causing an unnatural rise in temperature. Every day our air is being polluted by tons of gases, liquids, and solids that contain unwanted heat energy. This waste heat energy is given off by smokestacks, lights, exhaust from cars, hot water from factories and nuclear power plants. This unnatural heat in the atmosphere and water is eventually transferred to all parts of our planet. Thermal pollution endangers all life forms on planet Earth.

PERFORMANCE OBJECTIVES 18-5

1. Define thermal pollution.
2. Describe how thermal pollution occurs.
3. Explain how thermal pollution can be controlled and reduced.

SCIENCE TERMS 18-5

thermal pollution p. 429

18-4 (continued)

closed and the exhaust valve is opened. The crankshaft forces the piston into the cylinder. The upward-moving piston pushes waste and burned gases out through the exhaust valve.)
• **What happens next?** (The four cycles start over again with intake, compression, power, and then exhaust cycles.)

Section Review 18-4

1. By changing heat into mechanical energy
2. External-combustion engine and internal-combustion engine. External-combustion engine burns fuel outside the engine; internal-combustion engine burns fuel inside the engine.
3. Intake stroke, compression stroke, power stroke, exhaust stroke
4. Possible reasons might include ex-

Section Objective

To discuss the effects of thermal pollution

18-5 Thermal Pollution

Modern technology could not exist without the use of heat energy. Yet like many aspects of technology, the use of heat energy can be harmful to the environment.

CAREER
Ceramic Engineer

HELP WANTED: CERAMIC ENGINEER to develop laboratory equipment and pollution control devices. Applicant must have a college degree in ceramic engineering.

Perhaps the word *ceramics* brings to mind pottery and dishes. But to a **ceramic engineer,** the word means much more. For the world of ceramics goes far beyond the kitchen. A ceramic engineer develops products that are made of clay, sand, glass, and other materials that do not contain metal or plastic. These materials are all processed at high temperatures—650°C to 1650°C—in ovens called kilns.

A ceramic engineer may work in many fields, including energy development, art, pollution control, housewares manufacturing, and aerospace. A ceramic engineer may develop new types of dishes, construction materials, electric insulation, laboratory equipment, medical products, computer chips, and machine parts.

Ceramics are versatile because they are not good conductors of heat or electricity. Using ceramics, people are able to safely handle such extremely hot materials as molten metals or

high-voltage electric equipment. Also, ceramics can be made porous, waterproof, or airtight. Another advantage of ceramics is that they can be made into many different shapes—from hair-thin glass fibers for transmitting electronic messages to beautiful sculptures.

For information about a career as a ceramic engineer, contact the National Institute of Ceramic Engineers, 65 Ceramic Drive, Columbus, OH 43214.

---

plosion of hot gases may result in randomly directed energy; considerable energy may be lost due to friction or to the surrounding air, particularly in the exhaust stroke.

TEACHING STRATEGY 18-5

Motivation

Use a world map or globe. Point out the polar caps and explain that much of the earth's surface is covered with

ice. Point out the tropical regions at and near the equator. Point out the temperate zones between the equator and the poles. Lead students to discuss the possible consequences of the ocean waters rising and increasing world air temperatures.
• **What do you think could happen if all the icecaps at the poles melted?** (Accept all logical answers.)
• **What could happen to animal life in Africa?** (Accept all answers.)

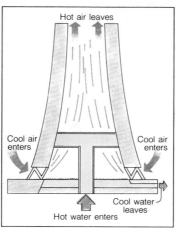

Hot air leaves

Cool air enters

Cool air enters

Cool water leaves

Hot water enters

Much of the heat generated by industrial processes cannot be used. It is waste heat. This waste heat is often released directly into the atmosphere or released as hot water that gets dumped into nearby rivers and lakes. **Thermal pollution** results. **Thermal pollution occurs when waste heat damages the environment by causing an unnatural rise in temperature.**

Thermal pollution endangers the survival of fish, plants, and animals. Fish are especially vulnerable to ❶ increases in water temperature. Some species will survive only a few hours at temperatures above 25°C.

What can be done to reduce thermal pollution? One solution is the use of a **cooling tower.** In a cooling tower, hot water from a factory or power plant is cooled as it flows through pipes. By the time the water is released into a nearby river or lake, it has cooled enough so that it poses no threat to the wildlife of the area.

Figure 18–14 *These cooling towers at the Three Mile Island Nuclear Power Plant in Pennsylvania are used to reduce thermal pollution of the air and water (left). Hot water from the power plant is cooled as it flows through pipes suspended in the tower (right).*

Figure 18–15 *The cooling system of a skating rink freezes the water to provide a smooth, hard surface for Olympic skater Tiffany Chin.*

SECTION REVIEW

1. What is thermal pollution?
2. What types of wildlife are threatened by thermal pollution?
3. What is the source of the heat that causes thermal pollution?
4. According to Figure 18–14, where does the excess heat go after the water is cooled in the cooling tower?

429

gradually rising. Point out that heat energy both from the sun and our modern technology and from the use of heat energy is causing this "heat blanket."

Tell students that this waste heat is causing thermal pollution. Explain that *thermal* means "heat."

• **What is pollution?** (Accept all answers, but lead students to suggest that it is making something "dirty or unclean" by discarding unwanted and unused substances into the environment.

Explain that thermal pollution occurs when waste heat damages the environment by causing an unnatural rise in temperature.

Section Review 18-5
1. Damage to the environment by the disposal of waste heat, which raises the temperature of the environment
2. Fish, plants, and other animals in and around the area where excess heat is released
3. Waste heat from factories and power plants
4. Into the air

• **What could happen to the orange and grapefruit orchards in California and Florida?** (Accept all logical answers.)
• **What could happen to the corn and soybean crops in Iowa, Illinois, and other midwestern states?** (Accept all answers.)
• **What could happen to the beef and pork industry throughout the country?** (Accept all answers.)
• **What could happen to the forests and parks in Montana, Oregon, Wyoming, and other northwestern states?** (Accept all answers.)
• **What could happen to the automobile industry?** (Accept all answers.)
• **What could happen to the way you dress, eat, and live?** (Accept all answers.)

Content Development
Explain that scientists are concerned that the temperature of the earth is

LABORATORY INVESTIGATION CONSTRUCTING A SOLAR COLLECTOR

BEFORE THE LAB

1. **Divide the class into groups of six students. Have each team bring one shoe box to school for the investigation.**
2. **Gather all materials at least one day prior to the investigation. You should have enough supplies to meet your class needs, assuming six students per group.**

PRE-LAB DISCUSSION

Have students read the complete laboratory procedure. Have students develop tentative hypotheses to the problem. Then discuss the procedure by asking questions similar to the following.

• **What is the purpose of the laboratory investigation?** (To find out if and how well a solar collector collects heat energy)

• **Why is it important to wrap the shoe box tightly with plastic wrap?** (To prevent heat loss)

• **What does the crumbled newspaper do?** (Insulates the box)

• **Why is it important to tilt the box?** (To allow the water to flow through the collector)

• **What does the tubing do?** (Carry water through the system and collect the solar energy.)

• **How much water should you pour through the system each time?** (250 mL)

• **Which water temperature should be recorded?** (The original liter of water and the water in the collecting beaker every second trial)

Tell the class to record the water temperatures to the nearest half or whole degree Celsius.

SKILL DEVELOPMENT

Students will use the following skills while completing this investigation.
1. Safety
2. Manipulative
3. Measuring
4. Recording
5. Comparing
6. Inferring
7. Applying
8. Observing

SAFETY TIPS

Alert students to be cautious about spilling water. Each drop of "lost" water represents heat collected but lost by carelessness, which could lead to inaccurate data and results.

Problem

How can solar energy be collected?

Materials *(per group)*

shoe box painted black on the inside and filled with newspaper painted black
rubber or plastic tubing, 1-mm diameter and about 1 m in length
funnel
ring stand and ring   graduated cylinder
thermometer   plastic wrap
2 250-mL beakers   pencil
container large   water
  enough to hold
  1 L of water

Procedure

1. Fill the inside of the shoe box with the crumpled newspaper. Use a pencil to punch a hole in each end of the box. See the accompanying diagram.
2. Insert the rubber or plastic tubing through the holes and position it inside the box as shown. Be sure that at least 10 cm of tubing is left sticking out of each end of the box.
3. Wrap the box tightly with plastic wrap.
4. Place the box in direct sunlight, tilting one end so that it is about 5 cm higher than the other end.
5. Attach the funnel to the tubing at the higher end of the box, using the ring stand and ring to hold the funnel in place.
6. Position one beaker at the other end of the tubing. This is the collecting beaker.
7. Fill the container with 1 L of water at room temperature. Measure and record the temperature of the water.
8. Using the graduated cylinder, pour 200 mL of water from the container to the other beaker.
9. Now pour 100 mL of water from the beaker into the funnel.

10. Repeat steps 8 and 9 so that you perform ten trials. *After every second trial, record the trial number and the temperature of the water in the collecting beaker. Remember to empty the water in the collecting beaker at the end of every second trial.*
11. Make a graph of your data. Plot the trial number along the X axis and the temperature along the Y axis.

Observations

1. How did the final water temperature compare with the initial temperature?
2. What happened to the water temperature as the number of trials increased? Does your graph support this observation?

Conclusions

1. What evidence do you have that solar energy is being collected?
2. How do you account for the different temperatures that you recorded?
3. What would happen if you placed the solar collector in direct sunlight for an hour before beginning the experiment?
4. Can you think of ways in which your solar collector might be made more effective?

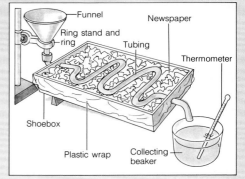

TEACHING STRATEGY FOR LAB PROCEDURE

1. You might ask the teams to write down what they *guess* the temperature rise will be after the second trial. Then before each successive temperature measure, they will have some evidence to make a reasonable estimate or prediction of the expected temperature.
2. Have the teams follow the directions carefully as they work in the laboratory.

CHAPTER REVIEW

SUMMARY

18–1 Heating Systems

❏ A central heating system generates heat for a building or group of buildings from one central location.

❏ Based on the way that heat is delivered, central heating systems are classified as direct or indirect systems.

❏ Major types of central heating systems include hot water, steam, radiant hot water, radiant electric, warm air, heat pump, and solar.

18–2 Insulation

❏ Insulation prevents heat loss by reducing the transfer of heat from a building by conduction and convection.

❏ Materials that provide good insulation are poor conductors of heat.

❏ A well-insulated building works as well in hot weather as it does in cold weather.

18–3 Cooling Systems

❏ Cooling systems use the process of evaporation to remove heat from the surroundings.

❏ A cooling system consists of a storage tank, freezer unit, compressor, condenser coils, and refrigerant.

❏ A refrigerant is a liquid that evaporates at a low temperature.

❏ Two common refrigerants are Freon and ammonia.

18–4 Heat Engines

❏ Heat engines convert heat energy into mechanical energy to do work.

❏ All heat engines involve the process of combustion, or the burning of a fuel.

❏ In an external-combustion engine, fuel is burned outside the engine. The steam engine is an external-combustion engine.

❏ In an internal-combustion engine, fuel is burned inside the engine. The gasoline engine is an internal-combustion engine.

❏ The four strokes in a gasoline engine are the intake stroke, compression stroke, power stroke, and exhaust stroke.

18–5 Thermal Pollution

❏ Thermal pollution occurs when waste heat damages the environment by causing an unnatural rise in temperature.

❏ One solution to thermal pollution is the use of a cooling tower.

VOCABULARY

Define each term in a complete sentence.

active solar heating	cooling tower	Freon	passive solar heating	spark plug
carburetor	cylinder	heat engine	piston	steam heating system
central heating system	diesel engine	heat pump system	power stroke	storage tank
combustion	exhaust stroke	hot water system	radiant electric system	thermal pollution
compression stroke	exhaust valve	insulation	radiant hot water system	turbine
compressor	external-combustion engine	intake stroke		warm air system
condenser coil	fiberglass	intake valve	refrigerant	
cooling system	freezer unit	internal-combustion engine	solar heating system	

431

---

source of the heat must be solar energy.

2. As the collector remained in the sun, it continued to absorb radiant energy. Thus one would expect the latter trials to produce a higher temperature than earlier trials.

3. The amount of heat transferred to the water would probably be greater since the collector had time to absorb more solar energy.

4. Increasing the surface area of the collector by enlarging the box or using more newspaper; increasing the surface area of the tubing by adding more loops; using reflectors such as mirrors to increase the amount of sunlight absorbed by the collector.

GOING FURTHER: ENRICHMENT

Part 1

Tell students to take a *very careful* look at the variables in this investigation. Have them try to control more of the variables. (For instance, if only a *total* of 250 mL of water was used, then the temperature for each repetition could be measured without being mixed with the other 750 mL of water in the large container. Students may create other ingenious methods to better control the variables.)

Part 2

Have students determine the amount of heat (calories) gained by the water as a result of the solar collector. They can use the formula for specific heat. (Multiply the total Celsius degree temperature rise in 1 L of water (1000 grams) by one calorie per gram Celsius degree. The product will be the number of calories of heat energy gained by the liter of water.) For example, if the temperature rise for 1 L of water was from 23° to 29°C, the amount of heat would be calculated as shown below. Heat gained by 1 L of water with 6°C temp. rise:

Heat gained = mass × temp. change × specific heat

Heat gained = $1000 \text{ g} \times 6°C \times 1 \text{ cal/gC}°$ Heat gained = 6000 cal

---

3. After the teams have completed the investigation, you might ask several teams to record their results on the chalkboard. Discuss the similarities and differences in the team results. Lead the class to suggest *logical* cause and effect explanations for any differences.

4. Discuss how the investigation relates to the chapter ideas by asking open questions similar to the following.

• **What happened to the "light" energy from the sun?** (The light energy was converted to heat energy, which raised the temperature of the water.)

OBSERVATIONS

1. Final temperature higher

2. Temperature of water increases as the number of trials increases.

CONCLUSIONS

1. Temperature of water increased, which means that heat was added. The

CHAPTER REVIEW

MULTIPLE CHOICE

1. a	**3.** b	**5.** b	**7.** c	**9.** b
2. c	**4.** d	**6.** d	**8.** a	**10.** b

COMPLETION

1. hot-water
2. heat pump
3. solar
4. solar collector
5. insulation
6. refrigerant
7. combustion
8. external-combustion
9. carburetor
10. thermal pollution

TRUE OR FALSE

1. F condensing
2. T
3. F passive
4. T
5. T
6. T
7. F turbine
8. F internal-combustion
9. T
10. F cooling tower

SKILL BUILDING

1. Diagrams will vary. Check for accuracy.
2. Vacuum: prevents heat transfer by convection; double-walled glass: reduces heat transfer by conduction; air space: reduces heat transfer by convection; cap: made of plastic, which is a nonconductor
3. Direct: warm air, heat pump; indirect: hot water, steam, radiant hot water, solar
4. a. and c. conducts heat poorly and prevents heat transfer by conduction and convection, b. reflects sun's rays, preventing heat transfer by radiation

ESSAY

1. Answers will vary. Each description should include the source of heat, how the heat is transferred, how the heat is circulated, and how the heating cycle begins again.
2. Liquid Freon in the storage tank is pumped to the freezer unit. There it evaporates, causing the surrounding area to become cool. The Freon vapor then flows to a compressor, where the pressure of the gas is increased. As the vaporized Freon passes through the condenser coil, it loses its heat and becomes a liquid.
3. A solar collector contains water, which is heated by the sun. This heated water is then transferred to the storage tank where it can later be used to heat a building or provide hot water.
4. Answers will vary, depending on the type of engine chosen.
5. The lake would probably be most affected because lakes tend to be small bodies of water and, thus, the amount of thermal pollution would raise the lake's temperature far more than if it were a larger body of water, such as the ocean. Because rivers are constantly moving, the water would not rise that much in temperature because the thermal pollution would be spread among a great deal of water passing through the river.
6. Fiberglass conducts heat poorly and prevents heat transfer by conduction. The air spaces in the fiberglass also serve to prevent heat transfer.

On a separate sheet of paper, write the letter of the answer that best completes each statement.

1. Which heating system involves a furnace and a blower?
   a. warm air   b. radiant electric   c. steam   d. hot water
2. Which of the following would *not* be part of an active solar heating system?
   a. water storage tank   b. solar collector   c. fuel tank   d. pipes
3. Which of the following is an insulating material?
   a. Freon   b. fiberglass   c. copper wire   d. ammonia
4. A cooling system removes heat from the surroundings through the process of
   a. condensation.   b. sublimation.   c. insulation.   d. evaporation.
5. In a cooling system, the compressor is used to
   a. transfer the refrigerant to the freezer unit.
   b. increase the pressure of the vaporized refrigerant.
   c. remove heat from the refrigerant.
   d. none of the above.
6. In a steam engine,
   a. fuel is burned outside the engine.   b. steam pushes against a piston or turbine.
   c. steam is heated in a boiler.   d. all of the above.
7. The correct order for the combustion process in a gasoline engine is
   a. intake stroke, exhaust stroke, compression stroke, power stroke.
   b. power stroke, intake stroke, compression stroke, exhaust stroke.
   c. intake stroke, compression stroke, power stroke, exhaust stroke.
   d. compression stroke, power stroke, intake stroke, exhaust stroke.
8. A diesel engine differs from a gasoline engine in that it
   a. takes in only air on the intake stroke.   b. has no cylinder.
   c. uses no compression stroke.   d. releases only air on the exhaust stroke.
9. A cooling tower reduces thermal pollution by
   a. enabling factories to waste less heat.
   b. cooling heated water before it is dumped into the environment.
   c. cooling the air around a factory or power plant.
   d. cooling bodies of water that have been damaged by waste heat.
10. Thermal pollution probably would not be a problem for
    a. fish living in the ocean near a busy industrial seaport.
    b. fish living in a mountain stream.
    c. fish living in a lake near a power plant.
    d. plant life on the bank of a river that flows past a large chemical factory.

On a separate sheet of paper, write the word or words that best complete each statement.

1. Hot water pumped through pipes is the basis of a _____ heating system.
2. Heat is taken from the outside air or ground in a _____ heating system.
3. Energy from sunlight is used by a _____ heating system.
4. A device for collecting solar energy is called a (an) _____.

5. Double-pane windows and weather stripping are examples of _____.
6. In a cooling system, the liquid to be evaporated is called the _____.
7. The burning of a fuel in an engine is called _____.

8. Fuel is burned outside the engine in a (an) _____ engine.
9. In a gasoline engine, gasoline is mixed with air in the _____.
10. The disposal of waste heat into the environment is called _____.

CONTENT REVIEW: TRUE OR FALSE

Determine whether each statement is true or false. Then on a separate sheet of paper, write "true" if it is true. If it is false, change the underlined word or words to make the statement true.

1. Steam gives off heat by evaporating.
2. In a radiant hot water system, hot water flows through a continuous coil of pipe in the floor of each room.
3. A building is heated naturally according to the placement of windows in an active solar heating system.
4. A material that helps to prevent the loss of heat from a building is called insulation.
5. A common refrigerant is Freon.

6. In a cooling system, a refrigerant loses its heat in the condenser coils.
7. In modern steam engines, steam pushes against a piston.
8. A diesel engine is an example of an external-combustion engine.
9. Thermal pollution is caused primarily by the disposal of heated water.
10. Thermal pollution can be reduced by the use of insulating towers.

CONCEPT REVIEW: SKILL BUILDING

Use the skills you have developed in the chapter to complete each activity.

1. **Making diagrams** Make a diagram that shows how a heat pump system gathers heat from the outside air and then uses this heat to warm the air inside a building.
2. **Applying concepts** Figure 17–6 on page 399 shows a diagram of a thermos bottle. In terms of insulation, explain the importance of the vacuum, double-walled glass bottle, air space, and cap.

3. **Classifying systems** Classify each of the following heating systems as direct or indirect: warm air, hot water, steam, heat pump, radiant hot water, solar.
4. **Applying concepts** Explain how each insulation material works: a. plastic foam used in a picnic cooler; b. aluminum foil covering a south-facing window in summer; c. goose down used in a ski jacket.

CONCEPT REVIEW: ESSAY

Discuss each of the following in a brief paragraph.

1. Choose one type of central heating system and describe how it works.
2. Explain how a cooling system operates.
3. Explain how a solar collector works.
4. Choose one type of heat engine and explain how it converts heat into mechanical energy to do work.

5. Which do you think would be *most* affected by thermal pollution: an ocean, a river, or a lake? Assume that each body of water is located near an industrial area. Explain your answer.
6. Explain why fiberglass is a good insulating material.

433

ADDITIONAL QUESTIONS AND TOPIC SUGGESTIONS

1. How does the greenhouse effect warm planet Earth? (Sunlight travels through the earth's atmosphere and hits the planet. Earth materials re-radiate infrared heat energy waves back toward space. Layers of water vapor and carbon dioxide in the atmosphere trap the infrared waves and reflect them back toward the planet. The heat energy bounces back and forth between the crust and the clouds. This greenhouse effect allows the planet to stay warm during cold nights and keeps our temperatures more constant.)

2. Some people suggest that we should replace internal-combustion engines with electric motors to eliminate thermal and soot pollution. Would this be a permanent solution? Why? (Probably not. Most of our electricity is generated by the burning of fossil fuels and at atomic energy plants. These generating plants create huge amounts of thermal and/or soot pollution. In addition, electric motors also produce waste heat when they run. Wind and/or water powered turbines would help reduce the heat at the generating plants, but we have too great a demand for these sources to supply us with all the energy we want and need.)

3. Explain why air conditioning increases thermal pollution. (Air conditioning does cool limited spaces such as houses, offices, and factories. However, the heat energy removed is concentrated and transferred to another place, such as to the air or to our streams and rivers. In addition, we create more random unwanted heat from the motors that power air conditioners.)

ISSUES IN SCIENCE

The following issues can be used as a springboard for class debate, or they can be assigned as a writing homework.

1. Public awareness of air pollution will certainly have an effect on the future design of heating systems. There may be a more widespread opinion on the use of electric or solar heating systems. Should the government subsidize industries in the development of new solar and/or electrical heating techniques. What is your opinion?

2. What is your opinion on the government spending money for the research and development of satellites for earth resource energy technology?

3. Scientists think our planet could continue to heat up because of thermal pollution. If that happens, the icecaps could melt and the atmosphere might become a thick layer of clouds. Some scientists think the thick clouds would reflect energy away from the planet and we would cool down. Other scientists think that the greenhouse effect would work even better and our planet would continue to heat up. What is your opinion?

How could we best relieve the problem of thermal pollution and stop creating an earth "heat blanket"?

Unit Five

HEAT ENERGY

ADVENTURES IN SCIENCE: JENEFIR ISBISTER:SHE DOES DIRTY WORK FOR CLEANER COAL

BACKGROUND INFORMATION

Coal contains two forms of sulfur: inorganic and organic. Inorganic sulfur is largely removed by the cleaning processes currently being used, but organic sulfur is not. It is the organic sulfur that would be removed by sulfur-eating bugs. Coal coming out of the northern Appalachian Mountains, which now contains too much organic sulfur to meet standards on sulfur content, could become usable with the help of micro-organisms.

Coal Bug One can separate the major type of organic sulfur from coal and produce a compound that can be washed away. Since coal contains several types of organic sulfur, bugs with an appetite for other types would have to be developed in order to more thoroughly clean up the coal.

Dr. Jenefir Isbister began her career in science as a medical technician. She became interested in microbiology when she returned to school at night to brush up on new medical technologies. She currently works at the Atlantic Research Corporation in Alexandria, Virginia, as a microbiologist.

Adventures in Science

JENEFIR ISBISTER: She Does

Jenefir Isbister knelt in the blackened soil outside a Pennsylvania coal mine. With a garden trowel, she scooped some dry black soil into a plastic box. The next day, she dug up some soil from outside a coal-processing plant near the laboratory in which she works. She even scooped up a little mud from the bank of a creek in her own backyard.

Why was Dr. Isbister collecting all this soil? "My boss asked me to find a microorganism to remove sulfur from coal," she explains. And such a microorganism might make its home in coal-rich soil. Dr. Isbister is an expert on microorganisms, or living things that are too small to be seen without special equipment. Microorganisms include a variety of bacteria.

Many microorganisms—often called microbes—feed upon nature's garbage, such as fallen leaves and the remains of dead animals and plants. The microbe that Dr. Isbister was searching for was one that eats the sulfur in coal—a sulfur-eating coal bug.

But why would Isbister be looking for such a thing? As she puts it, "A coal bug could help solve the problem of acid rain." In many parts of the world, acid rain is a serious problem whose effects include the death of trees, fish, and other living things.

Acid rain often is caused by burning coal that contains high levels of sulfur. The coal smoke produced contains sulfur dioxide. Sulfur dioxide chemically combines with water in the air to form sulfuric acid, a very strong acid. The acid falls to the earth as acid rain, acid snow, and even acid fog.

One way to reduce acid rain, then, is to remove as much sulfur as possible from the coal. Washing the coal before burning is the simplest method of scrubbing out the sulfur. But coal washing is expensive and removes only some of the sulfur. Prying more sulfur out of coal requires a chemical reaction—the kind of chemical reaction microbes produce when they dine.

434

TEACHING STRATEGY

Motivation

Write on the chalkboard the following sequence for the formation of acid rain: coal (containing sulfur) $\xrightarrow{\text{burns}}$ combines with oxygen→ forms sulfur dioxide (SO_2)→ combines with moisture in the air→ forms sulfuric acid (H_2SO_4)→ falls to earth as acid rain→ pollutes bodies of water and soil. Ask,

• **Where does acid rain begin?** (with the sulfur contained in coal)
• **Where does it end?** (with the pollution of rivers, lakes, soil)

Content Development

Refer to the acid rain sequence and ask,
• **Where do you think it is easier to solve a problem—where it begins or where it ends?** (where it begins)

Explain that for many years sci-entists have been working on removing sulfur from coal to prevent the formation of acid rain. Some of this work has been successful, but current techniques cannot remove all the sulfur, particularly from certain types of coal.

After students have read the article, ask,
• **What new technique for sulfur removal is being developed by Dr. Isbister?** (the use of microorganisms

"A sulfur-eating microbe would let us use high-sulfur coal," Dr. Isbister explains. And high-sulfur coal is inexpensive and plentiful.

So Dr. Isbister began collecting soil in the hope of finding a microbe that eats sulfur. "Soil is the best place to look for microorganisms that will grow under many conditions," she explains. "We didn't want bugs we had to baby!"

In the first step of experimentation, Dr. Isbister and Dr. Richard Doyle, a coworker at the Atlantic Research Corporation in Alexandria, Virginia, crushed each soil sample and placed a small amount of each in separate flasks of salt solution. "The solution keeps the microbes alive while we separate them from the soil," Isbister explains.

Dirty Work for *Cleaner* Coal

A special machine was then used to wash the bugs out of the soil in each flask. Liquid from the top of each flask was then added to another flask filled with nutrient broth. "It's a kind of soup that feeds the microorganisms," explains Isbister.

Next, the researchers added sulfur to each microbe broth. "We did lots of tests. After a long time, we found one solution that contained less sulfur than we had put in," says Isbister. The microbes in this broth had done the best job of eating sulfur. Surprisingly, the sulfur-eating microbes were the ones from her own backyard! Unfortunately, it had taken the microbes seven days to lower the sulfur level by only seven percent. "Seven percent is very little; seven days is horrible," says Isbister. "But it was a start. We had a little celebration."

Now the team added powerful chemicals to the broth, hoping to change the microbes' basic cell structure. The goal was to make the microbes hungrier for sulfur.

"I tested 250 chemical combinations," Isbister recalls. Finally, she found one com-

bination that caused the microbes to eat 80 percent of the sulfur in just 18 hours. "Then we really celebrated, and Dr. Doyle and I applied for a patent on Coal Bug One." Coal Bug One is the nickname the researchers have

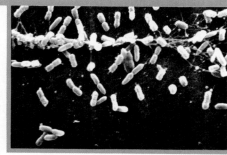

Coal Bug One, shown here in an electromicrograph (bottom), may solve the problem of burning high-sulfur coal (top).

given their sulfur-eating microbe. Two and one-half years of research had finally resulted in success.

Will Coal Bug One solve the problem of high-sulfur coal? "Coal Bug One eats just one of the many kinds of sulfur found in coal," Isbister replies. "So we'll need to find more bugs. But Coal Bug One is the first step."

435

ADDITIONAL QUESTIONS AND TOPIC SUGGESTIONS

1. What surprise did Dr. Isbister have when she discovered which bugs were eating sulfur? (The sulfur-eating bugs were from her own backyard—not the coal mines.)

2. What did Dr. Isbister do to increase the amount and rate of sulfur consumption by the bugs? (added chemicals to the "nutrient soup" she was feeding the bugs)

3. Can you explain how Dr. Isbister used the scientific method in her work? (She identified the problem: to get more sulfur out of coal. She formed a hypothesis: there must be microorganisms who would remove sulfur from coal. She set about collecting data by experimenting with various bugs. She analyzed and evaluated her first results as encouraging but not nearly good enough. Once again she identified the problem, this time to make the bugs eat more sulfur faster. Her hypothesis was that altering the chemical makeup of their food might do this. She experimented with different chemicals, then analyzed the results. She concluded that Coal Bug One could do the job.)

CRITICAL THINKING QUESTIONS

1. Can you infer from the article how it is possible to change the cell structure of a microbe? (by altering the diet of the microbe)

2. What economic benefit would result from the use of bugs to clean up coal? (It would be possible to burn inexpensive high-sulfur coal.)

who will eat the sulfur in coal)
- **How long did it take Dr. Isbister to develop Coal Bug One?** (two and one-half years)

Emphasize to students that scientists who develop new technologies must be patient and persistent. Often success comes to the person who keeps going at the point when most other people would give up.

Unit Five

HEAT ENERGY

ISSUES IN SCIENCE: HOTHOUSE EARTH: WILL THE GREENHOUSE EFFECT OCCUR?

BACKGROUND INFORMATION

The term *greenhouse effect* was first coined in 1896 by Swedish scientist Arrhenius. It comes from the analogy to an actual greenhouse, in which heat from the sun warms the inside of the greenhouse, then, instead of being reflected back into space, the heat is absorbed and trapped by the glass above. (A closed car sitting in the sun experiences a similar effect.) Arrhenius hypothesized correctly that gases released into the atmosphere by burning coal would contribute to the greenhouse effect and eventually produce a warmer earth.

Chemical pollutants that contribute to the greenhouse effect are chlorofluorocarbons, carbon dioxide, methane, and nitrous oxide. In addition to causing the greenhouse effect, these gases are also damaging the ozone layer in the atmosphere. It is the ozone layer that protects the earth from the sun's harmful ultraviolet rays. Scientists have measured a 30 to 50 percent depletion of ozone in the atmosphere over Antarctica. They feel that if this trend continues, the earth's people will be plagued by a higher incidence of skin cancer in the future.

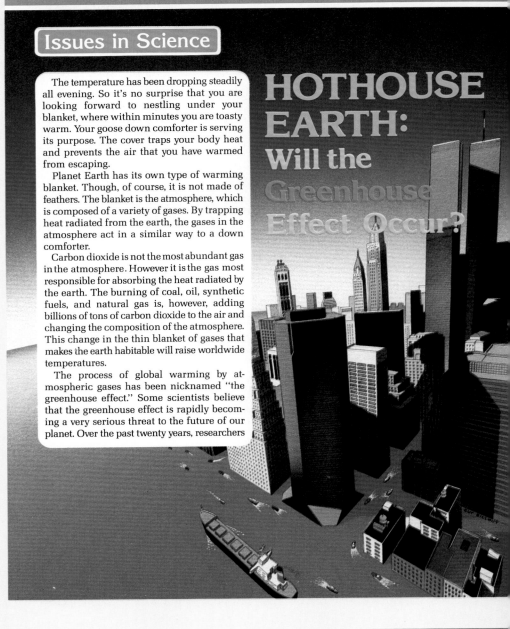

Issues in Science

HOTHOUSE EARTH: Will the Greenhouse Effect Occur?

The temperature has been dropping steadily all evening. So it's no surprise that you are looking forward to nestling under your blanket, where within minutes you are toasty warm. Your goose down comforter is serving its purpose. The cover traps your body heat and prevents the air that you have warmed from escaping.

Planet Earth has its own type of warming blanket. Though, of course, it is not made of feathers. The blanket is the atmosphere, which is composed of a variety of gases. By trapping heat radiated from the earth, the gases in the atmosphere act in a similar way to a down comforter.

Carbon dioxide is not the most abundant gas in the atmosphere. However it is the gas most responsible for absorbing the heat radiated by the earth. The burning of coal, oil, synthetic fuels, and natural gas is, however, adding billions of tons of carbon dioxide to the air and changing the composition of the atmosphere. This change in the thin blanket of gases that makes the earth habitable will raise worldwide temperatures.

The process of global warming by atmospheric gases has been nicknamed "the greenhouse effect." Some scientists believe that the greenhouse effect is rapidly becoming a very serious threat to the future of our planet. Over the past twenty years, researchers

---

TEACHING STRATEGY

Motivation

Begin by asking students,
• **How is the earth's climate kept suitable for human life?** (Answers may vary. Allow students to speculate.)
• **Would you be surprised if I told you that the earth has a blanket wrapped around it?**
Explain to students that the "blanket" is the earth's atmosphere.

By allowing the sun's rays to pass through in just the right amount, then absorbing some of the heat and radiating it back to earth, the atmosphere provides an automatic climate control that makes the earth hospitable to life.
• **What do you think would be the result if the composition of the earth's atmosphere were severely altered?** (The earth's climate could change; humans on earth might have problems continuing to live.)

Content Development

List on the chalkboard the possible effects of a hotter earth that are mentioned in the article. Then have students add to the list any other effects they can think of. Based on the part of the United States in which they live, students should consider how their lives might be affected if these predictions were to come true in the near future.

have watched the concentration of carbon dioxide increase considerably. A parallel increase in average global temperatures of about one-half Celsius degree has also been recorded.

To climatologists, these data represent a very strong link between the increase in atmospheric carbon dioxide and a rise in the earth's temperature. Scientists at the National Academy of Sciences agree that increased "emissions of greenhouse gases promise to impose a warming of unusual dimensions to a climate that is already unusually warm."

Scientists and climatologists are working hard to predict the possible magnitude of global warming. By using laboratory simulations and computer-generated graphs and charts, researchers have come up with this hypothesis: The average worldwide surface temperature could increase from 1.5 to 5.5 Celsius degrees by the year 2100. The consequences of such a drastic rise in the earth's temperature could be dramatic.

Polar icecaps and glaciers would melt, flooding vast tracts of land around the globe and submerging virtually all ports and harbors. At the same time, droughts would bake the grain-producing areas of the United States, Middle East, and Europe. Drinking water would be poisoned by ocean salts. Hurricanes, coastal storms, and tornadoes would occur more frequently.

As if that weren't enough, experts predict drastically altered weather patterns and changes in annual rainfall. As Robert Watson, director of NASA's upper atmospheric program, says, "Global warming is inevitable—it's only a question of magnitude and time. We can expect significant changes in climate in the next few decades."

Other researchers refuse to be so pessimistic. Recent studies by scientists at the American Geophysical Union Conference suggest that carbon dioxide buildup in the at-

If the greenhouse effect occurs, wheat fields such as these will be barren land.

mosphere might be only half as great as has been projected. There is evidence that the oceans could absorb a large amount of carbon dioxide produced by burning fossil fuels. Another cause for optimism is the discovery that an increase in atmospheric carbon dioxide causes clouds to become wetter and denser. These denser clouds reflect more sunlight than they let through. This fact suggests that ultimately there would be less heat for the atmosphere to trap and less heat to warm the globe. Some scientists theorize that the earth may even become cooler!

There is debate also over the need for immediate action. As John Hoffman of the Environmental Protection Agency proclaims, "We feel carbon dioxide is a very serious thing, but we think there is time to do research, and there is time to adapt." But others worry that time is running out and regulatory action to protect the environment must be taken now. What do you think?

437

ADDITIONAL QUESTIONS AND TOPIC SUGGESTIONS

1. How is the atmosphere like a blanket? (It traps heat from the earth's surface and prevents it from escaping.)
2. What effect of carbon dioxide could cause the earth to become cooler? (Carbon dioxide causes clouds to become wetter and denser; these clouds reflect more sunlight than they absorb.)

CRITICAL THINKING QUESTIONS

1. Do you think weather patterns in the United States today are different from those experienced by people in the 1880s? Explain your answer. (They probably are different because the earth has been getting warmer. It is possible that winters are less severe than they once were, and average temperatures in summer are higher.)
2. In a brief paragraph, interpret and react to the following statement: "Focusing on the dire events that might result from the greenhouse effect gives the public an excuse to dismiss what is really a manageable problem."
3. The planet Mars is deficient in carbon dioxide, and the planet Venus has an extremely thick layer of carbon dioxide. How do you think the climates of these planets are affected? (The climate of Mars is very cold, and the climate of Venus is extremely hot.)

CLASS DEBATE

Have students work in teams of four. Challenge each team to prepare *both* sides of the issue. Then have teams draw lots to see which viewpoint they will defend in the debate.

Unit Six
ELECTRICITY AND MAGNETISM

UNIT OVERVIEW

In Unit Six, students are introduced to electricity. Electric charge is explained on the basis of atomic structure, and static electricity is discussed. Students also learn about voltage, current, and resistance, as well as electrochemical cells. They explore the concept of the electric circuit. They also gain a practical understanding of electric power as a utility, and learn about the safe use of electricity.

Next, students study magnetism and magnetic poles, fields, and lines of force. They learn about compasses and the earth's magnetic properties. Finally, they study electromagnetism and electromagnetic induction and the practical applications of these concepts.

UNIT OBJECTIVES

1. **Describe the forces between and the atomic basis of electric charges.**
2. **Describe the effects of static electricity.**
3. **Define voltage, current, and resistance, and apply these concepts to circuit situations.**
4. **Describe the safe usage of electricity.**
5. **Describe magnetism and magnetic fields, poles, and lines of force.**
6. **Explain electromagnetism and electromagnetic induction, and describe practical applications of these concepts.**

INTRODUCING UNIT SIX

Begin your teaching of the unit by having students examine the unit-opener photograph, which shows a French high-speed train. Ask,
• **What seems unusual about the train's shape? Why does the train have this shape?** (The front end of the train is tapered or streamlined, which reduces air resistance, allowing the train to move more quickly.)

Point out that although the French TGV train is extremely fast, the Maglev trains being designed and tested will be much faster. Now have students read the unit introduction. The introduction should serve as the basis for various discussions that will better motivate students to study the chapters that follow.
• **Since Maglev trains have no wheels, is there any direct contact between the train and the rails?** (There are no rails, and the train appears to be levitated above the rails.)
• **What kind of force supports the train above the rails?** (A repelling force supports the train.)
• **Magnetism accounts for the properties of such trains. What is magnetism?** (Answers will vary. Students will learn the correct answer when they read Chapter 20.)
• **What role might electricity have to play in producing such magnetic forces? What is electricity, and how is**

Electricity and Magnetism

Passengers journeying from Lyon to Paris on the French *Train Grande Vitesse* are riding the fastest scheduled train in the world. On a test run in 1981, the TGV easily topped 380 kilometers per hour. But what makes this train so unusual is that it is not powered by gasoline or coal. An electric current drawn from overhead wires powers the TGV along its swift course.

The TGV, however, will soon lose its place as speed champion. For engineers in Japan, West Germany, and Britain are now involved in the development of maglev trains. Maglev stands for magnetic levitation. Because a maglev train has no wheels and makes no contact with a track, it appears to levitate in midair. Although this may seem to be some sort of magic, it is actually the application of basic principles of electricity and magnetism. Maglev trains are supported and propelled by the interaction of magnets located on the train body and on the track. A Japanese test model has already achieved a speed of 516 kilometers per hour. In this unit, you will learn about the world of electricity and magnetism. And you will gain an understanding of how magnets can power a train floating above the ground.

CHAPTERS

19 Electric Charges and Currents

20 Magnetism

The Train Grande Vitesse *picks you up and leaves you off in the center of the city. There are no trips to and from airports, which are often located some distance away from a city. And, there are no delays in takeoffs and landings. Travel over short to medium distances on this train is quicker than on a plane!*

439

it related to magnetism? (Answers will vary. Electricity, which involves a flow of charged particles called electrons, is related to magnetism, as students will learn. An electric current gives rise to magnetic forces, as will be explained in Section 20–4, which deals with electromagnetism.)

Chapter 19

ELECTRIC CHARGES AND CURRENTS

CHAPTER OVERVIEW

The concept of electric charge is introduced and related to subatomic particles. Forces of attraction and repulsion and electric fields are then discussed. Students next study the nature of static electricity. They are introduced to the concepts of voltage, electric current and resistance, and to Ohm's Law, which mathematically relates these quantities. Some of the methods by which current is produced are also discussed.

Students learn about the components of an electric current and about the differences between series and parallel circuits. Electric power and electric energy are then explained, and students are introduced to equations used in calculations involving these quantities. Finally, principles of electric safety are discussed.

INTRODUCING CHAPTER 19

Begin your introduction of Chapter 19 by asking students to observe the photographs on page 440, which contrast New York's nighttime skyline under normal conditions with its skyline during the 1965 blackout. Have them read the chapter introduction, or read it aloud yourself. Point out the importance of electricity in everyday life. Then ask,

• **Can you name some other routine aspects of life that were greatly affected during the blackout?** (Answers will vary. Students will think of various devices that ceased to operate and whose inability to function made certain ordinary tasks difficult or impossible to perform.)

• **What would you have done if you had been trapped in a subway train or elevator during the blackout?** (Answers will vary.)

• **What measures have you and your family taken (or what measures should be taken) to be better prepared to deal with possible future blackouts?** (Answers will vary. Some students may suggest stocking candles, flashlights, and nonperishable foods, storing water (in rural areas in which electrical household water pumps will be affected), or purchasing a household electric generator.)

Electric Charges and Currents 19

CHAPTER OBJECTIVES

After completing this chapter, you will be able to

19–1 Explain how electric charge is related to atomic structure.

19–1 Describe the forces that exist between charged particles.

19–2 Describe the effects of static electricity.

19–3 Relate voltage, electric current, and resistance.

19–3 Explain how electrochemical cells produce a flow of electrons.

19–4 Identify the parts of an electric circuit.

19–4 Compare a series and a parallel circuit.

19–5 Explain how electric power is calculated and purchased.

19–5 Describe how electricity can be used safely.

"Where were you when the lights went out?" Many people were asking each other that question the morning after November 9, 1965. On that day, shortly before the evening rush hour, a major blackout plunged the Northeastern United States and parts of Canada into total darkness. More than 200,000 square kilometers and over 30 million people were without electric power!

Electric typewriters stopped in midsentence. Elevators stopped in midair. Subways came to a screeching halt. And city traffic became a nightmare as all the traffic lights went out. Electric toothbrushes, hair dryers, toasters, refrigerators, and washing machines ceased to operate. In hospitals, doctors operated by candlelight, and auxiliary power systems kept important life-support equipment working.

For some, the blackout was an adventure—a challenge to see how well people could function without the energy they take for granted. For others, the blackout was a severe hardship. But for all, the power failure was a reminder of the importance of electricity in everyday life. It is hard to imagine a world without electricity.

Have you ever stopped to think about what electricity really is? Where it comes from and how it works? How it gets to your house and how you use it? You will learn the answers to these questions as you read this chapter. As for the blackout of 1965, perhaps someone you know was in the Northeast on that memorable day. If so, then you can ask the question, "Where were *you* when the lights went out?"

On November 9, 1965, a major blackout turned the bright, illuminated skyline of New York into darkness and left more than 30 million people in the Northeast without electricity.

441

TEACHER DEMONSTRATION

You may wish to perform the following demonstration in order to motivate students and to introduce them to this chapter. Turn on a faucet so as to produce a thin stream of water. Then rub a hard rubber or plastic comb with a piece of fur (or, alternatively, vigorously comb your hair with it). Ask,

- **What, if anything, will happen if I hold the comb near the stream of water?** (The stream will be deflected.)

Now actually place the charged comb very close to, but not directly into, the stream of falling water, recharging it just before doing so. The water will be deflected toward the comb.

- **Explain what has happened.** (Answers will vary. The charged comb has an excess of negatively charged electrons. Like-charged electrons in the water—or the more negative ends of the water molecules—are pushed away, causing the surface of the water nearest the comb to become positively charged, and thus to be attracted to the comb.)

TEACHER RESOURCES

Audiovisuals

Conductors and Insulators, 8mm film loop, PH Media *Current Flow and Measurement,* 8mm film loop, PH Media

Electricity at Work, 6 filmstrips with 3 cassettes, SVE *Looking into Electricity,* 2 filmstrips with 2 cassettes, LA

Books

Baker, Glenn and Leonard R. Crow, *Electricity Fundamentals,* Bobbs

Davidson, G., *Electricity in the House,* McKay

Gibson, W.M., *Basic Electricity and Electronics,* Prentice-Hall

Software

Electromagnetism, Prentice-Hall
Voltage, Current, and Resistance, Prentice-Hall

19-1 ELECTRIC CHARGE

SECTION PREVIEW 19-1

Students will be introduced to protons, neutrons, and electrons, and the electric charges of these particles. Force of attraction between unlike charges and forces of repulsion between like charges are then discussed. The development of a charge by objects is explained in terms of the movement of electrons into or out of the object. Finally, electric fields are discussed briefly.

PERFORMANCE OBJECTIVES 19-1

1. **Name the three principal subatomic particles and state their charges.**
2. **Describe the nature of forces that act between unlike charges and like charges.**
3. **Explain how an object can develop an overall electric charge.**
4. **Define electric field.**

SCIENCE TERMS 19-1

atom p. 442
subatomic particle p. 443
proton p. 443
neutron p. 443
electron p. 443
nucleus p. 443

electric charge p. 443
force of attraction p. 443
force of repulsion p. 443
electric field p. 445

19–1 Electric Charge

"It made my hair stand on end!" Perhaps you are familiar with this expression, which is often used to describe a frightening or startling experience. According to biologists, it is possible for human hair to stand on end in moments of extreme fear. But there is another force that can make hair stand on end. You probably have experienced it on a cold, dry day when your hair seemed to "fly" all around as you tried to comb it.

What you experienced was electricity. Electricity may also give you a shock if you walk along a carpet and then touch a metal doorknob. Electricity enables you to rub a balloon on your sleeve and make it stick to the wall. And electricity produces the awesome flashes of lightning in the sky.

What is electricity? Where does it come from? How does it move? To answer these questions, you must first understand atoms and charges, which are both related to electricity.

Subatomic Particles and Electricity

All matter is made up of **atoms.** An atom is the smallest particle of an element that has all the properties of that element. An element contains only one kind of atom. For example, carbon is made of only carbon atoms. Gold is made of only gold atoms.

Figure 19–1 *The metal sphere this girl is touching is part of a device called a Van de Graaff generator. This particular generator, located at the Ontario Science Center produces charges of static electricity great enough to make the girl's hair stand on end.*

TEACHING STRATEGY 19-1

Motivation

Ask students to discuss the role electricity plays in everyday life. They should be able to come up with a great many applications and can be led to the conclusion that most of the important activities that make up their day rely directly or indirectly on electricity—everything from waking up on time because of the ringing of their electric alarm clock, to preserving and cooking food, to transportation, to extending the activities of the daytime by means of electric lights. Ask them to imagine a world in which there were no electrical devices, and to think of how their ancestors were able to carry out everyday functions without the benefit of electricity.

Content Development

After students have been given a feeling for the many applications and aspects of electricity, lead them to wonder about the basis of this phenomenon. Introduce—or reintroduce—the concept of the atom to them. Discuss the most important subatomic particles and the concept of charge. You can help to make clear the concept of attractive and repulsive forces by means not only of charged objects (for example, like- and unlike-charged lightweight objects suspended near

Atoms are made of even smaller particles called **subatomic particles.** These subatomic particles include **protons, neutrons,** and **electrons.**

Protons and neutrons are found in the **nucleus,** or center, of an atom. Protons and neutrons account for most of the mass of an atom. Whirling around the nucleus is a cloud of electrons. Electrons occupy different energy levels, depending upon their distance from the nucleus.

Both protons and electrons have a basic property called **electric charge.** However, the kind of charge is not the same for both particles. Protons have a positive charge, which is indicated by a plus symbol (+). Electrons have a negative charge, which is indicated by a minus symbol (−). Neutrons are neutral. Neutrons have no electric charge.

Charge and Force

When charged particles come near one another, they give rise to two different forces. A force is a pull or push on an object. A force can pull objects together or it can push objects apart.

A force that pulls objects together is a **force of attraction.** A force of attraction exists between oppositely charged particles. So negatively charged electrons are attracted to positively charged protons. This force of attraction holds the electrons in the electron cloud surrounding the nucleus.

A force that pushes objects apart is a **force of repulsion.** A force of repulsion exists between particles of the same charge. So negatively charged electrons repel one another, just as positively charged protons do. **Electric charges behave according to this simple rule: Like charges repel each other; unlike charges attract each other.**

From your experience, you know that when you sit on a chair, pick up a pen, or put on your jacket, you are not attracted or repelled by these objects. Although the protons and electrons in the atoms of these objects have electric charges, the objects themselves are neutral. Why?

The number of electrons in an atom is equal to the number of protons in that atom. So the total negative charge is equal to the total positive charge. The atom is neutral. It has no overall charge.

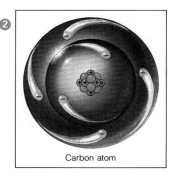

Carbon atom

Figure 19–2 *This atom of carbon shows the arrangement of the subatomic particles known as protons, neutrons, and electrons. Where is each particle found? What is the charge on each?* ❶

Figure 19–3 *When charged particles come near each other, a force is produced. The force can be either a force of attraction or a force of repulsion. What is the rule of electric charges?* ❷

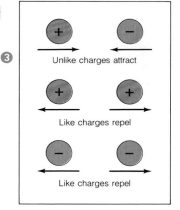

Unlike charges attract

Like charges repel

Like charges repel

443

one another from strings), but also of magnets. Do not become too involved in the specifics of the nature or magnitudes of forces; simply deal qualitatively with attractions and repulsions. Direct students' attention to Figure 19-3, which clearly shows the three different possibilities for charge interaction.

Skills Development

Skill: Designing an experiment
Ask students to design an experiment to test the way in which distance between charged objects affects forces of attraction and repulsion. They may come up with any of a wide variety of ways to measure how great a push or pull is exerted when the objects are at different distances apart.

Reinforcement
Have students do library research and prepare reports on Otto Van Guericke, Stephen Gray, Charles du Fay, Ewald Georg von Kleist, and Pieter van Musschenbroek, including each one's main contribution to the study of electricity.

Annotation Key

1. The force of attraction between the negatively charged balloon and positively charged wall makes the balloon "stick" to the wall. (Sequencing events)
2. There is a force of attraction between negatively charged balloon and part of wall that is positively charged. Unlike charges attract. (Applying concepts)
1. Thinking Skill: Applying concepts
2. Thinking Skill: Relating concepts

Sharpen Your Skills

Balloon Electricity
Skills: Hypothesizing, observing
Level: Remedial
Type: Hands-on
Materials: 4 medium-sized balloons

This activity will help reinforce the concept of moving charges and the fact that unlike charges attract. Have students relate their observations to the text discussion.

Sharpen Your Skills

Spark, Crackle, Move
Skills: Drawing conclusions, observing
Level: Average
Type: Hands-on
Materials: comb, wool carpet, metal pen, doorknob

This activity will help students observe the effects and buildup of static electricity. Have students relate their observations to the discussion in the text.

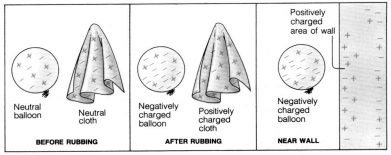

Figure 19–4 *Rubbing separates charges, giving the cloth a positive charge and the balloon a negative charge. When the negatively charged balloon is brought near the wall, it repels electrons in the wall. The nearby portion of the wall becomes positively charged. What happens next?* ❶

Sharpen Your Skills

Balloon Electricity

1. Blow up three or four medium-sized balloons.
2. Rub each balloon vigorously on a piece of cloth or article of clothing. Wool works especially well.
3. "Stick" each balloon on the wall. Note and record the day and time.
4. Every few hours, check the position of the balloons. Record the position as well as the day and time. If your balloons are very "sticky," you may have to extend your experiment overnight.

How long did the balloons stay attached to the wall? Why did the balloons eventually begin to slide and fall off the wall?

444

How, then, do objects such as balloons and strands of hair develop an electric charge if these objects are made of neutral atoms? The answer lies in the fact that electrons, unlike protons, are free to move. In certain materials, the negative electrons are only loosely held by the positive protons. These electrons can easily be separated from their atoms.

Rubbing separates charges on objects. When two objects are rubbed together, one object loses electrons while the other object gains these electrons. The object that gains electrons has an overall negative charge. The object that loses electrons has an overall positive charge. Remember that *only the electrons move*, not the protons. A neutral object develops an electric charge when it either gains or loses electrons.

If you rub a balloon against a piece of cloth, the cloth loses some electrons and the balloon gains these electrons. The balloon is no longer a neutral object. It is a negatively charged object because it has more electrons than protons. As the negatively charged balloon approaches the wall, it repels the electrons in the wall. The electrons in the area of the wall nearest the balloon move away, leaving that area of the wall positively charged. Using the rule of charges, can you explain why the balloon now sticks to the wall? ❷

Electric Fields

If two charged particles come close to each other, they will experience a force. If the two particles are alike in charge, the force will be one of repulsion. If the two particles are opposite in charge, the force will be one of attraction. The repulsion

---

19-1 (continued)

Motivation

The Greeks, as far back as the time of the philosopher Thales (600 B.C.), knew that when amber was rubbed with cloth, it attracted bits of straw or hair. Our word *electricity* comes from the Latin word *electrum,* which means "amber." The word *electrum* itself comes from a Greek word that means "shining."

Section Review 19-1

1. Protons, which are positively charged, and electrons, which are negatively charged.
2. Like charges repel each other; unlike charges attract each other.
3. Electrons from one object move onto another object, usually as the result of a disturbance such as rubbing. The object that loses electrons becomes positively charged; the object that gains electrons becomes negatively charged.
4. The positively charged particle experiences a force of repulsion while the negatively charged particle experiences a force of attraction. The force of repulsion felt by the positive particle is considerably stronger than the force of attraction felt by the negative particle. This is due to the difference in distance from particle X.

and attraction of particles occurs because charged particles have **electric fields** around them.

An electric field is the region surrounding a charged particle in which an electric force affecting other charged particles is noticeable. The electric field is strongest near the charged particle. It is weakest far away from the charged particle. The strength of an electric field depends upon the distance from the charged particle. As the distance from a charged particle increases, the strength of the electric field decreases.

SECTION REVIEW

1. What are the charged particles in an atom?
2. What is the rule of electric charges?
3. How does an object develop an electric charge?
4. A positively charged particle is placed 1 centimeter from positively charged particle X. A negatively charged particle is placed 10 centimeters from particle X. Compare the forces experienced by both the positively charged particle and the negatively charged particle.

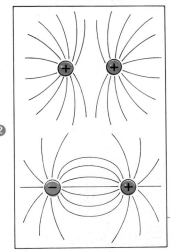

Figure 19–5 *Lines of force show the nature of the electric field surrounding two particles of the same charge (top) and two particles of opposite charge (bottom).*

19–2 Static Electricity

Section Objective

To define static electricity

When you read that the loss or gain of electrons produces an electric charge and electricity, you may have noticed that the words *electron* and *electricity* are similar. This similarity is no accident. Electricity depends upon electrons. In fact, **electricity** can now be defined as the energy associated with electrons that have moved from one place to another.

You are probably most familiar with electricity that flows through electric wires. But the movement of electrons is not always a continuous flow through a wire. Sometimes electrons can move from one object to another and then remain at rest. This type of electricity is called **static electricity.** The word *static* means "not moving," or "stationary."

Static electricity is the buildup of electric charges on an object. The electric charges build up because electrons have moved from one object to another. However, once built up, the charges do not flow. They remain at rest.

Sharpen Your Skills

Spark, Crackle, Move

1. Comb your hair several times in the same direction. Bring the comb near your hair but do not touch it.
2. Repeat step 1 but now bring the comb near a weak stream of water from a faucet.
3. In a darkened room, walk across a wool carpet and then touch the doorknob with a metal pen or rod.

445

19-2 STATIC ELECTRICITY

SECTION PREVIEW 19-2

In this section, students will be introduced to static electricity, which involves a buildup of charge. They also learn about three methods of electrically charging objects: friction, conductance, and induction. Conductors and insulators are described and contrasted. The electroscope, a device that can be used to detect electric charge and to demonstrate charging by conductance, is introduced.

Lightning is then explained as a static electricity phenomenon involving electric discharge, and Benjamin Franklin's investigation of this phenomenon is discussed. Finally, the concept of voltage, or potential difference, is introduced as a measure of the energy available to move electrons. The volt, or unit of voltage, is also introduced, as is the voltmeter, a device used to measure voltage.

PERFORMANCE OBJECTIVES

1. **Define and explain static electricity.**
2. **Contrast conductance and induction.**
3. **Describe the structure and use of the electroscope.**
4. **Explain what causes lightning.**
5. **Define voltage and state the unit in which it is expressed and the name of the device used to measure it.**

TEACHING STRATEGY 19-2

Motivation
Rub several balloons with a piece of fur or cloth, preferably wool. Stick the balloons to a classroom wall.
• **What causes the balloons to stick?** (They have gained electrons from the cloth, and now they repel electrons in the wall, leaving that area of the wall nearest them positively charged. The opposite charges attract one another.)

• **Why is this kind of electricity called static electricity?** (The electric charges have built up, but do not flow. Static means "unchanging.")
• **What do you predict will happen if charged balloons are brought close together? Why?** (They will repel one another because they have the same charge, and like charges repel.) Push several well-charged balloons close together to demonstrate what occurs. Bring out the fact that the reasoning,

hypothesis formation, and experimentation that are involved illustrate scientific method.

BACKGROUND INFORMATION

The magnitude of the force in an electric field is proportional to the product of the charges of the two objects, divided by the square of the distance separating the centers of the objects. This inverse square relationship accounts for the fact that the magnitude of electric forces decreases rapidly as distance increases.

TIE-IN/HOME ECONOMICS

Students may have noticed at home or in a home economics class, that certain materials, such as aluminum foil or thin copper pans, transfer heat and cool off quickly, whereas glass pans or plastic pan handles take a long time to heat up or, once heated, to cool down. This is because of the heat-conducting or heat-insulating properties of these materials. Most materials, such as metals, that are good at conducting electricity are good heat conductors due in part to the mobility of electrons in the atoms of these materials.

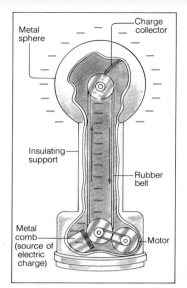

Figure 19–6 *A Van de Graaff generator produces static electricity by friction. Electrons supplied by a metal comb ride up a rubber belt to the top of the generator, are picked off by the charge collector, and transferred to the metal sphere. A large negative charge is built up and used to produce discharges of static electricity.* ❶

Figure 19–7 *A metal rod can be charged negatively (left) or positively (right) by conduction.*

Methods of Charging

An object can become charged with static electricity in three ways: friction, conduction, and induction. Rubbing a balloon with a piece of cloth is an example of charging an object by **friction.** The motion of the cloth against the balloon causes charges on both objects to separate. Since the electrons in the cloth are more loosely held than the electrons in the balloon, electrons move from the cloth to the balloon. What is the resulting charge on the cloth? On the balloon? ❶

If a hard rubber rod is rubbed with fur, friction separates charges on both the rod and the fur. Electrons are transferred from the fur to the rod. Because the rubber rod has gained electrons, it is negatively charged. The fur, which has lost electrons, is positively charged.

If a glass rod is rubbed with silk, electrons are transferred from the glass rod to the silk. The glass rod, which has lost electrons, is positively charged. What is the charge on the silk? ❷

Charging by **conduction** involves the direct contact of objects. In conduction, electrons flow through one object to another object. Certain materials allow electrons to flow freely. Materials that permit electric charges to move easily are called **conductors.** Most metals are good conductors of electricity. Silver, copper, aluminum, and mercury are among the best conductors.

Materials that do not allow electrons to flow freely are called **insulators.** Insulators do not conduct electric charges well. Good insulators include

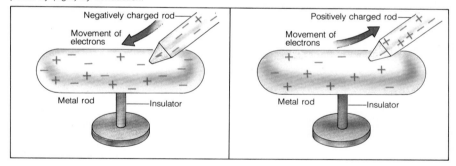

19-2 (continued)

Content Development

Direct student's attention again to Figure 19-5, which depicts lines of force between charges. Tie this field concept to the discussion of static electricity, pointing out the static nature of the field in this case. Later, you can contrast this with the changing electric field characteristic of flowing electricity. This will also help to prepare students for the concept of magnetic fields (treated in the following chapter), which result from changing electric fields.

Skills Development

Skills: Making observations, classifying objects

Ask students to experiment on a number of different materials (such as various plastics and fabrics) in order to determine which substances tend to be charged easily when rubbed. Students should work with different combinations of substances. They can also attempt to determine whether positive or negative charge develops in each by observing whether attraction or repulsion results when negatively charged balloon, for example, is brought near the charged object.

rubber, glass, wood, plastic, and air. The rubber tubing around an electric wire and the plastic handle on an electric power tool are examples of insulators. What do these insulators do? ❸

An object can acquire a charge by **induction.** Induction involves a rearrangement of electric charges. For induction to occur, a neutral object need only come close to a charged object. No contact is necessary. For example, a negatively charged rubber rod can pick up tiny pieces of paper by induction. The electric charges in the paper are rearranged by the approach of the charged rubber rod. The electrons in the area of the paper nearest to the rod are repelled, leaving the positive charges near the rod. Because the positive charges are closer to the negative rod, the paper is attracted.

The Electroscope

An electric charge can be detected by an instrument called an **electroscope.** A typical electroscope consists of a metal rod with a knob at the top and a pair of thin metal leaves at the bottom. The rod is inserted in a one-hole rubber stopper, which fits into a flask. The flask contains the lower part of the rod and the metal leaves. See Figure 19–10.

In an uncharged electroscope, the leaves hang straight down. When a charged object touches the metal knob, electric charges travel down the rod and into the leaves. The leaves spread apart, indicating the presence of an electric charge. Since the charge on both leaves is the same, the leaves repel each other and spread apart.

Figure 19–8 *Electric wires, often made of conductors such as copper, are covered by insulators such as rubber or plastic. Does an insulator conduct electricity?* ❹

Figure 19–9 *A charged rod brought near a conductor induces an electric charge in the*
❷ *conductor. Using this figure and Figure 19–7, compare the charge given to the metal rod by each charged rod when done by conduction and by induction.* ❺

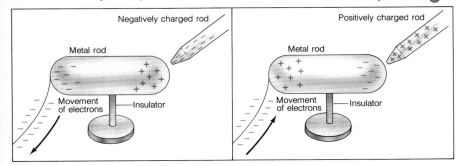

447

BACKGROUND INFORMATION

Metals tend to be good conductors of electricity because the outermost, or valence, electrons are not tightly held within individual metal atoms, but comprise a "sea" of electrons, which can flow easily within the metal.

ANNOTATION KEY

❶ Positive; negative (Relating concepts)

❷ Negative (Inferring)

❸ They prevent conduction of electricity to outside the wire or to the hand, eliminating shocks or burns. (Inferring)

❹ No (Applying concepts)

❺ By conduction, the charge on the metal rod is the same as the charge on the charged rod. By induction, the charge on the metal rod is opposite to the charge on the charged rod. (Interpreting illustrations)

❶ Thinking Skill: Applying concepts

❷ Thinking Skill: Relating concepts

Content Development

Carry out the conductance experiments described in the text by rubbing a hard rubber rod with fur and a glass rod with silk. Use the charged rods to pick up bits of paper by induction. Ask students to explain what happens in each case. Draw their attention to Figures 19-8 and 19-9, which help to schematize the two kinds of processes.

Reinforcement

Students who might have difficulty understanding conductance and induction can be encouraged to construct physical models of their own design to illustrate transfer of electrons. The electrons can be represented, for example, by colored pushpins that are inserted into a square of corkboard and that can be transferred to another corkboard, to illustrate conductance. Another, "uncharged" board (that is,

one that does not contain excess "electron" pins) can be brought near a "negatively charged" one, and some of the pins in the uncharged one can be moved to the end farthest from the charged board, to illustrate induction.

FACTS AND FIGURES

The leaves of a charged electroscope become discharged and come together partly because of cosmic radiation from space. Charged particles enter the electroscope at enormous speeds and produce electrical neutrality in the leaves by depositing or carrying away electrons.

TIE-IN/EARTH SCIENCE

Some biochemists and biologists have suggested that the energy from lightning in the primitive atmosphere of the earth produced complex organic, or carbon-containing, molecules, from the simple, inorganic ammonia, methane, and water vapor atmosphere present at the time. These molecules made possible the eventual development of life, these scientists conjecture.

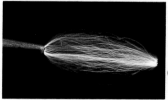

Figure 19–10 An electroscope is used to detect electric charges. Why do the leaves in this typical electroscope move apart when either a negatively charged rubber rod or a positively charged glass rod makes contact? ❶

Figure 19–11 The discharge of static electricity from one metal sphere to another can be seen as a spark (top). A more spectacular discharge of static electricity is lightning (bottom). Here lightning bolts light up the sky in Norfolk, Virginia.

448

An electroscope can be charged by conduction. A charged object is brought in direct contact with the knob of the electroscope. For example, if a negatively charged rubber rod touches the knob, electrons from the charged rubber rod move to the knob of the electroscope and then down the metal rod to the thin metal leaves. The leaves gain a negative charge, repel each other, and spread apart.

If a positively charged glass rod touches the knob of the electroscope, free electrons in the leaves and metal rod are attracted by the glass rod. The metal rod and knob conduct these electrons out of the electroscope to the glass rod. The loss of electrons causes the leaves to become positively charged. They repel each other and spread apart.

Lightning

Electrons that move from one object to another and cause the buildup of charges at rest, or static electricity, eventually leave the object. Usually these extra electrons escape into the air. Sometimes they move onto another object. The charged object loses its static electricity and becomes neutral. The loss of static electricity as electric charges move off an object is called **electric discharge.** Sometimes the discharge is slow and quiet. Sometimes it is very rapid and accompanied by a shock, a spark of light, or a crackle of noise.

One of the most dramatic examples of the discharge of static electricity is **lightning.** During a

---

19-2 (continued)

Content Development

Explain the use of the electroscope, directing students' attention to Figure 19-10. If an electroscope is available (or can be made easily), demonstrate its ability to be charged by conduction, using charged rubber and glass rods. Ask students to attempt to explain what happens on the basis of their knowledge of electric charge.

Motivation

Ask students to describe what they have observed during lightning storms that have occurred in the past. Ask them the following.

• **Where did the lightning originate and in what direction did it move?** (Although most students believe that all the lightning bolts they have observed moved from the sky downward toward the earth, many of the bolts probably moved in the other direc-

tion, appearances to the contrary.)

• **What causes lightning?** (It is a jumping of electrons to or from clouds that contain particles that have become electrically charged. Some of the energy during the discharge is released as light.)

• **What causes thunder?** (Some of the energy during the discharge is released as heat, which causes sudden expansion of the air, and therefore generates sound waves.)

HELP WANTED: ELECTRIC TROUBLE-SHOOTER for rural areas. High school diploma and interest in electricity required. We will train the right person.

Lightning rips the air as wind and hailstones batter the little town. Most of the area's electricity is out. The utility company sends out every available **trouble-shooter** to track down causes of the power failure.

Sometimes a trouble-shooter finds obvious problems, such as broken wires. But some-

times the source of trouble is hidden, and special equipment must be used to check transformers, switches, cables, and other equipment.

After locating the problem, a trouble-shooter may climb utility poles to repair or replace damaged equipment. In order to avoid harming people or property, it is necessary to be extremely safety conscious. A trouble-shooter must know exactly how electricity is generated and conducted.

A trouble-shooter also locates and repairs electric problems in homes, hospitals, schools, and other buildings. As technology changes and utility companies install new equipment, up-to-date methods for electric repair and maintenance must be learned.

Training for this career may be provided by private companies or by technical schools and community colleges. If you are interested in electricity and problem solving and would like more information about a career as an electric trouble-shooter, contact the International Brotherhood of Electrical Workers, 1125 15th Street NW, Washington, DC 20005.

storm, particles contained in clouds are moved about by the wind. Charges become separated, and there are buildups of positive and negative charges. If a negatively charged cloud forms near the surface of the earth, objects on the earth become electrically ❷ charged by induction. Soon electrons are jumping from the cloud to the earth. The result of this transfer of electrons is a giant spark called lightning.

Lightning can also occur as electrons jump from cloud to cloud. As electrons jump through the air, intense light and heat are produced. The light is the bolt of lightning you see. The heat causes the air to expand suddenly. The rapid expansion of the air is the thunder you hear. Lightning contains dangerously high amounts of electric energy. An average lightning bolt transfers 6 billion billion electrons between a cloud and the earth.

One of the first people to understand lightning as a form of electricity was Benjamin Franklin. In the mid-1700s, Franklin performed experiments

Sharpen Your Skills

Observing Static Electricity

1. Place two books about 10 cm apart on a table.

2. Cut tiny paper dolls or some other object out of tissue paper and place them on the table between the books.

3. Place a 20 to 25-cm square piece of glass on the books so that the glass covers the paper dolls.

4. Using a piece of silk, rub the glass vigorously. Observe what happens.

Using the rule of electric charges and your knowledge of static electricity, explain what you observed.

Sharpen Your Skills

Observing Static Electricity
Skills: Observing, hypothesizing, manipulative
Level: Enriched
Type: Hands-on
Materials: two books, tissue paper, scissors, square piece of glass

In this activity, students cause static electricity to build up on various objects and observe the effects of like charges attracting and unlike charges repelling. Make sure students relate their observations to the text discussion.

Enrichment
Have interested students do library research to gain more information on the physics of lightning and thunder phenomena. The students can prepare a written report and can also create charts illustrating the interesting energy conversions—involving electric energy, electromagnetic energy, heat energy, and mechanical energy—that are involved.

Motivation
Discuss the role of lightning rods in providing protection from lightning. You may wish to have students do library research on some of the various designs for such devices. They can also do research on whether such devices are used in the school, in their homes, or in nearby public buildings.

Other safety aspects related to the subject of lightning—for example, precautions to take if one is caught

outdoors during a lightning storm—can also be discussed.

HISTORICAL NOTES

Benjamin Franklin believed that substances contained what he called "electric fluid." He thought that friction between objects, such as that between rubber and fur or between clouds, removed some of the "fluid" from one object, causing it to be deficient in the "fluid," and transferred it to the other, causing it to have an excess of the "fluid." He theorized that these differences created the conditions for electrical attraction and repulsion. His theories, although crude, helped pave the way for progress in the understanding of electricity. The electron itself, the particle that accounts for electrical phenomena, was discovered by J. J. Thomson about a century after Franklin's death.

19-2 (continued)

Enrichment

Voltage is involved in any situation in which there is a difference in the potential electric energy of electrons in different parts of a system. The voltage acts as a sort of electromotive force that causes electrons to flow from the area of high potential energy toward the area of low potential energy. In this sense, voltage is analogous to potential energy differences between points that are at different distances from a body that exerts gravitational attraction and that causes other objects to move toward it, resulting in reduced potential energy.

Reinforcement

Students sometimes receive the faulty

Figure 19–12 *Benjamin Franklin's famous experiments (top) provided evidence that lightning is a form of static electricity that moves quickly through certain materials. Using these observations and the observation that pointed surfaces attract electricity, Franklin invented the lightning rod. Lightning rods attached to the tops of buildings provide a safe path for the lightning directly into the ground (bottom).*

450

that provided evidence that lightning is a form of static electricity, that electricity moves quickly through certain materials, and that a pointed surface attracts electricity. Franklin suggested that pointed metal rods be placed above the roofs of buildings as protection from lightning. These rods were the first **lightning rods.** Luckily for Franklin, he put a lightning rod on his roof. Shortly afterward, lightning struck his home!

Lightning rods work according to a principle called **grounding.** A discharge of static electricity usually takes the shortest path from one object to another. So lightning rods are attached to the tops of buildings and a wire connects the lightning rod to the ground. When lightning strikes the rod, which is taller than the building, it travels through the rod and the wire harmlessly into the earth.

Unfortunately, other tall objects such as trees can also act as grounders. That is why it is not a good idea to stand near a tree during a lightning storm. Why do you think it is also not a good idea to stand in an open field during an electric storm? ❶

Voltage: The Push of Electrons

It takes energy to move an object from one place to another. Even though electrons are very small, it still takes energy to move them. When you rub a balloon against your sleeve, you apply a force. This force moves electrons from the cloth to the balloon. You are able to apply this force because you have energy. The energy you expend goes to the electrons, which move. This energy is the "push" that makes electric charges move.

A measure of the energy available to move electrons is called **voltage.** Voltage is sometimes called potential difference. Voltage can be thought of as the "push" that makes electrons move. The higher the voltage, the more energy each electron carries. The more energy each electron carries, the more energy it can deliver, and the more work it can do.

Voltage is measured in units called **volts.** The symbol for volts is the letter "V." If you see the marking "10V," you know that it means ten volts. An instrument called a voltmeter is used to measure voltage.

impression that voltage is related to the number of electrons, high-voltage conditions being involved only when a great many electrons move. Actually, voltage depends on the energy of each electron and not at all on the number of electrons, which, as students will discover, is related to current.

Section Review 19-2

1. The buildup of electric charges on an object

2. Friction, conduction, induction
3. The metal leaves at the bottom of the metal rod move apart if the object has a charge.
4. Lightning is a discharge of static electricity that appears as a giant spark produced when electrons jump from cloud to cloud or from a cloud to the ground.
5. The energy available to move electrons; volts (V)
6. The lightning would not be able to

SECTION REVIEW

1. What is static electricity?
2. What are the three ways in which an object can acquire an electric charge?
3. How can you tell if an object touching an electroscope is neutral or has a charge?
4. What is lightning?
5. What is voltage? In what units is it measured?
6. What would happen if a lightning rod were made of an insulator rather than a conductor?

19–3 The Flow of Electricity

Section Objective

To relate electric current, voltage, and resistance

Once electrons are pushed into moving, they can be made to continue flowing provided they have a path and a source. A wire made of a suitable conducting material forms the path. A device that pumps electrons from one object to another is the source. The electrons are ready to flow. Your lamp will light, your stereo will play, your computer will work, and your oven will bake your favorite cookies!

Electric Current

The flow of electrons through a wire is called **electric current.** Current is measured according to how many electrons pass a given point during each second. The higher the electric current in a wire, the more electrons are passing through.

The symbol for current is the letter "I." The unit used to measure current is the **ampere (A),** or amp for short. One ampere is defined as the amount of current that flows past a given point per second. Among the instruments used to measure current are ammeters and galvanometers.

Resistance

Have you ever looked inside a clear light bulb and noticed a very thin piece of metal that glows when the light bulb is turned on? That piece of

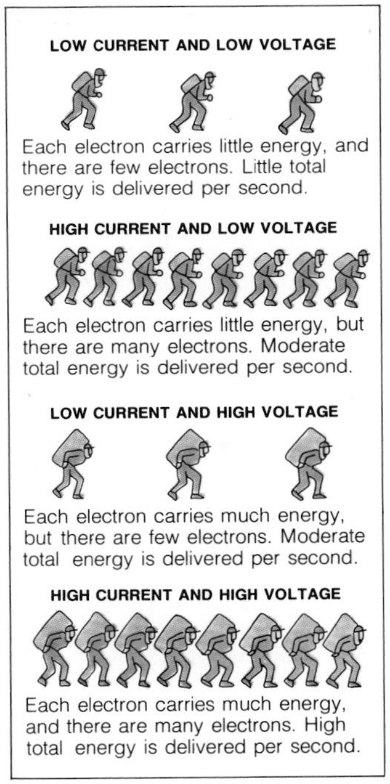

Figure 19–13 *Voltage is a measure of electron energy. Current is a measure of the rate of electron flow. In this figure, how is voltage represented? How is current represented?*

LOW CURRENT AND LOW VOLTAGE

Each electron carries little energy, and there are few electrons. Little total energy is delivered per second.

HIGH CURRENT AND LOW VOLTAGE

Each electron carries little energy, but there are many electrons. Moderate total energy is delivered per second.

LOW CURRENT AND HIGH VOLTAGE

Each electron carries much energy, but there are few electrons. Moderate total energy is delivered per second.

HIGH CURRENT AND HIGH VOLTAGE

Each electron carries much energy, and there are many electrons. High total energy is delivered per second.

451

19-3 THE FLOW OF ELECTRICITY

SECTION PREVIEW 19-3

This section introduces students to the concept of electric current. The ampere, the unit of current, is introduced, as are ammeters and galvanometers, devices used to measure current. The concept of resistance is discussed, and resistance, voltage, and current are related through Ohm's Law, $I = V/R$.

Dry cells, wet cells, and thermocouples are then analyzed as structures used for producing current. Finally, direct current and alternating current are contrasted.

PERFORMANCE OBJECTIVES 19-3

1. **Define electric current, state its unit, and name two devices used to measure it.**
2. **Define resistance and state its unit.**
3. **State and apply Ohm's Law.**
4. **Describe the structure and uses of dry cells and wet cells.**
5. **Contrast direct current and alternating current.**

SCIENCE TERMS 19-13

electric current p. 451
ampere p. 451
resistance p. 452
ohm p. 452
Ohm's Law p. 452
electrochemical cell p. 453
dry cell p. 453
battery p. 454

wet cell p. 454
voltaic cell p. 454
electrode p. 454
electrolyte p. 454
thermocouple p. 454
direct current (DC) p. 455
alternating current (AC) p. 455

travel down the rod, so it would find another pathway—probably through the building that the lightning rod is trying to protect. Thus a lightning rod made from an insulator would be useless.

TEACHING STRATEGY 19-3

Motivation

Allow students do some hands-on work with low-voltage dry cells, ammeters, voltmeters, light bulbs, and wires. Students can be asked to hypothesize on the effects of varying voltages and resistances, and can then demonstrate experimentally what actually occurs. Encourage students to use scientific method to "discover" Ohm's Law (at least qualitatively) on their own, with your supervision, and before they are formally introduced to it in the text.

Content Development

Carefully contrast current and voltage, both as to the nature of these quantities and as to the units used to measure them. Be sure to point out that current, which depends on the number of electrons, is not simply the flow of electrons but rather the rate of their flow per unit time.

BACKGROUND INFORMATION

Current, or the rate of flow of electric charge, is measured in amperes. The ampere unit itself, as a rate unit, is actually equal to a basic unit of electric charge, the coulomb, divided by a unit of time, the second. One coulomb is the amount of charge carried by 6.25×10^{18} electrons. A current of 1 ampere is equal to a flow rate of 1 coulomb per second.

Sharpen Your Skills

Electric Forces
Skills: Drawing conclusions, manipulative, observing, comparing, recording
Level: Average
Type: Hands-on
Materials: hard rubber comb, woolen cloth, cork, thread, glass rod, silk

This activity will help reinforce the concept that electric forces build up when electrons are forced to move from one object to another. Students should be able to relate their observations to the concept of like repels like and like attracts opposites.

19-3 (continued)

Content Development

Introduce the ohm as the unit of resistance. Then, after reviewing the concepts of voltage and current, introduce Ohm's Law.

$$I = V/R$$

Carry out sample calculations involving this equation in rearranged forms; using it, in separate problems, to solve for I, V, and R. Be sure to pay attention to the units involved and bring out the general point that I and R vary inversely, given a constant V.

Skills Development

Skills: Making comparisons, making illustrations

Have students plan and execute drawings that illustrate, in their own creative ways, the concepts of voltage, current, and resistance. Before they begin, direct their attention to Figure

---

---

metal is called a filament. As electric current passes through the filament, the filament resists, or opposes, the flow of electrons. As a result of this opposition, some of the electric energy is converted into heat and light.

Opposition to the flow of electricity is called **resistance.** The symbol for resistance is the letter "R." The unit of resistance is the **ohm** (Ω).

You will remember that some materials conduct electricity better than other materials. Wires made of good conductors, such as copper, have a low resistance. So electricity flows easily through copper wires. Wires made of poor conductors, such as iron, have a high resistance. These wires offer so much resistance that almost no current can flow. What is another name for a nonconductor? For what purpose are nonconductors used in wiring?

In addition to the material used to make a wire, the resistance of a wire depends upon its thickness, length, and temperature. Electrons move more easily through a thick wire. In a thin wire, there is less room for electrons to flow. So a thin wire offers more resistance to an electric current.

A longer wire offers more resistance than a shorter wire because the electrons have a greater distance to travel. So as the length of a wire increases, the resistance increases. Temperature affects resistance because the ability of a material to conduct electricity depends to a certain extent upon temperature.

Ohm's Law

An equation called **Ohm's law** relates electric current, voltage, and resistance. **Ohm's law states that the current in a wire is equal to the voltage divided by the resistance.**

$$current = \frac{voltage}{resistance}$$

or

$$I = \frac{V}{R} \qquad amperes = \frac{volts}{ohms}$$

Looking at this equation, what do you think will happen to the current if the resistance increases and the voltage remains the same? If the resistance

---

19-13, which helps to bring out the difference between high and low voltage and current situations.

Enrichment

Have advanced students do library research on the discovery of Ohm's Law and on its applications. They may wish to explain the applicability of the law in various simple technological devices such as rheostats, which make use of variable resistors to control current

and permit individualized control of brightness in lighting in such devices as "dimmers."

Common Errors

While completing the practice problems, students may rearrange equations such as Ohm's Law in incorrect ways. For example, in solving for V, given I and R, they may divide I by R instead of multiplying the two quantities. Review the simple algebra in-

What is the current through a wire that has a resistance of 30 ohms if the voltage is 45 volts?

Solution

Step 1 Write the formula

$$I = \frac{V}{R}$$

Step 2 Substitute given numbers and units

$$I = \frac{45 \text{ volts}}{30 \text{ ohms}}$$

$$I = 1.5 \text{ amperes}$$

Step 3 Solve for unknown variable

Practice Problems

❷ 1. What is the current flowing through a wire if the resistance of the wire is 20 ohms and the voltage is 40 volts?

❸ 2. A current of 0.5 amperes flows through a wire. What is the wire's resistance if the voltage is 50 volts?

ANNOTATION KEY

❶ Insulators, which prevent electricity from being conducted outside the wire (Applying concepts)

❷ 2 amps (Applying formulas)

❸ 25 volts (Applying formulas)

❹ Decreases; increases (Applying formulas)

❺ Increases (Applying formulas)

❶ Thinking Skill: Making comparisons

❷ Thinking Skill: Interpreting formulas

❸ Thinking Skill: Relating cause and effect

---

decreases and the voltage remains the same? What ❹ must happen to the resistance if the voltage increases while the current remains the same? ❺

Producing a Current

In order for a current to be produced, there must be a source of electrons. An **electrochemical cell** provides a steady supply of electric current. In an electrochemical cell, chemical energy produced by a chemical reaction is changed into electric energy.

DRY CELL The name **dry cell** is somewhat misleading, for the cell is not completely dry. It consists of a zinc can that contains a moist, pastelike mixture of chemicals. In the center is a solid carbon rod. As a chemical reaction takes place between the zinc and the paste, electrons are released. Attached to the zinc part of the cell is a negative terminal that picks up the electrons. Attached to the carbon ❸ rod is a positive terminal that has a shortage of electrons. The difference in number of electrons between the two terminals causes an "electron pressure" that pumps the electrons.

Sharpen Your Skills

Ohm's Law

Complete the following chart.

I (amps)	V (volts)	R (ohms)
	12	75
15	240	
5.5		20
	6	25
5	110	

453

Sharpen Your Skills

Ohm's Law
Skills: making calculations, applying
Level: Remedial
Type: Computational
    Students should use Ohm's Law to arrive at the following calculations. Row 1: 6.25; Row 2: 16; Row 3: 1100; Row 4: 0.24; Row 5: 22

---

volved in such rearrangements and also analyze the units that result from rearrangements. Demonstrate to students that such dimensional analysis can help reveal errors in manipulating equations and carrying out calculations.

Reinforcement
Encourage slower students to carry out many simple practice calculations involving Ohm's Law. They can make

up charts that show the various correct rearrangements of the equation and that display an assortment of values obtained by substituting different numbers and solving for the unknown.

Skills Development
Skills: Making graphs, analyzing data
Ask students to make a graph of the dependence of I upon R, given a con-

stant voltage—say, 10 volts. Students should substitute into Ohm's Law different values of I and solve for R. The results, when plotted, in terms of I (dependent variable, Y axis) versus R (independent variable, X axis), will reveal the inverse nature of the relationship. A hyperbole that asymptotically approaches each of the two axes will result. Be sure to give slower students assistance with the plotting of points and the drawing of a smooth curve.

TEACHER DEMONSTRATION

You can make a simple battery by cutting 20 5-cm squares of zinc sheeting, of copper sheeting, and of blotting paper. Pile them on top of each other in the order copper, blotting paper, zinc. A square of copper should be on the bottom and a square of zinc on the top. Tie the pile together with a thread. Attach one wire to the top plate and one to the bottom. Immerse the entire pile in a solution of sodium bicarbonate. When the blotting paper is soaked, remove the pile. Touch the free ends of the wires to a voltmeter to test the voltage. Ask students the following.

• **What is happening to produce a current?** (Electrons are flowing from the zinc end around to the copper end, and from each zinc inside to the copper below.)

• **What is the purpose of the sodium bicarbonate solution?** (It serves as an electrolyte, whose ions, or charged particles, conduct electricity.)

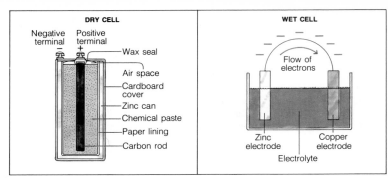

Figure 19–14 *Electrochemical cells, which include dry cells and wet cells, convert chemical energy into electric energy. What is a series of dry cells called? What is another name for a wet cell?* ❶

Figure 19–15 *The temperature difference between the hot junction and the cold junction in a thermocouple generates electricity. The greater the temperature difference, the greater the electric current. What is the energy conversion involved in the operation of a thermocouple?* ❷

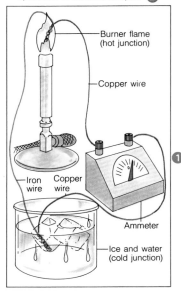

If a wire is connected to each terminal, the electrons will flow from the negative terminal through the wire to the positive terminal. As the chemical reaction continues, the electrons are pumped back to the negative terminal of the dry cell. In this way the negative terminal keeps its negative charge, and electrons can move through the complete path for a long time. A steady flow of current is established. The source of power for your portable radio or tape player is probably a dry cell such as the one just described. A series of dry cells connected to one another is called a **battery.**

WET CELL Another type of electrochemical cell is the **wet cell,** or **voltaic cell.** A typical car battery is a series of wet cells.

In a wet cell, two different metal plates called **electrodes** are placed in a conducting liquid called an **electrolyte.** In many wet cells the electrodes are made of zinc and copper. The electrolyte is hydrochloric acid.

As the zinc reacts with the hydrochloric acid, each zinc atom releases two electrons. An excess of electrons builds up at the zinc electrode. Once again, "electron pressure" pushes the electrons from the negative zinc electrode to the positive copper electrode. A wire connecting the two electrodes provides a pathway for a steady flow of electric current.

THERMOCOUPLE A **thermocouple** is a device that changes heat energy into electric energy. A thermocouple generates electricity as a result of temperature differences. In this device, the ends of a piece

---

19-3 (continued)

Content Development

Direct students' attention to Figures 19-14 and 19-15, which show a dry and a wet cell, and a thermocouple, respectively. Go over the features of these sources of current, and, if possible, demonstrate each in class. Ask students to try to analyze the processes occurring in each. Use your treatment of this topic to help reinforce what has already been learned about electrons, current, and voltage.

Motivation

You may wish to ask a student who has knowledge of automobiles to research and to present to the class information on automobile batteries, which are made up of a series of wet cells. The student may also explain the role of the battery and of the automobile electrical system as a whole. Alternatively, you may wish to arrange to have an industrial/automotive-arts teacher or a local auto mechanic address the class or even demonstrate the workings of an automobile battery and of an engine thermocouple.

Section Review 19-3

1. The rate of flow of electrons
2. Opposition to the flow of electricity
3. A chemical reaction causes the release of electrons. These electrons

of copper wire and a piece of iron wire are joined together, forming a loop. If one iron-copper junction is heated while the other is cooled, an electric current is generated. The greater the temperature difference between the junctions, the greater the current. Figure 19–15 shows a thermocouple with an ammeter attached to measure the current.

Thermocouples are used as thermometers in cars to show engine temperature. One end of the thermocouple is placed in the engine, while the other end is kept outside the engine. As the engine gets warm, the temperature difference produces a current. The warmer the engine, the greater the temperature difference—and the greater the current. This current in turn operates a gauge that shows engine temperature. Thermocouples are also used in ovens and gas furnaces.

Current Direction

Electrons moving through a wire can move continuously in the same direction or they can change direction back and forth over and over again. When electrons always flow in the same direction, the current is called **direct current,** or **DC.** The current in dry cells, batteries, and thermocouples is direct current. When electrons reverse their direction regularly, the current is called **alternating current,** or **AC.** The electricity in your home is alternating current. In the alternating current in your home, electrons change direction at a rate of about 60 times per second. Alternating current is the most commonly used current.

SECTION REVIEW

1. What is electric current?
2. What is resistance?
3. How does an electrochemical cell produce an electric current?
4. How does a thermocouple differ from a dry cell or battery?
5. What is direct current? Alternating current?
6. If the design of a dry cell keeps electrons flowing steadily, why do you think a dry cell goes "dead"?

Figure 19–16 *These electric power lines near Wagontire, Oregon, carry huge quantities of electricity to homes, offices, and other buildings in the area. What kind of current—DC or AC—is carried in these lines?* ❸

455

flow from a negative terminal to a positive terminal. Then the electrons are pumped back to the negative terminal to begin the cycle again.

4. A thermocouple changes heat energy into electric energy. A dry cell or battery changes chemical energy into electric energy.

5. The flow of electrons continuously in the same direction; the flow of electrons back and forth so that their direction is regularly reversed

6. The chemicals in the dry cell are eventually used up as a result of continuous chemical reaction.

19-4 ELECTRIC CIRCUITS

SECTION PREVIEW 19-4

In this section, students are introduced to an electric circuit as a complete path for an electric current. The parts of a circuit—electron source, load or resistance, wires, and switch—are discussed, and the concept of a closed circuit is covered. Finally, series circuits and parallel circuits are discussed and compared.

PERFORMANCE OBJECTIVES 19-4

1. Define electric circuit.
2. State the parts of a circuit and their functions.
3. Compare series and parallel circuits.

SCIENCE TERMS 19-4

series circuit p. 457
parallel circuit p. 457

19–4 Electric Circuits

❶ Try this experiment if you can. Connect one wire from a terminal on a dry cell to a small flashlight bulb. Does anything happen? Now connect another wire from the bulb to the other terminal on the dry cell. What happens? With just one wire connected, the bulb will not light. But with two wires providing a path for the flow of electrons, the bulb lights up.

In order to flow, electrons need a closed path through which to travel. **An electric circuit provides a complete, closed path for an electric current.**

Parts of a Circuit

An electric circuit consists of a source of electrons, a load or resistance, wires, and a switch. For a circuit that uses direct current, the source of electrons can be a dry cell or a battery. For a circuit that uses alternating current, the source of electrons is a generator at a power plant.

The load is the device that uses the electric energy. The load can be a light bulb, an appliance, a machine, or a motor. In all cases, the load offers some resistance to the flow of electrons. As a result, electric energy is converted into heat, light, or mechanical energy.

The switch in an electric circuit opens and closes the circuit. You will remember that electrons cannot

Figure 19–17 *No electricity can flow through an open circuit (left). When the switch is flipped on, the circuit is closed and electrons have a complete path through which to flow (right). What indicates a current is flowing through the circuit?* ❶

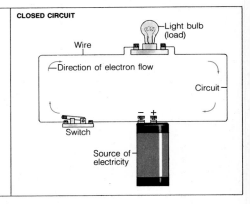
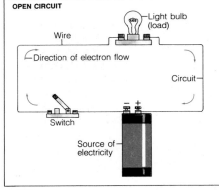

456

TEACHING STRATEGY 19-4

Motivation

Show students a simple electric circuit containing a small light bulb, a low-voltage dry cell, wires, and a switch. Open and close the switch several times and encourage students to do so as well. Ask,

• **What is happening?** (Electrons are flowing from one terminal of the dry cell, through a closed circuit, back to

the other terminal.)
• **What happens when the switch is opened? Why?** (Current can no longer flow because there is no longer a complete, closed path for electrons to travel along.)

Content Development

Reintroduce students to the circuit parts with which they are already familiar. Then discuss the nature of a circuit and the fact that circuits must

be closed. Ask them to observe the circuits shown in Figure 19-17, which helps to make this fact clear.

When you introduce series and parallel circuits, direct students' attention to Figure 19-18, which brings out the difference between the two types of circuits. If possible, construct actual series and parallel circuits in the classroom.

flow through a broken path. Electrons must have a closed path through which to travel. When the switch of an electric device is off, the circuit is open and electrons cannot flow. When the switch is on, the circuit is closed and electrons are able to flow. Remember this important rule: *Electricity cannot flow through an open circuit. Electricity can flow only through a closed circuit.*

Series and Parallel Circuits

As you just learned, an electric circuit consists of several parts: an electron source, a load, wires, and a switch. There are two types of electric circuits. The type depends on how the parts of the circuit are arranged.

If all the parts of an electric circuit are connected one after another, the circuit is a **series circuit.** In a series circuit, there is only one path for the electrons to take. Figure 19–19 illustrates a series circuit. The disadvantage of a series circuit is that if there is a break in any part of the circuit, the entire circuit is opened and no current can flow. Inexpensive holiday tree lights are often connected in series. What will happen if one light goes out in a circuit such as this? ❸

In a **parallel circuit,** the different parts of an electric circuit are on separate branches. There are several paths for the electrons to take in a parallel circuit. Figure 19–19 shows a parallel circuit. If there is a break in one branch of a parallel circuit,

Figure 19–18 *When severe weather conditions damage power lines, the flow of electricity is interrupted. Why?* ❷

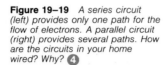

Figure 19–19 *A series circuit (left) provides only one path for the flow of electrons. A parallel circuit (right) provides several paths. How are the circuits in your home wired? Why?* ❹

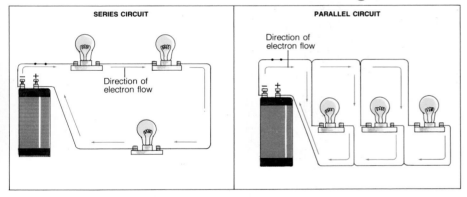

457

19-5 ELECTRIC POWER

SECTION PREVIEW 19-5

This section deals with the nature of electric power. The formula used to relate power, voltage, and current is then introduced.

$$P = V \times I$$

The unit of electric power, the watt, is then defined. Electric energy is then related to power and time by the equation

$$E = P \times t$$

and the kilowatt-hour is introduced. Finally, principles of electric safety are presented, and safety devices such as the fuse and circuit breaker are described.

PERFORMANCE OBJECTIVES 19-5

1. Define electric power and state and apply the formula that relates it to voltage and current.
2. Calculate electric energy, given power and time.
3. State the units of power and electric energy.
4. State six important safety rules relating to electricity.
5. Explain the use and operation of fuses and circuit breakers.

SCIENCE TERMS 19-5

power p. 458
watt p. 458
kilowatt p. 459
kilowatt-hour p. 460
fuse p. 461
circuit breaker p. 461

Figure 19–20 *Old types of tree lights used series circuits. Newer lights, such as these, are connected in parallel. What would happen to the lovely display if one bulb went out?* ❷

Section Objective

To define electric power

Figure 19–21 *These familiar electric appliances need electric power to operate. Each appliance has a different power requirement, or power rating. How is electric power calculated? In what unit is it measured?* ❸

458

electrons can still move through the other branches. The current continues to flow. Why do tree lights connected in parallel have an advantage over tree lights connected in series? Why do you think the electric circuits in your home are parallel circuits? ❶

SECTION REVIEW

1. What is an electric circuit?
2. What are the main parts of an electric circuit?
3. How does a series circuit differ from a parallel circuit?
4. Do you think that a circuit could be a combination of series and parallel connections? Explain your answer.

19–5 Electric Power

You probably use the word *power* in a number of different senses—to mean strength or force or energy. To a scientist, **power** is the rate at which work is done or energy is used. **Electric power is a measure of the rate at which electricity does work or provides energy.** In electric appliances, this energy is often converted to other forms of energy, such as heat, light, or mechanical energy. So electric power can be thought of as the rate at which the energy of an electric current is converted to other forms of energy.

Calculating Electric Power

Electric power can be calculated by using the following formula:

$$\text{power} = \text{voltage} \times \text{current}$$
$$\text{or}$$
$$P = V \times I$$

The unit of electric power is the **watt** (W). So the formula for power can also be written:

$$\text{watts} = \text{volts} \times \text{amperes}$$

According to this formula, one watt of power is delivered when a current of one ampere flows through a circuit whose voltage is one volt.

19-4 (continued)

Section Review 19-4
1. A complete, closed path for the flow of electrons
2. Source of electrons, load, wires, switch
3. In a series circuit, there is only one path for electron flow. In a parallel circuit, there are several paths for electron flow.
4. Yes. Separate sections of a circuit could be in parallel but be connected to each other or to other single resistances in series. Separate sections could be connected in series but be connected to each other in parallel.

TEACHING STRATEGY 19-5

Motivation
Ask students, in advance, to bring in (with their parents' permission) an electric utility bill. In class, explain that the information stated on the bill and the price of service relates to the quantity of electric energy used, which in turn depends on voltage, current, and time. As you go on to teach students the specifics regarding electric power and energy, explain in more detail how knowledge about these quantities and their calculations can be used to understand the information on their utility bills.

Sample Problem

What voltage is required to run a 75-watt light bulb if the current is 0.5 ampere?

Solution

Step 1	Write the formula	**power = voltage × current**
Step 2	Substitute given numbers and units	**75 watts = volts × 0.5 ampere**
Step 3	Solve for unknown variable	**75 = V × 0.5 = 75 ÷ 0.5 = 150 volts**

Practice Problem

❹ What is the power of an appliance that is operating at a current of 2 amps and a voltage of 120 volts?

To measure large quantities of power, such as the power used in your home, the **kilowatt (kW)** is used. One kilowatt is equal to 1000 watts. What is the power in watts of a 0.2-kilowatt light bulb? ❺

If you have ever looked at the label on a light bulb, hair dryer, or air conditioner, you probably are familiar with the units watts and kilowatts. Light bulbs are commonly 60, 75, or 100 watts.

Different appliances have different power ratings. As you might expect, the higher the rating, the greater the amount of electric energy needed to run ❷ the appliance. Figure 19–22 shows the power in watts for some common appliances.

Electric Energy

Have you ever noticed the electric meter in your home? This device measures how much energy your household uses. The electric company provides electric power at a certain cost. Their bill for this power is based on the total amount of energy a household uses, which is read from the electric meter.

The total amount of electric energy used depends on the total power used by all the electric appliances and the total time they are used. The formula for electric energy is

energy = power × time

or ❸

E = P × t

Figure 19–22 *This table shows the power used by some common appliances. Which appliance would use the greatest number of watts if operated for one hour?* ❻

POWER USED BY COMMON APPLIANCES

Appliance	**Power Used** *(watts)*
Refrigerator/freezer	600
Dishwasher	2300
Toaster	700
Range/oven	2600
Hair dryer	1000
Color television	300
Microwave oven	1450
Radio	100
Clock	3
Clothes dryer	4000

BACKGROUND INFORMATION

The term *power* is often used imprecisely by nonscientists, to refer to energy, force, and a number of other quantities. Power is actually a rate concept and is equal to energy used per unit time. Since energy is the ability to do work, power can also be defined as work done per unit time. Be sure to encourage students to use the term precisely.

ANNOTATION KEY

❶ If one light goes out, the others stay on. So that different lights and appliances can go on and off at different times, and so that a break in any part of the circuits does not disrupt the other electric lights and appliances (Relating concepts)
❷ Only one bulb would go dark. The rest of the display would remain lighted. (Applying concepts)
❸ Power equals voltage times current. Watts (Applying formulas)
❹ 240 watts (Applying formulas)
❺ 200 watts (Applying formulas)
❻ Range/oven (Interpreting tables)
❶ Thinking Skill: Interpreting formulas
❷ Thinking Skill: Making comparisons
❸ Thinking Skill: Interpreting formulas

Content Development

Define electric power clearly, and relate it and its unit to voltage and current. Carry out a number of sample calculations using the P = V × I equation. Discuss the power ratings of appliances and direct students' attention to Figures 19-21 and 19-22. Encourage them to compare the appliances listed. Go on to introduce the concept of electric power and the equation used to calculate its value.

Common Errors

When doing the practice problems, students may have difficulty manipulating the power-voltage-current equation. Be sure to show how the equation is to be rearranged to permit calculation of V or I, as students sometimes incorrectly multiply either of these quantities by P (rather than dividing it into P) to calculate the other quantity.

Reinforcement

You can easily demonstrate the validity of the E = P × t equation by noting that power is simply energy divided by time. Thus, the right side of the equation, P × t, reduces to

$$\frac{\text{energy}}{\text{time}} \times \text{time}$$

which clearly equals energy.

FACTS AND FIGURES

Chemically pure water is actually a rather poor conductor of electricity. However, any ordinary, nondistilled water contains in every milliliter large numbers of ions, or charged particles, that do conduct electricity. Thus ordinary water, which is actually a solution of salts, is a relatively efficient conductor. Even distilled water can quickly become a good conductor if any part of the body or clothing comes in contact with it, and ions become dissolved in it.

Electric energy is measured in **kilowatt-hours (kWh).**

energy = power × time

kilowatt-hours = kilowatts × hours

One kilowatt-hour is equal to 1000 watts of power used for one hour of time. You can imagine how much power this is by picturing ten 100-watt bulbs in a row, all burning for one hour. One kilowatt-hour would also be equal to a 500-watt appliance running for two hours.

To pay for electricity, the energy used is multiplied by the cost per kilowatt-hour. Suppose the cost of electricity is 8¢ per kilowatt-hour. How much would it cost to burn a 100-watt bulb for five hours? To use a 1000-watt air conditioner for three hours?

Electric Safety

Electricity is one of the most useful energy resources. But electricity can be dangerous if it is not used carefully. Here are some important rules to remember when using electricity.

1. Never handle appliances when your hands are wet or you are standing in water. Water is a fairly good conductor of electricity. If you are wet, you could unwillingly become an alternate path for the electric current!
2. Never run wires under carpets. Breaks or frays in the wires may go unnoticed. These breaks cause short circuits. A short circuit represents a shorter and easier path for electron flow and can cause shocks or a fire.
3. Never overload a circuit by connecting too many appliances to it. Each electric circuit is designed to carry a certain amount of current safely. An overloaded circuit can cause a short circuit.
4. Always repair worn or frayed wires to avoid short circuits.
5. Never stick your fingers in an electric socket or stick a utensil in a toaster that is plugged in. The electricity could be conducted directly into your hand or through the utensil into your hand.
6. Never come close to wires on power poles or to wires that have fallen from power poles or buildings. Such wires often carry very high voltages.

19-5 (continued)

Content Development

Carry out a number of examples involving calculation using the $E = P \times t$ equation. Take care to handle units correctly, and insist that students do so as well. Relate the calculations to practical situations, such as electric utility billing. You may wish to discuss some ways in which energy can be conserved in the home.

Take sufficient time to deal with principles involving electric safety. Review the rules given and ask students to come up with others. Finally, describe the role of fuses and circuit breakers and encourage students to learn the location of these devices in their home.

Skills Development

Skills: Applying concepts, relating cause and effect

Ask students to analyze their homes in terms of the electric safety rules discussed. They should check to see that none of the relevant rules is violated. If there are any potential difficulties, the students should record what the problems are and how they might result in a dangerous situation. The students should then inform their parents and should see to it that the problems are corrected.

Enrichment

Advanced students may wish to do library research on the history of the development of the concept of energy and its specific application to situa-

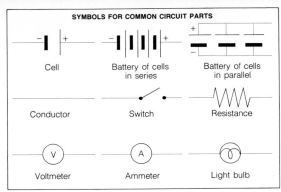

SYMBOLS FOR COMMON CIRCUIT PARTS

Cell

Battery of cells in series

Battery of cells in parallel

Conductor

Switch

Resistance

Voltmeter (V)

Ammeter (A)

Light bulb

Figure 19–23 *These symbols for common circuit parts are used to diagram any type of circuit—simple or complex. What are the advantages of using these symbols?* ❷

FUSES Your home has a great amount of electricity running through it. If too many appliances are all running at once or if the wires have become old and frayed, heat can build up in the wiring. The results can be dangerous. To protect against too much current flowing at once, your home may have **fuses** in a fuse box.

Inside each fuse is a thin strip of metal through which current flows. If the current becomes too high, the strip of metal melts and breaks the flow of electricity. So a fuse is an emergency switch.

CIRCUIT BREAKERS Like fuses, **circuit breakers** protect a circuit from becoming overloaded. Modern circuit breakers have a switch that flips open when the current flow becomes too high. These circuit breakers can easily be reset and used again once the problem has been found and corrected. Circuit breakers are easier to use than fuses. ❸

SECTION REVIEW

1. What is electric power? What is the formula for calculating electric power? In what unit is electric power measured?
2. What is electric energy? What is the formula for calculating electric energy? In what unit is electric energy measured?
3. Explain the purpose of fuses and circuit breakers. How is a fuse different from a circuit breaker?
4. If left running unused, which appliance would waste more electricity, an iron left on for half an hour or a television left on for one hour?

Sharpen Your Skills

Electricity in Your Home

Ask an adult to open the fuse box or circuit breaker box in your home. Describe the appearance of the fuses or circuit breakers. What different areas of your home do they protect?

Examine the appliances in your home for their power rating. Make a chart of this information. What is the relationship between an appliance's power rating and the amount of heat it produces?

461

LABORATORY INVESTIGATION
ELECTRICITY FROM A LEMON

BEFORE THE LAB

1. **Gather the necessary equipment at least one day prior to the investigation. You should gather enough equipment to meet your class needs, assuming two to six students per group.**

2. **For motivation purposes, you may wish to allow students to bring in their own coins and lemons.**

PRE-LAB DISCUSSION

Quickly review the basic concepts of electricity, such as current and the electric circuit. Ask students to propose and to discuss hypotheses regarding what will occur during the investigation, and why it will occur. Ask them also to consider what experimental findings will support or refute the hypotheses. Also, before they carry out the investigation, warn them not to oversand the coins, as they may expose base metal by doing so.

SKILL DEVELOPMENT

Students will use the following skills while completing this investigation.
1. Manipulative
2. Observing
3. Comparing
4. Hypothesizing
5. Inferring
6. Safety
7. Recording
8. Measuring
9. Applying

SAFETY TIPS

Remind students to be careful using scissors. Also tell them that juice from lemons that are used in the experiment should not be consumed, as metal salts have become dissolved in the juice.

TEACHING STRATEGY FOR LAB PROCEDURE

1. If you like, a voltmeter can be used instead of the compass and wire. If so, step 1 can be omitted.
2. It is important that the coins are sandpapered enough to remove any grease and any oxidation residue. Too much sanding, however, will expose only copper and the metals will not be different.

OBSERVATIONS

1. No
2. Yes
3. Yes

Problem

Can electricity be produced from a lemon, a penny, and a dime?

Materials *(per group)*

compass
cardboard box to fit the compass
bell wire
lemon
2 pennies
dime
sandpaper
scissors

Procedure

1. Wrap 20 turns of bell wire around the cardboard box containing the compass, as shown in the accompanying figure.
2. Roll the lemon back and forth on a table or other flat surface while applying slight pressure. The pressure will break the cellular structure of the lemon.
3. Use the pointed end of the scissors to make two slits about 1 cm apart in the lemon.
4. Sandpaper both sides of the dime and two pennies.
5. Insert the pennies in the two slits in the lemon. Only half of each penny should be inserted into the lemon, and the other half should stick out.
6. Touch the two ends of the bell wire to the coins. Observe any deflection of the compass needle. Record your observations.
7. Replace one of the pennies with the dime. Repeat step 6. Observe any deflection of the compass needle. If there is deflection, observe its direction. Record your observations.
8. Reverse the connecting wires on the coins. Observe any deflection of the compass needle and the direction of deflection. Record your observations.

462

Observations

1. Is the compass needle deflected when the two ends of the bell wire touch the two pennies?
2. Is the compass needle deflected when the two ends of the bell wire touch the penny and the dime?
3. Is the direction of deflection changed when the connecting wires on the coins are reversed?

Conclusions

1. Is an electric current produced when two pennies are used?
2. Is an electric current produced when a dime and a penny are used?
3. What is the purpose of breaking the cellular structure of the lemon? Of sandpapering the coins?
4. What materials are necessary to produce an electric current?
5. An electric current flowing through a wire produces magnetism. Using this fact, explain why a compass is used in this investigation to detect a weak current. What other device could be used to measure the current?
6. A dime is copper with a thin outer coating of silver. What would happen if the dime were sanded so much that the copper was exposed?

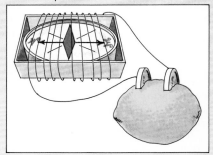

CONCLUSIONS

1. No
2. Yes
3. To allow the coins to touch the acidic lemon juice; to remove any grease or unwanted chemicals coating the coins
4. Two different metals and an electrolyte (lemon juice)
5. The needle on the compass is magnetic and will be attracted to the magnetic field set up when the electric current is produced. Thus, the needle

CHAPTER REVIEW

SUMMARY

19–1 Electric Charge
❏ All matter is made up of atoms.

❏ A force that pulls oppositely charged objects together is a force of attraction. A force that pushes similarly charged objects apart is a force of repulsion.

❏ An electric field is the region surrounding a charged particle in which an electric force affecting other charged particles is noticeable.

19–2 Static Electricity
❏ The buildup of electric charge is called static electricity.

❏ Objects can be charged by friction, conduction, and induction.

❏ A measure of the energy available to move electrons is called voltage (V), which is measured in units called volts (V).

19–3 The Flow of Electricity
❏ The flow of electrons through a wire is called electric current (I). Electric current is measured in units called amperes (A).

❏ Opposition to the flow of electricity is called resistance (R). Resistance is measured in units called ohms (Ω).

❏ Ohm's law states that the current in a wire is equal to voltage divided by resistance.

❏ In an electrochemical cell, chemical energy is changed into electric energy. A thermocouple changes heat energy into electric energy.

❏ In direct current (DC) electrons flow in the same direction. In alternating current (AC), electrons reverse their direction regularly.

19–4 Electric Circuits
❏ An electric circuit provides a complete, closed path for an electric current. Electricity can flow only through a closed circuit.

❏ A circuit in which there is only one path for the current is a series circuit. A circuit in which there are several paths is a parallel circuit.

19–5 Electric Power
❏ Electric power is a measure of the rate at which electricity does work or provides energy. The unit of the electric power is the watt (W). To measure large quantities of power, the kilowatt (kW) is used.

❏ Fuses and circuit breakers are used to protect against too much current flowing through a circuit at one time.

VOCABULARY

Define each term in a complete sentence.

alternating current (AC)	electric charge	electroscope	kilowatt-hour	series circuit
ampere	electric current	force of attraction	lightning	static electricity
atom	electric discharge	force of repulsion	lightning rod	subatomic particle
battery	electric field	friction	neutron	thermocouple
circuit breaker	electricity	fuse	nucleus	volt
conduction	electrochemical cell	grounding	ohm	voltage
conductor	electrode	induction	Ohm's law	voltaic cell
direct current (DC)	electrolyte	insulator	parallel circuit	watt
dry cell	electron	kilowatt	power	wet cell
			proton	
			resistance	

463

Part 2

Ask students to consider what may be happening on the chemical level during the investigation. Ask them also to consider how the quantitative data that are obtained might change if the data were collected over an extended period of time.

---

deflection shows whether or not an electric current has been produced. A voltmeter could also be used.

6. There would not be two different metals and no current would be produced.

GOING FURTHER: ENRICHMENT

Part 1

Make a voltmeter available to advanced students and allow them to repeat the investigation, using it in place of the compass, and connecting it in parallel. In this way, they will be able to obtain quantitative information on the potential differences involved. You may also wish to provide them with an ammeter, to be connected in series. This device will provide them with information on current magnitude and direction. The lemon setup should produce a current of about 0.5 volts.

CHAPTER REVIEW

MULTIPLE CHOICE

1. c	**3.** a	**5.** d	**7.** b	**9.** c
2. b	**4.** a	**6.** b	**8.** c	**10.** b

COMPLETION

1. nucleus
2. protons
3. distance
4. friction
5. negatively
6. electric discharge
7. ampere
8. thermocouple
9. series
10. power

TRUE OR FALSE

1. F repel/attract
2. T
3. F induction
4. F voltage
5. T
6. F voltage divided by the resistance
7. T
8. F closed
9. T
10. F should not use

SKILL BUILDING

1. a. The clothes have picked up static electricity, and clothes that are oppositively charged attract each other. **b.** Touching both terminals will complete circuit and the person will be shocked. **c.** The fuse is designed to burn out when the metal filament in the fuse overheats due to an overload or short circuit. If the correct fuse rating is not used, the fuse may not burn out and the overload or short circuit could cause a fire.
2. a. 120 watts **b.** .960 kilowatt-hours **c.** 6.7 cents
3. a. both **b.** series **c.** parallel **d.** series **e.** series
4. Rub the rubber rod with the fur and then touch the rod to the knob of the electroscope. This gives the electroscope a negative charge and the leaves should spread apart. Now bring a plastic ruler, rubbed with wax paper, and touch it to the knob of the electroscope. Observe what happens to the leaves. If the leaves collapse, the plastic ruler is positively charged.

ESSAY

1. Conduction (direct contact); friction (rubbing to separate charges); induction (approach of a charged object near a neutral object)

2. Insulator: does not conduct an electric current or allow electrons to flow. Conductor: allows electrons to flow easily. Use a conductor when you want an electric current to flow, such as in an electric wire. Insulators are most often used for safety purposes to prevent the flow of electrons. Insulators are usually coated around a conducting metal wire.
3. Answers will vary, but should reflect the basic safety rules discussed in the chapter.

4. The resistance of a wire depends on the material used, thickness, length, and temperature. Resistance can be increased by using a less-conductive material, by decreasing thickness of a wire, by increasing the length, and changing the temperature according to the material used.

Determine whether each statement is true or false. Then on a separate sheet of paper, write "true" if it is true. If it is false, change the underlined word or words to make the statement true.

1. Like charges <u>attract</u> each other; unlike charges <u>repel</u> each other.
2. A neutral object develops a negative charge when it <u>gains</u> electrons.
3. Charging by <u>conduction</u> involves a rearrangement of electric charges.
4. A measure of energy available to move electrons is called <u>friction</u>.
5. Materials that do not allow electrons to flow freely are called <u>insulators</u>.
6. Ohm's law states that the current in a wire is equal to <u>resistance divided by voltage</u>.
7. Copper is a <u>good</u> conductor.
8. An electric circuit provides a complete <u>open</u> path for an electric current.
9. The total amount of electric <u>energy</u> used depends on the total power used and the total time of use.
10. If an object gets lodged in an electric socket, <u>use</u> a utensil to remove it.

CONCEPT REVIEW: SKILL BUILDING

Use the skills you have developed in the chapter to complete each activity.

1. **Applying concepts** Provide an explanation for the following observations:
   a. Clothes dried in a dryer often stick together with "static cling."
   b. Never touch both terminals at the same time when working on a car battery.
   c. It is dangerous to use a 30-amp fuse in a circuit calling for a 15-amp fuse.
2. **Making calculations** A light bulb operates at 60 volts and 2 amps.
   a. What is the power of the light bulb?
   b. How much energy does the light bulb need in order to operate for eight hours?
   c. What is the cost of operating the bulb for 8 hours at a rate of 7¢ per kilowatt-hour?
3. **Identifying relationships** Identify each of the following statements as being a characteristic of (a) a series circuit, (b) a parallel circuit, (c) both a series and a parallel circuit:
   a. $I = V/R$
   b. The total resistance in the circuit is the sum of the individual resistances.
   c. The total current in the circuit is the sum of the current in each resistance.
   d. The current in each part of the circuit is the same.
   e. A break in any part of the circuit causes the current to stop.
4. **Designing an experiment** A plastic ruler is rubbed with waxed paper. The ruler gains an unknown charge. Describe an experiment you could perform using an electroscope, a rubber rod, and a piece of fur to determine the charge on the ruler.

CONCEPT REVIEW: ESSAY

Discuss each of the following in a brief paragraph.

1. Describe the three ways in which an object can be charged.
2. Compare an insulator and a conductor. How might each be used?
3. Discuss three safety rules to follow while using electricity.
4. Describe two ways in which the resistance of a wire can be increased.

465

ADDITIONAL QUESTIONS AND TOPIC SUGGESTIONS

1. Why are electrons much easier to remove from an object than protons are? (Electrons are much lower in mass. Also, unlike protons, they are not clustered together in the nucleus of the atom.)

2. Is it possible for a voltage to exist between two points without there also being a current? Explain. (Voltage is potential difference. There can be a difference in this potential energy between two points, even if no electrons are permitted to flow—for example, if a circuit in which there is a source of electricity is open.)

3. How is the current in a segment of wire affected if a parallel branch is attached at the ends of the segment? Explain. (The current, which is a measure of the number of electrons flowing past a point per unit time, is reduced, since some of the electrons that used to flow through the segment now flow through the parallel branch instead.)

4. What is the effect of each of the following on electric power: a. current is reduced; b. voltage is increased; c. a resistor is added? Explain in terms of the electric-power equation. (**a.** Power decreased in $P = V \times I$. **b.** Power increases, since V is increased in $P = V \times I$. **c.** Power decreases, since, by Ohm's Law, I is decreased if R is increased, and since $P = V \times I$.)

ISSUES IN SCIENCE

The following issues can be used as a springboard for class debate or assigned as a writing homework.

1. Do you think a third basic type of electric charge is possible? If so, how might a particle having such a charge be recognized? (Students may point out that, although there is no experimental evidence in favor of its existence, such a charge is at least theoretically possible. They may suggest that a particle having such a charge would be attracted to both positive and negative charges, since it would be unlike either and since unlike charges attract.)

2. The cost per kilowatt-hour of electricity charged by utility companies often decreases as the number of kilowatt-hours used increases. Does this seem fair? What might be an undesirable effect of this practice on energy conservation by individual households or companies? (Some students may feel that such discounting for increased use is fair and is analogous to other economic practices in which goods or services are involved. Others may stress the negative effect of not sufficiently discouraging overuse of energy resources by households or companies.)

Chapter 20
MAGNETISM

CHAPTER OVERVIEW

The properties of magnets are introduced in this chapter. Students learn about magnetism as a force of attraction or repulsion, and about magnetic poles and magnetic fields. Natural and induced magnetism are then discussed, and permanent and temporary magnets are contrasted.

Students read about the magnetic properties of the earth and about the behavior of compasses. Next, the basis of magnetism itself is explained in terms of electron spin, and the concept of magnetic domains is introduced.

Electomagnetism, or the relationship between electricity and magnetism, is discussed next. Oersted's discovery of the production of a magnetic field by an electric current is described. Applications of electromagnetism in devices such as electric motors, galvanometers, and doorbells are then treated. Next, students read about electromagnetic induction, the production of a current by motion of a conductor in a magnetic field. Finally, the principles of operation of generators and transformers are discussed.

INTRODUCING CHAPTER 20

Direct students' attention to the photograph on page 466. Ask whether any of them have observed an actual aurora. If some of the students have, ask,
• **What colors did you observe?** (Answers will vary. Many colors are typically present.)
• **What was the shape of the aurora, and how did it change?** (The shape, which changes rapidly, can vary considerably, often resembling a shimmering, shifting curtain.)
• **What causes auroras?** (They are light phenomena, resulting from collisions between particles in the upper atmosphere. Some of these particles are charged particles given off by the sun and trapped in the earth's magnetosphere, or magnetic field.)
• **Why do auroras occur over the extreme northern and southern parts of the earth?** (The earth's magnetic poles are located there.)

Magnetism

20

CHAPTER OBJECTIVES

After completing this chapter, you will be able to

20–1 Describe magnetism and the behavior of magnetic poles.

20–1 Relate magnetic fields and magnetic lines of force.

20–2 Describe the earth's magnetic properties.

20–2 Explain how a compass works.

20–3 Explain magnetism in terms of magnetic domains.

20–4 Describe how a magnetic field is created by an electric current.

20–5 Explain how electricity can be produced from magnetism.

20–5 Apply the principle of induction to motors, generators, and transformers.

The colored lights dance across the sky, growing bright and dim as they change shape. The choreography is never the same—each night a different cast of characters makes its entrances and exits on the darkened stage. When the show is over, the lights grow dim. For a short time, a faint glow remains. Then, once again, the sky is dark.

These colorful displays of light are called auroras. Perhaps you are more familiar with them by another name—the northern lights and the southern lights. At certain times of the year, auroras can be seen in the night sky near the Arctic Circle and the Antarctic Circle.

Auroras occur when charged particles blown out from the sun are trapped by the earth's magnetic field. As some of these particles collide with other particles in the upper atmosphere, visible light is given off.

Auroras provide evidence of how the earth behaves as a giant magnet in space. In this chapter you will learn more about the earth's magnetic field. You also will learn about magnets that can pick up everything from paper clips to huge pieces of scrap metal. And you will gain an understanding of the various applications of magnetism—applications that make your life easier and more comfortable.

A band of colors called an aurora dances across the sky in northern Alaska.

467

TEACHER DEMONSTRATION

You may wish to perform the following demonstration to motivate students and to introduce them to this chapter. Obtain a sample of the naturally magnetic mineral magnetite (lodestone). The sample should be large enough to be easily visible by the class and should have an elongated (rather than spherical) shape. Do not tell students the name of the mineral.

Use a string to hang the sample from a support. Ask students to observe the magnetite's orientation. Carefully rotate the support through 90°. But, before doing so, ask,

• **What will happen if the support is turned? Why?** (The mineral will keep its orientation. It is naturally magnetic and its north pole points toward the earth's magnetic north pole).

Use a compass to reveal the sample's magnetic orientation. Also, use the sample to pick up paper clips or small nails.

TEACHER RESOURCES
Audiovisuals
Electromagnetism, 8 mm film loop, PH Media

Electromagnets and Their Uses, 16 mm film, Cor

Magnets, filmstrip with cassette, LA

Magnets, Magnetism, and Electricity, 16 mm film, CRM/McGraw-Hill

Books
Chikazumi, Sushin and Stanley H. Charap, *Physics of Magnetism,* Krieger

Edminster, Joseph, *Schaum's Outline of Electromagnets,* McGraw-Hill

Kalvius, G.M. and R.S. Tebble, *Experimental Magnetism,* vol. 1, Wiley

McCraig, M., *Permanent Magnets in Theory and Practice,* Halstead

Software
Electromagnetism, Prentice-Hall

20-1 PROPERTIES OF MAGNETS

SECTION PREVIEW 20-1

The ancient Greeks discovered magnetite, a naturally occurring mineral. The magnetism it exhibits is a force of attraction or repulsion due to electron arrangements. Magnets have a north and a south pole, which, if the magnets are allowed to swing freely, point north and south, respectively. Like poles repel and unlike poles attract one another. The region in which such magnetic forces can act is called a magnetic field. Magnetic lines of force define the magnetic field of an object.

Materials can be magnetized by means of magnetic induction. Magnetized materials may be either temporary or permanent magnets, depending on whether they readily lose their magnetic properties.

PERFORMANCE OBJECTIVES 20-1

1. **Name a naturally magnetic mineral and describe its discovery.**
2. **Define magnetism.**
3. **Describe the properties of magnetic poles.**
4. **Define magnetic field and describe the appearance and use of magnetic lines of force.**
5. **Define magnetic induction, and contrast permanent and temporary magnets.**

20-1 Properties of Magnets

More than 2000 years ago, the Greeks living in a part of Turkey known as Magnesia discovered a mysterious rock. This rock could attract materials that contained iron. Because the rock was found in Magnesia, the Greeks named it magnetite. The Greeks noticed another interesting thing about this peculiar rock. If they allowed it to swing freely from a string, the same part of the rock would always face in the same direction. That direction was toward a certain northern star, called the leading star or lodestar. So magnetite also became known as lodestone.

The Greeks did not know it then, but they were observing a property of matter called **magnetism.** Certain materials, such as iron, exhibit the property of magnetism. **Magnetism is a force of attraction or repulsion due to an arrangement of electrons.**

Magnetic Poles

Magnetic forces, like electric forces, involve attractions and repulsions. The magnetic forces usually are strongest at the two ends of a magnet. These ends are called **poles.**

The simplest kind of magnet is a straight bar of iron. If a bar magnet is suspended horizontally on a string and allowed to swing freely, one end of the

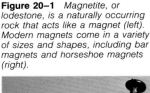

Figure 20-1 *Magnetite, or lodestone, is a naturally occurring rock that acts like a magnet (left). Modern magnets come in a variety of sizes and shapes, including bar magnets and horseshoe magnets (right).*

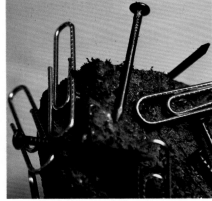

468

TEACHING STRATEGY 20-1

Cross Unit Reference

Upon completing this chapter, you may want to have students go to Chapter 28 Electronics and Computers. In this way, you can tie together the information students have learned about electricity and magnetism in Chapters 19 and 20 by showing some of the practical applications of such information.

Motivation

Make available to students a number of small horseshoe magnets with labeled poles. Also make strings and metal paper clips available and allow students to investigate magnetic properties such as attraction and repulsion and alignment of the magnets in north–south directions when allowed to swing freely. Ask them to consider what may account for the properties of magnets.

Content Development

As the various properties of magnets are introduced and explored, list the properties on the chalkboard. Ask the students the following.

• **Do the attraction and repulsion properties of magnets remind you of properties you studied earlier?** (Objects with like and unlike electric charges have similar properties of attraction and repulsion.)

• **Is it possible that magnets are sim-**

magnet will always point toward the north. The end of the magnet that points toward the north is called the **north magnetic pole.** The other end of the magnet, which points toward the south, is called the **south magnetic pole.** You have probably seen bar magnets marked with an "N" to show the north pole and an "S" to show the south pole. Perhaps you have seen horseshoe magnets too. The poles of a horseshoe magnet also are marked N and S.

When two magnets are brought near each other, they exert a force on each other. If two north poles are brought close together, they will repel each other. Two south poles will do the same thing. However, if the north pole of one magnet is brought near the south pole of another magnet, the poles will attract each other. The rule for magnetic poles is: *like poles repel each other and unlike poles attract each other.* How does this rule compare with the rule that describes the behavior of electric charges?

Magnetic Fields

Although magnetic forces are strongest at the poles of a magnet, they are not limited to the poles alone. Magnetic forces are felt around the rest of the magnet as well. The region in which magnetic forces can act is called a **magnetic field.**

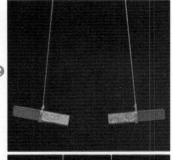

Figure 20–2 *Two bar magnets suspended by strings are free to move. What force is occurring between the magnets in each photograph? Why?* ❷

Figure 20–3 *You can see the magnetic lines of force in the pattern formed by iron filings placed on a glass sheet over a magnet. The diagram illustrates these lines of force. Where are the lines of force strongest?* ❸

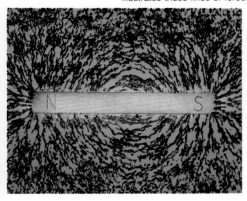
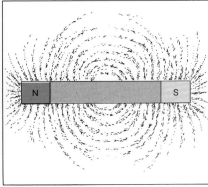

469

SCIENCE TERMS 20-1

magnetism p. 468
pole p. 468
north magnetic pole p. 469
south magnetic pole p. 469
magnetic field p. 469
magnetic lines of force p. 470
natural magnet p. 470
magnetic induction p. 470
temporary magnet p. 471
permanent magnet p. 471

TEACHER DEMONSTRATION

Explore the dependency of magnetic force on distance. Make use of a pole of a strong magnet in this demonstration. Hang a small iron object on a spring balance designed to measure force, and first measure the force of gravity, in newtons, acting on the object when it is far from the magnet. Subtract this value from subsequent readings. Hold the object (suspended from the spring balance) at various short distances above the magnet pole and record the resulting force on the object. Demonstrate that the force decreases rapidly with distance.

ANNOTATION KEY

❶ Same: Like charges repel each other and unlike charges attract each other. (Comparing)

❷ Top: repulsion; like poles Bottom: attraction; unlike poles (Interpreting photographs)

❸ Near the poles of the magnet (Interpreting illustrations)

❶ Thinking Skill: Making generalizations

❷ Thinking Skill: Observing

ply electrically charged objects, with a positive charge at one end and a negative charge at the other? How might you investigate this possibility? (Some students may incorrectly conclude that magnetism and electric charge are identical rather than simply related, as they turn out to be. Students may suggest testing magnets to see whether they attract electrically charged objects, such as rubbed balloons or glass rods. Actually carry out such tests to show that there is no such attraction and that magnets do not have net electric charges.)

Enrichment
Advanced students may wish to do library research to obtain more information on the discovery of magnetism and the properties of magnets. Have them report their findings to the class.

Sharpen Your Skills

Experiencing Magnetic Forces
Skills: Manipulative, observing, comparing, hypothesizing
Level: Remedial
Type: Hands-on
Materials: two bar magnets

This activity will enable students to actually feel the magnetic forces caused by bar magnets. Students will be able to feel the force of attraction when unlike poles are brought together, as well as the force of repulsion when like poles are brought together.

20-1 (continued)

Content Development

The strengths of the magnetic fields of different magnets can differ considerably. The magnetic field can thus be thought of as a quantity that can have different magnitudes. It is also a directional quantity. Since both magnitude and direction are involved, it is therefore a vector quantity. Magnetic field, or, more precisely, the magnetic induction of a field, is symbolized by the letter B with an arrow written above it to indicate its vector nature: B. The units in which B is measured are the tesla and the gauss (1 tesla = 10^4 gauss).

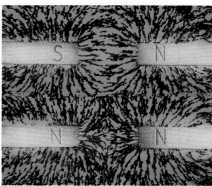

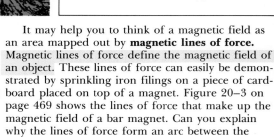

Figure 20–4 What do the lines of force around these magnets tell you about the interaction of like and unlike magnetic poles? ❶

Figure 20–5 This iron nail attracts metal paper clips. How can an iron nail be turned into a magnet? What is this process called? ❸

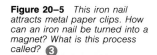

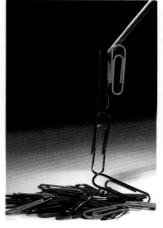

470

It may help you to think of a magnetic field as an area mapped out by **magnetic lines of force.** Magnetic lines of force define the magnetic field of an object. These lines of force can easily be demonstrated by sprinkling iron filings on a piece of cardboard placed on top of a magnet. Figure 20–3 on page 469 shows the lines of force that make up the magnetic field of a bar magnet. Can you explain why the lines of force form an arc between the north and south poles? ❷

Figure 20–4 shows the lines of force that exist between like and unlike poles of two bar magnets. The pattern of iron filings shows that like poles repel each other and unlike poles attract each other. Where are the lines of force always the most numerous and closest together? ❹

Magnetic Materials

When the Greeks discovered magnetite, or lodestone, they discovered what is known as a **natural magnet.** Natural magnets are naturally occurring substances that have magnetic properties.

Some materials can be made into magnets by stroking them in the same direction several times with strong magnets. Most of the magnets you probably have used are this type of magnet. The process by which a material is made into a magnet is known as **magnetic induction.**

You can see magnetic induction work by stroking an iron nail several times in the same direction

Skills Development

Skills: Making observations, identifying relationships, performing an experiment

Provide students with two bar magnets, sheets of paper, and iron filings. Have students use these materials to observe magnetic lines of force for one magnet alone, and for N–S, N–N, and S–S interactions between magnets. They should make sketches of what they observe.

Section Review 20-1

1. A force of attraction or repulsion due to an arrangement of electrons
2. Like poles repel each other and unlike poles attract each other
3. The region in which magnetic forces can act
4. Naturally occurring substances that have magnetic properties; a magnet made of a material such as soft iron that is easy to magnetize but that loses its magnetism quickly; a magnet that is

with a strong magnet. Soon the nail itself becomes a magnet. Some materials, such as soft iron, are easy to magnetize, but they also lose their magnetism quickly. Magnets made of these materials are called **temporary magnets.** Other magnets are made of materials that are more difficult to magnetize, but which tend to stay magnetized. Magnets made of these materials are called **permanent magnets.**

Cobalt, nickel, and iron are materials from which strong permanent magnets can be made. Most permanent magnets are made of a mixture of aluminum, nickel, cobalt, and iron. This mixture, which makes a very strong magnet, is called alnico.

SECTION REVIEW

1. What is magnetism?
2. State the rule that describes the behavior of magnetic poles.
3. What is a magnetic field?
4. What is a natural magnet? A temporary magnet? A permanent magnet?
5. Suppose that a bar magnet is suspended horizontally from a string. Describe a way to make the magnet rotate in a clockwise direction without touching the magnet.

20–2 The Earth As a Magnet

Why does one pole of a bar magnet suspended from a string always point north and the other pole always point south? The first person to suggest an answer to this question was an English physician named William Gilbert. In 1600, Gilbert proposed the idea that the earth itself is a magnet. He predicted that the earth would be found to have magnetic poles.

Gilbert's theory turned out to be correct. Magnetic poles of the earth were discovered. Today, scientists know that the earth behaves as if it has a huge bar magnet buried deep within it. **The earth exerts magnetic forces on magnets and compasses and is surrounded by a magnetic field that is strongest near the north and south magnetic poles.**

Sharpen Your Skills

Experiencing Magnetic Forces

❷

1. Take two bar magnets of the same size and hold one in each hand.

2. Holding the magnets with the two north poles facing each other, slowly bring the magnets together. What do you feel in your hands?

3. Now move the magnets apart. Hold them with the north pole of one facing the south pole of the other. Slowly bring the magnets together. What do you feel? What happens to the magnets?

Explain your observations in terms of magnetic forces.

Section Objective

To describe the earth's magnetic properties

❸

471

SECTION PREVIEW 20-2

Gilbert's theory that the earth acts like a magnet is presented. The earth's magnetic poles and its ability to exert magnetic forces are discussed. The earth's surrounding magnetosphere is then described. The behavior of compasses is explained next, and the discrepancy between magnetic and geographic poles is pointed out.

PERFORMANCE OBJECTIVES 20-2

1. **Describe the magnetic poles and magnetic field of the earth.**
2. **Define magnetosphere and explain its role in producing auroras.**
3. **Explain the behavior of compasses.**
4. **Distinguish between geographic and magnetic poles and explain magnetic variation.**

SCIENCE TERMS 20-2
magnetosphere p. 472
magnetic variation p. 473

---

difficult to magnetize, but which keeps its magnetism; usually made of cobalt, nickel, iron, or alnico
5. Hold a large, strong magnet near the bar magnet so that opposite poles are near each other. Slowly make a clockwise circle with the large magnet. It should pull the suspended magnet along in a clockwise rotation because of the attraction between the unlike poles.

TEACHING STRATEGY 20-2

Motivation

Draw students' attention to a world globe and ask them what properties would be observable if the earth were a magnet, as Gilbert correctly proposed. Then actually hold a strong bar magnet more or less parallel to the north–south axis of the globe and ask students to imagine the magnet imbedded in the globe. Ask,

● **How would free-swinging magnets and compasses behave when placed at different points of the globe?** (They would align themselves in a north–south (relative to the globe) orientation. Sophisticated students may then realize that the true magnetic north pole of the earth must be in the geographic south, in order for the north poles of magnets to point northward. Do not as yet remark on the correctness of this conclusion, which will be taken up shortly.)

TIE-IN/EARTH SCIENCE

Recent space probes, such as *Voyager 1* and *Voyager 2,* have revealed interesting details about the magnetic properties of other planets. Jupiter, for example, has an extremely strong magnetic field. The magnetosphere of this planet is one of the largest field "structures" in the solar system, and the temperatures reached by excited atomic particles in parts of this field are the highest yet measured.

HISTORICAL NOTES

Compasses have had a great inspirational effect on a number of scientists in the past. Albert Einstein, for example, in describing his early childhood, wrote that his favorite toy was a compass needle given to him by his father. Einstein claimed that he never lost the sense of scientific wonder that he first felt when he played with that "magical" needle.

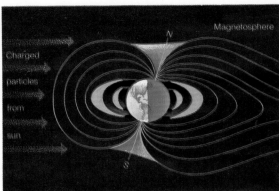

Figure 20–6 *The magnetosphere is made up of charged particles given off by the sun (left). These particles cause the formation of an aurora, such as the one shown in this photo taken by a satellite orbiting the earth (right).*

472

The region of the earth's magnetic field is called the **magnetosphere.** The magnetosphere, which extends beyond the atmosphere, is made up of charged particles that have been given off by the sun. Sometimes these particles collide with other particles in the upper atmosphere and light is given off. The result is the brightly colored aurora, which you read about in the introduction to this chapter.

Compasses

If you have ever used a compass, you know that a compass needle always points north. The needle of a compass is magnetized. It has a north pole and a south pole. The earth's magnetic field exerts a force on the needle just as it exerts a force on a bar magnet hanging from a string.

The north pole of a compass needle points to the north pole of the earth. As you learned, however, like poles repel and unlike poles attract. So the magnetic pole of the earth to which the north pole of a compass needle points must actually be a magnetic south pole. The same is true of the geographic south pole, which is actually a magnetic north pole. It would be too confusing, however, to try to convey this idea about the magnetism of the poles. So scientists accept the fact that the earth's magnetic north pole and magnetic south pole are named according to their locations near the geographic north pole and geographic south pole.

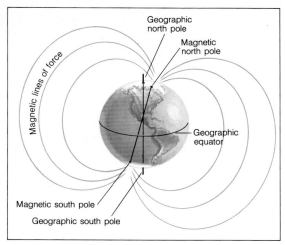

Figure 20–7 *You can see in this illustration that the geographic north and south poles are not located exactly at the magnetic north and south poles. Does a compass needle, then, point directly north?* ❶

A compass needle does not point exactly to the earth's geographic poles. It points to the magnetic poles. Scientists have discovered that the magnetic north pole is located in northeastern Canada, about 1600 kilometers from the geographic north pole. The magnetic south pole is located near the Antarctic Circle. Figure 20–7 shows the locations of the earth's magnetic and geographic north and south poles.

Because a compass points to the earth's magnetic poles, it does not show true north and south. The error in a compass caused by the difference in location of the earth's magnetic and geographic poles is called **magnetic variation.** The extent of magnetic variation is not the same for all places on the earth. Near the equator, magnetic variation is slight. As you get closer to the poles, the error increases.

SECTION REVIEW

1. In what ways is the earth like a magnet?
2. How does a compass work?
3. Why is the earth's magnetic north pole really a magnetic south pole?
4. What is meant by magnetic variation?
5. Why is magnetic variation close to the equator minimal, while near the poles the error is great?

473

less northeastward, rather than northward, direction. In parts of Alaska, compasses actually point eastward!

Content Development
There is strong geological evidence that the earth's north and south magnetic poles have "switched" a number of times in the past. Some scientists who have examined this evidence, which involves the orientation of magnetic minerals at different strata,

think that another switch of magnetic poles may occur in the not-too-distant future.

Reinforcement
Slower students might wish to sketch or obtain flat maps of the earth and label the magnetic poles. They can also draw in compasses at different geographic locations on the map and show the directions in which the needles point.

20-3 AN EXPLANATION OF MAGNETISM

SECTION PREVIEW 20-3

Magnetism is explained on the basis of electron motion—in particular, spin, which sets up a magnetic field. Unpaired electrons are presented as the basis for uncanceled, measurable magnetic fields. Grouping of fields into magnetic domains is discussed, and students are introduced to the idea that, in a magnetized object, the magnetic domains are lined up, and that magnetic properties are lost if the domain arrangement is randomized.

PERFORMANCE OBJECTIVES 20-3

1. **Explain magnetism in terms of electron spin.**
2. **Define magnetic domain.**
3. **Explain, in terms of the arrangement of magnetic domains, how an object can become magnetized or can lose its magnetic properties**

SCIENCE TERMS 20-3

magnetic domain p. 474

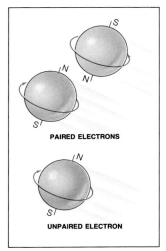

Figure 20–8 *Scientists believe that magnetism is due mainly to the spin of electrons. Since all objects have electrons, why aren't all objects magnetic?* ❶

20–3 An Explanation of Magnetism

If you bring a magnet near a piece of wood, glass, aluminum, or plastic, nothing happens. In addition, none of these materials can be magnetized. Yet materials such as iron, steel, nickel, and cobalt react readily to a magnet. And all of these materials can be magnetized. Why are some materials magnetic while others are not?

Scientists believe that magnetism is due to the motion of electrons, particularly their spin. The spin of an electron sets up a magnetic field around the electron.

In most atoms, electrons occur in pairs. Each electron in a pair spins in an opposite direction. So when electrons are paired together, their opposite spins cancel each other. The magnetic field of one electron is cancelled by the magnetic field of the other electron. No magnetism results.

Some metals, however, contain atoms with unpaired electrons. Usually, these unpaired electrons have a random arrangement. They are not lined up in any one direction. Their magnetic fields extend in many different directions. The force of magnetism is not felt, and the metal is unmagnetized.

Now, if all these individual magnetic fields are arranged in the same direction—that is, all north poles facing one way and all south poles facing the other way—the strength of the total magnetic field is greatly increased. The metal is magnetized.

A region in which the magnetic fields of atoms are grouped together is called a **magnetic domain.**

Figure 20–9 *In an unmagnetized substance, the individual magnetic fields extend in many different directions (left). When these magnetic fields are all arranged in the same direction, the substance becomes magnetized (right). What is the name for the region in which magnetic fields of atoms are grouped together?* ❷

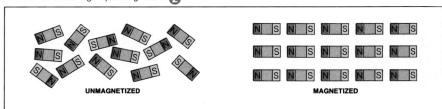

UNMAGNETIZED   MAGNETIZED

TEACHING STRATEGY 20-3

Motivation

Stroke an iron nail repeatedly with a strong magnet. Use the nail to attract a paper clip and support the nail and attached clip so that they are easily visible. Ask,
- **What has happened to the nail?** (It has become magnetized.)
- **Why has this happened?** (Answers will vary. The magnetic domains in the nail have lined up.)

After a short time, the clip will drop off. Ask,
- **Why has this happened?** (The magnetic domains have returned to a random arrangement.)

Content Development

Direct students' attention to Figures 20-8 and 20-9. Ask them to observe the paired and unpaired electrons in Figure 20-8, and explain the cancellation of magnetic fields that results from the pairing. Discuss Figure 20-9 in terms of random and aligned magnetic domains, taking care first to explain the concept of such domains as regions in which the magnetic fields of large numbers of atoms are overlapped and, in a sense, grouped together and unified. Use this concept to explain the property of certain materials to be magnetized and the ability

HELP WANTED: NUCLEAR MAGNETIC RESONANCE TECHNICIAN Familiarity with NMR scanner required. Must be sensitive to patients' needs. High school diploma and technical training necessary.

Aware that the patient is nervous, the technician calmly explains what is about to happen. Fear begins to disappear as the patient listens to the technician's comforting words.

The long tube-shaped machine that surrounds the patient's body, carefully explains the

nuclear magnetic resonance technician, uses a powerful circular magnet to produce clear three-dimensional images of the patient's internal organs. The painless procedure will reveal information about body structure and function that previously could be found only through surgery.

An NMR technician is trained to operate an NMR scanner. The technician must be able to follow a doctor's prescription and align the patient in the scanner so that the correct body section is imaged.

Some NMR technicians conduct laboratory research, order supplies, and handle administrative duties associated with NMR technology. Other NMR technicians are trained to examine the images produced by the NMR scanner and to recognize tumors or abnormal growths.

In some states, a license is necessary to run an NMR scanner. If you would like to find out how you can become an NMR technician, write to the American Society for Medical Technology, 330 Meadowfern Drive, Houston, TX 77067.

You can think of a magnetic domain as a miniature magnet. In an unmagnetized iron nail, for example, all the magnetic domains are pointing in different directions. See Figure 20–9. If a magnet comes near the nail, the magnetic domains temporarily line up so that like poles all point in the same direction. As soon as the magnet moves away from the nail, however, the domains go back to their original random arrangement.

Stroking the nail with a magnet will cause the domains to line up so that like poles all point in the same direction. The nail will act like a magnet. The nail will lose its magnetic properties as the domains return to a random arrangement.

The model of magnetic domains explains an interesting property of magnets. If you cut a magnet in half, the result is two smaller magnets. A piece cut from a magnet will have a north and south pole just like the original magnet. This is true no matter how many times the magnet is cut. A magnet is actually made up of thousands of smaller magnets.

Sharpen Your Skills

A Model of Magnetic Domains

1. Cut several index cards into small strips to represent magnetic domains. Label each strip with a north pole and a south pole.

2. On one sheet of posterboard, arrange the strips to represent an unmagnetized substance.

3. On another sheet of posterboard, arrange the strips to represent a magnetized substance.

Provide a written explanation for your model.

475

---

of magnets to be cut in two to produce two smaller magnets, each with a north and a south pole.

Enrichment
Ask advanced students to do library research on the nature of magnetic domains and on the development and experimental confirmation of the theory that such domains exist. Students can prepare written reports and also separate charts to illustrate the nature

of such domains and the steps in scientific method demonstrated by the historical development of the theory.

20-4 ELECTROMAGNETISM

SECTION PREVIEW 20-4

This section deals with electromagnetism, the relationship between electricity and magnetism. The students are first introduced to the experiments of Hans Christian Oersted. These experiments illustrated that an electric current gives rise to a magnetic field whose direction depends on the direction of the current. The structure and some of the uses of temporary magnets called electromagnets are then discussed. Finally, the electric motor, a device that converts electrical energy into mechanical energy, is described, as is the galvanometer, an instrument used to detect small currents.

PERFORMANCE OBJECTIVES 20-4

1. **Describe Oersted's experiment on currents and magnetic fields and state the principle he discovered.**
2. **Define electromagnetism.**
3. **Explain the structure and operation of electromagnets.**
4. **Describe the structure and use of electric motors and distinguish between direct and alternating current.**
5. **Describe the structure and use of galvanometers.**

SCIENCE TERMS 20-4

electromagnetism p. 477
electromagnet p. 477
electric motor p. 478
commutator p. 478
brush p. 479
galvanometer p. 479

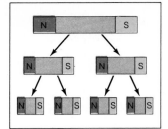

Figure 20–10 *You can see from this illustration that no matter how many times a magnet is cut in half, it retains its magnetic properties. First two and then four smaller magnets are formed. Why?* ❶

A magnet will lose its magnetic properties if the orderly arrangement of domains is destroyed. Banging a magnet with a hammer or dropping it repeatedly on the ground will knock the domains out of line. Since heat causes the particles of a substance to move faster, heating a magnet also will disrupt the arrangement of domains.

SECTION REVIEW

1. Which subatomic particle causes magnetic properties? How?
2. What is a magnetic domain? How does the model of magnetic domains explain magnetism?
3. How can the magnetic properties of a magnet be destroyed?
4. Describe how you could make a compass needle using a steel needle. Use the model of magnetic domains in your answer.

Section Objective

To relate electricity and magnetism

20–4 Electromagnetism

Here is an interesting experiment for you to try. Bring a compass near a wire carrying an electric current. The best place to hold the compass is just above or below the wire, but parallel to it. Observe what happens to the compass needle when electricity is flowing through the wire and when it is not. What do you observe? ❷

This experiment is very similar to one performed more than 150 years ago by the Danish physicist Hans Christian Oersted. His experiment led to an important scientific discovery about the relationship between electricity and magnetism.

Oersted's Discovery

In 1820, Oersted was lecturing a physics class when he noticed a wire lying above a compass. He observed that when current flowed through the wire, the compass needle was deflected, or turned, 90 degrees. When the direction of the current was reversed, the needle moved 90 degrees in the opposite direction. When no electricity flowed through the wire, the compass needle remained stationary.

476

20-3 (continued)

Section Review 20-3

1. Electron. The spin of electrons sets up magnetic fields.
2. A region in which the magnetic fields of atoms are grouped together. A substance is magnetized when all the magnetic domains are arranged in the same direction.
3. By dropping, hammering, or heating the magnet

4. Stroke the steel needle with a strong magnet. The magnetic domain of the needle will then line up and point in the same direction.

TEACHING STRATEGY 20-4

Motivation

Illustrate Oersted's experiment by connecting copper wires and a switch to the terminals of a low-voltage dry cell to create an open circuit. Place a

compass directly below and close to the wire, and orient the wire so that the compass needle is parallel to it. Ask,

• **What do you think will happen when the switch is closed?** (Most students, before reading Oersted's experiment, expect that nothing will happen, either because they do not expect magnetic force to be produced or because they expect that, if such a force is produced, it will be directed

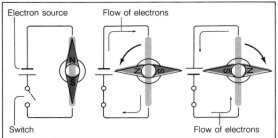

Figure 20–11 *According to Oersted's experiment, electric current flowing through a wire gives rise to a magnetic field. In the diagram on the left, no current is flowing so the compass needle is not deflected. In the other two diagrams, the needle is deflected as current flows through the wire. What happens when the flow of electricity is reversed?* ❸

For many years Oersted had believed that electricity and magnetism were related—now he had the evidence! As a result of his work, Oersted made a major contribution to the understanding of how electricity and magnetism are related.

An electric current flowing through a wire gives rise to a magnetic field whose direction depends upon the direction of the current. Thus, magnetism can be produced from electricity. Equally important was Oersted's discovery that a looped, or coiled, wire acted like a magnet when a current passed through it. The more coils the wire had, the stronger the magnet. It soon occurred to scientists that coiling a conductor around a piece of soft iron would produce an even more powerful magnet.

Electromagnets

The relationship between electricity and magnetism is called **electromagnetism.** Many applications of electromagnetism are part of your daily life. Powerful temporary magnets called **electromagnets** can be made by wrapping a coil of wire around a soft iron core and passing an electric current through the wire.

The strength of an electromagnet can be increased by increasing the number of loops of wire around the iron core. The electromagnet also will become stronger if the current or voltage that drives the current is increased.

An important property of an electromagnet is that it can be made to lose and then regain its magnetic properties by turning the current off and on. Can you think of a way in which this property of an electromagnet might be useful? ❺

Figure 20–12 *An electromagnet is produced when electric current passes through a wire looped around a nail or other piece of soft iron. How can the strength of an electromagnet be increased?* ❹ ❶

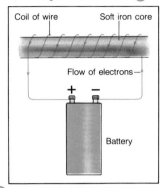

Coil of wire   Soft iron core

Flow of electrons

Battery

❷

BACKGROUND INFORMATION

The direction of the lines of force of the magnetic field produced by a current can be predicted by means of a left-hand rule. If the thumb of the left hand points in the direction of flow of electrons, the fingers curl in the direction (that is, from south to north) of the magnetic field. This rule is more conventionally stated as a right-hand rule, where the thumb points in the direction of flow of positive charge, which is opposite to that of the negatively charged electrons.

ANNOTATION KEY

❶ The orderly arrangement of magnetic domains is undisturbed when a magnet is cut in half. (Applying concepts)

❷ The needle is deflected by the magnetic field set up by the current. (Observing)

❸ The needle deflects in an opposite direction. (Interpreting illustrations)

❹ Increase current or increase number of loops of wire (Applying facts)

❺ Picking up objects to be moved from place to place (Inferring)

❶ Thinking Skill: Hypothesizing

❷ Thinking Skill: Identifying relationships

parallel to the wire and thus will tend to keep the compass needle in parallel alignment. Actually, the magnetic force will turn the needle so that it is no longer parallel to the wire.) Close and open the circuit several times. Ask,

• **Can you explain what has happened?** (A magnetic field has been produced, resulting in a perpendicular force that turns the needle so that it is no longer parallel to the wire.)

Content Development

Be sure to review the concept of electric current. Remind students that current is a measure of the flow rate of electrons and that, in a circuit, electrons move away from a negative terminal toward a positive terminal. Draw on the chalkboard a diagram to illustrate this. When you explain Oersted's experiment, illustrate on the board that the magnetic field lines of force flow around the current-

carrying wire, causing objects such as compass needles to align with them. If you wish, you may mention the left-hand rule at this point, especially for the benefit of advanced students.

Sharpen Your Skills

Making an Electromagnet
Skills: Manipulative, observing
Level: Remedial
Type: Hands-on
Materials: dry cell, nail, length of thin insulated wire

Students build a simple electromagnet in this activity and then determine which objects it will or will not pick\up.

Figure 20–13 *Large electromagnets can be used to pick up heavy pieces of metal. What is an important property of an electromagnet such as this?* ❶

ELECTRIC MOTOR An **electric motor** converts electric energy into mechanical energy that is used to do work. In order to understand the operation of an electric motor, imagine the following experiment. An electromagnet is connected to a dry cell. As the current flows, one end of the electromagnet becomes the north pole and the other end becomes the south pole. A compass can be used to determine which pole is which. The connections to the dry cell are then switched. The direction of the current is reversed. The poles of the electromagnet also are reversed. So by changing the direction of a current, the poles of an electromagnet can be reversed.

An electric motor contains an electromagnet that is free to rotate on a shaft, and a permanent magnet that is held in a fixed position. The current used to run an electric motor is AC, or alternating current. Alternating current is constantly changing
❶ direction. As the current changes direction, the poles of the movable electromagnet reverse. Thus, the relationship of the rotating electromagnet to the stationary permanent magnet is one of attraction, then repulsion, then attraction again. This alternating attraction and repulsion causes the electromagnet to spin on its shaft. The mechanical energy of the spinning turns the shaft of the motor, enabling the motor to do work.

If an electric motor were made to run on DC, or direct current, the movable electromagnet would not spin continuously. So an electric motor that runs on DC has a reversing switch called a **commutator.** A commutator is attached to the movable electromagnet. As the electromagnet turns, the commutator switches the direction of current so that the mag-

Figure 20–14 *As alternating current flows through the coils of wire, the poles of the movable electromagnet are reversed. The alternating attraction and repulsion between this electromagnet and the stationary electromagnet cause the movable electromagnet to spin on its shaft. Thus electric energy is converted into mechanical energy in a motor. What is the purpose of the commutator? Why would the motor not work without the commutator?* ❷

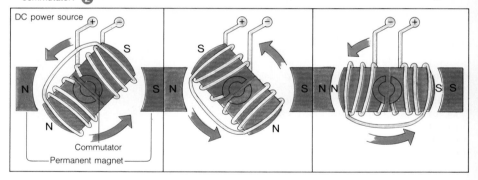

20-4 (continued)

Content Development
Relate the operation of the electric motor to the law of conservation of energy. Point out that some of the electrical energy is converted by such a device into mechanical energy, or energy of motion, which can be used to do work. Explain that most of the rest of the electrical energy is converted into heat energy, which in most cases is not useful for doing work. Point out that the total energy before the conversion is equal to the total energy afterward.

Provide other examples of conservation of energy, such as that occurring in an engine. This will help to tie the discussion of motors to other topics involving energy conversion, so as to illustrate the general principle involved.

Skills Development
Skills: Applying concepts, making observations
You may wish to construct a simple

electromagnet, wrapping a length of soft iron with many loops of insulated copper wire and connecting the ends of the wires to a low-voltage dry cell. Include a switch in the circuit. Scatter iron filings or small paper clips very near to the iron core, and then close the circuit. Open and close the circuit several times. Ask students to write down, without conferring, what they have observed. Also ask them to pro-

netic poles of the electromagnet reverse and the electromagnet spins. Electric current is supplied to the commutator through contacts called **brushes.** The brushes do not move, but simply touch the commutator as it spins. Electric motors are used in many household appliances—electric saws, electric can openers, food processors, refrigerators, and washing machines.

GALVANOMETER A **galvanometer** is an instrument used to detect small currents. The galvanometer consists of a coil of wire connected to an electric circuit and a needle. As current flows through the wire, the needle of the galvanometer is deflected. Because the needle will move in the opposite direction when the current is reversed, the galvanometer can be used to measure the direction of current.

Some other uses of electromagnets include doorbells, washing machines, telephones, and telegraphs. Electromagnets also are important in heavy machinery that is used to move materials such as scrap metal from one place to another.

SECTION REVIEW

1. How is magnetism related to electricity?
2. How is an electromagnet made?
3. How is an electromagnet different from a permanent magnet?
4. How does an electromagnet provide mechanical energy in an electric motor?
5. How is the effect of an electric current on a compass needle different from the effect of the earth's magnetic field on a compass needle?

20–5 Electromagnetic Induction

If magnetism can be produced from electricity, can electricity be produced from magnetism? Scientists who learned of Oersted's discovery asked this very question. In 1831, the English scientist Michael Faraday provided the answer.

Faraday discovered that an electric current could be generated, or induced, by moving a wire through

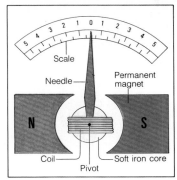

Figure 20–15 *As current flows through the coil of wire in a galvanometer, the magnet forces it to turn and the needle attached to it is deflected. The greater the current, the greater the deflection.*

Sharpen Your Skills

Making an Electromagnet

Obtain a low-voltage dry cell, nail, and length of thin insulated wire.

1. Remove the insulation from the ends of the wire.
2. Wind the wire tightly around the nail so that you have at least 25 turns.
3. Connect each uninsulated end of the wire to a post on the dry cell.
4. Collect some lightweight metal objects. Touch the nail to each one. What happens?

Section Objective

To explain how magnetism produces electricity

479

SECTION PREVIEW 20-5

Faraday's and Henry's experiments on electromagnetic induction, or production of a current by the motion of a conductor across magnetic lines of force in a magnetic field, are described. The structure and operation of the generator, a device in which principles of electromagnetic induction are applied to convert mechanical energy into electrical energy, are detailed. The production of alternating current by such a generator is then described. Finally, transformers, or devices that increase or decrease voltage in an alternating current, are discussed.

PERFORMANCE OBJECTIVES 20-5

1. **Describe Faraday's and Henry's experiments and state the principle of electromagnetism they discovered.**
2. **Define electromagnetic induction.**
3. **Describe the structure, operation, and uses of a generator, and explain the production of alternating current.**
4. **Describe the structure, operation, and uses of step-up and step-down transformers.**

SCIENCE TERMS 20-5

electromagnetic induction p. 480
generator p. 480
transformer p. 482
primary coil p. 482
secondary coil p. 482
step-up transformer p. 483
step-down transformer p. 483

---

pose an explanation for what has occurred. They can then be asked to read aloud what they have written.

SECTION REVIEW 20-4

1. Both involve the movement of electrons. An electric current flowing through a wire gives rise to a magnetic field whose direction depends on the direction of the current.
2. A coil of wire is wrapped around a piece of soft iron. An electric current

is passed through the wire. The strength of the electromagnet depends on the number of coils of wire and the amount of current.
3. An electromagnet can be made stronger or weaker; it can be turned off or on; its poles can be reversed.
4. As alternating current is passed through the electromagnet, its north and south poles continuously reverse. The electromagnet is alternately attracted to and repelled by the station-

ary permanent magnet in the motor. This continual attraction and repulsion causes the electromagnet to spin. The mechanical energy of the spin is used to turn a shaft to do work.
5. The earth's magnetic field will always cause a compass needle to point in the same direction—to the north. An electric current will cause the needle to point in a direction that is dependent upon the direction of the current.

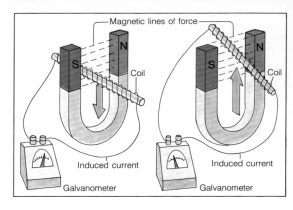

Figure 20–16 *When a conducting wire cuts across magnetic lines of force, electrons flow through the wire and a current is produced. What is this process called? What happens to the deflection of the needle in a galvanometer when the direction in which the lines of force are cut changes?* ❶

ANNOTATION KEY

❶ Electromagnetic induction. The deflection reverses as the induction current changes direction. (Interpreting illustrations)

❷ Opposite. In a motor, electric energy is converted to mechanical energy. (Comparing)

❸ Moving wheels (Relating concepts)

❶ Thinking Skill: Making generalizations

❷ Thinking Skill: Applying technology

Sharpen Your Skills

The History of Electricity
Skills: Research, writing comprehension
Level: Average
Type: Library

Students who complete this activity will obtain a solid working knowledge of many of the important scientists who contributed to the discovery of electricity and its many applications. Check students' reports for accuracy and to make sure they are well written and logically organized.

TEACHING STRATEGY 20-5

Motivation

Before explicitly teaching students about electromagnetic induction, demonstrate Faraday's and Henry's experiments. Twist copper wire to produce a number of loops large enough to allow a bar magnet to move within the helix formed by the loops. Ask,

• **What will happen if a bar magnet is placed in the space within the loops?** (Answers will vary. Actually nothing will happen unless the magnet or wire is moving.) Place the magnet within the loops and set the device down. Attach the ends of the wires to the posts of a galvanometer. No current will be produced.

• **What will happen if the magnet or the wire is moved?** (A current will re-

---

Sharpen Your Skills

The History of Electricity

Several scientists were responsible for establishing the relationship between electricity and magnetism. Using books and reference materials in the library, write a report about the scientists listed below. Include information about their lives as well as their contributions to a better understanding of electricity and magnetism.

Hans Christian Oersted
André Ampère
Michael Faraday
Joseph Henry
Nikola Tesla

480

---

sult, though most students will not expect this, especially if you have taken care to point out that there is no dry cell or other power source in the circuit.) Move the magnet, and then move the wire loops. A current will be produced in the wire.

• **Why do you think this happens?** (Answers will vary. The motion is causing the wire to cut across magnetic lines of force, or vice versa. This causes electrons to flow in the wire.)

---

a magnetic field. Faraday's discovery was duplicated at about the same time by an American scientist named Joseph Henry.

The process by which a current is produced by the motion of a conductor in a magnetic field is called **electromagnetic induction.** Electromagnetic induction involves magnetic lines of force.

❶ **When a conducting wire cuts across magnetic lines of force, a current is produced.** The same result is obtained when a magnet is moved in and out of coils of wire. It does not matter whether the conducting wire is moved or the magnet is moved. What is important is that there is motion within the magnetic field and magnetic lines of forces are cut.

Generators

An important application of electromagnetic induction is the operation of a **generator.** A generator is a device that converts mechanical energy into electric energy. How does this energy conversion compare with that in an electric motor? ❷

A generator consists of an insulated loop of wire and a U-shaped magnet that produces a magnetic field. The loop of wire, which is attached to a power source, is placed between the poles of the magnet. As the power source rotates the loop of wire clockwise, the wire cuts the magnetic lines of force and a current is induced.

As the loop of wire continues to rotate, the wire moves parallel to the magnetic lines of force. At this point no lines of force are being cut so no current is

---

Content Development

Lead into the topic of electromagnetic induction by reminding students that magnetism and electricity are related, as Oersted's experiments showed: magnetism can be produced by an electric current, which, you should now point out, involves a changing electric field. Since this connection exists, suggest that it should not be too surprising if an electric current could be produced from a changing mag-

produced. Further rotation moves the loop of wire to a place where magnetic lines of force are cut once again. But this time the lines of force are cut from the opposite direction. This means that the induced current is in the opposite direction. Because the direction of the electric current changes with each complete rotation of the wire, the current produced is AC, or alternating current.

Perhaps you own a bicycle that has a small generator attached to the back wheel to operate the lights. To turn the lights on, a knob on the generator is moved so that it touches the wheel. As you pedal the bike, you provide the mechanical energy to turn the wheel. The wheel then turns the knob. The knob is attached to a shaft inside the generator. The shaft rotates a coil of wire through magnetic lines of force. What happens to the lights when you stop pedaling? Why is this a disadvantage?

Most of the electric power you use every day comes from generators. Large generators at power plants must supply electric power for thousands of homes, offices, hospitals, schools, and stores. Turbines provide the mechanical energy for these large generators. Turbines are wheels that are turned by the force of moving steam or water. As the turbine rotates, it moves coiled wire in the generator through magnetic lines of force produced by a large and powerful magnet.

The large generators in power plants have many loops of wire rotating inside large electromagnets. The speed of the generators is controlled very carefully. The current also is controlled so that it reverses direction 120 times each second. Because two

Figure 20–17 *The force of moving water, such as this water at Hoover Dam on the Colorado River (top), is used to spin turbines (bottom) that help generate electricity by converting mechanical energy into electric energy.*

Figure 20–18 *Inside a generator (left), a loop of wire cuts magnetic lines of force to produce an electric current. What is the mechanical energy that is used to spin the generator on this bicycle?* ❸

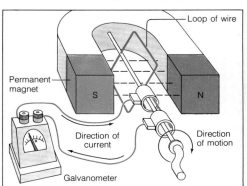

Loop of wire

Permanent magnet

S   N

Direction of current

Direction of motion

Galvanometer

HISTORICAL NOTES

Michael Faraday (1791–1867) was one of the greatest experimenters and theoreticians of all time. As well as discovering the principle of electromagnetic induction, he was the principal architect of the classical field theory that was later modified by James Clerk Maxwell and Albert Einstein.

Among his other accomplishments, Faraday discovered the principle of the electric motor and built a simple model of one. He also produced the first dynamo, stated the basic laws of electrolysis, and discovered that a magnetic field will rotate the plane of polarization of light.

conversion, a generator is the opposite of a motor: the former converts mechanical energy to electrical energy, and the latter converts electrical energy to mechanical energy.

Ask students to observe Figure 20-17, which shows a generator used at Hoover Dam.
• **What is providing mechanical energy?** (The water is providing this energy.)
• **How can you tell it is mechanical energy? What is mechanical energy?** (The water is moving and thus has mechanical energy, which is energy of motion.)

Reinforcement
For many students, the production and nature of alternating current are difficult to understand. For the benefit of such students, analyze carefully the structures and processes involved in AC production, drawing their attention to Figure 20-18. Ask them to construct a simple model, using a wire and a horseshoe magnet, and show them that as the wire loop is turned through a revolution, any given segment of it cuts through the lines of force first from one direction (say, up to down), then from the opposite direction (down to up). This produces differing directions of electron flow, and thus alternation of current direction.

netic field. Faraday's and Henry's experiments showed that such production does occur. Point out that such symmetries (for example, conversion of mechanical energy to heat energy suggests, correctly, the possible conversion of heat energy to mechanical energy) are common in science. Many theoretical scientists come to expect these symmetries and thus often hypothesize their existence before finding experimental evidence in support

of them. Such examples help to bring out that what are sometimes called aesthetic considerations (involving beliefs in the symmetry, beauty, and underlying simplicity and unity of nature) can play a major role in the creation of new and important hypotheses and theories.

Content Development
In teaching students about generators, point out first that, in terms of energy

HISTORICAL NOTES

Most engineers during the nineteenth century believed, incorrectly, that only DC electricity was useful in practical applications of electricity. Thus, early generators included inconvenient commutators, which converted the actually more usable AC current produced by the generator into DC current. Thus, although transformers, which could have been used in the transmission of the AC current, were invented as early as 1838 (by Joseph Henry), they were not used in transmission until after the usefulness of AC systems was demonstrated in Paris in 1883. American patent rights for the system, which was used in a London railway line and in Italy in 1884, were purchased by George Westinghouse, who set up the Westinghouse Electric Company. This, the first U.S. company to distribute alternating current, first transmitted it for lighting purposes in Buffalo, New York, in 1886.

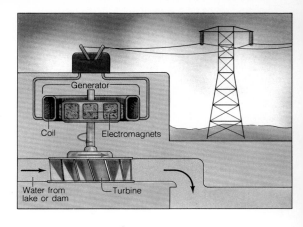

Figure 20–19 *In the operation of a generator, water spins a turbine, which in turn moves large electromagnets encased in coils of insulated wire. As the electromagnets move, the coiled wire cuts magnetic lines of force. Current is produced in the wire and conducted through power lines that eventually reach homes and other buildings.*

reversals make one complete cycle of alternating current, the electricity generated has a frequency of 60 hertz. Alternating current in the United States has a frequency of 60 hertz.

Transformers

The processes of electromagnetism and electromagnetic induction are combined in the operation of a **transformer.** A transformer is a device that increases or decreases the voltage of alternating current. A transformer operates on the principle that a current in one coil induces a current in another coil.

A transformer consists of two coils of insulated wire wrapped around the same iron core. One coil is called the **primary coil** and the other coil is called the **secondary coil.** When an alternating current passes through the primary coil, a magnetic field is created. The magnetic field varies in direction as a result of the alternating current.

Electromagnetic induction causes a current to flow in the secondary coil. This is because the secondary coil acts as if a magnet were suddenly pushed into it. Magnetic lines of force are cut, and current is induced.

If the number of loops in the primary and secondary coils are equal, the induced voltage of the secondary coil will be the same as that of the primary coil. However, if there are more loops in the secondary coil than in the primary coil, the voltage

---

20-5 (continued)

Motivation
You may wish to allow a student to demonstrate to the class the generation of electricity that allows the light on a bicycle to operate. If the generator can be readily removed and opened without damaging it, do so, and allow students to observe the knob, shaft, and magnet within the generator. You can then go on to explain the electromagnetic principles of its operation.

Content Development
Direct students' attention to Figure 20-20, which illustrates step-up and step-down transformers. Detail the structure and operation of each. You may wish to construct simple transformers and demonstrate their operation, using a low-voltage dry cell, wire, an iron ring, and two voltmeters.

Enrichment
Have advanced students do library research on the uses of step-up and step-down transformers. They should be encouraged to prepare charts that include cutaway drawings of devices that make use of such transformers. They can show the charts in class and present their findings orally to the class.

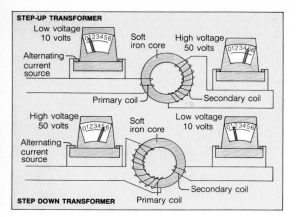

STEP-UP TRANSFORMER

Low voltage 10 volts — Soft iron core — High voltage 50 volts

Alternating current source

Primary coil — Secondary coil

High voltage 50 volts — Soft iron core — Low voltage 10 volts

Alternating current source

Secondary coil — Primary coil

STEP DOWN TRANSFORMER

Figure 20–20 *The processes of electromagnetism and electromagnetic induction are combined in the operation of a transformer. A transformer either increases or decreases the voltage of alternating current. A step-up transformer increases voltage. A step-down transformer decreases voltage. Which coil has the greater number of loops in each type of transformer?* ❶

of the secondary coil will be greater. Since this type of transformer increases the voltage, it is called a **step-up transformer.**

In a **step-down transformer,** there are fewer loops in the secondary coil than in the primary coil. So the voltage of the secondary coil is less than that of the primary coil.

Step-up transformers are used by power companies to transmit high-voltage electricity to homes and offices. They also are used in fluorescent lights and X-ray machines. In television sets, step-up transformers increase ordinary household voltage from 120 volts to 20,000 volts or more.

Step-down transformers reduce the voltage of electricity from a power plant so it can be used in the home. Step-down transformers also are used in doorbells, model electric trains, small radios, tape players, and calculators.

SECTION REVIEW

1. What is electromagnetic induction?
2. How can electric current be produced from a magnetic field?
3. What is the purpose of a generator?
4. What is the difference between a step-up and a step-down transformer?
5. Explain what must be the position of the loop of wire in a generator when the generator provides maximum current. Minimum current.

Figure 20–21 *A step-down transformer is used by power companies to reduce high-voltage electricity transmitted from power plants so it can be used in homes and offices.*

483

BACKGROUND INFORMATION

One of the reasons why electricity is transmitted in AC rather than DC form is that it is easy, using devices such as transformers, to change the voltage for an AC current, but there is no convenient way to do this for a DC current. It is important to be able to change voltage at two stages. First, the relatively low-voltage, high-current electricity produced by generators (whose moving parts would have to turn at impractically high speeds to produce high voltage) would, in transmission through wires, lose much power in heating the wires. This is demonstrated by the equation

$$P \text{ heat loss} = I^2R$$

which reveals that high values of I (current) produce very great power loss. Raising the voltage and proportionately lowering the current, I, produces the same total power (since P total = VI), but results in less unwanted loss of this power during transmission. Thus, step-up transformers are used before the generated electricity is transmitted. This high voltage turns out to be too dangerous and inconvenient for household use, however, so a step-down transformer is used to reduce voltage before it enters household wiring, or leaves the outdoor power lines.

Section Review 20-5

1. The process by which a current is produced by the motion of a conductor in a magnetic field

2. By moving a wire through a magnetic field, or by passing a magnet in and out of coils of wire, magnetic lines of force are cut and a current is induced.

3. To convert mechanical energy into electric energy.

4. A step-up transformer has more loops in the secondary coil than in the primary coil. The induced voltage is greater. A step-down transformer has fewer loops in the secondary coil. The induced voltage is less.

5. The loop of wire must be perpendicular to the magnetic lines of force. The loop of wire must be parallel to the magnetic lines of force.

LABORATORY INVESTIGATION
ELECTROMAGNETISM

BEFORE THE LAB

1. **Gather all materials at least one day prior to the investigation. You should gather enough to meet your class needs, assuming six students per group.**
2. **Make certain that the dry cell is of low voltage, that the nails used are made of iron or steel, and that the wire used is insulated bell wire.**
3. **Among the "other objects to be tested," include nonmetallic as well as metallic objects.**

PRE-LAB DISCUSSION

Before beginning this investigation, briefly review the basic principles of magnetism and Oersted's discovery. Then make sure that the laboratory procedure is clear to students. Also ask students to formulate hypotheses, based on the stated problem, regarding what will occur when the investigation is carried out.

SKILL DEVELOPMENT

Students will use the following skills while completing this investigation.
1. Safety
2. Manipulative
3. Observing
4. Recording
5. Comparing
6. Hypothesizing

SAFETY TIPS

Caution students not to operate the electromagnet—that is, not to have the circuit closed, with both wire ends connected to the dry-cell terminals—for more than a few seconds each time.

Problem

What factors affect the strength of an electromagnet? What materials are attracted to an electromagnet?

Materials *(per group)*

dry cell
5 nails, 10 cm long
2 meters of bell wire
6 paper clips
small piece of aluminum foil
penny or copper sheet
nickel
dime
other objects to be tested

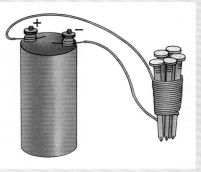

Procedure

1. Hold the five nails together and neatly wrap the wire around them. Do not allow the nails to overlap. Leave about 50 cm of wire at one end and about 100 cm at the other end.
2. Attach the shorter end of the wire to one terminal of the dry cell.
3. Momentarily touch the 100-cm end of the wire to the other terminal of the dry cell. **CAUTION:** *Do not operate the electromagnet for more than a few seconds each time.*
4. When the electromagnet is on, test each material for magnetic attraction. Record your results.
5. During the time the electromagnet is on, determine the number of paper clips it can hold.
6. Wrap the 100-cm end of wire over the first windings to make a second layer. You should use about 50 cm. There should be approximately 50 cm of wire remaining.
7. Connect the wire once again to the dry cell. Determine the number of paper clips the electromagnet can now hold. Record your results.

8. Carefully remove three nails from the windings. Connect the wire and determine the number of paper clips the electromagnet can hold. Record your results.

Observations

1. What materials are attracted to the electromagnet?
2. How many paper clips can the electromagnet hold in step 5? In step 7? In step 8?

Conclusions

1. What do the materials attracted to the magnet have in common?
2. When you increase the number of turns of wire, what effect does this have on the strength of the electromagnet?
3. How does removing the nails affect the strength of the electromagnet?
4. What general statement can be made about the factors that affect the strength of an electromagnet?

CHAPTER REVIEW

SUMMARY

20-1 Properties of Magnets

❏ Magnetism is a force of attraction or repulsion due to an arrangement of electrons.

❏ Like magnetic poles repel each other, while unlike poles attract each other.

❏ The region in which magnetic forces can act is called a magnetic field.

❏ There are three types of magnets: natural magnets, temporary magnets, and permanent magnets.

20-2 The Earth As a Magnet

❏ The earth is surrounded by a magnetic field that is strongest around the magnetic north and south poles.

❏ A compass needle does not point exactly to the earth's geographic north pole. It points to the magnetic north pole. The difference in the location of the earth's magnetic and geographic poles is called magnetic variation.

20-3 An Explanation of Magnetism

❏ Magnetism is created by electron spin.

❏ Magnetic domains are regions in which all the atoms' magnetic fields line up pointing in the same direction.

❏ A magnet will lose its magnetic properties if the orderly arrangement of the domains is destroyed.

20-4 Electromagnetism

❏ In 1820, Hans Christian Oersted discovered that a magnetic field is created around a wire that is conducting an electric current.

❏ The relationship between electricity and magnetism is called electromagnetism.

❏ An electric motor converts electric energy into mechanical energy that is used to do work.

20-5 Electromagnetic Induction

❏ In 1831, Michael Faraday discovered that an electric current can be produced from a magnetic field. This process is known as electromagnetic induction.

❏ One of the most important uses of electromagnetic induction is in the operation of a generator, which converts mechanical energy into electric energy.

❏ Electromagnetism and electromagnetic induction are combined in the operation of a transformer, which is a device that increases or decreases the voltage of alternating current.

VOCABULARY

Define each term in a complete sentence.

brush	magnetic field	north magnetic pole	step-down transformer
commutator	magnetic induction		step-up transformer
electric motor		permanent magnet	
electromagnet	magnetic lines of force	pole	temporary magnet
electromagnetic induction	magnetic variation	primary coil	transformer
electromagnetism	magnetism	secondary coil	
galvanometer	magnetosphere	south magnetic pole	
generator	natural magnet		
magnetic domain			

OBSERVATIONS

1. Answers will vary, depending on materials used in the investigation.
2. Students will find that the number of paper clips increased in step 7 from step 5, but decreased in step 8.

CONCLUSIONS

1. Made of iron or steel
2. Increases the strength
3. Decreases the strength
4. Strength is affected by the number of loops and the number of nails. (Some students may also point out that its strength could be increased by increasing the size of the dry cell.)

GOING FURTHER: ENRICHMENT

Part 1

Advanced students may wish to perform additional steps of a more quantitative nature, varying the number of turns of wire and making plots of (for example) number of paper clips held versus number of turns of wire.

Part 2

Ask students to propose hypotheses regarding variables untested in this investigation—for example, the effect on number of paper clips attracted if a higher-voltage dry cell were used. Do not have them actually test their hypotheses experimentally as a higher-voltage dry cell could present safety hazards. Encourage them to do library research to determine the answer instead.

CHAPTER REVIEW

MULTIPLE CHOICE

1. b	**3.** d	**5.** a	**7.** a	**9.** b
2. c	**4.** d	**6.** b	**8.** c	**10.** a

COMPLETION

1. lodestone/ magnetite
2. magnetic induction
3. magnetic variation
4. spin
5. domains
6. electromagnetism
7. electromagnet
8. electric motor
9. AC/alternating current
10. electromagnetic induction

TRUE OR FALSE

1. T
2. F repel
3. F natural
4. F magnetic north pole
5. F can
6. T
7. F temporary
8. T
9. T
10. F turbine

SKILL BUILDING

1. a. Needle is attracted by the earth's magnetic field **b.** Needle is acted upon by a magnetic field produced by an electric current flowing through a wire **c.** No magnetic lines of force are being cut, so no current is induced in the wire.

2. Electromagnetic induction involves mechanical energy. This energy moves the wire loop in the magnetic field so that lines of force are cut. The result is an energy conversion.

3. Check student diagrams. They should clearly show the various stages in the rotation perpendicular, then parallel, then perpendicular to the field.

4. For north–south, lines of force show attraction. For north–north, lines of force show repulsion.

5. Step-up transformer: a,f; step-down transformer: c,d; both step-up and step-down: b,e.

ESSAY

1. Electrified particles blown out from the sun are trapped by the earth's magnetic field. Some of these particles collide with other particles in the earth's upper atmosphere. As they do, visible light is emitted.

2. Natural magnets are naturally occurring substances that have magnetic properties. Temporary magnets are artificial magnets produced by magnetic induction. They are easy to magnetize, but then lose their magnetic properties quickly. Permanent magnets are also magnetized by magnetic induction, but they keep their magnetic properties.

3. Before a substance is magnetized, magnetic domains in the substance exist in a random arrangement. When the substance is magnetized, the magnetic domains line up so that like poles all point in the same direction.

4. Oersted discovered that a magnetic field is produced around a wire conducting an electric current. Faraday discovered that electricity can be induced from a magnetic field. The two discoveries are really opposite sides of the same coin: They show that electricity and magnetism are related in such a way that one can be produced in the presence of the other.

On a separate sheet of paper, write the letter of the answer that best completes each statement.

1. In a magnet, magnetic forces are strongest
   a. at the center. b. at the poles. c. around the edges. d. in the magnetic field.
2. The region in which magnetic forces can act is called a
   a. line of force. b. pole. c. magnetic field. d. field of attraction.
3. The region of the earth's magnetic field is called the
   a. atmosphere. b. stratosphere. c. aurora. d. magnetosphere.
4. The idea of the earth as a magnet was first proposed by
   a. Dalton. b. Faraday. c. Oersted. d. Gilbert.
5. Adjustments must be made for directions measured with a compass because
   a. a compass does not point to true north.
   b. a compass needle tends to lose its magnetism.
   c. the earth's magnetic poles are constantly changing.
   d. the earth's geographic poles are constantly changing.
6. Which of the following is not a magnetic material?
   a. lodestone b. glass c. cobalt d. nickel
7. The particle responsible for an atom's magnetic properties is the
   a. electron. b. neutron. c. proton. d. nucleus.
8. Which of the following will make a magnet lose its magnetic properties?
   a. stroking the magnet b. hanging the magnet from a string
   c. dropping the magnet d. cutting the magnet
9. A galvanometer is a device that is used to
   a. convert mechanical energy into electric energy. b. detect electric current.
   c. convert electricity into magnetism. d. detect a magnetic field.
10. The purpose of a generator is to
    a. convert mechanical energy into electric energy.
    b. convert electric energy into mechanical energy.
    c. use magnetism to do work.
    d. measure electric current.

On a separate sheet of paper, write the word or words that best complete each statement.

1. The natural magnet discovered by the Greeks is called _____.
2. The process by which artificial magnets are created is called _____.
3. The error in a compass is called _____.
4. The _____ of electrons creates a magnetic field in an atom.
5. Atomic magnetic fields group together in regions called _____.
6. The relationship between electricity and magnetism is called _____.
7. Wrapping a coil of conducting wire around a piece of iron makes a (an) _____.
8. A _____ converts electric energy into mechanical energy.
9. Current that constantly changes directions is called _____.
10. An electric current is produced from a magnetic field by _____.

CONTENT REVIEW: TRUE OR FALSE

Determine whether each statement is true or false. Then on a separate sheet of paper, write "true" if it is true. If it is false, change the underlined word or words to make the statement true.

1. The north pole of a magnet suspended horizontally from a string will point <u>north</u>.
2. Like poles of a magnet <u>attract</u> each other.
3. A naturally occurring substance with magnetic properties is a <u>permanent</u> magnet.
4. A compass needle points to the earth's <u>geographic north pole</u>.
5. Steel <u>cannot</u> be magnetized.
6. In a magnetized substance, <u>magnetic domains</u> point in the same direction.
7. Electromagnets are <u>permanent</u> magnets.
8. <u>Oersted</u> discovered electromagnetism.
9. In a generator, <u>mechanical</u> energy is converted to <u>electric</u> energy.
10. Large generators at power plants get their mechanical energy from <u>steam engines</u>.

CONCEPT REVIEW: SKILL BUILDING

Use the skills you have developed in the chapter to complete each activity.

1. **Identifying cause and effect** Explain each of the following observations:
   a. A compass needle points to the north.
   b. A compass needle is deflected 90 degrees when placed above a wire conducting an electric current.
   c. A compass needle is not deflected when a loop of wire in a generator is parallel to the magnetic lines of force.
2. **Applying concepts** The process of electromagnetic induction might seem to break the law of conservation of energy, which says that energy cannot be created. Explain why this is actually not so.
3. **Making diagrams** Use a diagram to show how the rotation of a wire loop in a generator first induces a current in one direction, then no current, then a current in the other direction.
4. **Making comparisons** How do the lines of force that arise when north and south poles of magnets are placed close together compare with the lines of force that arise when two north poles are placed together? Use a diagram in your explanation.
5. **Applying definitions** Indicate whether each of the following characteristics describes (a) a step-up transformer, (b) a step-down transformer, (c) both a step-up and a step-down transformer.
   a. Voltage in the secondary coil is greater.
   b. Involves electromagnetism and electromagnetic induction.
   c. Voltage in the primary coil is greater.
   d. Used in doorbells and model trains.
   e. Consists of two insulated coils wrapped around opposite sides of an iron core.
   f. More loops in the secondary coil.

CONCEPT REVIEW: ESSAY

Discuss each of the following in a brief paragraph.

1. Explain how an aurora is produced.
2. Compare the three types of magnets.
3. Using the theory of magnetic domains, explain how a substance is magnetized. How it loses its magnetism.
4. Describe the discoveries of Oersted and Faraday. How are these discoveries related?
5. Explain how a galvanometer works.
6. Explain the difference between an electric motor and an electric generator in terms of energy conversion.

487

---

5. A galvanometer consists of a coil of wire connected to an electric circuit and a needle similar to a compass needle. As electric current is passed through the wire, the needle is deflected. As current changes direction, the direction of deflection of the needle also changes.
6. Electric motor: electric energy to mechanical energy; Electric generator: mechanical energy to electric energy.

ADDITIONAL QUESTIONS AND TOPIC SUGGESTIONS

1. Given the fact that the earth's magnetic north pole is located in northeastern Canada, in which U.S. state would you expect the greatest magnetic variation from geographic north? Why? (Variation would be greatest in Alaska, since it lies so far north and is more or less west, rather than south, of the magnetic north pole.)

2. What would happen if an iron magnet were melted and then allowed to resolidify? (The iron would lose nearly all of its ability to act as a magnet because its magnetic domains would no longer be lined up, due to the flowing of atoms that would occur. A very slight amount of magnetization might remain, however, due to the influence of the earth's magnetic field.

3. A magnet cannot induce a current in a wire unless the magnet or wire is moving. Why then is it possible for an unmoving wire that carries a current to produce a magnetic field? Where is the movement, if any, in such a case? (The wire contains charged electrons, each of which produces an electric field. When there is a current, the electrons move, producing a changing electric field, which can give rise to a magnetic field, even though the wire, as a whole, is not moving.)

4. How is it that alternating current is useful for doing work, given that electrons from the power source do not flow in a stream into the devices used, but simply move back and forth? (The electrons from the power source have a voltage and carry energy, which is transformed into the device even though the electrons as a whole are not. The electrical energy is what makes the work possible.)

ISSUES IN SCIENCE

The following issue can be used as a springboard for class debate, or it can be assigned as a writing homework.

The turbines of electric generators can be turned by many energy sources, such as falling water, ocean tides, steam produced through the action of solar energy on water, and steam produced through the action of nuclear energy on water. Which of these energy sources should be developed for use to the greatest advantage in the future? (Answers will vary. Some of the energy sources—for example, falling water and tidal power—are of limited use in many regions. Others, such as solar power, offer considerable promise but require further development. Still others, such as nuclear power, have dangers associated with their use.)

Unit Six

ELECTRICITY AND MAGNETISM

ADVENTURES IN SCIENCE: ALAN MACDIARMID ELECTRIFIES PLASTIC

BACKGROUND INFORMATION

The plastic that MacDiarmid "electrified" was polyacetylene, which is derived from acetylene gas. Like all plastics, polyacetylene is a polymer. Along the polymer chain, carbon atoms are bonded to each other by shared electrons. The bonds alternate between single bonds and double bonds.

In the double bonds, electrons are more loosely held than in the single bonds. These double-bond electrons can be pried loose with the right chemical "crowbar." This crowbar proved to be iodine, which is used to dope the plastic. When iodine pulls one of the electrons loose, it creates an empty space that another electron can jump into. This movement of electrons— repeated down the chain with many double bonds—eventually becomes an electric current.

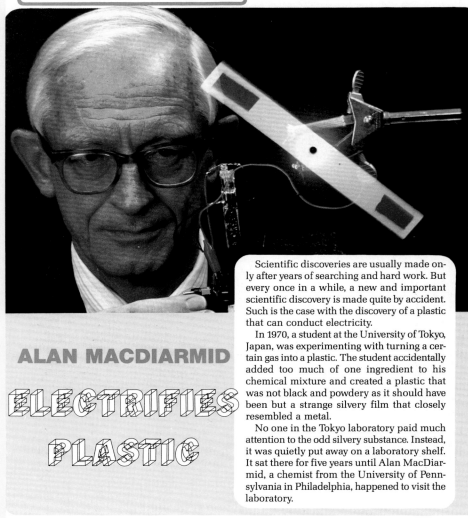

SCIENCE GAZETTE

Adventures in Science

ALAN MACDIARMID ELECTRIFIES PLASTIC

Scientific discoveries are usually only made after years of searching and hard work. But every once in a while, a new and important scientific discovery is made quite by accident. Such is the case with the discovery of a plastic that can conduct electricity.

In 1970, a student at the University of Tokyo, Japan, was experimenting with turning a certain gas into a plastic. The student accidentally added too much of one ingredient to his chemical mixture and created a plastic that was not black and powdery as it should have been but a strange silvery film that closely resembled a metal.

No one in the Tokyo laboratory paid much attention to the odd silvery substance. Instead, it was quietly put away on a laboratory shelf. It sat there for five years until Alan MacDiarmid, a chemist from the University of Pennsylvania in Philadelphia, happened to visit the laboratory.

488

TEACHING STRATEGY

Motivation

Begin by asking students,
• **Have any of you ever played musical chairs?** (probably most have)
• **How is the game played?** (Everyone marches to music around a row of chairs numbering one less than the number of people playing. When the music stops, everyone scrambles to get a seat.)

• **Would the game work if people were already sitting in the chairs?** (no) **Why not?** (There would be no empty seats to move into.)

Point out to students that in the article they are about to read, they will learn how electrons in a conducting material have quite a bit in common with people playing musical chairs.

Content Development

Review with students the definition of a conductor. Ask,
• **What materials are especially good conductors of electricity?** (metals)
• **What substances conduct electricity somewhat, but not as well as metals?** (metalloids, such as aluminum)
• **What substances do not conduct electricity?** (wood, plastic, rubber, glass; in general, nonmetals)

An Electrifying Discovery

World travel was nothing new to Alan Mac-Diarmid, who grew up in New Zealand. After graduating from the University of New Zealand in 1948, he made his way to the United States, then to England, and finally to Scotland. In 1955, he returned to the United States to become a professor of chemistry at the University of Pennsylvania. In 1966, this highly accomplished physicist became an American citizen.

When MacDiarmid saw the metallike plastic in the Tokyo laboratory in 1975, he was immediately fascinated by it. "I had never seen anything like it before," he says. He invited the Japanese chemist who ran the laboratory to return to Philadelphia with him to help investigate the new material. Before long, the scientists made an unexpected discovery. They found that if they added a tiny amount of impurity to the plastic, the plastic was suddenly able to conduct electricity. The impurity that makes a substance a conductor is called a dopant, and the process is known as doping. The scientists' discovery was startling because plastics usually are not conductors.

A Plastic Marvel

Metals are good conductors of electricity. Electrons in the atoms of metals can be easily "kicked" free. The hole left by a free electron can be filled by another electron. This in turn leaves a hole to be filled by another electron, and so on. As electrons leap from atom to atom, an electric current is conducted through the material.

In a plastic, the electrons are bound tightly to the atoms that make up the material. It is very difficult to kick these electrons free. But the behavior of electrons in the new plastic is different. Shared electrons that bond together adjacent carbon atoms in the plastic are only loosely held and can be pried loose by the right kind of chemical kick.

The dopant that the chemists added to the plastic provided that kick. The atoms of the dopant "stole" the loose electrons from the atoms in the plastic. The result was that an electron from a nearby atom jumped into the empty space. The space left by the jumping electron was filled by another electron, and so on. An electric current flowed. The new plastic was a conductor—and a very good one, indeed!

MacDiarmid's new plastic is now being used to build batteries. The plastic batteries weigh one-third less than regular batteries and release their electric energy much faster. It is hoped that these batteries will be a good source of energy for electric cars.

Scientists are exploring ways to make other kinds of conducting plastics, which they believe will have many future uses. Says Alan Heeger, a physicist who works with MacDiarmid, "Our dream is to make materials that will create a whole new technology."

These pieces of plastic developed by Alan Mac-Diarmid are formed from long chains of identical atomic units. Each unit consists of a carbon atom and a hydrogen atom. By doping this material, a current-conducting plastic is formed.

489

ADDITIONAL QUESTIONS AND TOPIC SUGGESTIONS

1. Why are metals good conductors of electricity? (Electrons in the atoms of metals can be easily kicked free.)
2. Why are easy-to-free electrons important in a conductor? (Electrons leaping from one atom to another form an electric current.)
3. How was MacDiarmid able to loosen electrons in the plastic? (by adding an impurity called a dopant)

CRITICAL THINKING QUESTIONS

1. What special advantages would plastic conductors have? (They would have the special properties of plastic—lightweight, flexible, easy to mold—which would be useful in making certain items such as batteries for electric cars.)
2. Plastic has long been used as a covering for wires and electronic devices such as telephones. Would MacDiarmid's plastic be useful in this way? Why or why not? (No. Plastic used to cover wires or telephones is used as an insulator; that is, a material that does not conduct electric current. Since MacDiarmid's plastic conducts electricity, it would need to be covered with an insulator itself.)

Also review with students the description of a polymer. Recall that plastics are polymers.

After students have read the article, discuss the role that accidental discoveries play in scientific research. Point out that although the initial discovery may be an accident, it is usually far from accidental that someone like MacDiarmid has the training and curiosity to recognize the discovery's importance and apply it in a useful way.

Unit Six

ELECTRICITY AND MAGNETISM

ISSUES IN SCIENCE: NUCLEAR POWER: PROMISE OR PERIL?

BACKGROUND INFORMATION

According to *Newsweek* magazine, "what happened" at Chernobyl is not known, but most "educated guesses" point to the following sequence of events.

1. The cooling system failed, resulting in the rapid overheating of fuel rods.

2. As temperatures rose drastically, the uranium fuel began to melt.

3. Operators flooded the reactor with water, but that only made matters worse. At this point, steam reacted with fuel, zirconium, and graphite to produce flammable hydrogen, methane, and carbon monoxide gases.

4. The gases built up over hours and violently exploded. The reactor and part of the reactor building were destroyed; lack of a containment structure exposed the inferno to the open air.

5. Melted fuel reacted out of control, producing radioactive materials that were sucked up into a cloud of deadly radiation.

6. Heavy lift helicopters tried to dump huge amounts of sand, lead, and boron on the burning plant, but nothing helped. The fires continued to smolder.

According to the *Newsweek* writer, the Chernobyl plant was outmoded (at least 30 years behind the times), poorly built, and lacking in basic safety backup equipment.

Issues in Science

NUCLEAR POWER: PROMISE OR PERIL?

A fiery explosion on April 26, 1986, rocked a city in the Soviet Union and terrified the rest of the world. The accident occurred at the Chernobyl Nuclear Power Plant, near Kiev. An explosion in a nuclear reactor blew off the roof of the plant and triggered a fire that burned for days. A cloud of radioactive particles rose into the air and was carried by winds throughout Europe. Chernobyl was the most serious nuclear accident in history.

Several people were killed instantly by the explosion at the Chernobyl plant. Others died soon after from burns or radiation poisoning. How many more will die in future years as a result of radiation remains unknown. But people may not be the only casualties of this explosion. The future of nuclear power in the United States has been gravely threatened by the accident at Chernobyl.

BENEFITS VERSUS RISKS

The popularity of nuclear power in the United States had begun to decline long before

TEACHING STRATEGY

Motivation

Begin by asking students how many of them remember hearing about the nuclear accident at Chernobyl. Encourage them to share what they remember, especially reactions to the accident they may have heard or read. Ask those students who seem knowledgeable about Chernobyl if the incident significantly affected their own attitudes toward nuclear power.

Content Development

Have students observe the diagram of a typical nuclear reactor found in Chapter 25 of this text. Explain that although the Chernobyl reactor was not identical to this one, the basic principles of operation were the same. Point out that the nuclear reactions that take place inside the reactor core generate enormous amounts of heat energy, and these reactions must be controlled if the reactor is going to operate safely. Share with students the information provided in the Background Information that describes what most experts believe happened when the Chernobyl reactor was destroyed.

the Chernobyl accident. Rising costs, delays in obtaining government licenses, and construction problems had plagued the nuclear power program. Public fears about the safety of nuclear power and the health hazards associated with nuclear wastes had prompted people to ask, "Is nuclear power worth it?" Accidents such as the one at Chernobyl have caused many people to answer, "No!"

People who are in favor of nuclear power say this attitude is not realistic. They argue that nuclear power is needed as a source of energy. Fossil fuels such as coal, oil, and natural gas presently supply most of the energy required to meet worldwide needs. But someday fossil fuels will run out. Once used up, these *nonrenewable* energy resources will be gone forever.

Critics of nuclear power say we can develop alternative energy resources. Energy from the sun, wind, rushing water, tides, and the earth's inner heat could meet our energy needs. These *renewable* resources could lessen our dependence on fossil fuels and nuclear energy. But proponents of nuclear power stress that these resources alone cannot satisfy the increasing energy needs of an increasing world population.

THE SAFETY ISSUE

People in favor of nuclear power claim that despite the Chernobyl accident, nuclear technology has a better safety record than coal, oil, and hydroelectric technology. To support this position, they cite the thousands of deaths caused by coal mine accidents, oil-drilling accidents, and dam failures.

Critics of nuclear power argue that the risks of conventional energy technologies are known and understood, while the dangers of nuclear power are not fully defined. They say that the possibility of more serious nuclear disasters exists, as the Chernobyl accident, unfortunately, has hinted at.

491

"Once again," says Robert Pollard, a nuclear power expert with the Union of Concerned Scientists, "this accident has brought home the idea that when you build a commercial nuclear power plant, you decide to accept the risk, however small, of killing a few thousand people."

Many critics add that large-scale accidents are not the only dangers of nuclear power. Small radiation leaks from nuclear plants, nuclear fuels, and nuclear waste dumps pose long-term health hazards to millions of people. These critics contend that no more nuclear power plants should be built until all the risks are known.

Supporters of nuclear power point to the progress of implementing safety procedures in nuclear power plants. Their prediction is that nuclear power plants of the future "will be perfectly safe."

Do you think the benefits of nuclear power outweigh the risks? Or are nations jeopardizing their future safety by turning to nuclear power? If nuclear energy becomes a dead issue, will it cause hardship or encourage the development of alternative energy resources?

ADDITIONAL QUESTIONS AND TOPIC SUGGESTIONS

1. What arguments against nuclear power had been voiced before the Chernobyl accident? (rising costs, delays in obtaining government licenses, construction problems, fears about public safety, health hazards associated with nuclear wastes)

2. Why do many people feel that we need to continue to develop nuclear power? (Someday fossil fuels will run out, and we need an energy source that can replace them.)

3. In what way are the risks and dangers of nuclear power different from the risks and dangers associated with coal and oil? (The hazards associated with coal and oil are known and understood; the hazards associated with nuclear power are not.)

CRITICAL THINKING QUESTIONS

1. Support or criticize the following statement:

"Every time there is an accident, everybody says, let's quit using this technology or that technology. The same thing happened after the *Challenger* explosion. Yet where would we be today if the Pilgrims and the pioneers had quit every time somebody got hurt?"

2. Experts seem to agree that the Chernobyl plant was at least 30 years behind the times, poorly built, and not properly equipped with safety equipment. Do you think this information should make a difference in the way Americans view the Chernobyl incident? (Answers will vary.)

CLASS DEBATE

Before the class debates the issue, take a poll to see how many students favor and how many oppose the continuing development of nuclear power. Keep the results of the poll secret. Then, after the class debate, take a second poll. Reveal the results of both polls and compare. Ask students to discuss how their views were changed by the debate.

Unit Seven
WAVES: SOUND AND LIGHT

UNIT OVERVIEW

In Unit Seven, students are introduced to the nature, types, characteristics, and interactions of waves. The properties of sound and the wave nature of sound are explained, as is the mechanism of hearing. The properties and wave nature of light are explained next. The entire electromagnetic spectrum is introduced. Students then explore light reflection and refraction, and light and pigment colors. Finally, mirrors, lenses, optical instruments, and light technology are discussed.

UNIT OBJECTIVES

1. **Describe the nature, types, characteristics, and interactions of waves.**
2. **Describe the properties of sound waves.**
3. **Describe the properties of electromagnetic waves.**
4. **Explain reflection and refraction of light.**
5. **Describe some of the technological applications of light.**

INTRODUCING UNIT SEVEN

Begin your teaching of the unit by having students examine the unit-opening photograph, which shows a beam of laser light. Ask them the following questions, which relate to the photograph.
• **How many colors of light are visible in the laser beam?** (Only one color is present.)
• **Does the beam spread out as it moves farther from its source? How does this compare with a beam of light from a flashlight?** (The laser beam does not appreciably spread out, especially when compared with a flashlight beam.)

Now have students read the unit introduction. This material should serve as the basis for various discussions that will better motivate students to study the chapters that follow. Here are some questions you may wish to pose to the class to initiate class discussions.
• **What other examples of communication made possible by light can you think of?** (Answers will vary. Some students may provide simple everyday examples, whereas others may be aware of sophisticated technological applications, as in holography and fiber optics.)
• **Lasers are especially useful in many other areas. Can you name**

Waves: Sound and Light

In 1979, Gary Finkle's world changed dramatically. A severe spinal-cord injury suffered in a swimming accident left Gary virtually without any feeling or movement below his shoulders. Everyone assumed he had no chance for an independent life. But they were wrong! A unique combination of light energy and a clever monkey gave Gary a new lease on life.

Gary became a charter member of a nonprofit organization that trains capuchin monkeys to help people such as himself increase their self-reliance and independence through the use of light. Here is how this unusual method works. Gary uses his mouth to control a small laser-beam pointer mounted on his wheelchair. With it he can direct his monkey, Jo, to do a number of tasks. Responding to the laser-beam signals, Jo brings Gary his snacks and even cleans away the scraps.

Gary's heart-warming story is just one of the many important applications of light. From primitive signal fires to modern fiber-optic technology and holograms, human beings have used light waves for communication. As you read the chapters in this unit, you will learn about light and another important wave—sound. And you will explore their many uses in your everyday world.

CHAPTERS

21 Waves

22 Sound

23 Light

24 Light and Its Uses

Laser light, a concentrated beam of coherent light, has many important and practical uses.

493

CHAPTER DESCRIPTIONS

21 Waves In Chapter 21, the nature of waves is explained, and transverse and longitudinal waves are contrasted. The basic characteristics of waves are explained, and wave speed, frequency, and wavelength are related. Finally, wave interactions are discussed.

22 Sound Chapter 22 deals with the wave model of sound. The transmission, properties, and interactions of sound waves are discussed. Noise and music are contrasted, and the mechanism of hearing is explained.

23 Light In Chapter 23, the nature of light and the relationship between light energy and the atom are described. Electromagnetic waves are discussed, and the particle and wave properties of light are contrasted. Reflection, refraction, and light and pigment colors are explained. Finally, the mechanism of sight is explained.

24 Light and Its Uses Chapter 24 deals with sources of light. Mirrors and lens are also treated. Finally, optical instruments and new technological applications of light are described.

---

some of these? (Areas include manufacturing, medicine, surveying, entertainment, computers, printing, and scientific measurement.)
• **What do you think makes laser light different from ordinary light?** (Answers will vary. As students will learn in Chapter 24, laser light is of a single frequency and is coherent; that is, its waves are in phase.)

Chapter 21
WAVES

CHAPTER OVERVIEW

So much of the phenomena that we experience, and even depend on, is energy transmitted as a wave. Everything from earthquakes and water waves which shape our earth, to the sound and light that deliver pleasure and important information about our immediate surroundings is based on waves.

This chapter looks at what a wave actually is and how it transmits energy. It categorizes waves according to the direction that the disturbance is moving with respect to the direction the wave is headed. The characteristics of waves such as wavelength, frequency, and amplitude are presented and used to describe differences in some familiar waves. How fast the energy is transmitted depends on the density and elasticity of the medium. The relationship between speed, wavelength, and frequency is also looked at.

The last section introduces students to the interactions that waves can have with medium changes, obstacles in the medium, and other waves. These interactions can be used to explain many phenomena, such as fuzzy shadows, the pencil in water that appears broken, and musical instruments.

INTRODUCING CHAPTER 21

Draw students' attention to the photograph on page 494. The most important thing for students to see in the picture is the transfer of energy. A difficult concept to get across to students is that energy is transferred thru a medium without transferring the medium. Have students read the text on page 495.
- **What do a water wave, sound waves, and a light wave have in common?** (They transfer energy.)
- **What other waves occur in nature?** (earthquake)
- **Does it transfer energy?** (yes)
- **Where did the energy come from that the water wave in the picture is carrying?** (wind or even an earthquake thousands of kilometers away perhaps)
- **If water waves arrive continually at the shore, why aren't the oceans empty?** (The energy is transferred to the beach, not the water.)
- **Where does the energy of the wave go after it hits the beach?** (Sound in the air moves particles of the beach and earth.)
- **If the water itself does not move toward the shore, how does a surfer get to the shore?** (He is surfing downhill. The energy not the water moves toward the shore.)

Waves 21

CHAPTER OBJECTIVES

After completing this chapter, you will be able to

21–1 Define a wave.

21–1 Describe the medium of a wave.

21–2 Compare transverse and longitudinal waves.

21–3 Identify the basic characteristics of waves.

21–4 Relate the speed, frequency, and wavelength of a wave.

21–5 Describe reflection, refraction, diffraction, and interference of waves.

This was it! The wave of the day. He had waited all morning for this one, passing up several good rides. But this wave belonged to him. It was as if it had traveled several thousand kilometers from the Arctic to the Pipeline in Hawaii just for him.

A couple of quick strokes and he was up on his surfboard. He drove down the face of the wave in an S-shaped turn. He drove again for distance and then hit full speed as he reached the bottom. The wave towered over him. The water thundered around him. He felt its awesome energy and knew if he could not keep ahead of the crushing weight of the water, he would be pulled under. But success was his this time. With a sense of accomplishment and an appreciation of nature's power, he rode the wave all the way to shore.

What is a wave? Where does a wave get its energy? How can a wave travel several thousand kilometers? As you read this chapter, you will find the answers.

A wave such as the "Pipeline" in Hawaii is an exhilarating reminder of nature's awesome energy.

495

TEACHER DEMONSTRATION

Most students are very interested in the sights and sounds of contemporary rock music. Play a video tape of a popular music video or as an alternative just play an audio tape. (You can add flashing lights, strobe light, colored lights, or anything else for excitement and interest.) Ask,

- **How did you know that the video was playing?** (Many answers are possible. Most will say they hear it or see it.)
- **What is really reaching your ears and eyes that carries this information?** (Energy, or waves)
- **How does this energy get to your ears and eyes?** (not fully explained here but basically waves)
- **Are the energy waves you see the same as the energy waves you hear?** (no)
- **What is different about them?** (This will be answered in the chapter.)
- **Which carries more energy?** (the light)

TEACHER RESOURCES

Audiovisuals

Color and Light: An Introduction, film, Coronet

Modern Concepts of Light, filmstrip, PH Media

Reflection of Light: Lenses, filmstrip, PH Media

Books

Browning, D. R., *Spectroscopy,* McGraw-Hill

Henderson, S. T., *Day Light and Its Spectrum,* Halsted

Middleton, T. H., *Light Refractions,* Stein & Day

21-1 NATURE OF WAVES

SECTION PREVIEW 21-1

In this section students will be introduced to the relationship between a wave, the energy it carries, and the medium it travels through. It looks at how the energy is transferred, what a wave is, what constitutes a medium, and what properties of the medium affect the way a wave moves through it.

PERFORMANCE OBJECTIVES 21-1

1. Explain what a wave is in terms of energy.
2. Recognize a few examples of wave phenomena.
3. List two properties of a medium that affect the speed of a wave.

SCIENCE TERMS 21-1

wave p. 496
medium p. 497

21-1 Nature of Waves

Drop a pebble into a still pond and observe the circular waves moving outward. Watch the waves moving across tall grass on a windy day. Observe the huge waves in the ocean during a storm. These examples illustrate wave motion. You might be surprised to discover that sound and light are also examples of wave motion. But sound waves and light waves are difficult to observe.

Waves and Energy

When a pebble is dropped into a still pond, the surface of the water is disturbed. The disturbance moves outward along the surface of the water as a series of **waves.** The disturbance is caused by energy traveling through the water. What is the source of this energy?

The pebble that is dropped into the water has kinetic energy because it is moving. Kinetic energy is energy of motion. When the pebble hits the water, some of its kinetic energy is transferred to nearby particles of water. These particles start to move as a result of the energy. Their movement transfers energy to neighboring water particles, which in turn move. As the water particles move, a wave is produced across the surface of the water. Energy is transferred from one place to another. **A wave is a disturbance that transfers energy through matter or space.** A wave is always the result

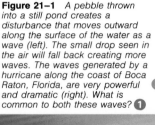

Figure 21–1 *A pebble thrown into a still pond creates a disturbance that moves outward along the surface of the water as a wave (left). The small drop seen in the air will fall back creating more waves. The waves generated by a hurricane along the coast of Boca Raton, Florida, are very powerful and dramatic (right). What is common to both these waves?* ❶

TEACHING STRATEGY 21-1

Motivation

Set up a pan or aquarium of water and float a cork in it. Explain to the students that pushing a pencil up and down in the water will make waves. Take a poll with this next question.

• **Will these waves make the cork move across the tank?** (no)

Be sure to move the pencil only up and down. The waves will move past the cork and it will move up and down but have very little horizontal motion.

Content Development

A small buzzer or bell that operates from a dry cell works nicely for demonstrating and discussing waves, energy, and media. Ring the bell. Discuss the energy transformations involved. Chemical energy of the battery is changed to electrical energy, which is changed to magnetic energy, which is changed to kinetic energy of the bell's arm, which is finally changed into sound energy. The bell itself is vibrating, bumping air molecules and transferring its energy to the surrounding air molecules, which bump other air molecules, which finally transfer their energy to your eardrums making them vibrate.

• **Is the bell moving air molecules all the way to your ear?** (no)

of energy moving from one place to another. It is important to note that when a wave moves through matter, the particles of matter do *not* move along with the wave. Only the energy that produces the wave moves with the wave.

Waves Through a Medium

A **medium** is any substance or region through which a wave is transmitted. Water is a medium for ocean waves. Air is a medium for sound waves. All phases of matter can act as a medium. For certain waves, a medium of matter is not required. These waves can be transmitted through a vacuum. Light is such a wave. Light from the sun, for example, travels to the earth through the vacuum of space.

A medium transfers wave energy but has no overall motion itself. The particles of the medium vibrate, or move, in small circles. The energy is transmitted from one place to another. But there is no movement of matter between these places. In other words, energy is transmitted *without* the movement of the medium as a whole.

If you have ever watched an object floating on water, you will understand wave motion and the transfer of energy. As the waves move past the object, the object bobs up and down. The waves continue to move forward, but the object remains in approximately the same place. Energy is transmitted, but matter is not.

Two properties of a medium affect the speed of a wave. One property is density. A wave moves more slowly in a denser medium. As the density of a medium increases, the speed of a wave decreases. Why? A denser medium has more inertia to overcome. It is harder to get the particles of a denser

Figure 21–2 *These wheat fields in Montana illustrate wave motion. The stalks of wheat sway back and forth as their energy is transmitted as waves. The stalks, however, do not move with the wave. What is the medium for these waves?* ❷

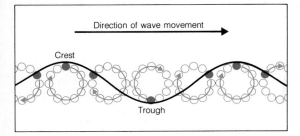

Figure 21–3 *As a wave moves through the medium of water, the individual water particles move in circles. The energy of the wave is transmitted without the movement of the medium as a whole. If you were viewing an object on the leftmost circle, how would its motion appear?* ❸

Direction of wave movement

Crest

Trough

497

TEACHER DEMONSTRATION

The motion of particles as a wave passes can be compared to the stretching of a spring or swinging of a pendulum. Attach a spring to a support and suspend a mass from it. Pull the mass down a bit to stretch the spring and release it to start it bouncing. The energy you gave it is analogous to the energy that a particle would encounter as a wave passes. The spring bounces back and forth but eventually returns to its rest position, just as particles in a medium may vibrate back and forth but eventually return to rest position. The same idea can be presented with the pendulum.

Put a glass jar over the bell.
• **Which is denser, glass or air?** (glass)
• **Is the energy from the bell transferred better through glass or air?** (air)
If a vacuum pump is available, withdraw the air from the bell jar and listen for the ring of the bell.
• **Why can't you hear the bell?** (Air is needed to transfer the energy.)
• **Is there any sound in space?** (no)

• **Do any waves travel through a vacuum?** (yes, light)

Reinforcement
Ask students to put an ear on to their desk and tap the desk with a pencil. Ask them to compare the intensity of the sound in air to that which they hear with their ear on the desk top.

21-2 TYPES OF WAVES

SECTION PREVIEW 21-2

This section classifies waves according to how the medium moves with respect to the direction of the wave. The discussion hinges upon a medium, which means that only mechanical waves are being classified, not electromagnetic waves. The wave is transverse if particles of the medium move at right angles to the direction of the wave and longitudinal if the motions are in the same direction. Some common examples of both types are given.

PERFORMANCE OBJECTIVES 21-2

1. **Classify those waves that require a medium as transverse or longitudinal.**
2. **Give some common examples of transverse and longitudinal waves.**
3. **Identify the crest and trough of a transverse wave.**
4. **Distinguish between a compression and rarefaction of a long wave.**

SCIENCE TERMS 21-2

transverse wave p. 498
crest p. 499
trough p. 499
compression p. 500
rarefaction p. 500
longitudinal wave p. 500

medium to respond to the energy of the wave and to start moving.

Another property of a medium that affects the speed of a wave is elasticity. Elasticity refers to the ability of a medium to return quickly to its original shape after being disturbed. A wave moves faster in a more elastic medium. For example, the speed of sound in steel is greater than it is in air. The elasticity of steel is greater than that of air.

SECTION REVIEW

1. What is a wave? What is a medium?
2. How does a wave move through a medium?
3. What two properties of a medium affect the speed of a wave?
4. At 25°C, the speed of sound in air is 346 m/sec. At 0°C, the speed of sound in air is 332 m/sec. Explain why the speed decreases as the temperature decreases.

21–2 Types of Waves

All waves are not the same. Ocean waves are a different type of wave from sound waves. Why? Although they both transfer energy through a medium, the movement of the disturbance through the medium is quite different. **Depending on the motion of the medium as compared to the movement of the wave, waves are classified as either transverse or longitudinal.**

Transverse Waves

An ocean wave is a **transverse wave.** A wave in which the motion of the medium is at right angles to the direction of the wave is a transverse wave.

You can make your own transverse wave by pulling up and down on a rope that has been attached at one end to a doorknob. The energy you give to the rope travels along the rope as a wave. But you will notice that the rope moves up and down while the wave moves forward. Your up-and-down motion is at right angles to the direction of the wave.

21-1 (continued)

Motivation

Point out that banging two rocks together underwater within a meter of an underwater swimmer can deafen the swimmer. This is because the speed and efficiency with which water transmits sounds are much better than that of air. Humpback whales can hear each other call for kilometers underwater.

Content Development

Steel is denser than air, and sound travels much quicker in steel. The elasticity, or how tightly bound the particles are, and the density work together to determine the speed of a wave. This discussion applies to mechanical waves such as sound.

Skills Development

Skill: Making predictions
Suspend equal masses from a stiff

• **Which will bounce faster? Why?**
(The stiffer one will bounce faster because it has a greater force trying to return it to its rest position. It is more elastic.)

Waves move faster through more elastic media. This can be better shown with a long Slinky than with a long spring. Movement in the Slinky is more slowly transferred than movement in the stiffer spring.

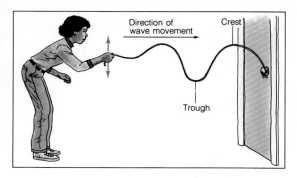

Direction of wave movement

Crest

Trough

Figure 21–4 *A rope attached at one end to a doorknob and pulled up and down will generate a transverse wave. How does the movement of the rope compare to the direction of wave movement?* ❶

Two important parts of a transverse wave represent the up-and-down motions of the particles of the medium. The **crest** of a wave is the high point. ❸ The crest represents the maximum displacement upward of a particle of the medium. The **trough** represents the maximum displacement downward of a particle of the medium. The trough is the low point of a wave. See Figure 21–4.

CAREER   *Geophysicist*

HELP WANTED: Experienced **GEOPHYSICIST** to lead an expedition in search of new sources of oil and natural gas. Knowledge of sonar devices helpful. College degree in geology required.

The first rays of sunlight draw long shadows of the people climbing into two trucks. The trucks roll out across the desert as the sun and the temperature steadily rise. A typical day for a **geophysicist** might begin this way.

The geophysicists' trucks carry devices that help detect underground oil. One device, called a thumper truck, carries a huge vibrator on its underside. As the truck slowly moves across the desert sand, the vibrator pounds the earth, sending sound waves downward through rock.

The sound waves from the thumper truck are reflected from the rock layers beneath the sand back to the earth's surface. Another device, called a seismograph, records the time it takes for the waves to travel. The geophysicist then studies the wave speeds to determine if the rock layers contain pockets of oil.

Geophysicists perform similar tests in the oceans to detect oil, gas, or minerals buried there. Other geophysicists use sound waves to make maps of the earth's surface and to study earthquakes and water and soil conditions.

If you would like information about a career as a geophysicist, contact the American Geophysical Union, Meetings and Members Program, 2000 Florida Avenue NW, Washington, DC 20009.

499

• **Why did the Indians put their ears to the ground or to the rails of a train track?** (The sound of coming trains or of buffalo stampedes travels faster in the rails or in the earth than in the air.)

Section Review 21-1
1. A disturbance that transfers energy through matter or space; any substance or region through which a wave is transmitted

2. The energy of the wave is transmitted without the movement of the medium as a whole.
3. Density and elasticity
4. Air at 0°C is denser than air at 25°C. Sound

TEACHING STRATEGY 21-2

Motivation
Operate a speaker that is exposed to show its movement. (Bring a stereo speaker or ask your audio visual department for a speaker that can be observed.) Show the production of waves in several other ways such as with tuning forks, guitar strings, rubber bands, or a drum. Have students pay attention to what motion is going on.
• **Is the wave motion in the same direction as the wave is moving or at right angles to it?** (same direction)
• **How does it compare to the motion of the cork on the water?** (The cork on the water shows motion at right angles to wave direction.)
• **Which is transverse?** (water)
• **Which is longitudinal?** (sound)

TEACHER DEMONSTRATION

Have students line up in the hall, holding hands. A transverse wave can be sent by having the student on the end raise his free hand, then the hand he is holding. The next student then raises the other hand. Each student in the chain raises the appropriate hand as the motion reaches him. A longitudinal wave can be demonstrated if students line up shoulder to shoulder. If you gently push on the end student and he gently pushes on the student beside him etc., a longitudinal wave will develop. This can lead to chaos but students remember the difference between transverse and longitudinal waves amazingly well.

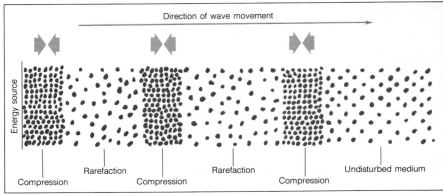

Figure 21–5 A longitudinal wave is a series of compressions and rarefactions. The motion of the molecules of the medium is parallel to the direction of wave movement. What happens to the molecules of the medium in a compression? In a rarefaction? ❶

Longitudinal Waves

Clap your hands together near your face. You hear a clap. Do you also feel any air striking your face? When you clap your hands, you crowd the air molecules together, causing a **compression** (kuhm-PREHSH-uhn). A compression is a space in the medium in which the molecules are crowded together. See Figure 21–5. This compressed band of air then moves forward. As it does, it leaves behind a space that contains much fewer molecules. A space in the medium in which there are fewer molecules is called a **rarefaction** (rair-uh-FAK-shun). See Figure 21–5.

As the compressed air molecules move forward, they collide with the air molecules next to them. These molecules also become compressed. Each layer of molecules pushes the next layer as the compressions move forward through the medium. Each compression is followed by a rarefaction. So rarefactions also move forward. As the layers move back and forth through the medium, compressions and rarefactions develop and "move" in a regular, repeating way. Energy is transmitted as a wave.

A wave that consists of a series of compressions and rarefactions is a **longitudinal** (lahn-juh-TYOOD-uhn-uhl) **wave.** In a longitudinal wave, the motion of the medium is parallel to the direction of the wave. In other words, the molecules of the medium move in the same direction the wave moves. Sound waves are longitudinal waves.

500

21-2 (continued)

Content Development

Have students diagram vibrating objects; at least one transverse and one longitudinal wave. Show the direction that the object is moving, the direction the media moves, and the direction the wave is moving. Label each as transverse or longitudinal. Draw and label the crest and trough for the transverse wave. Draw and label the compressions and rarefactions for the longitudinal wave.

Section Review 21-2

1. A wave in which the motion of the medium is at right angles to the direction of the wave
2. Molecules crowded together; space in which there are fewer molecules
3. A wave in which the motion of the medium is parallel to the direction of the wave

4. Longitudinal. The people move parallel to the direction of the wave. A series of compressions and rarefactions are formed.

TEACHING STRATEGY 21-3

Motivation

Slinkies work very well for showing wave characteristics. If you have or can borrow a ripple (or wave) tank, it is also very effective. A simple wave

SECTION REVIEW

1. What is a transverse wave?
2. What is a compression? A rarefaction?
3. What is a longitudinal wave?
4. Suppose that a long line is formed at a movie theater. Someone in back gives a big push. Everyone moves forward as this "push" moves toward the front. As people regain their balance, they move back. Which type of wave is generated? Explain your answer.

21–3 Characteristics of Waves

Section Objective

To describe the characteristics of a wave

There are many different kinds of waves. Sound waves, light waves, radio waves, microwaves, and ocean waves are but a few examples. All waves, however, share certain basic characteristics. **All waves have amplitude, wavelength, and frequency.** ③

Amplitude

A wave is a disturbance in a medium. The molecules in the medium are moved from their normal, or rest, position. The maximum distance the molecules are displaced from their rest position is called the **amplitude** (AM-plih-tyood) of the wave. The amplitude of a wave indicates the energy of that

Figure 21–6 *The basic characteristics of a wave are shown here. What is the high point of a wave called? The low point? What does wave amplitude measure?* ②

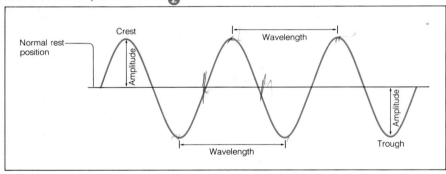

501

21-3 CHARACTERISTICS OF WAVES

SECTION PREVIEW 21-3

This section analyzes the quantifiable characteristics of all waves. Wavelength, frequency, and amplitude are discussed in detail.

PERFORMANCE OBJECTIVES 21-3

1. **Define wavelength, frequency, and amplititude.**
2. **Compare the characteristics of waves.**

SCIENCE TERMS 21-3

amplitude p. 501
wavelength p. 502
frequency p. 502
hertz p. 502

---

tank can be made by taking a shallow (3 to 5 cm) glass-bottomed tank about 50 cm × 50 cm. Put a light source below it and project the waves on the ceiling for all to see. With water in the tank, use a long, narrow object to push into the water at regular intervals and "make waves." Crests and troughs will appear brighter with dark bands between them. Make the waves more frequent and notice how the distance between the waves decreases by

one-half. Wavelength is the distance between two bright bands (crest to trough).

Content Development

Sound and light are the most commonly experienced waves students will be familiar with. Ask,
• **Sound is a longitudinal wave. How many compressions are hitting your eardrum every second you speak?** (Answers will vary.)

• **How would you perceive a sound with many compressions per sec? What would it sound like?** (high pitched)
• **Is there a limit to the frequencies we can hear?** (yes, about 20,000 Hz)
• **Is there a limit to the frequencies we can see?** (yes)
• **Which is a higher frequency, light you see or sounds you hear?** (light)
• **Which has waves closer together (shorter wavelength)?** (light)

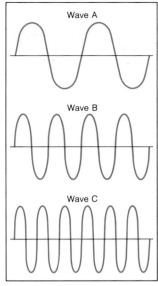

Figure 21–7 *Frequency is the number of complete waves per unit time. What is the frequency of Wave A? Wave B? Wave C?* ❶

wave. As the energy that generates a wave increases, the amplitude of the wave also increases. What happens to the crest and trough of a wave as amplitude increases?

Wavelength

The distance between two consecutive crests or troughs of a wave is called the **wavelength.** Actually, the wavelength can be measured from any point on a wave as long as it is measured to the *same point* on the next wave. Wavelength is usually measured in meters or centimeters. The symbol for wavelength is the Greek letter lambda (λ).

Frequency

The number of complete waves, or complete cycles, per unit time is called **frequency** (FREE-kwehn-see). For a transverse wave, you can think of frequency as the number of crests *or* troughs produced per unit time. For a longitudinal wave, frequency is the number of compressions *or* rarefactions produced per unit time. For example, if 100 complete cycles of compressions and rarefactions—100 compressions and 100 rarefactions—are carried by a medium in one second, the frequency of the wave is 100 cycles per second.

The unit used to measure wave frequency is called the **hertz (Hz).** This unit is named after Heinrich Hertz, who was one of the first scientists to study certain types of waves. A frequency of one hertz is equal to one wave, or cycle, per second: $1 \text{ Hz} = 1 \text{ wave/sec.}$

SECTION REVIEW

1. Define the three basic characteristics of waves.
2. What is the unit of wave frequency? How is it defined?
3. If the distance from a crest to a trough is 0.5 m, what is the wavelength?
4. Suppose that you notice 15 waves pass a point in 3 seconds. What is the frequency? How many waves would pass a point in 1 second if the wave frequency were two times greater?

Sharpen Your Skills

Waves on a Rope

1. Tie one end of a 3-m rope or coiled telephone cord to a stationary object. The knob of a door will work well.
2. Quickly move the other end of the rope up and down. Observe the resulting wave. What kind of wave do you produce?
3. Increase the speed of the up-and-down movement. What happens to the frequency? To the wavelength?
4. Increase the height to which you move your arm. What happens to the wave's amplitude?

502

21-3 (continued)

Reinforcement
Show a guitar string or tuning fork vibrating with low frequency and compare it to the motion of a string or fork vibrating at high frequency.
• **Which moves back and forth more times per second?** (the one lowest in pitch)
• **What is the difference between the sound wave produced from playing a certain note softly and playing the same note loudly?** (The amplitude or energy is greater with increased volume.)

Section Review 21-3
1. Amplitude, wavelength, frequency; maximum displacement from the rest position; distance between two consecutive crests or troughs; number of waves, or cycles, per unit time
2. Hertz; number of waves per second
3. 1 m
4. 5 Hz; 10 waves

TEACHING STRATEGY 21-4
Motivation
A very effective method of teaching this abstract relationship can be found in *Science Teacher,* May, 1981. In this article, "Getting in Step with Wavelengths", Charles McLaughlin asks students to become a wave. Have a day to honor ROY G. BIV. Students line

21–4 Speed of Waves

You have learned that the speed of a wave depends on the medium in which it travels. In a given medium, however, the speed of a wave is constant. The speed of a wave is determined by the number of waves passing in one second and the length of the wave. **The speed of a wave is equal to the frequency times the wavelength.**

$$\text{speed} = \text{frequency} \times \text{wavelength}$$

When the frequency of a wave is measured in hertz and the wavelength is measured in meters, the speed of the wave is measured in meters per second.

A wave with a frequency of 4 Hz and a wavelength of 2 m has a speed of 8 m/sec (4 Hz × 2 m = 8 m/sec). If the frequency of the wave were increased to 8 Hz, the wavelength would decrease to 1 m in the same medium. Why? In a given medium, the speed of a wave is constant. The speed must still be 8 m/sec. If the frequency is now 8 Hz, then the wavelength must be 1 m (8 Hz × 1 m = 8 m/sec). An increase in frequency requires a corresponding decrease in wavelength. What would happen to the frequency if the wavelength were increased? ❷

Sample Problem

What is the speed of a wave with a frequency of 100 hertz and a wavelength of 15 meters?

Solution

Step 1	Write the formula	**speed = frequency × wavelength**
Step 2	Substitute given numbers and units	**speed = 100 hertz × 15 meters**
Step 3	Solve for unknown variable	**speed = 1500 meters/second**

Practice Problems

❸ 1. A sound wave has a frequency of 110 Hz and a wavelength of 3.0 m. What is the speed of the wave?

❹ 2. What is the frequency of a wave that has a wavelength of 5.0 m and a speed of 250 m/sec?

503

21-4 SPEED OF WAVES

SECTION PREVIEW 21-4

This section deals with the relationship between the frequency, wavelength, and speed of a wave. The student is introduced to this relationship conceptually and then mathematically. It shows the importance of mathematical skills in quantifying scientific concepts. It demonstrates the scientific method by showing a systematic approach to solving problems using the relationship
speed = frequency × wavelength.

PERFORMANCE OBJECTIVES 21-4

1. **Predict increases or decreases in wavelength for a given increase or decrease in frequency.**
2. **Relate speed, frequency, and wavelength.**
3. **Solve mathematical problems involving wavelength and frequency.**

up according to height the day before the activity. The class is divided into seven small groups. The tallest ones are to wear red, the next tallest orange, and so on, to the shortest who wear violet the following day at school. ROY G. BIV refreshments may be served and ROY G. BIV prizes given away. Use your imagination.

Content Development
The motivational activity begins by asking the tall half of the class to line up fingertip to fingertip out in the hall. This separates them by one wavelength (approximately their height). Measure the average wavelength making certain that the students maintain constant wavelength (distance) and constant speed, have them walk by the door (perhaps to the tune of "Rainbow Connection"). Record the number of "waves" and the time for them to walk by. Determine the frequency of waves per second. Compute the speed of the waves. Perform the activity with the shorter half of the class, making sure they walk the same speed as the first group. Compare the wavelength, frequencies, and speeds of the two groups.
• **Why did more of the shorter people come by the door per second?** (higher frequency, they were closer together, shorter wavelength)

21-5 INTERACTIONS OF WAVES

SECTION PREVIEW 21-5

This section discusses wave behavior when waves encounter medium changes, obstacles, or other waves. It offers a basis for explaining many wave phenomena that we commonly experience by introducing reflection, refraction, diffraction, and interference.

PERFORMANCE OBJECTIVES 21-5

1. **Identify examples of reflection, refraction, diffraction, and interference.**
2. **Explain some common phenomena using these concepts.**

SCIENCE TERMS 21-5

reflection p. 504
incident wave
  p. 505
reflected wave
  p. 505
angle of incidence p. 505
angle of reflection p. 505
normal p. 505
law of reflection
  p. 505

refraction p. 505
diffraction p. 506
interference
  p. 506
constructive interference
  p. 506
destructive interference p. 506
antinode p. 507
node p. 507
standing wave
  p. 507

SECTION REVIEW

1. If the frequency and wavelength of a wave are changed, what happens to the speed? Why?
2. What is the relationship between wave speed, frequency, and wavelength?
3. A wave has a frequency of 10 Hz and a wavelength of 30 m. What is its speed?
4. If the frequency of the wave in question 3 were 20 Hz, what would be the wavelength?

21–5 Interactions of Waves

Waves traveling in the same medium move at a constant speed and direction. What would happen, however, if the waves encountered a different medium, reached an obstacle, or met another wave? Depending on the conditions, the waves would interact in a certain way with the medium. **The four basic wave interactions are reflection, refraction, diffraction, and interference.**

Reflection

Figure 21–8 shows water waves striking a barrier and bouncing back. This interaction is called **reflection** (rih-FLEHK-shuhn). Reflection is the bouncing back of a wave after it strikes a boundary that does *not* absorb the wave's energy. Imaginary

Figure 21–8 *Reflection is the bouncing back of a wave after it strikes a boundary that does not absorb its energy. According to the law of reflection, the angle of incidence equals the angle of reflection (right). This laser beam dramatically illustrates the reflection of light as it strikes a mirrored surface (left).*

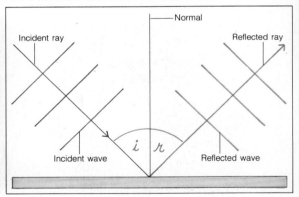

504

21-4 (continued)

Section Review 21-4

1. Remains the same. In a given medium, the speed of a wave is constant.
2. Speed equals frequency times wavelength.
3. 300 m/sec
4. 15 m

TEACHING STRATEGY 21-5

Motivation

Put your hand in front of a light source and project a fuzzy shadow on the wall or on a screen.
• **Why is the shadow fuzzy?** (Light bends around the edges of your finger. This is known as diffraction.)

Borrow a laser or make a ray box from a high-intensity light source inside of a box with a clean, narrow slit

in it about 1 cm long. It helps if the inside of the box is lined with aluminum foil. The beam is visible in the air only if it strikes particles such as chalk-dust or aerosol spray. Show the beam going into a tank of water (aquarium) at a small angle to the surface and notice the change in direction of the beam after it enters the water.
• **Why does the light change direction?** (It changes velocity and is refracted by the new medium.)

rays have been added to the diagram to show the direction of the incoming waves and the waves that are bounced back.

The incoming wave is called an **incident wave.** The wave that is bounced back is called a **reflected wave.** The angle formed by the incident ray and a line perpendicular to the barrier is called the **angle of incidence, i.** The angle formed by the same perpendicular line and the reflected ray is called the **angle of reflection, r.** The line perpendicular to the barrier is called the **normal.** The **law of reflection** states that the angle of incidence is equal to the angle of reflection.

Refraction

Waves do not bend as they travel through a medium. Waves travel in straight lines. However, when waves pass *at an angle* from one medium to another—air to water or glass to air, for example—they bend. The waves bend because the speed of the waves changes as the waves travel from one medium to another.

The bending of waves due to a change in speed is called **refraction** (rih-FRAK-shuhn). Refraction occurs because waves move at different speeds in different mediums. As waves pass at an angle from one medium to another, they may speed up or slow down.

You can see the results of the refraction of light. Place a pencil diagonally in a glass of water. The

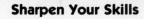
Figure 21–9 *This diagram illustrates how waves bend as they pass from air to water. The effect of refraction is shown in the accompanying photograph. Look back at Figure 21–8. Can you find evidence of refraction?* ❶

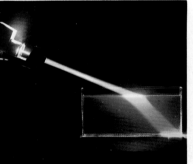

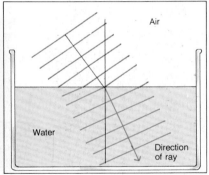

Air

Water

Direction of ray

505

Figure 21–10 *The refraction of light as it passes from one medium to another makes this flower stem look as if it were broken. Why does refraction occur?* **2**

pencil appears to be split into two pieces. The light waves traveling through air are slowed down and bent when they travel through water. You can observe refraction in another way. Place a coin in the bottom of an empty cup. Move the cup so that the coin is out of your line of sight. Then fill the cup with water. Does the coin become visible? **1**

Diffraction

The bending of waves around the edge of a barrier is called **diffraction** (dih-FRAK-shuhn). Diffraction is a result of a new series of waves being formed when the original waves strike a barrier. Perhaps you are familiar with the diffraction of sound waves. You can hear a band playing before you actually see them march around the corner into your line of sight. The sound waves reach you by bending around the corner of the building.

Interference

Suppose that you and a friend are holding the ends of a piece of rope. You both snap the ends at the same time. Two waves are sent toward each other. What will happen when the waves meet at the middle of the rope?

When two or more waves arrive at the same point at the same time, they interact with each other in a process called **interference.** The two waves combine to produce a single new wave. The two waves can combine in two different ways.

CONSTRUCTIVE INTERFERENCE If waves combine in such a way that the crests of one wave meet the crests of the other, **constructive interference** occurs. The crests of the two waves add together to form a single wave. The amplitude of the single wave is equal to the sum of the amplitudes of the two original waves. See Figure 21–11.

DESTRUCTIVE INTERFERENCE If waves combine in such a way that the crests of one wave meet the troughs of the other, **destructive interference** occurs. The crests and troughs combine by subtracting from each other to form a single wave. The ampli-

Sharpen Your Skills

Law of Refraction

Assemble the following materials:

2 rubber or wooden wheels firmly attached to an axle
large piece of velvet cloth or coarse sandpaper

1. Roll the wheels and axle across a smooth tabletop. Describe the direction of motion.

2. Place the velvet cloth or the coarse sandpaper on the table.

3. Roll the wheels again but in such a way that only one wheel moves across the rough surface. Describe the motion. What effect does this motion have on the direction of the wheels? What causes this to happen?

Explain how this activity illustrates refraction of waves.

506

21-5 (continued)

Content Development

Using the wave machine you have constructed, show interference by replacing the straight wave-maker (ruler) with two balls so that two circular waves will be generated. This would be much like the two speakers. You will see lines of brightness (nodes) where the water is still because of destructive interference. These will alternate with darker bands (antinodes) where constructive interference occurs. If the intensity of these bands is not clear, project the images onto a piece of poster paper below the tank instead of on the ceiling.

Motivation

Wet your finger and gently move it around the rim of a wine glass and listen to it "sing." It produces a standing wave. Change the frequency by adding water to the glass. Another demonstration is to place two speakers (stereo would work) about 1 to 2.0 m apart and send the same signal, preferably of constant frequency, to both speakers. This yields best results if there is little reflection from walls, so

have students stand around the speakers or take the demonstration outside. Have a student cover one ear and direct the other toward the speakers. As the student moves across in front of the speakers, the student should notice places that are louder and some that are softer. Ask,

• **What are the waves from the two speakers doing to cause this?** (constructive interference: louder; destructive interference: softer)

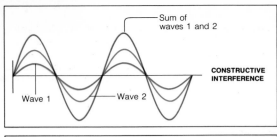

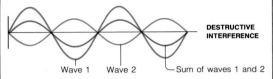

Figure 21-11 *When two waves arrive at the same place at the same time, they interfere with each other. The interference can be constructive or destructive. Which type of interference increases wave amplitude? Which type decreases wave amplitude?* ❸

tude of this wave is the difference between the amplitudes of the original waves. See Figure 21-11.

ANTINODES AND NODES   A point at which constructive interference causes maximum energy displacement is called an **antinode.** Any crest or trough may be called an antinode. A point at which destructive interference results in no energy displacement is called a **node.**

If both you and a friend continuously shake the ends of the rope up and down, something interesting occurs. Several points along the rope will not move. These are nodal points. Between the nodal points there are maximum displacements of the rope upward and downward. These are antinodal points. When constructive interference and destructive interference produce stationary nodes and antinodes, the resulting wave is called a **standing wave.**

SECTION REVIEW

1. What is the law of reflection?
2. What is refraction? Diffraction?
3. Compare constructive and destructive interference.
4. What is a standing wave?
5. Except for a connecting door, two rooms are separated by a soundproof wall. Explain why a sound produced in any part of one room can be heard anywhere in the other room.

Sharpen Your Skills

Waves in Your Bathtub

This activity works best at night with a bright bathroom light turned on.

1. Place about 2 cm of water in your bathtub. Tap the water with the eraser end of a pencil and observe the resulting wave.

2. Tap the water with the pencil laid flat and observe the resulting wave.

3. Place a ruler in the water as a barrier. Position the ruler so it forms a 45-degree angle with the flat pencil.

4. Tap the flat portion of the pencil and observe the reflected wave.

507

LABORATORY INVESTIGATION
OBSERVING WAVE PROPERTIES OF A SLINKY

BEFORE THE LAB
1. Obtain enough Slinkies for each group of students.

PRE-LAB DISCUSSION
Review with students the concepts of transverse and longitudinal waves, reflection, and standing waves, and the characteristics of frequency and wavelength. Students are asked to demonstrate some wave behavior, make observations about the behavior, and draw conclusions about the observations.

SKILL DEVELOPMENT
Students will use the following skills while completing this investigation.
1. Observing
2. Manipulative
3. Comparing
4. Relating
5. Inferring

SAFETY TIPS
Caution students not to overstretch the spring or release it quickly when it is stretched. This is for the safety of the Slinky. There are no specific hazards to the students.

TEACHING STRATEGY FOR LAB PROCEDURE
In step 6, instruct the students that gathering the first 20 cm together may not produce an observable wave. If not, they can push the Slinky together quickly in the direction of the other end.

OBSERVATIONS
1. Opposite
2. Increase
3. Decrease

CONCLUSIONS
1. Transverse because the movement of the particles of the medium is at right angles to the direction of the wave energy
2. Longitudinal because the movement of the particles of the medium is parallel to the direction of the wave energy
3. As rate increase, frequency increases and wavelength decreases
4. Type of wave, frequency, wavelength (amplitude)

GOING FURTHER: ENRICHMENT
Establish a standing wave with one antinode (or loop).
• **How long is the wave compared to the length of the spring?** (twice length of spring)
Make a standing wave with one additional antinode or two loops.
• **How do the wavelength and the length of the spring compare?** (They are equal.)
Continue making standing waves with one additional antinode each time. Draw a diagram each trial.
• **For a given vibrating object, is any wavelength possible for a standing**

Problem
What are the characteristics of a wave?

> **Materials** *(per group)*
> Slinky®, or other coiled spring

Procedure
1. On a smooth floor, stretch the spring to about 3 meters. Have one person hold the spring at each end. **CAUTION:** *Do not overstretch the spring.*
2. Make a loop at one end of the spring as shown in the accompanying figure.

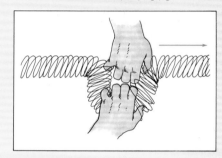

3. Release the loop and observe the motion of the wave. Observe the reflected wave.
4. Move one end of the spring back and forth on the floor. Draw a diagram of the wave you observe.
5. Repeat step 4, but this time increase the rate at which you move the spring back and forth.
6. Now squeeze together the first 20 cm of the spring, as shown in the accompanying figure.

508

7. Release the compressed section of the spring and observe the wave as it moves down the spring.

Observations
1. In step 3, is the reflected wave on the same or the opposite side as the original wave?
2. What happens to the frequency when you increase the rate at which the spring is moved back and forth?
3. What happens to the wavelength when you increase the rate at which the spring is moved back and forth?

Conclusions
1. Are the waves generated in steps 1 to 5 transverse or longitudinal? Explain your answer.
2. Are the waves generated in steps 6 and 7 transverse or longitudinal? Explain your answer.
3. What is the relationship between the rate at which the spring is moved back and forth and the frequency? And the wavelength?
4. What are three characteristics of a wave?

CHAPTER REVIEW

21-1 Nature of Waves

❏ A wave is a disturbance that transfers energy through matter or space.

❏ A medium is any substance or region through which a wave is transmitted.

21-2 Types of Waves

❏ A transverse wave is one in which the motion of the medium is at right angles to the direction of the wave.

❏ A crest is the maximum displacement upward of a particle of the medium.

❏ A trough is the maximum displacement downward of a particle of the medium.

❏ Molecules crowded together cause a compression. A rarefaction is a space in the medium in which there are fewer molecules.

❏ In a longitudinal wave, the motion of the medium is parallel to the direction of the wave.

21-3 Characteristics of Waves

❏ Amplitude is the maximum distance the molecules are displaced from their rest position.

❏ Wavelength is the distance from any point on a wave to the same point on the next wave.

❏ Frequency is the number of waves, or complete cycles, per unit time.

❏ The unit used to measure frequency is the hertz (Hz).

21-4 Speed of Waves

❏ The speed of a wave equals frequency times wavelength.

21-5 Interactions of Waves

❏ Reflection is the bouncing back of a wave after it strikes a boundary that does not absorb the wave's energy.

❏ The law of reflection states that the angle of incidence equals the angle of reflection.

❏ Refraction is the bending of waves due to a change in speed.

❏ Diffraction is the bending of waves around the edge of a barrier.

❏ Constructive interference adds waves together to form a single wave whose amplitude is the sum of the amplitudes of the original waves.

❏ Destructive interference combines waves to form a single wave whose amplitude is the difference between the amplitudes of the original waves.

❏ A standing wave is a wave with stationary nodes and antinodes produced by constructive interference and destructive interference.

VOCABULARY

Define each term in a complete sentence.

amplitude	constructive interference	hertz	medium	refraction
angle of incidence	crest	incident wave	node	standing wave
angle of reflection	destructive interference	interference	normal	transverse wave
antinode	diffraction	law of reflection	rarefaction	trough
compression	frequency	longitudinal wave	reflected wave	wave
			reflection	wavelength

509

wave? (no)
- **Why?** (Nodes must occur at the held ends.)
- **Why does a guitar string sound different in tonal quality when it is plucked near one end instead of in the middle?** (More harmonics are set in motion when plucked at the end.)

CHAPTER REVIEW

MULTIPLE CHOICE

1. d	**3.** a	**5.** d	**7.** b	**9.** d
2. b	**4.** a	**6.** c	**8.** c	**10.** b

COMPLETION

1. energy
2. at right angles
3. parallel
4. amplitude
5. wavelength
6. hertz
7. wavelength
8. incidence
9. constructive
10. node

TRUE OR FALSE

1. F energy
2. T
3. T
4. F longitudinal
5. F wavelength
6. T
7. F incident
8. F refraction
9. T
10. F standing

SKILL BUILDING

1. The elasticity of water is much greater than that of air. The elasticity factor is greater than the density factor in the case of water versus air. The greater elasticity causes a much faster speed of sound waves in water than in air.

2. Row 1: 75; Row 2: 375; Row 3: 400; Row 4: 200

3. To complete this activity, students must first infer that no change in speed occurs. **a.** no effect **b.** frequency decreases **c.** frequency increased

4. a. Amplitudes are almost equal but wave B is slightly higher. **b.** Wave B **c.** Wave B

ESSAY

1. Waves travel slower in denser media and faster in more elastic media.

2. Displacement of the medium is at right angles to direction of a transverse wave. Displacement of the medium is parallel to the direction of a longitudinal wave.

3. The wavelength increases and the speed remains the same.

4. The angle of the reflected wave equals the angle of the incident wave.

5. Constructive and destructive interference producing stationary nodes and antinodes

6. Sound waves pass from the jet to the house, through the atmosphere, and transfer this energy.

CONTENT REVIEW: MULTIPLE CHOICE

On a separate sheet of paper, write the letter of the answer that best completes each statement.

1. An example of a medium for a wave is
   a. air.   b. water.   c. space.   d. all of the above.

2. A medium transfers
   a. matter.   b. energy.   c. molecules.   d. air.

3. An ocean wave is an example of a
   a. transverse wave.   b. longitudinal wave.   c. standing wave.   d. stationary wave.

4. The maximum distance the molecules of a medium are displaced from their rest position is the
   a. amplitude.   b. wavelength.   c. frequency.   d. speed.

5. Wavelength is the distance between
   a. two consecutive crests.   b. two consecutive troughs.
   c. one point to the same point on the next wave.   d. all of the above.

6. In a given medium, if the frequency increases,
   a. the wavelength increases.   b. the speed increases.
   c. the speed remains constant.   d. the speed decreases.

7. The bending of waves due to a change in speed is called
   a. reflection.   b. refraction.   c. diffraction.   d. interference.

8. The bending of waves around the edge of a barrier is called
   a. reflection.   b. refraction.   c. diffraction.   d. interference.

9. The interaction of waves that meet at the same point at the same time is called
   a. reflection.   b. refraction.   c. diffraction.   d. interference.

10. A point where constructive interference produces maximum energy is called a (an)
   a. node.   b. antinode.   c. medium.   d. rarefaction.

CONTENT REVIEW: COMPLETION

On a separate sheet of paper, write the word or words that best complete each statement.

1. A wave is a disturbance that transfers _____.

2. In a transverse wave, the particles of the medium move _____ to the direction of the wave.

3. In a longitudinal wave, the particles of the medium move _____ to the direction of the wave.

4. The energy of a wave can be indicated by the _____.

5. The distance from any point on a wave to the same point on the next wave is called _____.

6. Frequency is measured in _____.

7. In the same medium, an increase in the frequency of a wave will cause a decrease in the _____ of the wave.

8. The law of reflection states that the angle of _____ equals the angle of reflection.

9. When two waves add together to form a single wave, the type of interference is _____.

10. A point of no energy displacement due to destructive interference is a (an) _____.

ADDITIONAL QUESTIONS AND TOPIC SUGGESTIONS

1a. Is a vibrating piano string a longitudinal or a transverse wave? (transverse)

1b. Is the wave it sends through the air longitudinal or transverse? (longitudinal)

2a. If all aspects of a piano string remained the same (tension, diameter) but the length was exactly doubled, what would happen to the wavelength of the sound? (It would double.)

2b. What would happen to the frequency of the sound? (It would be one-half the original frequency.)

3a. Would you be more likely to hear an oncoming motorboat if you were above or below water? (below water)

3b. Why? (Sound travels faster in water; it is more elastic.)

Determine whether each statement is true or false. Then on a separate sheet of paper, write "true" if it is true. If it is false, change the underlined word or words to make the statement true.

1. A medium transfers wave <u>matter</u>.
2. The <u>crest</u> of a wave is the maximum displacement upward.
3. Molecules spread out in <u>rarefaction</u>.
4. A <u>transverse</u> wave is a series of compressions and rarefactions.
5. The distance between two consecutive crests is one <u>amplitude</u>.
6. Frequency is measured in <u>hertz</u>.
7. The incoming wave is the <u>standing</u> wave.
8. The bending of waves due to a change in speed is called <u>reflection</u>.
9. When two waves combine to subtract from each other, <u>destructive</u> interference occurs.
10. Constructive interference and destructive interference producing stationary nodes and antinodes is called a <u>diffraction</u> wave.

CONCEPT REVIEW: SKILL BUILDING

Use the skills you have developed in the chapter to complete each activity.

1. **Applying concepts** Waves travel slower through a denser medium. Although water is denser than air, sound waves travel faster in water. Explain why.
2. **Making calculations** Complete the following table.

Speed (m/sec)	Frequency (Hz)	Wavelength (m)
150	2.0	
	250	1.5
200		0.5
	200	1.0

3. **Identifying relationships** State the effect on the frequency and speed of a wave if the amplitude is increased; wavelength is increased; wavelength is decreased.

4. **Interpreting diagrams** Answer the following questions using these diagrams.

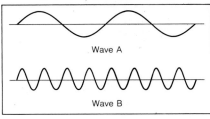

Wave A

Wave B

a. Which wave has the largest amplitude?
b. Which wave has the shorter wavelength?
c. Which wave has a higher frequency?

CONCEPT REVIEW: ESSAY

Discuss each of the following in a brief paragraph.

1. How do density and elasticity of a medium affect the speed of a wave?
2. Distinguish between transverse and longitudinal waves.
3. The frequency of a wave is decreased in a given medium. Describe what happens to the wavelength and speed.
4. Describe what happens to an incident wave after hitting a barrier at an angle.
5. Describe how a standing wave is produced.
6. Sometimes when a jet plane flies over your house you can actually feel the rooms shake. Explain why.

511

ISSUES IN SCIENCE

The following issue can be used for class debate or assigned as a writing homework.

Microwaves are being increasingly used in modern society. Microwave ovens are commonplace and microwave transmission of telephone conversations are common in remote areas where telephone lines are rare. Many people hail the use of microwaves as a sign of the technological advancement of society.

Others caution that microwaves can be very dangerous and that more precautions must be taken to protect consumers and people who live near microwave telephone and energy transmission centers. After research, take a side on this issue and prepare for a class debate on the increasing use of microwaves.

Chapter 22
SOUND

CHAPTER OVERVIEW

The everyday experiences of hearing are discussed and analyzed in this chapter. Many phenomena involving sound are familiar to us, but are never questioned, explained, or even identified. Here the behavior of sound is organized and explained in terms of a wave model.

Sound is a vibrational disturbance that propagates as a longitudinal wave as the medium vibrates forward and backward creating regions of rapidly varying air pressure. Because the propagation of the wave depends on the elasticity and inertia of the medium, the speed of the wave depends on both the phase and density of the medium.

The qualities of sound, loudness, pitch, and timbre, can be explained by describing the wave form, its amplitude, frequency, and overtones. These characteristics distinguish one sound from another. Wave interactions such as interference, resonance, and the Doppler effect can produce observable changes in sound waves. With this information, the difference between sound and noise is established as objective and not subjective. The chapter concludes with a description of the human ear.

INTRODUCING CHAPTER 22

Crack a whip or other long, flexible rope if you can. The tip of the whip is said to move faster than the speed of sound. What better way to lead in to a picture of the X-1, the first airplane to break the sound barrier. It takes the right stuff to fly faster than the speed of sound: the right engineering, the right mechanics, and the right pilot. (The right whip can break the sound barrier, but for most, the crack is probably the sound of the tip hitting the whip!)

Discuss with your students the concept of Mach number, which is simply the ratio of the speed of an object to the speed of sound in the surrounding medium. Discuss the existence of a "sound barrier." Both, though defined in the text on page 513, need clarification to dispel fanciful myths about a physical barrier and to clearly separate Mach number from *Star Trek*'s "warp factor."

Now have students focus on the photograph and text on pages 512 and 513. Point out that breaking the sound barrier involves moving faster than the speed of the sound that you are creating. Diagram a stationary sound source on the chalkboard as having emitted a series of concentric circles of increasing diameter. Evenly spaced circles will indicate that the

Sound 22

CHAPTER OBJECTIVES

After completing this chapter, you will be able to

22–1 Define sound.

22–1 Describe the transmission of sound.

22–2 Identify the properties of sound.

22–3 Classify wave interactions.

22–4 Distinguish between noise and music.

22–5 Explain how sound is heard.

Dawn broke over the Mojave Desert in California as Captain Chuck Yeager climbed into a tiny rocket plane called the X-1. On this Tuesday, October 14, 1947, Yeager was to attempt to break the sound barrier.

The speed of sound, which is called Mach 1, is 1056 kilometers per hour at an altitude of 12,000 meters. All previous attempts to reach this speed had ended in disaster. Many engineers claimed it was impossible to fly faster than the speed of sound. They said any plane that attempted to break the sound barrier would be torn apart.

At 9000 meters the B-29 mother plane dropped the X-1 from the bomb bay opening. Yeager fired the four rocket chambers and began climbing at a 45-degree angle. The acceleration was so violent that he had to strain to move his hands a few centimeters forward to the controls. The needle reached 0.96 Mach and then went clear off the scale. On the ground, the observers heard a tremendous explosion—the sonic boom. The X-1 had broken through the sonic wall! The plane and pilot were safe, and scientists had conquered yet another frontier.

In this chapter, you will learn about sound: What sound is, how it travels, how you hear. Also, you will learn more about those sounds most familiar to you— noise and music.

The pioneering flight of Chuck Yeager (inset) has made possible the now everyday flights of planes such as this at more than three times the speed of sound.

513

TEACHER DEMONSTRATION

Obtain an oscilloscope and a microphone from the physics laboratory or the audio-visual department. Attach the microphone to the vertical input and have fun. The only control that you may need to adjust after selecting an intermediate sweep frequency is the vertical gain, or amplification, so that the display remains on the screen.

Talk, sing, whistle, ring bells, strike tuning forks, and play every available instrument. Allow every student to see his or her voice.

Ask students to point out similarities and differences in the waves produced by different sources. All differences will be explained in this chapter.

Note that since measurements will not be made during the demonstration, the quality of the oscilloscope and microphone is not crucial, nor is the match between the two.

TEACHER RESOURCES
Audiovisuals
A Look at Sound, 16 mm film, Time-Life
Death Be Not Loud, 16 mm film, CRM/ McGraw-Hill
Learning About Sounds, 5 filmstrips with 5 cassettes, EBE
Matter and Energy: Sound, filmstrip with cassette, SVE

Books
Leitner, Bernard, *Sound: Space,* New York University Press
Nelkon, M., *Optics, Sound, and Waves,* Heinemann
Schafer, R. Murray, *The Tuning of the World,* Knopf
White, Frederick, *Our Acoustic Environment,* Wiley

sound has spread uniformly in all directions. A sound source moving faster than the speed of sound would always be at the leading edge of the waves that it produced. Diagram the waves as a series of egg-shaped lines of larger sizes drawn with the narrow end of each egg at the tail of the sound source. Opposite the source, the circles should look regular. Just above and below the source, the waves should overlap creating a thick line on the chalkboard. This is a region of intense rarefaction. As this region of rarefaction sweeps over the land, a sonic boom is heard. Ask,

• **Does everyone on the ground hear the sonic boom at the same time?** (Many think that everyone around would hear the crack just as the plane hits Mach 1, but the sonic boom is a continuous sound that trails the plane. Each observer hears the boom independently, depending on location.)

• **Why does the boom last so long?** (The boom is sustained by the many echoes it produces. Interested students may enjoy researching why two booms are sometimes created.)

• **Why did engineers fear the sound barrier?** (Some were concerned that the plane could not withstand the required acceleration or the intense rarefaction.)

22-1 WAVE MODEL OF SOUND

SECTION PREVIEW 22-1

What is sound? Sound is a vibrational disturbance that causes energy to be transmitted in a longitudinal wave. The molecules of the medium are made to vibrate back and forth, parallel to the velocity of wave propagation. Such a disturbance is best transmitted through elastic materials because the molecules must return to their original positions after the disturbance has passed. Thus, solids are better mediums for sound waves than liquids or gases.

The speed of sound is determined by the medium's elasticity and density. Increased elasticity enhances propagation, while increased density retards it. Because temperature affects density, the speed of sound in a given material increases as the temperature increases.

PERFORMANCE OBJECTIVES 22-1

1. Describe sound in terms of a wave.
2. Compare the phases of matter as to their ability to transmit sound.
3. Describe how the speed of sound is affected by the density of the medium through which it travels.
4. Compare the speeds of sound and light in air.

TEACHING STRATEGY 22-1

Take the opportunity to review the definitions of longitudinal and transverse waves from the previous chapter. Ask students to defend the description of sound as a longitudinal wave. While the strongest reason is that sound waves may not be polarized, students can picture a transverse water wave lifting an object as it passes, and a longitudinal sound wave pushing the object. An awareness of the response of the medium will make easy work of learning about the transmission and speed of sound.

22-1 Wave Model of Sound

A large boulder breaks loose from a high cliff and crashes to the bottom of a canyon. No one is present to hear the crash. Is there any sound? Perhaps you would answer no. But a scientist would likely disagree. In order to understand why, you must know more about the nature of sound.

Sound is a form of energy that causes molecules of a medium to vibrate back and forth. The molecules of the medium vibrate back and forth in a series of compressions and rarefactions. This series of compressions and rarefactions produces a wave in which the sound energy is transmitted. The motion of the molecules of the medium is parallel to the direction of movement of the wave. So sound travels through a medium as a longitudinal wave.

Is there sound produced when the boulder crashes to the canyon floor? The answer is yes. The crashing boulder causes compressions and rarefactions of the molecules of the air. These vibrations of molecules are transmitted through the air in the form of longitudinal waves.

Would sound be produced if the boulder crashed to the bottom of a canyon on the moon? Because the moon has no atmosphere, there is no medium to carry the sound waves. There are no molecules present to be compressed and rarefied. So there is no sound on the moon.

Figure 22-1 *Sound is a form of energy that causes molecules of a medium to vibrate back and forth, as you can clearly see from the splashes of water created by a vibrating tuning fork (left). If there are no molecules of a medium present, such as on the moon, there will be no sound. So astronaut Harrison Schmitt explores a lunar boulder in the silent world of the moon (right).*

514

Motivation

Ask students if a physician has ever listened to their heart or lungs with a stethoscope. Then ask:
• **Why do physicians use stethoscopes?** (To channel the sound gathered by a small object in contact with the body)

This example can lead off a discussion of which phases of matter are better conductors of sound. Rely on students' descriptions of solids, liquids, and gases to show that the arrangement of molecules in solids is best and that of gases is poorest for the transmission of sound.

Content Development

The contrast between the speed of sound and the speed of light is evident in a number of common occurrences in addition to the thunder and lightning example, such as trying to spot a plane overhead, watching a sporting

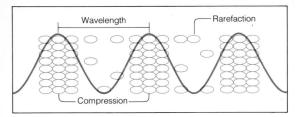

Figure 22–2 *A periodic series of compressions and rarefactions moves through a medium in the form of a longitudinal sound wave. In this diagram, a compression corresponds to a wave crest and a rarefaction to a wave trough. What is the distance between consecutive crests called?* ❶

Transmitting Sound

Because a sound wave is a series of compressions and rarefactions of molecules, materials that are elastic transmit sound easily. Elastic materials are those that return quickly to their original shape.

Solids are generally more elastic than either liquids or gases. The molecules in a solid do not move very far and bounce back very quickly as the compressions and rarefactions of a sound wave go by. Sound travels more easily through solids than it does through liquids or gases. Metals such as iron and nickel are very elastic and are, therefore, excellent transmitters of sound. Lead is not very elastic. How well do you think lead transmits sound? ❸

Most liquids are not very elastic. Sound is not transmitted as well in liquids as it is in solids. Gases are even more inelastic than liquids. So gases are the poorest transmitters of sound.

Another way of determining how well a medium transmits sound is to consider the arrangement of the molecules of the medium. The molecules of a solid are the most closely packed. Vibrations are most easily passed from one molecule to another in a solid. That is why you put your ear to a door to hear sounds on the other side. How would you describe the transmission of sound in a liquid and in a gas based on their molecular arrangement? ❹

Speed of Sound

The speed of sound in air is about 340 meters per second. This is considerably slower than the speed of light, which is almost one million times as great as the speed of sound. A familiar illustration of the difference in speeds of sound and light is a thunder-and-lightning storm. The sound of thunder reaches you *after* the light from a flash of lightning,

Figure 22–3 *Dolphins can "talk" and "listen" to each other because sounds are easily transmitted through water (top). When sound waves strike a hard surface, they are reflected (bottom). A reflected sound is called an echo. What is true about the series of compressions and rarefactions in an echo and in the original wave?* ❷

515

event in a large stadium, or enjoying a fireworks display. In each case, the slower speed of sound brings the aural information after the visual information has arrived; in the case of the fast plane, it is too late to be of any use.

The dependency of the speed of sound on elasticity and density comes logically from an understanding of the transmission of sound. The molecules of the medium are pushed forward by the sound wave and must re-

turn to their original positions. The density of the material affects the ability of the molecules to respond to the push of the wave; the inertia of the molecules slows the spread of the wave. Elasticity, the ability of a material to return to its original shape, affects the time that it takes the molecules to get back to their original positions; a very elastic medium is able to respond to the next wave very soon after an earlier wave passes.

ANNOTATION KEY

❶ 10 seconds (Making calculations)
❷ Greater (Applying concepts)
❸ Stone; rubber (Interpreting charts)
❹ Intensity, frequency, and quality (Relating facts)
❶ Thinking Skill: Applying concepts
❷ Thinking Skill: Making comparisons
❸ Thinking Skill: Making generalizations
❹ Thinking Skill: Applying definitions

SPEED OF SOUND

Substance	Speed (m/sec)
Rubber	60
Air at 0°C	331
Air at 25°C	346
Cork	500
Lead	1210
Water at 25°C	1498
Sea water at 25°C	1531
Silver	2680
Copper	3100
Brick	3650
Wood (Oak)	3850
Glass	4540
Nickel	4900
Aluminum	5000
Iron	5103
Steel	5200
Stone	5971

Figure 22–4 *The speed of sound varies in different mediums. In what medium does sound travel the fastest? The slowest?* ❸

even though both are produced at the same time! So if lightning occurs at a distance of 340 meters, it will take one second for you to hear the sound of thunder. How long would it take if the lightning were 3400 meters away? ❶

The speed of sound in a medium is determined by two factors. One factor that affects the speed of sound is temperature. You learned that the speed of sound in air is about 340 m/sec. This value is for air at a temperature of about 15°C. At 25°C, sound travels at 346 m/sec. And at 0°C, sound travels at only 331.5 m/sec.

As the temperature of a medium increases, the speed of sound increases. Sound travels faster at higher temperatures. When Chuck Yeager broke the sound barrier, he was flying at an altitude of 12,000 meters and a speed of 293 m/sec. At 12,000 meters the temperature is so cold that the speed of sound is only 290 m/sec. If you were watching a baseball
❶ game on a cold day, would the time difference between seeing the bat hit the ball and hearing it be greater or lesser? ❷

The nature of the medium also affects the speed of sound. Sound travels fastest in the most elastic materials. The speed of sound in water is 1500 m/sec. The speed of sound in steel is 5200 m/sec.

In materials in the same phase of matter, the speed of sound is slower in the denser material. Because the more massive molecules of the denser material have greater inertia, they do not move as
❷ quickly as the less massive molecules of the less dense material. The speed of sound in dense metals such as lead and gold is much less than the speed in steel or aluminum. Lead and gold are also less elastic—another reason why the speed of sound is slower in these metals.

SECTION REVIEW

1. What is sound? What kind of wave is it?
2. Compare the transmission of sound waves in solids, liquids, and gases.
3. What two factors affect the speed of sound?
4. Thunder is heard five seconds after a flash of lightning is seen. How far away is the lightning if the speed of sound in air is 340 m/sec?

22-1 (continued)

Motivation

Have two wire coat hangers on hand. Open one by untwisting the hook or cutting it just below the hook. Attach about a meter of heavy string to the open hanger to form a closed loop. Drop the good hanger. Call attention to the sound. Tell the students that the reason for the poor sound was that the air got in the way. Place the string over a student's head and have him lean forward so that the broken hanger hangs freely in front of him. Instruct him to hold the string against his ears. Strike the hanger. The student will hear deep, bell-like tones. Discuss and compare the transmission of sound in solids and gases.

Skills Development

Skills: Identifying patterns, making inferences, making calculations

Use Figure 22-4 as the basis for several exercises.

1. Use the speed of sound to group materials according to approximate density. Use a table of densities to check the groups. Are you correct? Discuss your "errors" in view of the second variable, elasticity, that affects the speed of sound.

2. What materials are considered elastic? Are resilient materials grouped together?

3. A fisher drops the anchor from a boat into the water. Who hears the splash first: the person whose ears are 3 m above the water or the fish 10 m below the water?

4. Does the variation of the speed of sound in air produce a noticeable difference from winter to summer?

Section Review 22-1

1. Form of energy that causes molecules of a medium to vibrate back and forth; longitudinal wave

2. Sound is transmitted best in solids, next best in liquids, and worst in gases.

3. Temperature and elasticity of medium

4. 1700 m

TEACHING STRATEGY 22-2

The properties of sound can be clearly explained in terms of its wave characteristics. In this section, the wave char-

22–2 Properties of Sound

Many different sounds reach your ears every hour of every day. Some sounds are pleasant. Some are unpleasant. Some sounds are loud, others soft. And some sounds, such as a song played on a guitar, are instantly recognizable and different from other sounds. There are many kinds of sounds, and each sound has its own special properties.

In Chapter 21 you learned about the characteristics of waves. All waves have amplitude, frequency, and wavelength. Since sound travels in longitudinal waves, it has these three characteristics. You will recall that amplitude indicates the energy of a wave. Frequency is the number of waves per unit of time.

In addition to amplitude and frequency, sound waves have the characteristic of interaction. **Amplitude, frequency, and wave interaction determine the properties of sound known as intensity, frequency, and quality.** The effects of these properties on the ear are loudness, pitch, and timbre (TAM-ber).

Intensity and Loudness

What is the difference between the sound of thunder and the sound of a handclap? The thunder has a great deal more energy than a handclap. The amount of energy in a wave is called **intensity.** Energy moves molecules of a medium from their rest positions. So intensity of a sound is determined by the amplitude of the sound wave. The larger the amplitude, the greater the intensity.

Figure 22–5 *You hear a variety of sounds every hour of every day. Some sounds are pleasant (left), others are unpleasant (right). All sounds have three basic properties. What are these properties?*

22-2 PROPERTIES OF SOUND

SECTION PREVIEW 22-2

The characteristics that we use to distinguish between different sounds include intensity, frequency, and quality. This section defines these characteristics in terms of everyday experiences and explains them in terms of the wave model of sound. The intensity of sound, what we detect as loudness, corresponds to the amplitude of the sound wave. Intensity is measured in units called decibels. The frequency of sound, heard as pitch, corresponds to the number of waves passing a given point per unit time. Frequency is measured in hertz (Hz). Quality, or timbre, refers to the complex wave shapes characteristic of different sources due to their unique combinations of overtones.

PERFORMANCE OBJECTIVES 22-2

1. Describe the properties of sound waves.
2. Explain how frequency and pitch are related.
3. Describe the Doppler effect.

SCIENCE TERMS 22-2

intensity p. 517	sonar p. 521
decibel p. 518	quality p. 521
pitch p. 519	timbre p. 521
ultrasonic p. 519	fundamental tone
Doppler effect	p. 521
p. 520	overtone p. 522

acteristics of amplitude, frequency, and wave interactions are used to describe intensity, pitch, and quality. These properties of sound should be familiar to most students. Your task is to label the properties precisely and relate the properties to wave characteristics.

Motivation
Make the same sound loudly and softly. Any instrument—including your voice—will do. Ask students to describe the difference between loud and soft. Focus the description on the source of the sound, how it is produced, and the amount of energy put into the wave. Strike a tuning fork and project its shadow using an overhead projector or another bright, localized source. The motion of the shadow will be an exaggeration of the motion of the tines. Call attention to the change in the amplitude of the vibration of the tines as the sound fades. Connect the amplitude with the intensity of the sound. Draw wave diagrams on the chalkboard showing the same frequency but different amplitudes, including one across the entire board of the amplitude gradually decreasing to zero but maintaining the same frequency. Ask if any students have observed the change in vibration of a loudspeaker as the volume control is adjusted on a stereo or radio.

Sharpen Your Skills

Viewing Vibrations
Skills: Observing, comparing, relating, applying, manipulative
Level: Average
Type: Hands-on
Materials: tuning fork, pencil, glass of water, cork, and string

In this activity, students are able to hear and observe sound wave vibrations as they pass through both air and water. Students should have little trouble completing this activity, but they may need some assistance in explaining their observations. If you have different tuning forks for them to work with, the activity will be greatly enhanced.

ANNOTATION KEY

1 Wavelength, amplitude, crest, trough, and frequency (Interpreting diagrams)
2 Jet engine and rocket engine (Interpreting charts)
3 Flute: high frequency; tuba: low frequency (Applying concepts)
1 Thinking Skill: Making comparisons
2 Thinking Skill: Applying definitions
3 Thinking Skill: Making comparisons

Sharpen Your Skills

Viewing Vibrations

Sound is caused by vibration. You can observe this by experimenting with a tuning fork.

1. Strike the prongs of a tuning fork with a pencil and then hold the fork close to your ear. What happens? What happens when you touch the prongs of the fork?

2. Next, strike the prongs of the tuning fork and place the ends of the prongs in a glass of water. What happens?

3. Tie a small piece of cork to a string and hold the string in one hand so the cork can swing freely. Strike the prongs of the tuning fork and hold one prong against the cork. Observe what happens.

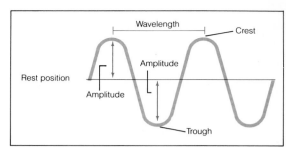

Figure 22–6 *Some of the basic characteristics of a sound wave can be seen in this diagram. What three characteristics can you identify?* 1

Intensity determines the loudness of a sound. The greater the intensity of a sound, the louder the sound is to the ear. Thunder sounds louder than a handclap because the intensity of thunder is much greater than the intensity of a handclap.

Intensity is measured in units called **decibels.** A sound with an intensity of 0 decibels is so soft that it 1 can barely be heard. Thunder, on the other hand, has an intensity of 120 decibels. Thunder is a very loud sound. Sounds with intensities greater than 120 decibels can actually cause pain in human beings. A jet engine has an intensity of about 170 decibels. This sound is very painful to human ears. So

Figure 22–7 *Decibel levels of some familiar sounds are shown in this table. Which sounds would be considered painful?* 2

INTENSITY OF SOUND

Sound	Decibels	Sound	Decibels
Threshold of human hearing	0	Heavy street traffic	70–80
Rustling leaves	10	Vacuum cleaner	75–85
Whisper	10–20	Loud music	90–100
Very soft music	30	Rock concert	115–120
Classroom	35	Threshold of pain	120
Average home	40–50	Jet engine	170
Conversation	60–70	Rocket engine	200

22-2 (continued)

Content Development

The intensity of sound may be measured in decibels. It is a relative measure defined in terms of the ratio of two intensities. Two sounds differ by one bel if they are in a ratio of ten to one. The bel is named for Alexander Graham Bell. The decibel is one tenth of a bel, making the decibel scale logarithmic to base ten. The threshold of hearing is arbitrarily called zero decibels. According to a logarithmic scale, 10 db is 10 times the intensity of 0 db, 20 db is 100 times the intensity of 0 db, 30 db is 1000 times the intensity of 0 db and so forth. Thus a 100 db reading of loud music is not double the intensity of a 50 db average home but is 100,000 times greater. Nor can two intensities simply be added if they occur at the same time: two vacuum cleaners do not add up to a rock concert!

Skills Development

Skill: Making comparisons

List a number of sounds such as a race car, refrigerator motor, birds chirping, helicopter, crowd, etc. Ask the students to arrange the sounds in order of increasing sound intensity. Compare with the representative sounds listed in Figure 22-7.

Reinforcement

Intensity corresponds to the amplitude of a sound wave. Since sound waves are longitudinal waves, the amplitudes correspond to the molecules' displacement forward or backward

ground crews exposed to this sound must wear special ear protection to avoid painful injuries. Music with an intensity above 85 decibels also can cause ear damage.

Frequency and Pitch

Sing the notes of the musical scale to yourself. Do you notice that the first "do" is a low note and the last "do" is a high note? Each note has its own **pitch.** The pitch of a sound is how high or low the sound is. Do not confuse high and low with loud and soft.

The pitch of a sound depends on how fast the molecules of a medium vibrate. Each complete vibration—one compression and one rarefaction—makes up a wave. So the pitch of a sound depends on the number of waves produced in a given time.

Frequency is the number of waves per unit time. The greater the frequency, the greater the number of waves in a given period of time. So pitch can now be defined as the property of sound that depends on the frequency of waves.

Sound waves that have a high frequency are heard as sounds of high pitch. A piccolo produces high-pitched sounds. Sound waves that have a low frequency are heard as sounds of low pitch. A tuba produces low-pitched sounds. A high note sung by a soprano may have a frequency of 1000 hertz. A low note sung by a bass may have a frequency of 70 hertz. A whistle has a high pitch because its frequency is about 1000 hertz. Thunder has a low pitch—its frequency is less than 50 hertz. You will recall that a frequency of one hertz is equal to one wave, or cycle, per second.

The human ear can hear sounds that range from about 20 hertz to about 20,000 hertz. Sounds with frequencies higher than 20,000 hertz are called **ultrasonic** (uhl-truh-SAHN-ihk) sounds. Most humans cannot hear ultrasonic sounds, but many animals can. Dogs can hear sounds with frequencies up to 25,000 hertz. Porpoises can hear sounds with frequencies up to 150,000 hertz! And bats actually produce ultrasonic sounds and then use their echoes to locate prey or to avoid bumping into objects. In this way, bats can fly about safely in the dark.

Figure 22–8 *The pitch of a sound depends on the frequency of the waves. How would you describe the frequency of the high-pitched sound of a flute? Of the low-pitched sound of a tuba?* ❸

519

FACTS AND FIGURES

It is sometimes imagined that molecules move vast distances in response to passing sound waves, but each molecule actually moves a surprisingly small distance. Sound intensities near the threshold of pain, as created by a military jet plane, displace the molecules of the air to a maximum of about .001 cm. Similarly, the pressure differential is only about ± 0.03 kPa, or about 0.0003 atm above and below the normal pressure of 1 atm or 101.3 kPa.

from their original positions in the medium. Diagrams of sound waves shown in Figures 22-2 and 22-6 can be misleading for students who have not mastered the differences between longitudinal and transverse waves. Both diagrams are graphs of the position of one molecule of the medium as a function of time; the amplitude of one molecule is shown as it responds to the passing sound wave. (Figure 22-2 could also be interpreted as a graph of pressure as a function of position.) Note that the amplitude of a wave corresponds to the maximum displacement of the molecules in one direction from their equilibrium, or rest, positions. There is nothing negative connoted by the graph passing below the rest position except to indicate that the particle has moved backward from the rest position. Formation of a trough requires the same energy as formation of a crest.

TEACHER DEMONSTRATION

An example of the Doppler effect is commonly found on the demonstration records that once came with stereo record players. It was included to prove to the consumer that stereo sound really existed by reproducing the sound of a passing train or racing car. The students will enjoy this and other sounds if such a demonstration record

22-2 (continued)

Content Development

The Doppler effect is a phenomenon that will enable you to reinforce the connection between pitch and frequency. The observer hears a higher pitch from an approaching race car because the waves are bunched together in front of the car. The car advances continuously thus shortening the period of the sound wave in air. The receding car similarly lengthens the period of the sound wave in air. The frequency of the source is not changed.

The moving source does not have to be accelerating. An accelerating source will produce a continuously

Sharpen Your Skills

The Doppler Effect

1. Cut a piece of hardboard that is 1/3 cm thick into a piece that measures 5 cm by 30 cm. Round off the corners with a file. This is your paddle.

2. Drill or punch a hole—large enough to allow a piece of sturdy twine to pass through easily—about 1 cm from one end of the paddle.

3. Thread 1 meter of heavy twine through the hole and tie one end to the paddle. Make sure you tie the twine securely!

4. CAUTION: *Operate the paddle outdoors and away from people, windows, and so on.* Have a friend stand several meters away while you whirl the paddle over your head like the blade of a helicopter. If the paddle does not twist and flutter, give the string several twists.

Have the observer describe the pitch of the sound. Does it change as the paddle approaches and as it moves away? Now have your friend whirl the paddle. What do you observe?

Figure 22–9 *As the train approaches the crossing (top), the listener hears a sound of higher pitch. As the train leaves the crossing (bottom), the listener hears a sound of lower pitch. What do the people in the train hear?* ❶

520

DOPPLER EFFECT Have you ever listened to the sound of a race-car engine as the car moves past you? As the race car approaches you, the pitch of ❶ the sound becomes higher. The pitch then becomes lower as the race car moves away from you.

The same effect occurs if you are on a train moving past a railroad crossing that has warning bells. The pitch of the bells increases, or gets higher, as you approach the crossing. The pitch of the bells decreases, or gets lower, as you move past the crossing. In either case, what you are observing is a change in the pitch of a sound due to the motion of either the sound source or the listener. A change in the frequency and pitch of a sound due to the motion of either the sound source or the observer is known as the **Doppler effect.**

When there is relative motion between a sound source and an observer, the frequency of the waves changes. As the sound source approaches the observer, compressions and rarefactions are generated from points that become closer and closer. Waves reach the observer sooner than they would have if the source had been producing them from its original position. The wave cycles reach the observer's ❷ ear more frequently. More waves per second mean a higher frequency and pitch.

When the source is moving away from the observer, sound waves are farther apart. The sound waves reach the observer later than they would have if the source were not moving. Fewer waves reach the observer. The decrease in frequency produces a sound of lower pitch.

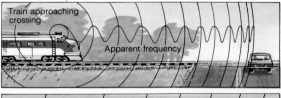

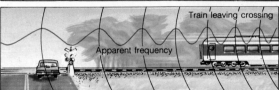

520

changing frequency, not just a shifted frequency. This should be made clear to avoid the misconceptions promoted by cartoons of falling objects.

Content Development

Chalkboard diagrams for a stationary source and moving observers are easier to draw and explain than those of a moving source, though the mathematics are slightly different if quantitative values are required. Draw a stationary

source as emitting a series of concentric, evenly spaced circles centered on the source. Contrast the frequencies measured by three observers: one at rest, one moving towards the source, and the third moving away from the source.

Motivation

Pose these thought questions to students.

1. In addition to measuring the depth

SONAR High-frequency ultrasonic waves are used in a system called "*so*und *n*avigation *a*nd *r*anging," or **sonar.** Sonar is used by ships to locate objects in the water or to determine underwater distances. In a sonar system, high-frequency waves sent out by instruments on a ship reflect off any solid object in the water. A detector on the ship picks up the reflected waves. The distance to the object is calculated by multiplying the speed of sound waves in water by one-half the time it takes the waves to make a round trip, or to go from the ship to the ocean floor and back to the ship.

Sound Quality

Why can you tell the difference between the sound of a trumpet and the sound of a flute even when they are both playing the same note? The instruments have a different sound **quality.** Sound quality is called **timbre.**

Why does each different sound source have a unique timbre? Sounds are produced by a source when it vibrates at a certain frequency. Actually, most objects that produce sound vibrate at several different frequencies at the same time. Each frequency produces a sound with a specific pitch. The blending of the pitches gives the sound its timbre.

How can a single source produce more than one frequency? Look at Figure 22–12 on page 522. The top diagram shows the *whole string* vibrating. When the whole string vibrates, the note produced is called the **fundamental tone.** The fundamental tone has the lowest possible frequency and pitch. At the same time, sections of the string are vibrating two times and four times faster than the fundamental tone, and producing sounds of higher pitch. This is

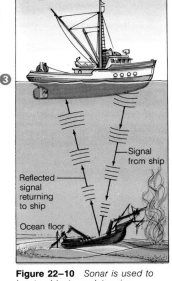

Figure 22–10 *Sonar is used to locate objects or determine distances under water. What two pieces of information must be known in order to calculate the distance from the ship to the object on the ocean floor?* ❷

Figure 22–11 *Sound waves can be converted into electric signals, which are displayed as a pattern of light on a screen. Here you can see the pattern produced by a harmonica (left) and a recorder (right) both sounding the same note. Notice the differences in the amplitude, wavelength, and frequency of the two sounds.*

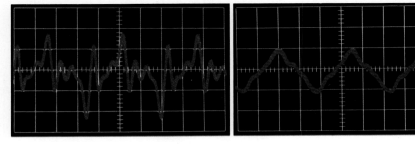

is available. Ask around. People who purchased their first stereos in the 1960s often have a copy in their record collections.

Some demonstrations of the Doppler effect, such as tying a tuning fork to a string and whirling it in a circle, are dangerous. Others, such as the one on page 520 are best done outdoors. Both can be confusing due to the forward and reverse motion and the possibility of obtaining a beat frequency if the circle is not large enough.

An alternate approach is to take a large aluminum ring stand pole, hold it at its center, strike an end against the floor, and then move it rapidly javelin-style towards one row of students at a time. They will hear the frequency shift distinctly.

of the oceans, what applications of a sonar system can you devise?
2. If you were the commander of a submarine, how could you fool the sonar system of an enemy ship?

Motivation
Ask students to describe the sounds of several musical instruments and explain why they prefer certain ones. Most students will respond with the word *quality* while only musicians can

be expected to know the word *timbre*. The music department may have an electronic keyboard that will simulate various instruments. While only the most expensive synthesizers can match actual instruments, a cheap model will do well here and be easier than locating several different instruments.

Enrichment
Pose these questions to advanced students.

1. Is the Doppler effect observable in water waves? Try it in your bathtub.
2. Why is the Doppler effect not noticeable when you are walking, or riding a bicycle?
3. Considering the immense speed of light, when could you expect to observe the Doppler effect for light waves?

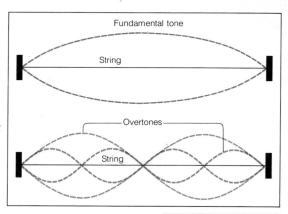

Figure 22–12 *A fundamental tone is produced when the whole string vibrates (top). When sections of the string vibrate faster than the fundamental tone, notes called overtones are produced (bottom). How does the pitch of overtones compare with that of the fundamental tone?* ❶

shown in the bottom diagram. The sounds of higher frequencies are called **overtones.** Sounds always have a fundamental tone and one or more overtones. The blending of the fundamental tone and the overtones produces the characteristic quality, or timbre, of a particular sound.

Without overtones, a trumpet and a flute would sound exactly the same. In fact, a violin, a clarinet, and your friend's voice would all have the same sound quality if it were not for overtones. Timbre is so unique for each person's voice that voice prints have been used to identify a person.

CAREER   *Piano Tuner*

HELP WANTED: PIANO TUNER to work in piano repair shop. Must be available for weekend work at concert halls. High school diploma required. Experience or technical training in piano repair and tuning helpful. Ability to play the piano useful but not necessary.

The talents of a **piano tuner** are needed to make a piano sound wonderful. The piano tuner first compares the pitch of one note on the piano with the pitch of a tuning fork. Then each string is tightened or loosened so that the tone is correct.

A piano tuner also adjusts the many parts that work together to produce the piano's beautiful tones. This may require realigning or replacing worn hammers, replacing broken strings, or rebuilding the wooden board that amplifies the strings' vibrations. Some piano tuners even rebuild pianos.

A piano tuner must have good hearing and manual dexterity. If you would like information about a career as a piano tuner, contact the Piano Technicians Guild, 9140 Ward Parkway, Kansas City, MO 64114.

SECTION REVIEW

1. Compare intensity and loudness.
2. How are frequency and pitch related?
3. What is the Doppler effect?
4. What is timbre?
5. What is a fundamental tone? An overtone?
6. The speed of sound in ocean water is 1530 m/sec. If it takes three seconds for an ultrasonic wave to make a round trip from a sonar device, what is the distance to the reflecting object?

22–3 Wave Interactions

Section Objective

To describe resonance and interference

Suppose that you are in your room listening to the stereo. The station starts playing your favorite song, so you turn up the volume. Whenever a particular note is made by the lead guitar, the glass on your desk starts vibrating. The glass might even shatter! Why?

Resonance

Sound is produced by vibrations in a medium. Every medium has its own frequency of vibration, or **natural frequency.** For example, one object may vibrate at 250 hertz, while another object vibrates at 510 hertz. So the first object has a natural frequency of 250 hertz, and the second object has a natural frequency of 510 hertz.

An object vibrating at its natural frequency can cause a nearby object to start vibrating *if that object has the same natural frequency.* The second object picks up some of the vibration energy of the first object and vibrates "in sympathy" with it. The glass on your desk absorbs some of the energy of the guitar when the two frequencies are the same. The glass vibrates in sympathy with the guitar.

The ability of an object to vibrate by absorbing energy of its own natural frequency is called resonance. A singer can shatter glass by singing a clear, strong, high-pitched note. If the natural frequency of the glass is the same as the natural frequency of the note sung by the singer, the glass will vibrate due to **resonance.** Glass is not very flexible.

❷

❸

523

SECTION PREVIEW 22-3

Every object has a natural frequency of vibration that is determined by its physical structure and dimensions. It is at this frequency that the object is most likely to absorb energy. Resonance describes the situation in which an object absorbs energy at its natural frequency. Sympathetic vibrations occur when one source is emitting waves of a frequency that can readily be absorbed by a second body and therefore sets the second body in oscillation.

Interference is the wave property that describes how two or more waves combine when in the same region of space. Waves may combine constructively or destructively. The resultant amplitude will be greater than either contributing wave if the two waves are in phase with each other. If the two waves are out of phase, the results may vary from a mixture of constructive and destructive interference to entirely destructive interference where the resultant amplitude is the difference between the two waves' amplitudes. Exactly opposite waves of equal amplitude may cancel each other entirely. Interference may be the result of two sound sources or of one source and its reflection. The study of sound by engineers concerned with interference and reverberation in buildings is called acoustics.

PERFORMANCE OBJECTIVES 22-3

1. **Define natural frequency of an object.**
2. **Describe an example of resonance.**
3. **Explain what may happen if two waves cross the same point at the same time.**
4. **Compare phase relationships required for constructive and destructive interference.**

SCIENCE TERMS 22-3

natural frequency p. 523
resonance p. 523
acoustics p. 525
reverberations p. 525

whole string vibrates; multiple vibrations produced when sections of the string vibrate faster than the fundamental wave
6. 2295 m

TEACHING STRATEGY 22-3

Motivation

Ask students if different objects in their houses rattle when a plane flies overhead, a truck rambles past, or a dog barks. Some may even be able to identify a particular type of plane or truck that makes a certain window, vase, or table vibrate. Many examples of sympathetic vibrations are common, including automobile rattles that occur only at certain speeds, pumping a swing in a playground, and the vibrations of a musical instrument when an identical instrument is played nearby.

TEACHER DEMONSTRATION
Tie several pendulums of various lengths with two pendulums of identical length to a horizontal string. Start one of the identical length pendulums in motion. Its energy will be transferred to its mate through resonance.

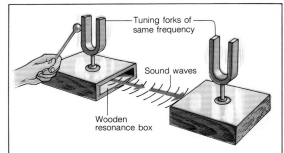

Figure 22–13 *When one tuning fork is set in motion it begins to vibrate at its natural frequency. These vibrations travel through the air and the wooden resonance box, which strengthens them. The tuning fork on the right will begin to vibrate "in sympathy" because it absorbs energy of its own natural frequency (right). Resonance caused the collapse of the Tacoma Narrows Bridge in November 1940 (left).*

So if the intensity of the sound is great enough, the glass will shatter.

You are applying the principle of reasonance every time you turn on your radio. Each radio station broadcasts at a specific frequency. When you turn the dial and tune in to a station, you are matching the frequency of your radio with the frequency of the broadcasting station. Can you think of some other examples of resonance?

Combining Sounds

In Chapter 21, you learned that waves produced at the same time can combine, or interact. You will remember that this combining of waves is called interference. Interference of waves can be constructive or destructive.

Sound waves produced at the same time from different sources can interfere constructively or destructively. When the sound waves are in phase, they combine to produce constructive interference. As a result of constructive interference, the intensity of the sound is increased. The sound is louder. Outdoor amphitheaters use band shells to amplify the music through constructive interference.

When the sound waves are out of phase, they combine to produce destructive interference. As a result of destructive interference, the intensity of the sound is decreased. The sound is softer. Destructive interference actually can produce "dead" spots in which no sound can be heard.

Dead spots are especially troublesome in large halls that have hard surfaces that bounce sounds back into the room. These reflected sounds

524

22-3 (continued)

Content Development
Careful chalkboard diagrams of waves in various phase relationships will emphasize the unique situation of being "in phase." Constructive interference occurs when two waves attempt to disturb a medium in the same direction at the same time. The resulting disturbance is the sum of the individual disturbances.

Destructive interference occurs when two waves attempt to disturb a medium in opposite directions at the same time. The resulting disturbance is again the sum of the two amplitudes, but one is considered negative due to its opposite direction. Total destructive interference is possible if the two waves are exactly equal in amplitude but opposite in phase.

Motivation
Strike a tuning fork and hold its base against various wooden objects: desk, door, closet, table, etc. until you find one that resonates. Resonance will make the sound louder but will also make it damp out sooner.

Motivation
Strike two slightly mismatched tuning forks. The beat frequency will be observed demonstrating both constructive and destructive interference. Have the students carefully describe what they hear and suggest an explanation.

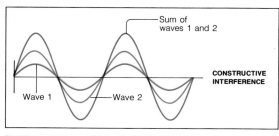

CONSTRUCTIVE INTERFERENCE

Sum of waves 1 and 2

Wave 1   Wave 2

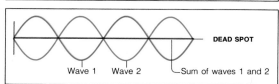

DESTRUCTIVE INTERFERENCE

Wave 1   Wave 2   Sum of waves 1 and 2

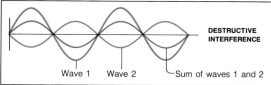

DEAD SPOT

Wave 1   Wave 2   Sum of waves 1 and 2

Figure 22–14 *Sound waves that are in phase can combine to produce constructive interference. Sound waves that are out of phase can combine to produce destructive interference. In some instances, destructive interference can produce "dead" spots. How do the intensities of the resulting sounds compare in these three types of wave interference?* ❷

Figure 22–15 *This amphitheater at Lincoln Center in New York City is designed to eliminate interference problems and produce the best possible sound.* ❸

interfere destructively and cancel each other. Engineers who work in **acoustics,** or the science of sound, try to design concert halls and auditoriums with no dead spots. Acoustical engineers must carefully design the shape, position, and materials of an auditorium to eliminate interference problems and provide the best possible sound.

Acoustics is also concerned with the occurrence of **reverberations** (rih-ver-buh-RAY-shuhnz). A reverberation is a combination of many reflected waves. During a long reverberation time, musical sounds can blend properly and produce a pleasing sound.

SECTION REVIEW

1. What is natural frequency?
2. What is resonance?
3. Distinguish between constructive and destructive interference in terms of sound intensity.
4. Describe constructive and destructive interference in terms of the combining of crests and troughs and the resulting amplitude.

525

Enrichment

Pose the following research questions to advanced students.
1. What is the purpose of the sounding board of a piano? Why do stringed instruments have odd-shaped cavities?
2. The Indian sitar has a set of strings that are never touched by the player. They match the strings that the player plays, but lie below them, out of reach. What is their function?
3. Why is the quality of sound from portable radios so different from that of sound systems with speakers in wooden cabinets? Why is the design of a speaker cabinet more than just a box big enough to hold the speaker?

Section Review 22-3

1. The frequency of vibration for a given object
2. Ability of an object to vibrate by absorbing energy of its own natural frequency
3. Constructive interference produces a sound of increased intensity. Destructive interference produces a sound of decreased intensity and possibly a dead spot.
4. Constructive interference: crests of one wave meet crests of another. Amplitude is increased. Destructive interferences: crests of one wave meet troughs of another. Amplitude is decreased.

22-4 SOUNDS YOU HEAR

SECTION PREVIEW 22-4

In this section, students will learn to differentiate between noise and music based upon wave properties. Music has a pleasing quality, identifiable pitch, and rhythm. A tie-in is made to the psychological and physiological effects of noise pollution.

PERFORMANCE OBJECTIVES 22-4

1. **Relate the characteristics of music and noise.**
2. **Discuss noise pollution.**

Figure 22–16 *A stringed instrument produces sound when the strings are set in motion by plucking or bowing. This traditional African drum is a percussion instrument, which vibrates when struck. A brass instrument such as the marching bugle tuba produces sound when a column of air is made to vibrate.*

22–4 Sounds You Hear

What is the difference between screaming and singing? Between the honk of a car horn and the high note of a violin? Screaming is noise; singing is music. The honk of a horn is noise; the note of a violin is music. Is the difference between noise and music simply a matter of personal taste? Perhaps you might be tempted to answer yes. After all, your music might be someone else's noise, and vice versa. But to a scientist, three characteristics of music set it apart from noise.

Music

A sound is music if it has a pleasing quality, a definite identifiable pitch, and a definite repeated timing called rhythm. Musical instruments produce sounds in several different ways. In woodwind and brass instruments—such as flutes, clarinets, trumpets, and trombones—columns of air are made to
❶ vibrate at various frequencies within the instruments. Percussion instruments, such as drums and cymbals, are set vibrating by being struck.

Stringed instruments are either plucked or rubbed to produce regular vibrations. The guitar, violin, and harp produce music in this way. The vi-
❷ bration produced has a certain frequency, and thus a certain pitch. But by changing the length, tightness, or thickness of the string, the string can be made to produce different pitches.

TEACHING STRATEGY 22-4

Motivation

Play a musical instrument properly and improperly to contrast music and noise. Tune a guitar string to show how tension affects pitch for a stringed instrument.

Content Development

In defining music and noise, keep close to the wave model of sound. Call students' attention to Figure 22-17. Use wave properties to identify those that are music.

Note that while the health effects of noise pollution are described under the heading "Noise," loud music can be equally debilitating. Refer back to Figure 22-7, the list of sound intensities.

Enrichment

Relate the discussion of stringed in-struments to earlier discussions of the speed of sound and fundamental tones. The pitch or frequency of a sound is determined by both speed and wavelength. For a stringed instrument, the minimum wavelength possible on a string, the fundamental, is determined by the length of the string. The speed of the wave in the string is determined by the string's elasticity and density. Thick strings are denser, reducing the speed of the

A shorter string vibrates at a higher frequency and produces a sound of higher pitch. The short strings of a ukulele produce higher pitched notes than the longer strings of a cello. The vibrating length of a string can be changed by the proper positioning of the fingers along the string. Musicians do this to produce the pitches they desire.

The more tension in a string, the higher the frequency of vibration and the higher the pitch. A stringed instrument is tuned by either tightening or ❸ loosening each string on the instrument. If a string is tightened, it produces a higher pitched sound. If loosened, it produces a lower pitched sound.

The strings on a bass guitar are thicker than the strings on a lead guitar. Thicker strings vibrate at a lower frequency than thinner strings. So thicker strings produce lower pitched sounds. What kinds of sounds do thinner strings produce? ❶

Noise

Why is the squeak of chalk on a chalkboard so unpleasant? It is noise. Noise is basically unwanted sound. Noise has no pleasing quality, no identifiable pitch, and no definite repeating pattern. Look at Figure 22–17. The four pictures are wave patterns of sound. A and B were produced by musical tones. Notice the repeating wave patterns. What were C and D produced by? Is there a repeating pattern? ❷

When noise reaches a level that causes pain or damages body parts, it becomes noise pollution. Noise pollution has become a major concern of society. For noise pollution can have a serious effect on people's health. The stress from listening to loud noises can raise a person's blood pressure and cause nervous tension. Studies of guinea pigs exposed to loud noises over a prolonged period of time show that noise can damage delicate tissues of the ear.

What can you do about noise pollution? In many countries, laws have been passed to prohibit noise pollution. People are not allowed to bring loud radios into public places. Of course, you don't have to ❹ wait for a law to follow this example. In your home, you can look for sources of noise pollution. Then you can determine which sources are within your control. You may not want to stop a loud appliance

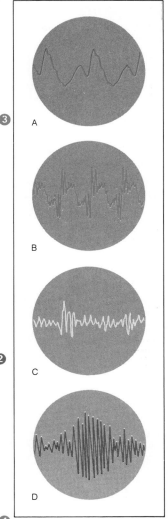

A

B

C

D

Figure 22–17 *These four wave patterns illustrate both music and noise. What distinguishes music from noise?* ❸

527

wave. Strings under more tension are more elastic, increasing the speed of the wave. Various combinations of tension, thickness, and length could produce the same pitch, but the overtones determine the timbre.

22-5 HOW YOU HEAR

SECTION PREVIEW 22-5

After identifying the ear as the human organ that detects sound, students will learn the parts of the human ear and the role each part plays in hearing.

PERFORMANCE OBJECTIVES 22-5

1. Describe the function of the outer ear.
2. Identify the parts that make up the middle ear and inner ear.
3. Discuss how sound vibrations are converted into an electrical signal.

SCIENCE TERMS 22-5

outer ear p. 528	anvil p. 529
ear canal p. 528	stirrup p. 529
eardrum p. 528	inner ear p. 529
middle ear p. 528	cochlea p. 529
hammer p. 528	

Sharpen Your Skills

Sound Through Bones
Skills: Relating, observing, comparing, manipulative
Level: Hands-on
Type: Remedial
Materials: fork

Students will readily discover through this activity that sound easily travels through bone and especially teeth. Students should be able to relate that a hearing aid is a device that transmits sound vibrations through bone in the skull, rather than through the anvil, stirrup, and hammer bones. You may want to point out that the first hearing aids were actually devices that the person held with their teeth so that sound vibrations could be transmitted through jaw bones to their ear. Such devices were called dentiphones.

---

in your kitchen. But placing a rubber pad under the appliance will lessen its noise level. In what other ways can you help prevent noise pollution? ❶

SECTION REVIEW

1. What is music?
2. Describe how a string can be made to produce different pitches.
3. Distinguish between music and noise.
4. Sounds with decibel levels between 60 and 100 can be annoying. Sounds above 100 decibels can cause damage to hearing. Classify the following sounds as either annoying or damaging: snowmobile, food blender, power mower, jet plane, loud rock band, subway train, police siren.

Section Objective

To describe how the body detects sounds

Sharpen Your Skills

Sound Through Bones

The bones in your body are excellent conductors of sound, and you can prove it.

1. Gently strike the prongs of a fork on the table and quickly place the handle of the fork against the bone behind your ear. What happens? Repeat this procedure using other bones in your body.

❶

2. Again strike a fork on the table. Put the handle of the fork between your teeth and bite down. Is the sound transmitted? Which is the better conductor, bone or teeth? How is this fact related to the operation of a hearing aid?

528

22–5 How You Hear

Do you remember the question posed at the beginning of this chapter about a boulder crashing to the bottom of a canyon? You learned that even if no one is around to hear the crash, a sound is still produced. For sound is a form of energy that causes molecules of a medium to vibrate back and forth.

If the question had been whether a sound is *heard*, the answer would have been no. In order for a sound to be heard, three things are needed. One, there must be a source that produces the sound. Two, there must be a medium to transmit the sound. And three, there must be an organ of the body that detects the sound. **In humans, the organ of the body that detects sound is the ear.**

How do you hear a series of compressions and rarefactions? Look at Figure 22–18. Hearing begins when sound waves enter the **outer ear.** The outer ear acts as a funnel for the sound waves. The waves move through the **ear canal** and strike a tightly stretched membrane called the **eardrum.** The vibrating air molecules cause the eardrum to vibrate very much like a musical drum.

Vibrations from the eardrum enter the **middle ear.** The middle ear contains the three smallest bones in the body. The first bone, the **hammer,** picks up the vibrations from the eardrum. The

---

22-4 (continued)

Section Review 22-4

1. A sound that has a pleasing quality, a definite identifiable pitch, and rhythm
2. Change length, tension, or thickness of string.
3. Music is pleasing to the ear, has a definite pitch and rhythm. Noise is unwanted sound that is unpleasant to the ear, has no definite pitch and has no rhythm.
4. Annoying: food blender, subway train, police siren
Damaging: snowmobile, power mower, jet plane, loud rock band

TEACHING STRATEGY 22-5

Depending on the students' science background, they may have studied the ear before. Take the opportunity to review the parts of the ear. Emphasize

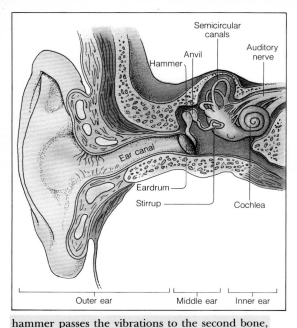

Semicircular canals
Auditory nerve
Hammer
Anvil
Ear canal
Eardrum
Stirrup
Cochlea

Outer ear | Middle ear | Inner ear

Figure 22–18 *This illustration shows the structure of the human ear. What are the three main parts of the ear?* ❷

hammer passes the vibrations to the second bone, the **anvil.** The anvil transmits the vibrations to the third bone, the **stirrup.** The stirrup then sets another membrane vibrating. This membrane transmits the vibrations to a liquid-filled **inner ear.**

The vibrations in the inner ear are channeled into the **cochlea** (КАНК-lee-uh). The cochlea is shaped like a snail shell and contains a special liquid and hundreds of special cells attached to nerve fibers. The nerve fibers join together to form one nerve that goes to the brain. The special cells detect movements in the liquid of the cochlea and convert them to electric impulses. The nerve fibers transmit the electric impulses to the brain, where they are interpreted as sound.

SECTION REVIEW

1. Name the three main parts of the ear.
2. What is the function of the eardrum?
3. Where are the nerve impulses interpreted as sound?
4. What would happen if the eardrum were torn?

Sharpen Your Skills

Model of a Wave

1. Using the wax from a lighted candle, attach a straight pin to one prong of a tuning fork.
2. Set up the apparatus as shown below.

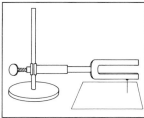

3. Place a sheet of carbon paper under the pin. Carefully adjust the height of the pin to lightly touch the paper.
4. Tap the opposite prong of the tuning fork.
5. Slowly and steadily pull the carbon paper under the pin. You may have to practice several times.
6. After several trials, cut out your best wave model and tape it to a sheet of paper.

Identify the basic wave characteristics. Explain why tapping the opposite prong produced a wave. Would the wave model be different if the prongs were reversed?

529

Sharpen Your Skills

Model of a Wave
Skills: Developing a model, manipulative, observing, comparing, relating, applying
Level: Enriched
Type: Hands-on
Materials: Wax from lighted candle, tuning fork, straight pin, ring stand, carbon paper

In this activity, students produce models of sound waves using a pin and carbon paper. Examine students' drawings for accuracy and make sure they can label all the basic parts of a typical wave. Students should be able to explain why tapping the opposite prong caused vibrations due to resonance. Some interested students may want to compare their device to the seismographs earth scientists use to study earthquake waves.

how the structure of each part of the ear is designed to respond to a particular characteristic of sound waves.

Motivation
Discuss the miraculous operation of the human ear by noting its range and sensitivity. Even an untrained person can detect a misplayed piano chord.

Content Development
Describe the parts of the ear in terms of how they respond to waves.

Reinforcement
Show the advantage of having two ears. Take about a meter of rubber tubing, mark its center, and insert a funnel in each end. Have a student sit facing a wall with the tube on a desk behind him while he holds a funnel to each ear. Tap the tube in various places. The student will be able to identify which side of center is tapped

based on the time delay to the more distant ear.

Section Review 22-5
1. Outer, middle, and inner ear
2. To transmit the compressions and rarefactions traveling through the outer ear to the middle ear
3. Brain
4. There would be a loss of hearing, since the vibrations could not be transferred to the middle ear.

LABORATORY INVESTIGATION
SPEED OF SOUND IN AIR

BEFORE THE LAB
1. Gather all materials at least one day in advance.
2. The glass tubing can be replaced by the plastic tubing sometimes used for packing golfclubs. It need not be transparent.
3. The 1000-mL graduate is required for its depth. Other vessels will suffice.

PRE-LAB DISCUSSION
Review the characteristics of sound waves with students prior to the investigation. Also review the properties of a medium that affect the speed at which sound passes through a medium.

SKILL DEVELOPMENT
Students will use the following skills while completing this investigation.
1. Safety
2. Manipulative
3. Computational
4. Observing
5. Recording
6. Inferring
7. Hypothesizing
8. Measuring
9. Applying

SAFETY TIPS
Caution students not to strike the tuning fork against hard surfaces, it may bend or chip. The tuning fork may contain enough energy to shatter the glass tube if they are allowed to touch.

TEACHING STRATEGY FOR LAB PROCEDURE
1. You might want to check that students are measuring the correct dimensions of the glass tube prior to their calculations.
2. You will have to provide students with the frequency of the tuning fork they are using.

OBSERVATIONS
1. Wavelength of tuning fork is dependent on the tuning fork used. However,

Problem
Can the speed of sound in air be calculated?

Materials *(per group)*
1000-mL graduated cylinder
hollow glass tubing, approximately 2.5 cm × 45 cm
tuning fork of known frequency
meterstick
water

Procedure
1. Fill the graduated cylinder with water to about 3 cm from the top.
2. Hold the hollow tubing in the water.
3. Strike the tuning fork against the heel of your shoe. Quickly place the fork just over the top of the hollow tube, as shown in the accompanying figure.
4. Move the hollow tube up and down until the *loudest* sound is heard. If there is more than one position in which the sound appears the loudest, choose the position in which the length of the tube above the water's surface is the shortest.
5. Record the length, L, of the air column to the nearest 0.1 cm.
6. Measure and record the inside diameter of the hollow tube to the nearest 0.1 cm.
7. Record the frequency of the tuning fork.

Observations
1. Calculate the wavelength of the tuning fork using the following formula:

   wavelength = (4 × L) + (1.6 × D)
       where L = length of the air column
             D = diameter of the tube
2. Calculate the speed of sound in air using the following formula:

   speed of sound = frequency × wavelength

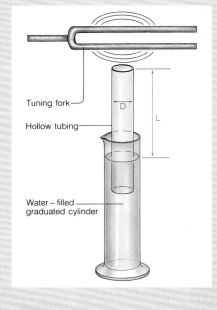

Tuning fork
Hollow tubing
Water-filled graduated cylinder
D
L

Conclusions
1. The speed of sound in air is about 34,500 cm/sec. How close is your calculation to this value?
2. How do you account for differences between your calculated value and the given value?
3. If a tuning fork with a different frequency were used, would you expect a different value for the speed of sound? Explain your answer.
4. If this investigation were performed at a temperature of 5C° above or below the actual temperature, would the speed of sound be different? Explain your answer.

---

student calculations should be checked for accuracy and should be reasonably close to the actual wavelength.
2. Student calculations will depend on their data, but should be reasonably close to the actual speed of sound. If students compute the speed of sound exactly as it is listed in the chart in this chapter, you can probably assume they copied the answer from the chart because their data will not be reliable enough to get the exact speed.

CONCLUSIONS
1. Student calculations may well be close to the actual speed of sound.
2. Accept all reasonable responses including experimental error, temperature of the room versus speed of sound under STP conditions, etc.
3. No. The frequency of the tuning fork does not change the speed of sound.
4. The speed would be different. The speed of sound is dependent on a num-

SUMMARY

22-1 Wave Model of Sound

❏ Sound is a form of energy that causes molecules of a medium to vibrate back and forth.

❏ Sound is a longitudinal wave.

❏ The speed of sound in air is about 340 meters per second at about 15°C.

22-2 Properties of Sound

❏ The amplitude of a sound wave determines the intensity, or loudness, of the sound.

❏ The frequency of a sound wave determines the pitch of the sound.

❏ The Doppler effect is a change in the frequency and pitch of a sound due to the relative motion of the source or the observer.

❏ The interaction of different frequencies in a sound wave determines the timbre.

❏ The lowest frequency of a vibrating object is called its fundamental tone. The higher frequencies are called its overtones.

22-3 Wave Interactions

❏ Every object has its own natural frequency of vibration.

❏ The ability of an object to vibrate by absorbing energy of its own natural frequency is called resonance.

❏ The intensity, or loudness, of a sound can be increased by constructive interference.

❏ The intensity, or loudness, of a sound can be reduced by destructive interference.

❏ Acoustics is the science of sound.

22-4 Sounds You Hear

❏ Music is sound that has a pleasing quality, a definite identifiable pitch, and a repeated pattern called rhythm.

❏ Noise is sound that does not have a pleasing quality, an identifiable pitch, or a repeating pattern.

❏ Over a period of time, loud noises can damage the ears and have other harmful effects on a person's health.

22-5 How You Hear

❏ In humans, the body organ that detects sound is the ear.

❏ The outer ear collects sound waves and sends them into the ear canal.

❏ The waves cause the eardrum to vibrate at the same frequency as the sound wave.

❏ The vibrations of the eardrum are transmitted to three small bones in the middle ear and then into the fluid in the cochlea.

❏ Special cells inside the cochlea detect the vibrations in the liquid and change them to electric nerve impulses.

❏ Nerve fibers carry the nerve impulses to the brain, where they are interpreted as sound.

VOCABULARY

Define each term in a complete sentence.

acoustics	eardrum	natural frequency	resonance
anvil	fundamental tone	outer ear	reverberation
cochlea	hammer	overtone	sonar
decibel	inner ear	pitch	stirrup
Doppler effect	intensity	quality	timbre
ear canal	middle ear		ultrasonic

531

ber of factors, one of which is temperature.

GOING FURTHER: ENRICHMENT

Part 1

Have students move the tube up until a second resonance is observed. It should be at 3 times the first resonance length. A third resonance will be at 5 times the first. Justify these as harmonic parts of the fundamental.

Part 2

Using their value for the speed of sound, have students determine the frequency of an unknown tuning fork using this method.

CHAPTER REVIEW

MULTIPLE CHOICE

1. d   3. c   5. c   7. d   9. b
2. a   4. d   6. b   8. a   10. d

COMPLETION

1. longitudinal
2. solid
3. faster
4. loudness
5. frequency
6. Ultrasonic
7. overtones
8. acoustics
9. music
10. nerve impulses

TRUE OR FALSE

1. T
2. F slower
3. F increases
4. F amplitude
5. F decibels
6. T
7. T
8. F amplitude
9. F Music
10. T

SKILL BUILDING

1. steel, wood, soup, oxygen gas
2. 20 sec
3. One observer could shout or fire a cap gun. The second observer would then shout or fire a cap gun upon hearing the sound. The first observer would measure the time taken to hear the return sound. Multiplying the speed of sound by the time would give the total distance (across and back). This distance would then be divided by 2 to find the distance across the river.
4. The process of resonance could explain the opening of the door. Some frequency of the radio waves used to communicate with the tower might be the same as the frequency that the garage door opener responds to (its natural radio wave frequency). The door opener would then operate as though the driver had sent a radio signal to it.
5. Graph should be a straight line with a slope of 0.6.
6. 336 m/sec; 346 m/sec; (graph line must be extended);
The change is 0.6 m/sec per °C.
7. The wind causes the air in the room to vibrate at its natural frequency. This is similar to a player causing the air in a wind instrument to vibrate by blowing into the mouthpiece.
8. Check students' diagrams. They should show **a.** High frequency, large amplitude **b.** Low frequency, small amplitude **c.** Low frequency, large amplitude.
9. The megaphone would collect more of the sound energy and send it into your ear, thus making the sounds louder.
10. a, b, e. Noise is produced by c and d.

ESSAY

1. Light travels faster than sound. You would see the drummer hit the drum before the sound waves reached you.

2. The molecules of the air are compressed and rarified by the sound energy of the handclap. The vibrations travel through the air as longitudinal waves. The waves are gathered by the outer ear and funneled through the ear canal. The eardrum, set in motion by the vibrations, passes the vibrations to the hammer, anvil, and stirrup of the middle ear. Another membrane is set in vibration and the vibrations enter the liquid-filled cochlea of the inner ear.

5. Loudness is measured in <u>hertz</u>.
6. Sonar uses <u>ultrasonic</u> waves.
7. Frequencies higher than the fundamental tone are called <u>overtones</u>.
8. Constructive interference increases the <u>frequency</u> of a sound wave.
9. <u>Noise</u> has a definite repeating pattern.
10. The organ that detects sound is the <u>ear</u>.

CONCEPT REVIEW: SKILL BUILDING

Use the skills you have developed in the chapter to complete each activity.

1. **Making comparisons** List the following materials from best to worst as transmitters of sound: a. steel b. oxygen gas c. soup d. wood.
2. **Making calculations** How long would it take to hear the thunder from a flash of lightning 6800 meters away? Assume the speed of sound in air is 340 m/sec.
3. **Designing an experiment** How could two observers on opposite banks of a river use sound to measure the river's width?
4. **Applying concepts** Automatic garage doors are operated by radio signals from a device that the driver has in the car. Explain why a garage door sometimes opens when an airplane overhead is communicating by radio with the control tower.
5. **Making graphs** Plot a graph showing how the speed of sound in air varies with the temperature, using the following data:

Temperature °C	Speed m/sec
−10	325
0	331
10	337
20	343

6. **Interpreting graphs** From your graph in question 5, determine the speed of sound in air a. at 18°C b. at 25°C. By how much does the speed of sound change for a change in temperature of 1°C?
7. **Relating concepts** Sometimes a whistling sound is heard in a room when a window is slightly open on a windy day. How is this observation related to the principle of a wind instrument?
8. **Identifying relationships** Draw a wave diagram to illustrate each of the following sounds: a. high-pitched and loud b. low-pitched and soft c. low-pitched and loud.
9. **Making predictions** The part of the ear that is outside the head collects the energy of sound waves and funnels it into the ear canal. What would be the effect on the loudness of sounds if you held the mouthpiece of a megaphone to your ear?
10. **Applying definitions** Overtones that sound well together are said to be in harmony. In order for sounds to be harmonic, their overtones must have frequencies that are whole-number multiples of the fundamental. Which of the following frequency combinations will produce harmonic sounds? What will the other combinations produce?
a. 256, 512, 768, 1024 Hz b. 128, 256, 1024 Hz c. 288, 520, 2048 Hz d. 128, 288, 480 Hz e. 512, 1024, 4096 Hz

CONCEPT REVIEW: ESSAY

Discuss each of the following in a brief paragraph.

1. If you were sitting in the last row of an auditorium during a concert, why might you see the drummer hit the drum before you actually heard it?
2. Trace the path of the sound of a handclap from the moment the clap is made to the moment you interpret the sound.
3. Describe the sound of a car whose horn has become stuck as it approaches you and then passes you.

533

The vibrations are converted to electric impulses by special cells lining the cochlea. The impulses are transmitted to the brain by nerve fibers of the auditory nerve. In the brain the impulses are interpreted as sound.
3. As the car approaches, the pitch increases. As the car passes, the pitch decreases. This is the Doppler effect.

ADDITIONAL QUESTIONS AND TOPIC SUGGESTIONS

1. A concert is to be broadcast live over the radio. You are lucky enough to get the last ticket to the concert. If your seat is in the last row 100 m from the stage and your friends are back home 100 km away listening to the radio, who will hear the music first? Recall that radio signals travel at the speed of light. (Your friends will hear the music 1000 times sooner.)
2. Is it possible to observe destructive interference of sound waves using your stereo system at home? What things limit your ability to do so? (reflections from walls, two ears at different locations, many musical notes of different frequencies, large speakers, more than two speakers, etc.) If the two speakers were 10 m apart, where might you expect to find destructive reinforcement for a pitch of 68 Hz if the speed of sound is 340 m/s. (wavelength is 5 m, destructive interference would occur at all points 2.5 m further from one speaker than the other)
3. Large structures such as towers, buildings and bridges have natural vibration frequencies. The Sears Building in Chicago sways back and forth at 0.1 Hz. What is its period of vibration? What can be done to prevent it from absorbing too much energy? (irregularly spaced supports, flexible connections, or a large unattached mass near the top to dampen vibrations as in the Citicorp Building in New York City). Why must marching soldiers break step when crossing bridges? (In 1831 a British troop destroyed a footbridge by marching in rhythm with its natural frequency.)
4. Usually big brother pushes little sister on the swing. Could little sister get big brother to swing as high? (Yes, with many small pushes at just the right frequency)

ISSUE IN SCIENCE

The following issue can be used as a springboard for class debate or may be assigned as a writing homework.

Noise pollution has become an increasingly serious health risk for people who live in cities or near loud sources of noise. Aside from damage to the ear, noise pollution has been connected to high blood pressure and problems associated with stress. Are our laws on noise pollution adequate? Should stricter laws be passed? Or do people have the right to make as much noise as they like?

Chapter 23
LIGHT

CHAPTER OVERVIEW

Light excites the most important of the senses, that of sight. A beam of light, starting in the atoms of the sun, starts its journey to the earth. Eight minutes later, it has reached the earth. Some of the light is absorbed and converted into heat energy. Some of the light is reflected from objects to your eyes making it possible to see the objects.

Light is much more than that. Light is made up of a stream of tiny packets of energy called photons. The amount of energy in the photon gives light particular characteristics that can be studied and controlled.

The question of what "light" is has been explained, reexplained, and the explanation has been modified many times. We do know light can be reflected, refracted, bent, and separated into color.

Light can be fascinating and stimulating. No matter what the source, the properties of light are similar in many ways.

INTRODUCING CHAPTER 23

Have students observe the opening photograph on page 534. Explain that the work done at various observatories depends on the equipment. Most of the work for astronomical observations is done over long periods of time and needs special equipment. Point out that today's refined equipment is designed for specific research programs and that there are more than 100 major astronomical observatories in more than 30 countries throughout the world working on various studies.

Explain that Kitt Peak is 2096 meters above sea level and 80 kilometers southwest of Tucson, Arizona.
- **Why do you think they would place an observatory so far away from everything?** (Accept all logical answers, but lead students to suggest that "clear pictures" can only be received when there is no outside interference, such as city lights or smog.)

Explain that Kitt Peak National Observatory houses two major optical telescopes and a radio telescope. Read the caption to the photograph.
- **What type of telescope would be required to do this special work?** (Accept all logical answers.)

Explain that the Robert R. McMath telescope is the largest solar telescope in the world. It has a system of three mirrors to produce an image.

Light

23

CHAPTER OBJECTIVES

After completing this chapter, you will be able to

23–1 Explain the relationship between light energy and the atom.

23–1 Describe the properties of electromagnetic waves.

23–2 Identify the parts of the electromagnetic spectrum.

23–2 Describe the uses of electromagnetic waves of different frequencies.

23–3 Distinguish between the particle and wave properties of light.

23–4 Compare regular and diffuse reflections.

23–5 Describe the process of refraction.

23–6 Account for the color of opaque and transparent objects.

23–6 Distinguish between colors of light and colors of pigments.

23–7 Explain how you see.

A laser beam arcs toward the moon from the McMath Solar Telescope on Kitt Peak, Arizona, and is reflected back to a telescope on the earth. Because the speed of light is known—thanks to Albert Michelson—the distance to the moon can be accurately measured.

The year is 1926. Albert Michelson is making a final check of his instruments. He has been working on this project for two long years. All his planning and preparation will be put to the test. Tonight he will accurately determine the speed of light.

Michelson has spent most of his career trying to obtain an accurate value for the speed of light. The method Michelson has chosen has made it necessary for him to determine the distance between two mountains in Southern California. Throughout the previous year, he supervised a team whose task it was to measure that distance. Descending the slope of Mount Wilson and ascending the slope of Mount San Antonio, the team finally made the measurement. It had taken more than a year to determine that the distance was exactly 25 kilometers!

Now that Michelson has an accurate value for the distance, he needs to measure the time it takes light to travel that distance. Light from a rotating mirror on Mount Wilson is transmitted to a mirror on Mount San Antonio. Then the light is reflected back to the rotating mirror on Mount Wilson. Michelson is able to measure the time it takes for the light to make the trip.

Once Michelson knows how long it takes the light to make a round trip, he can determine the actual speed of light by dividing the distance traveled by the travel time. But why would a scientist devote two years to measuring the speed of light? One reason is that the exact speed of light is important to an understanding of modern physics. Another reason is that like most scientists, Michelson was curious.

In this chapter you will learn more about the nature and properties of light. And you will gain an understanding of the important role light plays in your life—just as it did in Michelson's.

TEACHER DEMONSTRATION

Set a large pan of water in bright sunlight. Place a mirror in the pan of water and lean it against an inside edge. Adjust the mirror and pan so that a color band or spectrum appears on the wall. Ask,

• **What causes the color?** (Accept all answers at this point. Tell students they will be able to answer this question more fully after reading this chapter.)

TEACHER RESOURCES
Audiovisuals
Color and Light: An Introduction, 16 mm film, Cor
Reflection of Light: Lenses, filmstrip with cassette, PH Media
What Do You Know About Light?, filmstrip with cassette, LA

Books
Browning, D. R., *Spectroscopy,* McGraw-Hill
Henderson, S. T., *Day Light and Its Spectrum,* Halstead
Middleton, Thomas H., *Light Refractions,* Verbatum
Morris, Richard, *Light: From Genesis to Modern Physics,* Bobbs

Software
Life Cycle of Stars, Prentice-Hall

535

Also, housed at Kitt Peak is the N.U. Mayall telescope, which is one of the world's largest optical telescopes. The Kitt radio telescope has a reflector that is 11 meters in diameter.
• **How might daily observations using these three telescopes help scientists?** (Accept all answers, but encourage students to suggest that observations on a daily basis would be the only way to obtain accurate information and notice changes.)

• **Why do you think we need more information about light?** (Accept all logical answers.)

Point out that through these studies the distances to the various planets and stars have led us to space exploration. Say that light is needed by all living things. Therefore, the more we know about light, the better we can live.

Now have students read the chapter introduction. Make sure they

clearly understand how Michelson was able to deduce the speed of light through his investigations. Point out that even without sophisticated equipment (by modern standards), Michelson was able to use the scientific method and his powers of reasoning to come up with a very accurate number for the speed of light.

23-1 NATURE OF LIGHT

SECTION PREVIEW 23-1

Light is a form of energy. All types of light have certain properties in common. The atom is the source of all forms of light, whether visible or invisible. Light travels at the speed of 300,000 kilometers per second in a vacuum. All light has wavelengths. The wavelength varies with the amount of energy it contains. All light waves are transverse waves.

PERFORMANCE OBJECTIVES 23-1

1. **Explain the relationship between light energy and the atom.**
2. **Describe the properties of electromagnetic waves.**
3. **Explain how light travels.**

SCIENCE TERMS 23-1

photon p. 537
electromagnetic wave p. 538
polarized light p. 538

TEACHING STRATEGY 23-1

Motivation

Have students observe the photograph in Figure 23-1. Point out to students that light comes to us in many forms.
• **What do you think of when you think of the word "light"?** (Accept all logical answers.)
• **What are the other forms of light besides those we can see?** (Accept all logical answers.)
    Point out that light has many forms. Read the caption to Figure 23-1. Have the students observe the drawing in Figure 23-1.

Content Development

Point out that the atom is the source of all forms of light, whether visible or invisible. Explain that when an atom receives energy, the added energy is absorbed by the electrons. The atom becomes excited and forces the electrons to radiate this added energy in the form of tiny energy packets called photons.
• **Can you think of anything else that**

radiates energy? (Accept all logical answers.)
• **What would happen if we heated a metal rod in a hot fire?** (Most students will predict heat will be radiated from the rod.)
• **Would the metal rod glow and give off light?** (Most students will agree it would glow.)
    Point out to students that the atoms in the metal rod received extra energy from the fire. Explain that

---

23–1   Nature of Light

What do a microwave oven and a light bulb have in common? Are you surprised to learn that they both produce light? When you think of light, you probably think only of what you can see—rainbows, sunlight, city lights, fireworks, and television, for example. You probably do not think of radio waves, microwaves, infrared rays, ultraviolet rays, X-rays, and gamma rays. Yet these waves are all forms of light—invisible light.

Light Energy

The atom is the source of all forms of light, whether visible or invisible. According to modern atomic theory, tiny electrons moving about the nucleus of an atom are located in different energy levels within the electron cloud. Electrons located in a certain energy level have a specific amount of energy. However, an electron can absorb more energy. When energy is absorbed by an electron, the electron moves up to a higher energy level.
    The location of an electron in a higher energy level is an unstable condition. So eventually the

Figure 23–1 *Fireworks, amusement park lights, and moonlight are forms of light you are probably most familiar with (left). But they are not the only forms of light. All forms of light—visible and invisible—have their source in the atom. As a neutral atom absorbs energy, it becomes excited. Some of its electrons capture the energy and then release it in tiny packets (right). What are these packets called?* ❶

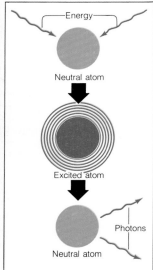

when the atoms became excited, the electrons radiated their added energy in the form of photons. Tell the students we feel this energy as heat and see it as light. Point out that the kind of light wave produced depends on the number of photons.

Content Development

Explain that energy given off by radiation is called radiant energy. Light comes to us in the form of radi-

electron loses its extra energy and falls back to its original energy level. As it does so, the electron releases its absorbed energy in the form of a tiny packet, or bundle, of energy called a **photon** (FOH-tahn). The photon contains the exact amount of extra energy that the electron absorbed.

Light is made up of a stream of photons, or tiny packets of energy. Some photons contain more energy than others. The energy of a photon depends on how much energy an electron in an atom absorbs and then releases. The amount of energy in a photon determines the kind of light wave produced. For example, photons of visible light contain ❶ a moderate amount of energy. X-ray photons, on the other hand, contain a good deal more energy. They are high-energy photons. Radio waves do not contain as much energy as visible light. Radio waves are made up of low-energy photons.

Electromagnetic Waves

Now you know two differences between light waves. Some light waves are visible while others are not, and the photons of different forms of light waves contain different amounts of energy. However, all light waves share several characteristics.

The speed of light is the same for all forms of light. The speed of light in a vacuum is 300,000 kilometers per second, 300,000 km/sec. The speed of all forms of light is slower in air, water, glass, and other materials.

All light waves are transverse waves. You will recall that in a transverse wave, the direction of wave energy is at right angles to the movement of ❷ the molecules of the medium. With a light wave, however, there are no moving molecules of the medium. There are only moving photons of energy.

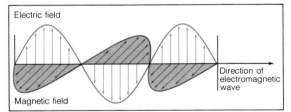

Shadows

A shadow is an area of darkness that is formed when an object blocks light from striking some surface. Often a shadow has two parts. When the light is completely blocked, the very dark umbra forms. The area outside the umbra receives some light and appears gray. This area is the penumbra.

With the sun or another light source behind you, observe your shadow or that of some other object. Identify the umbra and penumbra. Does the shadow change with the type of light source?

Figure 23–2 *In a transverse wave, the direction of the wave energy is at right angles to the electric and magnetic fields.*

537

Shadows
Skills: Applying, observing, relating, hypothesizing, manipulative
Level: Average
Type: Hands-on
Materials: sun or light source

In this activity, students easily see that light travels in a straight line and that when an object is placed in front of a light source, a shadow forms. Students should also be able to see the umbra and penumbra and note that the shadow should not change with different light sources, although the umbra and penumbra may appear different with stronger light sources.

ANNOTATION KEY

❶ Photons (Applying definitions)
❶ Thinking Skill: Making comparisons
❷ Thinking Skill: Applying concepts

---

ant energy. The sun, a light bulb, and a radio transmitter all give off some form of radiant energy. Point out that some light waves are visible while others are not. Explain that the photons in the light waves of visible light have only a moderate amount of energy, while the photons of X-ray light waves have a greater energy level. Tell students that radiant energy comes in waves. All the waves of radiant energy are called electromagnetic waves.

Skills Development
Skill: Developing a model
Divide the class into groups of three or four. Give each group a long rope. Have students sit on the floor to make the wave. One student should hold the rope without turning or moving it. Have a second student move the end of the rope back and forth to produce a "wave" in the rope.
• **What is the direction of the wave?** (Along the length of the rope)

• **What is the direction of the bumps in the wave?** (At right angles to the rope or direction of the wave)
• **How would you make the wave move faster?** (Move the end of the rope faster.)
• **How would you make the wave bumps larger?** (Move the ends of the rope farther.)

ANNOTATION KEY

❶ Sunglass lenses (Relating facts)
❷ Photon energy increases. (Interpreting illustrations)
❶ Thinking Skill: Making comparisons
❷ Thinking Skill: Applying technology
❸ Thinking Skill: Making generalizations
❹ Thinking Skill: Relating concepts

23-1 (continued)

Motivation

Show the class an electric light bulb (plugged in to light) and a small radio (turned on). Discuss the similarities and differences using questions such as the following.

• **How is a light bulb related to a radio?** (Answers will vary. Lead students to suggest that both light and radio signals are electromagnetic waves, and that electromagnetic waves can travel in a vacuum.)

• **How are the heat from a light bulb and the sound from a radio different?** (Sound does not travel in a vacuum. Light and heat will travel in a vacuum. To travel, sound needs a medium such as a gas, liquid, or solid.)

Content Development

Explain that in an electromagnetic wave, the moving photons generate both an electric and a magnetic field.

Figure 23-3 *Light waves that vibrate in all directions can be passed through a special filter to produce light waves that vibrate along a single plane only. This light is called polarized light. What is a common use of polarizing filters?* ❶

538

These fields are at right angles to each other and to the direction of wave energy. This is why they are considered transverse waves.

Section Review 23-1

1. Visible light, radio waves, microwaves, infrared rays, ultraviolet rays, X-rays, gamma rays

2. Tiny packet of energy produced when an electron drops from a higher energy level to a lower energy level

The moving photons of energy generate electric and magnetic fields. This is the reason light waves are called **electromagnetic waves.** An electromagnetic wave is both electric and magnetic in nature. The electric and magnetic fields are at right angles to each other and to the direction of wave energy. See Figure 23-2 on page 537.

Electromagnetic waves are different from other waves because they can travel in a vacuum. Electro-❶ magnetic waves do not need a medium through which to travel. Light can be transmitted with or without a medium. Sound needs a medium.

Polarized Light

Light that you can see contains transverse waves that are vibrating in many directions. If the light is passed through a special filter, light in which the waves vibrate in a certain uniform pattern is produced. This light is called **polarized light.** Polarized light is light whose waves vibrate along a single plane.

Polarizing filters contain a large number of parallel slits. Only those waves vibrating in the same plane as the slits pass through the filter. All other waves are reflected or absorbed. One of the most ❷ common uses of polarizing filters is in sunglasses. Polarized sunglasses cut down on glare.

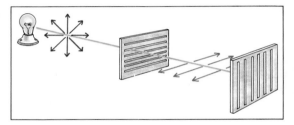

SECTION REVIEW

1. What are the various forms of light?
2. What is a photon?
3. What characteristics do all forms of light share?
4. Do you think light travels faster in air or in water? Explain your answer.

3. Speed, transverse waves, electromagnetic waves

4. In air. If light travels fastest in a vacuum, then the speed of light probably decreases as the density of the medium increases. Air is less dense than water, so light should travel faster in air.

23–2 Electromagnetic Spectrum

The different forms of electromagnetic waves are arranged in a particular order according to certain characteristics. These characteristics are photon energy, wave frequency, and wavelength. Since all electromagnetic waves travel at the same speed, speed is not used as a characteristic.

The arrangement of electromagnetic waves in order of their wavelengths, and thus their frequencies, is called the **electromagnetic spectrum.** See Figure 23–4. **The electromagnetic spectrum consists of radio waves, infrared rays, visible light, ultraviolet rays, X-rays, and gamma rays.**

Waves with the longest wavelengths have the lowest frequencies. Waves with the shortest wavelengths have the highest frequencies. Electromagnetic waves in the spectrum range from very short-wavelength, high-frequency gamma rays to very long-wavelength, low-frequency radio waves. Visible light is the small portion of the spectrum that you can detect with your eyes. The rest of the electromagnetic spectrum is invisible.

Figure 23–4 *The various forms of light that make up the electromagnetic spectrum are arranged according to their increasing frequency and decreasing wavelength. What happens to the photon energy of the waves as their frequency increases?* ❷

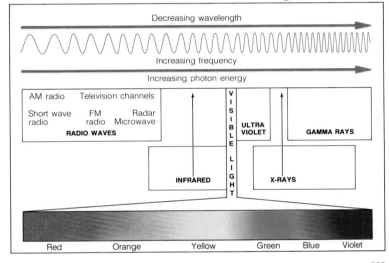

23-2 ELECTROMAGNETIC SPECTRUM

SECTION PREVIEW 23-2

The different kinds of electromagnetic waves are arranged in a specific order. This arrangement is called the electromagnetic spectrum. Electromagnetic waves have different lengths and frequencies. The more energy a photon has, the shorter the wave length and the higher the wave frequency. The electromagnetic spectrum consists of radio waves, infrared rays, visible light, ultraviolet rays, X-rays, and gamma rays.

PERFORMANCE OBJECTIVES 23-2

1. **Identify the parts of the electromagnetic spectrum.**
2. **Describe the uses of electromagnetic waves of different frequencies.**
3. **Explain the relationship between wave length and frequency.**

SCIENCE TERMS 23-2

electromagnetic spectrum p. 539
visible spectrum p. 540
invisible spectrum p. 540
radio wave p. 540
modulation p. 541
microwave p. 541
radar p. 541
infrared ray p. 542
ultraviolet ray p. 542
X-ray p. 543
gamma ray p. 543

TEACHING STRATEGY 23-2

Motivation

Show the class a picture of a large ocean wave with crests and troughs. Discuss the ocean wave using questions similar to the following.
• **What can you tell about the wavelength?** (The wavelength is very long.)
• **What can you tell about the frequency?** (Accept all logical answers.

Lead students to suggest that the frequency would also be long because it takes a long time for the total wave to move.)

Content Development

Explain that electromagnetic waves are classified by the amount of energy in the photons that make up the light waves. Point out that the length of the light wave is shorter when more energy is present in the photons. The

length of the light wave is longer when less energy is present in the photons. Explain that wave frequency is dependent on the length of the wave. Electromagnetic waves with short wavelengths have high frequencies. Electromagnetic waves with long wavelengths have low frequencies.

Tie a long rope to the back of a chair or door knob. Flip the rope to produce waves in the rope. Tell students that light moves in waves.

- **What is one wavelength?** (Accept all logical answers. Lead students to suggest the length of the wave is the distance between two of the tops or two of the bottoms of the waves.)
- **How do you think they measure wavelength?** (Accept all logical answers.)
- **How do you think they measure the frequency of a wave?** (Accept all logical answers.)

Draw a sketch of the rope wave on the chalkboard. Point out that the top of a wave is called a crest and the bottom of the wave is called a trough. Explain that the wavelength is the distance between two identical places on the wave pattern such as crest to crest, trough to trough, or any other identical place on the wave.

23-2 (continued)

Motivation

Pass a white light through a prism to obtain a spectrum. Tell students that when white light passes through a prism, the higher frequencies are refracted more than the lower ones. Discuss the spectrum with students.

- **How does this prove that white light has different frequencies?** (Accept all answers.)
- **Could scientists use this when working with light experiments?** (Accept all answers.) **How?** (Accept all logical answers. Lead students to suggest that by knowing that light will separate into frequencies and wavelengths, scientists can develop new theories, products, and knowledge.)

Content Development

Point out that the visible spectrum is the portion of the electromagnetic spectrum to which the eyes are sensitive. Explain that even though we see light as "white," it actually is a combination of colors. Red, at one end of the spectrum, has the lowest frequency; and violet, at the other

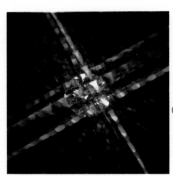

Figure 23–5 The visible spectrum is the portion of the electromagnetic spectrum to which your eyes are sensitive. As white light passes through this diamond it is broken up into the colors of the visible spectrum. What are these colors? ❶

The Visible Spectrum

As you look at the diagram of the electromagnetic spectrum in Figure 23–4 on page 539, notice that only a very small portion of the spectrum is visible light. The **visible spectrum** is the portion of the electromagnetic spectrum to which your eyes are sensitive. Although you may think of most light as being white light, you can see that the visible spectrum is broken down into different colors. White light is made up of many different colors of light.

The visible spectrum consists of light waves with frequencies between 430 trillion hertz and 760 trillion hertz. This range of frequencies includes all the colors of white light—red, orange, yellow, green, blue, and violet. Each color has a certain frequency.

Red has the lowest visible frequency at 430 trillion hertz. Red photons also have the lowest energy. Violet light has the highest visible frequency at 760 trillion hertz. Violet photons have the highest energy. Moving along the spectrum from red to violet, the frequency of the waves and the energy of the photons increase. What happens to the wavelength? Which color has the longest wavelength? The shortest? ❷

The Invisible Spectrum

Frequencies less than 430 trillion hertz or greater than 760 trillion hertz are invisible to the eye. Waves with frequencies that fall into this range make up the **invisible spectrum.**

RADIO WAVES   Electromagnetic waves with frequencies between 10,000 hertz and 1 trillion hertz are called **radio waves.** Radio waves have the lowest frequencies and the longest wavelengths in the electromagnetic spectrum. The wavelengths vary from 30 kilometers to less than 1 millimeter.

The main use of radio waves is communication, usually in the form of radio and television broadcasts. Such broadcasts are carried from a transmitting station to a receiving station by two methods: AM radio waves and FM radio waves.

When radio waves are transmitted, one of two characteristics of the waves can be varied—either

540

end of the spectrum, has the highest frequency.

- **What do you think happens to the wavelength in the various colors?** (Students should say they vary from a longer wave length in red to a shorter wave length in violet.)

Content Development

Explain that radio waves cannot be seen or heard but that a "radio" was developed to detect the waves and

change them to sound. Radio waves are the part of the electromagnetic spectrum called the invisible spectrum. Radio waves are normally described by their frequencies rather than their wavelengths. Radio waves are measured in kilohertz or megahertz. One kilohertz is one thousand waves per second. One megahertz is one million waves per second.

Remind students that radio waves are part of the invisible spectrum.

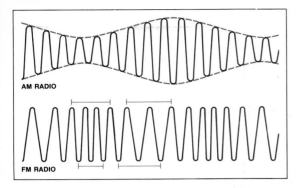

AM RADIO

FM RADIO

Figure 23–6 *AM radio waves are amplitude-modulated waves. FM radio waves are frequency-modulated waves. Because AM waves have longer wavelengths, they can bend around hills and buildings. The shorter wavelength FM waves are blocked by large objects. If you were traveling by car through the Rocky Mountains, which type of wave would be easier to receive on your radio?* ❸

the amplitude of the wave or the frequency. The variation in either amplitude or frequency of a wave is called **modulation** (mahj-uh-LAY-shuhn). AM means amplitude modulation and FM means frequency modulation.

Information is carried by AM radio waves as a pattern of changes in amplitude. See Figure 23–6. AM radio waves have frequencies between 500,000 hertz and 2 million hertz. Many radio stations transmit AM waves. The sound portions of most television broadcasts are carried as AM waves.

Information is carried by FM radio waves as a pattern of changes in frequency. See Figure 23–6. All FM radio waves have frequencies between 87 million hertz and 108 million hertz. Many radio stations transmit FM waves. The picture portions of most television broadcasts are carried as FM waves.

Because AM radio waves have longer wavelengths, they can bend around hills and buildings. The shorter-wavelength FM radio waves are blocked by large objects.

Radio waves with frequencies between one billion hertz and one trillion hertz are called **microwaves.** Microwaves are the highest-frequency radio waves. The wavelengths of microwaves are only a few centimeters. Microwaves are used for communication and for cooking.

Short-wavelength microwaves are used in **radar.** Radar, which stands for *ra*dio *d*etecting *a*nd *r*anging, ❹ is used in locating objects, calculating distances to objects, and monitoring automobile speed.

❸ **Figure 23–7** *Because microwaves are absorbed by most foods, they are used in cooking. Microwaves cause the molecules of the food substance to vibrate. This vibration increases the kinetic energy of the molecules, and so the temperature of the food increases. How do you think the speed of microwave cooking compares with other conventional methods?* ❹

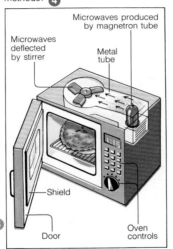

Microwaves produced by magnetron tube

Microwaves deflected by stirrer

Metal tube

Shield

Door

Oven controls

541

TIE-IN/ASTRONOMY

On Wednesday, January 7, 1987, Roger Lynds of the Kitt Peak National Observatory and Vahe Petrosian, Stanford University astronomy chairman, announced the discovery of three concave arcs. The arcs are estimated to be 1.9 million trillion miles long and glow with the luminosity of "hundreds of billions of suns." They are the largest structures found in the sky to date.

ANNOTATION KEY

❶ Red, orange, yellow, green, blue, violet (Identifying patterns)
❷ Wavelength decreases; red; violet (Relating facts)
❸ AM radio waves (Inferring)
❹ It is faster. (Applying technology)
① Thinking Skill: Interpreting diagrams
② Thinking Skill: Identifying patterns
③ Thinking Skill: Applying concepts
④ Thinking Skill: Applying technology

Skills Development

Skill: Applying concepts

If AM stations broadcast with radio frequencies from 535 kilohertz to 1605 kilohertz and FM stations broadcast with radio frequencies from 88 megahertz to 108 megahertz, what kind of station are the following radio stations?

• **Station KFMW at 108 is** (FM with 108 MHz)
• **Station ERTZ at 62 is** (FM with 62 MHz)
• **Station QPRG at 1250 is** (AM with 1250 KHz)
• **Station HPUI at 650 is** (AM with 650 KHz)
• **Station TYDX at 1490 is** (AM with 1490 KHz)
• **What are your local radio stations and what are their kilohertz or megahertz frequencies?** (Answers will vary.)

Radio waves are the longest waves of the invisible spectrum and have the lowest frequency. Explain that radio waves are longer than visible waves.

Tell students that the softness or loudness of a radio does not have anything to do with the frequency of the wave. But when radio waves are transmitted, either the amplitude or the frequency of the wave can be varied. Explain that AM is known as Amplitude Modulation and FM is known as Frequency Modulation. AM and FM radio waves are different kinds of waves. Explain that AM radio waves have longer wave lengths than FM radio waves. When you adjust your radio or television for sound, you are deciding what wavelength or wave frequency your radio or television receiver is to pick up.

23-2 (continued)

Motivation

Show students an electric hot plate or toaster with heating coils. Turn it on and allow the coils to become red.

• **What do you observe?** (Most students will say the red glow of the coils.)

Explain that the red coils are the "red" of the visible spectrum.

• **What else can you observe?** (Accept all logical answers.)

Reinforcement

Draw a sketch of a wave on the chalkboard. Review and point out the crest, trough, and wavelength.

Skills Development

Skill: Developing a model

Distribute a sheet of graph paper and metric ruler to each student. Tell students they are to draw a model of a wave. Have students draw a center line about 3 cm from the top of the graph paper. Then have them draw a single wave that has a) a wavelength of 10 cm, b) a crest 1 cm above the center line, and c) a trough 1 cm below the center line. Have students draw the following waves with 1 cm crests and troughs.

  Wave A = 2 waves per 10 cm
  Wave B = 5 waves per 10 cm
  Wave C = 10 waves per 10 cm
  Wave D = 20 waves per 10 cm
  Wave E = 40 waves per 10 cm
  Wave F = 100 waves per 10 cm

Tell the class to imagine that the 10 cm represents one second of time. Discuss the wave models using questions similar to the following.

• **What is the frequency of Wave A?** (Two waves per second, or 2 Hz)

• **What is the frequency of Wave B?** (Five waves per second, or 5 Hz)

• **What is the frequency of Wave C?** (Ten waves per second, or 10 Hz)

• **What is the frequency of Wave D?** (Twenty waves per second, or 20 Hz)

• **What is the frequency of Wave E?** (Forty waves per second, or 40 Hz)

• **What is the frequency of Wave F?** (One hundred waves per second, or 100 Hz)

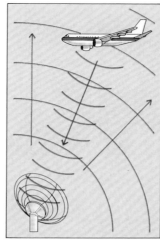

Figure 23–8 *In a radar device, a radio transmitter sends out high-frequency waves that bounce off objects and return as "echoes" picked up by a receiver.*

INFRARED RAYS Electromagnetic waves with frequencies slightly lower than visible red light are called **infrared rays.** Infrared rays cannot be seen, but they can be felt as heat. You can feel infrared rays as heat from the sun, a light bulb, or a stove.

All objects give off infrared rays. The amount of infrared given off by an object depends on the temperature of the object. Warmer objects give off more infrared rays than colder objects do. Infrared rays are used in cooking and in medicine.

ULTRAVIOLET RAYS Electromagnetic waves with frequencies just higher than visible violet light are called **ultraviolet rays.** The energy of ultraviolet photons is great enough to kill living cells. So ultraviolet lamps are often used in hospitals to kill germs and in processing plants to destroy bacteria and preserve food.

Ultraviolet rays are present in sunlight. When your body absorbs sunlight, ultraviolet rays cause

Figure 23–9 *Infrared light cannot be seen, but it can be detected as heat and used to produce a thermogram, or heat picture (left). Hotter areas appear as white, while cooler areas appear as blue and black. Note the dog's cold nose! When rocks containing fluorescent minerals are exposed to invisible ultraviolet light, they glow (center). X-rays are used to produce pictures of bones (right), such as these that show the growth of a hand from 2 years to 60 years.*

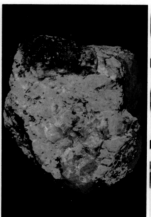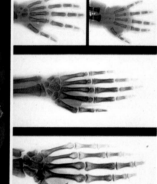

542

• **What happens to the wavelength as the frequency increases?** (The wavelength gets shorter.)

Content Development

Explain that in the electromagnetic spectrum, invisible waves are on both sides of the visible waves. The wavelengths of the invisible spectrum are both longer and shorter than the wavelengths in the visible spectrum. Explain that radio waves and infrared

your skin cells to produce vitamin D. Vitamin D is needed to make healthy bones and teeth. Ultraviolet rays can also make your skin tan. However, too much ultraviolet light can burn your skin.

X-RAYS Electromagnetic waves with frequencies just above ultraviolet are called **X-rays.** The energy of X-ray photons is great enough to pass easily through many materials, including your skin. Denser materials, however, absorb X-rays. Bone absorbs X-rays. When an X-ray picture of a part of your body is taken, the bones absorb the rays and the soft tissue does not. The picture that results shows the bones as white areas and the soft tissue as black. As you might expect, too much exposure to X-rays can be very harmful. Lead absorbs almost all the X-rays that strike it. Can you think of an important use of lead based on this property? ❶

GAMMA RAYS The highest-frequency electromagnetic waves are called **gamma rays.** Gamma rays have the highest-energy photons and shortest wavelengths of all the electromagnetic waves. Certain radioactive materials emit gamma rays. Gamma rays also come from outer space.

Gamma rays have tremendous penetrating ability—even greater than X-rays. The energy of gamma rays is so great that the photons can penetrate up to three meters of concrete! Gamma rays are used in medicine in the treatment of cancer. Excessive exposure to gamma rays, however, can cause severe illness.

SECTION REVIEW

1. What is the electromagnetic spectrum? List the kinds of waves that make it up.
2. In what three ways do forms of light differ?
3. What color has the lowest visible frequency? The highest visible frequency?
4. Moving along the spectrum from radio waves to gamma rays, what happens to frequency, wavelength, and photon energy?
5. Ultraviolet lights, or blacklights, give a violet glow. Are you seeing ultraviolet rays when you see ultraviolet light? Explain your answer.

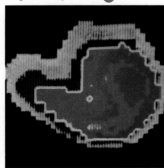

Figure 23–10 *This gamma camera image of the heart was produced when a patient was injected with a substance that gives off gamma rays. The camera detects the gamma rays and with the help of a computer creates an image. What kind of photon energy do gamma rays have?* ❷

543

• **Which wave would represent the infrared rays?** (Wave B)
• **Which wave would represent the visible light rays?** (Wave C)
Remind students that these model drawings are only models to help them understand the relative differences in the frequencies and wavelengths. Actual electromagnetic waves have very high frequencies and different actual wave lengths.

Section Review 23-2
1. The arrangement of electromagnetic waves in order of their wavelengths, and thus their frequencies; radio, infrared, visible light, ultraviolet, X-rays, gamma rays
2. In their frequency, photon energy, and wavelength
3. Red; violet
4. Frequency increases, wavelength decreases, photon energy increases
5. No. Ultraviolet waves are invisible to the human eye. Only the violet end of the spectrum is seen.

rays are longer than the rays of red light in the visible spectrum. The ultraviolet rays, X-rays, and gamma rays are shorter than the rays of violet light in the visible spectrum.

Skills Development
Skill: Applying concepts
Have students take out and observe the wave models they had previously sketched. Tell them to imagine that these wave drawings represent much

higher frequencies, such as those in the electromagnetic spectrum.
• **Which wave would represent the long radio waves with relatively low frequencies?** (Wave A)
• **Which wave would represent the very short gamma rays with the highest frequencies?** (Wave F)
• **Which wave would represent the X-rays?** (Wave E)
• **Which wave would represent the ultraviolet rays?** (Wave D)

23-3 PARTICLE, WAVE, OR BOTH?

SECTION PREVIEW 23-3

Although the wave theory of light seems to explain most of the properties and behavior of light, there are some unanswered problems. In radiations with low energy levels (long wavelengths), the wave theory seems to answer most of the questions. In radiations with high energy levels (short wavelengths), the questions can be answered only by the particle theory.

In the case of the photoelectric effect, the particle theory is the only answer. The photoelectric effect is the production of electrons by photons of light. Scientists directed violet light onto the surface of certain metals and noticed that energy was absorbed by the electrons in the atom of the metal. Enough electrons were knocked off the metal to form an electric current. After shining red light on the same metal, nothing happened. Yet, going to the center of the spectrum, yellow has both wave and particle properties.

PERFORMANCE OBJECTIVES 23-3

1. **Distinguish between the particle and wave properties of light.**
2. **Describe the frequencies in the electromagnetic spectrum that behave as particles, waves, or both particles and waves.**
3. **Explain the photoelectric effect.**

SCIENCE TERMS 23-3
photoelectric effect p. 544

Figure 23-11 *The energy of individual photons of violet light can produce an electric current. The energy of individual photons of red light cannot (left). The production of electrons by photons of light is called the photoelectric effect. Solar cells, such as these large arrays on a satellite in orbit around the earth, are one application of the photoelectric effect. What theory of light explains this effect?* ❶

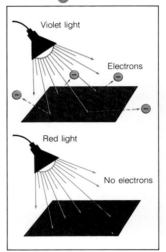

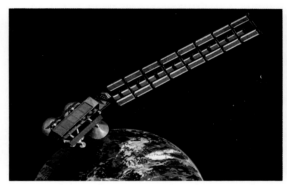

23-3 Particle, Wave, or Both?

Throughout this chapter, you have read about light as a wave and about the properties of light waves. The wave model of light, which has been the prevailing theory since the early 1800s, successfully explains most of the properties and behavior of light. However, in the early 1900s, scientists discovered something rather unusual about light, something that made them modify their wave theory.

Scientists shone violet light onto the surface of certain metals. The energy carried by photons of violet light was absorbed by electrons in the atoms of the metal plate. This photon energy knocked electrons out of the atoms in the metal plate. In fact, enough electrons were knocked off the metal plate to cause an electric current to flow. Since the experiment involved electrons and photons, this result came to be known as the **photoelectric effect. The photoelectric effect is the production of electrons by photons of light.**

Next, the scientists repeated the experiment with red light. Nothing happened! No matter how long the red light was shone or how bright it was, no electrons were ever knocked out of the metal's atoms. The dimmest violet light produced electrons, but the strongest red light did not!

As you know, photons of red light have less energy than photons of violet light. According to the wave theory, however, if red light strikes a metal plate as a continuous wave, then eventually the electrons should "soak up" enough energy so that they

---

Figure 23–12 *When two beams of light from two slide projectors intersect, they pass through each other without colliding. The images produced on each screen are clear. What theory of light explains this behavior?* ❷

can escape from their atoms. That does not happen. But suppose, in this case, light acts more like a stream of particles than like a wave. Then each individual red light photon, acting on its own, can never knock an electron from an atom. No single red light photon contains enough energy to do the job, no ❶ matter how long the light is on or how bright it is. On the other hand, violet light photons carry more energy than red light photons. So a single violet light photon can knock an electron right out of its atom. In the photoelectric effect, it certainly appears as if light acts more like individual particles than like a continuous wave!

The photoelectric effect can only be explained by a particle theory of light. The property of light waves known as interference can only be explained by a wave theory of light. Confused? Don't be. Scientists today describe light as both particlelike and wavelike. Scientists have not yet found a final solution to the problem of whether light is a particle or ❷ a wave. But this problem provides a good opportunity for you to remember that science is a way of explaining observations; it is not absolute knowledge.

SECTION REVIEW

1. What convinced scientists that light is a particle?
2. Why is light said to have a dual nature?
3. Which of the following electromagnetic waves would you expect to produce a photoelectric effect: radio waves, infrared waves, ultraviolet rays, X-rays, gamma rays?

Sharpen Your Skills

Light—Particle or Wave?

1. CAUTION: *Do this step outdoors.* Turn on two water hoses. Aim the stream of water from one hose across the path of the stream of water from the other hose. Observe carefully what happens to the stream of water particles in the second hose.

2. Darken a room and project a slide from a slide projector on the wall. Shine a flashlight beam across the projector beam in much the same way you did with the stream of water in step 1. Observe any effect on the projected picture.

Do the two streams of water particles act in the same way the two beams do? Explain your answer. Does this activity support a wave or particle theory of light? Explain your answer.

545

23-4 REFLECTION OF LIGHT

SECTION PREVIEW 23-4

If rays of light are always parallel and the angle of incidence equals the angle of reflection, then why do surfaces reflect light differently? On smooth surfaces, the image formed is clearly defined and looks exactly like the original. This type of reflection is called a regular reflection.

On surfaces that are not smooth, the image formed is "fuzzy" and the outline changes. This type of reflection is called a diffused reflection. This difference leads us to believe the type of surface that light strikes does determine the kind of reflection that is formed.

PERFORMANCE OBJECTIVES 23-4

1. **Compare regular and diffuse reflections.**
2. **Explain regular reflection in terms of the angles of incidence and reflection.**
3. **Explain the importance of diffuse reflections.**

SCIENCE TERMS 23-4

regular reflection p. 546
diffuse reflection p. 547

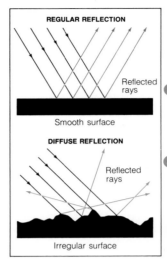

Figure 23–13 *Reflection from a smooth surface, or regular reflection, does not produce much scattering of light rays. Reflection from an irregular surface produces considerable scattering of light rays. The result is a diffuse reflection.*

Figure 23–14 *The castle you see is actually an image of the real thing, produced by light rays reflected from the surface of the water. What is reflection?* ❶

546

23–4 Reflection of Light

What happens to light when it strikes the surface of an object? Some of the light is absorbed by the object. The remaining light bounces off the surface of the object. Light that bounces off the surface of an object is said to be reflected. **The type of surface light strikes determines the kind of reflection that is formed.** No matter what type of surface light strikes, however, the angle formed by the incident ray and the normal equals the angle formed by the reflected ray and the normal. This is the law of reflection.

Kinds of Reflection

Why can you see your reflection in a mirror but not in a wall? In both cases light is reflected off a surface. In both cases, the angle of incidence equals the angle of reflection. So why is there a difference?

A mirror has a very smooth surface. The incident rays are always parallel to each other. Because the mirror has a smooth surface, the reflected rays will also always be parallel to each other. There is very little scattering of reflected light. The image formed is clearly defined and looks exactly like the object. This type of reflection is called a **regular reflection.**

The surface of a wall is not very smooth. A surface that is not smooth is often described as irregular. The incident rays are still parallel to each other. But because of the irregular surface, the reflected

---

TEACHING STRATEGY 23-4

Motivation

Place a wide-toothed comb in a beam of light falling on a piece of white cardboard. Tilt the cardboard so the beams passing between the teeth are several centimeters long.

- **How is the light traveling through the comb?** (Students should say in a straight line and through the spaces between the teeth.)

Point out that the light is traveling in straight parallel lines.

Place a mirror diagonally in the path of the light beams coming between the comb teeth to reflect the light to the ceiling and/or wall.

- **What happened to the light beam?**

(Most students will say the mirror "bent", "changed", "bounced", or "reflected" the beam of light.)

Content Development

Point out that when light strikes a surface the light rays are straight and parallel. Explain that the angle at which the rays hit the surface is called the "angle of incidence." The angle at which the rays leave the surface is called the "angle of reflection."

Skills Development

Skill: Interpreting diagrams

Have students observe Figure 23-13. Read the caption.

- **What do you observe about the light rays that reflect off a smooth surface?** (The rays are parallel. They bounce off at the same angle as they go in.)
- **What kind of smooth surfaces reflect light like this?** (Students are likely to suggest mirrors. Lead them to

rays are scattered in all directions. See Figure 23–13. The image formed is not clearly defined. Instead, it looks a bit "fuzzy," and the outlines of the image keep changing. Reflected light that is scattered in many different directions due to an irregular surface is called a **diffuse** (dih-FYOOS) **reflection.** ❸

Although diffuse reflections are not desirable for seeing your image, they are rather important. If the sun's rays were not scattered by reflecting off uneven surfaces and dust particles in the air, you would see only those objects that are in direct sunlight. In addition, the glare of the sunlight would be so strong that you would have difficulty seeing.

SECTION REVIEW

1. What is a regular reflection? How is it formed?
2. What is a diffuse reflection? How is it formed?
3. One example of a simple mirror is a still pool of water. Explain the difference in reflections from a still pool and a rippled pool.

CAREER   *Photographer*

HELP WANTED: PHOTOGRAPHER to work inside and outside the studio. Experience with light filters and a variety of lighting conditions preferred. Must be able to develop and print all materials. High school diploma required. Technical training or college preferred.

"Turn toward me just a bit and . . . hold it!" The shutter snaps and the **photographer** directs the model for another shot.

A photographer uses a variety of film, color filters, and lenses to adjust the camera to light conditions and to produce various images of the subject or model. Using light, color, and shadow, a photographer captures on film the mood or personality of the subject.

Photography plays an important role in fashion, science, journalism, and engineering. Some photographers work in studios where models or clients go to be photographed. Most photographers also must be ready to travel to other places to work. For science photographers this may mean frequent trips to laboratories. Photojournalists must often quickly catch action

shots at news events. Photography combines artistic ability with technical skill. Some knowledge of science, engineering, mathematics, or chemistry usually is necessary to prepare for a career in scientific, industrial, or journalistic photography. So a college education may be useful to a photographer.

If you would like to find out more about a career as a photographer, contact Professional Photographers of America, Inc., 1090 Executive Way, Des Plaines, IL 60018.

suggest that other flat shiny surfaces such as water, glass, and polished stone also reflect light in this manner.)
• **What kind of light rays are shown shining onto the irregular rough surface?** (Parallel light rays)
• **What happens to the rays when they reflect off an irregular surface?** (They bounce off in all directions.)
• **Why do they bounce off in all directions?** (The angles of the surface change.)

Content Development

Explain that on a smooth surface the reflected image is clear and the angle of incidence is equal to the angle of reflection. This type of reflection is called regular reflection. Explain that on rough surfaces the incident rays are still parallel, but the reflected rays are scattered in all directions. This type of reflection is called diffuse reflection.

Section Review 23-4
1. Clearly defined image that looks exactly like the object; smooth surface
2. Image that is not clearly defined ("fuzzy") and whose outlines keep changing; irregular surface
3. The regular surface of a still pool reflects a regular image. In a rippled pool, the waves of water also reflect regular images, but the overall image is distorted by the alternating height of each wave's trough and crest. The rippled pool overall is an irregular surface and scattering of reflected rays occurs.

23-5 REFRACTION OF LIGHT

SECTION PREVIEW 23-5

The bending of light due to a change in its speed is called refraction. Refraction occurs because light travels at different speeds through different mediums or different densities of the same medium. The amount by which a material refracts light is measured by its index of refraction.

The colors of light in the visible spectrum each have a different wavelength and frequency. Each wavelength or frequency of light is refracted by a different amount.

PERFORMANCE OBJECTIVES 23-5

1. Describe the process of refraction.
2. Explain how a prism refracts light to form a rainbow.
3. Explain the index of refraction.

SCIENCE TERMS 23-5

index of refraction p. 548
prism p. 549

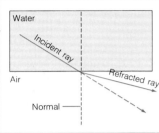

Figure 23–15 *As light passes from a less dense medium to a more dense medium, its speed decreases and it is refracted toward the normal (top). As light passes from a more dense medium to a less dense medium, its speed increases and it is refracted away from the normal (bottom). What do you think happens when light enters either medium parallel to the normal?* ❶

Figure 23–16 *The index of refraction is a comparison of the speed of light in air with the speed of light in a certain material. In which substance does light travel the slowest?* ❷

548

23–5 Refraction of Light

Light does not bend as it travels through a medium. Light travels in straight lines. What happens then when light passes from one medium to another? When light passes at an angle from one medium to another—air to water, glass to air, for example—it bends. The bending of light occurs because the speed of light changes. **The bending of light due to a change in its speed is called refraction.**

Refraction occurs because light moves at different speeds in different mediums. As it passes from one medium to another, it either speeds up or slows down. When light passes from a less dense medium to a more dense medium, it slows down. This is the case when light passes from air to water. When light passes from a more dense medium to a less dense medium, it speeds up. This is the case when light passes from glass to air. See Figure 23–15.

As you just read, light moves at different speeds in different mediums. Because its speed changes, light is refracted. The amount by which a material refracts light is measured by its **index of refraction.** The index of refraction is the comparison of the speed of light in air with the speed of light in a certain material. Since the speed of light in air is always greater than in any other material, the index of refraction of a certain material is always greater than one. The larger the index of refraction, the more the light rays are bent. Figure 23–16 gives the index of refraction for some substances.

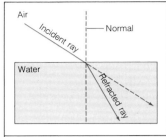

INDEX OF REFRACTION OF SOME COMMON MATERIALS

Material	Index of Refraction	Material	Index of Refraction
Air	1.00	Glass (ordinary)	1.52
Ice	1.31	Salt crystals	1.54
Water	1.33	Calcite	1.66
Methanol	1.33	Diamond	2.42

Content Development

Point out that the rod did not bend. Explain that this optical illusion was caused by the bending, or refracting, of light rays as they entered and left the air, water, and oil.

- **What do you predict might happen if we did the same thing using other clear liquids?** (Accept all answers.)

Explain that light travels faster in air than in water. Refraction occurs because light moves at different

speeds in different mediums. Because its speed changes, the light waves are refracted.

Skills Development

Skill: Interpreting diagrams

Have students observe the top diagram in Figure 23-15. Tell them to notice the reference line marked "normal." Have students use a protractor to measure the angle between the ingoing ray and the normal. Then have

Bending and Separating

You learned that white light is made up of all the visible colors. Each color corresponds to a particular frequency. If white light passes from air to glass, its speed changes and it is refracted. Each frequency of light is refracted by a different amount. Red, with the lowest frequency, is refracted the least. Violet, with the highest frequency, is refracted the most. Because each color is refracted a different amount, each color bends at a different angle. The result is a separation of white light into the six colors of the spectrum, or rainbow. See Figure 23–17.

The piece of glass that forms a spectrum is called a **prism** (PRIHZ-uhm). Notice that the light bends as it enters the prism and as it leaves it. The bending occurs as the light leaves the prism because the speed of light changes again as the light passes ❹ from glass back to air. At this point, which color is refracted the most? The least? ❸

Figure 23–17 *As white light passes through a prism, it is refracted. Since each frequency is bent a different amount, the white light breaks up into the colors of the spectrum (left and top right). Water droplets in the air act as tiny prisms, forming the visible spectrum better known as a rainbow (bottom right).*

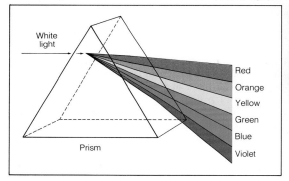

SECTION REVIEW

1. What is refraction?
2. What is the index of refraction?
3. Which color is refracted the most? The least?
4. Are longer or shorter wavelengths refracted at a greater angle?

them measure the angle between the normal and the refracted ray.
• **What did you find out about light moving from air to water?** (The refracted angle is less than the incoming angle.)
• **What does this mean?** (The light ray was refracted toward the normal.)
• **What happended to the speed of the light when it went from air to water?** (The light slowed down.)

Have students measure the same angles in the bottom diagram of Figure 23-15.
• **What did you find out about light moving from water to air?** (The refracted angle is more than the incoming angle.)
• **What does this mean?** (The light ray was refracted away from the normal.)
• **What happened to the speed of the light when it went from water to air?**

(The light sped up.)
Explain that the angle between the normal and the light ray entering a medium is called the "angle of incidence." Have students examine the angle that the light appears to refract. Point out that the angle between the normal and the refracted ray is called the "angle of refraction."

Section Review 23-5
1. Bending of light waves due to a change in the speed of light
2. The amount by which a material refracts light
3. Violet; red
4. Shorter wavelengths

23-6 COLOR

SECTION PREVIEW 23-6

When light strikes any form of matter, three things can happen: The light can be transmitted, absorbed, or reflected. Matter that allows light to pass through is called transparent. Transparent objects transmit the color you see, and all other colors are absorbed. An object that does not allow any light to pass through is called opaque. The color of an opaque object is the color it reflects. The waves of color that are not reflected are absorbed.

The frequency of a light wave determines its color. The colors of visible light are various mixtures of three frequencies of light, or three primary colors. The primary colors of light are red, blue, and green. The ability of colored light to combine and form new colors depends on the frequencies of the light.

Opaque pigments of any sort appear to have color because of the frequencies of light that are reflected from their surface. All other frequencies are absorbed.

PERFORMANCE OBJECTIVES 23-6

1. **Account for the color of opaque and transparent objects.**
2. **Distinguish between colors of light and colors of pigments.**
3. **Predict which colors will be transmitted, reflected, and/or absorbed by or from various substances.**

Figure 23–18 *A transparent substance transmits light readily, so objects seen through it are very clear (top). A translucent substance does not transmit light readily, so objects seen through it are unclear and lack detail (bottom). Which substance produces the most scattering of light?* ❶

23–6 Color

Here is something for you to try: Describe the clothes you are wearing today as precisely as you can *without* using colors. Pretty difficult, isn't it? The world you live in is full of colors. Just look around you and enjoy the colorful scenery!

When Light Strikes

In order to understand why objects have color, you must know what happens when light strikes the surface of an object. **When light strikes any form of matter, the light can be transmitted, absorbed, or** ❶ **reflected.**

When light is transmitted, it passes through the substance it strikes. If the light is transmitted readily, the substance is said to be **transparent.** Objects seen through transparent substances are very clear. Glass, water, and air are transparent. With transparent substances, there is no scattering of light.

If light is transmitted through a substance that scatters the light, the image seen is unclear and lacks detail. A substance that transmits light but no ❷ detail of that light is said to be **translucent** (tranz-LOO-suhnt). Waxed paper and frosted glass are translucent substances. A translucent substance produces a fuzzy image when you look through it.

A substance that does not transmit light is said to be **opaque** (oh-PAYK). A block of wood, a sheet of metal, and a piece of black cloth are opaque substances. When light strikes an opaque substance, it is either reflected or absorbed.

The Color of Objects

Why is grass green, an apple red, and a daffodil yellow? The answer to this question depends on the color of the light striking the object and whether the object is opaque or transparent.

OPAQUE OBJECTS An opaque object does not allow any light to pass through it. The light falling on the object is either reflected or absorbed. If the light is absorbed, can it reach your eyes? Obviously not. ❸ Only the light that is reflected reaches you. So the color of an opaque object is the color it reflects.

Think for a moment of a red apple. A red apple reflects red and absorbs all other colors. You see the red apple only by the light it reflects. What color do the green leaves on the stem of the apple reflect? ❷

Now think about an object that is white. White is the presence of all the colors of the visible spectrum. So what is being reflected from a white object? You are right if you said *all* the colors are reflected. No color is absorbed.

If all the colors are absorbed, then no color is reflected back to you. The object appears black. Black is the absence of color. Most objects reflect more than one color, however. These colors combine and produce a great variety of color mixtures.

TRANSPARENT OBJECTS Transparent objects allow light to pass through them. The color that is transmitted is the color that reaches your eyes. The other colors are absorbed. So the color of a transparent object is the color of light it transmits. Red glass absorbs all colors but red, which it transmits. Green glass transmits only green light. Ordinary window glass transmits all colors and is said to be colorless.

Primary and Complementary Light

Each color of the visible spectrum has its own wavelength and frequency. All the colors that you see are a result of how your eyes respond to various mixtures of three frequencies of light.

The three colors that can be mixed to produce light of any color are called the **primary colors.** The primary colors of light are red, blue, and green. Any color of light can be made by mixing red, blue, and green light in different ways.

Look at Figure 23–20 on page 552. You can see that if red light, blue light, and green light are mixed together, the result is white light. When the ❹ three primary colors are mixed together in equal amounts, the result is white light. All other shades of color can be produced by mixing the primary colors in different proportions. The color pink has more red light than blue and green light.

Any two colors that combine to form white light are called **complementary colors.** Yellow and blue are complementary colors, as are cyan and red. What is the third pair of complementary colors? ❹

Figure 23–19 *The color of an opaque object is the color it reflects. In white light, this apple appears red because it reflects red light (top). If only green light shines on it, it appears black (bottom). Why?* ❸

SCIENCE TERMS 23-6

transparent p. 550
translucent p. 550
opaque p. 550
primary color p. 551
complementary color p. 551
primary pigment p. 552

TEACHER DEMONSTRATION

Hold a glass prism in a beam of light. Have students observe the band of colors. Reaffirm that the rainbow of light produced is called the visible part of the electromagnetic spectrum.

ANNOTATION KEY

❶ Translucent substance (Relating facts)
❷ Green (Applying concepts)
❸ It reflects no light. (Relating concepts)
❹ Magenta and green (Inferring)
❶ Thinking Skill: Making generalizations
❷ Thinking Skill: Applying definitions
❸ Thinking Skill: Relating cause and effect
❹ Thinking Skill: Making observations

light to the same spot (the color on the screen should be white).

• **What happened when red and blue light were projected to the same spot?** (The spot was a magenta color.)

• **What happened when green and blue light were projected to the same spot?** (The spot was a bluish color. Tell students that this color is called cyan.)

• **What happened when red and green light were projected to the**

same spot? (The spot was a yellow color.)

Content Development

Point out that when color strikes a surface, three things can happen: the light will go through the substance, the light will be absorbed by the substance, or the light will be reflected by the substance. Explain that one or two of these things can happen at the same time. Point out that if the light

goes through the substance, we say the light was "transmitted." A substance that transmits light freely is called transparent. Many substances transmit and reflect light at the same time — part of the light is reflected, while the remaining light striking the surface is transmitted. Substances that both transmit and reflect light are called translucent. Objects behind translucent substances cannot be seen clearly. Substances that do not transmit light but absorb and reflect light are called opaque.

23-7 HOW YOU SEE

SECTION PREVIEW 23-7

We see color because our eyes send signals to the brain, a different signal for each wavelength of color. Light is seen through a series of steps that involves the various parts of the eye and the brain. The nerve cells in the retina called cones are responsible for your seeing color. Each cone is sensitive to a particular primary color.

When light enters the eye through the pupil, a lens in the eye refracts the light and produces an image on the retina. If the eyeball is too long, the image forms in front of the retina and the person is said to be nearsighted. If the eyeball is too short, the image forms behind the retina and the person is said to be farsighted.

PERFORMANCE OBJECTIVES 23-7

1. **Explain how you see.**
2. **Describe the parts of the eye.**
3. **Explain how each eye part helps us to see.**

SCIENCE TERMS 23-7

pupil p. 552
iris p. 552
retina p. 553
rod p. 553
cone p. 553
nearsightedness p. 553
farsightedness p. 553

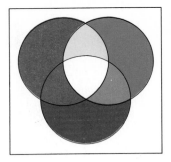

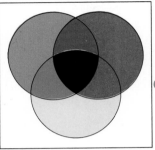

Figure 23-20 *The primary colors of light—red, blue, and green—combine to form white light (top). The primary pigments—yellow, cyan, and magenta—combine to form black (bottom). What is the relationship between the primary pigments and the complements of the primary colors of light?* ❶

Section Objective

To describe how you see

552

Primary and Complementary Pigments

You just learned that blue *light* and yellow *light* produce white *light*. Have you ever mixed blue paint and yellow paint? Was the mixture white? Definitely not. The mixture was green.

Paints are not sources of light. Paints are pigments. And the blending of pigments is different from the way your eyes blend the various colors of light. Pigments have a certain color because they absorb certain frequencies of the visible spectrum and reflect others.

The **primary pigments** are yellow, cyan, and magenta. Figure 23-20 shows how the primary pigments absorb and reflect light. When the three primary pigments are mixed in equal amounts, all colors are absorbed and the result is black. By looking at this figure, you may have noticed something interesting: The primary pigments are the complements of the three primary colors of light.

SECTION REVIEW

1. Compare transparent, translucent, and opaque substances.
2. Why would a green tree appear black under a blue light?
3. What are the primary colors of light? Of pigments? The complementary colors of each?
4. What happens when the primary colors of light are mixed in equal amounts? When the primary pigments are mixed in equal amounts?

23-7 How You See

You have learned what light is and how it is reflected and refracted. You know why an apple is red. And you can distinguish between the colors of light and of pigments. But how do you see light?

You see light through a series of steps that involves the various parts of the eye and the brain. Light enters the eye through an opening called the **pupil.** The colored area surrounding the pupil, called the **iris,** controls the amount of light that

---

23-6 (continued)

Content Development

Explain that the threads in students' clothing are dyed. Tell students that any time a pigment is used, such as in paint, dyes, or other "opaque" pigments, the color they see is due to the frequency of light that is being reflected. Point out that the primary colors of pigment are red, yellow, and blue.

• **What is the color of the classroom walls?** (Answers will vary.)

Explain that the paint absorbs most frequencies of light and reflects only the color of the wall. Point out that when pigments are mixed, the colors are those that the different pigments reflect. Point out that mixing pigments of the primary colors will produce pigments of the secondary colors. Red plus yellow produces orange. Blue plus yellow produces

green. Red plus blue produces purple.

Section Review 23-6

1. Transparent: transmits light without scattering: object seen clearly defined. Translucent: transmits light with scattering, so no details clearly seen; object seen as fuzzy. Opaque: reflects and absorbs light; transmits no light.
2. The green tree reflects only green light and absorbs the blue light. Since

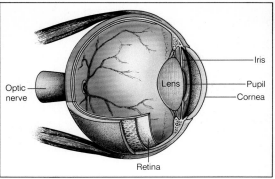

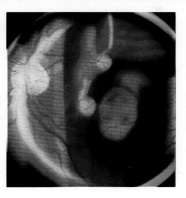

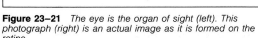

Figure 23–21 *The eye is the organ of sight (left). This photograph (right) is an actual image as it is formed on the retina.*

enters the pupil. A lens in the eye refracts the light and makes it converge on the **retina.** Muscles attached to the lens adjust its shape so that you can see objects both near and far away. The image that falls on the retina is inverted and smaller than the object.

The retina is made of light-sensitive nerves that transfer the image to the brain. The brain interprets the image as right-side up. Some of the nerve cells in the retina are called **rods.** Rods are sensitive to light and dark. Other nerve cells called **cones** are responsible for your seeing colors. Each cone is sensitive to a particular primary color.

Ideally, the image formed by the lens should fall directly on the retina. If the eyeball is too long, the image forms in front of the retina. A person has difficulty seeing objects at a distance but no trouble seeing objects nearby. This condition is called **nearsightedness.**

If the eyeball is too short, the image is focused behind the retina. The person can see distant objects clearly but has difficulty with nearby objects. This problem is called **farsightedness.** You will learn more about these conditions and how to correct them in Chapter 24.

SECTION REVIEW

1. What is the function of the iris? The pupil?
2. Where in the eye is the image formed?
3. What causes color blindness?

Content Development

Have students observe Figure 23-21. Explain that the eye is a light-tight compartment, spherical in shape. Light enters the eye through the opening called the pupil. The pupil is surrounded by the colored section called the iris. The iris is a muscle that opens and closes the pupil. The iris controls the amount of light that enters through the pupil. The retina is on the inside back of the eyeball. The retina is sensitive to light waves. When the light on the retina is too great, the brain automatically relieves the strain by sending nerve impulses to the muscles controlling the iris. The iris partially closes the opening in front of the eye lens so less light gets through to the retina.

Section Review 23-7

1. Controls the amount of light entering the eye. Opening through which light enters the eye
2. On the retina
3. Damage to the cones

---

there is no green light, no light is reflected.
3. Red, blue, green; yellow, cyan, magenta
4. White light results. Black results.

TEACHING STRATEGY 23-7

Motivation

Show the class an eye chart (usually available from the school nurse), a book, or any object.

• **What do you observe?** (Accept all logical answers.)
Have the class cover their eyes with a book or note pad.
• **What do you observe now?** (Accept all logical answers. Lead students to suggest that they may have heard your question but could not see the object because the book was in the way.) Explain that in order to see, light reflected off an object must reach our eyes.

LABORATORY INVESTIGATION REGULAR REFLECTION

BEFORE THE LAB
1. **This investigation can be done by individual students, or teams of two.**
2. **Gather all materials at least one day prior to the investigation. You should have enough supplies to meet your class needs, assuming one to two students per group.**

PRE-LAB DISCUSSION
Have students read the complete laboratory procedure. Discuss the procedure by asking questions similar to the following.
- **What is the purpose of the laboratory investigation?** (To find the relationship between the angle of incidence and the angle of reflection for regular reflection)
- **What do we mean when we say angle of incidence?** (The angle going to the mirror)
- **What do we mean when we say angle of reflection?** (The angle bouncing off the mirror)

Ask students to develop a hypothesis as to the relationship between the angle of reflection and the angle of incidence. Have them compare their original hypotheses to their observations once the investigation has been completed.

SKILL DEVELOPMENT
Students will use the following skills while completing this investigation.
1. Manipulative
2. Safety
3. Observing
4. Comparing
5. Relating
6. Applying
7. Recording
8. Measuring
9. Hypothesizing
10. Inferring

SAFETY TIPS
Alert students to be cautious with the mirrors and pins.

Problem
What is the relationship between the angle of incidence and the angle of reflection for regular reflection?

Materials *(per student)*
plane mirror
wood block
rubber band
4 straight pins
corrugated cardboard, 30 cm × 20 cm
graph paper cut to fit cardboard
metric ruler
protractor

Procedure
1. Tape the graph paper to the cardboard.
2. Draw a horizontal line one-third the distance from the top of the graph paper.
3. Attach the mirror to the wood block with a rubber band.
4. Place the *back edge* of the mirror on the line you drew in step 2.
5. Use the rubber band to attach a straight pin at the center of the mirror. Label this point A. See the accompanying figure.
6. Position a second pin approximately 10 cm in front of pin A. This pin must be in a direct line with pin A and with the image it produces in the mirror. Push the pin into the cardboard and label this point B.
7. Position another straight pin about 5 cm to the left of point B. Push the pin into the cardboard and label this point P.
8. Position a fourth pin so that it lines up with the image of pin A and the image of pin P. Push this pin into the cardboard and label the point R.
9. Remove all the pins and the mirror from the cardboard.
10. Draw a line from point B through point A to the horizontal line you drew in step 2.
11. Draw another line from point P to point C.
12. Draw a third line from point R to point C.
13. Use a protractor to measure the angle PCB and the angle RCB. Record these measurements.

Label the intersection of these two lines point C.

Observations
1. What is the size in degrees of angle PCB?
2. What is the size in degrees of angle RCB?

Conclusions
1. What is line BC called?
2. What is line PC called? Angle PCB?
3. Which line is the reflected ray? Which angle is the angle of reflection?
4. The law of reflection states that the angle of incidence is equal to the angle of reflection. Do your data verify this law? Explain your answer.
5. How do you account for any error in your results?

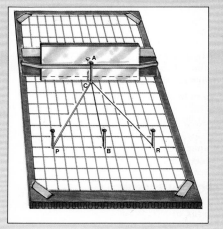

TEACHING STRATEGY FOR LAB PROCEDURE
1. Have students practice lining up and placing the pins in the proper places several times before measuring the angles.
2. Have the teams follow the directions carefully as they work in the laboratory.
3. Discuss how the investigation relates to the chapter ideas by asking open questions similar to the following.
- **What does the investigation illustrate about the angle of incidence and the angle of reflection?** (The angle of incidence equals, or almost equals, the angle of reflection.)
- **How could we be consistent with our angle measures?** (Repeat the activity and measure again. We could take several readings and average the results.)

CHAPTER REVIEW

SUMMARY

23-1 Nature of Light
❏ Light is made up of a stream of photons, or tiny packets of energy.

❏ All light energies are transverse electromagnetic waves.

❏ Polarized light is light whose waves vibrate along a single plane.

23-2 Electromagnetic Spectrum
❏ The electromagnetic spectrum includes radio waves, infrared waves, visible light, ultraviolet rays, X-rays, and gamma rays.

❏ The higher the frequency of an electromagnetic wave, the higher its photon energy and the shorter its wavelength.

23-3 Particle, Wave, or Both?
❏ Light can be explained as both particlelike and wavelike.

23-4 Reflection of Light
❏ The angle of incidence equals the angle of reflection.

❏ Regular reflection produces a clearly defined image that looks exactly like the object.

❏ Diffuse reflection is reflected light that has been scattered in many different directions.

23-5 Refraction of Light
❏ Refraction is the bending of light.

❏ The index of refraction is a measure of the amount by which a material refracts light.

❏ A prism separates white light into the six colors of the visible spectrum.

23-6 Color
❏ The color of an opaque object is the color of light it reflects.

❏ The color of a transparent object is the color of light it transmits.

❏ The primary colors of light are red, blue, and green. Primary colors combine to produce white light.

❏ Complementary colors of light combine to produce white light.

❏ Primary pigments are yellow, cyan, and magenta. Primary pigments combine to produce black.

23-7 How You See
❏ Nearsightedness occurs when the image falls in front of the retina.

❏ Farsightedness occurs when the image falls behind the retina.

VOCABULARY

Define each term in a complete sentence.

complementary color	infrared ray	photon	regular reflection
cone	invisible spectrum	polarized light	retina
diffuse reflection	iris	primary color	rod
electromagnetic spectrum	microwave	primary pigment	translucent
electromagnetic wave	modulation	prism	transparent
farsightedness	nearsightedness	pupil	ultraviolet ray
gamma ray	opaque	radar	visible spectrum
index of refraction	photoelectric effect	radio wave	X-ray

555

GOING FURTHER: ENRICHMENT

Part 1
Have students do the investigation two to three more times. Tell them to really aim for the best precision and accuracy possible as they line up the pins and measure the angles. Have the teams calculate an average for the angle of incidence and reflection.

Part 2
If curved mirrors are available, students might investigate to find out the relationship between the angles of incidence and reflection on curved mirrors. The relationship should be the same if the curve is constant.

OBSERVATIONS
1. Answers will vary, depending on the setup.
2. Answers will vary, depending on the setup. The size of the angle should be equal to or close to the angle PCB.

CONCLUSIONS
1. Normal
2. Incident ray; angle of incidence
3. RC; RCB
4. Since angle RCB is equal to angle PCB, the investigation does show that the angle of incidence equals the angle of reflection in regular reflection.
5. Most error will be due to inaccurate measurements when placing the pins at points P, B, R, and C.

CHAPTER REVIEW

MULTIPLE CHOICE

1. d   3. d   5. b   7. c   9. c
2. d   4. a   6. d   8. b   10. a

COMPLETION

1. atom
2. visible
3. radar
4. gamma rays
5. infrared rays
6. particle
7. regular
8. diffuse
9. refraction
10. opaque

TRUE OR FALSE

1. T   6. T
2. T   7. T
3. F visible   8. F prism
4. F infrared   9. T
5. F X-rays   10. F pupil

SKILL BUILDING

1. First electron. The higher the energy released, the higher the frequency.
2. The light that leaves the second prism would appear as white light. Check students' diagrams.
3. a. Black or gray absorbs all colors of the visible spectrum. This reduces glare caused by reflected light. **b.** Since white reflects all light, the clothing will help keep a person cooler on a hot day than darker clothing, which would absorb light. **c.** The green, yellow, and red produced by traffic lights is formed when the white light passes through colored filters. The color that is transmitted by each filter is the color that you see.
4. White; black; Colors of light combine by addition. Colors of pigment combine by subtraction.
5. a. Slower **b.** Away from normal **c.** Calcite
6. Because of the refraction of light, light rays from the sun that has already set are bent by the atmosphere toward your eyes. Check students' drawings to see if they accurately reflect this concept.

ESSAY

1. Speed, travel in a vacuum, electromagnetic waves, transverse waves
2. If light were a wave, then the energy of the wave as it is absorbed by a substance would be great enough to eventually knock out some of the electrons.

CONTENT REVIEW: MULTIPLE CHOICE

On a separate sheet of paper, write the letter of the answer that best completes the statement.

1. All light energies
   a. travel the same speed in a vacuum.   b. are transverse waves.
   c. are electromagnetic waves.   d. all of the above.
2. Each color of light has a different
   a. frequency.   b. energy.   c. wavelength.   d. all of the above.
3. The highest energy photons are
   a. radio waves.   b. infrared waves.   c. X-rays.   d. gamma rays.
4. Both wave and particle theory can explain how light
   a. reflects.   b. diffracts.   c. interferes.   d. all of the above.
5. The angle of reflection
   a. is sometimes less than the angle of incidence.
   b. equals the angle of incidence.
   c. is always greater than the angle of incidence.
   d. equals the angle of refraction.
6. The color that is refracted at the greatest angle is
   a. red.   b. yellow.   c. green.   d. violet.
7. An object that will *not* transmit any light is
   a. transparent.   b. translucent.   c. opaque.   d. all of the above.
8. The primary colors of light are
   a. red, yellow, blue.   b. red, green, blue.
   c. yellow, green, blue.   d. red, yellow, orange.
9. The primary colors of pigments are
   a. red, yellow, blue.   b. red, green, blue.
   c. yellow, cyan, magenta.   d. blue, cyan, magenta.
10. To see an object clearly, the image must fall exactly on the
    a. retina.   b. iris.   c. lens.   d. pupil.

CONTENT REVIEW: COMPLETION

On a separate sheet of paper, write the word or words that best complete each statement.

1. The _____ is the source of all forms of light.
2. The _____ spectrum contains all the colors you see.
3. Short-wavelength microwaves are used for _____.
4. The highest energy photons are _____.
5. _____ rays are felt as heat.
6. The _____ theory of light explains the photoelectric effect.
7. A clearly defined image is called _____ reflection.
8. A distorted image is produced by _____ reflection.
9. The bending of light is called _____.
10. _____ materials will only reflect or absorb light.

556

This does not happen with certain photons of light, no matter how long the light is shined on the substance.
3. Droplets of water in the atmosphere act as tiny prisms. White light passing through these droplets is separated into the colors of the visible spectrum.
4. When light strikes a smooth surface, all reflected rays are parallel to one another. So a regular reflection is produced. When light strikes an irregular surface, all the reflected rays are not parallel to one another, so a diffuse reflection is produced.
5. Light enters the eye through the pupil and is refracted as it passes through the lens. The light rays converge on the retina, which is made of light sensitive nerves that transfer the image to the brain in the form of nerve impulses. The brain interprets the nerve impulses and you see.

Determine whether each statement is true or false. Then on a separate sheet of paper, write "true" if it is true. If it is false, change the underlined word or words to make the statement true.

1. A particle of light is called a <u>photon</u>.
2. Light waves travel in a <u>vacuum</u>.
3. The <u>invisible</u> spectrum contains all the colors of the rainbow.
4. <u>Ultraviolet</u> radiation can be felt as heat.
5. Frequencies just above ultraviolet are called <u>gamma rays</u>.
6. The production of electrons by photons of light is called the <u>photoelectric</u> effect.
7. Reflected light that is scattered is called <u>diffuse</u> reflection.
8. A piece of glass that forms a spectrum is called a <u>lens</u>.
9. When all three primary pigments are mixed, the result is <u>black</u>.
10. Light enters the eye through the <u>iris</u>.

CONCEPT REVIEW: SKILL BUILDING

Use the skills you have developed in the chapter to complete each activity.

1. **Relating concepts** Two electrons drop from a higher energy level to a lower energy level. The first electron releases twice as much energy as the second electron. Which electron emits the higher frequency photon? Explain your answer.
2. **Applying concepts** A prism separates white light into the colors of the spectrum. What would happen if a second prism were placed in the path of the separated colors? Use a diagram in your answer.
3. **Identifying relationships** Using your knowledge of color and the behavior of light, answer the following.
   a. Why are roadways made of materials that are black or gray?
   b. Why is clothing worn for sports such as tennis usually white?
   c. How can traffic lights, which use white light bulbs, produce different colors?
4. **Making predictions** Cyan is a mixture of blue and green light. What color would result if cyan light were mixed with red light? What color would result if cyan pigment were mixed with red pigment? Explain your answers.
5. **Applying definitions** Using the table in Figure 23–16, answer the following:
   a. Does light go faster or slower when moving from methanol to glass?
   b. When light travels from diamond to air, is it bent toward or away from the normal?
   c. Light undergoes a greater velocity reduction going from air into which material, glass or calcite?
6. **Making diagrams** Explain why the sun you see setting has already set. Use a diagram in your answer.

CONCEPT REVIEW: ESSAY

Discuss each of the following in a brief paragraph.

1. What characteristics are common to all light waves?
2. Explain why the wave theory of light cannot explain the photoelectric effect.
3. How is a rainbow produced?
4. Describe how the surface light strikes is related to the type of reflection produced.
5. Describe how you see.

557

low bulb. The teacher wants you to produce seven different colors, how are you going to do it? (Answers will vary. All colors can be produced by projecting different combinations of the primary light colors.)

ISSUES IN SCIENCE

The following issue can be used as a springboard for class debate or assigned as a writing homework.

Some people think highway signs should be changed from the colors of yellow and black. Why do you think they originally selected the colors yellow and black? Do you think the sign colors should be changed? Explain your reasoning.

ADDITIONAL QUESTIONS AND TOPIC SUGGESTIONS

1. Explain how a diamond produces such brilliant colors? (Answers will vary but should be mainly based on refraction of light and the high index of refraction for diamond.)
2. Why is the sun at sunset still visible even though it is below the horizon? (Answers will vary but should be based on the refraction of light through the atmosphere.)
3. What happens when a colorblind person, blind to red, looks at an object emitting pure red light? (The object would appear black or gray. The person would not see the red at all because the cones sensitive to red light did not respond to the red wavelengths.)
4. Imagine you work the lights for a school program and the teacher gives you a red bulb, a blue bulb, and a yel-

Chapter 24
LIGHT AND ITS USES

CHAPTER OVERVIEW

Light is as fundamental to living as breathing is. Light fills all cosmic space. Light is emitted by the sun and the other stars in large amounts. We know the world largely because of light. We see our surroundings and build our life around the use of light.

There are several properties of light familiar to all of us. Some of the light we use is produced and given off by objects. These objects are known as luminous objects. Other objects reflect light and are known as illuminated objects.

When light strikes a surface, it is reflected, refracted, or absorbed. Light reflection causes interesting effects. The most common surface from which light waves reflect is a mirror. When the shape of a mirror is changed the image is changed. The usefulness of lenses to cause light refraction is basic to modern technology. When light passes through a lens, it bends. Lenses bend light because they refract light and change its speed.

INTRODUCING CHAPTER 24

Have students observe the photograph on page 558. Read the caption. Point out that the Hubble Space Telescope was named after Edwin Powell Hubble who grew up in Marshfield, Missouri. He joined the staff of the Mount Wilson Observatory in California in 1919 and made outstanding contributions to the study of the universe.

Explain that through the use of mirrors and lenses, the Space Telescope can gather light energy from all over the universe. Light energy comes from luminous objects. The sun, stars, candles, and light bulbs are all luminous objects that produce light waves and give off light.

Mirrors are commonly used as reflectors of light. The Space Telescope is equipped with a 2.4 meter mirror at one end. Based on the shape of its surface, a mirror is classified as plane, concave, or convex. A plane mirror has a flat surface. The surface of a concave mirror curves inward and the surface of a convex mirror curves outward. The images formed by the various mirrors differ in shape, type, size, and position.

The mirrors alone do not do everything expected of the telescope. Lenses allow the scientist to study the data received by the mirrors.

Light and Its Uses 24

CHAPTER OBJECTIVES

After completing this chapter, you will be able to

24–1 Distinguish between luminous and illuminated objects.

24–1 Describe incandescent, fluorescent, and neon light.

24–2 Explain how concave and convex mirrors form images.

24–2 List several uses of concave and convex mirrors.

24–3 Explain how convex and concave lenses form images.

24–3 Relate the images formed by convex and concave lenses to their uses.

24–4 Describe the operation and uses of several optical instruments.

24–5 Identify new applications of light technology.

What do the following numbers have in common: 14 billion light-years, 300,000 kilometers per second, 2.4 meters, and $1 billion? The answer is the Hubble Space Telescope, NASA's latest and most ambitious contribution to the study of the universe.

The Space Telescope is simply a 13-meter cylinder with a 2.4-meter mirror at one end—if that can be called simple! Built at a cost of more than $1 billion, the Space Telescope will be able to gather light from stars too distant or too dim to be studied clearly from the earth.

The new astronomical "eye in the sky" will be carried into space aboard a Space Shuttle and placed in orbit 500 kilometers above the earth's surface. The Space Telescope's reflecting mirror will gather light from objects in the universe as far away as 14 billion light-years. Light travels at 300,000 kilometers per second. In one year, light travels a distance of more than 9 trillion kilometers. This distance is called a light-year. The light the Space Telescope will gather might have left its source 14 billion years ago—about the time the universe was born!

The universe that scientists see will be expanded 350 times by the Space Telescope. The view the Space Telescope will afford is almost to the edge of the universe and the beginning of time!

In this chapter, you will learn more about telescopes and other instruments that use light. You will gain an understanding of how mirrors and lenses work. And you will look at some "light tools" whose future applications are as exciting and ambitious as those of the Hubble Space Telescope.

Technicians working on the 2.4-meter primary mirror of NASA's Hubble Space Telescope wear masks and special suits to maintain absolute cleanliness.

559

TEACHER DEMONSTRATION

Show the class several available light instruments such as a mirror, magnifying glass, overhead projector, 16 mm film projector, slide projector, microscope, telescope, or others that are available. Discuss the instruments using questions similar to the following.
• **How are these instruments similar?** (Accept all logical answers. Lead students to suggest that they all do something to or with light.)
• **How do these instruments use light?** (Accept all logical answers.)'
• **How do these instruments change light?** (Accept all logical answers.)

TEACHER RESOURCES

Audiovisuals

Color and Light: An Introduction, film, Coronet
Modern Concepts of Light, filmstrip, PH Media
Reflection of Light: Lenses, filmstrip, PH Media

Books

Browning, D. R., *Spectroscopy,* McGraw-Hill
Henderson S. T., *Day Light and Its Spectrum,* Halsted
Middleton, T. H., *Light Refractions,* Stein & Day

A lens is a curved piece of glass or plastic that bends light rays. There are two types of lenses, convex and concave. When light enters a lens, it always bends toward the thickest part of the lens. A concave lens is thicker at the edges and thinner in the center. When light rays enter a concave lens, they bend toward the outside edges and diverge. A convex lens is thicker in the center than at the edges. When light rays enter a convex lens, they bend toward the center and converge at a focal point. A magnifying glass is a common type of convex lens.

Explain that modern technology uses science discoveries to give us machines to help us in our daily lives. Science is constantly making now discoveries about energy and matter. Technology puts these discoveries to use. Today more and newer tools are being invented to use the energy of light.

24-1 SOURCES OF LIGHT

SECTION PREVIEW 24-1

Luminous objects give off energy in the form of light. A luminous object can produce incandescent light, fluorescent light, or neon light. Incandescent light is produced from heat. The sun, stars, candles, and light bulbs are all luminous objects that give off incandescent light. Fluorescent light and neon light are cool light produced by the electron bombardment of gas molecules. The type of gas and/or the type of coating on the tube determines the color of the light.

PERFORMANCE OBJECTIVES 24-1

1. **Distinguish between luminous and illuminated objects.**
2. **Describe incandescent, fluorescent, and neon light.**
3. **Explain the differences between hot and cool light.**

SCIENCE TERMS 24-1

luminous p. 560   fluorescent p. 561
illuminated   phosphor p. 561
   p. 560   neon p. 562
incandescent
   p. 560

Section Objective

To describe the ways in which luminous objects produce light.

Figure 24–1 *The aurora borealis, or northern lights, as seen over Fairbanks, Alaska (left), is a luminous light source. The light is produced when particles in the earth's upper atmosphere absorb and then release the energy of subatomic particles shot from the sun. Although the moon is shining brightly over the Sawtooth Mountains of Sun Valley, Idaho (right), it is doing so by reflected light. The moon is an illuminated object.*

24–1 Sources of Light

Almost all of the natural light the earth receives comes from the sun. The sun and other stars are called **luminous** (LOO-muh-nuhs) objects. A luminous object gives off its own light. Light bulbs, candles, campfires, and even fireflies are luminous objects.

Objects such as the moon can be seen because light shining on them is reflected, or bounced off. An object that can be seen only by reflected light is called an **illuminated** (ih-LOO-muh-nayt-ehd) object. You see the moon because sunlight is reflected off its surface. The moon does not give off its own light. How would you describe the pages of this book? The lamp in your room? ❶

As you learned in Chapter 23, light is a form of energy. A luminous object produces light when the electrons in its atoms give off energy. There are three different ways in which a luminous object can be made to give off energy in the form of light. These three ways determine the type of light produced. **A luminous object can produce incandescent light, fluorescent light, or neon light.**

Incandescent Light

Certain objects can be heated until they glow, or give off light. Light produced from heat is called **incandescent** (ihn-kuhn-DEHS-uhnt) light. An object

---

that gives off incandescent light is said to be incandescent. Ordinary light bulbs in your home are incandescent lights. They produce light when electricity is applied to them.

Inside the glass bulb of a light bulb is a thin wire filament made of the metal tungsten. Tungsten can be heated to over 2000°C without melting. When ❸ the light is switched on, electrons flow through the tungsten wire. Because the filament is thin, there is resistance to the electron flow. Electric resistance produces heat. Enough heat will cause the tungsten to glow as photons of visible light are emitted.

Figure 24–2 *This light bulb is incandescent because it produces light when electricity flows through the thin tungsten filament inside (left). If colored filters are placed over an incandescent light source, a variety of colors is produced (center). Certain living organisms, such as glowworms, are bioluminescent (right). They can produce light through chemical reactions in their bodies.*

Fluorescent Light

Light that is produced by the electron bombardment of gas molecules contained at low pressure is called **fluorescent** (floo-REHS-uhnt) light. Fluorescent light is cool light that uses much less electricity than incandescent light.

Fluorescent tubes, usually long and narrow or circular in shape, contain mercury vapor and argon gas. When electricity flows through the tube, electrons collide with the atoms of mercury vapor. The collisions produce photons of ultraviolet light. You cannot see this ultraviolet light. However, the inside of the tube is coated with special substances called **phosphors.** Phosphors absorb ultraviolet photons ❹ and begin to glow, producing visible light. The color that a fluorescent bulb produces depends on the phosphors used.

561

24-2 REFLECTION AND MIRRORS

SECTION PREVIEW 24-2

Mirrors are commonly used as reflectors of light. Based on the shape of its surface, a mirror is classified as plane, concave, or convex. A plane mirror has a flat surface and gives a virtual image. The virtual image of a plane mirror is the same size and rightside up. The surface of a concave mirror curves inward. The image of a concave mirror is inverted, or upside down. The surface of a convex mirror is curved outward. The image formed by a convex mirror is always rightside up and smaller than the object.

PERFORMANCE OBJECTIVES 24-2

1. **Explain how concave and convex mirrors form images.**
2. **List several uses of concave and convex mirrors.**
3. **Explain how concave mirrors form real images.**

SCIENCE TERMS 24-2

mirror p. 562
plane mirror p. 562
virtual image p. 563
concave mirror p. 563

optical axis p. 563
focal point p. 564
focal length p. 564
real image p. 564
convex mirror p. 565

24-1 (continued)

Section Review 24-1

1. Object that produces its own light; object seen by reflected light only
2. Electrons meet resistance as they flow through the tungsten filament. The resistance causes the filament to heat up, producing light.
3. Electrons collide with atoms of mercury vapor. Photons of ultraviolet light are produced. These photons are absorbed by the phosphors that coat the inside of the glass tube. Visible light is emitted.
4. Luminous; illuminated; illuminated; luminous

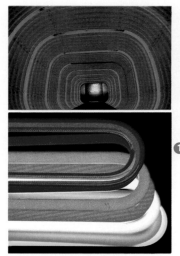

Figure 24–3 *The tubes lining the tunnel are producing fluorescent light (top). Tubes filled with neon and other gases produce different-colored light (bottom). Fluorescent light and neon light are often called gas discharge light.*

Section Objective

To classify mirrors according to the shape of their surfaces

Figure 24–4 *By using a series of mirrors correctly placed, an almost infinite number of images is produced by the reflection of light. What type of mirror is being used?* ❶

562

Neon Light

When electrons pass through glass tubes filled with gas, light is produced. The most common type of gas discharge light is **neon** light. Similar to fluorescent light, neon light is cool light. Neon light is bright red light. If other gases are added, however, different colors are produced.

Mercury vapor produces a greenish-blue light that does not create much glare. So mercury vapor lamps are used to light streets and highways. Sodium vapor lamps, which give off a bright yellow-orange light, use less electricity than mercury vapor lamps. In many locations, sodium vapor lamps are replacing mercury vapor lamps.

SECTION REVIEW

1. What is a luminous object? An illuminated object?
2. How does an incandescent bulb produce light?
3. How does a fluorescent source produce light?
4. Indicate whether the following are luminous or illuminated objects: incandescent light; the planet Mars; the planet Earth; neon light.

24–2 Reflection and Mirrors

You learned in Chapter 21 that reflection is the bouncing back of waves when they strike the surface of an object. The most common surface from which light waves are reflected is a **mirror.** Any smooth surface that reflects light and forms images can be used as a mirror. The surface of a mirror can be perfectly flat or it can be curved. **Based on the shape of its surface, a mirror is classified as plane, concave, or convex.**

Plane Mirrors

A mirror with a perfectly flat surface is a **plane mirror.** Figure 24–5 shows how an image of an object is formed in a plane mirror. Observe that the image appears to be behind the mirror. You know that this cannot be so, since the mirror is opaque

---

TEACHING STRATEGY 24-2

Motivation

Display plane, concave, and convex mirrors for the students to observe. Point out that mirrors are the most common surfaces from which clear, sharp images of light waves are reflected. Explain that mirrors are classified by the shape of the surface.

• **Where are mirrors used?** (Accept all logical answers.)

• **Where are plane mirrors used?** (Accept all logical answers.)
• **What kind of image is formed in a plane mirror?** (Accept all logical answers.)
• **Where are concave mirrors used?** (Accept all logical answers.)
• **What kind of image is formed in a concave mirror?** (Accept all logical answers.)
• **Where are convex mirrors used?** (Accept all logical answers.)

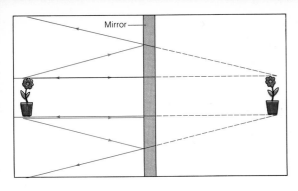
Mirror

Figure 24–5 *This diagram shows how an image is formed in a plane mirror. The reflected rays never really meet in front of the mirror. But if extended in back of the mirror, they come together and an image is formed. What kind of image is formed by a plane mirror? What characteristics of the image are illustrated here?* ❷

Figure 24–6 *These people are using an optical instrument known as a periscope to see an event that is actually blocked from their view (top). Light enters at the top of the periscope, is reflected from one mirror to the other, and then to the viewer's eye (bottom).*

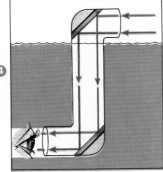

and no light can pass through it. As you can see from the figure, the reflected rays never really meet in front of the mirror. But if extended in back of the mirror, they come together and an image is formed.

The image formed by a plane mirror is rightside up, or erect, the same size as the object, and as far in back of the mirror as the object is in front of the mirror. The image is also reversed. Stand in front of a mirror and raise your *left* hand. Which hand of your image appears to be raised? ❸

The image formed by a plane mirror is called a **virtual image.** The word virtual means "not real." A virtual image only seems to be where it is. In other words, it can be seen only in the mirror. A virtual image cannot be projected onto a screen.

Concave Mirrors

A mirror can be curved instead of flat. If the surface of a mirror curves *inward*, the mirror is called a **concave mirror.** Most images formed by concave mirrors are inverted, or upside down. You can experiment with a concave mirror by looking at the inner surface of a shiny metal spoon. Move the spoon back and forth and observe what happens to your image.

Look at Figure 24–7 on page 564, which shows how a concave mirror forms an image. Notice the straight line drawn through the center of the mirror. This line is called the **optical axis.** Light rays

24-2 (continued)

Motivation

Cut a large, hollow rubber ball in half. Show the students the inside of the ball.

• **What do you predict would happen to the image if the inside of this ball had a mirror surface?** (Accept all logical answers.)

• **Do you predict the image would appear in front, at, or in back of the mirrored surface?** (Accept all logical answers.)

Content Development

Explain that when light rays hit the surface of a concave mirror, they reflect, producing an image in front of the mirrored surface. Point out that even though the surface is curved the law of reflection still applies. The angle of incidence is equal to the angle of reflection. Because a concave mirror is curved, the effects are different from those produced by a plane mirror.

Skills Development

Skill: Interpreting illustrations
Have students observe Figure 24-7. Point out that the optical axis is a straight line drawn through the center of the mirror. The light rays from the candle are hitting the surface of the concave mirror at different angles. Therefore, on reflection, the rays are not parallel but meet at a point called the focal point. Have students measure and record the angles of incidence and reflection in the diagram.

Have students draw a sketch of a concave mirror and a light source.

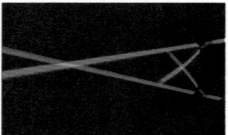

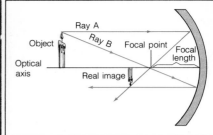

Figure 24–7 *A concave mirror reflects light rays so that they converge at a point called the focal point (left). You can see how an image is formed by a concave mirror by following ray A and ray B as they strike the mirror's surface and are reflected (right). What type of image is formed by a concave mirror? What is its size and position?* ❶

striking a concave mirror parallel to the optical axis are all reflected through the same point in front of the mirror. The point in front of the mirror where the reflected rays meet is called the **focal point.** The distance between the center of the mirror and the focal point is called the **focal length.** Follow ray A to see how it is reflected through the focal point.

Ray B passes through the focal point before it strikes the mirror's surface. Notice that it is reflected parallel to the optical axis. Light rays passing through the focal point before reaching the mirror are all reflected parallel to the optical axis. Where reflected rays A and B meet, an image is formed. ❶ The image is upside down, smaller than the object, and in front of the mirror. The image is a **real image.** A real image can be projected onto a screen because the light actually passes through the point where the image appears.

When a light source is placed exactly at the focal point of a concave mirror, something interesting

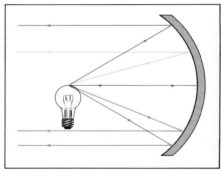

Figure 24–8 *If a light source is placed at the focal point, the reflected rays are all parallel to one another (left). No image is formed, but a concentrated beam of light, such as that produced in a searchlight, results (right). Where else are concave mirrors used to produce a powerful beam of light?* ❷

564

Have them draw in the lines to produce a diagram similar to Figure 24-7. Explain that the distance from the focal point to the center of the mirror is called the focal length.

Content Development

Explain that the image from a concave mirror can be real or virtual, depending on where the object is placed. If the object is outside the focal point, the image is a real image. It is called a

real image because the light rays actually focus and produce an image. Because the light actually passes through the point where the image appears, the image can be projected onto a screen.

Skills Development

Skill: Applying concepts
Divide the class into groups of three or four. Give each group a concave mirror (such as a concave makeup

happens. All the light waves are reflected back parallel to one another, and to the optical axis, in a concentrated beam of light. See Figure 24–8. If you open a flashlight, you will find a concave mirror behind the bulb. The bulb is placed at the focal point of the mirror so that the reflected light forms a powerful beam. Concave mirrors are placed behind car headlights to focus the light beam. Concave mirrors are used in searchlights and in spotlights.

If a light source is placed closer to a concave mirror than the focal point, none of the reflected rays meet. So a real image cannot be formed. Under such conditions, a concave mirror forms only a virtual image. The virtual image is larger than the object. This makes concave mirrors useful as shaving or makeup mirrors. ❷

Convex Mirrors

The surface of a **convex mirror** curves *outward* like the surface of a ball. Reflected rays spread out from the surface of a convex mirror, as you can see in Figure 24–9. The image formed by a convex mirror is always erect and smaller than the object. ❸ Like the image formed by a plane mirror, the image formed by a convex mirror appears behind the mirror.

Convex mirrors provide very large areas of reflection. For this reason, they are used in automobile side-view and rear-view mirrors to obtain a wider view. They are also used in stores to provide

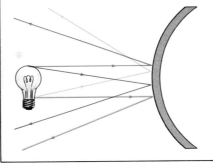

Figure 24–9 *Because a convex mirror spreads out reflected light rays from its very large area of reflection (right), it is often used to increase traffic visibility (left). What type of image does a convex mirror form?* ❸

Sharpen Your Skills

Using a Plane Mirror

1. Stand 1 or 2 meters away from a full-length mirror. Have a friend or classmate place pieces of masking tape at the points on the mirror where you see the top of your head and your feet.
2. Compare the distance between the pieces of tape with your height.
3. Without changing the position of the mirror, move so that you are a distance of 4 or more meters from it. Does your image still fill the space between the tapes? ❷

565

Sharpen Your Skills

Using a Plane Mirror
Skills: Observing, comparing, relating
Level: Average
Type: Hands-on
Materials: mirror, masking tape

In this activity, basic concepts regarding plane mirrors are observed. Students will note that the image in a plane mirror is a real image and the same size as the object. The size will not change as the student moves farther back.

• **What happened to the image?** (Accept all logical answers.)

Explain that when the light source is placed closer to a concave mirror than the focal point, none of the reflected rays meet. Therefore a virtual image is formed. Explain that if the light source is placed inside of the focal point toward the mirror, a real image will not be produced. Point out that in makeup mirrors the surface is concave. The virtual image is magnified and appears larger than the normal object.

Motivation

Point out that sometimes we want to concentrate light into a narrow beam. Take apart a flashlight. Show students the concave mirrored surface that reflects the light rays. Explain that the bulb is at the focal point of the concave mirror. This concentrates the light rays and produces a powerful beam.

• **Where else would we want a concentrated light formed?** (Accept all logical answers.)

Enrichment

Have students experiment using capital letters of the alphabet with stainless steel spoons and makeup mirrors to discover additional relationships about the size, positions, and kinds of images produced by concave mirrors with both long and short focal length mirrors.

---

mirror), a small pocket comb, a flashlight or other light source, and a sheet of white paper. Tell the class to focus the light onto the mirror. The light should be beyond the focal point.

Turn off the classroom lights to provide as much darkness as possible. The reflected rays of light should be visible in the darkened room.

Tell the students to place the comb teeth down in front of the light source. Have another student place the white paper in the reflected stream of light. Have them adjust the distance from the mirror until the inverted comb shows on the paper.

Have the student holding the comb, turn it over, thus allowing students to see that the image is inverted.

Skills Development

Skill: Making observations
Have students move the light closer to the mirror.

24-3 REFRACTION AND LENSES

SECTION PREVIEW 24-3

A lens is a curved piece of glass or plastic that is used to bend light rays so that they can be put to use. There are two types of lenses, convex and concave. A convex lens is thicker in the center than at the edges. When light rays enter a convex lens, the rays bend toward the center and converge at a focal point. A magnifying glass is a convex lens.

A concave lens is thicker at the edges and thinner in the center. When light rays enter a concave lens, they bend toward the outside edges and the light rays diverge.

PERFORMANCE OBJECTIVES 24-3

1. **Explain how convex and concave lenses form images.**
2. **Relate the images formed by convex and concave lenses to their uses.**
3. **Demonstrate how to find the focal point of a lens.**

SCIENCE TERMS 24-3

convex lens p. 567
concave lens p. 568

24-2 (continued)

Section Review 24-2

1. The surface of a plane mirror is perfectly flat. The surface of a concave mirror is curved inward. The surface of a convex mirror is curved outward.
2. Plane mirror: erect, same size as object, same distance behind mirror as object is in front; concave mirror: usually inverted and smaller than object, can be erect and larger than object; convex mirror: erect, smaller than object, behind mirror
3. Plane: periscopes, dress mirrors, other normal reflecting mirrors; concave: flashlights, searchlights, spotlights, headlights, telescopes, shaving

---

and makeup mirrors; convex: side-view and rearview mirrors, security mirrors
4. Convex mirror images are smaller than the objects. Telescopes must magnify the object.

TEACHING STRATEGY 24-3

Motivation
Place a convex lens between a candle and a piece of white paper. Place the

---

security guards with a complete view of shopping areas. However, convex mirrors give a distorted indication of distance. Objects appear to be farther away than they actually are. Why is this an important concern when using a car mirror? ❶

SECTION REVIEW

1. Describe the surface of a plane mirror. A concave mirror. A convex mirror.
2. Describe the image formed by a plane mirror. By a concave mirror. By a convex mirror.
3. What are some uses of each type of mirror?
4. Why are convex mirrors not used for telescopes?

24–3 Refraction and Lenses

Have you ever used a magnifying glass, a camera, or a microscope? If so, you were using a **lens** to form an image. A lens is any transparent material that refracts light. The light is said to be focused through the lens. Most lenses are made of glass or plastic and have either one or two curved surfaces. As parallel rays of light pass through the lens, they are refracted so that they either come together or

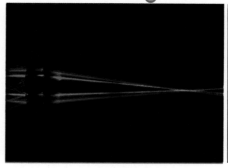
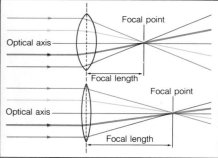

Figure 24–10 *A convex lens converges light rays because parallel rays of light are refracted toward the center—the thickest part—of the lens (left). What is the point at which the rays converge called? The degree to which the lens is curved determines the amount of refraction (right). How does the focal length of a very curved lens compare with the focal length of a slightly curved lens?* ❷

566

---

candle so that it is more than two focal lengths away from the lens. Adjust the paper until a clear, smaller inverted image is produced.
• **What does this tell us about a convex lens?** (Accept all logical answers. Lead students to suggest that a real inverted image can be produced and projected using a convex lens.)
• **Notice the size of the candle and the image. What happened?** (The image is smaller than the candle.)

spread out. **A lens that converges, or brings together, light rays is a convex lens; a lens that diverges, or spreads out, light rays is a concave lens.**

Convex Lenses

A lens that is thicker in the center than at the edges is called a **convex lens.** As parallel rays of light pass through a convex lens, they are bent toward the center—the thickest part of the lens. The light rays converge. The point at which the light rays converge is the focal point.

Light is refracted as it enters a lens and again as it leaves the lens. The amount of refraction depends on the degree to which the lens is curved. A very curved lens will refract light more than a lens whose surface is only slightly curved. In a very curved lens, the converging rays will meet at a focal point closer to the lens. Thus, the focal length of a very curved lens is shorter than that of a slightly curved lens. ❶

Because a convex lens converges light, it can form a real image. However, a convex lens can also

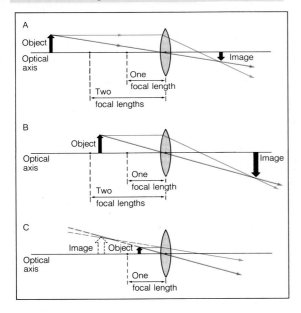

Sharpen Your Skills

Using Lenses

  1. Obtain two convex lenses, one of which is more curved than the other.
  2. Hold the more curved lens near your eye. Position the other lens an arm's length away.
  3. Select an object and move the farther lens toward or away from the object. Keep moving the lens until you see the object clearly through the combination of lenses.

  Is the focused image erect or inverted? Is it larger or smaller than the object? What kind of instrument have you made? ❶

Figure 24–11 *The type of image formed by a convex lens depends on where the object is placed in relation to the focal length of the lens. What type of image is formed in A and B? In C?* ❸

567

Sharpen Your Skills

Using Lenses
Skills: Relating, manipulative, observing, comparing, hypothesizing
Level: Average
Type: Hands-on
Materials: two convex lenses

  In this activity, students observe the properties of a convex lens. Students will note that the image is inverted and larger than the object. They have constructed a primitive telescope.

ANNOTATION KEY

❶ In order to maneuver the car safely, you must have a very accurate measure of distance. (Relating concepts)

❷ Focal point; focal length is shorter (Interpreting illustrations)

❸ Real; virtual (Interpreting illustrations)

❶ Thinking Skill: Relating cause and effect

Sharpen Your Skills

Reflection in a Spoon
Skills: Classifying, observing, manipulative
Level: Remedial
Type: Hands-on
Materials: spoon

  On the back side of the spoon, the image will be erect, smaller, and behind the mirror (convex). On the front side the image will be inverted and smaller (concave).

Measure the distance from the candle to the lens and from the lens to the image on the paper. Write the measurements on the chalkboard.

Place the candle so it is less than two focal lengths away from the lens. Adjust the paper until a clear, larger inverted image is produced.
• **What has happened to the image?** (Most students will say it got bigger.)

Have the students look through the lens at the candle.

• **Now how does it look?** (Most students should say erect and larger.)

Content Development

Point out that the image of a convex lens is produced at the focal point, just as it was in the concave mirror. Explain that a lens is like a mirror in one way. Both mirrors and lenses change the direction of parallel light rays. Mirrors only reflect light rays. A lens refracts or bends light rays. Point out

that a convex lens is thicker in the center and thinner on the edges. Convex lenses cause light rays to come together or converge. Sometimes people refer to a convex lens as a converging lens. The point at which the rays converge is called the focal point. The distance to the focal point from the lens is called the focal length.

TEACHER DEMONSTRATION

Hold a large convex lens between a piece of white paper or cardboard and a light source such as the sun. Adjust the lens until a small bright white spot appears on the paper.

- **What has happened to the light rays going through the lens?** (Accept all logical answers.)
- **What do you predict would happen if I continued holding this lens here?** (Accept all answers. Lead students to suggest the paper would begin to burn.)
- **Where do you think the focal point of the lens is?** (Accept all logical answers.)

24-3 (continued)

Motivation

Darken the classroom. Pass a light beam through a concave lens.

- **What is happening to the beam of light?** (Accept all logical answers.)
- **Will this lens focus at a point?** (Accept all answers.)
- **When would you predict we would use a lens of this shape?** (Accept all answers.)

Content Development

Point out that a concave lens is thicker at the edges and thinner in the center. Explain that when light rays pass through a concave lens, they diverge or bend outward. A concave lens is called a diverging lens. The images produced by diverging lens are erect and smaller than the object.

Skills Development

Skill: Making comparisons

Divide the class into groups of three or four. Give each group a convex and a concave lens. Have them record their findings when observing objects at a far distance and a near distance with each lens separately. Have them investigate and record their findings when they use both lenses "stacked" together.

- **What did you find out?** (Accept all logical answers. Have each suggestion explained thoroughly.)
- **How did the light rays travel?**

Figure 24–12 *A convex lens can be used as a magnifying lens when an object is placed between the lens and its focal point (top). Droplets of water act as convex lenses. Notice how they magnify the stem of this leaf (bottom).*

form a virtual image. The kind of image a convex lens forms depends on the position of the object.

If an object is placed at more than two focal lengths beyond a convex lens, the image formed is inverted and smaller than the object. The lens of a camera and the lens in your eye produce this type of image. See Figure 24–11 on page 567.

If an object is placed more than one focal length but less than two focal lengths beyond a convex lens, the image formed is inverted and larger than the object. This type of image is formed by the convex lens in a microscope or slide projector. See Figure 24–11 on page 567.

If an object is placed between a convex lens and its focal point, a virtual image is formed. The virtual image is erect and larger than the object. For this reason, convex lenses can be used as magnifying glasses. See Figure 24–12.

Concave Lenses

A lens that is thicker at the edges and thinner in the center is called a **concave lens.** As parallel rays of light pass through a concave lens, they are bent toward the edges—the thickest part of the lens. The light rays diverge.

All images produced by concave lenses are erect and smaller than the object. Concave lenses are most often used along with convex lenses to help form a sharper image.

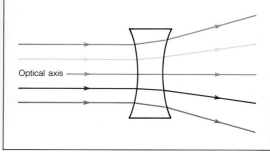

Figure 24–13 *A concave lens diverges light rays because parallel rays of light are refracted toward the edges—the thickest part—of the lens.*

Optical axis

568

(Accept all logical answers. Have each suggestion explained thoroughly.) Diagrams might be drawn on the chalkboard and discussed to illustrate how the light rays moved through each situation that was investigated.

Motivation

Partially blow up a plastic bag with a ziplock seal. Show the students the air-filled bag. Explain that it is the general shape of a convex lens, thicker in the center and thinner on the edges. Point out the curvature of the bag surface. Pull the bag at the edges to make it taut.

- **What happened to the curvature of the lenslike bag?** (Most students will say it flattened.)

Roll up the edges of the bag to force the air to the center.

- **Now what happened to the curvature of the lenslike bag?** (Most students will say the curvature increased.)

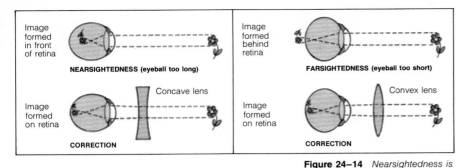

Figure 24–14 *Nearsightedness is corrected by using a concave lens. Why? Farsightedness is corrected by using a convex lens. Why?* ❶

Lenses and Vision

The lens of your eye is a convex lens. It is not a hard and rigid lens, but rather a soft and flexible one. So it can easily change shape to allow you to see clear images of objects both near and distant. Small muscles attached to the lens either relax or tighten and thereby control the curvature of the lens in order to focus images directly on the retina. How do you think the muscles move to allow you to see nearby objects? Distant objects? ❷

NEARSIGHTEDNESS Ideally, the image formed by the convex lens of the eye should fall directly on the retina. In certain cases, the image falls in front of the retina because the eyeball is too long. This condition is called nearsightedness. A nearsighted person has difficulty seeing distant objects clearly but no trouble seeing nearby objects.

The lens of a nearsighted person is too convex. The rays of light converge at a point in front of the retina. A correcting lens would have to make the light rays diverge before they enter the eye. So a concave lens is used to correct nearsightedness. See Figure 24–14. ❸

FARSIGHTEDNESS If the eyeball is too short, the image is focused behind the retina. This condition is called farsightedness. A farsighted person can see distant objects clearly but has difficulty seeing nearby objects. These objects appear blurred.

The lens of a farsighted person is not convex enough. The rays of light converge at a point

569

have to diverge before entering the lens of the eye.

• **What would you predict would happen to the lens of your eye if you were farsighted?** (Accept all logical answers.)

Explain that a person who is farsighted cannot see nearby objects. The lens of the eye of a farsighted person is not convex enough. The rays of light converge at a point behind the retina. They need a convex lens to correct their eyesight.

Reinforcement

Have students explore the paths of light rays through various concave and convex lenses. A comb placed in front of a flashlight or projector will produce individual rays that can be followed through the lenses. Students might make bulletin board diagrams of their investigations.

Enrichment

Have students make water lenses by *gently* placing one or several drops of water onto a glass slide. These lenses can be used to magnify newsprint. Students might try to make lenses that magnify the most using differing amounts of water. Clear, round glass jars can also be filled with water to make a different type of elongated lens.

Content Development

Point out that the lens of the eye is a convex lens. Explain that small muscles attached to the lens can change the shape of the curvature by relaxing or tightening. This control helps focus the images directly on the retina and allows a person to see far and near.

• **What would you predict would happen to your sight if the lens of the eye could not flatten?** (Accept all logical answers.)

Explain that when the lens does not flatten, the person cannot see distant objects. This condition is known as nearsightedness.

• **Can you predict what type of lens that person would have in her glasses?** (Accept all logical answers but ask for the reason behind their suggestion.)

Point out that a concave lens would have to be used for nearsightedness because the rays of light would

24-4 OPTICAL INSTRUMENTS

SECTION PREVIEW 24-4

Optical instruments are applications of light refraction and reflection. The amount of refraction depends on the thickness of the lens and the type of material. The amount of reflection and light gathering of a concave mirror depends on the diameter and curvature of the mirror. Optical instruments use different combinations of lenses and/or mirrors to converge or diverge light rays to perform the wanted result.

Some of the optical instruments we are most familiar with are simple combinations of lenses. A camera in its simplest form consists of a light-tight box, a convex lens to refract light, and photographic film. There are two kinds of telescopes, refracting and reflecting. The refracting telescope has two convex lenses, the objective lens, which brings light to a focus, and an eyepiece, which magnifies the image. A reflecting telescope reflects light by use of concave mirrors and then uses a lens to magnify the image.

PERFORMANCE OBJECTIVES 24-4

1. **Describe the operation of several optical instruments.**
2. **Make a model of a simple optical instrument.**

24-3 (continued)

Section Review 24-3

1. Convex lens is thicker in the middle. Concave lens is thicker at the edges.
2. Concave lens because the light rays must be diverged before entering the eye; convex lens because the light rays must be converged before entering the eye
3. A converging lens; convex lens

TEACHING STRATEGY 24-4

Motivation

If possible, get a camera that has lenses with different focal lengths.

behind the retina. A correcting lens would have to make the light rays converge before they enter the eye. So a convex lens is used to correct farsightedness. See Figure 24–14 on page 569.

SECTION REVIEW

1. Compare a convex lens and a concave lens.
2. What kind of lens is used to correct nearsightedness? Farsightedness? Explain your answer.
3. If you wished to examine a small object using a lens, would you choose a converging or diverging lens? Name the lens you would choose.

24–4 Optical Instruments

An optical instrument produces images by the reflection or refraction of light. **An optical instrument uses mirrors or lenses to produce images.** What optical instruments can you name?

Cameras

Just like the eye, a camera works by allowing light to enter through a lens. A camera lens, however, may be made up of several separate lenses. And the image produced by a camera lens falls on photographic film that contains chemical substances that are sensitive to light. Where does the image produced by the eye fall? ❶

Figure 24–15 *These three photographs were taken with lenses of different focal lengths. The size of the image depends on the focal length of the lens. Which photograph was taken with a camera lens of short focal length? Of long focal length?* ❷

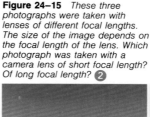

570

Have students observe Figure 24-19. Read the caption and show the lenses to students. Point out that cameras use a different-sized lens for each kind of picture. The reason for this is that a glass lens does not have the ability to change size like the lens in our eyes.

Content Development

Point out that a camera works much like an eye. The light is admitted through a shutter, similar to the iris of the eye, to a convex lens. Point out that most cameras today have several lenses. The convex lens converges the light and produces an image that is smaller, real, and inverted onto the photographic film.

Skills Development
Skill: Applying concepts
Do Sharpen Your Skills Forming an Image. Discuss students' findings with some of the following questions.

A camera contains a convex lens. The image formed by a camera is real and inverted. It is also smaller than the object. The size of the image formed on the film depends upon the focal length of the lens. A lens with a short focal length produces a small image. But because the image of the object being photographed is small, a wider area of the surroundings is included.

A lens with a long focal length produces a large image. With this kind of lens, the area of the surroundings is decreased as the size of the image is increased. See Figure 24–15.

The opening in the camera through which light enters is called the aperture. The size of the aperture controls the amount of light that passes through the lens and reaches the film.

Telescopes

Telescopes are used to view objects that are very far away. By using mirrors and lenses, telescopes produce enlarged images of distant objects.

A refracting telescope uses a series of lenses to focus and magnify light from distant objects. The larger the lenses used in a refracting telescope, the greater the light-gathering power. The refracting telescope at Yerkes Observatory in Wisconsin has a light-gathering power about 40,000 times greater than that of the human eye. The diameter of its largest lens is about 100 centimeters.

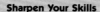
❷ **Figure 24–16** *The refracting telescope at Yerkes Observatory in Wisconsin (left) uses a series of lenses to form an image of a distant object (right). The Yerkes Observatory telescope is the world's largest refracting telescope.*

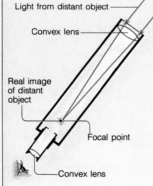

Light from distant object

Convex lens

Real image of distant object

Focal point

Convex lens

Explain that this model is sometimes called a pinhole camera. Some of the early cameras actually worked just like this model. Today cameras still use the same laws of light. Scientists and inventors have improved the camera by adding a variety of lenses, shutters, and types of film.

Enrichment
Interested students might use two convex lenses to make a simple telescope. First, have them use plastic clay to hold each lens upright. The lenses can then be moved until images are clear. This is the approximate distance that the telescope lenses need to be separated. Each lens can then be taped to paper towel tubes. One tube should fit inside the other. Additional sliding will adjust the lenses for various distances.

- **What do you observe about the image?** (The image is upside down. The image is smaller than the object.)
- **How do you think this happens?** (Accept all logical answers. Lead students to suggest that light rays traveled through the tiny hole and onto the wax paper.)
- **Is the image real or virtual?** (The image is real.)
- **How do you know the image is real?** (Real images can be projected.)

Explain that this tin-can model is a simple optical instrument that is very similar to our eye and a camera. Ask students the following questions.
- **Which part is similar to the pupil?** (The tiny hole)
- **Which part is similar to the aperture of a camera?** (The tiny hole)
- **Which part is similar to the retina?** (The wax paper)
- **Which part is similar to the film in a camera?** (The wax paper)

Sharpen Your Skills

Color Photography
Skills: Relating, report writing
Level: Average
Type: Library

Your students should find that color film is composed of eight layers: a top coat, a blue-sensitive emulsion layer, a yellow filter layer, a green-sensitive emulsion layer, a red-sensitive emulsion layer, a substrate, a film base, and a backing layer. Color film records images by breaking down white light into a three-component system as it passes through each of the layers. Each emulsion layer contains silver halide, which reacts to light. During development, silver metal is deposited where the film has been struck by light so that a complementary color negative image is eventually produced on the film.

24-4 (continued)

Content Development

Have students observe Figure 24-17. Point out that a reflecting telescope uses a concave mirror that will gather light from distant stars and galaxies. More light is gathered with less distortion by using a concave mirror. Explain that the concave mirror gathers the light and forms a small real image. The image is then reflected off a plane mirror to an eyepiece. The eyepiece is a combination of convex lenses that magnify the image.

Section Review 24-4

1. Camera: produces a real, inverted, smaller image on photographic film; telescope: using mirrors and lenses,

 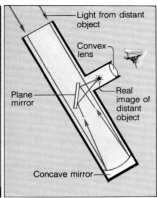

Figure 24–17 *The Hale Telescope at Mount Palomar in California (left) is one of the world's largest reflecting telescopes. Light rays from a distant object are reflected from one mirror to another to produce an image (right). What is the purpose of the convex lens?* ❶

A reflecting telescope uses a series of plane and concave mirrors to gather light from distant objects. The image formed by these mirrors is, however, relatively small. So a lens inside the eyepiece is used to magnify the image. The "200-inch" Hale telescope at Mount Palomar in California is one of the world's largest reflecting telescopes.

Microscopes

A microscope uses two convex lenses to magnify extremely small objects. One lens of the microscope is placed at the end of the tube. The other lens is in the eyepiece. The total magnification produced by the microscope is the product of the magnification of the two lenses.

SECTION REVIEW

1. Name three optical instruments. Explain what each does.
2. Compare a refracting and a reflecting telescope.
3. Which type of camera lens would be called a wide-angle lens—one with a short focal length or one with a long focal length? Which type would be called a telephoto lens?

Sharpen Your Skills

Color Photography

Color film is sensitive to the various frequencies of light. It can record the colors of an object.

Using books and other reference materials in your library, find out how color film works. Write a report that describes how the various colors are recorded on the film.

572

produces enlarged images of distant objects; microscope: uses lenses to magnify extremely small objects
2. Both telescopes are used to view distant objects by gathering light, focusing it, and magnifying it. A refracting telescope uses a series of lenses. A reflecting telescope uses a series of plane and concave mirrors. It also uses an eyepiece lens to magnify the image.
3. Short focal length; long focal length

TEACHING STRATEGY 24-5

Motivation

Tell students to imagine that they are going to have surgery. The doctor gives them a choice of operating tools, a laser or normal surgical tools.
• **What type of questions would you ask your doctor about the surgery?** (Accept all logical answers.)
• **Which one would you elect to have?** (Accept all answers.)

24–5 Light and Technology

To describe applications of light technology

Today, scientists have developed new and exciting ways to use light—from looking inside the human body to cutting through the body to producing three-dimensional images of body parts. **New developments in light technology include lasers, holography, and fiber optics.**

Lasers

Unlike white light, which is a mixture of all the frequencies of the visible spectrum, light from a **laser** is made up of only one frequency. Laser light is **coherent light,** or light that is in phase. This means that the crests and troughs of the light waves all move in the same direction at the same time. Light from a laser, then, travels in almost parallel lines with very little spreading. These characteristics make laser light an extremely powerful single-color light.

Different kinds of gases, liquids, and crystals are used to make lasers. One of the most common lasers is a ruby laser. A ruby laser consists of a solid rod made of ruby crystals. At each end of the rod is a mirror. One of these mirrors is a partial mirror. It does not reflect all the light that strikes it.

Wrapped around the rod is a tube called a flash tube, which provides energy in the form of bright flashes of light. The light is focused on and absorbed by atoms in the ruby crystals. When atoms absorb energy, their electrons move to higher energy levels. But the electrons do not stay there. Instead, they quickly drop back to their original levels. In the process of dropping back, the electrons give off the energy they absorbed. This energy is given off in the form of photons of light. All of the photons emitted have the same frequency and wavelength. They are all photons of the same color!

The process is repeated over and over so that a large number of photons are released. The photons are reflected back and forth between the mirrored ends of the rod, causing even more photons to be released. In this way, the light intensifies, or amplifies. When the light becomes intense enough, it passes through the partial mirror as a narrow beam of concentrated light.

Figure 24–18 *A laser produces an intense beam of coherent, single-color light (top). Such a beam of light can be used to diagnose eye diseases by monitoring the flow of blood through vessels in the retina (bottom).*

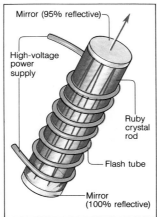

573

24-5 LIGHT AND TECHNOLOGY

SECTION PREVIEW 24-5

Modern technology uses scientific discoveries to give us machines that help us in our daily lives. Science is constantly making new discoveries about energy and matter. Technology puts these discoveries to use. Every day, more and newer sophisticated tools are being invented to use the light energy.

The laser, one of the most valuable of light tools, helps in the fields of medicine and business. Lasers are used in many types of surgery. The use of the laser in fiber optics allows doctors to see inside of patients. Optical fibers are replacing the wires in telephone and communication systems because of the greater number of messages that can be transmitted. Holograph systems are used in most grocery stores, credit cards, and for teaching many ideas in medicine and business.

PERFORMANCE OBJECTIVES 24-5

1. **Identify new applications of light technology.**
2. **Explain how laser technology is useful.**
3. **List uses of holography.**

SCIENCE TERMS 24-5

laser p. 573
coherent light p. 573
holography p. 574

hologram p. 574
fiber optic p. 575
optical fiber p. 575

• **Why would you select that type of surgery instead of the other?** (Accept all logical answers.)

Content Development

Point out that laser surgery is most often considered "bloodless surgery." Explain that a laser is light made up of only one frequency. Laser light is coherent light.

Content Development

Point out that different kinds of gases, liquids, and crystals are used to make lasers. Explain that a laser is a rod made or filled with one of these substances. Mirrors are placed on both ends of the rod. Wrapped around the rod is a flash tube, which provides energy in the form of light flashes. This energy is in the form of photons. As the process is repeated over and over, the energy intensifies and passes

through as a narrow beam of coherent light.

Enrichment

Have students write reports on the use of a laser in a particular machine such as a computer printer, video disc, audio disc, movie making, camera, satellites, or measuring distances.

24-5 (continued)

Motivation

Show students the universal bar code on several packages or cans from the grocery store.

- **How many of you have noticed these on the sides of packages?** (Most students will say they have.)
- **What does it do?** (Accept all logical answers. Lead students to suggest it puts the price of the package into the cash register.)
- **Why would this be an advantage to the grocer?** (Accept all logical answers.)
- **How do you predict it knows the price?** (Accept all logical answers.)

Content Development

Point out that when the package is moved over the scanner, a laser is used to instantly read the bar code. Explain that the "bars" in the code identify the manufacturer, product, and size. This information is picked up by the laser and transferred to a computer data bank where the current price is obtained. The information is then relayed back to the cash register display and a receipt is printed.

Content Development

Point out that holograph technology can use a laser light to produce a three-dimensional image of an object. The image is called a hologram. Discuss the possible applications of this kind of technology.

- **Where would a three-dimensional image be of use?** (Accept all answers.)

Explain that three-dimensional images are used by auto and machine tool manufacturers to find any defects in the parts. Medicine uses three-dimensional images to display the interior of body organs. Many television and movie presentations are working on developing a three-dimensional picture. Point out that using laser technology is expensive.

Skills Development

Skill: Applying technology
Discuss why companies find it cost effective to use laser technology.

Figure 24–19 *This hologram, or three-dimensional image of an object, was the first all-color hologram to be created. What kind of light is used in holography?* ❶

Lasers have uses in medicine, manufacturing, communication, surveying, entertainment, and even measuring the distance to the moon. Lasers are used in audio and video disks, computers, and printers. In the future, lasers may be used to produce an almost limitless supply of nuclear fusion energy.

Holography

One of the newest and most exciting uses of laser light is in **holography.** Holography is a technology that uses laser light to produce a three-dimensional image of an object or scene. The image is called a **hologram.**

Holograph systems are used with laser beams to scan the universal bar codes on grocery store items. Holograms have many other possible uses. They can store a tremendous amount of data in a limited space, give details of structural flaws in machine parts, display the interior of body organs, and bring three-dimensional TV pictures into your home.

CAREER · Holographer

HELP WANTED: HOLOGRAPHER Medical publisher needs a full-time holographer to create three-dimensional surgical instructions. College courses in photography, anatomy, and illustration preferred. Technical training in holography required.

A human eyeball, one meter tall, rotates slowly in the center of a classroom. Medical students watch as the instructor explains a complex surgical procedure. Occasionally, the instructor steps right through the eyeball as if it were a mirage! Yet it looks solid.

This realistic image is called a holograph or hologram. A **holographer** uses laser beams to create holographs. Holographs may be projected into the air, etched, or printed like a photograph. So knowledge of light, color, and art are important to a holographer.

A holographer may produce educational materials and amusing illusions for advertisements. Holographs are now used to show valuable art pieces worldwide while the originals remain safely stored. Holographers help produce holographic credit cards, passports, and licenses, which are difficult to duplicate.

Communication signals and films may be transmitted by holography. Because holographs can filter light and control wavelength, they may soon replace glass lenses and light filters.

If you would like to find out how to join the exciting field of holography, contact New York Holographics Laboratory, 34 W. 13th Street, New York, NY 10011.

- **Why would a manufacturer switch to using laser technology?** (Accept all logical answers. Lead students to suggest that the technology helps produce a better product at a lower cost than using older methods.)
- **Imagine that you own a large auto parts manufacturing plant. Would you install laser technology? Why or why not?** (Accept all logical answers.)
- **How is it possible for expensive technology to be cost effective?** (Accept all logical answers. Lead students to suggest that better products usually result in more sales. More sales lead to more profits with which to pay for the better technology.)

Motivation

Show students a long silk thread and a telephone wire. Point out that optical fibers are thinner than the thread.

- **If you had to string lines all over the world, which of these would you**

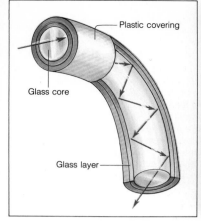
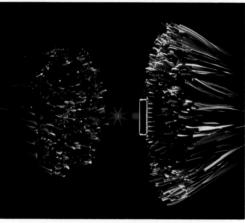

Figure 24-20 *Optical fibers are like "light pipes" because, through a series of continuous reflections, light is transported from one place to another (left). The single optical-fiber cable in the center of the photograph can carry as many messages in the form of high-intensity laser light as all the electric wires combined (right).*

Fiber Optics

Imagine a doctor being able to see inside a patient's body without having to perform surgery. Advances in the field of **fiber optics** have made this possible. Fiber optics deals with the transfer of light through long, thin flexible fibers of glass or plastic called **optical fibers.**

An optical fiber is like a "light pipe." A ray of light enters the fiber and is reflected so that it zigzags its way through the length of the fiber. See Figure 24-20.

Optical fibers are rapidly replacing electric wires in communication systems such as telephone systems. A single optical fiber can carry thousands of messages in the form of high-intensity laser light ❷ with extraordinary clarity. Optical fibers are also used in medicine, television signal transmission, and data processing.

SECTION REVIEW

1. Name three uses of lasers.
2. What is a hologram? An optical fiber?
3. Distinguish between white light and laser light.

575

dents to suggest that optical fibers have less corrosion, more reliability, less cost, less interference, less space, and can send more messages than metal wires.)
• **What are some disadvantages of using optical fibers?** (Many metal wires are already there, and this means additional labor to change the system.)
• **What do you think about replacing current metal wires with an optical fiber system? Should it be done?** (Accept all answers.)

Content Development

Point out that optical fiber instruments are used in many fields of medicine and industry. Explain that in medicine a long tube called a colonoscope is used to examine the inside of a patient's body. The high-intensity laser light gives the doctor an extraordinary view of the inside body tissues and organs. Explain that in industry, many companies are converting their data processing systems to use fiber optics instead of metal wire.

Section Review 24-5

1. Communication, surveying, audio and video discs, computers, printers
2. Three-dimensional picture formed by using laser light; long, thin, flexible fiber of glass or plastic that passes light through it by having the light be totally internally reflected
3. White light contains all the frequencies of the visible spectrum. Laser light contains only one frequency, is highly concentrated, and does not spread out.

use? (Accept all answers.)
• **Why would the thinner optical fiber be advantageous?** (Accept all logical answers.)

Skills Development
Skill: Interpreting diagrams
Have students observe Figure 24-20. Read the caption. Point out that a core of optical fibers is encased in a glass layer. Then an outside covering of flexible plastic is used.

• **What does each individual fiber in the core do?** (Carry impulses of data and information)
• **What is the purpose of the outer glass layer?** (To protect the inner fibers)

Skills Development
Skill: Applying technology
• **What are some advantages of using optical fibers instead of metal wire?** (Accept all logical answers. Lead stu-

LABORATORY INVESTIGATION
CONVEX LENSES

BEFORE THE LAB
1. **Divide the class into groups of three to six students.**
2. **Gather all materials at least one day prior to the investigation. You should have enough supplies to meet your class needs, assuming three to six students per group.**

PRE-LAB DISCUSSION
Have students read the complete laboratory procedure. Discuss the procedure by asking questions similar to the following.
- **What is the purpose of the laboratory investigation?** (To find the kinds of images produced by a convex lens)
- **What is a convex lens?** (A convex lens is like a magnifying glass. The lens is thicker in the center than at the edges.)
- **What is a real image?** (A real image is one that can be projected.)
- **What is a virtual image?** (A virtual image is one that we see but cannot project onto a screen.)

SKILL DEVELOPMENT
Students will use the following skills while completing this investigation.
1. Safety
2. Manipulative
3. Observing
4. Comparing
5. Recording
6. Measuring
7. Applying
8. Relating

SAFETY TIPS
Alert students to be cautious with the lens and light bulb. Remind the class to be sure that wires do not dangle and cause safety hazards.

TEACHING STRATEGY FOR LAB PROCEDURE
1. Have students practice lining up and placing bulb, lens, and screen in the proper places several times before measuring the distances.
2. Have the groups follow the directions carefully as they work in the laboratory.

Convex Lenses

Problem
What kinds of images are formed by a convex lens?

Materials *(per group)*
convex lens
lens holder
meterstick
light bulb and socket
blank sheet of paper

Procedure
1. Place the convex lens in the lens holder and position them at least 2 meters in front of the *lighted* bulb.
2. Position the paper behind the lens so a clear image of the bulb can be seen on the paper. The sheet of paper must be positioned vertically. Record the position and the relative size of the image.
3. Measure the distance from the lens to the paper. This is the focal length of the lens. Record the distance in centimeters.
4. Turn off the light bulb *when moving it.*
5. Move the bulb to a position that is greater than twice the focal length of the lens. Turn the bulb on. Record the position and relative size of the image.
6. Move the bulb to a position that is exactly twice the focal length. Record the position and relative size of the image.
7. Move the bulb to a position equal to the focal length. Record the position and relative size of the image.
8. Move the bulb to a position between the lens and the paper. This position is less than one focal length. Record the position and relative size of the image.

Object Distance (bulb to lens)	Image Position (erect or inverted)	Image Size

Focal length of lens _____

Observation
Describe the image formed in each step of the procedure for which you have made observations.

Conclusions
1. Is the image formed by a convex lens always erect? If not, under what conditions is the image inverted?
2. What happens to the size of the image as the bulb moves closer to the focal length? To the position of the image?
3. What happens to the size of the image as the bulb moves to less than the focal length? To the position of the image?

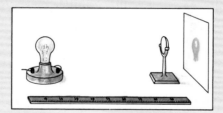

576

3. Discuss how the investigation relates to the chapter ideas by asking open questions similar to the following.
- **What happens when the bulb is very far away from the lens and screen?** (The image is formed at the focal point of the lens.)
- **What happens when the bulb is beyond twice the focal point of the lens?** (The image is between the focal point and twice the focal point, smaller, and inverted.)
- **What happens when the bulb is at twice the focal point in front of the lens?** (The image is at twice the focal point behind the lens, inverted, and the same size as the bulb.)
- **What happens when the object is between the focal point and twice the focal point?** (The image is beyond twice the focal point, inverted, and larger than the bulb.)
- **What happens when the bulb is at the focal point?** (No real image forms.)

SUMMARY

24-1 Sources of Light

❏ Luminous objects produce their own light.

❏ An illuminated object is seen only by reflected light.

❏ Light produced from heat is called incandescent light.

❏ Light that is produced by the electron bombardment of gas molecules contained at low pressure is called fluorescent light.

❏ Neon light is produced when electrons pass through glass tubes filled with neon gas.

24-2 Reflection and Mirrors

❏ A plane mirror has a perfectly flat surface and produces an image that is erect and the same size as the object.

❏ Concave mirrors curve inward and produce images that are usually inverted and magnified.

❏ Convex mirrors curve outward and produce images that are erect and smaller than the object.

24-3 Refraction and Lenses

❏ A convex lens converges light rays and produces real or virtual images, depending on the position of the object.

❏ A concave lens diverges light rays and produces erect images that are smaller than the object.

❏ To correct nearsighted vision, concave lenses are used. To correct farsighted vision, convex lenses are used.

24-4 Optical Instruments

❏ An optical instrument uses mirrors or lenses to produce images.

❏ A camera works by allowing light to enter through a convex lens.

❏ The image formed by a camera is real, inverted, and smaller than the object. The size of the image depends upon the focal length of the lens.

❏ A refracting telescope uses a series of lenses to focus and magnify light.

❏ A reflecting telescope uses a series of plane and concave mirrors to gather light.

❏ A microscope uses lenses to magnify extremely small objects.

24-5 Light and Technology

❏ Light from a laser is coherent, has a single frequency, and forms a very intense and concentrated beam.

❏ A hologram is a three-dimensional picture made from laser light.

❏ Optical fibers are long, thin, flexible fibers of glass or plastic that transmit light.

VOCABULARY

Define each term in a complete sentence.

coherent light	fluorescent	laser	phosphor
concave lens	focal length	lens	plane mirror
concave mirror	focal point	luminous	real image
convex lens	hologram	mirror	virtual image
convex mirror	holography	neon	
fiber optics	illuminated	optical axis	
	incandescent	optical fiber	

577

• **What happens when the bulb is inside the focal point?** (No real image is formed.)

OBSERVATIONS

Step 2: inverted and smaller; step 5: inverted and smaller; step 6: inverted and same size; step 7: no image formed; step 8: erect and enlarged

CONCLUSIONS

1. No. Image is inverted when the object is placed beyond the focal length.
2. Image gets larger, but stays inverted.
3. Enlarged and erect

GOING FURTHER: ENRICHMENT

Part 1

Have students do the investigation using a different magnifying glass with a longer or shorter focal point.

Part 2

Have the class use a concave makeup mirror and investigate the real images that are formed at the various distances from the focal point.

Part 3

Have the class use two lenses to make a simple refracting telescope and investigate the real and virtual images.

CHAPTER REVIEW

MULTIPLE CHOICE
1. a **3.** c **5.** b **7.** d **9.** b
2. b **4.** b **6.** d **8.** b **10.** d

COMPLETION
1. luminous
2. plane
3. concave
4. convex
5. concave
6. aperture
7. incandescent
8. laser
9. hologram
10. optical fiber

TRUE OR FALSE
1. F illuminated
2. T
3. T
4. F concave
5. F convex
6. F convex
7. F convex
8. T
9. T
10. T

SKILL BUILDING
1. Incandescent, since it gives off more heat than fluorescent
2. a. Laser light is of one frequency; white light is a combination of many frequencies. **b.** Laser light produces a beam that remains straight and does not diverge over distance. **c.** Laser light is produced when electrons absorb energy, move to a higher energy level, and then drop back to their original level, giving off photons of light. All the photons have the same frequency and wavelength and are of the same color. In this way light is amplified or strengthened by stimulating electrons to emit photons of energy.
3. 60 times
4. a. 3 cm **b.** 5 cm **c.** 25 cm
5. In the eye, light passes through the pupil; in the camera, light passes through the aperture. Muscles control the size of the pupil in the eye; the shutter controls the size of the aperture in a camera. In both, light passes through a lens and is refracted so that the light rays converge on the retina in the eye and on the film in the camera.
6. Accept all logical opinions on this topic.

ESSAY
1. Examples may include fire, sun, candle, lightbulb, stars.
2. The tungsten filament offers resistance to the flow of electrons. Electric resistance causes heat, which causes

photons of visible light to be emitted. In the fluorescent bulb, electricity flows through tubes containing mercury vapor and argon gas. Electrons collide with the atoms of mercury vapor, producing photons of ultraviolet light. The ultraviolet photons strike phosphors lining the tube, and the phosphors glow, producing visible light.
3. Real image is formed by the actual convergence of light rays. A real image can be projected onto a screen. A vir-

tual image is not really there because the reflected or refracted rays do not really meet. A virtual image cannot be projected onto a screen. A concave mirror forms a real image because it causes the rays to converge. A convex lens forms a real image because it causes the rays to converge.
4. The amount of bending in a convex lens is dependent on the wavelength or frequency. Since each color of the visible spectrum has a different wave-

---

CONTENT REVIEW: MULTIPLE CHOICE

On a separate sheet of paper, write the letter of the answer that best completes each statement.

1. A flashlight beam is seen because the light is
a. luminous.   b. illuminated.   c. fluorescent.   d. neon.
2. Which of the following does *not* belong?
a. luminous   b. illuminated   c. incandescent   d. fluorescent
3. The filament in an incandescent light bulb is
a. steel.   b. copper.   c. tungsten.   d. tin.
4. The photons released in a fluorescent light bulb are
a. infrared.   b. ultraviolet.   c. X-ray.   d. gamma.
5. The point in front of a mirror where reflected rays meet is the
a. focal length.   b. focal point.   c. aperture.   d. vertex.
6. As compared to the object, the image formed by a convex mirror is
a. erect and larger.   b. inverted and smaller.
c. inverted and larger.   d. erect and smaller.
7. The Hale telescope has a 5-meter
a. plane mirror.   b. convex mirror.   c. concave lens.   d. concave mirror.
8. The image formed by a convex lens in a telescope is
a. erect and enlarged.   b. inverted and enlarged.
c. inverted and smaller.   d. erect and smaller.
9. Farsightedness is corrected by a
a. convex mirror.   b. convex lens.   c. concave mirror.   d. concave lens.
10. Crests and troughs of each wave are lined up with all other waves in
a. incandescent light.   b. fluorescent light.   c. neon light.   d. laser light.

CONTENT REVIEW: COMPLETION

On a separate sheet of paper, write the word or words that best complete each statement.

1. The sun is a (an) _____ object.
2. A _____ mirror is perfectly flat.
3. A _____ mirror curves inward.
4. A _____ mirror curves outward.
5. A _____ lens diverges light.
6. The opening in the camera through which light enters is called the _____.
7. Light produced from heat is _____.
8. _____ is concentrated light with a single frequency.
9. A (An) _____ is a three-dimensional picture made with laser light.
10. A (An) _____ is a thin, flexible glass tube that transmits light.

CONTENT REVIEW: TRUE OR FALSE

Determine whether each statement is true or false. Then on a separate sheet of paper, write "true" if it is true. If it is false, change the underlined word or words to make the statement true.

1. The moon is said to be <u>luminous</u>.
2. Cool light is <u>fluorescent</u> light.
3. A plane mirror forms a <u>virtual</u> image.
4. Reflecting telescopes use <u>convex</u> mirrors.

578

5. <u>Concave</u> mirrors give an extra wide view.
6. <u>Concave</u> lenses are used in magnifying glasses.
7. The lens of the eye is a <u>concave</u> lens.

8. A camera lens produces an image that is inverted and <u>smaller</u>.
9. All laser light is <u>in phase</u>.
10. <u>Holograms</u> are three-dimensional images.

CONCEPT REVIEW: SKILL BUILDING

Use the skills you have developed in the chapter to complete each activity.

1. **Applying concepts** Suppose you are building an incubator and you need a source of heat. Would you use an incandescent or fluorescent light bulb? Explain your answer.

2. **Relating concepts** What characteristics of laser light can be used to explain the following statements:
   a. Laser light is never white.
   b. Laser light is useful in surveying.
   c. Laser stands for *l*ight *a*mplification through *s*timulated *e*mission of *r*adiation.

3. **Applying definitions** The lens at the end of a microscope tube has a magnification of 10×. The eyepiece lens has a magnification of 6×. What is the total magnification achieved by the microscope?

4. **Making calculations** When a convex lens produces a real image, the following relationship applies:

$$\frac{d_o}{d_i} = \frac{s_o}{s_i} \quad \text{or}$$

$$\frac{\text{object distance}}{\text{image distance}} = \frac{\text{object size}}{\text{image size}}$$

   a. What is the size of the image formed at 15 centimeters from a lens if the object is 4 centimeters tall and located 20 centimeters from the lens?
   b. An image measuring 2.5 centimeters is formed 10 centimeters from a lens. How large is the object if its distance from the lens is 20 centimeters?
   c. At what distance is a 2-centimeter image located if a 6-centimeter object located 75 centimeters from the lens produces this image?

5. **Making comparisons** Compare the structure and operation of a camera to that of the eye.

6. **Expressing an opinion** The technology is now available to place a series of mirrors in orbit. These mirrors would reflect light back to Earth in order to illuminate major urban areas at night. What do you think are some of the problems and the benefits that would result from such a project?

CONCEPT REVIEW: ESSAY

Discuss each of the following in a brief paragraph.

1. List five examples of luminous light.
2. How is light produced in an incandescent light bulb? In a fluorescent light bulb?
3. Compare a real image and a virtual image. Which type of mirror forms a real image? Which type of lens forms a real image?
4. Explain why when white light passes through a single convex lens different colors of the visible spectrum are focused at different points. Use a diagram to illustrate your explanation.
5. Describe the two vision problems. How is each corrected?
6. Describe how an optical fiber transmits light.

dows in your house to transfer more light into the room? How? (Answers will vary but students might suggest using concave lenses to diverge the light more or the use of mirrors.)
3. You found a small microfossil and would like to see it up close. What can you do to magnify the microfossil? (Use a magnifying glass or a series of convex lenses.)

ISSUES IN SCIENCE
The following issues can be used as a springboard for class debate or may be assigned as a writing homework.
1. Some people feel that the field of medicine is emphasizing the teaching and use of laser surgery over normal surgery with knives. What is your opinion? Explain your reasoning.
2. Many useful tools have been developed with the use of light energy. Do you predict that some day we will power automobiles and airplanes by light energy? Explain your answer.

length, each color is bent a different amount.
5. Nearsightedness: concave lens corrects; farsightedness: convex lens corrects

ADDITIONAL QUESTIONS AND TOPIC SUGGESTIONS

1. Imagine the electricity went out in your home. You have no flashlights but do have a candle, matches, a plane mirror, a convex mirror, a convex lens, and a concave lens. What type of arrangement would you set up to get the most light? Draw a sketch of how you would arrange the materials in a room. Explain your setup. (Answers will vary but should use the refracting rays of the concave and/or the convex lenses and the reflecting rays of the mirrors plus the candle and matches.)
2. Could you change the kind of win-

Unit Seven

WAVES: SOUND AND LIGHT

ADVENTURES IN SCIENCE: JOHN CAULFIELD'S WONDERFUL WORLD OF HOLOGRAPHY

BACKGROUND INFORMATION

Holography was invented by Dennis Gabor in 1947 in order to improve the electron microscope, which views and photographs objects with a beam of electrons. The lenses Gabor was using were so poor that he set out to create a way to take pictures without lenses.

When an ordinary camera takes a picture, the film records the intensity pattern of light reflected from the object being photographed. In order for a sharp image to form, a lens must be placed at the proper distance between the object and the film.

Holography records the direction as well as the intensity of the light reflected from an object. This complete light pattern is called a wave front. When a wave front strikes a photographic plate or film without a lens, no picture is produced. However, if the wave front is intersected at the film or plate by a second set of light rays, a reference beam, the wave front can be recorded and later reconstructed by proper illumination. The only lens needed for this process is the human eye. It is interesting to note that when the human eye views an object in the real world, the eye is reached by wave fronts exactly like those produced by a hologram, which explains why a hologram looks so real.

Adventures in Science

JOHN CAULFIELD'S WONDERFUL WORLD OF HOLOGRAPHY

Welcome to the wonderful world of holography! Or, as Isaac Asimov has described it, "the greatest advance in imaging since the eye." With a wide range of applications, holography is fast becoming a tool of the artist, scientist, surgeon, and city planner alike. What exactly is holography?

According to Dr. John Caulfield of the University of Alabama, holography is an unusual photographic technique that records a three-dimensional image so accurately that the image often appears to be real. Little wonder then that the term coined for this exciting technique comes from the Greek words *holos* and *gramma*, which mean "the whole message."

Conventional photography records images in two dimensions, producing photographs that appear flat. But holography adds a third dimension. So a holographic image, or hologram, has the same details of depth and texture that the original object has. In a series of steps, holography recreates the complex pattern of light that reflects off an object and makes it visible.

580

TEACHING STRATEGY

Motivation

Bring in several photographs of objects. Pictures of people, animals, a building, or a car work well. Ask,
- **When you see these objects in real life, how many dimensions do they have?** (three)
- **How can you tell?** (The objects all have length, height, and depth.)
- **How many dimensions does a photograph have?** (two) **Why?** (It is a flat piece of paper; it has only length and width.)

Display the photographs and ask,
- **How is your knowledge of these objects limited by the fact that the photographs have only two dimensions?** (Because the third dimension is hidden, you cannot really tell how deep an object is. Also, you can only see one view of the object, the view

First, a laser beam is directed at an object. The beam bounces off the object and onto a photographic plate. Another laser beam is directed at the plate. Together, the two beams form a pattern of light interference that looks like gray smudges. When still another laser beam is aimed at the plate in the second step of the process, the blurry message is unscrambled. Color is added by the artist, photographer, or scientist. The reconstructed image of the original scene or object is so real the temptation is to reach out and touch it.

"An interesting characteristic of the hologram," says Caulfield, who is a leader in the field of holographic applications, "is that the observer is able to see many different views of the image. It is like viewing a three-dimensional scene through a window. By moving to different parts of the window, we see the same scene from new angles."

This innovative technology is actually not that new. Holography was invented in 1947 by the Hungarian scientist Dennis Gabor. But because his techniques were unrefined, Gabor's experiments were ignored for nearly fifteen years. With the introduction of the laser in 1960, the field of holography bloomed. Today, holography is a growing technology with uses in fields as different as engineering and tennis! And John Caulfield is one scientist who intends to be in the forefront of this exciting science.

Caulfield's research includes developing images of things that *do not* exist or perhaps *cannot* exist! Such images are called synthetic holograms. Synthetic holograms have many important uses. For example, engineers can use them to design more efficient and pollution-free motors for cars and machines. Architects can use synthetic holograms to design buildings and to determine their best location in the actual landscape. And doctors can view computer-generated holograms of

parts of the human body before performing surgery.

More practical applications of holography include the use of printed synthetic holograms on credit cards and the use of holographic optical instruments to scan product codes on grocery items.

Holographic images of an airplane's instrument panel are projected directly in front of pilots as part of their training. And a recent development uses holography to guide aircraft through fog by creating holograms of the airport.

The world of holography grows as Dr. Caulfield and other scientists refine and expand the technology. With his interest in the technique of holography and his belief in its infinite applications, Caulfield is helping to prepare future scientists for the challenges that lie ahead. Holography is a young science with a bright, exciting future. As Caulfield notes, "We haven't yet seen the whole message of holography!"

Working in a laboratory at the University of Alabama, Dr. Caulfield deflects a laser beam toward an object for pulsed laser holography.

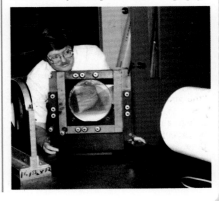

1. In what ways is a hologram different from a photograph? (It records objects in three dimensions; it shows an object from many different views; it can create images of objects that do not exist.)
2. What does holography recreate in order to produce an image? (the pattern of light that reflects off an object)
3. How are lasers used in the holographic process? (A laser beam directed at an object bounces off and onto a photographic plate. Another laser is beamed directly at the plate. A third laser is aimed at the plate to unscramble the pattern of light interference that resulted from the first two.)

CRITICAL THINKING QUESTIONS

1. Why do you think holograms are used on credit cards? (The complex light pattern that is recorded in a hologram would be very difficult to duplicate or copy. Thus the hologram acts as a protection against fraud.)
2. Why do you think synthetic holograms are helpful in designing new technological devices? (A synthetic hologram allows an inventor to see the thing that he or she imagines in tangible form. Then the inventor can evaluate and change the invention as he or she sees fit.)

from the angle at which the photograph was taken.)

Content Development
Explain to students that one of the advantages of a hologram is that it can show an object in three dimensions. It can also show the object from many different points of view. That is one of the reasons why we feel we can "reach out and touch" a hologram. Students may be amused to know that at the

CBS Laboratories in Stamford, Connecticut, there is a life-sized hologram of Dennis Gabor that looks so real that often people walk by and say, "Hello!"

Point out to students that holography did not come into its own until 1960, when the laser was introduced. It often happens in science that a new technology must be developed in order for someone's discovery or invention to be widely applied.

Unit Seven

WAVES: SOUND AND LIGHT

ISSUES IN SCIENCE: HYPERSONIC TRANSPORT: IS FASTER BETTER?

BACKGROUND INFORMATION

When an aircraft approaches the speed of sound, air begins to pile up in front of the aircraft, and the pressure waves, or sound waves, created by its motion can no longer move ahead of it. This significantly increases the drag on the plane. However, if the plane is powerful enough and properly streamlined, it will eventually move faster than the pressure waves and break the sound barrier.

As an aircraft flies faster than the speed of sound, it leaves behind itself two conical shock waves—one from its nose and the other from its tail. These shock waves cause the "sonic boom" heard on the ground as the plane passes overhead. In the hypersonic range, which is five or more times greater than the speed of sound, the angle of the cone decreases, causing the sonic boom to weaken by the time it reaches the ground. Thus the effects of sonic boom would be less with a hypersonic plane than with a supersonic plane.

Issues in Science

HYPERSONIC TRAVEL:

Is Faster Better?

Picture yourself as a busy New York rock star. Tough demands on your time are nothing new, but tomorrow's schedule seems impossible. You must attend an important breakfast meeting in London, sign contracts over lunch in New York, and perform before a sellout crowd at 8 P.M. in Los Angeles.

Can you do it?

You can if you prepare yourself for an exhausting twenty-six-hour trip that includes two supersonic flights and one subsonic flight. Aboard the supersonic transport, better known as the SST, travel is about twice the speed of sound, or 2400 kilometers per hour. Subsonic jetliners cruise at speeds between 800 and 1000 kilometers per hour. Thirty years ago, speeds such as these were only a dream. Today, they are a reality. But by the year 2000, they may be just a memory!

Need for Speed

By the year 2000, the wish of many travelers to go faster and faster may come true. The United States, Great Britain, and France are working on *hypersonic* airliner designs. Hypersonic transports, or HSTs, would fly at from five to eight times the speed of sound. In an HST, travel time from Los Angeles to Tokyo would be reduced from about ten hours to as few as two. And a flight from New York to San Francisco would be a mere 16 minutes—not five hours. Future predictions for the HST include round-the-world flights lasting no more than four hours!

Different Views

Some people believe that faster air travel could improve trade and cultural links between nations. And that's one reason why government and industry officials are urging the United States to build and use hypersonic airliners. Ben Rich of Lockheed Corporation

---

TEACHING STRATEGY

Motivation

Begin by asking students,
- **How many of you have ever taken an airplane trip?** (Probably many of them have.)
- **From where to where did you fly?** (Answers will vary.)
- **About how long did your trip take?** (Answers will vary.)

If a student's trip took four hours, for example, ask the student to speculate what it would have felt like if the trip had taken about 15 minutes. If anyone has flown halfway around the world, ask them what it would have felt like if their trip had taken only a few hours.

Content Development

Use the Motivation discussion as a lead-in to the subject of hypersonic travel. Explain that supersonic flights have been possible for several decades, but that in 1971, the U.S. government abandoned plans for the SST, or Supersonic Transport. According to a former professor of aerospace at Princeton, it was not environmental concerns that caused the SST's demise, but rather the projected high cost of operating the aircraft. High cost is one reason many people object to the possibility of hypersonic trans-

says, "Routine hypersonic flights between nations will be a reality by the end of the century."

Several aviation experts disagree, however. They feel that supersonic flight is not very practical and that hypersonic flight may be even less practical. These experts say commercial flights at speeds faster than the speed of sound have several drawbacks. One is cost. Planes burn more fuel at supersonic speeds. At faster speeds, the fuel use will be even greater and the costs higher. Another factor that adds to cost is the stress put on a plane's structure at supersonic speeds. As a result of this stress, supersonic planes require more frequent maintenance.

Furthermore, the critics argue, part of the speed advantage of hypersonic flights may be lost due to heavy traffic over and around major airports. A hypersonic plane might cross the Atlantic in less than an hour and then spend another half-hour waiting to land.

Another potential obstacle to commercial hypersonic flight is noise pollution. When an aircraft flies faster than sound, it creates shock waves in the air. These waves produce "sonic booms" that can be felt and heard on the ground. To protect people from sonic-boom effects, the U.S. Federal Aviation Administration (FAA) prohibits commercial supersonic flights over the United States.

Supporters of the hypersonic plane have no problem with the FAA limitation. As they see it, most of the HST flights would be over the ocean between the United States and the Far East. Trade between countries that rim the Pacific Ocean is greatly increasing. As a result, more and more people are flying between the United States and Japan, China, Singapore, and Australia.

To counter the argument of increased cost, supporters of the hypersonic plane claim that a significant portion of each trip could take

A long line of cars forms part of a protest march at Kennedy International Airport in New York. The target of the protest is the supersonic transport, or SST, whose noise level upon takeoff and landing has angered residents of the area.

place at higher altitudes than those used by conventional aircraft. Flying at higher altitudes uses less fuel and reduces operational costs.

No doubt, developing and building a hypersonic plane will be expensive. Aerospace industry specialists estimate that one hypersonic plane may cost $5 billion to $10 billion. Critics say it may cost twice that amount. But since HSTs may have uses outside the commercial-flight industry, supporters of the HST think that the high cost of developing the plane is justified. They support their position with the belief that the development effort would keep the United States in the forefront of the aviation industry.

Will the possible benefits to world trade, more efficient flight, and aviation advancement balance the costs in money and pollution? What do you think?

ADDITIONAL QUESTIONS AND TOPIC SUGGESTIONS

1. What disadvantages of hypersonic transport are mentioned in the article? (cost, noise pollution, having to work around the FAA restriction)
2. How does a supersonic or a hypersonic plane cause noise pollution? (by producing shock waves in the air when it flies faster than the speed of sound.)
3. A topic not mentioned in the article is safety of the proposed hypersonic planes. Research this topic and present arguments for and against hypersonic travel based on the safety factor.

CRITICAL THINKING QUESTIONS

1. Some supporters of hypersonic travel are saying that a person could leave New York after breakfast and have lunch in Tokyo. Why would this plan not work? (Because of the time differences between the two cities, the person would arrive in Tokyo shortly after midnight—a little off schedule for lunch!)
2. It's an old saying, "Time is money." Relate this cliche to the hypersonic travel issue, first from the point of view of a commercial airline, then from the point of view of an airline passenger. (Answers will vary.)

CLASS DEBATE

Have students research the issue further, then let each student choose which side he or she would like to defend. Then let students challenge each other to a debate.

port. However, a historian at the University of California at Berkeley points out that perhaps too much emphasis is being placed on the immediate commercial value of the aircraft. His view is that the technological advance should be made for its own sake, that it is something this country should be equipped with. Then once we have it, people will start using it.

Unit Eight
PHYSICAL SCIENCE AND TECHNOLOGY

UNIT OVERVIEW

In Unit Eight, students are first introduced to energy resources. Fossil fuels, solar energy, and nuclear energy are explored. Several alternative energy sources are also discussed. Land, air, and water pollution resulting from energy use are taken up next, as are possible methods of reducing pollution.

Chemical technology is then discussed. Students learn about the fuels obtained by fractional distillation of petroleum. They explore polymer formation and uses. Finally, the students read about electronic devices, including vacuum tubes, transistors, and integrated circuits. The operation of radios and televisions is described next. Students also learn about the development and operation of computers.

UNIT OBJECTIVES

1. **Describe some energy resources.**
2. **Discuss land, air, and water pollution, and describe methods used to reduce it.**
3. **Describe the production of fuels from petroleum.**
4. **Describe the formation and uses of polymers.**
5. **Explain the use of electronic devices and computers.**

INTRODUCING UNIT EIGHT

Begin your teaching of the unit by having students examine the unit-opening photograph, which shows steam being released from vents in the ground in Iceland. Ask students the following questions regarding this photograph.

• **Where is Iceland located? What is its climate like?** (Iceland is in the North Atlantic and has a fairly cold climate, although temperatures are not as low as might be expected, given its latitude.)

• **What energy sources are visible in the picture?** (Sunlight and steam are visible.)

• **Where is the steam coming from?** (It comes from volcanically heated underground water, and rises through vents.)

Now have students read the unit introduction. This material should serve as the basis for various discussions that will better motivate students to study the chapters that follow. Here are some questions you may wish to pose to the class to initiate class discussions.

• **How might the steam be used as an energy source?** (The steam can either be used directly, or it can be used first to heat water.)

• **What form of energy is contained by the steam?** (Potential heat energy,

Physical Science and Technology

Most countries mine coal and oil to produce energy. But Iceland, a small island nation in the North Atlantic, mines "volcanic fires." Iceland sits atop a volcanic belt covering one-third of its territory. The heat generated from this geothermal belt provides Icelanders with 30 percent of their total energy needs and 70 percent of their space-heating requirements.

In the past, Icelanders have used geothermal energy for hot springs bathing and laundering. Today, the uses have been expanded to include home heating, electricity production, and industrial manufacturing. No wonder Icelanders say, "Think well of the glowing embers."

Iceland's use of geothermal energy demonstrates how clean, inexpensive alternative energy sources can be used to meet people's energy needs. But the "glowing embers" are only one example. As you read the chapters in this unit, you will learn about alternative energy sources. And you will also learn how the union of science and technology promises to provide exciting and important developments for your future.

CHAPTERS

Solar energy can be used any time and place the sun shines. Geothermal energy comes from within the earth. It can be used even when the sun does not shine. The steam rising from the ground is produced when water is heated underground.

585

CHAPTER DESCRIPTIONS

25 Energy Resources Chapter 25 deals with resources such as fossil fuels and solar energy. Nuclear energy is also discussed, as are potential alternative energy sources.

26 Energy and the Environment In Chapter 26, the nature of pollution is discussed. Land, air, and water pollution are taken up. Methods for dealing with pollution are also described.

27 Chemical Technology Fuels derived from petroleum are discussed in Chapter 27, as is the process of fractional distillation. Formation of polymers from monomers is discussed. Finally, some important natural and synthetic polymers are described.

28 Electronics and Computers In Chapter 28, electronics is defined and discussed. Devices such as the vacuum tube and transistor are explained. The operation of radios, cathode-ray tubes, and televisions is also treated. Finally, the development and use of the computer are discussed.

as well as kinetic energy associated with temperature, is contained by the steam.)

• **In what other places in the world is natural steam energy made use of?** (A number of other countries, such as New Zealand, make extensive use of such energy.)

Chapter 25
ENERGY RESOURCES

CHAPTER OVERVIEW

In this chapter, students will learn about present and future energy resources. They will become aware of human dependence on energy and the need to ensure that the world's energy supply can keep pace with growing energy needs.

Students will learn about the three main types of fossil fuels and how these fuels formed in the earth. They will also learn that fossil fuels are in limited supply, and that alternative energy resources are being developed to at least partially replace them.

Students will read about the importance of the sun as an energy resource. Solar energy can be used directly, as in solar heating systems and solar cells, or indirectly, as in the use of wind and water power.

The development of nuclear energy will be discussed. Students will learn how energy is produced from nuclear reactions at a nuclear power plant.

In the last portion of the chapter, students will be introduced to potential alternative energy resources. These include gasohol, geothermal energy, biomass, and hydrogen power.

INTRODUCING CHAPTER 25

Have students observe the picture on page 586. Ask,
- **What kind of fuel do you see being used?** (wood)
- **For what types of things are these people dependent upon fuel?** (warmth, cooking, light)
- **For what types of things are we dependent upon fuel?** (the same things, plus power for automobiles, machinery, and appliances)
- **What types of fuel do we use?** (perhaps in some instances wood or coal, but mainly oil, gasoline, natural gas)

Have students read the chapter introduction. Compare the caveperson's energy crisis with the energy crisis of 1973. Ask,
- **What factors threatened to remove the cavepeople's source of energy?** (the fact that they did not know how to start a fire, plus the carelessness of the person who was supposed to watch the fire)
- **What could have solved the cavepeople's dilemma?** (knowledge of how to start a fire; greater vigilance on the part of the firekeeper; discovery of another fire source close to the cave)
- **What factors threatened to remove our source of energy in 1973?** (drastic reduction of oil shipments due to a limited supply of oil, probably

Energy Resources 25

CHAPTER OBJECTIVES

After completing this chapter, you will be able to

25–1 Explain how fossil fuels formed on the earth.

25–1 Define hydrocarbon and combustion.

25–2 Describe several direct uses of solar energy.

25–2 Explain how power derived from moving water and wind is related to the sun.

25–3 Compare the processes of nuclear fission and nuclear fusion.

25–3 Describe the parts of a nuclear reactor.

25–4 Discuss the importance of alternative energy resources.

25–4 List several potential alternative energy resources.

The time: 75,000 years ago. Huddled together in a dim cave, the hunters prepare for a long, cold night. A smoldering fire provides the only warmth as a chilling darkness settles over the land. One member of the group agrees to keep the fire going while the others sleep. The hunters do not know how to start a fire. They have carried the glowing embers for this fire from the remains of a forest fire started by lightning.

The night is quiet. The fire-keeper's eyes grow heavy. Soon he is asleep. The fire goes out. The hunters have lost their only source of light and heat. It is humankind's first energy crisis.

The time: 1973. Cars line up for at least 4 kilometers. As the sun peeks over the horizon, a young man selling coffee and doughnuts makes his way through the sea of automobiles. The more sociable motorists use the opportunity to visit with neighbors. Others read the morning paper or try to sleep. The rest just sit in their cars and scowl.

An early morning traffic jam? No, the first experience with an oil shortage for the United States. Shipments of oil to the United States have been drastically reduced. Motorists wait in line for what has become a most precious commodity—gasoline.

Fortunately, the oil crisis of 1973 did not last long. The discovery of new oil fields plus efforts to conserve fuel produced a relative abundance of oil by 1986. But the shortages of the 1970s were dramatic indications of how dependent people are on fuel and how dangerously close they are to running out of it.

Every day you use energy from fuel to heat your home, power your car, operate appliances, and cook your food. What would your life be like if that energy were not available? In this chapter, you will learn about various energy resources for present and future use. With that information, you should be better able to answer the question.

Early people used fire for cooking, for light and heat, and to ward off dangerous animals.

587

TEACHER DEMONSTRATION

Obtain several devices such as an oil lamp, a kerosene lamp, a candle lantern, a kerosene heater, a camping stove. Display each item and the type of fuel it uses. Discuss the function of each item, then carefully demonstrate how each item is used. (**CAUTION:** *Make sure the classroom is properly ventilated, or conduct the demonstration outdoors. Do not allow students to handle the items once they are ignited.*)

Point out that there was a time not too long ago when devices such as these were depended upon for heat and light. Ask,

• **Can you think of other nonelectrical devices that would provide warmth and light? What types of fuel would they use?** (Answers will vary.)

TEACHER RESOURCES
Audiovisuals
Nuclear Energy, 3 filmstrips, PH Media
Solar Energy, 2 filmstrips, Learning Arts
The Power and Energy Crisis: Technological Challenge of the Future, 2 filmstrips, PH Media
The Sunbeam Solution, film, Time-Life

Books
Chauliaquet, C., et al., *Solar Energy in Building*, Wiley
Hagel, J., *Alternative Energy Strategies: Constraints and Opportunities*, Praeger

brought about by overuse of known oil resources)
• **What factors prevented the shortage from continuing?** (conservation of oil resources; discovery of new oil fields)

Point out that the problems and solutions were similar in both instances—the people involved needed to be more careful, and they also needed to increase their knowledge of how to obtain and use energy resources. Continue the discussion by having students list the ways in which they use energy from fuel every day. To sharpen their awareness of what life would be like without fuel, ask,
• **Have you ever experienced a power blackout due to a storm or other problem?** (probably most have)
• **What types of things did you have to do without?** (electric lights, television, refrigeration, heat or air conditioning)

• **How did you go about solving the problems presented by this loss of power?** (Answers will vary. Probably they will include turning to alternative power sources, such as candles or battery-operated devices.)

25-1 FOSSIL FUELS

SECTION PREVIEW 25-1

In this section, students will be introduced to the three main fossil fuels—coal, oil, and natural gas. Students will learn that these fuels are valuable as energy sources because they are rich in hydrocarbons.

Students will read about four stages of coal formation, each of which results in a different type of coal. They will learn about the formation of petroleum and natural gas, and how these resources are used as fuels.

Students will come to understand that the conditions under which fossil fuels formed no longer exist. Because of this, conservation of fossil fuels is an important issue in today's world.

PERFORMANCE OBJECTIVES 25-1

1. Identify the three main fossil fuels.
2. Describe the four types of coal and how each is formed.
3. Describe the formation of oil and natural gas, and explain how each is obtained and used.
4. Discuss the need to conserve fossil fuels.

SCIENCE TERMS 25-1

fossil fuel p. 588
hydrocarbon p. 588
combustion p. 588
peat p. 588

lignite p. 588
bituminous coal p. 588
anthracite p. 588
nonrenewable resource p. 590

25-1 Fossil Fuels

Most of the energy you use every day comes from **fossil fuels.** Fossil fuels formed hundreds of millions of years ago when layers of dead plants and animals were buried beneath sediments such as mud, sand, silt, or clay. Over millions of years, heat and great pressure changed the sediments into rock and the plant and animal remains into fossil fuels.

❶ The three main fossil fuels are coal, oil, and natural gas.

The reason fossil fuels are so useful as energy sources is due to their chemical makeup. Fossil fuels are rich in **hydrocarbons.** Hydrocarbons are substances that contain the elements hydrogen and carbon. When hydrocarbons in fossil fuels are combined with oxygen at high temperatures, heat and light energy are released. This process—which you probably call burning—is known as **combustion.**

Other types of fuels also give off heat and light during combustion. People have burned wood as a fuel ever since they learned how to start a fire. But wood and other fuels do not produce as much energy as fossil fuels. A kilogram of coal, for example, ❷ provides twice as much heat as a kilogram of wood. The heating values of oil and gas are more than three times that of wood. In addition, fossil fuels are easier to transport, store, and use.

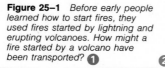

Figure 25-1 *Before early people learned how to start fires, they used fires started by lightning and erupting volcanoes. How might a fire started by a volcano have been transported?* ❶

588

Coal

Coal is a solid fossil fuel. There are four types of coal, each of which represents a different stage in the development of coal. Each can be used as a fuel.

The first type of coal is **peat.** Peat is a soft substance made of decayed plant fibers. When peat undergoes pressure from rocks piled above it, it is converted into **lignite** (LIHG-night). Lignite, the second type of coal, is soft and has a woody texture.

If even more pressure is applied to lignite, it ❸ turns into **bituminous** (bigh-TOO-muh-nuhs) **coal.** Bituminous coal, the third type of coal, is often called soft coal. Bituminous coal is the most plentiful type of coal on the earth. It takes tremendous pressure to change bituminous coal into **anthracite** (AN-thruh-sight), the fourth type of coal. Anthracite

---

TEACHING STRATEGY 25-1

Motivation

A few days before the lesson, have students survey adult family members or neighbors and ask how their homes were heated when they were children. (Encourage students to include some senior citizens.) Have students tally their results on the chalkboard. Then take a survey of the class to find out how students' homes are heated.

Content Development

Refer to the Motivation discussion and note the home heating systems that depend upon fossil fuels. (These include coal, oil, and natural gas.) Point out that coal was the first fossil fuel to be used in home heating, then oil, then more recently, natural gas.

Point out that in the United States today, only 1 percent of all coal produced is used for home heating. The majority of coal produced (about 71

percent) is used to produce energy for electric power plants.

Skills Development

Skill: Interpreting maps

Have students observe the map in Figure 25-2. Ask,

• **Are all of the coal deposits in the United States concentrated in one particular area?** (no)
• **Are they concentrated in several areas?** (yes)

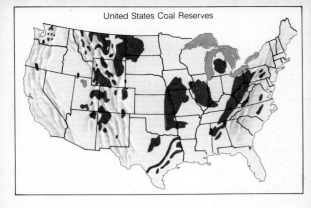

United States Coal Reserves

Figure 25–2 Coal miners dig for coal in deep mine shafts under the earth (right). Major coal reserves are located throughout the United States (left). Where is the coal deposit nearest your home located? ❷

is very hard and brittle. Few deposits of anthracite are located in the United States.

Oil and Natural Gas

Unlike coal, the plants and animals from which oil and natural gas formed probably lived in the earth's oceans. When they died, they sank to the ocean floor and were covered by sediments. In time, the layers of sediments changed into sandstone, limestone, or shale. Pressure from these rock layers, in addition to great heat and the action of certain bacteria, changed the plant and animal remains into oil and natural gas.

Rocks such as sandstone and limestone have tiny pores through which oil and gas can seep. When oil ❹ and natural gas were first formed, they probably seeped through the sandstone and limestone layers. In time, the oil and gas that were covered by harder rocks through which they could not seep formed pools. The oil and gas became trapped in natural "pockets" under the harder rocks.

Oil that is drilled from beneath the earth is called crude oil, or petroleum. Some of the fuels that can be obtained from petroleum are gasoline, kerosene, heating oil, and jet fuels. In Chapter 27, you will read about other petroleum products.

Although almost all of the petroleum used in the world today is obtained from oil wells, some petroleum is located near the surface of the earth. Two sources of this petroleum are tar sands and oil

Figure 25–3 Petroleum and natural gas are often found in the same deposit. Why is natural gas usually found above petroleum? ❸

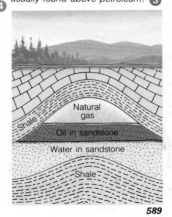

Natural gas

Shale

Oil in sandstone

Water in sandstone

Shale

589

TIE-IN/SOCIAL STUDIES

The presence of coal deposits or oil fields in a particular location greatly affects the economic and social development of that area. Have students research the development of a typical coal mining town, focusing especially on the problems that people face because the use of coal in the United States has changed. Then have students research the growth of an area in which oil has been discovered.

ANNOTATION KEY

❶ The lava would have ignited a tree limb or stump, which could then have been carried back to the cave or campsite. (Inferring)

❷ Answers will vary, depending on location. (Interpreting maps)

❸ Natural gas is less dense. (Applying concepts)

❶ Thinking Skill: Classifying

❷ Thinking Skill: Making comparisons

❸ Thinking Skill: Sequencing events

❹ Thinking Skill: Making observations

• **What are these areas?** (the Appalachian region; some of the Midwestern and Southwestern states; some of the Rocky Mountain states)
• **Are there areas of the U.S. in which there are no major coal deposits?** (yes)
• **What are these areas?** (West Coast; New England; parts of the Great Lakes region)

Natural gas

Oil

Figure 25–4 *To obtain petroleum and natural gas, geologists drill through rock layers covering the fuel deposits (left). The petroleum obtained from deposits in Alaska is piped through the Alaska pipeline (right).*

Sharpen Your Skills

Where Is the Oil?

Using books and other reference materials in the library, find out where the major oil fields in the world are located. Make a map showing these oil fields. Be sure to include oil fields that have recently been discovered, as well as areas that are presently believed to contain oil.

590

shale. Tar sands are layers of sand soaked with thick, gooey petroleum. Oil shale is a gray rock that can contain droplets of oil within the rock. Unfortunately, obtaining oil from both tar sands and oil shale is not economical.

Natural gas is usually found along with petroleum. Because natural gas is less dense than petroleum, it often is located above petroleum deposits. The most common natural gas is methane. Methane and other types of natural gas are used as fuels to heat homes. Methane also is used in gas stoves.

Fossil Fuel Shortages

Fossil fuels are **nonrenewable resources.** Nonrenewable resources are formed by nature over millions of years. Once they are used up, they cannot be replaced. So the gasoline lines of 1973 could return. Even worse, some scientists believe that if people continue to use oil at the present rate, the United States may be out of oil by the year 2060. The worldwide supply of oil may be used up by 2080. A resource that took hundreds of millions of years to form will be used up in the span of a few thousand years. Do you now understand why

---

conservation of nonrenewable resources such as fossil fuels is such an important topic—not just for scientists but for everyone throughout the world?

SECTION REVIEW

1. What are the three main types of fossil fuels?
2. What is the name for substances made of the elements hydrogen and carbon?
3. Why is natural gas usually found on top of petroleum deposits?
4. Most scientists believe that oil and natural gas formed beneath the ocean floor. However, a great amount of oil and natural gas are now found beneath dry land. Explain how this could have occurred.

Figure 25–5 *Oil shale may contain enough oil to be ignited.*

25–2 Solar Energy: Direct and Indirect

Section Objective

To describe direct and indirect uses of solar energy

Life on earth could not exist without the energy given off by the sun. Without this **solar energy,** plants would not grow, rain would not fall, and wind would not blow. Planet Earth would be so cold and dark that nothing could survive.

Scientists estimate that the amount of solar energy falling on a 200-square-kilometer plot near the equator is enough to meet the world's energy needs! As you can see, tapping this solar energy certainly would help conserve fossil fuels. **Solar energy can be used directly from the sun or indirectly, such as using wind or water power to produce usable energy.** ❶

Direct Solar Energy

Direct solar energy means taking energy straight from the sun and using it. The main problem with direct solar energy is that it is difficult to collect, convert, concentrate, and store.

PASSIVE SOLAR ENERGY Direct solar energy can be either passive or active. An example of passive use would be positioning windows in a house so that the

591

25-2 SOLAR ENERGY: DIRECT AND INDIRECT

SECTION PREVIEW 25-2

In this section, students will be introduced to the uses of solar energy, both direct and indirect. Direct use of solar energy consists of taking energy straight from the sun and using it. Indirect uses of solar energy include the harnessing of wind power and water power.

Students will learn that direct use of solar energy can be active or passive. They will also learn that solar energy can be converted into electricity by means of a photovoltaic cell.

As students read about indirect uses of solar energy, they will discover how blowing wind can produce useful energy. They will also discover how the movements of rivers, streams, and tides can be harnessed to produce useful energy.

PERFORMANCE OBJECTIVES 25-2

1. **Distinguish between direct and indirect uses of solar energy.**
2. **Distinguish between active and passive uses of solar energy.**
3. **Explain how a solar cell converts sunlight into electricity.**
4. **Explain how water and wind power provide useful energy.**

SCIENCE TERMS 25-2

solar energy p. 591
solar collector p. 592
photovoltaic cell p. 592
hydroelectric p. 593
tidal power p. 593

---

other parts of the world, and compare to coal use in the United States. (They should find that in less industrialized nations, coal is used in industry and home heating to a greater extent than it is in the United States.)

Section Review 25-1

1. Coal, oil, and natural gas
2. Hydrocarbons
3. It is less dense than petroleum.
4. The oceans dried up or the land

beneath the oceans rose up above the waterline.

TEACHING STRATEGY 25-2

Motivation

Have students observe Figure 25-6. Ask,
• **What distinctive feature do you notice about the design of these buildings?** (slanted, glass-covered surfaces)
• **What do you think will happen to these glass surfaces when the sun**

shines on them? (They will become hot.)
• **Have you ever had an experience of glass becoming hot when exposed to sunlight?** (Answers will vary. A typical example is a closed car becoming hot from sitting in the sun.)

If possible, obtain other photographs of buildings designed to utilize solar energy. Display the photographs and discuss the use and placement of glass to obtain solar energy.

TEACHER DEMONSTRATION

The following demonstration will illustrate how solar energy can be used to boil water.

In a sunny spot, clamp a small Pyrex test tube half full of water on a ring stand. Hold a concave mirror so that sunlight is reflected and focused on the tube. To heat the water faster, you may wish to have three or four students assist you by also holding mirrors. Have students note the time it takes for the water to boil. Discuss the use of mirrors to intensify the radiant energy.

BACKGROUND INFORMATION

An active solar system is defined as any system that makes use of a technological device. Such devices include solar collectors, pumps, heat exchangers, and fans. A passive system utilizes only those things that would normally be part of a building. These include the positioning of windows, the use of thermal materials in floors and walls, and the use of glass enclosures to trap sunlight.

25-2 (continued)

Content Development

Refer to the Motivation discussion and point out the passive and active uses of solar energy in the photographs and pictures you displayed. Point out that in passive uses of solar energy, the positioning of windows is often augmented by the use of thermal materials in the walls and floors of the house. These materials absorb the heat brought in through the windows during the day, then radiate the heat into the house at night.

Content Development

To help students better understand the use of a solar collector in an active solar heating system, write the following steps on the chalkboard.
1. Water in solar collector heated by sun's energy
2. Hot water pumped to storage tank
3. Hot water circulated through house as needed to provide heat
4. Cooled water returned to solar collector to be heated again
• **Why is the water cool when it returns to the solar collector?** (It has given up its heat to warm the house.)

Figure 25–6 *These solar collectors reflect the sun's rays toward a tower of water, where enough heat energy is absorbed to heat the water (left). The solar collectors on the roof of this school in Denver, Colorado, supply most of the school's energy (right). Are these solar collectors an example of the direct or indirect use of solar energy?* ❶

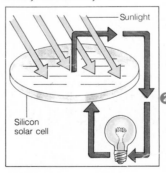

Figure 25–7 *A solar cell, or photovoltaic cell, converts sunlight directly into electricity.*

Sunlight

Silicon solar cell

592

amount of sunlight absorbed would be enough to heat the house. The obvious problem with passive solar energy for home heating is that when the sun stops shining, the source of heat is removed.

ACTIVE SOLAR ENERGY Active solar energy involves collecting the sun's energy in a device called a **solar collector.** In a typical solar collector, a large, dark ❶ surface covered with glass or plastic absorbs energy from the sun. Water is actively pumped through pipes or a large, flat surface inside the collector. The water is warmed by the sun's energy. The warm water is then stored to provide heat and hot water for some future time. What advantage does ❷ active solar heating have over passive solar heating?

Although the use of passive and active solar heating has been successful in many homes, it has not gone far to meet the energy needs of society as a whole. In order to provide energy for offices, schools, factories, hospitals, and apartment complexes, some type of central solar power plant must be designed.

SOLAR CELLS A solar cell, or **photovoltaic cell,** is a device that converts sunlight directly into electricity. Most solar cells are "sandwiches" of very thin layers of silicon and metal. When sunlight strikes ❷ the surface of this sandwich, electrons flow across the layers. This flow of electrons is electric current, which can be used to do work. Unfortunately, the amount of electricity produced by a single solar cell is very small. Huge numbers of cells are needed to produce useful amounts of electricity.

Point out that many types of heating systems circulate hot water through pipes. Some students may have heating systems in their homes in which water is heated in a boiler by a fuel such as gas or oil, then circulated through pipes to radiators or baseboard heaters.

Reinforcement

Some students may have difficulty distinguishing between direct and indirect, active and passive uses of solar energy. On the chalkboard, write the word *Direct* on one side and *Indirect* on the other side. Under Direct write the words *Active* and *Passive.* Have students list examples of each type of energy use. Emphasize that indirect use of the sun's energy implies that the sun's energy produces something such as wind or rain, which in turn can be tapped as an energy source. Also emphasize that active and passive are

Solar cells were first used on a large scale in 1959 to generate electricity aboard the United States space vehicle *Vanguard I*. Since then, they have been used to generate electricity on most spacecraft. Can you think of a reason why solar cells would be especially effective in space? ❸

One disadvantage of solar cells has been their cost. In 1959, electricity from solar cells cost about $500 per watt. Now it is down to $6 per watt. Although the efficiency of solar cells has been greatly improved, energy experts say that the cost will have to be lowered to $1 per watt in order to compete with the cost of electricity obtained from fossil fuels.

Indirect Solar Energy: Water Power

Energy from the sun causes water to evaporate from oceans and lakes. This water vapor condenses to form clouds in the atmosphere. When the water vapor falls back to the earth as rain or snow, it produces rushing rivers and streams.

There is tremendous power in moving water. Since ancient times, people have used that power to turn mill wheels. By the late 1800s, most water mills had been replaced by steam engines. But with the invention of the electric light bulb in 1879, water power became important once again as a means of generating electricity. Why is water power an indirect use of solar energy? ❹

The mechanical energy in falling or flowing water is used to generate usable electricity in a **hydroelectric** power plant. Hydroelectric means "using water to produce electricity." At a hydroelectric plant, dams hold back millions of tons of water. Some of the water is allowed to pass through pipes and is then channeled past turbines within the plant. The rushing water spins the blades of a turbine in an electric generator to produce electricity. Although new plants are built each year, the number of areas in which a dam can be built is limited. In this sense, hydroelectric power is limited. ❸

In the past few years, another way of producing hydroelectric power has been developed. This method, often referred to as **tidal power,** involves using the rise and fall of tides. In areas where the difference between high and low tides is great, the

Sharpen Your Skills

Dinosaur Power

Almost 100 million years ago, a dinosaur called *Stegosaurus* roamed the earth. Some scientists believe *Stegosaurus* used solar energy in an unusual way.

Using books and other reference materials in the library, find out what the *Stegosaurus* looked like. Then predict what part of its body might have been used to absorb solar energy.

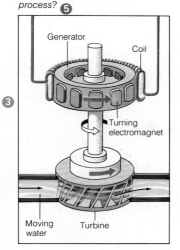

Figure 25–8 *Inside a generator at a hydroelectric plant, the mechanical energy of moving water is used to spin a turbine. The spinning turbine, in turn, causes large electromagnets to spin. The spinning electromagnets generate electricity. What energy conversion is involved in this process?* ❺

Generator

Coil

Turning electromagnet

Moving water

Turbine

593

Sharpen Your Skills

Dinosaur Power
Skills: Predicting, applying
Level: Enriched
Type: Library

Students will discover through research that many scientists believe the large raised plates running down the back of the stegosaurus may have been used to collect solar energy to help this coldblooded reptile maintain its body temperature.

TIE-IN/EARTH SCIENCE

The process by which the earth's water supply is replenished is called the water cycle. The cycle begins as energy from the sun causes water on the earth to evaporate. The water vapor forms clouds, then eventually condenses. The condensed water vapor falls to the earth as precipitation. When some of this new water evaporates, the cycle begins all over again.

ANNOTATION KEY

❶ Direct (Applying concepts)
❷ Heat is still available at night or on cloudy days. (Inferring)
❸ Intensity of sunlight is great and there are no clouds to obstruct the sunlight. (Relating concepts)
❹ The sunlight is not used directly, but its effects on water are applied to produce energy. (Applying definitions)
❺ Mechanical energy of moving water converted into electric energy (Applying concepts)
❶ Thinking Skill: Applying technology
❷ Thinking Skill: Applying technology
❸ Thinking Skill: Sequencing events

different ways of using the sun's energy directly.

Skills Development
Skill: Relating concepts
• **In the discussion of fossil fuels in the last section, what concern was raised about future use of this resource?** (These fuels are non-renewable because the conditions under which they formed no longer exist. Thus we may someday run out

of fossil fuels.)
• **Does this same problem exist with regard to solar energy?** (no)
• **Why not?** (The sun shines every day, and never stops producing energy.)
• **What special problems do exist with regard to using solar energy as a primary energy source?** (It is difficult to collect and store, and so far no way has been designed to use solar energy on a large scale.)

Although hydroelectric power produces almost no pollution, the building of a dam can upset the ecological balance in an area. Have students research the effects that a hydroelectric power plant can have on the environment.

FACTS AND FIGURES
Use of tidal power is limited to coastal regions where the difference between high tide and low tide is usually greater than 8 meters.

BACKGROUND INFORMATION
When air is heated, its density decreases. The warm air rises, producing an area of low pressure. Cooler, denser air, which produces an area of high pressure, moves in underneath the warm air. It is this movement of air that creates wind.

Figure 25–9 *For centuries, the mechanical energy of moving water has been used to turn water mills (left). Today, falling water at Boulder Dam is used to generate electricity (right). Are water mills and hydroelectric plants direct or indirect uses of solar energy?* **1**

movement of water during changes in the tides can be used to spin a turbine and generate electricity. Tidal power plants are in use in France, Canada, and the Soviet Union. However, tidal power as an energy resource is quite limited since there are relatively few areas in the world in which tidal power plants can be built.

CAREER   *Hydroelectric Plant Operator*

HELP WANTED: HYDROELECTRIC PLANT OPERATOR Must have mechanical skills or power-plant operation experience. Work includes maintaining equipment and supervising other employees. High school diploma required.

A huge, light-green water pipe extends from one reservoir at the top of a cliff to another reservoir at the bottom of the cliff. During the day, gravity pulls water down through the pipe to turn turbines and generate electricity. At night, water from the lower reservoir is pumped back into the upper reservoir.

A **hydroelectric plant operator** oversees the daily flow of millions of liters of water up and down through the pipe. The operator makes sure that the electric generating plant's turbines and other equipment are working properly. The operator monitors meters and gauges and records the amount of water that is released from the upper reservoir or that is pumped from the lower reservoir.

The operator routinely checks safety devices. During power failures, the operator may

have to start up or reverse the flow of water or repair faulty equipment. A hydroelectric plant operator must have mechanical skill and the ability to deal with emergencies quickly and efficiently.

Most hydroelectric power plant operators have a high school diploma plus several years of technical training. If you would like to learn more about this career, contact the International Union of Operating Engineers, 1125 17th Street NW, Washington, DC 20036.

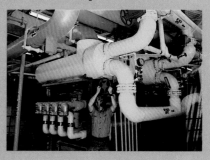

25-2 (continued)

Content Development
Review with students the idea that energy can change from one form into another. Point out that energy from the sun is called radiant energy. (Radiant energy is actually produced by nuclear reactions on the sun's surface.) The energy of rushing water or blowing wind is mechanical energy.

Ask,
- **What happens to the mechanical energy of rushing water when it reaches a generator at a hydroelectric power plant?** (It spins a turbine, which in turn causes electromagnets to spin. The spinning electromagnets generate electricity, thus converting mechanical energy into electric energy.)

Skills Development
Skill: Identifying cause and effect
Wind generators were very popular on American farms during the 1930s. Yet there were days when little or no electricity was generated, and there were times when the wind generators fell apart.
- **What conditions do you think caused these occurrences?** (Calm days, with little or no wind, caused little or no electricity to be produced. Storms

Indirect Solar Energy: Wind Power

Solar energy does not heat the earth evenly. It is the uneven heating of the earth by solar energy that causes winds to blow. Throughout history people have used the wind to propel sailing ships, turn mill wheels, and pump water. Why is wind power an indirect use of solar energy? **2**

In 1890, a Danish inventor developed a windmill that could generate electricity. The movement of the wind caused the windmill to spin. The spinning windmill was connected to a turbine in a small electric generator. As the wind blew, an electric current was generated. Wind generators became very popular with American farmers. They were widely used until the 1940s. But wind generators had some serious disadvantages. Can you think of what some of these disadvantages might be? **3**

When the United States faced serious oil shortages in the 1970s, interest in wind energy was renewed. The use of new materials and designs made possible the development of tough, efficient wind generators. Some of these look like giant egg beaters. Others look like weather vanes. Still others look like huge cylinders. Most can adjust to changing wind conditions, and all can withstand storms. **1**

Energy planners do not expect wind energy to meet the energy needs of the world. But they do believe that the increased use of wind generators will save fuel and reduce air pollution.

Figure 25–10 *This experimental windmill "farm" at Altamont Pass in California consists of several thousand windmills that generate electricity. Is this a direct or indirect use of solar energy?* **4**

Sharpen Your Skills

Timing Tides
Skills: Making calculations, comparing, relating
Level: Average
Type: Computational

This activity provides some basic background information on tide changes and also reinforces mathematical skills. Students should find that a high tide will occur at 6:50 AM on Wednesday and at 7:40 AM on Thursday.

ANNOTATION KEY

❶ Indirect (Applying definitions)

❷ The sunlight is not used directly, but its effects on atmosphere create winds, which can be used to generate electricity. (Applying definitions)

❸ Generators do not work on calm days. Because wind blows at different speeds, amount of electricity produced varies greatly from day to day. (Inferring)

❹ Indirect (Applying definitions)

❶ Thinking Skill: Applying technology

or especially high winds would knock the wind generators down, blowing them apart.)

• **Why do you think farmers switched to hydroelectric power when it became available in the 1940s?** (Rushing water is much more reliable than wind—only a broken dam might interfere with its ability to produce electricity.)

Enrichment
Ask students to use reference materials in the classroom or library to find out more about the formation of precipitation and wind. Then have students make diagrams to illustrate how solar energy produces the energy of rushing water, and how solar energy produces wind power.

25-3 NUCLEAR ENERGY

SECTION PREVIEW 25-3

In this section, students will discover how energy is released during nuclear fission and nuclear fusion. Fission is the splitting of an atomic nucleus into two smaller nuclei; fusion is the joining of two atomic nuclei into a single larger nucleus.

Students will learn that most useful energy comes from nuclear fission. They will read how this energy is converted into electricity at a nuclear power plant, and how a fission reaction is initiated and controlled in a nuclear reactor.

Students will become aware of the limitations of using nuclear fission as an energy source. They will also discover why nuclear fusion is, as of yet, not a useful source of energy.

PERFORMANCE OBJECTIVES 25-3

1. **Explain how energy is released during nuclear fission and fusion.**
2. **Explain how energy from nuclear fission is converted into electricity.**
3. **Name and describe the parts of a nuclear reactor.**
4. **Discuss some problems associated with the use of nuclear energy.**

SCIENCE TERMS 25-3

strong force
p. 596
nuclear energy
p. 596
nuclear fission
p. 596
nuclear chain re-
action p. 597

core p. 597
moderator p. 597
control rod p. 597
nuclear fusion
p. 599

SECTION REVIEW

1. List three ways in which solar energy is used directly.
2. What is the relationship between hydroelectric power and solar energy?
3. In what ways is solar energy used in your home? Considering the region in which you live, what other forms of solar energy might be appropriate for use in your home?

Section Objective

To explain how energy is released during nuclear fission and nuclear fusion

25–3 Nuclear Energy

You may recall that the nucleus of an atom contains protons and neutrons. The force that binds protons and neutrons in the nucleus is called the **strong force.** Scientists have long known that if the strong force could be broken, vast amounts of nuclear energy would be released. In other words, if the nucleus of an atom could be split, a new and powerful energy source would be found. This energy, called **nuclear energy,** is the energy locked within the nucleus by the strong force.

Nuclear Fission

In 1938, the first **nuclear fission** (FIHSH-uhn) reaction was carried out. **Fission is the splitting of an atomic nucleus into two smaller nuclei, during which nuclear energy is released.** A fission reaction does not happen on its own. It must be made to happen. The most common fission reaction involves the splitting of a uranium-235 nucleus.

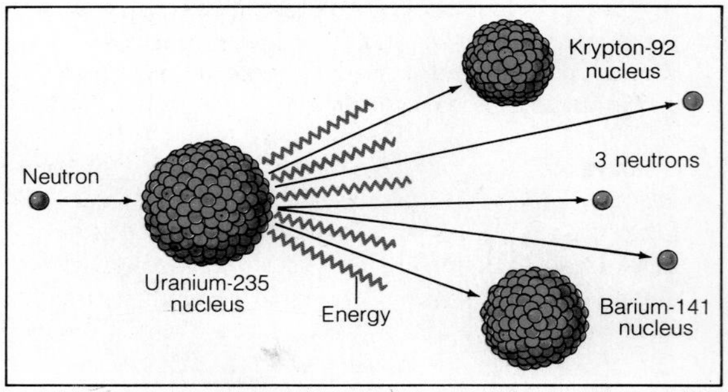

Figure 25–11 *In this diagram of a chain reaction, a uranium-235 nucleus is bombarded by a neutron "bullet." What are the products of this fission reaction?* ❶

596

25-2 (continued)

Section Review 25-2
1. Active solar system; passive solar system; solar cells
2. Solar energy evaporates water, which returns to earth as rain and snow. Rushing rivers, fed by rain and snow, are used in hydroelectric plants.
3. Answers will vary, depending on the region in which students live.

TEACHING STRATEGY 25-3

Motivation
Display a cluster of marbles on a large, flat surface. (The marbles should be as tightly packed as possible.) Take one marble and shoot it into the cluster so that the cluster breaks apart. Ask several students to try the same thing, challenging them to break the cluster into two parts that are nearly equal.

Point out that success depends upon aiming the shooter marble very carefully, and shooting it with a sufficient amount of energy.

Content Development
Use the Motivation activity to lead into a discussion of nuclear fission. Explain to students that in a fission reaction, the nucleus of an atom breaks apart, just as the cluster of marbles broke apart. Point out that the "shooter" in a

To split a uranium-235 nucleus, scientists must shoot a "nuclear bullet" into the nucleus. The nuclear bullet in a fission reaction is a neutron. When a neutron strikes the uranium-235 nucleus, the nucleus is split into a krypton-92 nucleus and a barium-141 nucleus. During this process, two or three more neutrons are released from the uranium-235 nucleus. Energy is released as well. See Figure 25-11.

Each neutron released during a fission reaction is capable of starting another fission reaction by splitting another uranium-235 atom. The neutrons released by each of these reactions then split several more atoms. One neutron striking one uranium-235 ❷ atom initiates a chain of nuclear fission reactions. The process in which the splitting of one atom causes the splitting of additional atoms is called a **nuclear chain reaction.**

If a nuclear chain reaction is uncontrolled, the resulting energy that is released will create an atomic explosion. That is just what happens in an atomic bomb. However, if the chain reaction is carefully controlled, the energy that is released can be a valuable energy resource. Controlled chain reactions take place in nuclear power plants.

Nuclear Power Plants

The energy produced during nuclear fission is mostly heat energy. In a nuclear power plant, this heat energy is used to convert water into steam. The steam then passes through a turbine in an electric generator. The steam spins the blades of the turbine. So nuclear power plants produce electricity from the energy locked within the nucleus.

Fission reactions in a nuclear power plant are produced and controlled in nuclear reactors. The three main parts of a nuclear reactor are the **core,** ❸ **moderator,** and **control rods.**

CORE The core is the central part of a nuclear reactor. It is within the core that nuclear fission takes place. To begin a fission reaction, nuclear fuel rods are placed in the core. The most common nuclear fuel is uranium-235. When neutrons strike the rods of uranium-235, nuclear fission begins. If the

597

BACKGROUND INFORMATION

A reactor requires a specific amount of fuel to maintain a chain reaction. This amount is called the *critical mass*. The critical mass varies according to the size and design of the reactor. If the amount of fuel is less than the critical mass, the chain reaction will die out. If the amount of fuel is greater than the critical mass, the reactor will overheat.

BACKGROUND INFORMATION

The reactions that take place inside a nuclear reactor release radiation. Some of this radiation is in the form of gamma rays. Gamma rays are the most penetrating form of radiation, requiring several centimeters of lead or concrete to stop them. Gamma rays are also the most dangerous form of radiation, for they have the ability to kill the cells of living things.

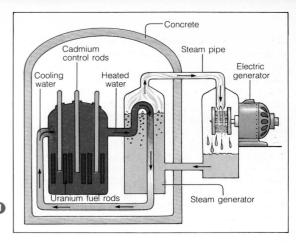

Figure 25–12 *This illustration shows the design of a typical nuclear reactor. How is the heat that is produced during a chain reaction converted into electricity?* ❶

Figure 25–13 *Before being placed in a reactor, nuclear fuel rods are carefully checked (top). If the nuclear fuel rods are placed at just the right distance from one another, a chain reaction will occur (bottom). What is the most common fuel for nuclear fuel rods?* ❷

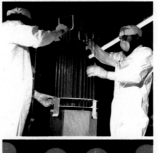

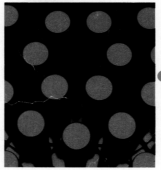

fuel rods are placed at just the right distance from one another, a chain reaction occurs. It is important to note that the nuclear fuel rods in a nuclear reactor cannot explode due to fission. That is, a nuclear explosion similar to an atomic bomb is impossible in a nuclear reactor.

MODERATOR The neutrons released during fission move very fast—too fast to be absorbed by other uranium nuclei. So the neutrons must be slowed down. A material that slows down neutrons is called a moderator. The most common moderator used in the United States is water.

CONTROL RODS In order for a nuclear reaction to produce useful energy, the overall speed of the reaction must be carefully controlled. This task is accomplished with control rods. In most reactors, the control rods are made of the element cadmium. Cadmium rods have the ability to "soak up" neutrons. By placing control rods deep in the reactor core, extra neutrons are absorbed and the fission process is slowed down. By pulling the control rods out of the reactor a bit, the fission reaction is speeded up as more neutrons become available to split uranium-235 nuclei.

There was a time not too long ago when energy experts predicted that nuclear power would become

---

25-3 (continued)

Content Development

Continue using the marbles as a model of nuclear fission. Ask,
• **Suppose I place several clusters of marbles fairly close together, then shoot a marble into one cluster. What might happen to some of the marbles that are released when the cluster breaks apart?** (They might hit other clusters of marbles.)
• **What will happen if they hit the clusters with quite a bit of energy?** (They will break the clusters apart.)

Point out that this is what happens in a nuclear chain reaction. The neutrons released in the first fission reaction act like the stray marbles— they target other nuclei of uranium-235. These nuclei split apart and in turn release neutrons, and so on.

Skills Development
Skills: Interpreting diagrams, relating concepts
Have students observe the diagram of a nuclear reactor in Figure 25-12. Ask,
• **Where in the reactor is water heated?** (in the core)
• **What is the pathway of the water once it is heated?** (It leaves the reactor and goes into the steam generator.)
• **What happens to the water once it reaches the steam generator?** (It

changes water into steam, thereby losing its heat and becoming cool.)
• **What is the pathway of the water once it has cooled?** (It leaves the steam generator and returns to the core of the reactor.)
• **What then happens to the water?** (It is reheated and the cycle begins again.)
• **Can you think of an energy system studied earlier in this chapter that recycles water in much the same way?**

the world's leading source of energy. Just one 1.25-centimeter pellet of uranium-235 can produce as much energy as 615 liters of fuel oil. And eight such pellets would be enough to supply all your home energy needs for one year. Yet the experts' predictions did not come true. What went wrong?

Aside from the potential safety problems associated with nuclear power plants, the main reason nuclear power has not become a more important energy resource is an economic one. The costs of building such plants have risen tremendously in the last decade. Electricity derived from nuclear power ❷ plants costs *more* than electricity derived from other sources. And it is estimated that the costs will go even higher.

Is nuclear power from fission a lost cause? Not at all. Scientists are trying to find ways to make nuclear power safer and cost effective. If they succeed, nuclear power may become an even greater source of energy in the future.

Nuclear Fusion

Just as splitting an atomic nucleus releases energy, so does combining two atomic nuclei. **The combining of atomic nuclei is called fusion.** In fact, **nuclear fusion** produces far more energy than nuclear fission. It is fusion that produces the energy given off by stars such as our sun.

Within the sun, enormous heat and pressure cause the nuclei of hydrogen atoms to fuse into a helium atom. During this process, some of the mass of the hydrogen nuclei is converted into energy. Scientists have found a way to produce energy through nuclear fusion. However, the energy produced is uncontrolled and destructive. The explosion of a hydrogen bomb is a nuclear fusion reaction.

To be able to produce a controlled fusion reaction that generates useful energy is a long-standing dream of many scientists. But it is very likely that by the year 2000 nuclear fusion will become a reality. Since a nuclear fusion reactor would use hydrogen from water, an unlimited supply of fuel would be available. This fact, plus the fact that nuclear fusion likely will be nonpolluting, explains why scientists want this dream to become a reality.

Figure 25–14 *Three Mile Island in Pennsylvania was the site of a serious nuclear power plant accident. Radiation escaped into the atmosphere when the reactor's cooling system failed and the nuclear core overheated.*

599

FACTS AND FIGURES

A 1.25-cm fuel pellet of uranium-235 can produce as much energy as 800 kg of coal, 615 L fuel oil, or 650 L gasoline. Eight such pellets would provide enough energy to meet all the needs of an average home for one year.

BACKGROUND INFORMATION

Most nuclear fusion reactions involve the joining of hydrogen atoms to form helium atoms. Temperatures of several million degrees Celsius are required for a fusion reaction. At such high temperatures, matter does not exist in an ordinary physical state. The form of matter that exists while fusion takes place is called *plasma*.

ANNOTATION KEY

❶ Heat from reaction boils water into steam. Steam then spins a turbine in an electric generator. (Interpreting diagrams)
❷ Uranium-235 (Relating facts)
❶ Thinking Skill: Sequencing events
❷ Thinking Skill: Applying concepts

Have students research Einstein's work and find out how it explains the energy released during a nuclear fission reaction.

Enrichment
One of the most serious accidents that can happen at a nuclear power plant is a core meltdown. Have students find out what a core meltdown is, and how it occurs. Also ask them to find out if any core meltdowns have occurred, what the consequences were, and what precautions are taken to prevent core meltdowns.

Skills Development
Skill: Making a model
Divide the class into groups of five or six students. Challenge each group to use familiar materials to make a model of a nuclear reactor. Have each group display their model and describe it to the class.

(solar heating system)
• **How is water recycled in this system?** (Water is heated in the solar collector, then is circulated to give heat to the house. Then it returns to the collector to be reheated.)

Reinforcement
To review the terms associated with the production of nuclear energy, write each of the following words or phrases on an index card: nuclear reactor, core, moderator, nuclear fuel, fuel rods, control rods, fission, chain reaction, nuclear power plant. Place the cards face down on a table and have students take turns drawing a card. Each student must give the definition of the word or phrase on the card that he or she has drawn.

Enrichment
In 1905, Albert Einstein presented a theory that relates mass and energy.

25-4 ALTERNATIVE ENERGY SOURCES

SECTION PREVIEW 25-4

In this section, students will read about the need to develop alternative energy resources. Some of these resources include gasohol, geothermal energy, biomass, and hydrogen power.

Students will learn that two alternative types of fuel are gasohol and biomass. Gasohol is a mixture of alcohol and gasoline that can be used to power automobiles. Biomass is fuel from plants and other organic materials that can be burned for cooking and home heating.

Students will read about an alternative energy source called geothermal energy. Geothermal energy is the energy that comes from hot springs and geysers.

A potential resource that is not yet practical to use is hydrogen power. Students will read about some of the possibilities and problems associated with this resource.

PERFORMANCE OBJECTIVES 25-4

1. **Discuss the need for the development of alternative energy resources.**
2. **Identify various alternative energy resources currently being developed by scientists.**
3. **Discuss the use of gasohol and biomass as alternative fuels.**
4. **Describe geothermal energy and explain how it is used.**
5. **Discuss the potential use of hydrogen power as an energy source.**

SCIENCE TERMS

gasohol p. 601
fermentation p. 601
geothermal energy p. 601
geyser p. 602
biomass p. 603
electrolysis p. 603

 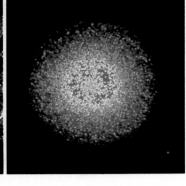

Figure 25–15 *Tiny hydrogen pellets placed in the chamber of an experimental fusion device are bombarded with a beam of electrons (left). When a pellet reaches temperatures of more than 70 million degrees Celsius, it undergoes nuclear fusion (right). If it could be fully developed, why would nuclear fusion be a source of energy that could meet worldwide needs?* ❶

SECTION REVIEW

1. What type of nuclear reaction involves splitting an atomic nucleus? Combining two atomic nuclei?
2. What is the "bullet" used in a fission reaction?
3. How is the rate of the chain reaction in a nuclear reactor controlled?
4. Why would safe economical nuclear power provide a good alternative to the dwindling supply of fossil fuels?

25–4 Alternative Energy Sources

Today, there are enough energy resources to meet the world's needs. Why then must people be concerned about conserving energy resources? The answer is twofold. One reason people must look for new, clean sources of energy is pollution. There are several pollution problems associated with many energy resources. You will read about some of these pollution problems in Chapter 26. The other reason people must develop new energy resources is the future energy needs of society. The present available supply of energy resources cannot be used up ❶ today without preparing for tomorrow. Today's generation must use energy wisely to ensure its availability for future generations. **Throughout the world, scientists are working to develop alternative energy resources, such as gasohol, geothermal energy, biomass, and hydrogen power.**

600

25-3 (continued)

Section Review 25-3

1. Fission; fusion
2. Neutron
3. Cadmium control rods are pushed in or pulled out to control the number of neutrons available in the chain reaction.
4. Nuclear energy can be used on a very large scale, just as fossil fuels are. By using nuclear energy, our supplies of fossil fuels would be conserved and could be applied to areas in which nuclear power is not appropriate.

TEACHING STRATEGY 25-4

Motivation

Have students study the graph in Figure 25-19. Ask,
• **What resource produces nearly half the energy we use in the United States?** (oil)

Gasohol

Almost all cars in the United States are powered by gasoline. During the gas shortages of the 1970s, however, scientists began looking for alternatives to gasoline. One alternative that was developed was **gasohol.** Gasohol is a mixture of gasoline and alcohol. Ethanol, or ethyl alcohol, is the alcohol commonly used. Gasohol is widely used today in South America.

Ethanol is obtained by the action of yeast cells on various grains such as corn, wheat, and barley. The yeast converts the sugar in the grain into ethanol and carbon dioxide in a process called **fermentation** (fer-muhn-TAY-shuhn). Today, scientists are experimenting with cars that run entirely on ethanol. How does gasohol conserve fossil fuels? ❷

Geothermal Energy

You may not realize it, but there is a lot of energy beneath your feet. Molten rock deep within the earth has an average temperature of about 1800°C. This heat is called **geothermal energy.** You do not

Figure 25–16 *Grains such as corn are combined with yeast cells to produce ethanol. What is the name of this process?* ❸

Figure 25–17 *This geothermal well in Iceland is a source of hot water (left). In a geothermal power plant, cold water is pumped into the earth where it is heated, returned to a power plant, and used to generate electricity (right). How else might the cold water pumped into the earth be used to generate electricity?* ❹

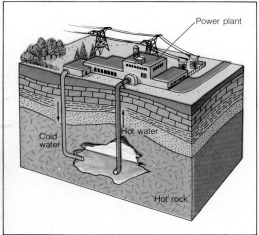

FACTS AND FIGURES

The United States has only 6 percent of the world's population, but it uses 33 percent of the world's energy.

ANNOTATION KEY

❶ Nonpolluting and has an unlimited source of hydrogen fuel from ocean water (Applying concepts)

❷ Gasohol saves on gasoline, which is produced from the fossil fuel petroleum. (Relating concepts)

❸ Fermentation (Applying definitions)

❹ Heat converts it to steam, which spins a turbine. (Inferring)

❶ Thinking Skill: Applying technology

past several hundred years, and how it may need to change again in the next several hundred if we are to survive. Ask,

• **What was the principle source of energy in American homes 200 years ago?** (wood)

• **What types of energy needs did this fuel supply?** (heating and cooking)

• **What were the principle forms of transportation at this time?** (walking, horses)

• **What provided light for homes and power for appliances?** (candles and oil lamps; the only "appliances" were devices used by hand)

Point out that the change in energy use over the last 200 years is due largely to technological advancement. Also point out that the same technology that uses so much energy can be put to work to help solve the problems of future energy needs.

• **How can technology be used now to prepare for the day when fossil fuels are no longer abundant?** (It can be used to develop alternative energy resources.)

• **How can people help prevent a shortage of fossil fuels?** (by conserving energy; by supporting the development of new resources; perhaps even by going into a career that contributes to the development of new resources)

• **What two resources together supply about the same amount of energy?** (coal and natural gas)

• **Are these resources renewable or nonrenewable?** (nonrenewable)

• **What do you think would happen in the United States if these resources were no longer available?** (Ninety percent of our energy would no longer be available; the very comfortable lifestyle we are used to would be drastically affected because there would be limited power for appliances, transportation, and heating; technology and industry would come to a near halt as power for factories would be severely limited; even the energy needed to develop new energy sources would be limited.)

Content Development

Use the Motivation activity to lead into a discussion of how energy use in the United States has changed over the

The best "hot spots" provide water that has a temperature between 150° and 350°C.

BACKGROUND INFORMATION

Geysers are formed when, deep in the earth, molten rock heats solid rock above. Water from the earth's surface seeps into the earth and touches the rock, which is hot enough to change the water into steam. The steam then moves up through cracks in the earth's surface.

ANNOTATION KEY

❶ Biomass (Applying definitions)
❷ 90 percent (Interpreting charts)
❶ Thinking Skill: Sequencing events
❷ Thinking Skill: Applying technology

notice this heat because you are shielded by about 64 kilometers of the earth's crust.

In some places, there are cracks and weak spots in the earth's crust. These cracks and weak spots are often called hot spots. Water in hot spots becomes heated by contact with hot rocks. Frequently, this water bursts forth from the earth in fountains of steam and boiling water known as **geysers.** Geysers and hot groundwater are used in Iceland to heat homes and greenhouses. In Italy, New Zealand, the Soviet Union, and the United States, water heated underground is used to spin turbines and generate electricity.

Hot spots can be used to produce geothermal energy in another way. Cold water is often pumped into hot spots in the earth. The heat in the hot ❶ spots turns the water into steam. Because the number of hot spot regions on the earth is limited, however, it is unlikely that geothermal energy can keep pace with the world's growing energy needs.

Biomass

Any material that can be burned is a combustible material. Combustible materials can be used in a variety of ways. They can be used to heat water and produce steam. The steam can then be passed through a turbine to generate electricity. Combustible materials also can be burned to generate heat for homes and factories. One group of combustible

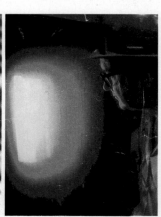

Figure 25–18 *From sugar cane grown in Hawaii (left), tiny pellets of fibrous wastes are formed (center). These fuel pellets can then be burned in a factory (right). What general term is used to describe combustible materials that come from living things?* ❶

25-4 (continued)

Skills Development
Skills: Interpreting diagrams, comparing, inferring
Have students observe the diagram of a geothermal power plant in Figure 25-17. Ask,
• **How is water heated in this power plant?** (It is pumped into the earth, where it comes into contact with hot rock.)

• **Where does the water go once it is heated?** (back to another part of the power plant to generate electricity)
• **Although the diagram does not show it specifically, can you infer what probably happens to the water once it has given up its heat to generate electricity?** (It is probably pumped back into the ground to be reheated.)
• **How is a geothermal power plant similar to a nuclear power plant?** (In both cases, water is heated by an en-

ergy source, then used to generate electricity.)
• **How is a geothermal power plant similar to an active solar heating system?** (In both cases, water is heated by a natural source, then pumped to a place where it can be used to provide energy.)

Skills Development
Skill: Comparing
Have students compare the possible

materials is known as **biomass.** Biomass includes plants, animal wastes, and all other forms of matter that come from living things.

Biomass has been used as a fuel for heating purposes for thousands of years. Wood is the main form of biomass used for combustion. Other forms of combustible vegetation include corn husks, waste fibers from sugar cane, sunflowers, and seaweed. In many parts of the world, animal wastes are dried in the sun and used as heating fuel.

One advantage of biomass is that it is renewable. Biomass fuels can continually be grown. Scientists are experimenting with ways to use biomass more economically and efficiently. However, as long as fossil fuels remain relatively inexpensive, biomass will not be a major source of energy worldwide.

Hydrogen Power

The only truly unlimited energy source on earth, other than sunlight, is hydrogen. Oceans, rivers, and lakes all contain hydrogen in the form of water. Hydrogen can be burned in place of fossil fuels. The problem with using the hydrogen in water is that it is bound to oxygen atoms. A water molecule, you may recall, contains 2 hydrogen atoms bonded to 1 oxygen atom.

To obtain hydrogen for combustion, a water molecule must be decomposed. The decomposition of water usually is done by passing an electric current through water. The process of decomposing water is called **electrolysis.** However, it takes more electricity to produce hydrogen during electrolysis than can be obtained by burning hydrogen at an electric generating plant. So at this time, hydrogen power does not appear to be a major energy source.

SECTION REVIEW

1. What is gasohol?
2. Use the definition of geothermal energy to explain the meaning of the prefix *geo-* and the suffix *-thermal*.
3. What is biomass? How can it be used to produce electricity?
4. How would building a house partially beneath the earth's surface help conserve energy?

Figure 25–19 *This chart shows the sources of energy used in the United States. How much energy is presently obtained from fossil fuels?* ❷

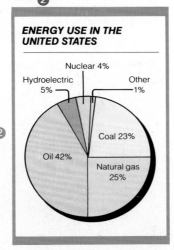

ENERGY USE IN THE UNITED STATES

Nuclear 4%
Hydroelectric 5%
Other 1%
Coal 23%
Oil 42%
Natural gas 25%

603

BACKGROUND INFORMATION

The largest geothermal electric generating complex in the world is located at The Geysers in California. It is owned and operated by Pacific Gas and Electric Company (PG&E). PG&E is considered a pioneer in the techniques of turning geothermal energy into electricity.

Geothermal energy plants have two advantages over hydroelectric power plants: They do not require the damming of rivers, and they do not pollute the atmosphere with smog from combustion products. The one disadvantage of using geothermal energy is that drilling to reach the hot rock is very expensive.

FACTS AND FIGURES

In Iceland, nearly 80 percent of all homes receive heat and hot water directly from hot springs and geysers.

Enrichment

Have students use the information in the text and Background section above to draw a diagram that shows the formation of a geyser. Point out that in a geothermal power plant, this natural process is enhanced by facilitating the flow of water to and from the hot rock.

Section Review 25-4

1. Combination of gasoline and ethanol
2. Geo = earth; thermal = heat
3. Biomass is all forms of matter that come from living things. Burning biomass can heat water and produce steam, which can be used to spin a turbine.
4. Temperature variations beneath the ground are less than those above the ground. Thus, houses would lose less heat in the winter and be cooler during the summer. In both cases, less energy is needed to warm or cool the house.

use of hydrogen power with the direct use of solar energy.
• **In what way is hydrogen power similar to solar energy?** (Both hydrogen and sunlight are unlimited resources on earth.)
• **What problem exists with regard to hydrogen that does not exist with regard to solar energy?** (Hydrogen is not usually found in the free state, so it is much harder to obtain than sunlight.)

• **If hydrogen were used as an energy source how would its use be different from that of solar energy?** (Solar energy can provide electricity directly by means of solar cells; hydrogen would have to be burned as fuel at a power plant in order to provide electricity. Also, solar energy can directly provide heat and hot water for a home, whereas hydrogen would have to be burned as a fuel to power a heating system.)

LABORATORY INVESTIGATION
SOLAR HEATING

BEFORE THE LAB
1. **Note that this lab must be done on a day when there is plenty of sunshine.**
2. **At least one day prior to the investigation, gather enough materials for your class, assuming six students per group.**
3. **The water should be allowed to stand for several hours in order to come to room temperature.**
4. **The metal or plastic containers should all be the same size.**

PRE-LAB DISCUSSION
Review the use of a solar collector to heat water in an active solar heating system. Ask,
- **What color is the inside of a solar collector usually painted?** (black)
- **Does this fact influence your hypothesis for this investigation?** (Answers may vary, but most will probably say yes.)
- **What is the variable in this investigation?** (the color of the paper surrounding the container of water)
- **What factors in the investigation must be carefully controlled?** (starting temperature of the water, amount of exposure to sunlight, amount of water in each container)

SKILL DEVELOPMENT
Students will use the following skills while completing this investigation.
1. Observing
2. Manipulative
3. Measuring
4. Safety
5. Recording
6. Relating
7. Applying
8. Inferring
9. Hypothesizing

SAFETY TIPS
Remind students to handle the thermometers carefully and to exercise caution when puncturing the lids of the containers.

Problem
Does the color of an object affect the amount of solar energy it absorbs?

Materials *(per group)*

black and white construction paper
2 metal or plastic containers with plastic lids
2 Celsius thermometers
water
scissors and tape
clock or watch

Procedure
1. Tape two layers of black paper around one container. Tape two layers of white paper around the other one.
2. Using the scissors, carefully punch the center of each lid to make a hole large enough to hold a thermometer. **CAUTION:** *Handle the scissors carefully.*
3. Fill each container with water at room temperature and cover them with plastic lids.

604

4. Carefully insert a thermometer through the hole in each lid. Make sure the bulb of the thermometer is just below the surface of the water. **CAUTION:** *Be careful when handling the thermometer.*
5. Place the containers on a sunny windowsill. Make sure each is in direct sunlight.
6. Record the temperature of the water in each container every 3 minutes for 36 minutes. Place your data on a data table.

Time (min)	3	6	9	12	15	18	21
Temperature (°C)							

Observations
1. During which time interval did the temperature in the black container begin to rise? During which time interval did the temperature in the white container begin to rise?
2. What was the final temperature of the water in the black container? In the white container?
3. Make a graph of your data, plotting temperature on the vertical axis and time intervals on the horizontal axis.

Conclusions
1. How effectively did the sun's solar energy heat the water in the containers?
2. Does the color of an object affect the amount of solar energy it absorbs?
3. What hidden variable might have an effect on your results?
4. Based on this experiment, what color clothing would you be likely to wear in the winter? In the summer?

TEACHING STRATEGY FOR LAB PROCEDURE
1. Point out to students that for accurate results, both containers of water must be filled to the same level.
2. The recording of the temperature every three minutes will probably go most smoothly if members of the lab group take turns reading the thermometer.
3. Suggest to students that they plot the temperatures of both containers on the same graph, using different color pencils.

OBSERVATIONS
1. Answers will vary depending on the intensity of the sunlight. However, the black jar should show a rise in temperature sooner than the white jar.
2. Answers will vary, but the black jar should show a higher final temperature.
3. Students' graphs should be consistent

CHAPTER REVIEW

SUMMARY

25–1 Fossil Fuels

❏ The three main types of fossil fuels are coal, oil, and natural gas.

❏ Fossil fuels have high heating values because they are rich in hydrocarbons.

❏ The four types of coals are peat, lignite, bituminous, and anthracite.

❏ Many fuels are produced from petroleum.

❏ Natural gas usually is found above deposits of petroleum. The most commonly used natural gas is methane.

❏ Fossil fuels are a nonrenewable resource whose supplies are running out.

25–2 Solar Energy: Direct and Indirect

❏ Energy given off by the sun is called solar energy.

❏ Solar energy can be used directly or indirectly.

❏ Active and passive solar heating systems are examples of direct solar energy.

❏ Solar cells, or photovoltaic cells, convert sunlight into electricity.

❏ Hydroelectric power is power derived from moving water.

❏ At a hydroelectric plant, moving water is used to spin a turbine and produce electricity.

❏ The movements of tides can be used to generate electricity.

❏ Windmills connected to a generator use the power of the wind to produce electricity.

❏ Both hydroelectric power and wind power are indirect uses of solar energy.

25–3 Nuclear Energy

❏ Nuclear energy is the energy locked within the atom by the strong force.

❏ Fission is the splitting of an atomic nucleus into two smaller nuclei.

❏ In a nuclear power plant, a nuclear chain reaction produces heat energy that can be used to convert water into steam and spin a turbine.

❏ The three main parts of a nuclear reactor are the core, moderator, and control rods.

❏ The combining of atomic nuclei is called nuclear fusion.

25–4 Alternative Energy Sources

❏ Gasohol is a mixture of gasoline and ethanol.

❏ Heat from deep within the earth is called geothermal energy.

❏ The burning of biomass can be used to convert water into steam, which can then spin a turbine and produce electricity.

❏ Hydrogen found in water represents an unlimited supply of hydrogen fuel.

❏ At the present time, it takes more energy to produce hydrogen from water than can be obtained by burning hydrogen.

VOCABULARY

Define each term in a complete sentence.

anthracite	electrolysis	hydrocarbon	nuclear chain reaction	photovoltaic cell
biomass	fermentation	hydroelectric	nuclear energy	safety system
bituminous coal	fossil fuel	lignite	nuclear fission	solar collector
combustion	gasohol	moderator	nuclear fusion	solar energy
control rod	geothermal energy	nonrenewable resource	peat	strong force
core	geyser			tidal power

605

Part 2

At the end of the lab, students are asked how they would choose clothing for summer and winter, based on their observations. Continue this discussion by asking,

• **In what other situations would you be able to apply the knowledge you gained during this investigation?** (Answers will vary. Some possible situations include choosing a color for an automobile; choosing a color for the surface of a patio or deck; choosing a color for a house or roof; choosing a color for a camping tent; choosing a color for cooking equipment if you want to use solar energy.)

---

with their data.

CONCLUSIONS

1. Solar energy should be very effective in heating the water.
2. The black jar absorbed more solar energy.
3. One possible hidden variable is the position of the jars—one in more direct sunlight than the other. Also, many classroom thermometers will show slight variances in temperature, even when no such variances exist.
4. Wear black outfits in winter and white outfits in summer.

GOING FURTHER: ENRICHMENT

Part 1

Have students perform a similar experiment in which the variable is the size of the container. (Let the color of both containers be black.)

CHAPTER REVIEW

MULTIPLE CHOICE

1. b	**3.** c	**5.** c	**7.** b	**9.** c
2. c	**4.** b	**6.** b	**8.** b	**10.** a

COMPLETION

1. heat/light
2. solid
3. Anthracite
4. nonrenewable
5. solar energy
6. solar cell or photovoltaic cell
7. neutron
8. control rod/cadmium
9. Geothermal energy
10. electrolysis

TRUE OR FALSE

1. T
2. F peat
3. F above
4. F active
5. T
6. F indirect
7. F splitting
8. F cannot
9. T
10. F Electrolysis

SKILL BUILDING

1. Accept all logical predictions. Make sure illustrations are appropriate for predictions.
2. Renewable: wood, hydroelectric power, sugar cane, geothermal energy, hydrogen; nonrenewable: coal, petroleum, tar sands, natural gas, nuclear energy
3. The reaction would proceed too rapidly, perhaps causing an explosion or overheating of the reactor.
4. Check student maps for accuracy. Geothermal locations should include Italy, New Zealand, Soviet Union, and United States (California, Hawaii). Tidal locations should include France, Canada, and Soviet Union.
5. Answers will vary.
6. Answers will vary, but make sure students back up opinions with facts from the text and/or other resource materials.
7. Direct: solar cell, passive solar heating; indirect: fossil fuel, hydroelectric power, biomass; neither: geothermal energy, hydrogen
8. The gas was hydrogen, which combined with oxygen during combustion to produce water.

ESSAY

1. Solar cells produce electricity from the sun, which is a great advantage because the sun's energy is unlimited. However, electricity produced by solar cells is relatively expensive.
2. A fission reaction is controlled by controlling both the speed and number of neutron bullets. A material called a moderator is added to the reactor to slow neutrons down. Then metal control rods are used to speed up or slow down the rate of the reaction.
3. A chain reaction begins when a single neutron hits a uranium-235 nucleus. As the nucleus splits, it releases 2 to 3 more neutrons, which then go on to split other uranium atoms, and so on.
4. Solar energy is available every single day and it will never run out or need to be recreated.
5. Accept all logical answers, but the most obvious example is hydrogen. Hydrogen is extremely abundant in ocean waters. But it is difficult to obtain from ocean water and, as such, is not a par-

3. Natural gas is usually found <u>below</u> petroleum.
4. Collecting solar energy and storing it in the form of hot water is an example of <u>passive</u> solar heating.
5. Hydroelectric power is an <u>indirect</u> use of solar energy.
6. Windmills are a <u>direct</u> use of solar energy.

7. Fission is the <u>combining</u> of atomic nuclei.
8. An accident at a nuclear power plant <u>can</u> cause an atomic explosion.
9. Geysers are fountains of steam and boiling water that gush from within the earth.
10. <u>Fermentation</u> is the process of decomposing water molecules into hydrogen and oxygen.

Use the skills you have developed in the chapter to complete each activity.

1. **Making predictions** Using your imagination and the information provided in this chapter, think about how primitive people may have discovered fire and how they learned to start fires. Prepare a colorful diagram to illustrate your supposition.
2. **Classifying resources** Classify each of the following resources as renewable or nonrenewable: coal, natural gas, wood, hydroelectric power, sugar cane, geothermal energy, hydrogen, nuclear energy, petroleum, tar sands.
3. **Making inferences** Based on the description of control rods, what do you think would happen if the control rods in a nuclear reactor failed to function?
4. **Making maps** Choose geothermal energy or tidal energy. Find out where in the world these energy resources are used. Make a map to display these locations.
5. **Making observations** Over a period of several days, keep a list of the ways in

which you use energy produced by fuels. Be sure to identify the fuel that produces each type of energy.
6. **Expressing an opinion** Write a short essay that expresses your opinion about the following statement: "These dire predictions about running out of oil are greatly exaggerated. And even if we do run out, I feel confident that human beings, with all their resourcefulness, will find another way to produce the energy they need."
7. **Classifying solar energy** Classify each of the following as a direct or indirect use of solar energy: solar cell, fossil fuel, geothermal energy, hydroelectric power, biomass, hydrogen power, solar heating.
8. **Drawing conclusions** In 1937, the German airship *Hindenburg* exploded in midair. As a result of the combustion of the gas that filled the *Hindenburg,* water formed. What can you conclude about the gas that filled the *Hindenburg* airship?

Discuss each of the following in a brief paragraph.

1. Discuss the advantages and disadvantages of a solar cell.
2. Explain how a nuclear reactor controls a fission reaction.
3. Explain what is meant by a nuclear chain reaction.
4. What is the greatest advantage of direct solar energy over other energy sources?

5. Do you agree with the statement, "Just because a resource is abundant does not make it a valuable resource"? Explain your answer.
6. Should petroleum be conserved and saved for future generations?

607

ticularly valuable resource at this point in time.
6. Accept all logical answers, both pro and con.

ADDITIONAL QUESTIONS AND TOPIC SUGGESTIONS

1. How many different forms of energy can you identify in the process by which wind is converted into useful energy? (Radiant energy from the sun warms the earth unevenly, causing wind to blow. The wind at this point has kinetic energy because it is moving. The wind then turns a windmill, which is mechanical energy. The mechanical energy of the windmill is changed to electric energy as it generates an electric current. This electricity can power an appliance to do work, which is mechanical energy; it can power an electric heating system, which is heat

energy; or it can light lamps, which is radiant energy.)
2. How would the latitude of an area influence the effective use of direct solar energy in that area? (Areas closest to the equator would have sunlight for about the same period of time (12 hours) every day of the year. Areas near the poles would have little sunlight during summer or winter but nearly 24 hours of sunlight during the opposite season. Also, the sun's rays strike areas near the equator directly, but they shine more at an angle as one moves toward the poles. This makes the sunlight near the equator more intense.)
3. Compare the energy changes involved when a battery generates an electric current with the energy changes involved when a solar cell generates an electric current. (In a battery, a chemical reaction creates an electric current, thus converting chemical energy into electric energy. In a solar cell, sunlight strikes the cell and causes electrons to flow, thus changing radiant energy into electric energy.)

ISSUES IN SCIENCE
The following issues can be used as a springboard for class debate or assigned as a writing homework.
1. The generation of electricity at a nuclear power plant also generates nuclear wastes. A great controversy exists as to how and where these wastes should be disposed of. Find out more about this issue, then write a short essay that addresses the question, "Would I want a nuclear waste disposal site in my community?"
2. Work with a partner. Present a debate in which each of you supports one of the following statements:

"I think we should go back to the good old days when the only fuel we needed was wood, and the only driving machine was a horse and buggy. That would solve the 'energy crisis'!"

"I think modern technology is the answer to all of our energy problems. As long as scientists keep discovering new resources and new methods of using them, we will always have enough energy."

Chapter 26
ENERGY AND THE ENVIRONMENT

CHAPTER OVERVIEW

Pollution is a byproduct of human society. It is nothing new. Early humans had garbage dumps and fouled waterways with their wastes. Because their numbers were small, the pollution they produced was easily diluted and assimilated into the environment. As populations increased, people and their pollutants became more concentrated. Population growth is not the only cause of pollution. **Pollution occurs whenever people use matter and energy.** People living in a modern industrial, technological society produce more pollution per person than people living in less developed countries. For example, the United States has about 5 percent of the world's population but uses about 30 percent of the world's natural resources and produces over 33 percent of the world's pollution. Some studies indicate that half of these mineral and energy resources are wasted.

This chapter examines how the search for and the use of energy causes pollution. The chapter covers land, air, and water pollution, then explores some of the many ways pollution can be reduced. Chapter 26 ends by pointing out that pollution control is everyone's responsibility.

INTRODUCING CHAPTER 26

Have students study the illustration on page 608. The nuclear plant explosion and fire was by far the worst nuclear disaster in history. The fire released a radioactive cloud that spread far outside the Soviet Union. At least 31 Soviets died in the reactor fire. The radiation—more than was released at Hiroshima and Nagasaki—may eventually cause at least 4000 deaths. This radiation pollution dramatically demonstrated how one country's activities can affect another country.

Although Chernobyl will go down in history, students should be made aware that many other forms of pollution are also caused by the human need for energy. Acid rain and the dramatic buildup of carbon dioxide in our atmosphere have the potential to make Chernobyl look like a minor accident. Point out that as the number of people on earth increases, the demand for energy resources goes up and up and pollution increases. Have students propose ways to reduce such pollution.

Energy and the Environment

26

CHAPTER OBJECTIVES

After completing this chapter, you will be able to

26–1 Define pollution.

26–2 Describe the ways in which obtaining and using energy can cause land pollution.

26–3 Describe the ways in which obtaining and using energy can cause air pollution.

26–3 Relate the burning of fossil fuels to the formation of acid rain.

26–4 Describe the ways in which obtaining and using energy can cause water pollution.

26–4 Discuss other sources of water pollution.

26–5 Discuss how conservation and new technologies can reduce land, air, and water pollution.

The first sign of danger came with the southeast wind. Instruments at a Swedish nuclear power plant detected twice as much radioactivity in the atmosphere as usual on April 28, 1986. At first the Swedes feared a malfunction in their own plant. But it soon became apparent that the excess radioactivity was being carried by winds from the Soviet Union.

It was not long before the story broke. An explosion and fire at the Chernobyl nuclear power plant in the Russian Ukraine had released a huge cloud of radioactive dust. The cloud was blown by winds across Poland and into Scandinavia. Later the wind shifted and blew the deadly cloud over Switzerland and Italy. Everywhere the cloud was blown, people were warned to avoid contaminated water, vegetables, and milk. About 25 people in the vicinity of Chernobyl died. Thousands more may develop serious health problems.

The accident at Chernobyl undoubtedly will have an effect on the further development of nuclear power. Once thought to be the energy solution of the future, nuclear power is now viewed with skepticism.

Our society could not exist without sources of energy. Yet we must keep in mind that using energy brings with it certain pollution problems. In this chapter, you will learn about some of the causes of pollution as well as some of the solutions to pollution. Despite its tragic outcome, the accident at Chernobyl has had one important effect. It has made people more aware than ever before of the necessity to reduce pollution.

The fire at the Chernobyl nuclear power plant in the Soviet Union resulted in a cloud of radioactivity that spread over neighboring countries. How many people will be affected by this radioactivity will not be known for at least twenty years.

609

TEACHER DEMONSTRATION

This demonstration shows that burning any fuel produces pollutants. Ideally you will have some kitchen matches, a candle, an alcohol lamp, and a Bunsen burner available. Any combination will do.

Light the match and ask the students what they observe. Let the match go out and ask,

- **How many saw any pollution?** (Most students should see grayish white smoke when the match is lit and extinguished.)

Light another match and hold it 2 to 3 cm from a beaker that you or a student is holding with tongs. Carbon will accumulate on the beaker. Ask,

- **Where did the black stuff come from?** (from the smoke of the burning match) **What is it?** (tiny carbon particles)

Repeat the demonstration using the candle, the alcohol lamp, and the Bunsen burner. Ask,

- **Which heat source produced the most carbon?** (candle)

Point out that even these simple burning technologies produce some pollution (in this case, carbon), but as burning technologies evolved from campfires to Bunsen burners, better fuels produced less pollution. Today scientists are looking for even better ways to burn fuels and reduce the pollution that comes from them.

TEACHER RESOURCES

Audiovisuals

Air Pollution: Take a Deep Deadly Breath, Parts 1 and 2, film, CRM/McGraw-Hill

Air Pollution—The Facts, film, American Lung Association

Our Polluted Planet, filmstrip, Encyclopaedia Britannica

Water Pollution, filmstrip, BFA Educational Media

Books

Brewer, R., *Principles of Ecology,* Saunders

Chanlett, E.T., *Environmental Protection,* McGraw-Hill

Royston, M.G., *Pollution Prevention Pays,* Pergamon

26-1 POLLUTION—WHAT IS IT?

SECTION PREVIEW 26-1

Students will be introduced to the terms *renewable* and *nonrenewable* natural resources in this section. The idea of ecological balance and how humans affect that balance is also covered. This section defines pollution as "things that make the environment worse." Pollution is one form of environmental changes that usually has undesirable side effects.

PERFORMANCE OBJECTIVES 26-1

1. **Describe ways environmental balance can be upset.**
2. **Compare renewable and nonrenewable resources.**
3. **Explain the relationship between getting and using energy and pollution.**
4. **Compare the effect of using renewable energy sources with the effect of using nonrenewables.**

SCIENCE TERMS 26-1
pollution p. 610

ANNOTATION KEY

❶ Make people more aware of the problem, pass stricter laws and enforce them, peer pressure (Relating cause and effect)

❷ Land reclamation (Applying definitions)

❶ Thinking Skill: Making generalizations

❷ Thinking Skill: Applying technology

26–1   Pollution—What Is It?

Our environment is like a great treasure house—in it we have everything we need for life. Air, water, food, and energy all exist in such abundance that it is hard to imagine ever being without them. Yet that is just what might come to pass. For despite the richness of natural resources, a delicate balance between plenty and want exists in our environment. **The balance in our environment can be upset by the way in which we obtain and use our natural resources.** If we use renewable resources faster than they can be replaced, the balance will be upset. If we too quickly consume nonrenewable resources, ❶ which cannot be replaced, the balance will be upset. If in the process of obtaining or using one resource we pollute another resource, the balance will be upset. It is this problem of pollution that needs our attention.

Pollution is the release of substances into the environment that changes the environment for the worse. Most pollution is the result of human activities. Although pollution cannot be blamed entirely on the use of energy resources, a great deal of pollution is directly tied to energy use. Our heavy dependence on fossil fuels has made pollution a major concern in the last several decades. In obtaining and using the energy we need, people have polluted the land, air, and water.

Figure 26–1 *Keeping our natural resources beautiful is something everyone is interested in (left). Yet litter discarded by careless people can quickly upset the balance in our environment (right). How can such littering be prevented?* ❶

610

TEACHING STRATEGY 26-1

Begin this section with a review of the terms *renewable* and *nonrenewable resources* and *environment*. Remind students that energy operates ecosystems, and humans are an important part of ecosystems. Natural ecosystems function entirely on energy inputs from the sun. Ecosystems that have large human populations need additional sources of energy. Ask,

• **What are these additional sources of energy? Are some more important than others? Do some cause more pollution than others?** (Accept all answers at this point.)

Motivation

• **Is all pollution the result of human activities? Is there such a thing as natural pollution?** Toss out these two questions and let the students debate the answers for a few minutes. You

might ask for a vote on whether things like earthquakes and volcanic eruptions fit the definition of pollution.

Concept Development
Pollutants do not have to cause physical harm. Noise and heat pollution often cause psychological distress. Unpleasant sights and foul odors may offend the senses but do not cause lasting harm.

1. Compare renewable and nonrenewable resources.
2. What is pollution?
3. How might an increase in the use of renewable energy sources help maintain a balanced environment?

26–2 Land Pollution

The use of coal as a fuel was an important step in the industrialization of our nation. Yet our environment has often paid heavily for the use of coal.

Coal near the surface of the ground is obtained by a process called **strip mining.** In strip mining, entire hills are cut apart by large earth-moving machines. This process badly damages the land. In addition to scarring the landscape, strip mining can cause land pollution.

During the strip-mining process, fertile topsoil is buried under piles of rock. When the rock is exposed to moisture and rain, acids and other dangerous chemicals seep out of the rock. Rainwater carries the acids into the ground, polluting nearby soil. The acids also may be carried into nearby streams, causing water pollution as well.

This pollution, however, need not occur. Coal mining companies can take steps to restore the land to its original condition. The process of restoring the land is called **land reclamation.** See Figure 26–2. In 1978, Congress passed a law that required mine owners to reclaim the land whenever possible.

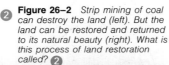

Figure 26–2 *Strip mining of coal can destroy the land (left). But the land can be restored and returned to its natural beauty (right). What is this process of land restoration called?*

26-2 LAND POLLUTION

SECTION PREVIEW 26-2

This section examines the pollution problems relating to coal mining, toxic wastes, and nuclear waste disposal. Most students have mental images of coal mines as deep, dark tunnels. Some are, but explain that most of the coal mined today comes from large strip mines such as the one in Figure 26-2.

PERFORMANCE OBJECTIVES 26-2

1. **Describe ways in which obtaining coal damages the environment.**
2. **Define land reclamation.**
3. **Explain how toxic wastes can pollute the land.**
4. **Identify the source of most nuclear wastes.**
5. **Compare low-level nuclear wastes with high-level nuclear wastes.**

SCIENCE TERMS 26-2

strip mining p. 611
land reclamation p. 611
toxic p. 612
nuclear waste p. 612

be replaced, their wise use will ensure that there will always be enough of such resources to help maintain a balance in our environment.

TEACHING STRATEGY 26-2

Motivation

Use an overhead projector to project an outline map of the United States on the board. Ask students to go to the board and draw in the location of the major U.S. coal deposits. After they have made their selections, display or pass out copies of a map showing the actual locations of U.S. coal reserves. Maps can be obtained from the U.S. Department of Energy or your school library. Have students compare the location of their coal deposits with the actual coal deposits.

Content Development

Students and the press often use the terms *ecology* and *environment* incorrectly. Ecology is the study of the relationships of living things with each other and with the physical environment. The environment is the sum or product of all the living and nonliving things that surround or influence an organism.

Reinforcement

Have students try to identify as many of the kinds of land pollutants (litter) as they can find in Figure 26-1.

Section Review 26-1

1. Renewable resources can be replaced by nature; nonrenewable resources cannot be replaced by nature.
2. Release of substances that change the environment for the worse
3. Because renewable resources can

TEACHER DEMONSTRATION

Students usually associate acids with liquids and have a difficult time believing that acids can come from rocks or minerals such as coal. To demonstrate the acidity of coal, crush a 5-g sample of coal into a fine powder. Measure about 25 mL of water into each of two beakers. Measure the acidity of the water using blue litmus paper. (It should remain blue.) Then add the crushed coal to one of the beakers. Have students predict what color the litmus paper will be if you test the water again. Repeat the litmus paper test. (It should still be blue.) Test the beakers each day for five days. The litmus paper in the beaker with the coal will gradually turn pink, then red, as the acid from the coal leaches into the water. Ask,

• **What was the purpose of the second beaker of water?** (control)

ANNOTATION KEY

❶ Wastes seep in groundwater or are transported by rain into lakes and streams. (Relating cause and effect)

❶ Thinking Skill: Applying technology

26-2 (continued)

Content Development

Coal is a concentration of hydrocarbons that was fixed by plants during the process of photosynthesis eons ago. There are four types of coal that are classified according to age. *Peat* is the youngest; you can still see the plant fibers in peat. *Lignite,* or brown coal, is just compressed peat. *Bituminous* coal is lignite that is older and more compressed. It is often called soft coal. *Anthracite* is hard coal. It is almost pure carbon and is very hard and brittle. Bituminous is the most abundant coal in the United States.

Figure 26-3 *One of the most serious causes of land pollution is the leaking of toxic wastes from improperly stored or maintained barrels (left). As proof of the danger, notice the special equipment the scientists must wear while examining leaking wastes in a toxic waste dump in New Jersey (right). How does the leaking of toxic wastes cause water pollution as well as land pollution?* ❶

Figure 26-4 *Low-level nuclear wastes are being buried at this dump site in Hanford, Washington.*

Obtaining and using certain energy resources can pollute the land. Strip mining is but one example. Another example involves solid wastes from factories. Solid wastes from factories may contaminate the land with **toxic,** or poisonous, chemicals. Factories that produce fuels and petrochemicals from petroleum are a major source of this type of land pollution. When improperly stored in barrels buried under the soil, toxic wastes can seep into the land.

Perhaps the most threatening form of land pollution today is the disposal of **nuclear wastes.** Nuclear wastes are radioactive substances associated with the use of radioactive materials or the production of nuclear power.

Nuclear wastes are classified as either low-level or high-level wastes. Low-level wastes have relatively short half-lives. The half-life of a radioactive substance is a measure of its rate of decay. Low-level wastes decay quickly. The disposal of these wastes usually does not cause major pollution problems. The wastes can be isolated from the environment until they are no longer radioactive.

High-level wastes, however, have half-lives of about 10,000 years or more. Isolating these substances from the environment for that length of time is practically impossible. A common practice has been to seal these wastes in concrete or glass containers and then bury the containers deep within the earth. The problem with this procedure is that the containers may eventually corrode or leak. The nuclear wastes can then escape, polluting the land. As the radioactive substances seep out, they also can find their way into underground water sources and contaminate the water supply.

Content Development

Low-level nuclear waste is very dilute and that is one of the major problems. To economically remove and store millions of liters of radioactive water, the radioactivity must be concentrated. To date producers have found it easier to store these low-level wastes where they were produced. However, if a major leak or spill occurs, these wastes can accumulate and concentrate in food chains very quickly.

Motivation

Have students investigate half-life by using their lab table drawers or small boxes and 100 pieces of popcorn. Working in small groups, have the students label two adjacent sides of the drawer A and B. Give each group 100 kernels of unpopped popcorn and have them dump it into the drawer. Shake the drawer so the popcorn rolls around. Remove, count, and record the kernels that are pointing directly

HELP WANTED: RANGE MANAGER to specialize in environmental impact due to oil, gas, and coal operations. College degree in range management required.

It is a short helicopter ride to the densely wooded hills. From the air, the **range manager** compares the landscape below with the geologic maps of the area. A petroleum company for which the range manager works plans to mine the coal and natural gas buried within these rolling hills.

A range manager develops conservation plans for the area that is to be mined. A range manager writes an environmental impact statement. This is a report that outlines the possible effects of mining activities on the environment. The report explains what could happen to the land, air, water, plants, people, and wildlife of the area.

After mining or drilling operations are complete, a range manager develops a plan to restore or reclaim the area to a natural and productive site. Occasionally, a former mining site

is turned into a recreation area or park. A range manager oversees this type of recreational land development.

To become a range manager, a college student studies many subjects. These include science, economics, communications, computers, and resource management. If you would like information about a career as a range manager, write to the U.S. Department of Agriculture, Soil Conservation Service, 14th and Independence Avenue SW, Dept. 0054, South Building, Washington, DC 20250.

SECTION REVIEW

1. Describe two ways in which strip mining damages the land.
2. What term is used for nuclear wastes that have very long half-lives?
3. Describe how a pollutant buried underground in one area might cause pollution many kilometers away from the burial site.

26–3 Air Pollution

Section Objective

To identify and describe major sources of air pollution

Imagine a place where the sky is always gray, the buildings are blackened by smoke, and the air smells like rotten eggs. Do you think people would choose to live in such a place? The people of Donora, Pennsylvania, did in the 1940s.

The city of Donora boasted one of the largest steel mills in the world. The economy of the city

613

26-3 AIR POLLUTION

SECTION PREVIEW 26-3

This section introduces students to the Donora air pollution disaster that was caused by the buildup of pollutants due to a temperature inversion. The disaster represents a turning point in the efforts to regulate air pollution by local and state governments. This section also briefly discusses acid rain and other types of aerial pollutants.

PERFORMANCE OBJECTIVES 26-3

1. **Describe how a temperature inversion affects air quality.**
2. **Explain the formation of acid rain.**
3. **Relate some human health problems to air pollution.**
4. **Describe major sources of air pollution.**

SCIENCE TERMS 26-3
temperature inversion p. 614
acid rain p. 615

at sides A and B. This represents about one half-life.

Give the drawer a shaking and repeat the counting and recording. This represents another half-life. Students should be able to estimate the number of kernels they are going to get on the next two or three "half-lives" they investigate.

Section Review 26-2
1. Fertile topsoil is buried under rocks; water causes acids and other dangerous chemicals to seep out of rocks and into nearby soil.
2. High-level nuclear wastes
3. Pollutant may enter groundwater or be carried by streams far from burial site.

TEACHING STRATEGY 26-3

Begin this section by explaining how many people felt "the solution to pollution is dilution." For generations, this attitude was applied to both water and aerial wastes. If you dumped wastes in the water, it was no longer your problem. If you built a high enough smokestack, then aerial wastes were no longer your problem. This attitude did not matter when there were just small amounts of wastes, but as cities grew and the industrial revolution spread, so did pollution. Soon, rivers and the air were receiving more wastes than they could dilute.

• **Where do wastes in the water or air go?** (Lead the discussion to the idea that earth is a closed system; a spaceship moving around the sun.)

Sharpen Your Skills

Greenhouse Effect

The carbon dioxide released into the air by motor vehicles and the burning of fossil fuels by industry have created what scientists call the greenhouse effect. Using reference books in the library, write a report on the greenhouse effect. Include in your report how adding carbon dioxide to the atmosphere increases the greenhouse effect. Also include predictions made by scientists about how the greenhouse effect may change the earth's climate, as well as the results of such changes.

was thriving as mills and factories operated 24 hours a day. Millions of tons of coal were burned every hour to provide energy for this growing industrial center. And the people of Donora reasoned that the gray sky, the smoke, and the smell were the price they had to pay for progress.

But in October 1948, the price became too high. The air had become almost unbreathable. Noontime looked like late evening. People could barely see. A temperature inversion had settled over the city.

A **temperature inversion** occurs when cool air near the earth's surface becomes trapped under a layer of warmer air. Normally, air near the surface ❶ is able to rise, taking pollutants with it. But during a temperature inversion, pollutants are trapped in the layer of cool air near the earth. The temperature inversion in Donora lasted four days.

Since the Donora disaster, which caused the death of 20 people and the hospitalization of thousands more, cities and states have passed laws to help control emissions of pollutants from factories and power plants. Yet the problems associated with burning coal and other fossil fuels still remain.

Coal and other fossil fuels contain sulfur impurities. When a fossil fuel is burned, sulfur combines

Figure 26–5 *During a temperature inversion, cool air containing pollutants becomes trapped near the ground under a layer of warm air (left). Temperature inversions are a serious problem in some major cities, such as Los Angeles (right). What group of people might be particularly affected by a temperature inversion?* ❶

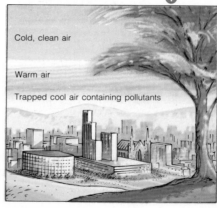

Cold, clean air

Warm air

Trapped cool air containing pollutants

614

26-3 (continued)

Motivation

History repeats itself for those who ignore it. In 1273, Edward I outlawed the use of high-sulfur coal in London. Yet, some of the worse air pollution disasters ever recorded occurred in that city. In 1911, more than 1100 Londoners died from coal smoke. In 1952, more than 4000 people were

killed. Disasters also occurred in 1956, 1957, and 1962. Air pollution is often thought of as an inconvenience; in fact, it is a damaging and dangerous killer.

Content Development

Along some parts of the California coast, cool air from the Pacific Ocean is held near the ground and temperature inversions frequently occur. These inversions are unhealthy but

usually do not directly result in death. Point out that disasters often call attention to a problem that has been around for a long time. Disasters often mobilize people and government for short periods of time. They tend to distract from the overall, long-term impacts of the problem. Today's emissions of sulfur dioxide, particulate matter, and small amounts of radioactive substances from all U.S. coal-fired power plants cause an estimated

with oxygen in the atmosphere to form various sulfur oxides. When sulfur oxides react with moisture in the air, droplets of weak sulfuric acid form in the atmosphere. The droplets eventually mix with rainwater to form **acid rain.** You will learn more about acid rain and its relationship to water pollution in the next section.

Although much air pollution comes from the industrial burning of coal and other fossil fuels, the most significant source of air pollution is motor vehicles. Gasoline and diesel fuels do not burn completely in the engines of cars, buses, and trucks. Unburned fuel vapors and carbon dioxide are released into the atmosphere. These pollutants can burn and irritate the eyes. They also can damage the lungs, particularly of people who already have breathing problems. Air pollution due to motor vehicles also can damage plant life.

Other pollutants contained in the exhausts of motor vehicles are nitrogen oxides. Nitrogen oxides are compounds in which nitrogen is combined with oxygen. In the atmosphere, nitrogen oxides may combine with water vapor to form droplets of weak nitric acid. The nitric acid may fall to the earth as acid rain in much the same way sulfuric acid does.

Figure 26–6 *Air pollution in Japan can become so severe that a warning bell is rung to alert people to stay indoors. Why do you think these people are wearing masks?* ➋

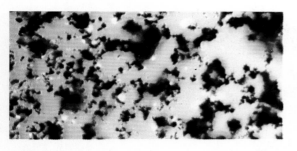

Figure 26–7 *Some of the pollutants released in car exhaust fumes are shown in this unusual photograph of auto exhaust particles. How can this type of pollution be decreased?* ➌

SECTION REVIEW

1. What is the chief source of air pollution?
2. How does a temperature inversion increase the damaging effects of pollutants released into the atmosphere?
3. What problems would be caused for a city such as Donora, Pennyslvania, if the activities of factories were curbed?

615

10,000 premature deaths, more than 100,000 cases of respiratory disease, and several billion dollars in property damage each year.

the layers of air under normal conditions.

26-4 WATER POLLUTION

SECTION PREVIEW 26-4

Students learn more about the formation and effect of acid rain in this section. This is a serious global problem that industrial nations are beginning to address. The section also covers water pollution from offshore oil wells and thermal pollution from power plants. Students will briefly review some of the nonenergy related causes of water pollution.

PERFORMANCE OBJECTIVES 26-4

1. **Describe the effects of acid rain on aquatic organisms.**
2. **Explain how burning fossil fuels pollutes air, water, and land.**
3. **Give an example of how our search for energy causes pollution.**
4. **Identify the causes and effects of thermal pollution.**
5. **List three effects of water pollution.**

SCIENCE TERMS 26-4
thermal pollution p. 618

TEACHING STRATEGY 26-4

Review the causes and formation of acid rain covered in the previous section. This section covers what happens when the acids return to earth. Point out that the exact chemistry of what is popularly called acid rain is still a subject of considerable debate. A more precise term is acid deposition because the acids reach earth as dry particles as well as being dissolved in rain and snow.

Motivation
Many students will have had some kind of personal experience with water pollution. Ask them to share their experiences with the class. Re-mind students that water pollution has many forms. Sometimes you can see or smell the pollutants, but much of the time the pollution is so dilute that it takes expensive scientific instruments to measure it. Some pollutants, like mercury and lead, are measured in parts per billion (ppb).

Content Development
Acid deposition is a serious and grow-ing problem in North America, Japan, Europe, and the Soviet Union. Normal rainfall is slightly acidic (pH about 5.6), but acid deposition has pH values as low as 1.9 (fog in California). Re-mind students that a whole number decrease in pH represents a tenfold increase in acidity. Some Adirondack lakes are 500 times more acidic than normal lakes. Studies have shown that damage to U.S. crops, fish, wildlife, and materials costs about $2.5 billion a year.

26-4 Water Pollution

The lake, once teeming with life, now seems strangely empty. The surrounding land is quiet—too quiet. Nearby plants and trees have withered. Animals who once depended on the lake area for food have left or died. This lake and its inhabitants are victims of acid rain.

In the last section, you read how emissions from factories and motor vehicles can cause droplets of sulfuric acid and nitric acid to form in the atmosphere. When these droplets fall to the earth as acid rain or acid snow, they change the acidity, or pH level, of the waterways fed by the acid rain. Most organisms can survive in only a narrow range of water acidity. By increasing the water's acidity, acid rain kills many of the organisms living there. At the same time, acid rain damages the plant life on which the rain falls. Throughout parts of the United States, lakes and forests are being destroyed by acid rain.

Acid rain begins as air pollution. As rain falls to the earth the problem becomes water pollution. Then as the acid rain seeps into the soil, land pollution results. In this example of a "pollution chain," all aspects of the environment are damaged.

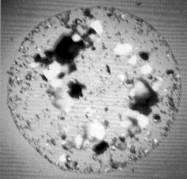

Figure 26-8 *Acid rain can severely damage the plants and animals living in lakes and ponds (left). This photograph shows the pollutants in a single drop of acid rain (right). What are the two acids contained in acid rain?* ❶

616

Figure 26–9 *This oil spill occurred when a supertanker ran aground in the Delaware River near Philadelphia, Pennsylvania. The oil killed many plants and animals in the river and polluted nearby shores.*

Fossil Fuels and Water Pollution

Strip mining for coal releases pollutants into the soil and water. Burning fossil fuels creates water pollution by producing acid rain. Unfortunately, there are even other ways in which our energy needs contribute to water pollution.

Both obtaining and using energy resources are major causes of water pollution. Here is one example. Petroleum is often found under the sea floor. To obtain petroleum, offshore oil wells are constructed. And although great precautions are taken, drilling accidents do occur. As a result of such accidents huge amounts of oil spill into oceans and lakes. Oil spills also occur when tankers carrying oil are damaged so that they leak their oil into the surrounding water.

Oil spills are also an environmental disaster. Plants and animals that come in contact with the oil are often destroyed. If the oil reaches the shore, it contaminates beaches and may contribute to the death of shore-dwelling organisms. Despite improved cleanup technology, oil spills remain one of the most difficult types of water pollution to remedy.

Nuclear Power and Water Pollution

A great amount of hot water is generated in a nuclear power plant. The heat from this water is usually transferred to a nearby body of water, such

---

Sharpen Your Skills

Local Pollution

Conduct a survey of the area in which you live to determine the extent of air, land, and water pollution.

Draw a map of the area that you select. Draw in any major landmarks, streets and roads, rivers, streams and lakes, and factories. Label north, south, east, and west on the map. Then make a key using a different symbol for each type of pollution and mark any polluted areas on the map.

1. Which sections of the area were the most polluted? With what kinds of pollution?

2. Which kinds of pollution in the area were difficult to identify and estimate? Why?

617

---

transported long distances, these sources will become larger sources of pollution.

Although oil spills are difficult and very expensive to clean up, the long-term effects of crude oil spills are not long-lasting. Studies show that most marine life recovers in three to five years. Oil that has been refined seems to cause much more damage than unrefined oil.

Skills Development
Skill: Designing an experiment
Oil and water do not mix. Challenge students to design and conduct an experiment to determine which common laundry detergent causes 1 mL of cooking oil to mix with 10 mL of water. Be certain students control how much detergent they use.

Motivation
• **How many people have seen rainbows on the street or in a parking lot after it has rained? What caused the rainbow?** (thin layers of oil reflecting parts of sunlight).

Point out that oil is a major pollutant in storm water runoff. This water is not treated in sewage plants but goes directly into surface waters.

Content Development
Almost 6 billion kilograms of oil are added to the oceans each year. About 15 percent comes from natural sources, the remaining 85 percent comes from human activities. Forty percent comes from runoff; about 20 percent comes from tanker spills and routine tanker cleaning; less than 1 percent comes from ruptures or "blowout" from offshore wells. As more oil is drilled from the ocean and

Sharpen Your Skills

The Year 2050
Skills: Making predictions, inferring, report writing
Level: Average
Type: Vocabulary/writing
This activity will allow students to use their imaginations, along with the information presented in the text. Accept all well-written, logical short stories.

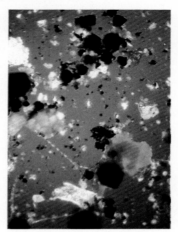

Figure 26–10 In this photograph, you can see some of the emissions given off at a nuclear power plant. Although such emissions often leak into the air, they can pollute the land and water as well. How? ❷

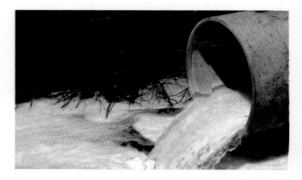

Figure 26–11 Although it may look like this sewage is being dumped into a nearby river, the sewage has actually been treated at a sewage treatment plant so that it is safe to discharge. Do you think sewage treatment should be mandatory? Give reasons for your answer. ❸

618

as a lake or stream. The temperature of the body of water rises. The increase in temperature in bodies of water such as lakes is called **thermal pollution.** Most water-dwelling organisms can survive only in a narrow temperature range. When the water temperature rises, many organisms are destroyed. In what ways are thermal pollution and acid rain similar? ❶

You have read how radioactive wastes from nuclear power plants and other uses of radioactive materials can pollute the land. In much the same way, radioactive wastes can pollute our water supplies. Radioactive wastes stored in containers dumped into the sea may leak out of the containers and become a long-term water pollutant.

Other Sources of Water Pollution

Although using and obtaining energy is a major source of water pollution, it is by no means the only source. Many factories dump solid wastes directly into nearby water or onto land that has water underground. Such dumping is especially serious because groundwater is the most important source of drinking water in the United States. Sewage, too, is often released into rivers and streams. Chemicals used on farmlands to improve the growth of plants or to kill harmful insects also may enter and pollute the groundwater.

Water pollution limits the amount of wildlife that can live in the water, affects supplies of drinking water, and destroys recreational areas. To prevent further water pollution, federal laws have been passed to prohibit industry from dumping certain

---

26-4 (continued)

Enrichment
International laws not outlaw the dumping of radioactive wastes in the world's oceans. Have students conduct library research to find out which countries have agreed to abide by this law and which ones have refused to support it.

Content Development
There is a tremendous number of pollutants that end up in our water supply. Some, such as sediments from erosion, are natural, but most are the byproducts of humans. Inorganic chemicals, minerals, and synthetic, organic chemicals are commonly found in both surface and groundwater.

In the process of breaking down sewage, decomposer organisms use up

large quantities of oxygen, so fish and other forms of aquatic life cannot survive. Nutrient enrichment causes the natural process of succession to rapidly increase, leading to "cultural eutrophication." The nutrients support the growth of large quantities of algae, which cloud the water and affect all the organisms living there.

Section Review 26-4
1. Acid rain changes the acidity, or

chemical wastes into the earth's waters. Wastewater treatment systems are being constructed to remove pollution from rivers and lakes. What other steps might be taken to stop water pollution and save one of the earth's most important natural resources? **4**

SECTION REVIEW

1. How does acid rain damage organisms living in lakes or streams?
2. Using acid rain, describe the relationship between burning fossil fuels and the pollution of water, air, and land.
3. Why would an ocean be much less affected by thermal pollution than a lake?

26–5 Pollution—What Can Be Done?

The problems of environmental pollution will not go away. To the contrary, they will worsen as population increases. But there is something that can be done about pollution. **Pollution can be reduced by conserving energy, by finding cleaner ways to use energy, and by using alternative clean energy sources.**

Conservation

Conservation is the wise and careful use of resources. When we conserve our energy resources, we benefit the environment in two ways. First, our nonrenewable resources will last longer. Second, pollution will be reduced.

There are many ways that energy can be conserved at home. Doing full loads in the washing machine or dishwasher instead of several small loads will save energy. Turning the thermostat down a few degrees in the winter and turning the air conditioner up a few degrees in the summer will save energy. And making sure that a house or apartment is well insulated also will save energy.

Because a great amount of energy is used by motor vehicles, changing driving habits can make a

Sharpen Your Skills

The Year 2050

2

Write a short story that describes what you think life will be like in the year 2050. The focus of your story should be the kinds of energy resources used and the environmental problems that may exist.

619

26-5 POLLUTION— WHAT CAN BE DONE?

SECTION PREVIEW 26-5

This section introduces students to some of the ways pollution can be reduced. Conservation of energy and nonrenewable resources are both discussed. The development of new technologies that use energy more efficiently and new pollution control technologies are also covered. The section ends by reminding students that they play an important role in determining the fate of the earth.

PERFORMANCE OBJECTIVES 26-5

1. **Define and give examples of conservation.**
2. **Explain how conservation can save energy resources and reduce pollution.**
3. **Identify some common materials that can be recycled.**
4. **Give examples of how technology can reduce pollution.**

SCIENCE TERMS 26-5

conservation p. 619
recycling p. 620

---

pH level, of water. Because many organisms can live only in a narrow pH range, acid rain kills many organisms.
2. Burning fossil fuels releases nitrogen and sulfur oxides into the air. They combine with water vapor to produce droplets of sulfuric and nitric acid, which fall to earth as acid rain. These droplets pollute the atmosphere by acting directly on plant life, as well as artificial structures such as buildings and statues. Acid rain that

falls on land causes land pollution. Acid rain that falls into water causes water pollution.
3. Because the ocean is so much larger, thermal pollution causes much less of a change on overall ocean temperatures than on temperatures of standing bodies of water such as lakes.

TEACHING STRATEGY 26-5

Students should understand that they

are an important part of the solution to the problems of energy supply, demand, and pollution. Emphasize that anyone who is not part of the solution, is part of the problem.

Motivation
Ask students to list the five things they dislike the most about your city or town. After they have completed their lists, ask them to decide if the problems will increase or decrease in the next ten years. Survey the class for a list of the problems and if the problem will be bigger or smaller after a decade has passed.
• **What can you do to help resolve these problems?** (Point out that ten years from now, most of them will have been voters for *five* years.)

TIE-IN/SOCIAL STUDIES

The economics of conservation is difficult for some students. Use the light bulb as an example of how the initial cost is more, but eventually you save both energy and money. For example, if a regular bulb costs a dollar and a conserving bulb costs three dollars but lasts four times as long and costs only one-fourth as much to operate, the bulb represents a good economic and social investment.

Sharpen Your Skills

Car Pooling
Skills: Observing, recording, comparing, relating, applying
Level: Remedial
Type: Hands-on

Through this activity, most students will note that cars, in general, do not contain more than one passenger. As such, car pooling is not a concept that has been widely accepted. Students should be able to relate the idea that increasing car pooling would help lessen air pollution tremendously.

26-5 (continued)

Content Development

The term *conservation* has different meanings to different people. It does not mean "doing without or not using." The essence of the conservation ethic is wise and careful use of all natural resources. Conservation should become part of our lifestyle; an important part of how we live, work, and play.

The United States has made tremendous progress in reducing energy waste. New cars get better gas mileage; new appliances require less energy to operate; and new homes are better designed and insulated. Yet studies continue to show that how a car is maintained and driven is critical to obtaining maximum efficiency. Different families in similar homes use significantly different amounts of electricity and natural gas. This evidence shows that human behavior is a critical factor in any conservation scheme.

Enrichment

Review the methods used to read an electric meter and have students take readings on their home meters at the beginning and end of a 24-hour period. Calculate the average kilowatt-hours consumed. Challenge the students to see if they can reduce the class average by getting their families to make a special effort to conserve electricity for the next 24 hours.

Figure 26–12 *Many tons of paper are being recycled at this recycling center. Recycling will help save many trees, from which paper is made. What materials do you recycle?* ❶

real difference in the quality of our environment. The use of car pools and public transportation saves fuel and reduces air pollution. So does keeping a car well tuned and in good operating condition. And don't forget the most ancient form of transportation—walking!

A form of conservation that has received considerable public attention is **recycling.** You probably have a recycling center in your neighborhood or town. In recycling, substances that can be used again from discarded articles are reclaimed and sent to factories. Recycling has been very successful in reclaiming paper, glass containers, and aluminum cans.

New Technologies

New technologies can reduce pollution by creating cleaner and more efficient ways of obtaining and using energy resources. Technology also can help develop alternatives to fossil fuels.

The burning of coal has been made less damaging to the environment by the use of scrubber systems. A scrubber system works like a shower. As sulfur oxides are released from burning coal, a high-pressure spray of water dissolves them before they can react with water in the atmosphere. Scrubber systems and other antipollution systems can be placed in smokestacks to prevent the release of pollutants into the atmosphere.

Pollution from automobile exhaust has been reduced by equipping cars with pollution-control

Content Development

New technologies can and do reduce pollution, but they are costly to purchase and usually require regular maintenance. In the long run, it is cheaper and more effective to remove the pollutants from fossil fuels before they are burned. Technologies that improve energy efficiency reduce en-

---

Sharpen Your Skills

Car Pooling

Select a *safe* spot where you can observe cars as they go by. Be sure you can see into each car. Do not use a busy highway because there would be no way to check every car. Try to be at your site at different times each day for several days. Keep a record for ten minutes each day of the number of people in each car that goes by. Make a chart to present your findings.

1. How many cars have only the driver? At what times of day? How many have one, two, three, or more passengers?

2. How might the environment benefit from car pooling?

620

devices. This type of pollution could be further reduced by the development of engines that burn fuel more completely.

Scientists are working on new methods of ocean-drilling for oil in order to reduce the possibility of underwater leaks. In addition, several new methods have been developed for dealing with oil spills. These include vacuum systems that can pump oil out of the water and certain types of absorbents that can soak up oil near the shore.

In Chapter 25, you learned about ways in which scientists are working to find alternatives to fossil fuels. If a clean, renewable source of energy such as solar energy or nuclear fusion could be used on a large scale, many of our pollution problems would be solved.

Everyone's Responsibility

At the beginning of this chapter, you read that pollution is caused mainly by the activities of people. It is important to realize that the activities of people can also stop pollution. And everyone—young or old, scientist or nonscientist—can help.

SECTION REVIEW

1. What is conservation?
2. How can new technologies reduce pollution?
3. How does recycling reduce pollution and conserve important resources?
4. In what ways can you personally reduce pollution?

Figure 26–13 *Pollutants released into the air from factory smokestacks cause acid rain and other forms of air pollution. Can such pollution be decreased without having to close the factory?* ❷

Figure 26–14 *Almost everyone is opposed to pollution. These people have taken to the streets of Washington, D.C., to protest against the pollution due to toxic wastes.*

621

ergy needs. For example, new refrigerators require half as much energy as those made a decade ago, and energy experts claim they can be designed to use half again what they currently use. Ask students to identify some of the technologies that have increased energy efficiency. They should identify new materials, microcircuits, and smaller, more efficient motors. Point out that some of the new light bulbs currently on the market produce the same amount of better quality light using one-fourth the energy of older-type bulbs.

Content Development

New developments in solar electric technologies are greatly reducing the cost of photovoltaic cells. Polycrystalline and amorphous silicon panels are both cheaper to make than the familiar single crystal panels. Solar electric power can make a substantial contribution to decreasing our need for fossil fuels.

Motivation

Write on the chalkboard, "Think globally but act locally." Ask students what they think the expression means. Ask them for some specific examples of things they can do locally. Remind them of the list of things they dislike most about their city and have them identify *one* thing they can fix or change. Then encourage them to act responsibly and change it.

Section Review 26-5

1. The wise and careful use of resources
2. By developing cleaner and more efficient ways to obtain and use energy resources and by developing alternative clean energy sources
3. Reduces pollution by reducing litter; conserves resources by reusing materials such as metal and glass, thereby lessening pollution because fewer of these materials must be manufactured
4. Answers will vary, but conserving electricity will likely be on most students' lists.

LABORATORY INVESTIGATION
OBSERVING AIR POLLUTION

BEFORE THE LAB
Be certain you have enough petri dishes for each group. Watch glasses can also be used if they are about the same size, or you can have the students convert all the data to particles per square centimeter.

If some of the samples come back with very large numbers of particles, students might have to estimate the number of particles. Estimates can be made by counting all the particles in a sample number of grid squares.

PRE-LAB DISCUSSION
Demonstrate how to put *thin* layers of petroleum jelly on the petri dishes. Fingers work well. Students can number the petri dishes if they record the number and the exact location in their lab book. Ask:

• **What is the purpose of the petri dish with the cover?** (control) Have the students decide on a safe place to keep this control.

Encourage students to select a variety of sites for their pollutant traps. Review their proposed locations before they set them out. After the students have set out their petri dishes ask them to rank the petri dishes in order from the one that will collect the most air pollutants to the one that will collect the fewest. Students should write their hypotheses and try to identify some of the variables that will influence how many particles of air pollution will be collected in each location.

SKILL DEVELOPMENT
Students will use the following skills while completing this investigation.
1. Safety
2. Comparing
3. Observing
4. Applying
5. Relating
6. Recording
7. Measuring
8. Graphing
9. Hypothesizing
10. Manipulative

SAFETY TIPS
Be certain that the petri dishes are placed in secure places where they will not be disturbed by other students or where they will not fall on people.

TEACHING STRATEGY FOR LAB PROCEDURE
You might want to modify the procedure so one group brings in their traps after one day, another group after two days, and another after three days. Just cover the petri dishes until every group has completed their "pollution trapping."

OBSERVATIONS
1. Comparisons will vary, depending on location. Students should find a wide range of pollutant levels in their different dishes.
2. Comparisons will vary, depending on locations selected for each dish.

Problem
How can you observe solid particles in the atmosphere that cause air pollution?

Materials *(per group)*

6 petri dishes	1 petri dish cover
petroleum jelly	glass-marking pencil
graph paper	magnifying lens

Procedure
1. Coat the flat surface of each petri dish with a thin layer of petroleum jelly.
2. Immediately place the cover over one of the petri dishes. Put this dish aside.
3. Place the other five petri dishes in locations where they will be exposed to the outside air yet will not be disturbed.
4. Use the marking pencil to write the name of the location on the side of each dish.
5. Do not disturb the dishes for three days.
6. Collect the dishes after three days. Place each dish, one at a time, on the graph paper. Use the magnifying lens to count the number of particles in each part of the graph paper grid. Total the number of particles in each dish. Record your data on a data table similar to the one on this page.

Observations
1. Compare the data from each location.
2. Compare your data with data from other groups. Record the locations of the data from other groups, as well as the number of solid particles counted in each dish.

Conclusions
1. Which dish was the control in this investigation? Explain your answer.
2. The solid particles you counted were evidence of air pollution. How can you account for the difference in the number of particles at the various locations?
3. How can you explain the difference in the number of particles found in other locations by your classmates?
4. Make a graph of your data, plotting location on the horizontal axis and number of particles counted on the vertical axis. What conclusions can you draw?

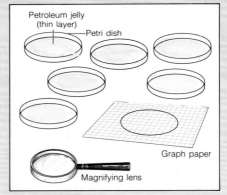

Dish	Number of Particles
1	
2	
3	
4	
5	
6	

622

622

CHAPTER REVIEW

SUMMARY

26–1 Pollution—What Is It?

❏ The balance in our environment can be easily upset by the ways in which we obtain and use energy resources.

❏ Pollution is the release of unwanted substances into the environment.

26–2 Land Pollution

❏ Strip mining causes land pollution by burying fertile topsoil under rocks and by the action of acids that seep out of the rocks when exposed to water.

❏ Land damaged by strip mining can be restored by land reclamation.

❏ Both obtaining and using energy resources contribute to land pollution.

❏ High-level nuclear wastes may take many thousands of years to decay and become non-radioactive. Because of their long half-lives, such wastes are difficult to store safely.

26–3 Air Pollution

❏ Burning fossil fuels releases many polluting emissions into the atmosphere.

❏ During a temperature inversion, pollutants are trapped in a layer of cool air near the earth's surface.

❏ Most air pollution is due to motor vehicle exhausts.

❏ Sulfur oxides and nitrogen oxides released during the burning of fossil fuels can combine with water in the atmosphere to form droplets

of sulfuric acid or nitric acid. These acids fall to earth as acid rain.

26–4 Water Pollution

❏ Acid rain has damaged many lakes, streams, and other waterways, as well as plant life near such bodies of water.

❏ Both obtaining and using energy resources are major causes of water pollution.

❏ Thermal pollution occurs when bodies of water, often near nuclear power plants, are heated above their normal temperatures. Thermal pollution can destroy plant and animal life in such bodies of water.

❏ Aside from using energy resources, water can be polluted by the dumping of solid wastes, litter, sewage, fertilizers, and pesticides.

26–5 Pollution—What Can Be Done?

❏ Conservation is the wise and careful use of natural resources.

❏ Pollution can be reduced by conservation of energy resources.

❏ Recycling useful solid wastes can help reduce pollution?

❏ New technologies are being developed to lessen pollution due to fossil fuels.

❏ Alternative energy sources also can help lessen fossil fuel pollution.

❏ Reducing pollution is not just a task for scientists, it is a job for everyone.

VOCABULARY

Define each term in a complete sentence.

acid rain	pollution	thermal pollution
conservation	recycling	
land reclamation	strip mining	toxic
nuclear waste	temperature inversion	

623

CONCLUSIONS

1. The dish with the cover on it.

2. Air pollution can vary from place to place, depending on the nature of each location. The number of pollutants near a factory, for example, would be expected to be higher than the number of pollutants in a closed room.

3. Answers will vary, depending on class results.

4. Check student graphs for accuracy. Their explanation and conclusions

should be consistent with their graphed data.

GOING FURTHER: ENRICHMENT

Part 1

Encourage the students to repeat the experiment around their homes. They should find different kinds and different numbers of pollutants in their neighborhood than they do around school.

Part 2

Ask students

1. If the rank they hypothesized at the beginning of the experiement was close to their results.

2. If there is some way they could selectively collect only certain kinds of pollutants.

3. How they could re-do the experiment to reduce the variables at each site.

4. To develop a scheme to classify the various particles of air pollution they collected.

CHAPTER REVIEW

MULTIPLE CHOICE
1. b 3. c 5. c 7. d 9. d
2. d 4. b 6. c 8. a 10. c

COMPLETION
1. pollution
2. Coal
3. nuclear wastes
4. temperature inversion
5. sulfuric acid/acid rain
6. nitrogen oxides/water
7. oil spill
8. thermal pollution
9. recycling
10. Conservation

TRUE OR FALSE
1. F unwanted
2. F renewable
3. F low-level
4. F coal
5. T
6. F incompletely
7. F is often
8. T
9. F all
10. T

SKILL BUILDING
1. Check student drawings to make sure they show a pollution chain going from the air to the water and land.
2. Check student maps for accuracy.
3. **a.** burning of high-sulfur coal in factories **b.** hot water released from power plant into nearby lake **c.** drastic increase in the use of cars **d.** air pollution becomes so severe that it poses serious health risks for general population.
4. Accept all logical, well-written essays on this topic.
5. Accept all logical, well-written reports.
6. Burning garbage might well decrease land pollution, but it would drastically increase air pollution. If scrubber systems and other forms of technology allow the "clean" burning of garbage, this idea would be more environmentally sound.

ESSAY
1. Turn off lights and appliances when not in use; keep heat down to a comfortable level; insulate properly.

2. Our environment has a delicate balance. Obtaining energy resources can upset this balance by causing the scarring of land (strip mining) and the destruction of waterways (oil spills). Using energy resources—such as burning fossil fuels, which causes air pollution—can also upset the balance.
3. Our environment cannot really be separated into land, air, and water. Pollution chains often form in which a pollutant released into the air, for example, is brought back to the land through rain, and then is washed into waterways by water runoff.
4. Conservation is the wise use of our natural resources. It involves not only reducing the use of various energy resources, but also reducing the polluting effects of such resources. By reducing pollution, people are taking an active part in conserving our natural resources—both for themselves and for future generations.

On a separate sheet of paper, write the letter of the answer that best completes each statement.

1. Pollution has become a major problem largely because of the
   a. abundance of natural resources.   b. dependence on fossil fuels.
   c. use of renewable resources.   d. decrease in energy consumption.
2. Obtaining and using energy resources have resulted in pollution of
   a. land.   b. air.   c. water.   d. all of these.
3. Coal near the surface of the ground is obtained through
   a. power shovels.   b. deep mine shafts.   c. strip mining.   d. land reclamation.
4. Poisonous wastes that contaminate the land are called
   a. nuclear fuels.   b. toxic wastes.   c. low-level wastes.   d. petrochemicals.
5. High-level nuclear wastes are difficult to dispose of because they
   a. are large and bulky.   b. are poisonous.
   c. have long half-lives.   d. have short half-lives.
6. A temperature inversion occurs when
   a. winds do not blow.   b. warm air is trapped under cool air.
   c. cool air is trapped under warm air.   d. warm air rises above cool air.
7. The major source of air pollution is
   a. nuclear wastes.   b. burning coal.   c. industrial wastes.   d. motor vehicles.
8. The release of excess heat into nearby bodies of water is called
   a. thermal pollution.   b. acid rain.
   c. groundwater pollution.   d. toxic waste pollution.
9. Water pollution
   a. limits wildlife.   b. limits drinking-water supplies.
   c. destroys recreational areas.   d. all of these.
10. The burning of coal has been made less polluting due to
    a. offshore drilling.   b. recycling.
    c. scrubber systems.   d. motor vehicle antipollution devices.

On a separate sheet of paper, fill in the word or words that best complete each statement.

1. The release of unwanted substances into the environment is called _____.
2. _____ can be obtained by strip mining.
3. Radioactive products of a nuclear power plant are called _____.
4. A _____ occurs when a layer of cool air is trapped under warmer air.
5. Sulfur oxides combine with water in the atmosphere to form droplets of _____ _____, which fall to the earth as _____.
6. Nitric acid forms in the atmosphere when _____ combine with _____.
7. An accident or leak in a petroleum tanker at sea may result in a (an) _____.
8. A rapid increase in the temperature of a lake or river may be caused by _____.
9. Reclaiming materials from glass and aluminum containers and paper is called _____.
10. _____ is the wise and careful use of natural resources.

Determine whether each statement is true or false. Then on a separate sheet of paper, write "true" if the statement is true. If it is false, change the underlined word or words to make the statement true.

1. Pollution is the release of <u>any</u> substance.
2. Resources that can be replaced once used up are called <u>nonrenewable</u> resources.
3. Nuclear wastes that have a short half-life are called <u>high-level</u> wastes.
4. The air pollution in Donora, Pennsylvania, was caused by the burning of <u>natural gas</u>.
5. The impurity in coal that leads to acid rain is <u>sulfur</u>.
6. Gasoline burns <u>completely</u> in a car engine.
7. Oil released into the ocean <u>is not</u> fatal to sea plants and animals.
8. The release of <u>sewage</u> into waterways is an example of water pollution.
9. Conservation is the wise use of <u>nonrenewable</u> resources.
10. <u>Solar energy</u> is an example of a renewable resource.

CONCEPT REVIEW: SKILL BUILDING

Use the skills you have developed in the chapter to complete each activity.

1. **Making diagrams** Make a chart or diagram that shows a pollution chain in which acid rain begins as air pollution and then becomes water and land pollution.
2. **Making maps** Find out where coal is mined around the world. Make a map that shows each area of coal mining. Use different colors to show coal deposits that have high-sulfur content or low-sulfur content.
3. **Relating cause and effect** Identify a possible cause for each of the following:
   a. acid rain forms
   b. temperature of a lake rises dramatically
   c. United States runs out of oil
   d. more and more people use car pools
4. **Expressing an opinion** Write a brief essay that either supports or refutes the following statement: "I think this whole environmental thing has gone too far. Once industrial profits go down because of all this government interference, the country will be worse off than before."
5. **Relating concepts** Write a short report in which you discuss how each of the following groups might react to the problem of acid rain in a certain area:
   a. tourists
   b. owners of industry
   c. wildlife preservationists
   d. fishermen
6. **Applying concepts** One serious form of land pollution is garbage and litter. Instead of being disposed of in solid-waste dumps, garbage and litter can be burned. Why is burning garbage not an environmentally sound idea? How could it become an environmentally sound idea?

CONCEPT REVIEW: ESSAY

On a separate sheet of paper, discuss each of the following in a brief paragraph.

1. How can you conserve energy in the home?
2. Explain how the balance in our environment is related to obtaining and using energy resources.
3. Explain why land, water, and air pollution cannot really be separated from one another.
4. How is conservation related to reducing pollution?

625

ADDITIONAL QUESTIONS AND TOPIC SUGGESTIONS

1. Why is it important to control pollution?
2. Explain why air, land, and water are considered renewable resources.
3. If fossil fuels cause so much pollution, why do we still use them?
4. Why are fossil fuels considered stored solar energy?
5. What are some of the benefits of conserving energy?
6. What are some ways you can conserve energy at home? At school?

ISSUES IN SCIENCE

The following issues can be used as a springboard for class debate, or they can be assigned as a writing homework.
1. Acid rain is an acknowledged international problem, yet most industrial countries are doing very little to resolve the problem. Some people argue that the amount of acid rain produced by each industry is difficult to calculate and that the costs of cleaning up their emissions greatly exceed the benefits to the environment. What are the estimated costs of controlling acid rain? Who pays the costs and what are some of the estimates for reducing emissions?
2. Some critics of solar energy technologies claim that the energy required to build most solar collectors exceeds the amount of energy they will ever collect. Does this "net energy" issue have any merit? How are the figures for embodied energy calculated?
3. How much solar energy is available where you live? Contact the U.S. Department of Energy or your state energy office and get maps showing the amount of direct solar radiation available in the United States. Calculate how many square meters of land it would take to provide all the energy needs of a typical residence (30 kilowatt hours per day).

Chapter 27

CHEMICAL TECHNOLOGY

CHAPTER OVERVIEW

In this chapter, students will learn about the many products that come from petroleum. These products include fuels, such as home heating oil and gasoline, and synthetic substances, such as nylon, plastics, and synthetic rubber.

Students will discover that raw petroleum, which is called crude oil, contains many different parts, or fractions. These fractions can be separated by a process known as fractional distillation.

Students will read about the many products we use every day that are made from petrochemicals. Petrochemicals are produced by polymerization, a process by which many molecules are chemically bonded together to form long chains called polymers. Students will also read about some polymers that occur in nature, such as silk, cotton, and cellulose. Students will come to understand that synthetic materials made from polymers are useful because they are flexible, strong, lightweight, and long lasting.

INTRODUCING CHAPTER 27

Direct students' attention to the photograph on page 626. Ask,
• **What do you see in this picture?** (a lot of snow and ice, and four people standing in the middle of it)
• **Does this look to you like the kind of environment in which you would expect to find a valuable natural resource?** (Answers may vary, but most students will probably say no.)

Explain that this is a photograph of the area near Prudhoe Bay on the Arctic Ocean, on the Northern coast of Alaska. In 1968, a rich oil field was discovered in this area, an oil field that is believed to be the largest oil deposit in North America. The total oil reserves in this area are said to be as much as 50 billion barrels.
• **Have you ever heard of the Alaska Pipeline?** (Answers may vary. Some students may have discussed the Pipe-

line in their social studies classes.) Encourage any students who have heard about the Pipeline to share what they know. Then point out that between 1974 and 1977, a 1290-km pipeline was constructed to join the Prudhoe Bay area with Valdez, an ice-free port on the Southern coast of Alaska. From Valdez, the valuable oil from Prudhoe Bay is shipped abroad.

Review with students the formation of fossil fuels, explaining that fos-

Chemical Technology 27

CHAPTER OBJECTIVES
After completing this chapter, you will be able to

27–1 Identify the major fractions of petroleum.

27–1 Describe the process of fractional distillation.

27–2 Explain how polymers are formed from monomers.

27–2 Describe the process of polymerization.

27–2 List some important natural and synthetic polymers.

Somewhere near Prudhoe Bay on the bone-chilling north coast of Alaska, four scientists stand on a vast barren plain. The view is awesome. All that meets the eye is a white landscape dotted with icy shades of green and blue. But the landscape was not always this stark. Millions of years ago this region was covered with forests. Animals and microscopic organisms made their homes among the trees, grasses, and giant ferns. A hot sun beat down on the lush vegetation.

Over millions of years, the plants and animals that flourished in the forests of Alaska died out and were buried. Time, heat, and the pressure of layers of sediment transformed the remains of these organisms into a black, thick liquid. Oil!

The scientists who stand on the ice and snow of Prudhoe Bay are looking for oil. Oil is one of the world's most important and valuable resources. Oil is a source of energy that warms homes and powers cars, planes, trains, and ships. Oil is a source of chemicals used to manufacture clothing, medicines, paints, records and cassette tapes, and thousands of other products used every day.

How does a gooey, black fluid from inside the earth get to be a pair of sneakers, an aspirin, or a tape that holds Bruce Springsteen's voice? In this chapter, you will find out more about the important role oil plays in making your life more comfortable and enjoyable.

Millions of years ago, this area on the north coast of Alaska was covered by a lush tropical forest. Today, it is covered by a blanket of ice and snow. Yet deep beneath the surface, the remains of organisms that once lived in the tropical forest have collected as droplets of oil.

627

TEACHER DEMONSTRATION

Bring in samples of several materials such as plastic food wrap, a piece of Teflon cookware, a pair of pantyhose, a plastic food-storage container, a shirt or blouse made of a synthetic fabric, an aspirin, a rubber washer or other plumbing component, a container of antifreeze. Make a display of the items and have students observe them. Ask,

• **In what way are these items similar?** (Answers will vary, but students should be guided to recognize that all are made from synthetic materials. By the end of the chapter, they will understand that all are made from petrochemicals.) Encourage students to recognize the diversity of the items by asking,

• **Can you classify these items according to how each is used?** (food preparation and storage: plastic wrap, plastic container, Teflon cookware; articles of clothing: shirt or blouse, pantyhose; car maintenance: antifreeze; home maintenance: washer; medicine: aspirin)

TEACHER RESOURCES
Audiovisuals
Mechanism of an Organic Reaction, film, CHEM Study
Synthesis of an Organic Compound, film, CHEM Study

Books
Cantow, H. J. (ed), *Polymer Chemistry,* Springer-Verlag
Driver, W. E., *Plastics Chemistry and Technology,* Van Nostrand Reinhold
Jenkins, A. D., *Polymer Science,* Elsevier

sil fuels were formed from the remains of dead plants and animals. Remind students that the three main fossil fuels are coal, oil, and natural gas.

Have students read the text on page 627. Ask,

• **How was oil formed in Alaska?** (At one time, the climate of Alaska was warm. Many plants and animals flourished in this climate. As they died out, they were buried. Eventually time, heat, and pressure turned their remains into oil.)

• **If the climate of Alaska had always been what it is today, do you think that oil would have formed in this area? Why or why not?** (Answers may vary, but it is unlikely that oil would have formed because little wildlife and vegetation would have been present.)

Explain to students that the discovery of rich oil fields has greatly enhanced Alaska's economy because oil is an extremely valuable resource.

• **What makes oil such a valuable resource?** (Answers may vary, but students should be guided to recognize that from oil an enormous variety of products can be produced, and that many of these products are essential or extremely valuable to our lives. Oil is the world's leading energy resource, and oil is also the raw material from which many important synthetic substances are produced.)

27-1 FUELS FROM PETROLEUM

SECTION PREVIEW 27-1

In this section, students will learn how petroleum is separated into its useful parts by fractional distillation. They will learn that fractional distillation takes place in a fractionating tower, where crude oil is heated to a temperature of about 385°C.

Students will learn about the various products that are produced from a barrel of crude oil. They will come to understand that because each fraction of petroleum has a different boiling point, raw petroleum can be vaporized and then condensed to draw off each separate substance.

PERFORMANCE OBJECTIVES 27-1

1. **Explain how petroleum is separated into its useful parts by fractional distillation.**
2. **Identify the products obtained from a barrel of crude oil.**
3. **Describe how each fraction of petroleum separates in a fractionating tower.**

SCIENCE TERMS 27-1

petroleum p. 628
fraction p. 628
fractionating tower p. 628
distillation p. 628

To describe how fractional distillation separates petroleum into its various components

27-1 Fuels from Petroleum

The oil that gushes from deep within the earth is a mixture of chemicals called crude oil, or **petroleum.** Petroleum is usually black or dark brown. But it can be green, red, yellow, or even colorless. Petroleum may flow as easily as water or it may ooze slowly like thick tar. The color and density of petroleum depend on the substances that make it up. By itself, petroleum is almost useless! But the different parts, or **fractions,** of petroleum are among the most useful chemicals in the world.

Petroleum is separated into its useful parts by a process called fractional distillation. The process of **distillation** involves heating a liquid until it vaporizes and then allowing the vapor to cool until it condenses back into a liquid. The different fractions of petroleum have different boiling points. So each fraction vaporizes at a different temperature. The temperature at which a substance boils is the same as the temperature at which it condenses. Thus, each fraction will condense back to a liquid at a different temperature. By drawing off each fraction as it condenses, petroleum can be easily separated into its various parts.

Fractional distillation of petroleum is done in a **fractionating tower.** The process of separating petroleum into its fractions is called refining. At a

Figure 27–1 *Geologists drill through the earth's surface to find crude oil, which is then recovered by devices such as an oil rig (left). The first oil well in the United States was drilled in 1859 in Pennsylvania (right). What is another term for crude oil?* ❶

628

TEACHING STRATEGY 27-1

Motivation

Draw on the chalkboard two beakers filled with liquid. Label one beaker water: boiling point = 100°C. Label the other beaker carbon tetrachloride: boiling point = 76.5°C.

- **Suppose you had a mixture of these two liquids, and you wanted to separate them. How would you go about it?** (Allow students to suggest whatever plans they wish.) If no one has suggested taking advantage of the difference in boiling point, ask,

- **What physical property of the two liquids is listed on the chalkboard?** (boiling point)

- **How might this property be useful in separating the two liquids?** (One would boil before the other, leaving the other liquid behind.)

Note that although this is true, simply boiling the mixture does not solve the problem, because one liquid will "disappear" as it vaporizes into the air.

- **How can we be sure to retrieve both liquids?** (Answers may vary. After students have studied this section, they will understand that the mixture must be vaporized, then condensed to retrieve the original liquids.)

Content Development

Use the Motivation activity to lead into

Figure 27–2 *Petroleum is separated into fractions in fractionating columns in an oil refinery (left). Each fraction condenses at a different temperature and is drawn off in collecting vessels located at fixed points along the column (right).*

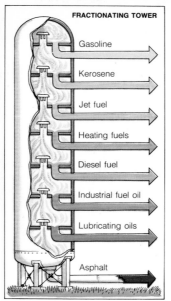

FRACTIONATING TOWER

Gasoline

Kerosene

Jet fuel

Heating fuels

Diesel fuel

Industrial fuel oil

Lubricating oils

Asphalt

Figure 27–3 *This illustration shows the amount, or percent yield, of each fraction that can be obtained from a barrel of crude oil. Which fraction represents the highest percent yield?* ❷

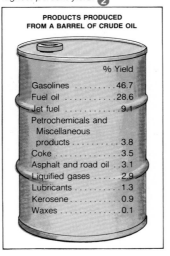

PRODUCTS PRODUCED
FROM A BARREL OF CRUDE OIL

	% Yield
Gasolines	46.7
Fuel oil	28.6
Jet fuel	9.1
Petrochemicals and Miscellaneous products	3.8
Coke	3.5
Asphalt and road oil	3.1
Liquified gases	2.9
Lubricants	1.3
Kerosene	0.9
Waxes	0.1

FACTS AND FIGURES

Boiling points for various fractions of petroleum:
Asphalt: above 400°C
Lubricating oils: 325–350°C
Diesel fuel: 275–325°C
Kerosene: 175–275°C
Gasoline: 30–175°C

ANNOTATION KEY

❶ Petroleum (Applying definitions)
❷ Gasolines: 46.7% (Interpreting charts)
❸ Gasolines (Interpreting illustrations)
❶ Thinking Skill: Applying technology
❷ Thinking Skill: Sequencing events

refinery, fractionating towers may rise 30 meters or more. Petroleum is piped into the base of the fractionating tower and heated to about 385°C. At this temperature, which is higher than the boiling points of most of the fractions, the petroleum vaporizes.

Figure 27–2 shows a typical fractionating tower. When the petroleum vaporizes, the fractions rise up the tower. As they rise, they cool and condense. Some fractions condense at high temperatures. These fractions condense near the bottom of the tower and are drawn off to collecting vessels. Other ❷ fractions continue to rise in the tower. As they rise, they cool even more before they condense. These fractions are drawn off at higher levels in the tower. As a result of this vaporization–condensation process, the various fractions of petroleum are separated and collected.

You will notice in Figure 27–2 that asphalt is collected at the bottom of the fractionating tower. Asphalt vaporizes at a temperature that exceeds the temperature in the tower. When the other fractions vaporize, asphalt is left behind as a liquid that simply runs out of the bottom of the tower. Which fraction in the tower condenses at the lowest temperature? ❸

a discussion of fractional distillation. Write the information from Facts and Figures on the chalkboard.
• **If these are some of the essential components of petroleum, how might they be separated from one another?** (by boiling, or vaporizing, the petroleum)
• **What must be done once the mixture has been vaporized?** (The temperature must be lowered in order to condense the vapors into liquids.)

• **Why is it necessary to condense the vapors?** (In the vaporized state, it is difficult or impossible to collect the substances. Also, they are useful as liquids, not as gases.)

Have students observe the fractionating tower in Figure 27-2. Ask,
• **What do you notice about the order of substances in the tower?** (Those with the lowest boiling points are at the top, and those with the highest boiling points are at the bottom.)

• **Why is this the case?** (Those that condense at a lower temperature have more time to rise in the tower as the vapor is cooled.)

27-2 PETROCHEMICAL PRODUCTS

SECTION PREVIEW 27-2

In this section, students will be introduced to the many useful products that are made from petrochemicals. These products include plastics, synthetic fibers, and medicines.

Students will learn that petrochemical products are made possible by a process called polymerization. Polymerization involves the chemical bonding of molecules to make gigantic chains called polymers.

Although most of the polymers discussed in this section are synthetic materials made from petroleum, students will also read about natural polymers. These include cotton, wool, cellulose, and proteins.

PERFORMANCE OBJECTIVES 27-2

1. **Define polymer and describe the process of polymerization.**
2. **Identify petrochemicals produced by polymerization.**
3. **Describe some of the products made from petrochemicals.**
4. **Discuss the usefulness of products made from petrochemicals.**

SCIENCE TERMS 27-2

polymer p. 630
monomer p. 630
amino acid p. 632
polymerization p. 632

SECTION REVIEW

1. What physical property forms the basis of fractional distillation?
2. Why do substances with low boiling points condense near the top of a fractionating tower?
3. How would you separate three substances—A, B, and C—whose boiling points are 50°C, 100°C, and 150°C, respectively?

Section Objective

To identify petrochemicals produced by polymerization

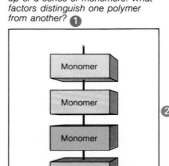

Figure 27–4 *A polymer is made up of a series of monomers. What factors distinguish one polymer from another?* ❶

Monomer

Monomer

Monomer

Monomer

POLYMER

630

27–2 Petrochemical Products

Ride a bicycle down your street and you are probably gliding along on a product of petroleum, or a petrochemical product. The rubber in the ❶ inner tube is made from petrochemicals. Put on your winter jacket and you are probably keeping yourself warm with a petrochemical product—the lining of your jacket is made from petrochemicals.

Polymer Chemistry

One simple definition of chemistry is the "making and breaking of bonds." In a chemical reaction, the chemical bonds that hold atoms together in molecules are broken. The atoms are rearranged, different bonds are formed, and new molecules are produced. The petrochemical products that are part of your life come from the making and breaking of chemical bonds in petrochemicals. A general term for this process is polymer chemistry. And polymer chemistry involves **polymers** (PAHL-ih-merz).

The term polymer comes from the Greek words *polys*, meaning "many," and *meros*, meaning "parts." The word "parts" refers to a grouping of atoms ❷ called a molecular unit. A molecular unit alone is not a polymer. But many molecular units strung together in a series form a unique polymer.

The individual molecular units that form a polymer are called **monomers** (MAHN-uh-merz). You can think of a polymer as a series of monomers all bonded together one after another. The type of monomers and the length and shape of the polymer chain determine the physical properties of the polymer.

27-1 (continued)

Section Review 27-1
1. Boiling point
2. They must rise the highest before they cool and condense into a liquid.
3. Heat the substance to above 150°C and then allow it to cool so that liquid condenses at a different temperature (150°C, 100°C, 50°C) and separates out.

TEACHING STRATEGY 27-2

Motivation
Have students observe the photographs in Figure 27-5. Ask,
• **How many of these products have you used?** (Answers will vary.)
• **In what ways did you find these products useful?** (Answers will vary. Try to guide students to consider the special properties of the synthetic materials, such as the nonstick Teflon.)

• **Have you ever used similar products not made from these materials that were less practical or more difficult to use?** (Answers will vary. Probably many students have used cookware that was not coated in Teflon, or have tried to cover food with something less convenient than plastic wrap.)

Content Development
Point out to students that 75 years ago

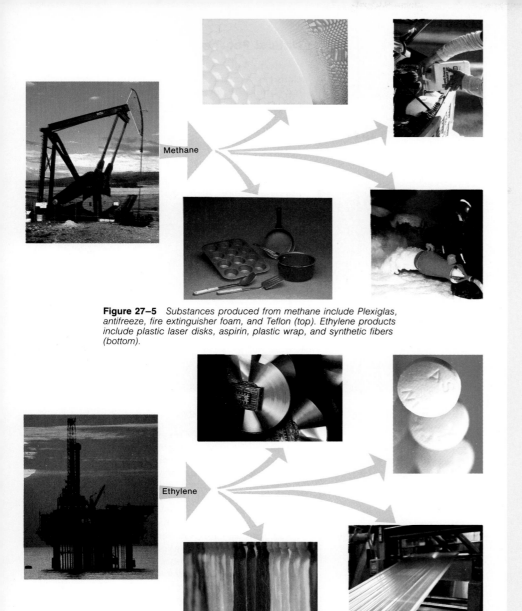

Figure 27–5 *Substances produced from methane include Plexiglas, antifreeze, fire extinguisher foam, and Teflon (top). Ethylene products include plastic laser disks, aspirin, plastic wrap, and synthetic fibers (bottom).*

most of the synthetic substances we take for granted had not even been thought of. Thanks to chemical technology, and polymer chemistry in particular, we have available such a wide variety of useful products.

Skills Development
Skill: Making a model
Divide students into groups of three or four. Challenge each group to create a three-dimensional model of a polymer, using whatever materials they wish. (Students may find it helpful to refer to Figure 27-4.) Some groups may enjoy researching the structure of a particular polymer and using that as a basis for their model.

Reinforcement
Review with students the formulas for methane (CH_4) and ethylene (C_2H_4). Remind students that both substances are hydrocarbons, meaning that they contain hydrogen and carbon. Emphasize that petroleum, which is a fossil fuel, is rich in hydrocarbons.

BACKGROUND INFORMATION

There are two types of polymerization reactions. The first of these is *addition polymerization*. In addition polymerization, bonding between monomers is accomplished by opening the double bonds between carbon atoms in molecules such as ethylene. As a result, no atoms are eliminated during the reaction. Polymers such as Teflon and Plexiglas are made by this process.

The second type of polymerization reaction is called *condensation polymerization*. In this type of reaction, atoms must be eliminated in order for the bonds to form. The joining of amino acids to form proteins is an examples of a condensation reaction. Atoms of hydrogen and oxygen are eliminated, making water a byproduct of protein formation. The polymer Dacron is also formed by the condensation process.

Sharpen Your Skills

Homemade Adhesives
Skills: Designing an experiment, manipulative, comparing, applying, relating
Level: Average
Type: Hands-on
Materials: flour, water, egg white

In this activity, students compare the adhesive strength of two homemade adhesives. Have students compare the adhesive strength of the flour paste and egg white glue to some synthetic adhesives.

Figure 27–6 *In the past, rubber was obtained from rubber trees (left). Today, the rubber used in products such as these truck tires is manufactured in factories (right). What type of polymer is rubber obtained from rubber trees? From factories?* ❶

Sharpen Your Skills

Homemade Adhesives

1. Mix flour and water to make a paste.
2. Separate the white from the yolk of a raw egg. Egg white is a natural adhesive.
3. Compare the "sticking strength" of the flour paste and the egg white by using each to lift objects of increasing mass.

632

Natural Polymers

Most of the polymers you will read about in this chapter are made from petrochemicals. Some polymers, however, occur in nature. Cotton, silk, wool, and natural rubber are all natural polymers. Cellulose and lignin, important parts of wood, are natural polymers. In fact, all living things contain polymers. Protein, an essential ingredient of living matter, is a polymer. The monomers from which proteins are made are called **amino acids.** Combined in groups of one hundred or more units, amino acid monomers form many of the parts of your body—from hair to heart muscle.

Synthetic Polymers

Although the term polymer may be new to you, the polymers produced from petrochemicals are probably quite familiar. Polymers produced from petrochemicals are called synthetic polymers. Petrochemical products such as rubber and plastic wrap are synthetic polymers. Synthetic polymers are used to make fabrics such as nylon, rayon, orlon, and ❶ dacron. Plastics, used in many products from kitchen utensils to rocket engines, are petrochemical products made of polymers. The list goes on and on.

The first polymer was manufactured in 1909. Since then, **polymerization** (puh-lihm-uhr-ih-ZAY-shuhn) has come a long way. **Polymerization is the process of chemically bonding monomers to form polymers.** Most early polymers consisted of fewer

---

27-2 (continued)

Skills Development

Skill: Observing
Divide the class into groups of three or four. Have each group tour the classroom and list all the objects that they believe are made of polymers. Have the groups report their findings, then discuss.

Content Development

As students begin to see how many products come from petroleum, impress upon them the loss that we would suffer if petroleum were no longer available. Point out that if alternative fuels are developed, the useful fractions of petroleum will still be used extensively to make polymers.

Enrichment

The discovery of nylon in the 1940s is an interesting story. Have students research this topic and report to the class.

Reinforcement

To review the difference between natural polymers and synthetic polymers, have students collect pairs of similar objects—made from a natural polymer; the other made from a synthetic

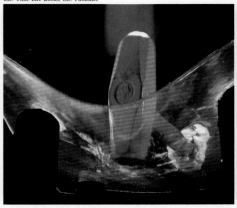

Figure 27–7 *Polymer technology has produced some amazing materials. This sheet of plastic simply bends no matter how hard it is struck by a hammer (left). This extra-thin sheet of plastic is not damaged by temperatures over 1000°C. But as you can see from the boiling water, it does allow the transfer of heat (right).*

than two hundred monomers. Today's polymers may contain thousands of monomers. The numerous ways in which these monomers can be linked may be very complex. They include single chains, parallel chains, intertwining chains, spirals, loops, and loops of chains!

Polymer chemistry has produced synthetic materials that are strong, light, heat resistant, flexible, and long lasting. These properties give polymers a wide range of uses. For example, polymers are used as substitutes for human tissue, such as bones and arteries. These polymers must last a lifetime and withstand the wear and tear of constant use. Polymer adhesives, rather than thread, are often used to ❷ hold clothes together. Polymers are replacing glass, metal, and paper as containers for food. The cup of hot chocolate you may have held today did not burn your hand because it was made of a white insulating polymer. Polymer materials also are used for rugs, furniture, wall coverings, and curtains. Look around you and see how many polymers you can spot. And remember to thank petroleum for all these useful polymers.

Figure 27–8 *Polymers are used to build artificial body parts such as this artificial heart (top) and this artificial knee joint (bottom). What important properties must polymers used in artificial body parts have?* ❷

TEACHER DEMONSTRATION

This demonstration shows the preparation of the synthetic fiber nylon. You will need the following materials: adipyl chloride solution (0.25 M in hexane), hexamethylene diamine solution (0.50 M in 0.50 M NaOH), acetone (in alcohol), paper clip, small beakers, graduated cylinder.

1. Bend apart the paper clip, leaving a hook at one end.

2. Pour 5 mL hexamethylene diamine solution into one beaker.

3. Slowly add 5 mL adipyl chloride solution. A white film should form as the two solutions meet.

4. Put the paper clip into the beaker, hooking around the white film. Then slowly lift the paper clip from the beaker.

5. This white substance is the polymer nylon. Continue removing the nylon from the beaker until none remains.

6. Place the nylon in a beaker and wash it. Rinse with acetone and let it dry.

polymer. For example, a student might bring in a bowl made of wood, which contains the natural polymers cellulose and lignin, and a bowl made of plastic.

BACKGROUND INFORMATION

Some common polymers and their uses are listed below.

1. **Dacron:** textiles, arterial grafts, parachutes
2. **Nylon 66:** tire cord, textiles, brush bristles, netting, carpet, sutures
3. **Polyethylene:** tubing, prosthetic devices, packaging materials, kitchen utensils, paper coating
4. **Polypropylene:** rope, protective clothing, textiles, carpet
5. **Polystyrene:** containers, boats, coolers, insulation, furniture
6. **Polyvinyl chloride (PVC):** rubber substitute, cable covering, tubing, rainwear

TIE-IN/LIFE SCIENCE

In 1944, the development of a synthetic membrane that worked like a natural membrane made possible the invention of an artificial kidney. Another use of synthetic membranes is in skin substitutes for burn victims.

On July 4, 1986, a figure that represents freedom to people of the United States and most of the world was honored with a huge birthday party. The figure is the Statue of Liberty. Almost everywhere you looked that day there were replicas of the one hundred-year-old statue. The replicas were cast from almost every material imaginable: chocolate, ice, aluminum, glass, plastic, concrete, plaster, and—like the original statue—copper.

Producing the molds from which these statues were formed kept many **patternmakers** busy for months before the celebration. A patternmaker produces molds for new car parts, new board game pieces, machine parts, and many other products.

Using blueprints that show how the finished product should look, a patternmaker first makes a model of the new product. The model is usually made of clay, wood, or plaster. The model is then pressed into clay, sand, plaster, or other materials to make a hollow mold. The finished piece is then cast, or formed, from this mold.

Frequently, a mold is used to shape new synthetic materials. So a patternmaker must be familiar with the chemical technology that is used to develop new materials. A high school diploma and courses in art, math, mechanical drawing, and metalworking are required to become a patternmaker. Usually a patternmaker learns the skills of the trade through a five-year apprenticeship. For information about a career as a patternmaker, contact the American Foundrymen's Society/Cast Metals Institute, Inc., Golf and Wolf Roads, Des Plaines, IL 60016.

Polymer materials also can be mixed and matched to produce substances with unusual properties. Different plastics and synthetic fibers are combined to make punctureproof tires and bulletproof vests. Layers of polymer materials can be combined to make waterproof rain gear.

Polymer chemistry also is important in the transportation industry. Each year the number of polymer parts in cars, planes, and trains increases. A plastic car engine has been built and tested. This engine is lighter, more fuel efficient, and more durable than a metal engine.

Figure 27–9 *Synthetic fibers are one of the many products formed from polymers. What is the name of the process of chemically bonding monomers to form polymers?* ❶

27-2 (continued)

Reinforcement

Have students make a collection of fabric-content labels, noting those that list synthetic polymers and those that list natural polymers. Encourage them to take special notice of fabrics that include a mixture of synthetic and nonsynthetic fibers, such as 45 percent cotton and 55 percent polyester.

- **What advantages do you think a mixture of synthetic and natural fibers might have?** (A possible answer might be combining certain wear-resistant qualities of synthetic fibers with the feel and appearance of natural fibers.)

Enrichment

Challenge students to find out the specific monomers that make up Dacron, polypropylene, and polyvinyl chloride (PVC). Then have them use their findings to draw structural formulas for a portion of each polymer.

Skills Development

Skill: Inferring

Point out to students that superstrength glue is made from polymers. Ask,

- **What does this tell you about the chemical bonds of polymers?** (They must be very strong and difficult to break.)

Figure 27–10 *The scientist is holding a thin strand of Kevlar, a polymer five times stronger than steel (right). Ropes of Kevlar have replaced steel in lines used to hold ships at dock (left).*

Devices that produce electricity also are being improved with polymers. Polymer batteries and solar electric cells will soon be available. These developments are expected to increase the use of solar energy and improve energy conservation. Recently, a new polymer was developed that can conduct electricity almost as well as metals such as copper. One of the scientists who developed this polymer described its possible use "as a lightweight, rechargeable battery about as thick as a sheet of paper." As you can see, polymers made from petroleum are extremely important today. And they will be even more important in the future.

SECTION REVIEW

1. What is the relationship between a monomer and a polymer?
2. List three examples of natural polymers.
3. What is the name of the process in which monomers are chemically bonded to form polymers?
4. What might be some of the economic side effects of increased use of polymers in automobiles?

635

Section Review 27-2
1. A polymer is a long chain of monomers.
2. Cotton, silk, wool, natural rubber, cellulose, lignin, protein
3. Polymerization
4. Answers will vary but may include more emphasis on discovering and purchasing petroleum, less demand for steel, increased fuel efficiency of cars.

LABORATORY INVESTIGATION COMPARING NATURAL AND SYNTHETIC POLYMERS

BEFORE THE LAB

1. **At least one day prior to the investigation, gather together enough materials for your class, assuming six students per group.**
2. **If you have difficulty obtaining linen, silk can be used instead. If you have difficulty obtaining acetate, acrylic fiber can be substituted.**

PRE-LAB DISCUSSION

Begin the discussion by asking students,

● **Why do you think synthetic fabrics were invented?** (Answers may vary. Probably synthetic fabrics were invented in order to obtain fabrics with certain properties, such as water repellency or the ability to "wash and wear" with little or no ironing. Also, it is possible that at certain times in certain places, natural fabrics may have been in short supply, or difficult or expensive to obtain.)

After students have read the lab, ask,

● **What is being investigated in this lab?** (the properties of natural vs. synthetic fabrics)

● **What is the variable in this investigation?** (the different types of fabric, and whether the fabric is made from natural or synthetic polymers)

● **What is the control?** (the things that will be done to the fabrics)

● **What is your hypothesis as to the outcome of the investigation?** (Answers will vary, but should reflect an expectation to see a difference in properties between synthetic and natural fibers.)

SKILL DEVELOPMENT

Students will use the following skills while completing this investigation.
1. Safety
2. Manipulative
3. Comparing
4. Observing
5. Recording
6. Inferring
7. Applying
8. Relating

SAFETY TIPS

Remind students to wear safety goggles and rubber gloves during the lab. Caution them to avoid splashing bleach on skin or clothing.

At the end of the lab, emphasize the need to dispose of liquid wastes properly.

Problem

How do natural and synthetic polymers compare in strength, absorbency, and resistance to chemical damage?

Materials *(per group)*

12 Styrofoam cups	marking pen
liquid bleach	scissors
water	paper towel
oil	rubber gloves
medicine dropper	metric ruler
mild acid (lime juice, vinegar, or lemon juice)	
3 samples of natural polymer cloth: wool, cotton, linen	
3 samples of synthetic polymer cloth: polyester, nylon, acetate	

Procedure

1. Record the color of each cloth.
2. Label six Styrofoam cups with the names of the six cloth samples. Also write the word "bleach" on each cup.
3. Cut a piece about 2 square centimeters from each cloth. Put each piece in its cup.
4. Wearing rubber gloves, carefully pour a small amount of bleach into each cup.
5. Label the six remaining cups with the names of the six cloth samples and the word "acid." Then pour a small amount of the mild acid into each and repeat step 3.
6. Set the cups aside for 24 hours. Meanwhile, proceed with steps 7 through 9.
7. Using the remaining samples of cloth, attempt to tear each.
8. Place a drop of water on each material. Note whether the water forms beads or is absorbed. If the water is absorbed, record the rate of absorption.

9. Repeat step 8 using a drop of oil.
10. After 24 hours, carefully pour the liquids in the cups into the sink or into a container provided by your teacher. Dry the samples with a paper towel.
11. Record any color changes.

Observations

1. Which material held its color best in bleach? In acid?
2. Which materials were least resistant to chemical damage by bleach or mild acid?
3. Which material has the strongest fiber or is hardest to tear?
4. Which materials are water repellent?

Conclusions

1. Compare the natural and synthetic polymers' strength, absorbency, and resistance to chemical damage.
2. Which material would you use to manufacture a laboratory coat? A farmer's overalls? A raincoat? An auto mechanic's shirt?

OBSERVATIONS

1. wool
2. cotton, linen
3. polyester
4. polyester, nylon

CONCLUSIONS

1. The synthetic polymer polyester was the strongest in terms of being hardest to tear. The synthetic polymer polyester absorbed the least amount of

SUMMARY

27-1 Fuels from Petroleum

❏ Crude oil, or petroleum, is made up of different parts called fractions.

❏ Although petroleum has no practical uses, its fractions have many important uses.

❏ Petroleum is separated into its components through a process called fractional distillation.

❏ During fractional distillation, petroleum is heated to a temperature at which most of its fractions vaporize. As the fractions rise up the fractionating tower, they cool and condense at different temperatures. The liquid fractions are drawn off and separated at different levels in the tower.

27-2 Petrochemical Products

❏ Substances derived from petroleum are called petrochemicals.

❏ Most petrochemical products are polymers.

❏ A polymer is a series of molecular units called monomers.

❏ The process of chemically combining monomers to make a polymer is called polymerization.

❏ Natural polymers include cotton, silk, wool, natural rubber, cellulose, lignin, and protein.

❏ Proteins are made of amino acids.

❏ Synthetic polymers include rubber, plastics, and fabrics such as nylon, orlon, rayon, and dacron.

❏ Polymers are usually strong, lightweight, heat resistant, flexible, and long lasting.

❏ Polymers can be mixed and matched to form substances that are waterproof, punctureproof, or electrically conductive.

VOCABULARY

Define each term in a complete sentence.

amino acid   fractionating   petroleum
distillation   tower   polymer
fraction   monomer   polymerization

CONTENT REVIEW: MULTIPLE CHOICE

On a separate sheet of paper, write the letter of the answer that best completes each statement.

1. Crude oil is
   a. a single substance.   b. gasoline.   c. asphalt.   d. a mixture.
2. The physical property used to separate petroleum into its parts is
   a. melting point.   b. boiling point.   c. density.   d. solubility.
3. The highest temperature in a fractionating tower is about 385°C because that is
   a. below the boiling point of most petroleum fractions.
   b. above the boiling point of most petroleum fractions.
   c. equal to the boiling point of most petroleum fractions.
   d. below the melting point of most petroleum fractions.
4. Of the following, the least likely to vaporize in a fractionating tower is
   a. kerosene.   b. gasoline.   c. asphalt.   d. heating fuel.

637

Part 2

Have students take an inventory of their clothing and record five items made from synthetic fibers and five items made from natural fibers. Have them write a brief statement describing how each garment has worn so far, noting any problems or benefits. For example, a student might write, "Dacron blouse: Needs no ironing after it is washed, but color has not stayed as bright as I had hoped." Have students share and compare their lists in a class discussion.

water while the synthetic polymers polyester and nylon absorbed the least amount of oil. The natural polymer wool was the most resistant to chemical wear from bleach and acid.

2. Lab coat: cotton, linen; farmer's overalls: polyester; raincoat: polyester, nylon; auto mechanic's shirt: polyester, nylon

GOING FURTHER: ENRICHMENT

Part 1

Have students perform a similar experiment using synthetic rubber and natural rubber, or plastic and wood. Encourage the students to compare the usefulness of items made from these substances, based on the properties they discover.

CHAPTER REVIEW

MULTIPLE CHOICE

1. d	3. a	5. c	7. a	9. c
2. b	4. b	6. b	8. c	10. d

COMPLETION

1. petroleum
2. distillation
3. fractionating; refinery
4. boiling point
5. Petrochemical products
6. monomers
7. cellulose; lignin
8. Amino acids
9. Polymerization
10. synthetic

TRUE OR FALSE

1. F crude oil
2. T
3. F fractional distillation
4. T
5. F condenses
6. F 385°C
7. F polymer; monomer
8. T
9. T
10. F synthetic

SKILL BUILDING

1. Conclusions will vary, but students should readily perceive that the majority of petroleum products are used for various types of fuels, particularly gasoline. Students may point out that by decreasing the use of fuels used in transportation, perhaps through increased mass transit, more of the petroleum can be used for other products or can be conserved for future needs.

2. Answers will vary, depending on students' choices for objects. Predictions should be logical in terms of characteristics of new polymers, but they do not have to be necessarily feasible at the present time.

3. Students should point out that materials used in an engine must be durable, withstand vibrations, and be able to withstand high temperatures that build up in a car engine. Furthermore, materials used in engines should be lightweight in order to conserve fuel. Materials used in safety belts should be flexible but very strong and able to withstand the stresses involved during an accident. Materials used in seat cushions should be soft and comfortable but must also be durable to provide for the car's lifetime of wear and tear.

4. Without fossils, Alphaland is the least logical choice to explore for oil, since oil is derived from the remains of ancient plants and animals. Since Gammaland has fossils, the possibility of oil does exist. However, fossils in Gammaland are not deeply buried, indicating that they have not been underground long enough and have not had to withstand enough pressure to be changed into petroleum. The fact that Gammaland is very cold is irrelevant. The most logical choice to explore for oil would be in Betaland. There the fossils are deep enough to have been buried long ago and under great pressure.

5. The process of distillation involves
   a. vaporization and condensation. b. freezing and melting.
   c. vaporization and melting.   d. freezing and condensation.
6. A polymer is made up of a series of
   a. atoms.   b. monomers.   c. fuels.   d. synthetic molecules.
7. An example of a natural polymer is
   a. wool.   b. plastic.   c. crude oil.   d. copper.
8. An example of a synthetic polymer is
   a. natural rubber.   b. protein.   c. rayon.   d. cotton.
9. The process of chemically bonding monomers to form polymers is called
   a. distillation.   b. fractionation.   c. polymerization.   d. refining.
10. An example of a polymer product is
   a. lead tubing.   b. crude oil.   c. water.   d. plastic.

CONTENT REVIEW: COMPLETION

On a separate sheet of paper, write the word or words that best complete each statement.

1. Oil that gushes from deep within the earth is called crude oil, or _____.
2. The process of _____ involves heating a liquid until it vaporizes and then allowing it to cool until it condenses.
3. To separate crude oil into its useful components, a _____ tower is used at a _____.
4. Each fraction of petroleum has a different _____.
5. _____ are products made from petroleum.
6. A polymer consists of many _____ bonded together.
7. The natural polymers _____ and _____ are important components of wood.
8. _____ are the monomers from which proteins are made.
9. _____ is the process in which monomers are chemically bonded to form polymers.
10. Polymers manufactured from petroleum are called _____ polymers.

CONTENT REVIEW: TRUE OR FALSE

Determine whether each statement is true or false. Then on a separate sheet of paper, write "true" if it is true. If it is false, change the underlined word or words to make the statement true.

1. Petroleum taken directly from the earth is called asphalt.
2. Petroleum can be separated into its different parts, or fractions.
3. The process of separating petroleum into its components is called boiling.
4. Heating a liquid to its boiling point turns it into a vapor.
5. When a vapor evaporates, it changes back to a liquid.
6. In a fractionating tower, petroleum is heated to about 85°C.
7. A monomer is a long chain of polymers.
8. Silk is an example of a natural polymer.
9. Polymerization involves the chemical bonding of monomers into polymers.
10. Plastics are examples of natural polymers.

ESSAY

1. Answers will vary, depending on students' selections. Make sure students' essays are well written and logical.
2. There are no right or wrong answers to this issue. Some students will show great concern for the environment and may suggest cutting back on our use of petroleum. Others may feel the need for petroleum products outweighs the pollution problems. Still others may suggest using petroleum products, but

Use the skills you have developed in the chapter to complete each activity.

1. **Making graphs** Figure 27–3 shows the yield in percent of products that are derived from petroleum. On a sheet of graph paper, plot the type of product on one axis and the percentage yield of that product on the other. What conclusions can you draw from your finished graph?

2. **Making predictions** Select five objects in your home that are made from naturally occurring substances such as wool or silver. For each object, predict whether a synthetic polymer may be developed to replace the naturally occurring substance. Describe the characteristics each synthetic polymer should have to make it more suitable than the naturally occurring substance.

3. **Applying technology** You are an engineer whose task is to design a car that is fuel efficient yet meets all of the current standards for safety and durability. What kinds of materials would you consider using? What properties must the materials used in the engine have? The materials used in safety belts? The materials used in seat cushions?

4. **Analyzing data** You are an oil prospector who has sent three scientists to explore three regions of the earth—Alphaland, Betaland, and Gammaland. You get the following reports.
Alphaland: No fossils in rocks at any depth. Warm climate for millions of years. Betaland: Fossils at great depths. Present climate warm. Gammaland: Fossils at relatively shallow depths. Present climate very cold.
You can choose only one location at which to sink a well. Based on your data, which location would you choose? Explain your answer.

CONCEPT REVIEW: ESSAY

Discuss each of the following in a brief paragraph.

1. Describe some of the uses of synthetic polymers in your life. Then describe what changes you would have to make in your life style if these polymers were not available.

2. Many people use and enjoy the products derived from petroleum. However, some of the chemical processes used to make these products, as well as the burning of petroleum fuels, add to the pollution of the air, the land, and the water in the United States. So people often must decide whether manufacturing a certain product is worth the damage done to the environment. In other words, people often must make a trade-off between products they want and the effects on the environment. What is your feeling on this issue?

639

Also, synthetic polymers have more special properties than natural polymers, such as the ability to repel water or withstand high temperatures or punctures.)

2. Why is a height of 30 meters or more necessary for a fractionating tower? Could not a shorter tower be used? (The tower must be tall enough to allow the fractions to rise high enough to separate. If a shorter tower was used, several fractions that condense at low temperatures would probably collect together at the top.)

3. What advantages would a food container made of polyethylene have over a food container made of metal, glass, or paper? (Metals tend to conduct heat and react chemically with other substances such as acids. Polyethylene would probably keep food at a desired temperature more easily and would provide safe storage for acidic foods such as cut fruits. The advantages of polyethylene over glass are that it will not crack or shatter, and it is lighter weight. Paper containers are handy as throwaways, but they tend to absorb food juices, lose their shape quickly, and catch fire easily. None of these things are true about polyethylene containers.)

ISSUES IN SCIENCE

The following issues can be used as a springboard for class debate or assigned as a writing homework.

1. The proposed construction of the Alaska Pipeline in the early 1970s prompted tremendous criticism from conservationists, who were able to block the pipeline's construction for several years. Find out why the conservationists objected, and why they were eventually overruled. Then express your own opinion on the issue.

2. Despite the popularity of synthetic fabrics, many people will not buy a garment unless it is marked 100 percent natural fiber. They feel that synthetic fibers "don't breathe," are not good for their skin, and are "not organic." Take a position on this issue, and explain why you will or will not wear synthetic fabrics.

finding methods to make sure such products do not pollute the environment.

ADDITIONAL QUESTIONS AND TOPIC SUGGESTIONS

1. In what ways do the properties of natural polymers resemble those of synthetic polymers? In what ways do they differ? (Natural polymers such as those contained in wood, cotton cloth, and human tissues provide strength and durability, as synthetic polymers do. Natural polymers, however, are usually more prone to damage than synthetic polymers. An example of this would be a wooden spoon versus a plastic spoon. The wooden spoon might burn, dry out, become discolored, become worn, or react chemically with other substances. The plastic spoon would tend to be more resistant to these stresses.

Chapter 28

ELECTRONICS AND COMPUTERS

CHAPTER OVERVIEW

This chapter traces the development of electronic instrumentation from its inception to its application in computers.

Electronics is the study of the release, behavior, and effects of electrons as it relates to use in helpful devices. Electronics began with the invention of the vacuum tube diode, which serves as a one-way valve for electrons. Vacuum tube diodes are used as rectifiers. Vacuum tube triodes are amplifiers.

Modern electronics began with the use of semiconductors to make solid-state diodes and transistors. Produced by doping crystals like silicon with impurities, solid-state devices can replace many large vacuum tubes with a single, tiny integrated circuit.

A discussion of radio and television tells how electromagnetic signals are produced, transmitted, amplified, and used to create audio and video signals. The operation of the cathode ray tube is detailed.

The final section deals with computers, their main parts, and their need for programs. The binary number system is introduced and explained as the only language a computer can handle.

Electronics and Computers 28

CHAPTER OBJECTIVES

After completing this chapter, you will be able to

28–1 Define electronics.

28–1 Describe the structure and applications of vacuum tubes.

28–1 Relate semiconductors to the operation of transistors and integrated circuits.

28–2 Explain how a telephone and a radio work.

28–3 Describe the operation of a cathode-ray tube and its use in television.

28–4 Discuss the development and the components of a modern computer.

28–4 Use the binary system to represent numbers.

It was 1952, and not many people were familiar with computers. In fact, there were some who had never even heard the word! But on Election Day of that year, the inevitable happened. Millions of Americans came face to face with the computer age for the first time. For some it was a rather shocking encounter.

The presidential contest that year pitted Republican Dwight D. Eisenhower against Democrat Adlai E. Stevenson. Early in the evening, even before the voting polls had closed, newscaster Walter Cronkite announced to television viewers that an "electronic brain" was going to predict the outcome of the election.

The "electronic brain" was the huge UNIVAC I computer. For weeks before the election, computer scientists had been feeding district-by-district results of the presidential elections of 1944 and 1948 into UNIVAC's computer memory. They also had instructed the computer how to analyze the early 1952 voting returns by comparing them with the results of the last two elections.

What UNIVAC predicted, based on just 3 million votes, was a landslide victory for Eisenhower. A shocked and disbelieving nation sat by their television sets into the early hours of the morning, convinced that the "electronic brain" had made a giant mistake.

UNIVAC was not wrong, however. When all the votes were counted, the computer's prediction turned out to be remarkably close to the actual results. As Eisenhower became president, the computer age dawned for most Americans. In this chapter, you will learn about some of the devices that have brought the computer age to where it is now.

This photographer's view of computer technology shows some of the basic hardware—chips, multichip board, and computer cable.

641

TEACHER DEMONSTRATION

Visit a television repair shop and obtain an electron gun from a broken television picture tube. Display the gun to the class without identifying it. Mention that this is the heart of something very important to them. Can anyone identify the device? The actual operation of the electron gun is quite simple compared to the processing of the television signal before it reaches the picture tube.

TEACHER RESOURCES

Audiovisuals

Computer Hardware: What It Is and How It Works, 4 filmstrips, The Center for Humanities

Computers in Our Society, 5 filmstrips, Encyclopaedia Britannica

Books

Dertouzos, M. L., and J. Moses (eds.), *Computer Age: A Twenty-Year View,* MIT Press

Slotnick, D. L., and J. L. Slotnick, *Computers: Their Structure, Use, and Influence,* Prentice-Hall

Ask students to list the computer-controlled devices that they have encountered just this morning. The list will be staggering. Integrated circuits are found in refrigerators, radios, alarm clocks, toasters, microwave ovens, garage door openers, etc. The integrated circuit is essentially a computer since it processes information according to a program and acts upon the results.

28-1 ELECTRONIC DEVICES

SECTION PREVIEW 28-1

Electronics is defined in this section as the study of the release, behavior, and effects of electrons as it relates to use in helpful devices.

Students learn that electronics had its start with the vacuum tube and its applications as diodes, amplifiers, and rectifiers.

Modern electronics began with the invention of solid-state devices, sandwiches of semiconductors that behave in the same manner as vacuum tubes but with more precision and efficiency. Transistors and integrated circuits have miniaturized the world of electronics.

PERFORMANCE OBJECTIVES 28-1

1. **Define electronics.**
2. **Explain why a vacuum tube diode is actually a one-way gate for electric current.**
3. **Describe the function of an amplifier.**
4. **Compare p-type semiconductors and n-type semiconductors.**
5. **Compare transistors with a triode vacuum tube.**

SCIENCE TERMS 28-1

electronics p. 642
vacuum tube
  p. 643
diode p. 643
rectifier p. 643
amplifier p. 644
triode p. 644
semiconductor
  p. 645

solid-state device
  p. 645
doping p. 645
transistor p. 646
integrated circuit
  p. 646
chip p. 646

Your world would be very different without electricity and the numerous devices that use electricity. Were you awakened this morning by the buzz of an alarm clock and the flash of numbers? Did you rely on a radio or a cassette player to get the day started with music? Did your breakfast include food that was warmed in a microwave oven? Can you get through the day without using the telephone?

Few people can answer these questions without realizing that electric devices make life easier and more enjoyable. The branch of technology that has developed electric devices is called **electronics.** Electronics is a branch of physics. **Electronics is the study of the release, behavior, and effects of electrons as it relates to use in helpful devices.**

Electronic technology can be traced to the nineteenth century, when electricity was used to power simple devices such as lamps, heaters, and welding arcs. In such devices, the kinetic energy of moving electrons was converted into heat and light energy. The flow of electrons, however, was not modified or regulated in any precise way. Today, scientists and engineers know that if electrons are carefully controlled, they can be made to carry messages, magnify weak signals, draw pictures, and even do arithmetic!

Figure 28-1 *The control panel in an airplane consists of electronic instruments that make flying easier, more accurate, and safer (left). Here are some electronic devices that you may be familiar with (right). What energy conversion is involved in electronic devices?* ❶

TEACHING STRATEGY 28-1

While this chapter may stand alone, it employs many terms and concepts that were mentioned in earlier chapters about chemistry, electricity, waves, and light. One strategy is to use the entire chapter as a reinforcement for earlier lessons. View each piece of technology as an application of science that students already know by calling attention to the words and concepts developed throughout the year. You may ask students to turn back in the text to reread definitions and explanations as they read this chapter.

Motivation

We cannot escape electronics in the modern world. The students can be challenged to name a career that has not been influenced by improvements in electronic technology. They will be hard-pressed to find one. Under-standing electronics is now essential for professions as diverse as agriculture, medicine and auto mechanics.

Contrast electronics with the study of electromagnetism. This would be an appropriate time to point out the similarities and differences between science and technology.

Content Development

For students unsure of how AC current manages to do anything, discuss

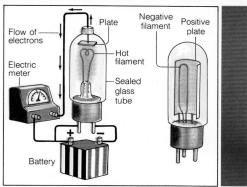

Figure 28–2 *A diode is the simplest type of vacuum tube. In a diode, electrons flow from the negatively charged filament to the positively charged plate, creating a one-way flow of electrons. Diodes are used as rectifiers in many electronic devices. Why?* ❷

Vacuum Tubes

The ability to control electrons carefully began with the invention of the **vacuum tube.** The vacuum tube is a one-way valve, or gate, for a flow of electrons. Electrons are permitted to move in only one direction through the vacuum tube.

The simplest type of vacuum tube is called a **diode.** A diode consists of a filament, or wire, and a plate. The filament is negatively charged, and the plate is positively charged. Electrons flow from the negatively charged filament to the positively charged ❷ plate. Both the filament and the plate are contained in a sealed glass tube, from which almost all the air has been removed. How does this fact explain the name given to this tube? ❸

Because vacuum tubes produce a one-way current, they have many applications in electronics. Two important applications of vacuum tubes are as ❸ rectifiers and amplifiers. Vacuum tubes also acted as switches in early electronic computers.

Rectifiers

A **rectifier** is a vacuum tube diode that converts alternating current (AC) to direct current (DC). The current supplied to your home by an electric power plant is alternating current. In alternating current, the electrons move back and forth, not just in one

how it is the energy and information that gets transferred. The electrons themselves do not have to go very far to pass on the energy and information. The situation has a weak analogy to the motion of the particles of a medium disturbed by a longitudinal wave. Remind the students that we do not purchase batteries to get electrons and that we do not buy electrons from the local power company.

Content Development
Pass around several vacuum tubes. Magnifying glasses may be helpful for viewing the electrodes of some tubes. Viewing can certainly be enhanced by breaking and removing the glass. Have students identify as many parts as they can, using Figure 28-2 as a reference. Dead tubes can be obtained from local television repair shops.

TEACHER DEMONSTRATION

Display two radios: one, a modern transistor radio, the other a table-top model containing vacuum tubes. Display the insides of each. If the parts of a vacuum tube are visible, point them out to the class.

Turn both devices on for the same amount of time at the same volume. Make note of the energy wasted by the older radio in the forms of heat and light.

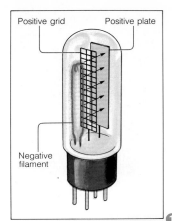

Figure 28–3 *A triode vacuum tube consists of a filament, a plate, and a grid. The addition of the grid allows the electron flow to be amplified, or strengthened (top). Triodes are used in microphones to amplify sound (bottom).*

644

direction. Certain household appliances cannot operate on alternating current. They need direct current. So these appliances have rectifiers built into their circuits. As the alternating current passes through the rectifier, it is changed into direct current.

Rectifiers are used in devices such as televisions, stereos, and computers. Converters that allow you to plug battery-operated devices into household electric outlets contain rectifiers.

Amplifiers

An **amplifier** is an electronic device that increases the strength of an electric signal. In an amplifier, a small input current is converted to a large output current. The large output current produces a stronger signal. The strengthening of a weak signal is called amplification. Amplification is perhaps the most important function of an electric device.

Amplifiers are **triode** vacuum tubes. A triode consists of a filament, a plate, and a wire screen, or grid. The addition of the grid allows the flow of electrons between the negatively charged filament and the positively charged plate to be better controlled. The invention of the triode was responsible for the rapid growth of the radio and television industry.

Amplifiers strengthen both sound and picture signals. The signals that carry sound and picture information are often very weak as a result of traveling long distances through the air. By the time an antenna picks up the signals, they are too weak to produce an accurate copy of the original signal. Radio and television amplifiers strengthen the incoming signals. Fully amplified signals can be millions or billions of times stronger than the signal picked up by the antenna!

Without amplifiers, devices such as hearing aids, public-address systems, tape recorders, and radar would not operate. Amplifiers also are essential to the operation of medical instruments used to diagnose certain injuries and diseases. Human heart waves and brain waves can be studied by doctors because the weak electric signals given off by these organs are amplified.

28-1 (continued)

Motivation
To show that household current is AC, obtain a digital clock that has red light-emitting diodes forming the numerals. With the clock plugged in, move it rapidly in front of the students. A darkened room is best. The numbers will appear as dashed lines showing that they actually are flashing on and off at 60 Hz.

Content Development
The notion of a small signal producing a larger signal is disturbing to some students, and it ought to be disturbing in light of the law of conservation of energy. The small signal fed to an amplifier does not produce a large output signal, rather it controls a large current, causing the large current to take the shape of the small input signal. An analogy might be drawn to a crowd at a sporting event.

The crowd is capable of creating large noises. The cheerleaders cannot make as much noise as the crowd, but they can signal the crowd to make certain noises. The cheerleaders control the loud sounds of the crowd with their own weaker signals.

Semiconductors

Electronic technology took a giant step with the discovery of **semiconductors.** Semiconductors are materials that are able to conduct electric currents better than insulators but not as well as metals. Devices that use semiconductors are called **solid-state devices.**

Silicon and germanium, two metalloids, are the most commonly used semiconductors. These elements have crystal structures that cause them to act like diodes. In these two elements current passes easily in one direction but not in the other.

Solid-state devices have several advantages over vacuum tubes. Using crystals of semiconductors makes solid-state devices much smaller and lighter than vacuum tubes. A tiny piece of semiconductor material can be made into a very small crystal diode. Such a diode gives off less heat, uses far less power, is more dependable, and lasts longer.

To increase the conductivity of semiconductors, certain impurities must be added to them. Adding ❸ impurities to semiconductors to increase their conductivity is called **doping.**

There are two types of semiconductors. These types are based on the impurity used to dope the semiconductor. If the impurity contributes extra electrons to the semiconductor, the semiconductor is called an n-type, meaning negative-type. Silicon doped with arsenic is an n-type semiconductor. Semiconductors that have fewer electrons, or extra protons, are called p-type semiconductors. What do you ❷ think p-type means? Silicon doped with gallium is a p-type semiconductor.

Figure 28–4 *Radios that used vacuum tubes were large, heavy, and cumbersome. They also gave off a considerable amount of heat. Radios that use semiconductors* ❸ *can be made extremely small. In addition, they are more dependable, last longer, use less power, and give off less heat. What are devices that use semiconductors called?* ❶

Figure 28–5 *Doping a semiconductor increases its conductivity. What impurity is used to make an n-type semiconductor? A p-type?* ❸

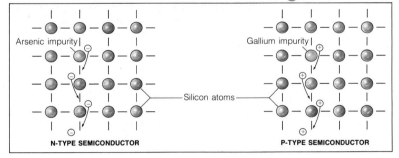

Arsenic impurity

Gallium impurity

Silicon atoms

N-TYPE SEMICONDUCTOR

P-TYPE SEMICONDUCTOR

Content Development

A crystal diode of very small size can be constructed from a tiny piece of silicon and a thin platinum wire. The silicon acts as a cathode and the platinum as a collecting plate. Since the electrons travel directly from the silicon to the platinum, the cathode does not have to be heated, nor does the device require a vacuum. Semiconductor diodes are even smaller, with the platinum wire replaced by another tiny crystal. This requires that the crystals' affinity for electrons be enhanced or diminished by doping it with impurities; that is, loading it with extra electrons or protons.

Reinforcement

Moving from vacuum tubes to semiconductors should require little motivation since today's students are far more familiar with transistors than with their bulky predecessors. Ask students how large vacuum tubes could possibly be made to fit inside a tiny transistor. Of course they cannot, but the semiconductor devices are essentially atom-sized versions of their large counterparts.

Transistors

Semiconductors also are used to make solid-state devices called **transistors.** A transistor—a sandwich of three semiconductor crystals—is used to amplify an electric current or signal. It is the arrangement of the impurities in the semiconductors that enables them to act as amplifiers. A weak signal, corresponding to a weak current, enters the transistor and is amplified so that a strong signal is produced.

Transistors come in a variety of shapes and sizes. Perhaps you are familiar with some of them. Transistors are commonly used in radios, televisions, stereos, computers, and calculators. The small size, light weight, and durability of transistors has helped in the development of communication satellites.

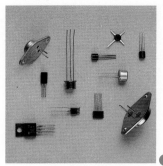

Figure 28–6 *Transistors come in a variety of shapes and sizes. What does a transistor do?* ❶

Integrated Circuits

An **integrated circuit** combines many diodes and transistors on a thin slice of silicon crystal. This razor-thin piece of silicon is often called a **chip.** A single integrated circuit, or chip, may contain thousands of diodes and transistors in a variety of complex combinations.

To turn a silicon chip into an integrated circuit, it must be doped in some places with arsenic and in other places with gallium. Certain areas of the chip become diodes, while other areas become transistors. Connections between these diodes and transistors are then made by painting thin "wires" on the chip. Wires are attached to the integrated circuit so it can be connected to other devices.

Figure 28–7 *An integrated circuit, or chip, contains thousands of diodes and transistors in complex combinations on a thin slice of silicon crystal. Here, you see the size of a chip in comparison to the wafer from which it is made (left). This photograph of a computer chip, magnified 175 times by a scanning electron microscope, shows the integrated circuit paths. A human hair is wider than 150 of these paths (right).*

directed toward the third material, the collector. The base acts as a barrier between the two currents. The current to the collector is controlled by the current to the emitter since it creates a voltage between the edges of the base. The transistor amplifies a weak signal by allowing the weak signal to control a large current. The large current in your portable radio is supplied by the battery. The weak signal comes from the radio station.

Content Development
Since a semiconductor's effects involve only a few atoms, the size of a diode or transistor need only be a few atoms thick. Integrated circuits combine many diodes and transistors on single crystals. A thin slice of silicon called a wafer is coated with an insulator that leaves the silicon exposed in certain areas. These exposed places receive a coating of a second semiconductor of opposite type, thus forming a diode.

Integrated circuits are used as amplifiers and switches in a wide variety of devices. Computers and microcomputers, calculators, radios, watches, washing machines, refrigerators, and even robots use integrated circuits.

SECTION REVIEW

1. What is electronics?
2. What is a vacuum tube? How is a vacuum tube used as a rectifier? As an amplifier?
3. What is a semiconductor?
4. How are semiconductors used to make integrated circuits? What are some advantages of the use of integrated circuits?

Figure 28–8 *A computer scientist designs a new computer chip by first drawing a large version and then having the design miniaturized.*

28–2 Transmitting Sound

The birth and growth of the communications industry has been due to advances in electronic technology. Since the first telegraph line in 1844, people have become accustomed to instant communication. Each improvement in the speed, clarity, and reliability of a communication device has been based on a discovery in the field of electronics.

Telephone Communication

The first telephone was invented in 1876 by Alexander Graham Bell. Although modern telephones hardly resemble Bell's, the principle on which all telephones work is the same. **A telephone sends and receives sound by means of electric currents.** A telephone has two main parts.

TRANSMITTER The transmitter is located behind the mouthpiece of a telephone. The transmitter converts sound waves into a pattern of electric waves. The electric waves travel over wires to a receiver.

Sound waves produced when a person speaks into a telephone cause vibrations in the transmitter. These vibrations vary according to the particular sound. The vibrations regulate the amount of electric current produced and sent out over telephone

Section Objective

To describe how sound-transmitting devices work

Figure 28–9 *The first telephone was invented in 1876 by Alexander Graham Bell. Today, you push buttons or dial to make calls. But up until the early 1950s, telephone calls were placed by switchboard operators, whose familiar phrase was, "Number, please."*

647

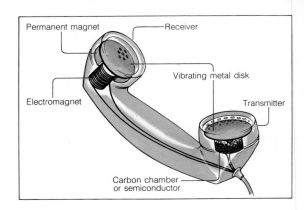

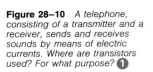
Figure 28–10 *A telephone, consisting of a transmitter and a receiver, sends and receives sounds by means of electric currents. Where are transistors used? For what purpose?* ❶

wires. You can think of the electric current as "copying" the pattern of the sound waves.

RECEIVER The receiver, located in the earpiece, converts the pattern of electric waves sent out by a transmitter back into sound. The receiver uses an electromagnet to produce this conversion.

Electric current transmitted by another telephone activates the electromagnet. The electromagnet ❶ moves in such a way that it causes vibrations in a thin, round metal disk attached to it. The vibrations produce sound waves that are heard by the listener.

Alexander Graham Bell used carbon grains in the transmitter to convert sound to electricity. Today's telephones use a small semiconductor crystal. Transistors then amplify the electric signal. In modern telephone earpieces, semiconductor devices have replaced electromagnets.

Radio Communication

All devices that produce sound—such as radios, stereos, and tape recorders—are closely related to the telephone. They all involve the interconversion of sound and electric energy.

❷ **Radios work by changing sound vibrations into electromagnetic waves, or radio waves.** The radio waves, which travel through the air at the speed of light, are converted back into sound vibrations when they reach a radio receiver.

648

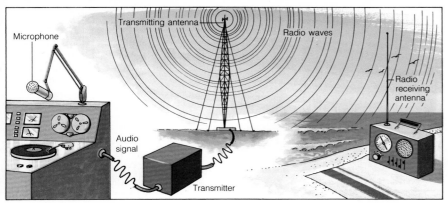

Figure 28–11 *Radios work by converting sound vibrations, usually produced at a broadcast station, into electromagnetic waves. The waves are amplified by a transmitter and then sent out into the air from a transmitting antenna. Picked up by a receiving antenna, the radio waves are converted back into sound waves by a* ❸ *receiver. What else does the receiver do with the radio waves?* ❷

A radio program usually begins at a radio station. Here, a microphone picks up the sounds that are being broadcast. An electric current running through the microphone is disturbed by the sound vibrations in such a way that it creates its own vibrations that match the sound.

The electromagnetic waves that represent the sounds of a broadcast are now sent to a transmitter. The transmitter amplifies the waves and sends them to a transmitting antenna. The antenna sends the waves out into the air as radio waves. Why do you think many radio stations locate their antennas at high elevations or open areas or on top of towers? ❸

Radio waves are converted back into sound waves by means of a radio receiver. A radio receiver picks up and amplifies the radio waves originally sent out from a radio station. When a radio receiver picks up sounds corresponding to a specific frequency, it is described as being tuned in. The main parts of a radio are the antenna, tuner, amplifier, and loudspeaker.

SECTION REVIEW

1. What are the two main parts of a telephone? What energy conversions are made in each part?
2. Describe the broadcast of a radio program.
3. How have solid-state devices affected telephones and radios?

649

Enrichment

Amplifiers are required to prevent telephone signals from fading out over long distances. The energy is gradually lost due to the fact that the current heats the wire. Telephone signals are often converted into light, which looses less energy, requires no wires, and travels a little faster. Fiber optics provides a method of sending a narrow beam of light through a plastic strand no thicker than a human hair.

The fiber acts as a pipe for light. A laser, or even a light-emitting diode, sends a pulsed beam of light corresponding in rhythm with the varying sound wave into one end of the fiber. The light bounces off the walls of the fiber again and again in glancing reflections as if the surface of the fiber were a mirror. A light-sensitive diode at the other end converts the light back into an electrical signal.

28-3 TRANSMITTING PICTURES

SECTION PREVIEW 28-3

This section explains the operation of the cathode-ray tube. Electrons are emitted by a hot filament and directed at a phosphorescent screen. The position and intensity of the electron beam is changed so that as the phosphorescent material in different areas emits different amounts of light, a picture is formed.

A color television picture tube has three electron beams aimed at materials that emit light of different colors. The pictures are formed as the three materials emit different amounts of the primary colors.

PERFORMANCE OBJECTIVES 28-3

1. Describe the operation of the cathode-ray tube.
2. Explain why a color television picture tube requires three electron guns.

SCIENCE TERMS 28-3

cathode-ray tube p. 650

28-3 Transmitting Pictures

Can you imagine that people once thought television was useless? About fifty years ago, that was exactly what many people thought about the demonstration of early television. Of course, what these people were seeing were blurry black-and-white images of other people waiting in the next room to have their turn to see television!

Cathode-ray Tubes

Television images are produced on the surface of a special type of vacuum tube called a **cathode-ray tube,** or **CRT.** Cathode-ray tubes are also responsible for images produced by computer displays, video games, and radar devices.

A cathode-ray tube is an electronic device that uses electrons to produce images on a screen. The electrons, moving as a beam, sweep across the screen and cause it to glow. The screen glows because it is coated with fluorescent material. Fluorescent material glows when struck by electrons.

The electrons in a CRT come from the negatively charged filament within the sealed glass vacuum tube. An electric current heats the metal filament and causes electrons to "boil" off it. The electrons are accelerated toward the screen and focused into a narrow beam. The moving electrons produce a magnetic field that can be used to control the direction of the beam. Electromagnets placed outside the CRT cause the beam to change its

Figure 28–12 A cathode-ray tube is a sealed evacuated tube in which a beam of electrons is focused on a screen coated with fluorescent material (bottom). As electrons strike the fluorescent material, visible light is given off and an image is formed (top).

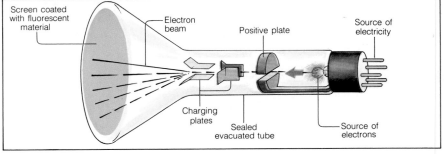

Screen coated with fluorescent material
Electron beam
Positive plate
Source of electricity
Charging plates
Sealed evacuated tube
Source of electrons

650

You might want to discuss whether the fact that people read more in earlier times than today is an advantage or a disadvantage to today's students over students of yesterday.

Content Development
While the creation, transmission, and reception of a television signal is more complicated than that of radio, the production of the picture itself is rather simple, electrically speaking.

The behavior of the electron beam is easy to explain according to the rule that opposite charges attract and like charges repel. Figure 28-12 shows an electrostatic deflection system. The negative electrons are accelerated from the negative electrode toward the positive plate. Some pass through a narrow opening in the plate and form a beam. The charging plates change the direction of the beam. The size of the opposite charges on each

direction, making it move rapidly up and down and back and forth across the screen.

At each point where the beam of electrons strikes the fluorescent material of the CRT screen, visible light is given off. The brightness of the light is determined by the number of electrons that strike the screen. The more electrons, the brighter the light. The continuous, rapid movement of the beam ❷ horizontally and vertically across the screen many times per second produces a pattern of light, or a picture, on the screen. The electron beam in a CRT traces 525 lines as it zigzags up and down, creating a whole picture 30 times each second.

Television Transmission

A cathode-ray tube in a color television differs from a simple cathode-ray tube in two important ways. One, the screen of a color television is coated with three different materials placed close together in clusters of dots or in thin stripes at each point on ❸ the screen. Such material glows with a different color of light—red, blue, or green—when struck by

Figure 28–13 *The CRT in a color television contains three electron guns—one each for red, blue, and green signals. The screen of the CRT is coated with three different fluorescent materials, each of which glows with a different primary color of light when struck by a beam of electrons. What is the purpose of transistors in CRTs?* ❶

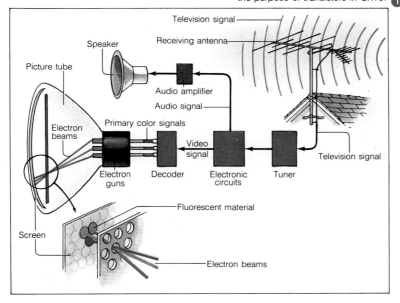

pair of plates is carefully controlled so that as it changes, the force on the negative electrons in the beam changes. The electrons' vertical and horizontal paths change accordingly.

A second type of cathode-ray tube is controlled magnetically. As described in the text, but not illustrated, an electromagnet surrounds the outside of the neck of the tube. The magnetic field of this coil, or yoke, directs the electron beam. Due to the nature

of the magnetic force on a moving charge, this system is somewhat more difficult to explain.

Motivation
Students can be asked to transmit a single picture to other students by calling out a series of numbers. Each number represents the brightness of a spot: from zero for black to three for bright white. Establish a number for the width and height of the picture,

perhaps ten by twenty. Include a check number that would indicate the start of a new picture.

This exercise will impress students with the enormous amount of information received by a television set each second and with the speed at which the television is able to process this information.

Enrichment
Discuss the storage of television signals on magnetic tape and laser disks.

Skills Development
Skill: Sequencing events
Have students use Figure 28-13 to trace the sequence of events that take place from the time a television signal reaches their antenna to the time they see the picture on their television screen. You might want to suggest that some students research and report back to the class on the sequence of events involved when the televis[...] signal is transmitted through a [...] system, rather than through th[...]

28-4 COMPUTERS

SECTION PREVIEW 28-4

Computers are described as electronic devices that perform calculations and process information. A brief history of the computer begins with Hollerith's punch cards and leads up to integrated circuits.

The physical parts of the computer's hardware, central processing unit, main storage, input devices, and output devices, are explained along with the interactions among them. Common examples are stated. The need for computer programs is stressed as is the binary system. The binary system is the only system that a digital computer can use. Practice is provided for conversion of decimal numbers into binary and for adding binary numbers.

PERFORMANCE OBJECTIVES 28-4

1. **Trace the role of electronics in the growth of computers.**
2. **List the parts of a computer and their functions.**
3. **Describe the binary system.**

SCIENCE TERMS 28-4

computer p. 652	disk drive p. 655
hardware p. 654	output device
central proces-	p. 655
sing unit p. 654	modem p. 655
computer pro-	data bank p. 656
gram p. 654	software p. 656
main memory	binary system
p. 654	p. 656
input device	bit p. 657
p. 655	byte p. 657

Section Objective

To relate the basic computer components to computer operation

a beam of electrons. Various colors are produced by adjusting the strengths of the electron beams. For example, red is produced when electrons strike only the red material. Purple is produced when electrons ❶ strike red and blue material. When do you think white is produced?

The other difference is that a color television CRT contains three electron guns—one each for red, blue, and green signals. The information for controlling and directing the beams is coded within the color picture signal that is transmitted from a TV station.

All cathode-ray tubes, including those in televisions, use transistors. The transistors amplify the electric signals received by the CRT. These signals cannot be used unless they are amplified.

SECTION REVIEW

1. What is a cathode-ray tube?
2. Describe the operation of a cathode-ray tube.
3. How does a color television CRT differ from a simple CRT?
4. Photographs of a TV picture taken with an ordinary camera often show part of the screen filled. Explain why.

28-4 Computers

A **computer** is an electronic device that performs calculations and processes information. A modern electronic computer can do thousands of calculations per second. At equally incredible speed, it can file away billions of bits of information in its memory. Then it can rapidly search through all that information to pick out particular items. It can change numbers to letters to pictures to sounds—and then back to numbers again.

Using these abilities, modern computers are guiding spaceships, navigating boats, diagnosing diseases and prescribing treatment, forecasting ❶ weather, and searching for ore. Computers can make robots move, talk, and obey commands. Computers can play games and make music. They even can design new computers!

28-3 (continued)

Section Review 28-3

1. An electronic device that uses electrons to produce images on a screen
2. An electric current heats a metal· filament in the CRT, which then gives off electrons. The electrons are accelerated through a magnetic field, which focuses the electrons into a beam. Electromagnets placed outside the CRT cause the beam of electrons

to change its direction. At each point where the electrons strike the fluorescent material of the CRT screen, visible light is given off. The brightness of the screen depends on the number of electrons that strike the screen.
3. In a color television, the screen is coated with three different materials that can glow with either red, green, or blue light. The color CRT also differs from other CRTs in that it has

three electron guns, rather than just one. Each gun contains and controls the information about a particular color, either red, green, or blue.
4. The electron beam in a CRT creates a whole picture 30 times per second. If the shutter speed on the camera is faster than this, the photograph will only show a partial picture since the entire picture will take $\frac{1}{30}$ of a second to appear on the screen.

Computer Development

The starting point of modern computer development is considered to be 1890. In preparation for the United States census that year, Herman Hollerith devised an electromagnetic machine that could handle information punched into cards. The holes allowed small electric currents to pass and activate counters. Using this system, Hollerith completed the 1890 census in one-fourth the time it had taken to do the 1880 census! Hollerith's punch card became the symbol of the computer age.

The first American-built computer was developed in 1946 by the United States Army. The Electronic Numerical Integrator and Calculator, or ENIAC, consisted of thousands of vacuum tubes and occupied a warehouse. It cost millions of dollars to build and millions of dollars to maintain. It was constantly breaking down and had to be rebuilt each time a new type of calculation was done. ENIAC required great amounts of energy, generated huge amounts of heat, and was very expensive. By today's standards, ENIAC was slow. It could do only 100,000 calculations per second!

The first general purpose computer was introduced in 1951. It was called the Universal Automatic Computer, or UNIVAC. UNIVAC was certainly an improvement over ENIAC, but it was still large, expensive, and slow.

Increased demand for computers encouraged more advanced computer technology. Technical breakthroughs such as transistors and integrated circuits reduced the size and cost of computers. They also increased the efficiency, speed, and uses of

Sharpen Your Skills

Computing Speed

Shuffle a deck of playing cards. Have a friend time you as you sort the cards, first into the four suits, and then from the 2 through the ace in each suit. Determine how many "sorts" you made. Remember, each time you place a card somewhere, it is a sort. Calculate how many sorts you made per second.

A bank check-sorting machine can make 1800 sorts a minute. How long would it take this machine to do the same number of sorts you did? How much faster than you is this machine?

Figure 28–14 *The uses of computers are many and varied. Computer applications include the identification of worldwide ozone concentrations (left), the aerodynamic design of cars (center), and the determination of controls and seat positions in automobiles (right).*

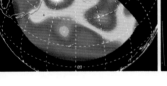
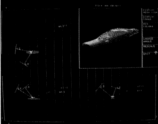
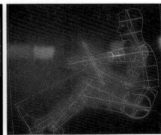

653

Sharpen Your Skills

Computing Speed
Skills: Comparing, making calculations
Level: Average
Type: Computational
Materials: deck of playing cards
The number of sorts students can make per second will vary, but will be substantially slower than the bank machine. Have students relate the speed of the machine to the many applications of computers that require fast computational calculations.

ANNOTATION KEY

❶ When electrons strike red, blue, and green (Inferring)
❶ Thinking Skill: Applying technology
❷ Thinking Skill: Relating cause and effect

Sharpen Your Skills

Telephone and Radio History
Skills: Relating, report writing
Level: Average
Type: Library
This activity will help students grasp the historical developments that occurred in the building of the telephone and radio. Students will be quite interested in the story of Alexander Graham Bell and his working on the telephone, as well as the early work Marconi did on the radio.

TEACHING STRATEGY 28-4

Motivation
Computers are everywhere. Every integrated circuit chip is a computer. These dime-sized computers are difficult to spot since they are hidden in cars, watches, toys, and appliances. Discuss the pervasive use of computers and how an understanding of their limitations can only enhance one's ability to use them advantageously.

Even professionals using computers are occasionally misled by the results if they do not fully understand what the computer can and cannot do for them.

Content Development
The holes in the punch cards of Herman Hollerith, the founder of IBM, allowed small electric currents to pass, activating counters. The cards were effectively mechanical switches, turning on and off currents. Every computer breakthrough has consisted of either a better way of storing information, such as replacing the holes, or a faster way of turning a current on and off, such as replacing the mechanical switches. The improvements are based on electronic technology—first vacuum tubes then semiconductors and now integrated circuits. Integrated circuits can do a billion calculations each second!

Figure 28–15 *Early computers used large vacuum tubes such as these, which were neither fast nor reliable (left). Tiny computer chips have replaced the larger transistor boards in modern computers. Here, you see the size of a chip as compared to the eye of a needle (right).*

computers. And equally important, they brought the computer within everyone's reach.

The future of computers lies in both the very small and the very large. Integrated circuits called **microprocessors** can hold the entire processing capability on one small chip. At the other extreme, groups of computers are being linked together to form supercomputers.

Computer Hardware

Computer **hardware** refers to the physical parts of a computer. **Computer hardware includes a central processing unit, main storage, input devices, and output devices.**

The brain of a computer is the **central processing unit,** or **CPU.** A CPU controls the operation of all the components of a computer. It executes the arithmetic and logic instructions that it receives in the form of a **computer program.** A computer program is a series of instructions that tells the computer how to perform a certain task. A computer program can be written in one of several different computer languages.

The main storage of a computer is often referred to as the **main memory.** The main memory contains data and operating instructions that are processed by the CPU. In the earliest computers, the main memory consisted of thousands of vacuum tubes. Modern computer memory is contained on

Figure 28–16 *Computer hardware includes a central processing unit, main memory, an input device, and an output device. What is the function of each?* ❶

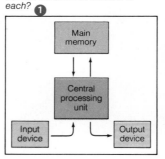

654

28-4 (continued)

Motivation
If a computer is available, display the computer and all its components. Have students identify each part and classify the various parts in terms of main memory, input device, or output device.

Content Development
Have the class write a detailed program that adds two numbers. Emphasize that the CPU can only do one thing at a time, including trivial details such as turning on the input device, checking if data is there, getting data, reading data, storing data, etc. Students can act out the parts of the computer with instructions and data printed on cards. Count the number of individual steps required to add the

two numbers. Mention that the human brain must also do each and every step.

chips. The most advanced memory chip can store as much information as 1 million vacuum tubes can.

Data are fed to the central processing unit by an **input device.** One common input device is a keyboard. A keyboard looks very much like a typewriter. Using a keyboard, a person can communicate data and instructions directly to a computer. Other input devices include magnetic tape, optical scanners, and disk or diskette drives.

A **disk drive** reads information off a disk or diskette and enters it into the computer's memory or into the CPU. Information from a disk drive can be placed into a computer very quickly.

Information produced by the computer can be removed and stored on a disk. So a disk drive is also an **output device.** An output device receives data from the central processing unit. Output devices include printers, cathode-ray tubes, magnetic-tape drives, and voice synthesizers. Even robots are output devices!

Like a disk drive, a **modem** is an input and output device. A modem changes electronic signals

CAREER   *Computer Artist*

HELP WANTED: COMPUTER ARTIST to direct a series of animated educational videos. High school diploma, technical training, and a lively imagination required. Knowledge of computer programming helpful.

Just a few years ago, computer programmers were frustrated by the difficulties they faced when trying to make an image appear three-dimensional on a flat computer monitor. But today, even things that have never actually been seen, such as the details of subatomic particles, can be produced with three-dimensional clarity by a **computer artist.**

A computer artist creates scientific, technical, or artistic images through computer graphics. A computer artist may be required to write computer programs. Depending on the capabilities of the computer being used, the program can be written to allow simple two-dimensional outlines or realistic-looking three-dimensional images.

A computer artist combines creativity with practical knowledge of computers. Computer artists create special effects for movies, educational materials, advertisements, and other types of artwork. Most animated films and cartoons are drawn and colored by computer artists.

If you would like more information about becoming a computer artist, contact the National Computer Graphics Association, 2722 Merrilee Drive, Fairfax, VA 22031.

Content Development
Simulate computer logic circuits by constructing DC electric circuits. Use batteries, lamps, and switches. Arrange two switches in series with a lamp to form an "and" gate. The lamp should light when both switches are closed. Arrange two switches in parallel to each other and in series with a lamp to simulate an "or" gate. The lamp will light if either switch is closed.

Skills Development
Skills: Sequencing events, applying concepts

Have students observe Figure 28-16. Then have them imagine a piece of information that they want entered on the computer, acted upon by the computer, and demonstrated on the computer screen. Have students sequence the events that would occur, using the terms main memory, CPU, input device, and output device.

Figure 28–17 *Computers are used to study body mechanics (left) and to design circuitry for future computers (right). What is the name for the program, or set of instructions, a computer follows?* ❶

from a computer into sounds that can be carried over telephone lines. It also changes the sounds back into computer signals. A modem allows a computer to communicate with other computers, often thousands of kilometers away. As computers link in ❶ this way, they form a network in which information can be shared. A modem allows use of this network by accessing information from a central **data bank.** A data bank is a vast collection of information stored in a large computer.

The Binary System

Computer hardware would be useless without **software.** Software is the program or set of programs the computer follows. Software must be precise because a computer cannot think on its own. It can only follow instructions. For example, to add two numbers, a program must tell a computer to get one number from memory, hold it, get the other number from memory, combine the two numbers, and print the answer. After completing that instruction, the computer must be told what to do next.

A computer executes instructions by counting with just two numbers at a time. The numbers are 0 and 1. The system that uses just these two numbers is called the **binary system.** The operation of all computers is based on the binary system.

Computer circuits are composed of diodes. As you learned, diodes are gates that are either open ❷ or closed to electric current. If the gate is open, current is off. If the gate is closed, current is on. To a

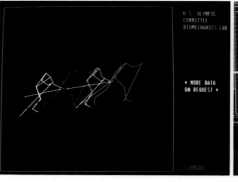
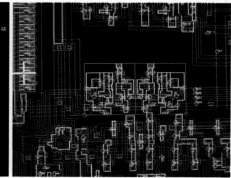

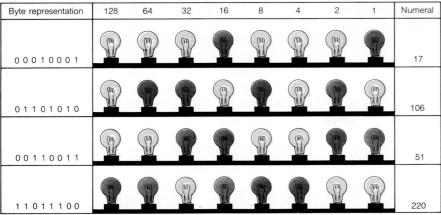

Byte representation	128	64	32	16	8	4	2	1	Numeral
0 0 0 1 0 0 0 1									17
0 1 1 0 1 0 1 0									106
0 0 1 1 0 0 1 1									51
1 1 0 1 1 1 0 0									220

computer, 0 is current off and 1 is current on. Each digit, then, acts as a tiny electronic switch, flipping on and off at unbelievable speed.

Each single electronic switch is called a **bit**. A string of bits—usually 8—is called a **byte.** Numbers, letters, and other symbols can be represented as a byte. For example, the letter A is 01000001. The letter K is 11010010. The number 9 is 00001001. See Figure 28–18. What do you think the code for the number 7 is? For the number 83? What is the value of the largest number that can be represented by one byte? ❸

You do not need to be reminded of the importance of computers. You have only to look around you! The uses of computers are many, and their presence is almost universal. Any list of computer applications cannot really be completed today. For by the time today is over, another new application will have been devised.

SECTION REVIEW

1. What are the four hardware components of a computer system? What is the function of each?
2. What is a modem? How is it related to a data bank?
3. How is the binary system used by a computer?
4. Show how the following numbers would be represented by a byte: 175, 139, 3, 45, 17.

Figure 28–18 *All computers execute instructions by using the binary system. The off/on positions of these light bulbs correspond to the off/on positions of electronic switches, or bits. What is the name for a string of 8 bits?* ❷

657

representation when various ages are added together. Allow students to use Figure 28-18 as a reference tool when doing these calculations.

Section Review 28-4

1. Central processing unit (CPU): "brain" of computer, performs all arithmetic calculations and runs all software programs; main memory: contains data and operating instructions that are processed by the CPU;

input device: feeds data into the computer; output device: receives, displays, or stores data from the CPU
2. A modem is both an input and an output device. It can input or output information over phone lines and can connect the computer user with huge banks of information (data banks) for use by the computer operator.
3. The binary system is a mathematical system using only two numbers, 0 and 1. Since the switches in a computer can be in one of two positions, either on or off, the binary numbers refer to a switching position.
4. 10101111; 10001011; 00000011; 00101101; 00010001

LABORATORY INVESTIGATION THE FIRST CALCULATOR: THE ABACUS

BEFORE THE LAB

An abacus can easily be constructed by stringing beads or other objects on string in a cardboard box. Do not let the lack of commercial apparatus deter you from this investigation.

PRE-LAB DISCUSSION

The abacus provides a concrete example of an abstract concept—that of place value in a number system. Young children can be taught to recognize and understand large numbers using an abacus.

Here the abacus is used to represent the types of manipulations that a computer makes in handling numbers. Warn students that they will be slow at first, but with practice surprising speed and accuracy can be achieved.

SKILL DEVELOPMENT

Students will use the following skills while completing this investigation.
1. Manipulative
2. Computational
3. Applying
4. Relating

SAFETY TIPS

No special safety precautions are necessary for this investigation.

TEACHING STRATEGY FOR LAB PROCEDURE

You will want to circulate through the room, offering assistance to students who are unable to grasp, at first, the use of an abacus.

OBSERVATIONS

1. The settings should be as follows: a) units column: upper bead down, one lower bead up; tens column: upper bead up, one lower bead up; b) units column: upper bead down, two lower beads up; tens: upper bead down, three lower beads up; hundreds: upper bead up, two lower beads up; c) units: upper bead down, one lower bead up; tens: upper bead up, one lower bead up; hundreds: upper bead up, no lower beads up; thousands: upper bead down, no lower beads up; d) units: upper bead down, no lower beads up; tens: upper bead up, one lower bead up; hundreds: upper bead up, two lower beads up; thousands: upper bead down, one lower bead up; ten thousands: upper bead up, one lower bead up; hundred thousands: upper bead down, three lower beads up; millions: upper bead up, one lower bead up.

2. Students must add the proper number of beads to show the correct answers: 7, 15, and 183, respectively.

CONCLUSIONS

1. Base 10, or decimal number system
2. A computer works in base 2, or the binary number system
3. All numbers can be counted in the binary system. The only number that can be represented by an 8-bit byte is 16 (00010000).

Purpose

To determine how an abacus works as a counting machine

Materials (per group)

Abacus

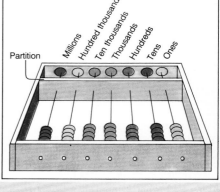

Procedure

1. The columns of beads on the abacus represent, from right to left, units of ones, tens, hundreds, thousands, ten thousands, hundred thousands, and millions.
2. The single bead in the upper section of each column, above the partition, equals five beads in the lower section of that column.
3. Always start from the lower section of the far right, or ones, column.
4. Count to three by sliding three beads up from the lower section of the ones column to the partition.
5. Continue counting to eight. Slide the fourth bead up to the partition. You should be out of beads in this section. Slide all four beads back down and slide the single bead from the upper section of this column down to the partition. Remember that the top bead equals five lower beads. Continue counting from six to eight by sliding the beads in the lower section of the ones column up to the partition. Before doing any further counting, check with your teacher to see that you are using the abacus correctly.
6. Continue counting to twelve. Slide the last bead in the ones column up to the partition. You should now have a total of nine. And you should be out of beads in the ones column. Slide all these beads back to their original zero position. Slide one bead in the lower section of the tens column up to the partition. This repre-

sents ten. Continue counting in the ones column until you reach twelve.

Observations

1. Count to each of these numbers on the abacus: 16, 287, 5016, 1,816,215.
2. How would you find 8 + 7 on the abacus? Start by counting to eight on the abacus. Then continue adding seven more beads. Find the following sums: 7 + 8, 3 + 4, 125 + 58.

Conclusions

1. On what number system is the operation of the abacus based?
2. How does this compare with the operation of a computer?
3. Could the numbers you counted in the Observations be represented on a computer? Which numbers could be represented with an 8-bit byte? Give the representation for these numbers.

658

CHAPTER REVIEW

SUMMARY

28–1 Electronic Devices

❏ Electronics is the study of the release, behavior, and effects of electrons as it relates to use in helpful devices.

❏ In a vacuum tube, electrons are permitted to move in only one direction.

❏ A rectifier is an electronic device that converts alternating current to direct current.

❏ An amplifier is an electronic device that increases the strength of an electric signal.

❏ Semiconductors are materials that are able to conduct electric currents better than insulators but not as well as metals.

❏ Adding impurities to semiconductors to increase their conductivity is called doping.

❏ An integrated circuit combines diodes and transistors on a thin slice of silicon crystal.

28–2 Transmitting Sound

❏ A telephone sends and receives sound by means of electric currents.

❏ A telephone has two main parts: a transmitter and a receiver.

❏ Radios work by changing sound vibrations into electromagnetic waves, or radio waves.

28–3 Transmitting Pictures

❏ A cathode-ray tube, or CRT, is an electronic device that uses electrons to produce images on a screen.

❏ The screen in a color television cathode-ray tube is coated with three different materials to produce the various colors.

❏ A cathode-ray tube in a color television contains three electron guns—one each for red, blue, and green signals.

28–4 Computers

❏ Early computers were large, expensive, slow, and subject to breakdown.

❏ Integrated circuits called microprocessors can hold the entire processing capability on one small chip.

❏ Computer hardware consists of a central processing unit, main storage, input devices, and output devices.

❏ A computer program is a series of instructions that tells the computer how to perform a certain task.

❏ The operation of all computers is based on the binary system.

VOCABULARY

Define each term in a complete sentence.

amplifier	data bank	modem
binary system	diode	output device
bit	disk drive	rectifier
byte	doping	semiconductor
cathode-ray tube	electronics	software
central processing unit	hardware	solid-state device
chip	input device	transistor
computer	integrated circuit	triode
computer program	main memory	vacuum tube
	microprocessor	

659

GOING FURTHER: ENRICHMENT

Part 1

Have students perform simple subtraction exercises on the abacus. You may have to help them with the method to employ for the first subtraction exercise.

Part 2

Have students design an abacus that works on the binary system. Have them repeat the investigation using this abacus.

CHAPTER REVIEW

MULTIPLE CHOICE

1. b   3. c   5. a   7. c   9. c
2. a   4. b   6. b   8. d   10. b

COMPLETION

1. electronics
2. amplifier
3. silicon/ germanium
4. doping
5. integrated circuit
6. transmitter/ receiver
7. cathode-ray tube, or CRT
8. central processing unit, or CPU
9. modem
10. binary

TRUE OR FALSE

1. T
2. F semiconductors
3. F electric
4. T
5. F three
6. F ENIAC
7. T
8. F input
9. T
10. T

SKILL BUILDING

1. Check students' drawings, which should be similar to Figure 28-16.
2. The correct order is vibrating vocal cords produce sound, sound vibrates a metal plate, mechanical energy is converted into an electric signal, an electromagnet is energized, a vibrating magnet produces sound.
3. 54,000 pictures
4. Both: magnetic tape, disk drive; input: typewriter keyboard, punched cards, optical scanner; output: CRT, voice synthesizer
5. 10011; 111001; 11011111; 10100001; 10000001; 11111111
6. Check students' programs more for the logic they employ than whether the program could actually be run by a computer. Students should not be expected to be computer programmers, but they should be able to apply what they have learned into what the program would need to tell the computer and how the computer would run the program.

ESSAY

1. They are more compact, use less energy, are more reliable, and are much faster than vacuum tubes.

2. A rectifier is a diode vacuum tube that converts alternating current (AC) to direct current (DC). An amplifier uses a triode vacuum tube to increase the strength of an input signal.
3. An integrated circuit combines many diodes and transistors on a thin slice of silicon crystal, often called a chip. To turn the silicon chip into an integrated circuit, it must be doped in some places with arsenic and in other places with gallium.

4. The cathode-ray produces free electrons. The beam of electrons passes through magnetic plates, which focus the beam. Electromagnets cause the beam to change direction, making it move rapidly up and down and back and forth. When the electrons strike the picture tube, fluorescent material on the tube glows. By directing the electrons' intensity, the amount of glow on the screen is increased or reduced, creating a picture.

CONTENT REVIEW: MULTIPLE CHOICE

On a separate sheet of paper, write the letter of the answer that best completes each statement.

1. Diode vacuum tubes are used as
   a. transistors.   b. rectifiers.   c. amplifiers.   d. triodes.
2. Which electronic device was important to the rapid growth of the radio and television industry?
   a. triode   b. diode   c. punch card   d. disk drive
3. Which of the following is a semiconductor?
   a. copper   b. plastic   c. silicon   d. oxygen
4. A sandwich of three semiconductor crystals used to amplify an electric signal is a (an)
   a. diode.   b. transistor.   c. integrated circuit.   d. modem.
5. Radios work by changing sound vibrations into
   a. electromagnetic waves.   b. gamma rays.   c. electric current.   d. bytes.
6. Which is *not* an advantage of the use of solid-state devices in telephones and radios?
   a. smaller size   b. increased cost
   c. better amplification   d. greater energy efficiency
7. Which of the following is *not* an application of a computer?
   a. store data   b. perform complex calculations
   c. rectify alternating current   d. design new computers
8. The physical parts of a computer are collectively referred to as computer
   a. software.   b. peripherals.   c. programs.   d. hardware.
9. Which of the following is computer software?
   a. printer   b. disk drive   c. program   d. memory
10. In the binary system, the number 86 would be represented as
    a. 01100110.   b. 01010110.   c. 10101001.   d. 11010010.

CONTENT REVIEW: COMPLETION

On a separate sheet of paper, write the word or words that best complete each statement.

1. The branch of physics that deals with the behavior of electrons as it relates to use in helpful devices is called _____.
2. An electronic device used to increase the strength of an electric signal is called a (an) _____.
3. Two common semiconductors are _____ and _____.
4. Adding impurities to semiconductors to increase their conductivity is called _____.
5. Diodes and transistors combined on a thin slice of silicon is a (an) _____.
6. The two main parts of a telephone are the _____ and the _____.
7. An electronic device that uses electrons to produce images on a screen is called a (an) _____.
8. The brain of a computer is called the _____.
9. The device that allows computers to communicate with one another is a (an) _____.
10. The number system on which the operation of all computers is based is called the _____ system.

660

CONTENT REVIEW: TRUE OR FALSE

Determine whether each statement is true or false. Then on a separate sheet of paper, write "true" if it is true. If it is false, change the underlined word or words to make the statement true.

1. A device that converts alternating current to direct current is a <u>rectifier</u>.
2. The conductivity of <u>transistors</u> is between that of conductors and insulators.
3. A telephone sends and receives sound by means of <u>magnetic</u> current.
4. The beam of electrons in a <u>cathode-ray tube</u> produces a picture.
5. A color television CRT has <u>two</u> electron guns.
6. The first American-built computer was <u>UNIVAC</u>.
7. <u>Microprocessors</u> are integrated circuits that can hold the entire processing capability of a computer on one chip.
8. <u>Output</u> devices feed data to a computer.
9. A <u>data bank</u> is a vast collection of information stored in a large computer.
10. A string of bits, usually eight in number, is called a <u>byte</u>.

CONCEPT REVIEW: SKILL BUILDING

Use the skills you have developed in the chapter to complete each activity.

1. **Making diagrams** Draw a diagram that shows how the four main hardware components of a computer are related.
2. **Sequencing events** The sentences below describe some of the energy conversions required for a local telephone call. Arrange them in their proper order.

   Sound vibrates a metal plate.
   An electromagnet is energized.
   A vibrating magnet produces sound.
   Vibrating vocal cords produce sound.
   Mechanical energy is converted into an electric signal.
3. **Making calculations** The pictures on a television screen last for one-thirtieth of a second. How many pictures are flashed on a screen during a 30-minute program?
4. **Classifying computer devices** Many methods of putting data into a computer are similar to methods of getting data out of a computer. Identify each of the following as an input device, an output device, or both: typewriter keyboard, CRT, printer, optical scanner, magnetic tape, disk drive, punched cards, voice synthesizer.
5. **Applying definitions** Write the following numbers in binary form: 19, 57, 1, 95, 161, 129, 255.
6. **Applying concepts** A program is a list of instructions that tells a computer how to perform a task. Write a program that describes the steps involved in your task of waking up and arriving at school for your first class.

CONCEPT REVIEW: ESSAY

Discuss each of the following in a brief paragraph.

1. In what ways are semiconductor diodes and transistors better than their vacuum-tube ancestors?
2. Compare the functions of rectifiers and amplifiers. What type of vacuum tube is used for each?
3. Use the following terms in one or two sentences to describe an integrated circuit: diodes, silicon crystal, chip, transistors, doping.
4. Describe how a cathode-ray tube creates a picture.

661

ISSUES IN SCIENCE

The following issues can be used as a springboard for class debate, or they can be assigned as a writing homework.

1. Vacuum tubes are essentially obsolete, now that the production of semiconductor devices have been perfected. Many other modern inventions have also become obsolete within a century of their invention: The fountain pen and the telegraph are two. What other "modern" inventions are obsolete? Can you predict several items that will be replaced by improved versions?

2. Television has had a profound impact upon society. Could the inventors have forseen the positive and negative effects of television? Do the positive effects outweigh the negative? Should the development of the television have been stopped until only positive effects could be assured?

3. Do you think that computers will ever reach the level of "artificial intelligence?" What is your definition of artificial intelligence? How do experts define it? If computers only do what they are told, can they ever really think?

ADDITIONAL QUESTIONS AND TOPIC SUGGESTIONS

1. List the various ways that music can be stored for playing at a later time. Explain how the information is stored in each case. Describe the energy conversions that are required to make the stored information into sound again.

2. Explain the roles of the three filaments in the triode vacuum tube. If energy cannot be created, how does an amplifier amplify?

3. Distinguish between AC and DC currents. What two things must the converter that enables you to plug in your portable radio do to the 110-volt AC household current? How can semiconductor diodes be used in a converter?

Unit Eight
PHYSICAL SCIENCE AND TECHNOLOGY

ADVENTURES IN SCIENCE: STAN OVSHINSKY: PIONEERING A NEW TYPE OF GLASS

BACKGROUND INFORMATION

Although the orderly arrangement of atoms in a crystal makes it possible for an electric current to flow, this same orderliness can make crystals difficult to produce in the laboratory. Crystals must be grown slowly, in a scrupulously clean, controlled environment. This is to ensure that each atom links properly to its neighbor.

Amorphous materials such as glass are much easier to make because the atoms are arranged randomly. The ingredients need only be melted together in a crucible. Thus ovonic devices are easier to produce than similar devices made from crystalline materials.

Adventures in Science

STAN OVSHINSKY: PIONEERING A NEW TYPE OF GLASS

One day in the late 1960s, physicist Hellmut Fritzsche paid a visit to Stan Ovshinsky. Ovshinsky, a self-taught inventor, claimed to have developed a kind of glass that could conduct electricity. Even more startling than Ovshinsky's claim of invention was his suggestion that this new electronic glass could surpass transistors.

Fritzsche, like most physicists of the day, did not believe such a thing was possible. After all, glass is an insulator, not a conductor. And the idea of making computer chips or transistors out of it was ridiculous. "Just lead me into the laboratory," he told Ovshinsky. "Let me do the experiments and at the end of the day I'll explain this mystery to you." By the end of the

662

TEACHING STRATEGY

Motivation
Remind students of their study of "electrified plastic" in Unit Six Adventures in Science. Recall that MacDiarmid's discovery was important because it had been previously believed that plastic could not conduct an electric current. Ask,
• **Would you expect glass to conduct an electric current?** (Answers may vary. The correct answer is no.)

Point out that in this Adventure lesson, they will read about someone who discovered a way to "electrify" glass.

Content Development
Write the word *amorphous* on the chalkboard. Ask,
• **What does this word mean?** (without form)

• **Why is this word used to describe a substance such as glass?** (In glass, atoms are arranged randomly, and the material does not have the rigid shape of a crystalline solid.)

Have students compare and contrast Ovshinsky's discovery to that of MacDiarmid. Point out that while MacDiarmid's discovery came about quite by accident, Ovshinsky had pondered the possibility of glass conductors for a long time. He finally made

day, however, Fritzsche had changed his tune. "I cannot explain it," he told Ovshinsky. "All I can say is that it is the most important thing I've ever seen."

A RADICAL NOTION

The operation of almost all modern electronic products is based on devices made from crystals of specific elements. The atoms in a crystal are arranged in an orderly fashion. This arrangement lets electricity flow freely through the crystal. In amorphous materials such as glass, the atoms are flung around randomly, or haphazardly. So it is difficult for an electric current to pass through amorphous materials.

But Ovshinsky believed that if he chose the right mixture of elements, he could melt them together into a glasslike material that would have the same kind of electronic properties as crystals. It was a radical notion, but as it turned out, a correct one. Yet it took Ovshinsky almost ten years to prove it.

AN AVID LEARNER

Stanford Ovshinsky grew up in Akron, Ohio. He spent his childhood experimenting with chemicals in the basement of his home and reading all the books he could get. But because the budding inventor did not like school, he never considered going to college. "I just wasn't interested," he says. "I was interested in what was going on out in the world." So after graduating from high school, Ovshinsky became a machinist.

Then, as now, what really interested Ovshinsky was how things actually work. This fascination included the human brain as well as machinery. Over the next ten years, Ovshinsky learned as much as he could about the brain. He was looking for links between the workings of the brain and the workings of machines similar to the ones he used in his shop. Human brain cells, he knew, have no orderly structure. Yet the cells are able to store and process information in much the same way that computers do. Ovshinsky reasoned that if brain cells could store and process information, so could amorphous materials such as glass.

ELECTRONIC GLASS

For nine years Ovshinsky and his wife, who has a Ph.D. in biochemistry, worked to create electronic switches out of a type of glass called chalcogenide. They sandwiched a thin layer of the glass between two pieces of metal. When a strong current was used, the glass allowed it to pass through. Ovshinsky's electronic glass had the ability to act as a semiconductor—an ability that up until then had been a property only of crystals.

The Ovshinskys continued to develop electronic devices using chalcogenide. One of their inventions is a device similar to the memory switches in computers. But their device continues to store its memories even after the power is shut off!

Today, products using Ovshinsky's invention bear the name ovonic devices. They include inexpensive and efficient solar cells.

Stan Ovshinsky at work with his wife, Iris.

663

ADDITIONAL QUESTIONS AND TOPIC SUGGESTIONS

1. What made Ovshinsky think that a material such as glass might be able to conduct an electric current? (Human brain cells, which store and process information in much the same way as a computer, are made of amorphous material.)
2. What kind of glass did Ovshinsky discover could be made to conduct electricity? (a type of glass called chalcogenide)
3. What did he do to this glass? (sandwiched it between two pieces of metal)

CRITICAL THINKING QUESTIONS

1. Why are materials that can conduct electricity so important? (Technological devices such as computers, calculators, radios, televisions, and even robots depend upon the flow of electricity. Thus there is a continual demand for a wide variety of materials that can conduct an electric current.)
2. Why is ovonic glass useful in solar cells? (When the sun's rays strike a solar cell, an electric current is produced. Thus it is necessary for the cell to be made of materials that conduct electricity.)

his discovery by working to prove his idea correct.

Unit Eight

PHYSICAL SCIENCE AND TECHNOLOGY

ISSUES IN SCIENCE: NUCLEAR WASTE: WHAT CAN BE DONE WITH DEADLY GARBAGE?

BACKGROUND INFORMATION

There are two main classifications of radioactive wastes: high-level and low-level. High-level radioactive waste consists of spent fuel from commercial nuclear power plants and the highly radioactive materials resulting from atomic energy defense activities. According to the Nuclear Regulatory Commission, this waste must be permanently isolated.

Low-level radioactive wastes include products such as those used in medical diagnosis and treatment, as well as discarded filters and protective clothing from nuclear power plants and other industries. Most low-level wastes decay rather quickly. The disposal of low-level wastes is the responsibility of the states in which they are produced.

In January 1983, the President signed into law the Nuclear Waste Policy Act (NWPA) of 1982. The NWPA established a national policy for the safe storage and disposal of high-level radioactive wastes. The law requires the U.S. Department of Energy to site, construct, and operate geologic repositories, and to be ready to accept waste for disposal by the end of January 1998. The Department is also directed to assist utilities in providing adequate and safe at-reactor storage for spent fuel.

Issues in Science

NUCLEAR WASTE:

What can be done with DEADLY GARBAGE?

"Arbitrary, . . . uncaring, and unreasonable," protested the governor of Texas.

"I am worried about earthquakes and groundwater contamination," declared the governor of Washington.

"Nevada has already done its share," fumed that state's governor.

The topic that has aroused such argument and emotion—and made its way to the state capital—is garbage. But not ordinary garbage. This waste is nuclear waste—the deadliest garbage of all.

In 1984, after a two-year study, the federal government selected Texas, Washington, and Nevada as sites in which to bury 40,000 tons of nuclear waste—radioactive nuclear waste!

Radioactive trash is generated primarily by the nation's 95 nuclear power plants. Each year, nearly 2000 tons of this waste are produced. By the year 2020, there will be about 100,000 tons of radioactive waste in need of a burial site. Permanent disposal sites that present no health and safety hazards must be found for this deadly garbage.

If we cannot find a place on the earth to get rid of nuclear garbage, why not send it into space? Rockets loaded with nuclear wastes could be launched into orbit between the earth and Venus. Traveling at the right speeds, the rockets could stay in orbit for a million years or more without bumping into either planet.

Critics of this idea point to its cost and potential danger. An accident during rocket launch could harm thousands of people. These critics believe that we should not seek a solution in the stars but on the earth.

664

TEACHING STRATEGY

Motivation

Begin by asking students,

• **What do you do with garbage at your house or apartment?** (put it in trash cans or garbage disposals; put it out for garbage collection)

• **What do you think would happen if no one came to take the garbage away?** (It would begin to smell; it would pile up and look bad; it would take up a lot of room; it could eventually cause disease.)

Explain to students that they are going to read about a type of garbage that never goes away—because unlike ordinary garbage, it cannot be buried or placed in an ordinary dump.

Content Development

Review with students the concepts of radioactive decay and half-life. Point out that high-level radioactive wastes have half-lives that are long enough to keep the materials radioactive for thousands, millions, perhaps billions of years. Note that these wastes are temporarily being stored in on-site "swimming pools" at nuclear power plants, but that many pools are becoming too crowded. Also, these wastes are potentially too dangerous to just let them "sit around" at a reactor site.

The Antarctic ice sheet is more than 2500 meters thick in some places. Could nuclear wastes be buried under this huge frozen blanket? No, according to some critics of this idea. Not enough is known about the behavior of ice sheets. And what is known is not comforting. For example, ice sheets move rapidly about every 10,000 years. Their movement might allow the wastes to get loose. In addition, nuclear wastes produce a tremendous amount of heat—enough heat, in fact, to melt the ice. Where the ice melted, nuclear radiation might leak out into the oceans and the air.

If not under the Antarctic ice sheet, then how about a nuclear cemetery under the ocean floor? Thick smooth rock layers have been building up there for millions of years. Nuclear wastes deposited in these rock layers probably would remain there almost forever.

But as with other proposals, there are problems with this idea. At present, the technology to do the job does not exist. And not enough is known about the various forces to which such rock is exposed.

With ice sheet cemeteries and underwater graveyards all but impossible, one idea still remains. That idea is to put nuclear wastes in "rooms" dug out of underground rock.

In order to determine the best place to bury nuclear wastes, scientists must know all they can about the rock. Here are the properties scientists have determined are best. The rock must be strong, heat resistant, and waterproof. The rock must be at least 6100 meters deep. And the ground where the rock exists must be very dry and free of earthquakes and other geologic problems. These rock properties seem to be characteristic of rock layers in Texas, Washington, and Nevada.

There are four kinds of rocks that scientists believe will be the best: basalt, granite, salt, and tuff. Each of these rocks, however, has certain properties that also make it unsuitable for burying radioactive wastes.

So far, scientists have been unable to find the perfect graveyard for nuclear wastes. But the search goes on. Unfortunately, in the meantime the wastes pile up, and people continue to be concerned about their land, water, and—most importantly—their health.

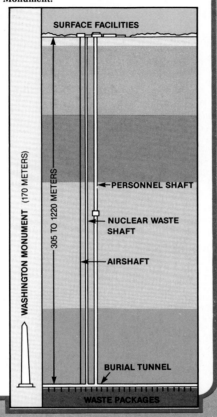

Nuclear wastes must be buried deep below the earth's surface. This diagram shows the parts of a proposed burial site. The relative depth is shown by a comparison with the Washington Monument.

ADDITIONAL QUESTIONS AND TOPIC SUGGESTIONS

1. Based on the amount of nuclear waste waiting to be disposed of, calculate how many years this "garbage" has been piling up. (about 20)

2. France has found a method of disposing of wastes from nuclear power plants that seems to be working. Find out what this method is and whether the United States plans to try it. (In France, radioactive materials are converted into salts, mixed with molten glass, cast into ingots, then buried in the ground. The United States plans to use this method to dispose of liquid radioactive wastes from the military.)

CRITICAL THINKING QUESTIONS

1. Why is it so difficult to contain radioactive wastes? (Radiation can penetrate all but the densest materials, and after thousands and thousands of years it is possible that even these materials could be penetrated.)

2. Even if a particular site seems safe for disposal of nuclear wastes now, why might it not remain safe for thousands of years? (The earth changes in many ways over time. Changes in the earth's crust or oceans could take place, thereby greatly changing the characteristics of a particular area.

3. How could radioactive wastes buried deep in the earth contaminate the water supply of an area? (If any radiation leaked out, it could contaminate the groundwater contained in the soil. Also, particles of contaminated soil could be carried into rivers and oceans.)

CLASS DEBATE

This issue is not so much a "for or against" issue as it is a problem that needs a solution. The controversy develops as people disagree as to what should be done, or as citizens oppose the building of a waste site in their community.

Students may enjoy debating this issue as if they were members of Congress. In this way they would have ample opportunity to present, support, and oppose various courses of action.

For Further Reading

> If you have an interest in a specific area of Physical Science or simply want to know more about the topics you are studying, one of the following books may open the door to an exciting learning adventure.

Chapter 1: Exploring Physical Science

Lapp, R.E., and the editors of Time-Life Books. *Matter.* New York: Time.

Ruchlis, H. *Discovering Scientific Method.* New York: Harper and Row.

Chapter 2: Properties of Matter

Adler, I. *The Wonders of Physics: An Introduction to the Physical World.* New York: Golden Press.

Asimov, I. *A Short History of Chemistry.* Garden City, NY: Anchor Books.

Chapter 3: Classification of Matter

Asimov, I. *Building Blocks of the Universe.* New York: Abelard-Schuman.

Dickinson, E. *Colloids in Foods.* New York: Elsevier.

Chapter 4: Structure of Matter

Adler, I., and R. Adler. *Atoms and Molecules.* New York: John Day.

Frisch, O.J. *Working with Atoms.* New York: Basic Books.

Chapter 5: The Periodic Law

Kelma, P., and A.H. Stone. *Mendeleev: A Prophet of Chemical Elements.* Englewood Cliffs, NJ: Prentice-Hall.

Seaborg, G.T., and E.G. Valens. *Elements of the Universe.* New York: Dutton.

Chapter 6: Families of Elements

Smith, N.F. *The Inside Story of Metal.* New York: Messner.

Weeks, M.E., and H.M. Leicester, *Discovery of the Elements.* New York: Chemical Education Publishing Company.

Chapter 7: Atoms and Bonding

Asimov, I. *How Did We Find Out About Atoms?* New York: Walker.

Snell, C.T. *Chemistry Made Easy.* New York: Chemical Education Publishing Company.

Chapter 8: Chemical Reactions

Carona, P.B. *Chemistry and Cooking.* Englewood Cliffs, NJ: Prentice-Hall.

Woodburn, J.H. *Excursions into Chemistry.* Philadelphia: Lippincott.

Chapter 9: Solution Chemistry

Gilfond, H. *Water: A Scarce Resource.* New York: Watts.

Stone, A.H. *The Chemistry of a Lemon.* Englewood Cliffs, NJ: Prentice-Hall.

Chapter 10: Carbon Chemistry

Cross, W. *Coal.* Chicago: Children's Press.

Kraft, B. *Oil and Natural Gas.* New York: Watts.

Chapter 11: Nuclear Chemistry

Asimov, I. *How Did We Find Out About Nuclear Power?* New York: Walker.

Fermi, L. *The Story of Atomic Energy.* New York: Random House.

Chapter 12: Motion

Dalton, S. *Caught in Motion.* New York: Van Nostrand Reinhold.

Valens, E. *Motion.* New York: World.

Chapter 13: Forces

Ipsen, D.C. *Isaac Newton: Reluctant Genius.* Hillside, NJ: Enslow.

Milgrom, H. *First Experiments with Gravity.* New York: Dutton.

Chapter 14: Forces in Fluids

Adkins, J. *Moving Heavy Things.* Boston: Houghton Mifflin.

Grey, J. *The Facts of Flight.* Philadelphia: Franklin Institute Press.

Chapter 15: Work, Power, and Simple Machines

James, E. *The Simple Facts of Simple Machines.* New York: Lothrop.

Weitzman, D. *Windmills, Bridges and Old Machines: Discovering Our Industrial Past.* New York: Scribner's.

Chapter 16: Energy

Adler, I. *Energy.* New York: John Day.

Satchwell, J. *Energy at Work.* New York: Lothrop.

Chapter 17: Heat

Adler, I. *Hot and Cold: The Story of Temperature From Absolute Zero to the Heat of the Sun.* New York: John Day.

Cobb, V. *Heat.* New York: Watts.

Chapter 18: Uses of Heat

Kavaler, L. *A Matter of Degree: Heat, Life and Death.* New York: Harper.

Stone, A.H., and B. Siegel. *The Heat's On.* Englewood Cliffs, NJ: Prentice-Hall.

Chapter 19: Electric Charges and Currents

Asimov, I. *How Did We Find Out About Electricity?* New York: Walker.

Cooper, A. *Electricity.* Morristown, NJ: Silver Burdett.

Chapter 20: Magnetism

Arley, N. *Exploring Magnetism.* New York: Watts.

Vogt, G. *Electricity and Magnetism.* New York: Watts.

Chapter 21: Waves

Kentzer, M. *Waves.* Morristown, NJ: Silver Burdett.

Pierce, J. *Almost All About Waves.* Cambridge, MA: MIT Press.

Chapter 22: Sound

Kettlekamp, L. *The Magic of Sound.* New York: Morrow.

Stevens, S.S., and F. Warshorsky. *Sound and Hearing.* New York: Time-Life.

Chapter 23: Light

Adler, I. *The Story of Light.* New York: Harvey House.

Ubell, E. *The World of Color and Candle.* New York: Atheneum.

Chapter 24: Light and Its Uses

Maurer, A. *Lasers: Light Wave of the Future.* New York: Arco.

Muirden, J. *How to Use an Astronomical Telescope.* New York: Linden.

Chapter 25: Energy Resources

Cross, W. *Petroleum.* Chicago: Children's Press.

Knight, C. *Harnessing the Sun.* New York: Morrow.

Chapter 26: Energy and the Environment

Hoke, J. *Solar Energy.* New York: Watts.

Satchwell, J. *Future Sources.* New York: Watts.

Chapter 27: Chemical Technology

Cobb, V. *The Secret Life of Hardware: A Science Experiment Book.* New York: Lippincott.

Milne, L., and M. Milne. *Nature's Great Carbon Cycle.* New York: Atheneum.

Chapter 28: Electronics and Computers

Knight, D. *Robotics: Past, Present & Future.* New York: Morrow.

O'Brian, L. *Computers.* New York: Watts.

The metric system of measurement is used by scientists throughout the world. It is based on units of ten. Each unit is ten times larger or ten times smaller than the next unit. The most commonly used units of the metric system are given below. After you have finished reading about the metric system, try to put it to use. How tall are you in metrics? What is your mass? What is your normal body temperature in degrees Celsius?

COMMONLY USED METRIC UNITS

Length   The distance from one point to another

meter (m)

(a meter is slightly longer than a yard)

1 meter = 1000 millimeters (mm)

1 meter = 100 centimeters (cm)

1000 meters = 1 kilometer (km)

Volume   The amount of space an object takes up

liter (L)

(a liter is slightly larger than a quart)

1 liter = 1000 milliliters (mL)

Mass   The amount of matter in an object

gram (g)

(a gram has a mass equal to about one paper clip)

1000 grams = 1 kilogram (kg)

Temperature   The measure of hotness or coldness

degrees Celsius (°C)

0°C = freezing point of water

100°C = boiling point of water

METRIC — ENGLISH EQUIVALENTS

2.54 centimeters (cm) = 1 inch (in)
1 meter (m) = 39.37 inches (in)
1 kilometer (km) = 0.62 miles (mi)
1 liter (L) = 1.06 quarts (qt)
250 milliliters (mL) = 1 cup (c)
1 kilogram (kg) = 2.2 pounds (lb)
28.3 grams (g) = 1 ounce (oz)
$C° = 5/9 \times (F° - 32)$

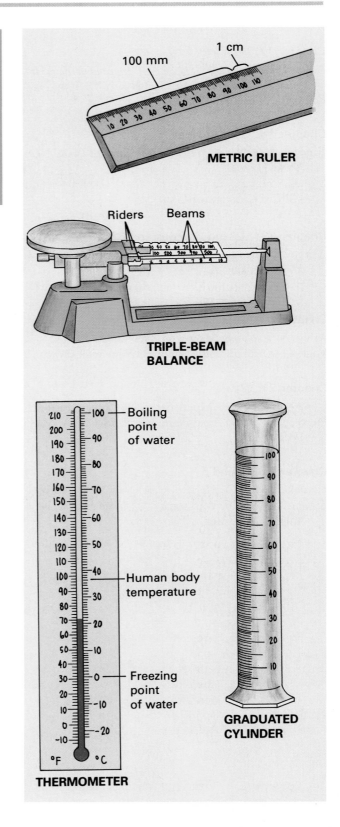

METRIC RULER

TRIPLE-BEAM BALANCE

THERMOMETER

GRADUATED CYLINDER

> One of the first things a scientist learns is that working in the laboratory can be an exciting experience. But the laboratory can also be quite dangerous if proper safety rules are not followed at all times. To prepare yourself for a safe year in the laboratory, read over the following safety rules. Then read them a second time. Make sure you understand each rule. If you do not, ask your teacher to explain any rules you are unsure of.

Dress Code

1. Many materials in the laboratory can cause eye injury. To protect yourself from possible injury, wear safety goggles whenever you are working with chemicals, burners, or any substance that might get into your eyes. Never wear contact lenses in the laboratory.

2. Wear laboratory aprons or coats whenever you are working with chemicals or heated substances.

3. Tie back long hair to keep your hair away from any chemicals, burners and candles, or other laboratory equipment.

4. Remove or tie back any article of clothing or jewelry that can hang down and touch chemicals and flames before working in the laboratory.

General Safety Rules

5. Read all directions for an experiment several times. Follow the directions exactly as they are written. If you are in doubt about any part of the experiment, ask your teacher for assistance.

6. Never perform activities that are not authorized by your teacher. Obtain permission before "experimenting" on your own.

7. Never handle any equipment unless you have specific permission.

8. Take extreme care not to spill any material in the laboratory. If spills occur, ask your teacher immediately about the proper cleanup procedure. Never simply pour chemicals or other substances into the sink or trash container.

9. Never eat in the laboratory. Wash your hands before and after each experiment.

First Aid

10. Report all accidents, no matter how minor, to your teacher immediately.

11. Learn what to do in case of specific accidents such as getting acid in your eyes or on your skin. (Rinse acids on your body with lots of water.)

12. Become aware of the location of the first aid kit. But your teacher should administer any required first aid due to injury. Or your teacher may send you to the school nurse or call a physician.

13. Know where and how to report an accident or fire. Find out the location of the fire extinguisher, phone, and fire alarm. Keep a list of important phone numbers such as the fire department and school nurse near the phone. Report any fires to your teacher at once.

Heating and Fire Safety

14. Again, never use a heat source such as a candle or burner without wearing safety goggles.

15. Never heat a chemical, you are not instructed to heat. A chemical that is harmless when cool can be dangerous when heated.

16. Maintain a clean work area, and keep all materials away from flames.

17. Never reach across a flame.

18. Make sure you know how to light a Bunsen burner. (Your teacher will demonstrate the proper procedure for lighting a burner.) If the flame leaps out of a burner toward you, turn off the gas immediately. Do not touch the burner. It may be hot. And never leave a lighted burner unattended!

19. A test tube or bottle that is being heated should be pointed away from you and others. Chemicals can splash or boil out of a heated test tube.

20. Never heat a liquid in a closed container. The expanding gases produced may blow the container apart, injuring you or others.

21. Never pick up a container that has been heated without first holding the back of your hand near it. If you can feel the heat on the back of your hand, the container may be too hot to handle. Use a clamp or tongs when handling hot containers.

Using Chemicals Safely

22. Never mix chemicals for the "fun of it." You might produce a dangerous, possibly explosive substance.

23. Never touch, taste, or smell a chemical that you do not know for a fact is harmless. Many chemicals are poisonous. If you are instructed to note the fumes in an experiment, gently wave your

hand over the opening of a container and direct the fumes toward your nose. Do not inhale the fumes directly from the container.

24. Use only those chemicals needed in the activity. The lids should be kept on chemicals that are not being used. Notify your teacher whenever chemicals are spilled.

25. Dispose of all chemicals as instructed by your teacher. To avoid contamination, never return chemicals to their original containers.

26. Be extra careful when working with acids or bases. Pour such chemicals over the sink, not over your work bench.

27. When diluting an acid, pour the acid into water. Never pour water into the acid.

28. Thoroughly rinse with water any acids on your skin or clothing. Immediately notify your teacher of any acid spill.

Using Glassware Safely

29. Never force glass tubing into a rubber stopper. When inserting glass tubing into rubber stoppers or rubber tubing, use a lubricant and a turning motion. Your teacher will demonstrate the proper way to insert glass tubing.

30. Never heat glassware that is not thoroughly dry. Use a wire or asbestos screen to protect glassware from any flame.

31. Keep in mind that hot glassware will not appear hot. Never pick up glassware without first putting the back of your hand near it to see if it is hot.

32. If you are instructed to cut glass tubing, fire-polish the ends first to remove sharp edges.

33. Never use broken or chipped glassware. If glassware breaks, notify your teacher and dispose of the glassware in the proper trash container.

34. Never eat or drink from laboratory glassware. Thoroughly clean glassware before putting it away.

Using Sharp Instruments

35. Handle scalpels or razor blades with extreme care. Never cut material toward you; cut away from you.

36. Notify your teacher immediately if you are cut in the laboratory.

End-of-Experiment Rules

37. When an experiment is completed, clean up your work area and return all equipment to its proper place.

38. Wash your hands after every experiment.

39. Turn off all candles and burners before leaving the laboratory. Check that the gas line leading to the burner is off as well.

> This mathematics refresher is designed to review those topics that may trouble you when you study physical science. You may wish to study this material before working on problems presented in the text. The material in this Appendix, although not presented in great detail, is sufficient to enable you to solve the chapter problems.

Working with Fractions

1. Addition and Subtraction: Same Denominators

To add or subtract fractions that have the same denominator, add or subtract the numerators, then write the sum or difference over the denominator. Express the answer in lowest terms. (See Examples 2 and 3.)

Examples

1. $\dfrac{1}{5} + \dfrac{2}{5} = \dfrac{1+2}{5} = \dfrac{3}{5}$

2. $\dfrac{5}{14} + \dfrac{1}{14} + \dfrac{1}{14} = \dfrac{5+1+1}{14} = \dfrac{7}{14} = \dfrac{1}{2}$

3. $\dfrac{11}{12} - \dfrac{5}{12} = \dfrac{11-5}{12} = \dfrac{6}{12} = \dfrac{1}{2}$

4. $\dfrac{4}{7} - \dfrac{2}{7} - \dfrac{1}{7} = \dfrac{4-2-1}{7} = \dfrac{1}{7}$

2. Addition and Subtraction: Different Denominators

To add or subtract fractions that do not have the same denominator, find the least common denominator. Express the fractions as equivalent fractions using the least common denominator. Then add or subtract the numerators. Write the sum or difference over the denominator. Express the answer in lowest terms. (See Example 2.)

Examples

1. $\dfrac{1}{2} + \dfrac{1}{3} = \dfrac{3}{6} + \dfrac{2}{6} = \dfrac{3+2}{6} = \dfrac{5}{6}$

2. $\dfrac{2}{5} + \dfrac{1}{10} = \dfrac{4}{10} + \dfrac{1}{10} = \dfrac{4+1}{10} = \dfrac{5}{10} = \dfrac{1}{2}$

3. $\dfrac{7}{8} - \dfrac{1}{4} = \dfrac{7}{8} - \dfrac{2}{8} = \dfrac{7-2}{8} = \dfrac{5}{8}$

4. $\dfrac{7}{8} - \dfrac{1}{3} = \dfrac{21}{24} - \dfrac{8}{24} = \dfrac{21-8}{24} = \dfrac{13}{24}$

3. Multiplication

To multiply two or more fractions, multiply the numerators to obtain the numerator of the product. Multiply the denominators to obtain the denominator of the product. Because it is easier to work with smaller numbers, whenever possible divide any numerator and denominator by their greatest common factor before multiplying. (See Examples 3 and 4.) Express the answer in lowest terms. (See Example 2.)

Examples

1. $\dfrac{7}{8} \times \dfrac{3}{5} = \dfrac{7 \times 3}{8 \times 5} = \dfrac{21}{40}$

2. $\dfrac{1}{2} \times \dfrac{1}{3} \times \dfrac{2}{5} = \dfrac{1 \times 1 \times 2}{2 \times 3 \times 5} = \dfrac{2}{30} = \dfrac{1}{15}$

3. $\dfrac{1\!\!\!\diagup 4}{7_{\,1}} \times \dfrac{3\!\!\!\diagup 9}{16_{\,4}} = \dfrac{1 \times 3}{1 \times 4} = \dfrac{3}{4}$

4. $\dfrac{1}{2_{\,1}} \times \dfrac{4\!\!\!\diagup 8}{16_{\,3}} \times \dfrac{1\!\!\!\diagup 3}{7} = \dfrac{1 \times 4 \times 1}{1 \times 3 \times 7} = \dfrac{4}{21}$

4. Division

To divide one fraction by another, invert the divisor and then multiply the two fractions. Express the answer in lowest terms.

Examples

1. $\dfrac{1}{2} \div \dfrac{1}{3} = \dfrac{1}{2} \times \dfrac{3}{1} = \dfrac{1 \times 3}{2 \times 1} = \dfrac{3}{2} = 1\dfrac{1}{2}$

2. $\dfrac{2}{5} \div \dfrac{8}{15} = \dfrac{1\!\!\!\diagup 2}{5_{\,1}} \times \dfrac{3\!\!\!\diagup 15}{8_{\,4}} = \dfrac{1 \times 3}{1 \times 4} = \dfrac{3}{4}$

3. $\dfrac{2}{3} \div \dfrac{4}{5} = \dfrac{1\!\!\!\diagup 2}{3} \times \dfrac{5}{4_{\,2}} = \dfrac{1 \times 5}{3 \times 2} = \dfrac{5}{6}$

4. $\dfrac{9}{16} \div \dfrac{3}{4} = \dfrac{3\!\!\!\diagup 9}{16_{\,4}} \times \dfrac{1\!\!\!\diagup 4}{3_{\,1}} = \dfrac{3 \times 1}{4 \times 1} = \dfrac{3}{4}$

Converting a Fraction to a Decimal

To convert a fraction to a decimal, divide the numerator by the denominator, carrying the answer to the required number of decimal places.

Examples

1. Convert $\dfrac{2}{5}$ to a decimal.

$$5\overline{\smash{\big)}\,2.0} \quad \begin{array}{c}.4\\ \underline{2\,0}\end{array} \quad = \quad .4$$

2. Convert $\frac{2}{7}$ to a two-place decimal.

$$
\begin{array}{r}
.285 \\
7\overline{\smash{)}2.000} \\
\underline{1\,4} \qquad = \quad .29 \\
60 \\
\underline{56} \\
40 \\
\underline{35} \\
5
\end{array}
$$

3. Convert $\frac{45}{85}$ to a three-place decimal.

$$
\begin{array}{r}
.529 \\
85\overline{\smash{)}45.000} \\
\underline{425} \qquad = \quad .529 \\
250 \\
\underline{170} \\
800 \\
\underline{765} \\
35
\end{array}
$$

Converting a Fraction to a Percent

To convert a fraction to a percent, divide the numerator by the denominator and multiply the result by 100 percent.

Examples

1. Convert $\frac{18}{25}$ to a percent.

$$
\begin{array}{r}
.72 \\
25\overline{\smash{)}18.00} \\
\underline{17\,5} \qquad .72 \times 100\% = 72\% \\
50 \\
50
\end{array}
$$

2. Convert $\frac{7}{50}$ to a percent.

$$
\begin{array}{r}
.14 \\
50\overline{\smash{)}7.00} \\
\underline{5\,0} \qquad = \quad .14 \times 100\% = 14\% \\
2\,00 \\
2\,00
\end{array}
$$

3. Convert $\frac{7}{4}$ to a percent.

$$
\begin{array}{r}
1.75 \\
4\overline{\smash{)}7.00} \\
\underline{4} \qquad 1.75 \times 100\% = 175\% \\
3\,0 \\
\underline{2\,8} \\
20 \\
20
\end{array}
$$

Converting a Percent to a Decimal

To convert a percent to a decimal, write the number without the percent sign and move the decimal point two places to the left.

Examples

1. Convert 84% to a decimal.
84% = .84

2. Convert 0.6% to a decimal.
0.6% = .006

3. Convert 160% to a decimal.
160% = 1.60, or 1.6

4. Convert 27.5% to a decimal.
27.5% = .275

Working with Ratios and Proportions

A ratio compares two numbers. A ratio is often written as a fraction in which the number being compared is the numerator and the number to which it is compared is the denominator. The fraction is then expressed in lowest terms. A ratio also may be written with a colon.

Examples

1. Express the ratio of 12 to 4.

12 to 4 $= \dfrac{12}{4} = \dfrac{3}{1}$, or 3 : 1

2. Express the ratio of 4 to 12.

4 to 12 $= \dfrac{4}{12} = \dfrac{1}{3}$, or 1 : 3

3. Express the ratio 25 cm to 75 cm.

25 cm to 75 cm $= \dfrac{25}{75} = \dfrac{1}{3}$, or 1 : 3

Proportions

A proportion is a mathematical sentence that states that two ratios are equivalent. To write a proportion, place an equal sign between the two equivalent ratios. In this case, the equal sign stands for "is the same as." You can use a colon instead of a fraction.

Examples

1. Write as a proportion: 6 compared to 9 is the same as 8 compared to 12.

$\dfrac{6}{9} = \dfrac{8}{12}$, or 6 : 9 = 8 : 12

2. Write as a proportion: 56 is to 14 as 76 is to 19.

$\dfrac{56}{14} = \dfrac{76}{19}$, or 56 : 14 = 76 : 19

To write a proportion in which the value of one number is unknown, use X to represent the unknown number.

Examples

1. Some number compares to 45 as 8 compares to 10.

$\frac{X}{45} = \frac{8}{10}$, or X : 45 = 8 : 10

2. Some number compares to 30 as 9 compares to 54.

$\frac{X}{30} = \frac{9}{54}$, or X : 30 = 9 : 54

To find the value of the unknown number in a proportion, cross multiply, then divide both sides of the equal sign by the number that precedes X. Check your answer by substituting the value you found for X in the original proportion.

Examples

1. $\frac{X}{45} \diagdown \frac{8}{10}$

10 × X = 8 × 45

10X = 360

$\frac{10X}{10} = \frac{360}{10}$

X = 36

2. $\frac{X}{30} \diagdown \frac{9}{54}$

54 × X = 9 × 30

54X = 270

$\frac{54X}{54} = \frac{270}{54}$

X = 5

Working with Equations

An equation is a mathematical sentence that contains a variable and an equal sign. An equation expresses a relationship between two or more quantities. A formula is a special kind of equation. A formula shows relationships between quantities that are always true. A formula is a mathematical rule. In physical science, you will be dealing with formulas. In Appendix D, you will find a list of the formulas used in this textbook.

To solve a formula, follow these three steps:
Step 1 Write the formula.
Step 2 Substitute given numbers and units.
Step 3 Solve for the unknown variable.

Examples

1. Using the formula for the area of a circle, $A = \pi r^2$, calculate the area of a circle whose radius is 2 cm:

Step 1 Write the formula. $A = \pi r^2$

Step 2 Substitute given numbers and units.

$A = \frac{22}{7} \times (2 \text{ cm})^2$

Step 3 Solve for the unknown variable.

$A = \frac{22}{7} \times 4 \text{ cm}^2 = \frac{88 \text{ cm}^2}{7} = 12.5 \text{ cm}^2$

2. Using the formula for density, $D = \frac{m}{v}$, find the mass of a sample of aluminum whose volume is 5 cm^3 and whose density is 2.7 g/cm^3:

Step 1 Write the formula. $D = \frac{m}{v}$

Step 2 Substitute given numbers and units.

$2.7 \text{ g/cm}^3 = \frac{m}{5 \text{ cm}^3}$

Step 3 Solve for the unknown variable.

m = 2.7 g/cm^3 × 5 cm^3

m = 13.5 g

1. Density (Chapter 1)

$$\text{density} = \frac{\text{mass}}{\text{volume}} \qquad D = \frac{m}{v}$$

2. Volume of a Regular Solid (Chapter 1)

volume = height × length × width

$$v = h \times l \times w$$

3. Speed (Chapter 12)

$$\text{speed} = \frac{\text{distance}}{\text{time}}$$

4. Acceleration (Chapter 12)

$$\text{acceleration} = \frac{\text{final velocity} - \text{original velocity}}{\text{time}}$$

5. Momentum (Chapter 12)

momentum = mass × velocity

6. Force (Chapter 13)

force = mass × acceleration

7. Weight (Chapter 13)

weight = mass × acceleration due to gravity

$$w = m \times g$$

8. Pressure (Chapter 14)

$$\text{pressure} = \frac{\text{force}}{\text{area}}$$

9. Work (Chapter 15)

work = force × distance

$$W = F \times d$$

10. Power (Chapter 15)

$$\text{power} = \frac{\text{work}}{\text{time}}$$

$$P = \frac{W}{t} \quad \text{or} \quad P = \frac{F \times d}{t}$$

11. Work Input (Chapter 15)

work input = effort force × effort distance

$$W_I = F_E \times d_E$$

12. Work Output (Chapter 15)

work output = resistance force × resistance distance

$$W_O = F_R \times d_R$$

13. Mechanical Advantage (Chapter 15)

$$\text{mechanical advantage} = \frac{\text{resistance force}}{\text{effort force}}$$

$$MA = \frac{F_R}{F_E}$$

14. Efficiency (Chapter 15)

$$\text{efficiency} = \frac{\text{work output}}{\text{work input}} \times 100$$

$$\text{Efficiency} = \frac{W_O}{W_I} \times 100$$

15. Mechanical Advantage of a Lever (Chapter 15)

$$\text{mechanical advantage} = \frac{\text{effort arm length}}{\text{resistance arm length}}$$

16. Kinetic Energy (Chapter 16)

$$\text{kinetic energy} = \frac{\text{mass} \times \text{velocity}^2}{2}$$

$$\text{K.E.} = \frac{m \times v^2}{2}$$

17. Gravitational Potential Energy (Chapter 16)

gravitational potential energy = weight × height

18. Einstein's mass–energy relationship (Chapter 16)

energy = mass × speed of light^2

$$E = m \times c^2$$

19. Heat Gained or Lost (Chapter 17)

$$\begin{matrix}\text{heat gained} \\ \text{or lost}\end{matrix} = \text{mass} \times \begin{matrix}\text{change in} \\ \text{temperature}\end{matrix} \times \text{specific heat}$$

Heat gained or lost = $m \times \Delta T \times$ s.h.

20. Ohm's Law (Chapter 19)

$$\text{current} = \frac{\text{voltage}}{\text{resistance}}$$

$$I = \frac{V}{R}$$

$$\text{amperes} = \frac{\text{volts}}{\text{ohms}}$$

21. Electric Power (Chapter 19)

electric power = voltage × current

$$P = V \times I$$

watts = volts × amps

22. Electric Energy (Chapter 19)

electric energy = power × time

$$E = P \times t$$

23. Wave Speed (Chapter 21)

speed = frequency × wavelength

24. Law of Reflection (Chapter 21)

angle of incidence = angle of reflection

NAME	SYMBOL	ATOMIC NUMBER	ATOMIC MASS†	NAME	SYMBOL	ATOMIC NUMBER	ATOMIC MASS†
Actinium	Ac	89	(227)	Neon	Ne	10	20.2
Aluminum	Al	13	27.0	Neptunium	Np	93	(237)
Americium	Am	95	(243)	Nickel	Ni	28	58.7
Antimony	Sb	51	121.8	Niobium	Nb	41	92.9
Argon	Ar	18	39.9	Nitrogen	N	7	14.01
Arsenic	As	33	74.9	Nobelium	No	102	(255)
Astatine	At	85	(210)	Osmium	Os	76	190.2
Barium	Ba	56	137.3	Oxygen	O	8	16.00
Berkelium	Bk	97	(247)	Palladium	Pd	46	106.4
Beryllium	Be	4	9.01	Phosphorus	P	15	31.0
Bismuth	Bi	83	209.0	Platinum	Pt	78	195.1
Boron	B	5	10 8	Plutonium	Pu	94	(244)
Bromine	Br	35	79.9	Polonium	Po	84	(210)
Cadmium	Cd	48	112.4	Potassium	K	19	39.1
Calcium	Ca	20	40.1	Praseodymium	Pr	59	140.9
Californium	Cf	98	(251)	Promethium	Pm	61	(145)
Carbon	C	6	12.01	Protactinium	Pa	91	(231)
Cerium	Ce	58	140.1	Radium	Ra	88	(226)
Cesium	Cs	55	132.9	Radon	Rn	86	(222)
Chlorine	Cl	17	35.5	Rhenium	Re	75	186.2
Chromium	Cr	24	52.0	Rhodium	Rh	45	102.9
Cobalt	Co	27	58.9	Rubidium	Rb	37	85.5
Copper	Cu	29	63.5	Ruthenium	Ru	44	101.1
Curium	Cm	96	(247)	Samarium	Sm	62	150.4
Dysprosium	Dy	66	162.5	Scandium	Sc	21	45.0
Einsteinium	Es	99	(254)	Selenium	Se	34	79.0
Erbium	Er	68	167.3	Silicon	Si	14	28.1
Europium	Eu	63	152.0	Silver	Ag	47	107.9
Fermium	Fm	100	(257)	Sodium	Na	11	23.0
Fluorine	F	9	19.0	Strontium	Sr	38	87.6
Francium	Fr	87	(223)	Sulfur	S	16	32.1
Gadolinium	Gd	64	157.2	Tantalum	Ta	73	180.9
Gallium	Ga	31	69.7	Technetium	Tc	43	(97)
Germanium	Ge	32	72.6	Tellurium	Te	52	127.6
Gold	Au	79	197.0	Terbium	Tb	65	158.9
Hafnium	Hf	72	178.5	Thallium	Tl	81	204.4
Helium	He	2	4.00	Thorium	Th	90	232.0
Holmium	Ho	67	164.9	Thulium	Tm	69	168.9
Hydrogen	H	1	1.008	Tin	Sn	50	118.7
Indium	In	49	114.8	Titanium	Ti	22	47.9
Iodine	I	53	126.9	Tungsten	W	74	183.9
Iridium	Ir	77	192.2	Unnilennium	Une	109	(266?)
Iron	Fe	26	55.8	Unnilhexium	Unh	106	(263)
Krypton	Kr	36	83.8	Unniloctium	Uno	108	(265)
Lanthanum	La	57	138.9	Unnilpentium	Unp	105	(262)
Lawrencium	Lr	103	(256)	Unnilquadium	Unq	104	(261)
Lead	Pb	82	207.2	Unnilseptium	Uns	107	(262)
Lithium	Li	3	6.94	Uranium	U	92	238.0
Lutetium	Lu	71	175.0	Vanadium	V	23	50.9
Magnesium	Mg	12	24.3	Xenon	Xe	54	131.3
Manganese	Mn	25	54.9	Ytterbium	Yb	70	173.0
Mendelevium	Md	101	(258)	Yttrium	Y	39	88.9
Mercury	Hg	80	200.6	Zinc	Zn	30	65.4
Molybdenum	Mo	42	95.9	Zirconium	Zr	40	91.2
Neodymium	Nd	60	144.2				

†Numbers in parentheses give the mass number of the most stable isotope.

Glossary

When difficult names or terms first appear in the text, they are respelled to aid pronunciation. A syllable in SMALL CAPITAL LETTERS receives the most stress. The key below lists the letters used for respelling. It includes examples of words using each sound and shows how the words would be respelled.

Symbol	Example	Respelling
a	hat	(hat)
ay	pay, late	(pay), (layt)
ah	star, hot	(stahr), (haht)
ai	air, dare	(air), (dair)
aw	law, all	(law), (awl)
eh	met	(meht)
ee	bee, eat	(bee), (eet)
er	learn, sir, fur	(lern), (ser), (fer)
ih	fit	(fiht)
igh	mile, sigh	(mighl), (sigh)
oh	no	(noh)
oi	soil, boy	(soil), (boi)
oo	root, rule	(root), (rool)
or	born, door	(born), (dor)
ow	plow, out	(plow), (owt)

Symbol	Example	Respelling
u	put, book	(put), (buk)
uh	fun	(fuhn)
yoo	few, use	(fyoo), (yooz)
ch	chill, reach	(chihl), (reech)
g	go, dig	(goh), (dihg)
j	jet, gently, bridge	(jeht), (JEHNT lee), (brihj)
k	kite, cup	(kight), (kuhp)
ks	mix	(mihks)
kw	quick	(kwihk)
ng	bring	(brihng)
s	say, cent	(say), (sehnt)
sh	she, crash	(shee), (krash)
th	three	(three)
y	yet, onion	(yeht), (UHN yuhn)
z	zip, always	(zihp), (AWL wayz)
zh	treasure	(TREH zher)

absolute zero: temperature at which all molecular motion ceases; $0°K$, $-273°C$

acceleration (ak-sehl-uh-RAY-shuhn): rate of change in velocity

acid: compound with a pH below 7 that tastes sour, turns blue litmus paper red, reacts with metals to produce hydrogen gas, and ionizes in water to produce hydrogen ions; proton donor

acid rain: droplets of weak sulfuric acid and nitric acid that form in the atmosphere and mix with rainwater

actinoid series: second row of rare-earth elements in the periodic table, which with the exception of three elements are radioactive and synthetic

activation energy: energy needed to form a short-lived, high-energy, extremely unstable molecule whose atoms are rearranged to form products in a chemical reaction

active solar heating: heating system that uses a solar collector to store heat from the sun and an arrangement of hot water heater and pipes to circulate heat throughout a building

alcohol: substituted hydrocarbon in which one or more hydrogen atoms have been replaced by an –OH group, or hydroxyl group

alkali metal: element in Group IA

alkaline earth metal: element in Group IIA

alkane: straight-chain or branched-chain saturated hydrocarbon in which all the bonds between carbon atoms are single covalent bonds

alkene: unsaturated hydrocarbon in which at least one pair of carbon atoms is joined by a double covalent bond

alkyne: unsaturated hydrocarbon in which at least one pair of carbon atoms is joined by a triple covalent bond

alloy: solution of two metals or a metal and a nonmetal that has the properties of a metal

alpha decay: release of an alpha particle, or helium nucleus, from the nucleus of a radioactive atom

alternating current (AC): electrons moving back and forth through a wire, changing direction over and over again

amino acid: organic acid that contains carbon, hydrogen, oxygen, nitrogen, and sometimes sulfur and phosphorus; monomer from which proteins are made

amorphous (uh-MOR-fuhs) **solid:** solid that loses its shape under certain conditions

ampere: unit used to measure electric current

amplifier: electronic device that increases the strength of an electric signal

amplitude: (AM-plih-tyood): maximum distance the molecules of a medium are displaced from their rest position

angle of incidence (i): angle formed by the incident ray and a line perpendicular to the barrier (normal)

angle of reflection (r): angle formed by a line perpendicular to the barrier (normal) and the reflected ray

anthracite (AN-thruh-sight): hard, brittle coal formed when bituminous coal undergoes pressure

antinode: point at which constructive interference of waves causes maximum energy displacement

aqueous (A-kwee-uhs) **solution:** solution in which the solvent is water

Archimedes' principle: principle that states that the buoyant force on an object is equal to the weight of the fluid displaced by the object

aromatic hydrocarbon: ring of 6 carbon atoms joined by alternating single and double covalent bonds; has a strong, often pleasant odor

atom: smallest particle of an element that has the properties of that element

atomic mass: average of the masses of all the existing isotopes of an element

atomic mass unit (amu): unit used to measure the masses of subatomic particles; a proton has a mass of 1 amu

atomic number: number of protons in the nucleus of an atom

average speed: measure of speed obtained by dividing the total distance by the total time

balanced force: force that is opposite and equal to another force

base: compound with a pH above 7 that tastes bitter, is slippery to the touch, turns red litmus paper blue, and ionizes in water to produce hydroxide ions; proton acceptor

battery: series of dry cells connected to one another

Bernoulli's principle: principle that states that the pressure in a moving stream of fluid is less than the pressure in the surrounding fluid

beta decay: release of a beta particle, or negatively charged electron, from the nucleus of a radioactive atom

bimetallic strip: strip consisting of two different metals that expand at different rates and cause the strip to bend; switch in a thermostat

binary system: number system that uses only the numbers 0 and 1, on which computer operation is based

binding energy: energy associated with the strong force

biomass: plants, animal wastes, and all other forms of matter that come from living things, which can be burned to generate heat

bit: single electronic switch in a computer

bituminous (bigh-TOO-muh-nuhs) **coal:** soft coal formed when lignite undergoes pressure

boiling: process in which particles inside a liquid as well as those on the surface change to a gas

boiling point: temperature at which a substance changes from the liquid phase to the gas phase

boiling point elevation: increase in the boiling point of a pure liquid solvent caused by the addition of solute

Boyle's Law: law that states that the volume of a fixed amount of gas varies inversely with the pressure of the gas

Brownian motion: constant movement of particles in a colloid

brush: contact through which electric current is supplied to the commutator in an electric motor

bubble chamber: instrument used to detect radioactivity using a superheated liquid

buoyancy (BOI-uhn-see): force of a fluid that pushes an object up

byte: a string of bits, usually 8 bits

calorie: unit used to measure heat

calorimeter (kal-uh-RIHM-uh-tuhr): instrument used to measure the heat given off in chemical reactions

carbohydrate: organic molecule of carbon, hydrogen, and oxygen in which there are two atoms of hydrogen for every atom of oxygen

carboxyl group: –COOH, group that characterizes all organic acids

carburetor (KAHR-buh-rayt-uhr): part of an internal-combustion engine in which gasoline is turned into vapor and mixed with air in the intake stroke

catalyst (KAT-uhl-ihst): substance that increases the rate of a reaction but is not itself changed by the reaction

cathode-ray tube (CRT): electronic device that uses electrons to produce images on a screen

Celsius (SEHL-see-uhs): metric temperature scale on which water freezes at 0° and boils at 100°

centimeter (cm): one-hundredth of a meter

central heating system: system that generates heat for an entire building or group of buildings from one central location

central processing unit (CPU): brain of a computer, which controls and processes information, controls the operation of all the components, and executes the arithmetic and logic instructions it receives

centripetal (sehn-TRIHP-uh-tuhl) **acceleration:** acceleration that is directed toward the center of a circular path

Charles's Law: law that states that the volume of a fixed amount of gas varies directly with the temperature of the gas

chemical bonding: combining of atoms of elements to form new substances

chemical change: process by which a substance becomes a new and different substance

chemical energy: energy that bonds atoms or ions together

chemical equation: expression in which symbols and formulas are used to represent a chemical reaction

chemical formula: combination of chemical symbols usually used to represent a compound

chemical property: property that describes how a substance changes into a new substance

chemical reaction: process in which the physical and chemical properties of the original substance change as a new substance with different physical and chemical properties is formed

chemical symbol: shorthand way of representing an element

chemistry: study of what substances are made of and how they change and combine

chip: razor-thin piece of silicon

circuit breaker: switch that flips open when the current flow becomes too high, thus breaking the circuit and stopping the flow

cloud chamber: instrument containing evaporated alcohol; used to detect radioactivity

coefficient (koh-uh-FIHSH-uhnt): number placed in front of a symbol or formula in a chemical equation that indicates how many atoms or molecules of the substance are involved in the reaction

coherent light: light that is in phase

collision theory: theory that says that reacting molecules must collide with sufficient energy if they are to form products

colloid (KAHL-oid): homogenous mixture that is not a true solution

combustion: process in which hydrocarbons in fossil fuels are combined with oxygen at high temperatures and heat and light are released; the burning of a fuel

commutator: special reversing switch in an electric motor that runs on DC that switches the direction of the current so that the magnetic poles of the electromagnet reverse and the electromagnet spins

complementary color: one of two colors that combine to form white light

compound: two or more elements chemically combined

compound machine: combination of two or more simple machines

compression (kuhm-PREHSH-uhn): space in a medium in which the molecules are crowded together

compression stroke: process in an internal-combustion engine in which the gasoline-air mixture is compressed in a cylinder and ignited by a spark from a spark plug

compressor: part of a cooling system where the pressure of the refrigerant vapor is increased

computer: electronic device that performs calculations and processes information

computer program: series of instructions that tells a computer how to perform a certain task

concave lens: lens that is thicker at the edges and thinner in the center so that it diverges light rays

concave mirror: mirror with a surface that curves inward

concentrated solution: solution in which a lot of solute is dissolved in a solvent

concentration: measure of the amount of a substance in a given unit of volume; amount of solute dissolved in a certain amount of solvent

condensation (kahn-duhn-SAY-shuhn): change of a gas to a liquid

condenser coil: part of a cooling system that cools the refrigerant vapor and changes it back into a liquid

conduction (kuhn-DUHK-shuhn): heat transfer through a substance or from one substance to another by the direct contact of molecules; method of charging objects with static electricity that involves the direct contact of objects

conductor: material that permits electric charges to move easily

cone: nerve cell in the retina of the eye that is sensitive to a primary color

conservation: wise and careful use of natural resources

constant speed: speed that does not change

constructive interference: process in which waves combine in such a way that the crests of one wave meet the crests of the other

control rod: rod usually made of cadmium that controls the speed of a nuclear reaction

control setup: part of an experiment that does not contain the variable

convection (kuhn-VEHK-shuhn): heat transfer in liquids and gases as molecules move in currents

conversion factor: fraction that always equals one, which is used for dimensional analysis

convex lens: lens that is thicker in the center than at the edges so that it converges light rays

convex mirror: mirror with a surface that curves outward

cooling system: system that removes heat from a building, room, or other space through evaporation

cooling tower: part of a factory or power plant in which water containing waste heat is cooled as it flows through pipes

core: central part of a nuclear reactor, where nuclear fission takes place

corrosion: gradual wearing away of a metal due to a chemical reaction in which the metal element is changed into a metallic compound

covalent bonding: chemical bonding in which electrons are shared rather than transferred

crest: high point of a wave; maximum displacement upward of a particle of the medium

crystal (KRIHS-tuhl): solid in which the particles are arranged in a regular, repeating pattern

crystal lattice: huge numbers of ions grouped together in a regular, repeating pattern

crystalline solid: solid made up of crystals

cubic centimeter (cm³ or cc): metric unit used to measure the volume of solids; equal to a milliliter

cycloalkane: saturated hydrocarbon ring

cylinder: tube in an external-combustion engine in which a piston moves back and forth; part of an internal-combustion engine in which a piston moves and compresses the gasoline-air mixture to one-seventh of its original volume

data: recorded observations and measurements

data bank: vast collection of information stored in a large computer

decay series: series of steps by which a radioactive nucleus decays into a nonradioactive nucleus

deceleration (dee-sehl-uh-RAY-shuhn): decrease in velocity

decomposition reaction: chemical reaction in which a complex substance breaks down into two or more simpler substances

denatured alcohol: ethanol to which a poisonous compound such as methanol has been added

density: mass per unit volume of a substance

destructive interference: process in which waves combine in such a way that the crests of one wave meet the troughs of the other

diatomic element: two atoms covalently bonded

diesel engine: internal-combustion engine in which only air is taken in during the intake stroke

diffraction (dih-FRAK-shuhn): bending of waves around the edge of a barrier

diffuse (dih-FYOOS) **reflection:** reflected light that is scattered in many different directions due to an irregular surface; produces a "fuzzy image"

dilute solution: solution in which there is a little solute dissolved in a solvent

dimensional analysis: converting one unit to another

diode: simplest type of vacuum tube consisting of a filament and a plate

direct current (DC): electrons continuously moving in the same direction through a wire

disk drive: input/output device that reads information off a disk or diskette and enters it into or receives it from a computer's memory, or CPU

dissociation: separation of ions from a compound during solution

distillation: process that involves heating a liquid until it vaporizes and then allowing the vapor to cool until it condenses back into a liquid

doping: adding impurities to semiconductors to increase their conductivity

double-replacement reaction: chemical reaction in which different atoms in two different compounds replace each other

drag: opposition to thrust caused by fluid friction

dry cell: electrochemical cell that consists of a positive electrode, a negative electrode, and a pastelike electrolyte

ductile: able to be drawn into a thin wire

effervescence (ehf-er-VEHS-ehns): escape of a gas from a liquid solution

efficiency: comparison of work output to work input

effort arm: distance from the effort force to the fulcrum

effort distance (d_E): distance through which a machine moves, or distance through which the effort force is applied to a machine

effort force (F_E): force that is applied to a machine

electric charge: positive or negative condition of a particle due to unequal numbers of protons and electrons in the atom

electric current: flow of electrons through a wire

electric discharge: loss of static electricity as electric charges move off an object

electric field: region surrounding a charged particle in which an electric force affecting other charged particles is noticeable.

electricity: energy associated with electrons that have moved from one place to another

electric motor: motor that converts electric energy into mechanical energy

electrochemical cell: cell in which chemical energy produced by a chemical reaction is changed into electric energy

electrode: metal plate in a wet cell

electrolysis: process of decomposing water into hydrogen and oxygen by passing an electric current through water

electrolyte: conducting liquid in a wet cell

electromagnet: powerful temporary magnet made by wrapping a coil of wire around a soft iron core and passing an electric current through the wire

electromagnetic energy: energy produced by moving electric charges

electromagnetic force: force of attraction or repulsion between particles in an atom

electromagnetic induction: process by which a current is produced by the motion of a conductor in a magnetic field

electromagnetic spectrum: arrangement of electromagnetic waves in order of their wavelengths, and thus their frequency

electromagnetic wave: wave that is both electric and magnetic in nature; light wave

electromagnetism: relationship between electricity and magnetism

electron: subatomic particle with a negative charge

electron affinity: tendency of an atom to attract electrons

electron cloud: space in which electrons are likely to be found

electron-dot diagram: representation of the electron-sharing that takes place in covalent bonding

electronics: study of the release, behavior, and effects of electrons as it relates to use in helpful devices

electroscope: instrument, consisting of a metal rod with two thin metal leaves at one end, used to detect radioactivity; instrument that can detect an electric charge

element: simplest type of pure substance

endothermic (ehn-duh-THER-mihk) **reaction:** chemical reaction in which energy is absorbed

energy: ability to do work

energy conversion: change in the form of energy

energy level: most likely location in an electron cloud in which an electron can be found

ester: compound that results from the chemical combination of an alcohol and an organic acid

esterification: reaction that produces an ester

evaporation (ih-vap-uh-RAY-shuhn): vaporization that takes place at the surface of a liquid

exhaust stroke: process in an internal-combustion engine in which gases are expelled from the cylinder through the exhaust valve

exhaust valve: part of an internal-combustion engine through which gases are expelled from the cylinder

exothermic (ehks-uh-THER-mihk) **reaction:** chemical reaction in which energy is released

experimental setup: part of an experiment that contains the variable

external-combustion engine: engine in which fuel is burned outside the engine; a steam engine

family: column of elements in the periodic table; group

farsightedness: condition in which a person has difficulty seeing nearby objects

fat: large complex ester formed from the reaction between the alcohol glycerol and fatty acids that is a solid at room temperature

fermentation (fer-muhn-TAY-shuhn): process in which yeast converts the sugar in a grain into ethanol and carbon dioxide

fiberglass: common insulating material consisting of long thin strands of glass packed together

fiber optics: field that deals with the transfer of light through long thin flexible fibers of glass or plastic called optical fibers

first law of motion: Newton's law that states that an object at rest will remain at rest and an object in motion will remain in motion at constant velocity unless an unbalanced force acts upon it

flammability (flam-uh-BIHL-uh-tee): ability to burn

fluid friction: friction produced when an object moves through a fluid

fluorescent (floo-REHS-uhnt): type of light produced by the electron bombardment of gas molecules contained at low pressure

focal length: distance between the center of the mirror or lens and the focal point

focal point: point in front of a mirror where the reflected rays meet

force: push or pull that gives energy to an object, causing it to start moving, stop moving, or change its motion

force of attraction: force that pulls objects together

force of repulsion: force that pushes objects apart

fossil fuel: fuel formed over hundreds of millions of years by heat and great pressure on plant and animal remains

fraction: petroleum part with its own boiling point

fractionating tower: place where fractional distillation of petroleum takes place

frame of reference: object or point from which movement is determined

freezer unit: part of a cooling system in which the liquid refrigerant absorbs heat and evaporates

freezing: change of a liquid to a solid

freezing point: temperature at which a substance changes from the liquid phase to the solid phase

freezing point depression: lowering of the freezing point of a liquid solvent by dissolving a solute in it

Freon (FREE-ahn): common refrigerant used in cooling systems

frequency (FREE-kwuhn-see): number of complete waves, or complete cycles, per unit time

friction (FRIHK-shuhn): force that opposes the motion of an object; method of charging an object with static electricity

fulcrum (FUL-kruhm): fixed point at which a lever pivots

fuse: device containing a thin metal strip that melts and breaks the flow of electricity if the current becomes too high

galvanometer: instrument used to detect small currents

gamma decay: release of gamma rays, or electromagnetic waves of very high frequency and energy, from the nucleus of an atom

gamma ray: highest frequency electromagnetic wave

gas: matter with no definite shape or volume

gasohol: mixture of gasoline and alcohol

Geiger counter: instrument designed to detect and measure radioactivity by producing an electric current in the presence of a radioactive substance

generator: device that converts mechanical energy into electric energy

geothermal energy: heat energy deep within the earth's crust

geyser: fountain of steam and boiling water that bursts forth from the earth through a crack or weak spot in the earth's crust

gram (g): one-thousandth of a kilogram

gravitational (grav-ih-TAY-shuhn-uhl) **potential energy (G.P.E.):** energy that is dependent on height above the earth's surface

gravity: force of attraction between all objects in the universe

grounding: providing a path for the discharge of static electricity to reach the earth

group: column of elements in the periodic table; family

half-life: amount of time it takes for half the atoms in a given sample of a radioactive element to decay

halogen (HAL-uh-juhn): element in Group VIIA

halogen derivative: substituted hydrocarbon that contains halogens

hardware: physical parts of a computer

hard water: water that contains large amounts of dissolved metal ions

heat conductor: substance that conducts heat more effectively than other substances

heat energy: internal motion of particles of matter

heat engine: machine that changes heat energy into mechanical energy in order to do work

heat of fusion: amount of heat needed to change a substance from the solid phase to the liquid phase

heat of vaporization: amount of heat needed to change a substance from the liquid phase to the gas phase

heat pump system: heating system that takes heat from the outside air and brings it inside

heat transfer: movement of heat from a warmer object to a colder one

hertz (Hz): unit used to measure wave frequency; one wave per second

heterogeneous (heht-uhr-uh-JEEN-ee-uhs) **matter:** matter that has parts with different properties

heterogeneous mixture: mixture that does not appear to be the same throughout

hologram: image produced by holography

holography: technology that uses laser light to produce a three-dimensional image of an object or scene

homogeneous (hoh-muh-JEEN-ee-uhs) **matter:** matter that has identical properties throughout

homogeneous mixture: mixture that appears to be the same throughout

horsepower (hp): 745.56 watts; originally, the power necessary for a strong horse to move a 750-newton object one meter in one second

hot water system: heating system in which hot water is pumped through pipes to a convector that heats the room through convection currents

hydrocarbon: organic compound that contains only hydrogen and carbon

hydroelectric: using water to produce electricity

hydrogen ion: proton produced by an acid dissolved in water

hydronium ion (H_3O^+): hydrated hydrogen ion

hydroxide ion: ion produced when a base is dissolved in water

hydroxyl group: –OH, group that characterizes all organic alcohols

hypothesis (high-PAHTH-uh-sihs): proposed solution to a scientific problem

illuminated (ih-LOO-muh-nayt-uhd): able to be seen only by reflected light

incandescent (ihn-kuhn-DEH-suhnt): type of light produced from heat

incident wave: wave coming in toward a barrier

inclined plane: slanted surface used to raise an object

index of refraction: measure of the amount by which a material refracts light

indicator: compound that shows a definite color change when mixed with an acid or a base

induction: method of charging an object with static electricity that involves a rearrangement of electric charges

inert: not readily combining with other elements to form compounds

inertia (ihn-ER-shuh): tendency of objects to remain in motion or stay at rest unless acted upon by an unbalanced force

infrared ray: electromagnetic wave with a frequency slightly lower than visible red light

input device: device used for feeding data into the central processing unit of a computer; keyboard, magnetic tape, optical scanner, disk or diskette drive

insoluble: unable to be dissolved in water

insulation: prevention of heat loss by reducing the transfer of heat that occurs by conduction and convection

insulator: material that does not allow electrons to flow freely; substance that does not conduct heat easily

intake stroke: process in an internal-combustion engine in which the gasoline is vaporized, mixed with air, and transferred from the carburetor through the intake valve to a cylinder

intake valve: part of an internal-combustion engine through which the gasoline-air mixture is transferred from the carburetor to a cylinder

integrated circuit: circuit that combines many diodes and transistors on a thin slice of silicon crystal

interference: process in which two or more waves arriving at the same point at the same time combine to produce a single new wave

internal-combustion engine: engine in which the burning of fuel takes place inside the engine; a gasoline engine

internal energy: energy contained in a substance

invisible spectrum: waves with frequencies less than 430 trillion hertz or greater than 760 trillion hertz that are thus invisible to the human eye

ion: charged particle formed when an atom gains or loses electrons

ionic bonding: chemical bonding that involves a transfer of electrons

ionization (igh-uhn-ih-ZAY-shuhn): process of removing an electron and forming ions: formation of ions from solute molecules by the action of a solvent

ionization energy: energy needed for ionization

iris: colored area surrounding the pupil of the eye that controls the amount of light that enters the pupil

isomer: organic compound that has the same molecular formula as another organic compound but a different structure

isotope (IGH-suh-tohp): atom of an element that has the same number of protons as another atom of the same element but a different number of neutrons

joule (J): one newton-meter; unit in which energy is measured

Kelvin scale: metric temperature scale on which 0° represents absolute zero, the boiling point of water is 373°, and the freezing point of water is 273°

kilogram (kg): basic unit of mass in the metric system

kilometer (km): 1000 meters

kilowatt (kW): 1000 watts

kilowatt-hour: 1000 watts of power used for one hour of time; measure of electric energy

kinetic (kih-NEHT-ihk) **energy:** energy that a moving object has due to its motion; energy of motion

kinetics: study of reaction rates

land reclamation: process of restoring land

lanthanoid series: first row of rare-earth elements in the periodic table; soft, malleable metals that have a high luster and conductivity

laser: device that concentrates light into a narrow intense beam

law: scientific theory that has been tested many times and is generally accepted as true

law of conservation (kahn-ser-VAY-shuhn) **of energy:** law that states that energy can be neither created nor destroyed by ordinary means

law of conservation of mass: law that states that matter can be neither created nor destroyed in a chemical reaction

law of conservation of momentum: law that states that the total momentum of any group of objects remains the same unless outside forces act on the objects

law of reflection: law that states that the angle of incidence is equal to the angle of reflection

law of universal gravitation: Newton's law that states that all objects in the universe attract each other by the force of gravity

lens: any transparent material that refracts light

lever: a bar that is free to pivot, or move about, a fixed point when an effort force is applied

lift: upward force

lightning: discharge of static electricity

lightning rod: pointed metal rod placed above the roof of a building as protection from lightning

lignite (LIHG-night): soft woody type of coal formed when peat undergoes pressure

lipid (LIHP-ihd): any of the class of organic compounds consisting of fats and oils

liquid: matter with no definite shape but with a definite volume

liter (L): basic unit of volume in the metric system

longitudinal (lahn-juh-TYOOD-uhn-uhl) **wave:** wave consisting of a series of compressions and rarefactions in which the motion of the medium is parallel to the direction of the wave

lubricant: substance that changes sliding friction to fluid friction

luminous (LOO-muh-nuhs): giving off its own light

luster: shininess

machine: device that makes work easier by changing the size or direction of the applied force

magnetic domain: region in which the magnetic fields of atoms are grouped together

magnetic field: region in which magnetic forces act

magnetic induction: process by which a material is made into a magnet

magnetic lines of force: lines that define the magnetic field of an object

magnetic variation: error in a compass caused by the difference in location of the earth's magnetic and geographic poles

magnetism: force of attraction or repulsion due to an arrangement of electrons

magnetosphere: region of the earth's magnetic field

main memory: main storage of a computer that contains data and operating instructions

malleable: able to be hammered into a thin sheet

mass: amount of matter in an object

mass number: sum of the protons and the neutrons in the nucleus of an atom

matter: anything that has mass and volume

mechanical advantage (MA): number of times a machine multiplies the effort force

mechanical energy: energy associated with motion

medium: any substance or region through which a wave is transmitted

melting: change of a solid to a liquid

melting point: temperature at which a substance changes from the solid phase to the liquid phase

meniscus (mih-NIHS-kuhs): point at the bottom of the curve of the liquid in a graduated cylinder

metal: element that is a good conductor of heat and electricity, is shiny, has a high melting point, is ductile and malleable, and forms positive ions

metallic bond: bond formed by the atoms of metals, in which the outer electrons of the atoms form a common electron cloud

metalloid (MEHT-uhl-oid): element that has properties of both metals and nonmetals

meter (m): basic unit of length in the metric system

metric system: standard system of measurement used by all scientists

microprocessor: integrated circuit that can hold the entire processing capability of a computer on one small chip

microwave: radio wave with a frequency between 1 billion hertz and 1 trillion hertz

milligram (mg): one-thousandth of a gram

milliliter (mL): one-thousandth of a liter

millimeter (mm): one-thousandth of a meter

mirror: any smooth surface that reflects light and forms images

miscible (MIHS-uh-buhl): able to be dissolved in another liquid

mixture: matter that consists of two or more substances mixed together but not chemically combined

modem: input and output device that changes electronic signals from a computer into sounds that can be carried over telephone lines and vice versa

moderator: material that slows down neutrons in a nuclear reaction

modulation (mahj-uh-LAY-shuhn): variation in either amplitude or frequency of a wave

molecule (MAHL-uh-kyool): combination of atoms formed by a covalent bond

momentum: mass of an object multiplied by its velocity

monomer (MAHN-uh-mer): smaller molecule that joins with other smaller molecules to form a polymer

motion: change in position relative to a frame of reference

natural magnet: naturally occurring substance that has magnetic properties

nearsightedness: condition in which a person has difficulty seeing objects at a distance

neon: type of light produced when electrons pass through glass tubes filled with neon gas; bright red light

network solid: covalently bonded substance that does not have a low melting point

neutralization (noo-truhl-uh-ZAY-shuhn): reaction of an acid with a base to produce a salt and water

neutron: subatomic particle with no electric charge

newton-meter (N-m): unit of work; joule

noble gas: element in Group VIIIA

node: point at which destructive interference of waves results in no energy displacement

nonelectrolyte: substance that forms an aqueous solution that does not conduct an electric current

nonmetal: element that is a poor conductor of heat and electricity, has a dull surface, low melting point, is brittle, breaks easily, and forms negative ions

nonrenewable resource: natural resource that cannot be replaced by nature

normal: line perpendicular to the barrier

north magnetic pole: end of the magnet that points toward the north

nuclear chain reaction: continuous series of fission reactions

nuclear energy: energy released by the splitting of the nucleus of an atom; energy locked within the nucleus by the strong force

nuclear fission (FIHSH-uhn): splitting of an atomic nucleus into two smaller nuclei of approximately equal mass, during which nuclear energy is released

nuclear fusion: joining of two atomic nuclei of smaller masses to form a single nucleus of larger mass

nuclear radiation: particles and energy released by radioactive decay

nuclear waste: radioactive substance associated with the use of radioactive materials or the production of nuclear power

nucleus (NOO-klee-uhs; plural: nuclei, NOO-klee-igh): small dense positively charged center of an atom

ohm: unit of resistance

Ohm's Law: law that states that the current in a wire is equal to the voltage divided by the resistance

oil: large complex ester formed from the reaction between the alcohol glycerol and fatty acids that is liquid at room temperature

opaque (oh-PAYK): unable to transmit light

optical axis: straight line drawn through the center of a mirror or lens

optical fiber: long thin flexible fiber of glass or plastic

orbital motion: motion that results from the combination of the object's forward inertia and the downward pull of gravity on an object

organic acid: substituted hydrocarbon that contains the –COOH group, or carboxyl group

organic chemistry: study of carbon compounds

organic compound: compound that contains carbon

output device: device that receives data from the central processing unit of a computer, such as a printer, cathode-ray tube, magnetic tape drive, or voice synthesizer

oxidation number: number of electrons an atom gains, loses, or shares when it forms chemical bonds

parallel circuit: electric circuit in which the different parts of the circuit are on separate branches

particle accelerator: instrument in which artificial transmutation takes place

passive solar heating: heating system in which a building is heated directly by the rays of the sun

peat: soft type of coal made of decayed plant fibers

period: horizontal row of elements in the periodic table

periodic: repeating according to the same pattern

periodic law: law that states that the physical and chemical properties of the elements are periodic functions of their atomic numbers

permanent magnet: magnet made of a material that is difficult to magnetize but stays magnetized

petroleum: crude oil

phase: state in which matter can exist: solid, liquid, gas, or plasma

phase change: physical change of matter from one phase to another

phosphor: substance that absorbs ultraviolet photons and glows, producing visible light

photoelectric effect: production of electrons by photons of light

photon (FOH-tahn): tiny packet of energy

photovoltaic cell: device that converts sunlight directly into electricity

physical change: change in which physical properties of a substance are altered but the substance remains the same kind of matter

physical property: property of a substance that can be observed without changing the identity of the substance

physics: study of forms of energy and the laws of motion

piston: metal plate in a combustion engine that moves back and forth in a cylinder and passes mechanical energy to a connecting rod, which does work

plane mirror: mirror with a perfectly flat surface

plasma: high-energy phase of matter

polarity (poh-LAR-uh-tee): property of a molecule with oppositely charged ends

polarized light: light whose waves vibrate along a single plane

pole: end of a magnet

pollution: release of substances into the environment that changes the environment for the worse

polyatomic ion: group of covalently bonded atoms that acts like a single atom when combining with other atoms

polymer (PAHL-ih-mer): giant molecule made up of smaller molecules joined together; many molecular units strung together in a chain

polymerization (puh-lihm-er-ih-ZAY-shuhn): process of chemically bonding monomers to form polymers

potential (poh-TEHN-shuhl) **energy:** energy stored in an object due to its position

power: rate at which work is done, or the amount of work done per unit time

power stroke: process in an internal-combustion engine in which the explosion of hot gases forces the piston back down and energy is transferred from the piston to the wheels of the car

precipitate (prih-SIHP-uh-tayt): insoluble substance that crystallizes out of a solution

precipitation: process by which a precipitate forms

pressure: "push" that fluids exert on an object; force that acts over a certain area

primary coil: coil of insulated wire wrapped around an iron core in a transformer that creates a magnetic field when alternating current passes through it

primary color: one of three colors that can be mixed to produce light of any color; red, blue, or green

primary pigment: yellow, cyan, or magenta

prism (PRIHZ-uhm): piece of glass that forms a spectrum when white light is passed through it

product: substance that is produced by a chemical reaction

projectile: any object thrown in the air that moves forward due to its inertia and accelerates downward due to gravity

projectile motion: curved path of a projectile

property: characteristic of a substance

protein: organic compound made up of amino acids

proton: subatomic particle with a positive charge

pulley: chain, belt, or rope wrapped around a wheel

pupil: opening in the eye through which light enters

pure substance: substance made of only one kind of material having definite properties

quark (kwahrk): particle that makes up all other known particles in the nucleus of an atom

radar: radio detecting and ranging; short-wavelength microwaves used in locating objects, calculating distances to objects, and monitoring speed

radiant electric system: heating system in which electricity passes through wires or cables that resist the flow of current and give off heat through radiation

radiant hot water system: heating system in which hot water runs through a continuous coil of pipe in the floor of a room, and heats the room through radiation

radiation (ray-dee-AY-shuhn): energy given off when certain substances decay; heat transfer through space

radioactive: giving off radiation

radioactive decay: spontaneous breakdown of an unstable atomic nucleus

radioactivity: release of energy and matter that results from changes in the nucleus of an atom

radioisotope: artificially produced radioactive isotope of a common element

radio wave: electromagnetic wave with a frequency between 10,000 hertz and 1 trillion hertz

rarefaction (rair-uh-FAK-shuhn): space in a medium in which there are fewer molecules

reactant (ree-AK-tuhnt): substance that enters into a chemical reaction

reaction rate: measure of how quickly reactants turn into products

real image: image formed by a mirror or lens that is the result of the actual converging of light rays

rectifier: vacuum tube diode that converts alternating current to direct current

recycling: form of conservation in which discarded materials that can be used again are sent to factories where they are reclaimed

reflected wave: wave that bounces back from a barrier

reflection (rih-FLEHK-shuhn): bouncing back of a wave after it strikes a barrier that does not absorb the wave's energy

refraction (rih-FRAK-shuhn): bending of waves due to a change in speed

refrigerant: liquid that is evaporated in a cooling system

regular reflection: reflected light in which the rays are reflected parallel to each other with very little scattering; produces a clearly defined image

resistance: opposition to the flow of electricity

resistance arm: distance from the resistance force to the fulcrum

resistance distance (d_R): distance through which the resistance force is applied, or distance through which the object moves

resistance force (F_R): force applied by a machine

retina: part of the eye on which light converges to form an image

rod: nerve cell in the retina of the eye that is sensitive to light and dark

rolling friction: friction produced when an object rolls over a surface

safety system: system in a nuclear power plant, consisting of a cooling system and a concrete casing around the reactor, that helps prevent nuclear accidents

saturated hydrocarbon: hydrocarbon in which all the bonds between carbon atoms are single covalent bonds

saturated solution: solution that contains all the solute it can possibly hold at a given temperature

scientific method: systematic approach to problem solving

screw: inclined plane wrapped around a cylinder to form a spiral

secondary coil: coil of insulated wire wrapped around an iron core in a transformer in which a current flows

second law of motion: Newton's law that states that force equals mass times acceleration

semiconductor: material that is able to conduct electric currents better than insulators but not as well as metals

series circuit: electric circuit in which all the parts of the circuit are connected one after another

single-replacement reaction: chemical reaction in which an uncombined element replaces an element that is part of a compound

sliding friction: friction produced when two solid objects slide over each other

slope: slant of a line connecting two points that indicates the change in the Y axis as compared to the change in the X axis

software: programs a computer follows

soft water: water that does not contain metal ions

solar collector: device that collects the sun's energy

solar energy: energy given off by the sun

solar heating system: heating system that uses the energy of the sun to produce heat

solid: matter with a definite shape and a definite volume

solid-state device: device that uses semiconductors

solubility: maximum amount of solute that can be dissolved in a definite amount of solvent at a specific temperature

soluble: able to be dissolved

solute (SAHL-yoot): substance that is dissolved in a solution

solution (suh-LOO-shuhn): homogeneous mixture in which one substance is dissolved in another substance

solvent (SAHL-vuhnt): substance that does the dissolving in a solution

south magnetic pole: end of a magnet that points toward the south

spark plug: part of an internal-combustion engine that produces an electric spark that ignites the fuel

specific gravity: comparison, or ratio, of the mass of a substance to the mass of an equal volume of water

specific heat: ability of a substance to absorb heat energy

speed: distance traveled by a moving object per unit of time

standing wave: wave that results when constructive interference and destructive interference produce stationary nodes and antinodes

starch: carbohydrate made of a long chain of sugar molecules hooked together

static electricity: buildup of electric charge on an object

steam heating system: heating system in which steam is forced through pipes from a boiler to a convector, which heats the room through convection currents

step-down transformer: transformer that decreases the voltage in alternating current

step-up transformer: transformer that increases the voltage in alternating current

storage tank: part of a cooling system that holds the refrigerant

strip mining: process in which entire hills are cut apart by large earth-moving machines to obtain coal

strong force: force that binds protons and neutrons in the nucleus

structural formula: formula that shows the kind, number, and arrangement of atoms in a molecule

subatomic particle: proton, neutron, or electron

sublimation (suhb-lih-MAY-shuhn): change from the solid phase of matter directly into the gas phase

subscript: small number placed to the lower right of a chemical symbol that gives the number of atoms of the element in the compound

substituted hydrocarbon: hydrocarbon formed when one or more hydrogen atoms in a hydrocarbon chain or ring is replaced by a different atom or group of atoms

sugar: carbohydrate

supersaturated solution: solution that is made to hold more solute at a given temperature than is normal

suspension: heterogeneous mixture in which the solute particles are larger than atoms, ions, or molecules

synthesis (SIHN-thuh-sihs) **reaction:** chemical reaction in which two or more simple substances combine to form a new, more complex substance

synthetic element: element produced by artificial transmutation; transuranium element

temperature: measure of the motion of molecules

temperature inversion: condition that occurs when cool air and pollutants near the earth's surface are trapped under a layer of warm air

temporary magnet: magnet made of a material that is easily magnetized but quickly loses its magnetism

terminal velocity: velocity reached when the pull of gravity equals the air resistance and the falling object no longer accelerates

theory: most logical explanation of events that occur in nature

thermal expansion: expansion of a substance due to heat

thermal pollution: damage to the environment by waste heat that causes an unnatural rise in temperature of air or in bodies of water such as lakes and streams

thermocouple: device that changes heat energy into electric energy

thermometer: instrument used for the measurement of temperature

thermostat (THER-muh-stat): device that helps control temperature in an indoor area or in an appliance

third law of motion: Newton's law that states that for every action there is an equal and opposite reaction

thrust: forward force

tidal power: power produced by the rise and fall of tides

tincture (TIHNK-chuhr): solution in which alcohol is the solvent

toxic: poisonous

tracer: radioactive element whose pathway through the steps of a chemical reaction can be followed

transformer: device that increases or decreases the voltage of alternating current

transistor: sandwich of three semiconductor crystals used to amplify an electric current or signal

transition metal: element that has properties similar to other transition metals and to other metals but whose properties do not fit in with those of any other family.

translucent (tranz-LOO-suhnt): able to transmit light but no detail of that light

transmutation: process by which the nucleus of an atom changes so that a new element is formed

transparent: able to transmit light readily

transuranium element: element produced by artificial transmutation; synthetic element

transverse wave: wave in which the motion of the medium is at right angles to the direction of the wave

triode: vacuum tube that consists of a filament, a plate, and a wire screen, or grid

trough: low point of a wave; maximum displacement downward of a particle of the medium

turbine: paddle wheel in an external-combustion engine that rotates, producing mechanical energy

ultraviolet ray: electromagnetic wave with a frequency just higher than visible violet light

unbalanced force: force that is not opposite and equal to another force and causes motion or a change in motion

unsaturated hydrocarbon: hydrocarbon in which one or more of the bonds between carbon atoms is a double covalent or triple covalent bond

unsaturated solution: solution that contains less solute than it can possibly hold at a given temperature

vacuum tube: one-way valve, or gate, for a flow of electrons

valence electron: electron in the outermost energy level of an atom

vaporization (vay-puhr-ih-ZAY-shuhn): change of a liquid to a gas

variable: factor that is being tested in an experiment

velocity: speed in a given direction

virtual image: image formed by a mirror or lens in which the rays of light do not actually converge

viscosity (vihs-KAHS-uh-tee): resistance of a liquid to flow

visible spectrum: portion of the electromagnetic spectrum to which human eyes are sensitive; light waves with frequencies between 430 trillion hertz and 760 trillion hertz

volt: unit of voltage

voltage: measure of the energy available to move electrons

voltaic cell: wet cell

volume: amount of space an object takes up

warm air system: heating system in which heated air is forced through ducts to vents and moves throughout the room by convection currents

watt (W): one joule per second; unit of electric power; volts times amps

wave: disturbance that transfers energy through matter or space

wavelength: distance between two consecutive crests or troughs of a wave

weak force: force that is responsible for radioactive decay

wedge: inclined plane that moves

weight: response of mass to the pull of gravity

wet cell: electrochemical cell that consists of a positive electrode, a negative electrode, and a liquid electrolyte; voltaic cell

wheel and axle: lever that rotates in a circle, made of two wheels of different sizes

work: product of a force applied to an object and the distance through which the force is applied; force times distance

work input (W_I): work done on a machine

work output (W_O): work done by a machine

X-ray: electromagnetic wave with a frequency just above ultraviolet

Index

Fischer/VISUM/Woodfin Camp; bottom: Ken Karp; **357** Hank Morgan/Rainbow; **358** top left: Alan Goldsmith/The Stock Market; top right: Mike Yamashita/Woodfin Camp; bottom: Ken Karp; **359** center: Ken Karp; right: Ken Karp; **360** Palmer/Kane/The Stock Market; **362** Walter Frenck/Odyssey Productions; **363** Philip Jon Bailey/The Picture Cube; **364** top: Gabe Palmer/The Stock Market; bottom left: Hugh Rogers/Monkmeyer Press; bottom right: Dr. E.R. Degginger; **370** NASA; **372** top: Hale Observatories; bottom left: Arjen Ueraik/The Stock Market; bottom right: P. Degginger/H. Armstrong Roberts; **373** top: Jean Paul Nacivet/Leo deWys; bottom: Malcom S. Kirk/Peter Arnold; **374** left: Tom Martin/The Stock Market; right: John Blaustein/Woodfin Camp; **375** David Madison/Duomo; **376** top: Wally McNamee/Duomo; bottom: Paul J. Sutton/Duomo; **377** left: Dan Helms/Duomo; right: J. Alex Langley/DPI; **378** top: Knotts Berry Farms; bottom: Thomas Braise/The Stock Market; **379** Bruce Curtis/Peter Arnold; **380** top: Russ Kinne/Photo Researchers; bottom: John Scheiber/The Stock Market; **383** top: Leo deWys; bottom: The Granger Collection; **388** Randa Bishop/DPI; **389** Don Siddle/Liaison; **390–391** Dan McCoy/Rainbow; **391** Karen Kasmauski/Wheeler Pictures; **392** Dr. Ray Clark & Mervyn Goff/Science Photo Library/Photo Researchers; **394** C. Allan Morgan/Peter Arnold; **398** Phil Degginger; **400** Jack C. Whitt/DPI; **401** Werner Wolff/Black Star; **402** left: Mark A. Mittelman/Taurus Photos; right: Clyde H. Smith/Peter Arnold; **405** Jack McConnell/DPI; Steve Fuller/Peter Arnold; **406** Dan McCoy/Rainbow; **408** left: Richard Choy/Peter Arnold; right: Dr. E.R. Degginger; **409** Peter Arnold; **410** Ken Karp; **411** Bill Ross/West Light/Woodfin Camp; **416** Jet Propulsion Lab; **418** Gabe Palmer/The Stock Market; **422** top left: Paolo Koch/Photo Researchers; top right: Arthur Tress/Photo Researchers; bottom: J. Alex Langley/DPI; **423** top: Jerry L. Holt/Photo Researchers; bottom: NASA/Photo Researchers; **424** C. Bonington/*Daily Telegraph Magazine*/Woodfin Camp; **426** Marilyn Leger/DPI; **428** Davidson/Magnum/Corning Glass Works; **429** top: Bill Pierce/Woodfin Camp; bottom: Adam J. Stoltman/Duomo; **434** Robert Severi; **435** top: Collier/Condit/Stock Boston; bottom: Atlantic Research Corp., Alexandria, Virginia; **436** Guy Billout/*Discover* magazine; **437** Roy H. Blanchard/DPI; **438** David Barnes/The Stock Market; **440** top: Steve Elmore/The Stock Market; bottom: Harry Grossman/DPI; **442** Michael Phillip Manheim; **447** Ken Karp; **448** top: Russ Kinne/Photo Researchers; bottom: Randa Bishop/DPI; **449** David Pollack/The Stock Market; **450** top: Culver Pictures; bottom: I. Kennedy/International Stock Photo; **455** Paul Shambroom/Photo Researchers; **457** John V.A. Neal/International Stock Photo; **458** top: Thomas Braise/The Stock Market; bottom: Ken Karp; **466** Ned Haines/Photo Researchers; **468** left: Ken Karp; right: Richard Megna/Fundamental Photographs; **469** all: Richard Megna/Fundamental Photographs; **470** all: Richard Megna/Fundamental Photographs; **472** The University of Iowa; **475** Jon Riley/Medichrome Div./The Stock Shop; **477** Ken Karp; **478** Dick Durrance/Woodfin Camp; **481** top: Terrence Moore/Woodfin Camp; center: Steve Firebaugh/The Stock Market; bottom: Richard Megna/Fundamental Photographs; **483** Peter Vadnai/The Stock Market; **488** Joe McNally/*Discover* magazine 6/84, Time Inc.; **489** Joe McNally/*Discover* magazine 6/84, Time Inc.; **490** Ed Cooper/H. Armstrong Roberts; **491** Philip Jon Bailey/Stock Boston; **492** Chuck O'Rear/West Light/Woodfin Camp; **494** Duomo; **496** left: M. Dohrn/Science Photo Library/Photo Researchers; right: Stuart Cohen/Stock Boston; **497** C. West/The Stock Market; **499** Hank Morgan/Photo Researchers; **504** O. Andrews/Leo deWys; **505** Fundamental Photographs; **506** Ken Karp; **512** both: U.S. Air Force Photo; **514** left: Richard Steedman/The Stock Market; right: NASA; **515** Lowell Georgia/Photo Researchers; **517** left: Jim Anderson/Woodfin Camp; right: Tim Davis/Photo Researchers; **519** top: Michael Melford/Wheeler Pictures; bottom: Stephen Green-Armytage/The Stock Market; **521** both: Fundamental Photographs; **522** Ken Karp; **524** AP Wide World Photos; **525** Jules Zalon/DPI; **526** top: Robert Frenck; bottom left: Margaret McCarthy/Peter Arnold; bottom right: Micky Palmer/DPI; **534** National Optical Astronomy Observatories; **536** Lee L. Waldman/The Stock Market; **540** Akuma Takegami/International Stock Photo; **542** left: Dr. R.P. Clark & M. Goff/Photo Researchers; center: Terry Dominco/Earth Images; right: Biophoto Assoc./Photo Researchers; **543** Howard Sochurek/Woodfin Camp; **544** NASA; **545** Ken Karp; **546** Charles E. Dorris/Photo Unique; **547** Erwin & Peggy Bauer/Bruce Coleman; **549** top: Cesar Paredes/The Stock Market; bottom: Sil Strung/The Stock Market; **550** both: Ken Karp; **551** both: Ken Karp; **553** Lennart Nilsson/Behold Man; **558** NASA/Science Source/Photo Researchers; **560** left: Ned Haines/Photo Researchers; right: Sharon Beals/Photo Researchers; **561** left: Runk/Schoenberger/Grant Heilman; center: Chris Collins/The Stock Market; right: P.A. Hinchliffe/Bruce Coleman; **562** top: Joel Gordon; center: John Maher/The Stock Market; bottom: Dan McCoy/Rainbow; **563** Ron Watts/Black Star; **564** top: Richard Megna/Fundamental Photographs; bottom: M.J. Pettypool/Uniphoto Picture Agency; **565** Michael Heron/Woodfin Camp; **566** Fundamental Photographs; **568** top: A.G.E. Foto Stock/Peter Arnold; center: John Scheiber/The Stock Market; bottom: Fundamental Photographs; **570** all: Tom Stack; **571** Yerkes Observatory; **572** Hale Observatories; **573** Alexander Tsiaras/Science Source/Photo Researchers; **574** top: Nancy Safford/Woodfin Camp; bottom: Ken Karp; **575** William James Warren/West Light; **580** Hologram-Dan Schweitzer-Paradox-1985—6/Photography Ronald R. Erickson 1986; **581** University of Alabama in Huntsville; **582** David Burnett/Contact; **583** Martin Levick/Black Star; **584** Jerry Liebmann/Leo deWys; **588** Soames Summerhays/Photo Researchers; **589** Vince Streano/The Stock Market; **590** The Stone Flower Studio/DPI; **591** Dick Durrance/Woodfin Camp; **592** left: D. Kirkland/Sygma; right: Tom McHugh/Photo Researchers; **594** top left: Jeffrey E. Blackman/The Stock Market; top right: Vic Bider/The Stock Market; bottom: Alexas Urba/The Stock Market; **595** Viviane Holbrooke/The Stock Market; **598** top: U.S. Department of Energy; bottom: Jerry Mason/Photo Researchers; **599** Russ Kinne/Photo Researchers; **600** left: Sandia National Laboratories; right: University of Rochester; **601** top: Edward Sonner/DPI; bottom: Barry Griffiths/Photo Researchers; **602** all: Paul Chesley/Photographers Aspen; **604** Ken Karp; **610** left: Art Sokoloff/DPI; right: Keith Gunnar/Bruce Coleman; **611** left: Bob Hahn/Taurus Photos; right: Cary Wolinsky/Stock Boston; **612** top left: Chris Collins/The Stock Market; top right: Mike Yamashita/Woodfin Camp; bottom: James Mason/Black Star; **613** Chris Jones/The Stock Market; **614** J. Barry O'Rourke/The Stock Market; **615** top: Hans Paul/Woodfin Camp; bottom: Roger J. Cheng; **616** left: Roger J. Cheng; right: Roger J. Cheng/Atmospheric Science Research Center; **617** Larry Lefever/Grant Heilman; **618** top: Roger J. Cheng/Atmospheric Science Research Center; bottom: Tom Stack; **620** Chris Jones/The Stock Market; **621** top: Chris Reeberg/DPI; bottom: Walley McNamee/Woodfin Camp; **626** American Petroleum Institute; **628** left: J. Alex Langley/DPI; right: North Wind Picture Archives; **629** Dr. E.R. Degginger; **631** top clockwise: Jim Merithew/Picture Group; Michael Furman/The Stock Market; Ken Karp; Seth H. Goltzer/The Stock Market; Ken Karp; bottom clockwise: Vince Streano/The Stock Market; © Joel Gordon; Ken Karp; © Joel Gordon; © Ted Horowitz/The Stock Market; **632** left: William E. Ferguson; right: Hal Yaeger/DPI; **633** top left: Life Science Library/Giant Molecules/Photograph by John Zimmerman © 1986 Time, Inc., Time-Life Books, Inc. Publisher; top right: Life Science Library/Giant Molecules/Photograph by Donald Miller © 1986 Time, Inc., Time-Life Books, Inc. Publisher; bottom top: Dan McCoy/Rainbow; bottom bottom: Dan McCoy/Rainbow; **634** top: Palmer/Kane/The Stock Market; bottom: Life Science Library/Photography by Bruce Roberts © Time-Life Books, Inc.; **635** E.I. duPont de Nemours; right: E.I. duPont de Nemours; **636** Ken Karp; **640** Joel Gordon; **642** left: Chris Sorensen; right: Ken Karp; **643** Ken Karp; **644** Roy Morsch/The Stock Market; **645** Ken Karp; **646** top: Ken Karp; bottom left: Joel Gordon; bottom right: Alfred Pasieka/Taurus Photos; **647** top: Chuck O'Rear/Woodfin Camp; bottom: Culver Pictures; **650** Ken Karp; **653** left: NASA/Science Source/Photo Researchers; center: Hank Morgan/Photo Researchers; right: George Hailing/Photo Researchers; **654** left: IBM; right: Joel Gordon; **655** Ken Karp; **656** left: Dan McCoy/Rainbow; right: C. Mula & Haramaty/Phototake; **662** Henry Groskinsky/*Discover* magazine 11/84, Time Inc.; **663** Henry Groskinsky/*Discover* magazine 11/84, Time Inc.; **664** Glenn Cruickshank/West Stock.

PERIODIC TABLE

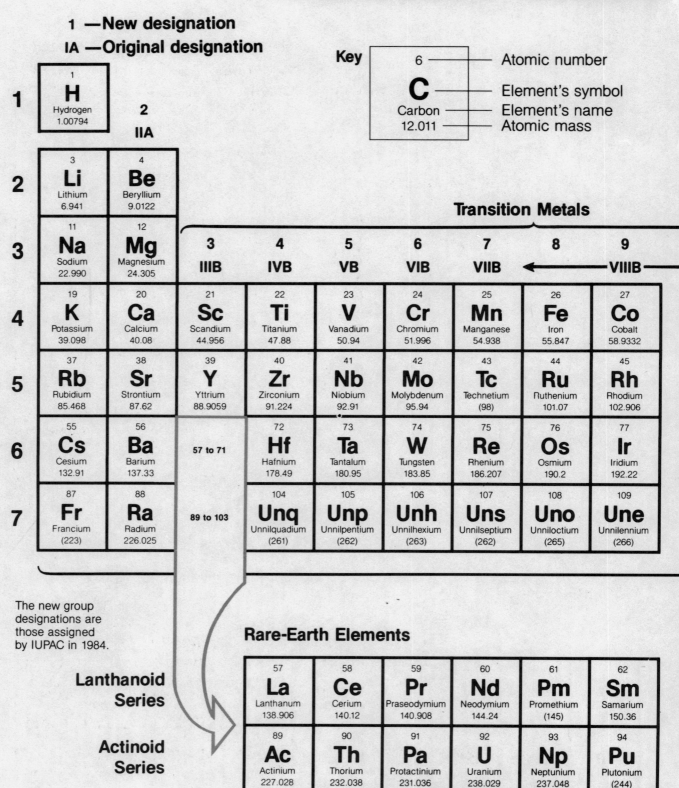

1 — New designation
IA — Original designation

Key

6	Atomic number
C	Element's symbol
Carbon	Element's name
12.011	Atomic mass

Transition Metals

1 IA	2 IIA	3 IIIB	4 IVB	5 VB	6 VIB	7 VIIB	8 ←	9 VIIIB →
1 **H** Hydrogen 1.00794								
3 **Li** Lithium 6.941	**4** **Be** Beryllium 9.0122							
11 **Na** Sodium 22.990	**12** **Mg** Magnesium 24.305							
19 **K** Potassium 39.098	**20** **Ca** Calcium 40.08	**21** **Sc** Scandium 44.956	**22** **Ti** Titanium 47.88	**23** **V** Vanadium 50.94	**24** **Cr** Chromium 51.996	**25** **Mn** Manganese 54.938	**26** **Fe** Iron 55.847	**27** **Co** Cobalt 58.9332
37 **Rb** Rubidium 85.468	**38** **Sr** Strontium 87.62	**39** **Y** Yttrium 88.9059	**40** **Zr** Zirconium 91.224	**41** **Nb** Niobium 92.91	**42** **Mo** Molybdenum 95.94	**43** **Tc** Technetium (98)	**44** **Ru** Ruthenium 101.07	**45** **Rh** Rhodium 102.906
55 **Cs** Cesium 132.91	**56** **Ba** Barium 137.33	57 to 71	**72** **Hf** Hafnium 178.49	**73** **Ta** Tantalum 180.95	**74** **W** Tungsten 183.85	**75** **Re** Rhenium 186.207	**76** **Os** Osmium 190.2	**77** **Ir** Iridium 192.22
87 **Fr** Francium (223)	**88** **Ra** Radium 226.025	89 to 103	**104** **Unq** Unnilquadium (261)	**105** **Unp** Unnilpentium (262)	**106** **Unh** Unnilhexium (263)	**107** **Uns** Unnilseptium (262)	**108** **Uno** Unniloctium (265)	**109** **Une** Unnilennium (266)

The new group designations are those assigned by IUPAC in 1984.

Lanthanoid Series

Actinoid Series

Rare-Earth Elements

57 **La** Lanthanum 138.906	58 **Ce** Cerium 140.12	59 **Pr** Praseodymium 140.908	60 **Nd** Neodymium 144.24	61 **Pm** Promethium (145)	62 **Sm** Samarium 150.36
89 **Ac** Actinium 227.028	90 **Th** Thorium 232.038	91 **Pa** Protactinium 231.036	92 **U** Uranium 238.029	93 **Np** Neptunium 237.048	94 **Pu** Plutonium (244)